Advanced Excel

for scientific
data analysis

third edition

Robert de Levie

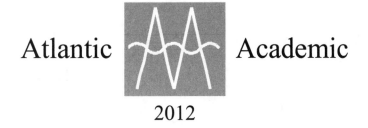

Atlantic Academic

2012

Atlantic Academic LLC,
21 Atlantic Place,
Orr's Island, Harpswell,
Maine 04066 USA

First edition: 2004
Second edition: 2008
Third edition: 2012

Library of Congress Cataloguing-in-Publication Data:
de Levie, Robert
Advanced Excel for scientific data analysis — 3rd edition
ISBN: 978-0-98-471230-4
1. Chemistry, Analytic — Data Processing
2. Electronic Spreadsheets 3. Microsoft Excel

QD75.4.E4D43 2012

9 8 7 6 5 4 3 2 1

Printed in the United States of America

Dedication

This book is dedicated to the memory of Leonardo Volpi (1957-2010) who, through his many well-crafted, freely downloadable and open-access contributions, almost single-handedly made Excel into a high-quality platform for numerical analysis. Readers of this book will encounter Volpi's contributions in almost every chapter, and will especially note his great enlargement of Excel's capabilities in matrix algebra in chapter 10, and his extension of Excel beyond the double-precision limit in chapter 11.

Leonardo Volpi was born and raised in Piombino in Tuscany, Italy, and studied electronic engineering at the University of Pisa, from which he graduated in 1983. Since 1989 he worked in the Information and Communication Technology group of the Enel Group, Italy's largest power company, as a Technical Systems Integrator. He was always generous and helpful, and surrounded himself with a group of colleagues and coworkers, his 'foxes' (a wordplay on his name), who in turn helped him with his work on solving general problems of numerical analysis, which he then made available on his website http://digilander.libero.it/foxes. All serious Excel users will sorely miss him, while gratefully building on his legacy.

Preface

Even more than its earlier editions, the present volume will take its readers far beyond the standard spreadsheet fare provided by Microsoft. While its contents have been expanded by the inclusion of a number of new features, its general organization is unchanged from that of the second edition. After the introduction you will find three chapters on least squares analysis, followed by two on Fourier transformation and related methods, and one on digital simulation. The next chapter describes in some detail how to use VBA to write user-designed functions and macros to expand the reach of the spreadsheet and make it solve *your* problems. The three final chapters illustrate how user-designed functions and macros can improve some standard numerical methods, facilitate the uses of matrix algebra, and can greatly enhance the accuracy of the spreadsheet.

The most visible change in this third edition is its significantly enlarged page format, because the earlier edition had reached its practical thickness limit. The text has undergone a number of useful updates, with more emphasis on visual representations such as error surfaces, and the inclusion of several entirely new sections: chapter 1 sections 2.4 through 2.7 and 5.2; chapter 4 sections 21, 23, 24, and 26; chapter 5 section 11; chapter 7 sections 4 and 7; chapter 8 sections 3, 16, and 22; chapter 9 sections 2.10, 2.11, 4.4, and 6.3; chapter 10 sections 11, 12, 16, 17, 19 and 20, as well as much of chapter 11. Chapter 4 now includes a brief discussion of a Levenberg-Marquardt routine that consistently outperforms Solver on the NIST standard reference tests, and chapter 9 contains a novel algorithm for the numerical differentiation of mathematical functions that, for reasons outside of my control, did not make it into the second edition, and caused me to change publishers. Moreover, the recent, quite substantial extension of Volpi's Xnumbers.xla by John Beyers to XN.xla and XN.xlam has been incorporated throughout this book, because it can be used throughout Excel (on the spreadsheet, in functions, and in subroutines) with all recent pc versions of Excel, from 2000 through 2010. All the needed add-ins are freely downloadable from my website, http://www.bowdoin.edu/~rdelevie/excellaneous, which now doubles as a convenient transfer station for the many contributions by Volpi, Beyers, and others that are described in this book.

*****

Science and engineering progress through a mixture of three essential ingredients: ideas, tools, and experiments. Excel is a ubiquitous and rather intuitive computational program that, through the selfless efforts of people like Leonardo Volpi and John Beyers, has now become a serious numerical analysis tool. As such, it is a means to an end, a distinction that was obviously lost on a reviewer of an earlier edition of this book who advised readers not to use Excel "for anything serious like curing cancer". No software will cure cancer, but it can surely assist in that and other worthwhile scientific and engineering efforts, if only because of its low psychological entrance barrier, open architecture, wide distribution, and computational prowess.

This book is intended for those who are already familiar with the Excel spreadsheet, and who want to explore what it can offer them in the physical sciences and engineering. It is not intended as an introduction to Excel, nor is it meant for those who are already comfortable with high-performance general-purpose numerical software platforms such as Fortran or C, with programs that can do symbolic math such as Mathematica or Maple, with more specialized numerical packages such as Matlab or statistical ones like SPSS, SAS or R, and therefore may not find it worthwhile to investigate what Excel can do for them. All such programs can perform most any task that can be done on Excel, and as a consequence of Volpi's work, Excel can now also perform many tasks performed by those high-performance numerical analysis packages, even though the extra computational overhead of its user-friendliness makes the spreadsheet unsuitable for really large problems, and an extensive library of statistical applications still remains to be written. However, for most small and medium-sized scientific and engineering computations, the choice of platform often depends primarily on its availability as well as on one's prior familiarity with that particular software, and both of these criteria often tend to favor the spreadsheet.

Long before the opening up of the internet, two innovative programs, word processing and spreadsheets, had already fueled the explosive development of desktop and laptop computers and their current, wide distribution makes them uniquely suitable for a close examination of their capabilities. At present, whether we like it or not, Excel is by far the most widely distributed numerical software platform in the world. In my own experience, as a teacher charged with introducing incoming graduate chemistry students to numerical data analysis, I found that most students preferred the low barrier to learning, the open structure, and the visual and numerical immediacy of the spreadsheet to more formal languages such as Fortran or C, even though the latter at that time were certainly much more powerful, and already came with impressive subroutine libraries. Its user-friendliness makes the spreadsheet an excellent teaching tool, even if its openness and great flexibility can also be its Achilles heel, as described in chapter 11, and an accountant's headache. Developing VBA and incorporating it into Excel was Microsoft's masterstroke that made it overtake its main competitors, Lotus 1-2-3 and QuattroPro, and this book fully exploits that aspect. Unfortunately, the unwillingness of Microsoft to promptly correct sub-optimal software has turned off many potential users, especially engineers and statisticians. Although Microsoft has not changed its habits, the work of Volpi and Beyers goes a long way towards overcoming that problem.

*****

The introductory chapter surveys some of the standard features of Excel, and therefore can serve as a brief refresher. It also contains some more advanced material that needed to be introduced there in order to be available in subsequent chapters. However, the novice user of Excel is urged first to consult a manual, or an introductory book, as can usually be found on the shelves of a local library or bookstore.

This book has two main parts. Chapters 2 through 7 deal with some of the main analysis methods used in science and engineering, specifically least squares analysis, Fourier transformation, and rudimentary digital simulation, as applied to the Excel spreadsheet. The emphasis is not so much on their mechanics, but on their proper use. The next four chapters, 8 through 11, focus more strongly on implementing these methods with custom functions and macros in those cases for which Excel does not provide the needed software.

In order to avoid possible confusion, we will adopt several definitions and distinctions that are not part of common English usage, and therefore need a brief explanation. In data analysis, one often deals with experimental uncertainty in the data. In this connection we will follow a convention adopted by most physical scientists, viz. to distinguish between their *accuracy*, i.e., how close these data are to their true values, and their *precision*, i.e., how reproducible they are under the experimental conditions used. This is a useful general distinction, even though precision and accuracy may sometimes get entangled in the data analysis.

Amongst numbers we will distinguish between measured *variables*, i.e., experimentally determined quantities such as distance, time, current, voltage, absorbance, wavelength, concentration, and pH, and computed *parameters*, the model-based constants that we extract from experimental data, such as speed, acceleration, resistance, molar absorptivity, equilibrium constant, etc. This distinction is not necessarily a physical one, e.g., acceleration can be determined directly, or derived from measuring distance as a function of time. Moreover, fitting parameters may be purely empirical, in which the "model" is some convenient mathematical function that appears to fit. But it is always useful in data analysis to separate the directly measured data from those derived from them during the analysis, and to consider how that data analysis itself can sometimes affect the results.

In working with graphs, Microsoft distinguishes between a *chart* and a *plot*. A chart contains the actual data, just as a canvas contains a painting, while the plot contains the chart plus its immediate surrounding, including axis labels, just as a frame surrounds a painting and, in a museum setting, may also include an explanatory label. Likewise, we will differentiate between an *array* (a set of data) and a *range* (a set of spreadsheet cells) and, when discussing VBA procedures, between *functions* (self-updating code) and *subroutines* (code that only responds when called). *Macros* are a special type of subroutine, callable from the spreadsheet, just as public functions are a callable subset of all (public and private) functions.

*****

The predecessor of this book, *How to use Excel in analytical chemistry and in general scientific data analysis* (Oxford Univ. Press 2001) focused on the responsible use of statistics in analytical chemistry, and to this end contained a number of add-in macros. The present book addresses a much more general readership, but continues the emphasis of its predecessor. The second edition added some of Leonardo Volpi's routines, especially for matrix functions (Matrix.xla) and for extended-precision macros (Xnumbers.dll). The latter add-in has become obsolete with Excel version 2007, and is replaced in the present edition by the more powerful and flexible XN.xla(m), as extended by John Beyers. As a consequence, there is some overlap between the various add-ins described in this book, and the user sometimes has several more or less equivalent options, for both functions and macros, even though other areas are still underrepresented, such as the statistical approaches chemists often describe as chemometric, or more sophisticated numerical simulations. I hope that some statistician(s) thoroughly familiar with those fields will step in to fill this void.

Most of the instructions in this book apply to versions of Excel for IBM-type personal computers starting with Excel 97, although some new features (such as cell comments) have only been available in more recent versions of Excel, and may therefore not work in the earliest versions. The specific instructions in this book were mostly tested in Excel 2000 and 2003, still my favorite versions. In 2007 Excel underwent a major cosmetic facelift, which affected neither its underlying computational engine nor VBA, but changed the names of many first-line commands, a real nuisance for old-timers.

Differences in Excel on an IBM-type personal computer or on a Macintosh are relatively minor, such as using Ctrl‿click instead of right-click, and the Option key instead of the Alternate key. (The linking symbol ‿ is used here to indicate that the Ctrl key should remain depressed while clicking. We use it instead of the more common + because you will be less inclined to type it.) Appendix A.8 lists some other differences between pc and Mac commands. Excel versions 1 through 4 used a completely different macro language, and are therefore *not* suitable for use with this book, since none of the custom functions and macros described here will work in those early versions. If you have such an early version, it is high time to upgrade.

Idiosyncratic notation has been kept to a minimum, with three exceptions. The notation 3 (2) 9 is used as convenient shorthand for the arithmetic progression 3, 5, 7, 9 (i.e., starting at 3, with increment 2, ending at 9). The linking symbol ‿ is used to indicate when keys should be depressed simultaneously, as in Alt‿F11 or Ctrl‿Alt‿Del. And the symbol $\oslash$ will identify deconvolution, complementing the more usual symbol $\otimes$ for convolution. These symbols are based on the fact that, in the Fourier transform domain, deconvolution is associated with division (/) just as convolution is with multiplication ($\times$).

Especially in the first few chapters of this book an effort has been made to show the reader how to use Excel 2007 and 2010, in which the look and feel and, more importantly, the names of many of its first-line commands were changed to sell old wine in new bottles. Despite those changes, the material in this book is applicable to these recent versions of Excel.

Excel 2007 and 2010 will accept your earlier Excel spreadsheets, but are *not* fully backward compatible, and its use may therefore require you to make some changes. For scientific data analysis, there is little to recommend upgrading from Excel 2003 to its newer versions, and much to discourage it if you were already an experienced user before 2007. One can of course run Excel 2003 on the new Vista platform to gain its supposedly improved immunity to viruses and other unwanted intrusions.

Excel 2007 has largely done away with toolbars. Instead you will find a series of ribbons that display the most popular choices but were often renamed, take up more space for fewer options, and consequently require frequent ribbon-changing. Fortunately, many (though not all) of the old hotkey commands still work in Excel 2007/10. There was also a useful change in Excel 2007/10, its greatly increased spreadsheet size, but the corresponding instruction set was not given a corresponding update or expansion. (The "64-bit" versions of Excel 2010 offer 64-bit cell *addressing*, but unfortunately still no 64-bit *computing*.)

The expansion of the spreadsheet area in Excel 2007 required extending the column designations to three letters. Therefore, before importing your pre-existing functions into Excel 2007/10, check whether it uses names that will now become cell addresses and, if so, change them. We use the marker ⓞⓩ,⑩⑩ to indicate, especially in the first chapters, where Excel 2007/10 requires an approach different from that of its earlier versions. For the sake of uniformity we will indicate the old *hotkey* commands (by underlining specific letters), most of which still apply, even though the instruction itself may be called by a different name in the most recent versions.

*****

The focus of this book is on the *numerical analysis of experimental data*, such as are usually encountered in the physical sciences and in engineering. Much of such data analysis is nowadays performed with one of two approaches, least squares analysis or Fourier transformation, which therefore form the first major subject areas of this book. But the emphasis is neither on numerical analysis as an abstract mathematical subject, nor on its specific computer implementations, but on analyzing experimental data and extracting the best possible information from them, and to explain the basic principles involved, primarily by example. We therefore relegate most of the numerical manipulations to functions and macros, and in this book focus instead on how best to *use* these tools. With such understanding, with the tools described, and with knowing how to make your own Excel tools when none are already available, this book aims to make the spreadsheet do *your* bidding, not so much by prettying up its display, as by exploiting its considerable computational capabilities to the fullest. And in case Excel's built-in facilities and its many add-ons don't provide what you need, this book describes how to make Excel routines to fill *your* specific needs, shows you many specific examples (and pilferable parts) in the associated MacroBundle, and has a number of MacroMorsels specifically illuminating aspects of VBA that might otherwise cause you some coding difficulties.

In the current edition we have incorporated many more graphical aids, especially those that can visualize central concepts such as (the logarithm of) SSR, the *s*um of *s*quares of the *r*esiduals, i.e., the quantity usually minimized in least squares routines. The shapes of such plots can often alert us to potential difficulties with the associated data analysis.

If you want to use the rectangular spreadsheet array for linear algebra (they are clearly made for each other) but feel constrained by the limited set of matrix instructions provided by Excel, you will find many additional tools in chapter 10. If you require scientific, engineering, and statistical functions that Microsoft does not have, need higher accuracy than Excel can provide, or precision higher than the IEEE 754 standard "double precision", read chapter 11. In short, this book empowers you to do much more with Excel than you might otherwise have thought possible.

As much as feasible, the material is illustrated with practical examples taken from the scientific literature, and specific instructions are provided so that you can reproduce the analyses, and can then modify them to suit you own needs. Real examples have the advantage that they often highlight realistic applications, but there is a second reason to favor real measurements over made-up examples, viz. the fundamental difference between "pure" mathematics on the one hand, and numerical computation and the physical sciences on the other. In pure math, numbers are well-defined, hard objects, while in numerical computation and in the physical sciences they are usually somewhat fuzzier and softer. This is readily seen for criteria such as $x < 0$, $x = 0$, and $x > 0$, which are absolute in math, but can become vague due to numerical round-off errors in computation and/or to experimental errors in scientific data.

Since this book deals with the application of numerical software to scientific data, this softness is often emphasized, and methods to minimize its effects are stressed. Least squares methods, e.g., tend to minimize the effects of random experimental errors, deconvolution those of systematic ones, while careful choice of algorithms and/or use of extended numberlength can reduce computational errors. Fourier transformation and singular value decomposition allow us to filter out less significant signals from those of interest, and hybrids between these various methods can often combine some of their best aspects. Such tools can and should play a role in data analysis, i.e., in converting experimental numbers into useful information.

*****

Almost all of the special routines described in this book can be downloaded as open-access functions, macros and subroutines. Where necessary, short introductions are given to the topics being introduced, but you will not find any conjectures, propositions, lemmas or theorems here, but instead simple explanations of the basic principles involved, often accompanied by a few crucial equations. You will not encounter any screenshots of Excel dialog boxes either, or any templates to fill in, but plenty of illustrations of actual spreadsheets, often accompanied by a listing of the explicit instructions used. This makes this text useful for individual study as well as for an introductory course in applied numerical analysis in the physical sciences and engineering, especially when its worked examples are combined with projects of the student's own choosing. I have had my students in courses using this book work on a wide variety of topics, from the ups and downs of the stock market and the tides (some contrast!) to an analysis of the supposedly equivalent (but evolutionarily maintained, and therefore almost certainly significant) synonyms in the four-letter amino acid code, where the Word-related VBA commands operating on letters and strings came in handy.

As always I will be grateful for reader's comments, corrections, and suggestions. Please address these to rdelevie@ bowdoin.edu.

Acknowledgements

First I would like to express my indebtedness to Leonardo Volpi and his many coworkers, who built much of the material described in this book, and to John Beyers and his brother Steve, who have continued its development and further extension. It is the marvel of the Internet and of the spirit of open access software, that Excel has now been transformed from a competent business software package to a first-rate instrument for scientific data analysis, while fully retaining the ease of use and visual rather than command-line-based orientation of the spreadsheet. It is an ironic consequence of that same Internet that I have so far met in person none of those mentioned here, and have corresponded only with a few of them: Leonardo Volpi, John Beyers, David Heiser, and Simonluca Santoro. Here, then, listed alphabetically, are the names of others whom I have only met on paper as contributing to this book: Eric Braekevelt, R. C. Brewer, Ricardo Martinez Camacho, Wu Chinswei, Lieven Dossche, Berend Engelbrecht, Rodrigo Farinha, Mariano Felici, Arnoud de Grammont, Hans Gunter, David F. Haslam, Michael Hautus, André Hendriks, Richard Huxtable, Ton Jeursen, Jianming Jin, John Jones, Michael Kozluk, Giovanni Longo, Bruno Monastero, Javie Martin Montalban, Sebastián Naccas, Takuya Ooura, Kent Osband, Robert Pigeon, Simon de Pressinger, Roger Price, Luis Isaac Ramos Garcia, James R. Ramsden, Michael Richter, Iván Vega Rivera, Michael Ruder, Mirko Sartori, Gerald Schmidt, Gabriel Simmonds, Vidas Sukackas, David Sloan, Ken Thompson, Christopher Titus, Abel Torres, Alfredo Álvarez Valdivia, Franz Josef Vögel, Shaun Walker, Gregg B. Wells, P. J. Weng, Yong Yang, Vladimir Zakharov, Jakub Zalewski, Thomas Zeutschler, Shanjie Zhang and Oldgierd Zieba. In the name of the readers and users of this book: thank you all for your generous contributions.

Numerous friends, colleagues and students have contributed to this book, corrected some of its ambiguities, and made it more intelligible. I am especially grateful to Bill Craig for invaluable help on many occasions, to Whitney King, Panos Nikitas, Carl Salter, and Brian Tissue for their many helpful comments, especially on the chapters on least squares, to Peter Griffiths and Jim de Haseth for commenting on the chapter on Fourier transformation, to Peter Jansson for valuable comments on deconvolution, to Philip Barak for letting me use his elegant equidistant least squares macro, to Simonluca Santoro for letting me incorporate his beautiful contour diagrams, and to Harry Frank, Edwin Meyer, Caryn Sanford Seney, and Carl Salter, for sending me experimental data that are so much more realistic than simulations would have been. I gladly acknowledge the various copyright holders for permission to quote from their writings or to use their published data, and I am grateful to William T. Vetterling of Numerical Recipes Software for permission to incorporate some programs from *Numerical Recipes* in the sample macros.

I am very grateful for the many helpful comments and suggestions from colleagues and friends, especially from John Beyers, Stephen Bullen, Bosco Emmanuel, Steve Feldberg, David Heiser, Nemad Jeremic, Linde Koch, Ernest Lippert, Jan Myland, Keith Oldham, Hans Pottel, Simonluca Santoro, Mohammad Tajdari, Joel Tellinghuisen, and alphabetically last but helpwise first and foremost, Leonardo Volpi. My wife Jolanda was the great facilitator whose love, support, forbearance, proofreading, and help made it all possible.

Copyright credits

About the author

Robert de Levie is the author or co-author of more than 160 papers in analytical chemistry and electrochemistry, and of several books: an early *Spreadsheet Workbook for Quantitative Chemical Analysis*, McGraw-Hill (1992), a textbook on the *Principles of Quantitative Chemical Analysis*, McGraw-Hill (1997), an Oxford Chemistry Primer on *Aqueous Acid-Base Equilibria and Titrations*, Oxford University Press (1999), *How to use Excel in Analytical Chemistry and in General Scientific Data Analysis*, Cambridge University Press (2001), and the book you now read, of which the first two editions (2004, 2008) were published by Oxford University Press.

He was born and raised in the Netherlands, earned his Ph.D. in physical chemistry at the University of Amsterdam under the tutelage of Jan A. A. Ketelaar, spent two years as a postdoc with Paul Delahay in Baton Rouge, LA, and for 34 years taught analytical chemistry at Georgetown University in Washington, DC. For ten of those years he was the US editor of the *Journal of Electroanalytical Chemistry*. Now an emeritus professor, he lives on Orr's Island, ME, and is associated with Bowdoin College in nearby Brunswick, ME, where he can be reached at rdelevie@bowdoin.edu.

Contents

8 *Write your own macros* 335

Chapter *1*
Survey of Excel

1.1 Spreadsheet basics

A spreadsheet is laid out as a page in an accountant's ledger, i.e., as a sheet with rows and columns. Because it is electronic rather than actual, the used part of the spreadsheet can be quite large, in which case only a small part of it is visible at any one time on the monitor screen. For that reason, the most important information is usually kept *at the top* of the spreadsheet, where it is easily found, rather than at the bottom of the columns, as would be common on paper. Especially, summary figures as well as final numerical results and conclusions are preferably placed at or near the top of the spreadsheet. When you start a new spreadsheet, it is therefore good practice to leave plenty of room at the top.

The spreadsheet is typically surrounded by several bars (together with ribbons in the more recent Excel versions 2007 and 2010). Here is the run-down for Excel 2003 and the largely similar Excel 97 and Excel 2000: the top bar is the (typically blue) Title Bar, used to drag the sheet, and also containing in its right corner the Minimize, Maximize, and Close buttons. Below this you will see the Menu Bar, starting with File, Edit, View, Insert, … . Then comes the Standard Toolbar, with icons for a sheet, an open folder, a diskette, a printer, etc., and finally a Formula Bar with windows for the cell address and cell formula. Clicking on View ⇨ Toolbars allows you to select or deselect some of these and many other toolbars. At the bottom of the spreadsheet you will find the Status Bar (initially showing Ready) and, below the spreadsheet, the Windows Task Bar with its Start button.

In Excel 2007 the Title and Menu bars are modified, and share a large round Office button (Excel 2010 returned to a File tab), while the Standard toolbar is replaced by ribbons, selected by a modified Menu bar which now has Ribbon Tabs. The Formula and Status bars are retained. Most confusingly, many top-level instructions have been renamed, and while most of the earlier-used hotkeys are still functional, they are no longer shown by underlining. Fortunately, these cosmetic changes only affect the top-level instructions; at lower levels, no changes were made, hotkeys are still indicated as such, and the underlying computing engine is essentially unaffected. In this book we will use the nomenclature of Excel 2003, still its most popular and most widespread version, show its hotkeys, and indicate with ⓪⑦, ⑩: when those mnemonic hotkeys have changed in Excel 2007/10.

The rows and columns define individual cells denoted by column letter(s) and row number(s) shown at the top and left respectively. The right-hand side has a scroll bar, and the bottom contains sheet tabs and a scroll bar. Inside that spreadsheet frame, the top left-hand cell is A1, to its right is B1, below B1 is B2, etc. A cell can contain one of three different items: a label, a number, or an instruction. In the absence of contrary information, labels start with a letter, numbers with a digit, and instructions (i.e., formulas or functions) with the equal sign, =. When a cell contains an instruction, it will show the corresponding numerical result; the underlying instruction can be seen in the *formula window* in the formula bar when that particular cell is highlighted. At the same time, the cell address is shown in the *address window* in the same formula bar. As *default*, i.e., unless otherwise instructed, Excel displays labels as left-justified, and numbers as right-justified.

The most basic mathematical operations of a spreadsheet are listed in appendix A.1. Note that multiplication must use an asterisk, *, division a forward slash, /, and exponentiation a caret, ^. Numerous built-in functions are listed in appendices A.2 through A.7. Section 1.9 shows a first example of a user-defined function, and in chapter 8 you will learn how to write your own functions and macros.

In general, copying instructions to another cell assumes *relative* addressing. This uses rules like those in chess, where the knight in one move can only reach squares with a given relative position with respect to its starting point, in this particular example either two steps sideways and one step up or down, or one step sideways plus two up or down. Relative addressing can be overridden by using the dollar sign, that symbol of stability, in front of the column letter and/or row number, thereby making that part of the address *absolute*. The function key F4 (typically above the numerals on the keyboard) toggles through the four possible permutations, say, from A1 to $A$1, A$1, $A1, A1, $A$1, etc.

A highlighted cell or cell block has a heavy border surrounding it, and a *handle*, a little dark square, at its bottom-right corner. By highlighting two adjacent cells containing different numbers, and by then dragging the corresponding handle, one can conveniently generate a row or column of numbers in arithmetic progression.

Exercise 1.1.1:
 (1) Place the numbers 0, 1, 2, and 3 in cells B3, B4, C3, and C4, respectively. Highlight the block B3:C4, grab its handle, and move it down or sideways. Note that one can drag only vertically or horizontally at the time, but can still make a block such as shown in Fig. 1.1 by dragging twice, e.g., first down and then, after momentarily releasing the handle, sideways (or vice versa). Note that this trick does not work for letters or other text, which is simply repeated. Try it.

	A	B	C	D	E	F	
1							
2							
3		0	2	4	6	8	
4		1	3	5	7	9	
5		2	4	6	8	10	
6		3	5	7	9	11	
7		4	6	8	10	12	
8		5	7	9	11	13	
9		6	8	10	12	14	
10		7	9	11	13	15	
11		8	10	12	14	16	
12		9	11	13	15	17	
13		10	12	14	16	18	
14		11	13	15	17	19	
15		12	14	16	18	20	

Fig. 1.1.1: The square B3:C4 (here shown with gray background) as extended by dragging its handle (not shown here) sequentially in two directions.

The more general way to fill a row or column uses a formula that is copied. In the example of Fig. 1.1.1, the result shown could have been obtained by entering the value 0 in cell B3, the formula =B3+1 in cell B4, copying this to B5:B15, entering the instruction =B3+2 in cell C3, and copying this to the block C3:F15. While this takes slightly more initial effort, it is not restricted to arithmetic progressions, and is also modified more readily and more reliably, especially when all constants involved are specified in separate cells, say B1 and C1, and are then called by their absolute addresses, as in =B3+$B$1 for cell B4, and =B3+$C$1 in C3, and the latter instructions are then copied down.

In complicated mathematical expressions it is often convenient to use easier to read, easier to remember, and therefore less error-prone symbolic range names rather than their cell addresses. In Excel you can also assign such names to constants, i.e., to parameters with an absolute address. The simplest method to assign such names is to highlight the cell containing the constant to be named, and then to move the mouse pointer to the Name Box on the Formula Toolbar, click on the cell address, type the name, and press Enter (on the Mac: Return). You can also use the sequence Insert ⇨ Name ⇨ Define, and then type the desired name in the Define Name dialog box. For fancier, so-called dynamic named ranges, see http:/www.ozgrid.com/Excel/advanced-dynamic-ranges.htm.

07, 10: Starting with Excel 2007, the above sequence of instructions no longer exists as such (and hotkeys are no longer automatically displayed by underlining), but was replaced by For<u>m</u>ulas ⇨ Define Na<u>m</u>e ⇨ <u>D</u>efine Name or AltMMD, while the Define Name dialog box is now called the New Name box. As a concession to old-time users, in Excel 2007 and Excel 2010 you can still use (most of) the corresponding hotkeys. In the above example of <u>I</u>nsert ⇨ <u>N</u>ame ⇨ <u>D</u>efine, depress in this order the Alt, I, N, and D keys, to yield the equivalent Name Manager dialog box. (The hotkeys are case-insensitive, i.e., it doesn't matter whether you use lowercase or caps. In older versions of Excel you may have to keep the Alt key down while you press the subsequent keys in succession.) The hotkeys may or may not yield the old instructions when they begin with the letter F, which used to specify <u>F</u>ile, but in Excel 2007 refers to the Office Button. (In Excel 2010 it is a <u>F</u>ile tab again.) Old-timers may also want to make their own Quick Access Toolbar, as described in section 1.2.8.

If you want to restrict the name definition to a given sheet, use the Define Name dialog box, and precede the name with that of the worksheet plus an exclamation mark, as in Sheet1!K1a. You can then define K1a differently on the next page. When the sheet is relabeled, the attached sheet name in the assigned cell name is updated automatically.

Note that the given name cannot be the same as an existing Excel instruction (such as Range, Next, End) or as a valid cell address: A2 or AB2 cannot function as names, but single letters (except R and C) and combinations such as AA or A2B can, because they cannot be confused with possible cell addresses. The letters R and C, either alone or followed by a number, cannot be used, because they would be interpreted in terms of the row/column notation. This restriction also applies to, e.g., function names: you can name a function to convert degrees Fahrenheit to degrees centigrade F2C, but Excel will not let you call its counterpart C2F.

The size expansion of Excel 2007 has invalidated many cell addresses that are valid in earlier versions, such as Ka1 or ABC3, and it is therefore best to change them, even if you keep using an earlier version of Excel, just in case you or someone else later imports that spreadsheet into Excel 2007 or beyond. You can readily change them into, e.g., K1a or AB3C.

Formulas typically refer to the contents of other cells. Once you have completed the formula, click on it in the formula bar, so that you will see the cells to which it refers, outlined in color-coded boxes with a corresponding coloration in the formula. It is quite common to make mistakes in assigning cell addresses, especially for cells in a different row and column, and the above check will catch most of those errors while you still remember how the just-completed formula is supposed to work.

It is sometimes convenient to add explanatory comments to spreadsheet formulas. This can be accomplished by incorporating the N function, which will convert values into numbers. Because it will translate text into zero, it can be added to formulas in such a way that it does not affect the calculation, but will show *in the formula box* when that cell is active. Say that you want to compute the sum of squares of the residuals, i.e., the differences between the squares of equivalent values in, e.g., C9:C87 and F9:F87. You can do that with the Excel instruction `=SUMXMY2(C9:C87,F9:F87)`, and you can include a label such as `=SUMXMY2(C9:C87,F9:F87)+N("SSR")`, or a more explicit comment such as `=SUMXMY2(C9:C87, F9:F87)+N("The sum of squares of the residuals")`, with the explanatory text within quotation marks inside brackets. Keep it short enough to fit inside the formula box. Better yet, you can attach a *cell comment*, a text box that can either be displayed continuously, or be displayable whenever the pointer hovers for a while over the comment indicator, a small red triangle in the top right-hand corner of the cell. A cell comment is added with <u>I</u>nsert ⇨ Co<u>m</u>ment or by right-clicking on the cell and selecting Insert Comment.

1.2 Setting up the spreadsheet

We now make sure to be all on the same wavelength. In this book we will use a number of auxiliary programs that come with Excel but that may not have been installed on your computer, e.g., if the software was installed using the 'Typical' option. Any resulting omissions are best remedied now, before you continue using this book. Moreover, you will need additional tools, some specifically developed for this book, others very powerful yet freely downloadable add-ins. Below we list these various components, and ways to make them available on your spreadsheet.

1.2.1 Data Analysis ToolPak

The Data Analysis ToolPak (or a variation of that name, depending on the Excel version used) contains many useful tools, including a random number generator, a data sampler, and many statistical tools such as anova, F-tests and t-tests. It may already be part of your spreadsheet, so first check whether you find it in the menu under Tools, usually at or near the very bottom. (Excel 2000 and 2003 have shortened menus that show only their most often used parts. The rest is still available, but you must either let the mouse pointer hover over that menu for a few seconds, or click on the chevron at the bottom of the menu to get the full display.) If it is not listed under Tools, check in the menu list under Add-Ins: it (and the associated (Data) Analysis ToolPak – VBA) may just need to be activated there. Otherwise, in the Add-Ins dialog box, click on Browse, and locate the drive, folder, and file for the (Data) Analysis ToolPak add-in; it is usually found in the MicrosoftOffice\Office\Library\Analysis folder. Then run the Setup program to install it. **07**,**10**: Click on the Office Button (**10**: File tab) ⇨ Excel Options (at the bottom of the dialog box) ⇨ Add-Ins ⇨ under Manage: at the bottom of the Add-ins box select Excel Add-ins and press Go… ⇨ click on Analysis ToolPak, Analysis ToolPak – VBA, and Internet Assistant – VBA, and (now that you are at it) Solver Add-in. Click OK.

1.2.2 Solver

Solver is an add-in, automatically included in the Full installation, but left out with skimpier installation protocols. (Why this is done defies logic, because Solver is one of the more useful features of Excel, available also in Lotus1-2-3 and QuattroPro.) When you don't find it listed under Tools on the Excel main menu bar, get the Excel or Office CD, and install it. (**07**,**10**: See under 1.2.1.) If your computer uses centrally administered software, you may have to involve the IT department to activate as Solver.

The above lets you *use* Solver, but (except in **07**,**10**) doesn't allow you to *call* Solver as a subroutine, as is done by, e.g., the custom macros ColumnSolver and SolverScan of the MacroBundle, as described in chapter 4. To permit such automatic calls of Solver requires the following additional action. First click on the Start button and, in the resulting menu, on Search, For Files or Folders ... (or Find ⇨ Files or Folders). In the Find: All Files dialog box, under the tab Name & Location, in the Name: window type Solver.xla, and, if necessary, enter Systemdisk[C:] in the Look in: window, activate Include subfolders, and click on Find now. Jot down where Solver.xla is located. (If you have Microsoft Office, it most likely is in Systemdisk[C:], Program Files, Microsoft Office (with or without a version number), Office, Library, Solver.) Exit the Find dialog box, which will bring you back to the spreadsheet, select the VBA editor with Alt⌣F11 (on the Mac: Opt⌣F11), then go to Tools ⇨ References, which will display the References – VBAProject dialog box. Click on Browse, select Files of type: Microsoft Excel Files (*.xls, *.xla), and now that you know where to find it, navigate your way to Solver.xla, and Open it. This will return you to the References – VBAProject dialog box, where you now use the Priority up button to bring it up, so that it is listed contiguously with the other, already activated add-ins. Click OK; from then on (i.e., until you reload or upgrade Excel) VBA will know how to find Solver when called from a macro.

07,**10**: For the Mac, you can freely download Solver from http://www.solver.com/mac/index2008.html for Excel2008, or from http://www.solver.com/mac/index.html for Excel 2011.

1.2.3 VBA Help file

Also check whether the VBA Help File has been activated and, if not, do so. This file contains help files specific to VBA, the computer language used in custom functions and subroutines.

MovieDemo4 in section 1.6 uses the VBA instruction `Volatile`. How would you find out what it does? Since it operates only in VBA, the Excel Help file does not list it, but the VBA Help file does. Likewise, the VBA Help file includes extensive information on how to use Solver as a VBA-driven function, material you would otherwise have a hard time finding. Last but not least, the VBA Help file displays a pop-up list of options when you type a VBA instruction followed by a period. Otherwise you would have to memorize Excel's Object Model or consult its Object Browser.

1.2.4 Downloading special software for this book

It is strongly recommended that users of this book install a number of free, open-access add-ins. They can all be downloaded from my excellaneous website. (You need not worry because I am not trying to sell you anything: these downloads are all free, don't install any cookies or spyware, and can be removed easily and completely if you don't like or don't need them anymore, just by deleting the contents of the folder in which you have put them.) I wrote most of the MacroBundle, and all of the MacroMorsels, but the most powerful add-in packages, such as those of Leonardo Volpi and John Beyers, can of course be downloaded directly from their original websites. With the explicit permission from their authors, I have merely collected them on my website for your convenience. I don't claim any authorship of them, but can attest to their being extremely useful for scientific data analysis, and free of any promotional stuff.

But first you need to decide on a space for these files. In principle you can put them anywhere, either together or scattered over your desktop and/or throughout your computer. I suggest that you put them all together in one folder, with a simple name such as AllAddIns and distinct from the existing AddIns files of Excel, kept in an easily reachable place, with all major packages in their own subfolders. This also makes it easy to update or remove them.

Point with your cursor to an empty space on your desktop, right-click, then click on New ⇨ Folder. An icon in the shape of a manila folder will appear, with its (temporary) name New Folder highlighted. (If a New Folder already exists, the name will be New Folder (2) or something like it.) With the cursor pointing to its highlighted name, right-click to open the associated pop-up menu, select Rename, type AllAddIns, or whatever other name you prefer, and click Enter. Double-click on the file to open it: you will mainly see an empty white window with its new name showing in its title bar. Then in this folder, using the same sequence of right-clicking and then clicking on New ⇨ Folder, make subfolders and name them MacroBundle, MacroMorsels, XN, Matrix, etc. Exit any folder by hitting its close button, ⊠.

If you like to keep your desktop clutter-free, you might prefer to keep your AllAddIns folder just below the surface, such as in MyDocuments. Alternatively you might want to put the subfolders in files that Excel has already called AddIns, such as Tools ⇨ Add-Ins, or in the AddIns file where VBA will look first, which is most readily found by opening Excel, clicking Alt⌣F11 to open the VBEditor, and then selecting Add-Ins to get to the Add-Ins Manager. Even more hidden from view is the file Add Reference, which you also find in the VBEditor, but now under Tools ⇨ References by clicking the Browse button. For the sake of simplicity I will assume, in what follows, that you keep all your add-ins in an AllAddIns file on your desktop. If not, put it elsewhere, and make a note of where you put it.

Once you have decided on the file name and location, you need to do three things: (1) download the file and store it in your AllAddIns file, (2) install it so that Excel knows where to find it, and (3) install XN and Matrix in the VBEditor if you intend to write your own functions and macros, so that you can use their functions in your VBA code. Downloading will be essentially the same for all add-in files, provided that you have an unzip routine on your computer (because some of these files might be too large to reach you otherwise) and have a pdf reader for the associated help files. Various unzip routines are available on the web, some of them free, and a free pdf reader is available from http://get.adobe.com/reader/. On the other hand, these routines require different installation procedures, which will be described in detail below. But first, here is how you download the MacroBundle from my excellaneous website.

Go to the internet, click on my website at http://www.bowdoin.edu/~rdelevie/excellaneous, click on *downloads* in its opening paragraph, then in the Downloads section double-click on *MacroBundle*, and in the FileDownloads dialog box click on Open. A text file with the heading MacroBundle will appear. If it opens in Word, click on <u>E</u>dit ⇨ Select A<u>l</u>l, otherwise highlight its top line, and use Shift‿PageDown to highlight the entire file. Copy it to the Clipboard (e.g., with Ctrl‿c), then click on the AllAddIns folder to open it, then on the MacroBundle subfolder, and paste the copied text with, e.g., Ctrl‿v. Return to the Desktop, and likewise download the MacroMorsels, which you place in the MacroMorsels subfolder.

You can avoid having to type in the sample macros used in this book, and their test data, by down-loading the files SampleData and SampleFunctionsAndMacros. You can store these in their own subfold-ers, or just place them as such in the AllAddIns folder. For legality's sake, also download the short GNU General Public License, which specifies what you can do with the above routines without having to ask for specific permission. Return to the desktop; you have now successfully downloaded all these files.

For chapter 10 you will need to download Matrix.xla, which deserves its own subfolder. Matrix.xla extends the number of matrix operations from Microsoft's puny handful to well over one hundred, includ-ing multiple tools for a variety of matrix functions, including for eigenfunctions, eigenvectors, and singu-lar value decomposition. A brief listing of its functions can be found in Table 10.9.1. If you are interested in matrix algebra you may also want to download BigMatrix.xla.

Much of chapter 11 depends heavily on XN.xla (**07**,**10**: XN.xlam), which from now on will often be referred to as XN. It is primarily software to get past the double-precision restraints of the IEEE-754 dou-ble-precision protocol used by Excel. XN also contains a large number of useful double-precision and quadruple-precision tools that will be used in many other places throughout this book.

An additional, very worthwhile add-in, Optimiz.xla, is used for high-precision optimizations, of which section 4.24 especially highlights the Levenberg-Marquardt routine that consistently outperforms Solver in tests using the NIST Standard Reference Data sets for nonlinear data fitting. (**10**: Solver can now compute in 64-bit, quadruple precision, even though Excel cannot.)

Finally, there are several loose items that were taken from Volpi's website: Volpi's dedicated spread-sheets Random_plot.xls and Simonluca Santori's IsoL.xls. Place these in the AllAddIns file, with their explanatory notes, as well as the reference file for the MathParser mentioned in section 8.16.

Download all of these, or at least the ones in the left-hand column of Table 1.2.1, and put them in sep-arate subfolders in your AllAddIns file, even if you may not yet know what they can do for you. (**07**,**10**: right-click, and select Properties ⇨ General ⇨ Unblock). Together they will take up about 33 MB; Table 1.2.1 breaks that down into its component parts. And if, after reading this book, you find some of them not useful to you, just delete them; it is as simple as that. While 33 MB was considered huge in terms of the 1981 memory limit of 1 MB of IBM's first personal computers, it fills up less than 5% of a modern CD, less than 0.5% of an 8 GB USB stick, and an even smaller fraction of your computer memory. Just a few high-resolution pictures will take up more memory space.

MacroBundle	1.0 MB	SampleFunctionsAndMacros	0.3 MB
MacroMorsels	0.3 MB	SampleData	0.2 MB
Matrix.xla	8.6 MB	BigMatrix.xla*	4.3 MB
XN.xla(m)	7.4 MB	IsoL.xls*	1.1 MB
Optimiz.xla*	7.1 MB	Random_Plot.xls*	3.2 MB
GNU General Public License	0.1 MB	Reference for clsMathParser	0.4 MB

Table 1.2.1: Approximate memory requirements of the various suggested downloads, after unzip-ping. *Routines marked with an asterisk have not yet been verified to work with Windows7 or Vista.

1.2.5 Installing the MacroBundle & MacroMorsels

The MacroBundle and MacroMorsels are .doc text files that you can read with Microsoft Word. After reading chapter 8, the code in the MacroMorsels (and perhaps even the MacroBundle) may make sense to you, and may become useful as building blocks for any functions and macros you may want to develop yourself. Initially, however, we will treat the MacroBundle as a collection of black boxes. They are, intentionally, the simplest possible form of macros, without the fancy UserForms that allow tighter controls on input data and may give your macros a more professional look, but that make them less transparent to beginners and take extra time to learn to program.

Near its beginning, the MacroBundle has a description of how to place it, as is (i.e., explanatory comments and all), in an Excel module, by downloading it, and then pasting it directly into an Excel VBEditor module. First, copy the MacroBundle to the Clipboard with Ctrl⌣c. To find the module, open Excel, and click on Alt⌣F11. When you see a dark area without any text, in the Menu bar above it click on Insert ⇨ Module. Then paste the MacroBundle in the module with Ctrl⌣v. The Excel workbook in which you have placed it will then 'know' what to do with the MacroBundle, and will automatically save it with its contents (⓿⓿,⓿⓿: save as .xls*m*, otherwise the macros will *not* be saved). After installation of the Macro-Bundle, go back to the spreadsheet, click on Alt⌣F8 or Tools ⇨ Macro ⇨ Macros, and see the just installed macros listed. For easy access to them, in that list find and double-click on InsertMBToolbar, which will create a MacroBundle Toolbar so that these macros are now only one or two clicks away. (⓿⓿: All functions and subroutines, including macros, are accessed in the Developer Ribbon. Activate the Developer Ribbon with Office ⇨ Excel Options, select the Popular tab, and put a check-mark next to Show Developer Tab in the Ribbon. ⓿⓿: As for Excel 2007 but now use the File tab instead of the Office button.)

For the MacroMorsels follow the same procedure. No toolbar is provided for them, since you will not need them that often. The SampleFunctionsAndMacros need not be loaded in a VBEditor module at this time; you can access individual parts in them when you need those, at which time you highlight the needed part, copy it, and insert it in your VBEditor module. The SampleData do not need any installation, because their relevant parts are to be pasted into the spreadsheet itself whenever needed.

For legality's sake, also download the short GNU General Public License, which specifies what you can do with the above routines without having to ask for specific permission. (In short: you have automatic permission to use, copy, share and even pilfer everything in these files, at your own responsibility and risk, as long as this software and/or any of its components are neither sold nor used in or for other direct commercial purposes, including promotions and advertising. Moreover, they cannot be incorporated without written permission in for-profit software. And when you use these routines (or significant parts thereof) in your publications, please refer to their source, so that others can learn about their existence.

If you intend to use one or more macros of the MacroBundle as provided, you can place them in a workbook called Personal.xls (or Personal Macro Workbook in the Mac), which will open automatically (though invisibly) every time you open Excel. You can find it under Tools ⇨ Macro ⇨ Record New Macro under Store macro in:. If, however, you want to modify the routines in the MacroBundle to suit your own needs, it is better to keep them out of Personal.xls, because if you ever get tempted to modify them inside Personal.xls and end up inadvertently writing an infinite loop (as at some point you will), you may have trouble extricating yourself from it. But if you place these routines in any other Excel spreadsheet, they will be saved only with that particular spreadsheet (and in Excel 2007/10 only when you save them specifically *with* macros, as an .xlsm or .xltm). You must either load them again in any new spreadsheet where you intend to use them (which is what I prefer), or otherwise have another open spreadsheet containing them (but which can be minimized, so that it takes up no spreadsheet space).

1.2.6 Installing Matrix.xla, BigMatrix.xla, XN.xla(m) & Optimiz.xla

The installation of Matrix.xla will be used here as our model. (For ⓪⑦,⑩: substitute XN.xlam for XN.xla. Note that Matrix.xla, BigMatrix.xla, and Optimize.xla do not have .xlam versions, and the latter two may or may not run in Vista.) We will assume that you have downloaded Matrix.xla in a subfolder Matrix in the AllAddIns file on the desktop, as described in section 1.2.4. Note that Excel already has several files called AddIns, which is confusing. We therefore suggest that you use a different name, such as *All*AddIns. If you named your files differently, and/or placed them somewhere else, make corresponding changes in the instructions given below. You can install these files now, or wait until you need to do so. For the sake of convenience, and in order to avoid unnecessary repetition, we describe the process here.

Some of these add-in files come in compact .zip format, which in Windows 2007/10 might be blocked because of security measures. Before unzipping them, therefore choose Properties, select the General tab, and click Unblock Apply OK. Otherwise you might need to do this for every individual file, which can get rather tedious, especially for the .chm helpfiles. Make sure to *read* these help files in order to use the new configuration settings.

Installation in Excel.

(1) Open Excel, and go to Tools ⇨ Add-Ins. (⓪⑦: Office button or ⑩: File tab, then ⓪⑦,⑩: ⇨ Excel Options ⇨ Add-Ins ⇨ Go. From Excel Options, click Trust Center ⇨ Trust Center Settings ⇨ Macro Settings ⇨ Trust Access to the VBA project. Make sure that the add-in is in a Trusted Location in the Trust Center; if not, select Add New Location and type its address. When, upon opening an Excel workbook with the add-in, you get a Security Warning, click on Options ⇨ Enable this content. You might also want to Enable automatic update in Trust Center Settings ⇨ External Content.

(2) In the Add-Ins dialog box, click on the `Browse` button.

(3) In the resulting Add-Ins dialog box, go to the Up One Level icon (a manila folder with an ⌐ at the top), and repeatedly click on it until you have reached the Desktop. If you have put your AllAddIns folder somewhere else, now go down to where it is located.

(4) Double-click on the AllAddIns folder, then on the Matrix subfolder.

(5) Click in the File name window, type Matrix.xla, and click OK. Do *not* specify its version number; this will make it easier to replace a given version of Matrix.xla by an update.

(6) This will get you back to the earlier Add-Ins dialog box, which will now show Matrix and Linear Algebra for Excel v.2.3, preceded by a tick mark.

(7) Click OK. This will close the dialog box. You will now see a Matrix dialog box with an OK and a book button. Press that OK button.

(8) You have now installed Matrix.xla in Excel. The formula bar will show a book icon with a white M on a blue background; clicking on that icon will display a short (4-item) Matrix Toolbar. Clicking the icon once more will delete the toolbar: the icon is a toggle switch for the toolbar.

(9) The toolbar contains a number of useful macros, some of which we will use later. But regardless of whether or not the toolbar shows, you will have access to the functions of Matrix.xla via the Paste Function icon f_x. Click on it, and select Function category: All, then scroll down the window labeled Function names: till you reach function names starting with an M, such as `MAbs`, `MAdd`, and so on, including the names of such unmistakable matrix functions as `MCholesky`, `MEigenvalJacobi`, or `MEigenvec`.

When you have forgotten where you hid Matrix.xla, click on the Start button (at the left-hand bottom), select Search, click on All files and folders, in the window labeled All or part of the file name: type Matrix.xla, click search, and voilà, you will see where you had placed that file. When opening a spreadsheet already linked to Xnumbers.xla, you need to Edit ⇨ Links and Change Source in order to link it to XN.xla.

There is a bug in some versions of Excel that does not allow you to Change Source (when you have lots of data) unless you click on Tools ⇨ Options, select the Calculation tab, under Calculation click on the round button in front of Automatic, and exit with OK. (⓪⑦,⑩: From the 2007 Office Button, or the 2010 File tab, under Excel Options, select Formulas ⇨ Calculation Options.)

Installation in VBA.

(1) If you want to use these matrix functions in custom-made routines, such as you might want to write yourself, you must also install Matrix.xla in VBA. The procedure is analogous to that for Excel, and thus should now be rather easy. However, if you only will use Matrix.xla(m) as provided, you need not do this – anyway, you can always do it later when the need arises. Here is how you do it.

(2) In the Excel spreadsheet, click Alt⌣F11.

(3) In the resulting VBEditor or Visual Basic menu bar, click on Tools ⇨ References to get to the References – VBA Project dialog box.

(4) Click on the Browse button to get to the Add Reference box.

(5) Use the Up One Level icon to get to the Desktop, then click to open AllAddIns, then Matrix.xla (or maneuver from there to wherever you have stored Matrix.xla).

(6) In the Add Reference box, click inside the File name window to activate it, then type Matrix.xla.

(7) Make sure that the Files of type: window selects Microsoft Excel Files (*.xls, *.xla).

(8) Push the Open button to return to the References – VBA Project box. This should now list VBAMatrix, with a tick mark.

(9) Press the Priority Up arrow till the line VBAMatrix is contiguous with the other tick-marked (i.e., active) reference files, which may take more clicks than you care for. Once done, click OK.

(10) Return to the spreadsheet with Alt⌣F11.

For XN.xla follow the same installation procedures. I use XN.xla6051-7A, and for Excel 2007/10 you might want to load the corresponding XN.xlam6051-7M version, the fastest versions with up to 630 decimals. There may be a newer version when you read this, and/or you may want to use a different packet size, with a larger maximal numberlength but a slower execution time. The specific version used will show in the Add-Ins box as Xnumbers followed by its version number and, when entered, will show an Xnumbers box for Multi-Precision Floating Point Arithmetic and Numerical Methods for EXCEL. Push the (rather misleadingly labeled) Exit button to install a purple book icon with the letter X. You can again check that XN is installed by clicking on the Paste Function icon and scrolling down to function names starting with x, where you will now find such function names as x_And, x2Dbl, xBinomial, xCplxA-CosH, xEval, xMatInv, xRegLinCoef, and many more.

Clicking on the X-book icon will bring up a three-item XN Toolbar, which contains macros and, under Help, two very useful help files, the Function manager which lists all functions and macros of XN, and the very extensive Help-on-line manual. The toolbar will toggle on and off by clicking on the X-book icon. XN installed in the VBEditor shows in its References – VBA Project box as Xnumbers60.

Incidentally, the second (2008) edition of this book described and used the related Xnumbers.dll, which is useful for making macros. For the sake of continuity, Xnumbers.dll can still be downloaded from Volpi's or my website, but I will not use it in the present edition, because it will no longer be supported. It has been superseded by XN.xla (**07**,**10**: XN.xlam), which is more convenient, more powerful, and can be used throughout Excel, i.e., on the spreadsheet, in VBA functions, and in VBA macros. Moreover, XN also works in Excel 2007/2010, which Xnumbers.dll will not.

BigMatrix and Optimiz only need to be installed in Excel, not in VBA, because they only contain macros, and lack VBA-callable functions. Once BigMatrix and Optimiz are installed, they are inserted in the Tools menu, from which you can call them. They both have manuals: that for BigMatrix is obtained with Tools ⇨ Big Matrices ⇨ Manager ⇨ Help, that for Optimiz through Tools ⇨ Optimiz ⇨ Info version, and then clicking on the book icon.

To uninstall an item from the AllAddIns collection, delete or remove the xla(m) file. When asked in a dialog box whether you indeed want to delete it, answer in the confirmative.

1.2.7 Links to R

Excel is a general-purpose software package designed for business applications, and it cannot be all things to all people. Leonardo Volpi has done much to add scientific and engineering functionality to Excel, but it is still weak in its statistical tools. This is where R comes in, a free, open-access command-line language that contains a quite extensive and still growing collection of statistical packages. A recent, very interesting link to R is provided by the RExcel add-in that can connect Excel to R, a (Unfortunately, RExcel doesn't work on the Mac.) A related program, Rcmdr (J. Fox et al., http://socserv.socsci.mcmaster.ca/jfox /Misc/Rcmdr/) works on Windows, MacIntosh, and Unix computers, displays R script and output windows, and also makes it possible to place any R program on the Excel menu. A lavishly illustrated book by R. M. Heiberger and E. Neuwirth, *R Through Excel* (Springer 2009), shows many simple, worked-out examples using both RExcel and Rcmdr. This must do until one or more statisticians, building on the work of Volpi and Beyers, will contribute sophisticated statistical routines for Excel.

1.2.8 Links to commercial software

As illustrated in this book, the great flexibility of the spreadsheet allows us to incorporate many personalized tools as custom functions and macros. Moreover, there are powerful aids available, often freely downloadable, which further extend these possibilities. The popularity of the spreadsheet also led many specialized commercial software providers to make their products spreadsheet-compatible. Here we will merely mention a few examples of two different types of such adaptations: add-ins that, after installation, function as if they were part of Excel, and links with other products. There are too many of such add-in products to even attempt a complete listing. They usually complement Excel in areas that the spreadsheet lacks, such as symbolic mathematics, or where Excel is particularly weak, such as in statistics.

Examples of the first category are the interfaces between Excel and *Maple* and *Mathematica*, mathematics packages that can do both numerical *and symbolic* mathematics. Both certainly 'know' more math than most graduating math majors, and both have superb 3-D graphics. Maple includes its Excel add-on package in its basic software, whereas Wolfram Research requires its users to buy a separate *Mathematica link for Excel*. These add-ins make Maple or Mathematica directly accessible through Excel, including their extensive collections of functions in its Standard Add-on Packages, and still more in its specialized packages (which again must be purchased separately) such as those in electrical engineering, mechanical engineering, and real-time 3-D visualization. The user must buy (or have institutional access to) both Excel and Maple or Mathematica, plus (in the case of Mathematica) the rather expensive link between them.

In order to access such functions once Excel and, e.g., Mathematica, have been installed and linked, the Mathematica command on the spreadsheet must be wrapped in quotes and then identified as a Mathematica instruction, as in =Math("6!+8!"), which yields the sum of the factorials of 6 and 8 as 41040. This expression can be applied to the contents of, e.g., cells C3 and D3 respectively with the command =Math ("#1!+#2!",C3,D3), and can then be copied to other places in the spreadsheet just like any other Excel function, using relative, absolute, or mixed addressing. Of course, Excel also provides a factorial function, and the same result can therefore be obtained more easily as =FACT(6)+FACT(8) or =FACT(C3)+FACT(D4), but Mathematica contains a wealth of functions Excel doesn't have.

It is also possible to embed Mathematica functions in Excel macros, and to manipulate Mathematica using Excel's VBA. Still, the software systems are so different, and their links so non-intuitive, that many users with access to both may opt to keep and use them separately.

An example of the second category is the set of 76 statistical routines provided by the Numerical Algorithms Group (NAG) as its Statistical Add-Ins for Excel. These add-ins, specially made for Excel, might be a way around some of the documented deficiencies in Excel (see section 1.13) but to my knowledge they have not yet been tested against the NIST standards. Some of these routines overlap with functionality built into Excel (though often at higher accuracy), while others significantly extend the power of Excel, such as the principal component and factor analysis routines. A free 30-day trial of the NAG add-in for Excel is available at http:/extweb.nag.com/local/excel.asp, or from secondary freeware/shareware distributors such as www.download.com.

1.2.9 Choosing the default settings

In Excel, as in Windows, almost anything can be changed. It is useful to have *default settings*, so that one need not specify everything every time Excel is started. It is often helpful for the novice to have fewer (potentially confusing) choices. Once you have become familiar with Excel, you may want to make changes in those default settings to make the spreadsheet conform to your specific needs and personal taste. Here are some of the common defaults, and how to change them.

By default, Excel displays the standard and formatting *toolbars*. Excel has many other toolbars, which can be selected with View ⇨ Toolbars. You can even make your own toolbar with View ⇨ Toolbars ⇨ Customize. An existing toolbar can be positioned anywhere on the spreadsheet simply by dragging the two vertical bars at its left edge (when it is docked in its standard place) or by dragging its colored top (when not docked). **07,10**: The above commands will not work in Excel 2007, which replaced the standard and formatting toolbars by a set of ribbons. But there is still a customizable Quick Access Toolbar next to the Office Button, which you can use to make your own Excel 2007 toolbar, as described in section 1.2.8.

Many aspects of the spreadsheet proper can be changed with Format ⇨ Style ⇨ Modify (**07,10**: Alt⌣OS), including the way *numbers* are displayed, which *font* is used, and cell *borders*, *colors*, and *patterns*.

Many Excel settings can be personalized in Tools ⇨ Options. Under Tools ⇨ Options ⇨ General you can specify, e.g., the number of *entries* in the *Recently used file list*, change the *Standard font* (e.g., from Arial to a more legible serif font such as Times New Roman) or perhaps use a different font *Size*. Here you can also set the *Default file location* (from C:\My Documents) and define another *Alternate startup file location*.

Under the View tab (i.e., under Tools ⇨ Options ⇨ View) you can toggle the appearance of *spreadsheet Gridlines* on or off. Under the Edit tab (Tools ⇨ Options ⇨ Edit) you can (de)select to *Edit directly in the cell*, which allows you to edit in the cell (after double-clicking) rather than in the formula bar. Here you can also *Allow cell drag and drop* or disallow it, and specify whether and how to *Move selection after enter*, i.e., you might prefer the cursor to stay put rather than move down one cell after each data, text, or formula entry. (**07,10**: Alt⌣TO likewise opens the Excel Options dialog box, where you can find these same options, albeit under freshly renamed categories.)

Excel does not make *backup files* by default. If you wish to change this, use Files ⇨ Save As ⇨ Options or Files ⇨ Save As ⇨ Tools ⇨ General Options and select Always create backup. (**07,10**: Use AltFALG.) You can also automate periodic saves with Tools ⇨ Add-Ins by activating the Autosave Add-In. (**07,10**: Office Button ⇨ Excel Options, click on Save, then activate Save AutoRecover and specify the interval.)

When you print with the Print button on the Standard Toolbar, you use the default printing settings. File ⇨ Page Setup provides many alternatives, including *number of copies*, *paper size* and *orientation*, etc., depending on the printer used. (**07,10**: Office Button ⇨ Print.)

In Excel 97 through 2003, browse in Tools ⇨ Customize to see (and select) your Toolbars and their Commands. You can click on a command and then use the button to get its Description.

Likewise, in Excel 97 through 2003, the default setting for the graph type is accessible after you activate a chart to make the Chart menu available. Select Chart ⇨ Chart Type, and under Chart type pick your choice, XY(Scatter), and Set as default chart. Even better, you can define the format of the default chart. Say that you dislike the gray background and the horizontal gridlines that Excel puts in its XY plots. Make a graph the way you like it, e.g., with a white background (activate the plot area, select Format Plot Area, then select Area None or the white square) and without the gridlines (activate a gridline, right-click, or double-click on the Mac, and select Clear). With the chart still activated (so that the C̲hart button is accessible in the menu toolbar) click on C̲hart ⇨ Chart T̲ype, select the Custom Types tab, click on the U̲ser-defined option button, then on A̲dd. In the next dialog box, specify its N̲ame, give an (optional) D̲escription, S̲et as default chart, and exit with OK. Then, the next time you highlight a block and invoke I̲nsert ⇨ C̲hart you will get the selected format by pushing the F̲inish button on step 1 of the Chart Wizard. Or, faster, highlight the area involved, and type Alt‿i, Alt‿h, Alt‿f (for I̲nsert ⇨ C̲hart ⇨ F̲inish).

In Excel 2000 and Excel 2003, the menu bars and toolbars initially display only those items that you have used most recently; the others are out of view, even though they are still available by clicking on the chevron at the bottom of the menu, or by waiting a few seconds. If you don't like this feature, go to V̲iew ⇨ T̲oolbars ⇨ C̲ustomize, select the O̲ptions tab, and undo the checkmark for Me̲nus to show recently used commands first. (**07**,**10** have replaced these toolbars by ribbons, with space to display everything plus lots of space to spare.)

1.2.10 Making your own 2007 toolbar

07,**10**: If you prefer to use a single toolbar rather than (or in addition to) the set of Excel 2007 ribbons, you can customize the Quick Access Toolbar next to the Of̲fice Button. You can then enter your favorite icons, click Alt to find their hotkey (a number followed by a letter, as in 0J) and even, if you want, switch the ribbons off with Ctrl‿F1 while retaining this toolbar. (The ribbons will return as soon as you click Ctrl‿F1 again, so that you retain full access to all Excel 2007 commands. The presence of a toolbar containing the commands you use most often will greatly reduce the number of times you would otherwise need to switch between ribbons.) Excel still uses its earlier toolbars at all its lower levels. Moreover, you can still make your own toolbar in VBA, as illustrated in section 8.21, but this will show only in the Developer ribbon, whereas the Quick Access toolbar is always displayed.

To create your own general-purpose Excel 2007 toolbar, click on the tiny Customize Quick Access Toolbar arrow to the right of the Quick Access Toolbar, click on Mi̲nimize the Ribbon, then on M̲ore Commands, under Choose commands from: pick All Commands, select your favorites and, one-by-one, A̲dd them or double-click on them. The macros come from the category Macros, a list that includes some Excel functions, such as LinEst, and any add-in macros you may have entered. Arrange them to taste with the up and down buttons.

Here is a set of icons that I would incorporate in the Quick Access Toolbar if, for some reason, I should have to use Excel 2007: New, Open, Save As, Print Preview, Print, Paste Special, Name Manager, Undo, Redo, Find, GoTo, Insert Chart, Fill Color, Font Color, Font Size, Bold, Italic, Symbol, Split, Align Left, Center, Align Right, Orientation, Borders, Clear Comments, and Formula Auditing. Mind you, all this only takes up about half of a single row on my monitor screen, leaving plenty of space for the workbook name. I might even add a few macros, such as Propagation, LS0, LS1, SolverAid, ForwardFT, and InverseFT. (Macros take up little space on the Quick Access Toolbar, but are all shown with the same, generic macro icon. Hover over them with your pointer to find their names, and click Alt if you want to find the associated hotkeys.) In this way you can do most of your work with the pesky ribbons out of sight, and without having to relearn many new names for old commands that you use routinely. Incidentally, none of this affects the Formula Bar just above the working area of the spreadsheet, which since Excel 2003 contains the icon f_x for the Insert Function, or the Status Bar just below that working area, which now has a useful zoom feature.

1.2.11 Switching from pre-07 Excel to a more recent version of Excel, or vice versa

Until 2007, Excel users had come to expect forward-compatibility for any updates, but this no longer applies to Windows Vista, Office 2007 and Office 2010. Be prepared for a number of changes in the 'look and feel' of Excel when you switch from earlier versions of Excel to Excel 2007, primarily in the replacement of toolbars with wider but less densely populated ribbons, forcing the user to switch repeatedly between ribbons. Moreover, many common commands have merely been renamed. Therefore, those used to the older versions should count on spending some time before becoming familiar with the new spreadsheet environment and its new nomenclature.

As already mentioned, if you have to switch between earlier versions of Excel and its later incarnations, you may have to change names assigned to constants. That, however, is the unavoidable consequence of the increase in spreadsheet size, which makes addresses out of almost all two- and three-letter combinations followed by a number. Obviously, some old names can no longer be assigned to constants, because Excel would not know whether you mean to call a cell address or an assigned name, in which case it will interpret the name as an address. You can usually avoid this problem by making a relatively small name change, such as moving a number between rather than after the letters, e.g., K1a instead of Ka1, or by using names with four or more letters.

Apart from the above, you may not encounter any problems in going from pre-07 Windows and Office to Vista and Office 2007 or Office 2010. All your spreadsheets should run, and all your add-in functions and subroutines should work. The operating word here is *should*, because there are some major hitches, especially with sophisticated add-ins that use compiled (.dll) kernels, such as Xnumbers. So far I have neither encountered or heard of any difficulties with the simpler add-ins that use non-compiled code, which the VB Editor interprets line-by-line, such as those in the MacroBundle and the MacroMorsels.

Moving in the reverse direction is of course more complicated. The mechanics are simple enough: if you want to make the 2007 or 2010 spreadsheet available to Excel 5 or Excel 95, save it as an Excel 5.0/95 Workbook (*.xls); if the intended user has a more recent version, save it as an Excel 97/2003 Workbook (*.xls). Obviously, if you have used more than 256 columns (i.e., beyond the letter combination IV), and/or more than 65536 rows, the additional cells will be truncated. And any functions new to Excel 2007 or 2010 will also be lost. This means that there is no gain in using Excel 2007 when those spreadsheets must be shared with those still using earlier versions of Excel. Error messages will alert you to the possibility of such losses, although they lack specificity as to what cells are affected, and merely identify the problems as involving "some" formulas or "some" cells.

Such losses can be avoided by using a Compatibility Pack for Office XP or Office 2003, a freely downloadable facility that lets users of XP or 2003 open, use, and save the 2007 and 2010 versions of Word, Excel, and PowerPoint. There is no comparable solution for users of earlier versions.

Incidentally, when you save an Excel 2007 spreadsheet, make sure to specify the .xls*m* format, since the default Excel 07 format for file saving, .xls*x*, will *not* retain any macros, while earlier versions did.

1.3 Making 2-D graphs

Graphs form an integral part of science and technology, because well-designed visual images are usually interpreted more readily than data sets. Excel makes it easy to generate publication-quality 2-D graphs. In order to make a graph, we first must have something to show in it. Below we will use *simulated* data, generated with the (Data) Analysis ToolPak. See section 1.2.1 if you cannot find ToolPak listed under Tools.

But first a brief technical excursion. In Excel, graphs are made of at least two largely independent blocks: the *chart* area, and the smaller *plot* area. To these you can add other independent blocks, such as legends, labels, and other textboxes; the latter can be placed anywhere within the chart area. The data are shown inside the plot area. The larger chart takes up the total space of the graph, and contains the plot area plus a region surrounding it on all four sides, which may contain text. Thus, the chart surrounds the plot in the same way as a mat surrounds a drawing or watercolor painting. Axis labels and legends can be either inside or outside the plot area, but must be within the chart area. In this book, most chart borders have been deleted, but (with the exception of some 3-D plots in section 1.4) the plot borders have been retained.

Exercise 1.3.1:

(1) Enter the sequence 1, 2, 3, ... , 1000 in A1:A1000. From now on, such an arithmetic progression will be denoted by its first and last members and, within brackets, its increment, i.e., as 1 (1) 1000. In recent versions of Excel this can also be accomplished as follows: enter the starting value (here: 1 in cell A1), highlight it, then use <u>E</u>dit ⇨ F<u>i</u>ll ⇨ <u>S</u>eries. In the resulting dialog box, specify Series in <u>C</u>olumns, Type <u>L</u>inear, <u>S</u>tep value: 1, Sto<u>p</u> value: 1000, OK.

(2) Open the Data Analysis ToolPak with <u>T</u>ools ⇨ <u>D</u>ata Analysis, then in the Data Analysis dialog box use the scroll bar and select Random Number Generation. In its dialog box, select <u>D</u>istribution: Normal (for Gaussian noise), click on the round 'option' or 'radio' button to the left of <u>O</u>utput Range, click on the corresponding window, and enter N1:N1000 (it is easy to remember that we have synthetic *n*oise in column N), then click OK.

(3) In cell B1 enter the instruction =10+N1, then double-click on the handle of cell B1 to copy this instruction to B2:B1000. The newly copied column acquires the length to which the adjacent column is filled contiguously, and will not work when there are no adjacent, contiguously filled columns.

(4) With column B still highlighted, use Shift⌣← (by simultaneously depressing the Shift and back arrow keys) to extend the highlighting to the two-column block A1:B1000, then use <u>I</u>nsert ⇨ C<u>h</u>art, select XY(Scatter), pick your style of Chart sub-type (with markers and/or lines), and <u>F</u>inish. (In general do *not* use the Line chart, which assumes that all points are equidistant, i.e., that all *x*-values are equally spaced, regardless of whether or not this is true.)

(5) Click on the superfluous Legend box (which will then display its 8 handles), and delete it (with the Delete key). Your graph should now resemble Fig. 1.3.1.

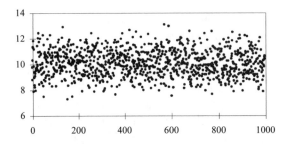

Fig. 1.3.1: A simulated data set of 1000 data with an average value of 10 and Gaussian noise with a standard deviation of 1.

We can modify the various components of the graph by right-clicking (on the Mac, use Ctrl⌣click instead) or double-clicking on them. The most often modified elements are the function shown, and the axes. Click on the data and try out some of the options available in the F<u>o</u>rmat Data Series dialog box. These include smoothing the curves using a cubic spline (Smoothed line under the Pattern tab) and, for multiple data sets, the use of a secondary axis (highlight the series, click on F<u>o</u>rmat ⇨ <u>S</u>elected Data Series and, under the Axis tab, click on <u>S</u>econdary axis). Click on the numbers next to the horizontal axis, then change their font and size using the font and size windows on the formatting toolbar. Click on the vertical axis and try out some of the many options available in the Format Axis dialog box, including (under the Scale tab) using a logarithmic and/or reversed axis. Click on the background to get the Format Plot Area dialog box, or on the graph edge to find the Format Chart Area dialog box instead. Or, for more drastic changes, look under <u>C</u>hart, which appears in the Menu bar instead of <u>D</u>ata when the graph is activated. In the following exercise we will import a label, calculate 9-point averages and their standard deviations, and display these as error bars.

In ❼,❿ you likewise highlight the area you want to graph, then select the Insert ribbon, click on Scatter, then on the choices shown (points with or without straight or smooth curves), at which point you automatically switch to the Design ribbon of the Chart Tools. You can then select from a number of (in my opinion rather tasteless) Chart Styles or, alternatively, click on the line, right-click, and select <u>F</u>ormat Data Series, which gives you a wide choice of options, including many decent ones. The above examples involve a single function or data set. In order to introduce another data set with the same abscissa (horizontal axis), just highlight that set, copy it to the clipboard with Ctrl⌣c, click on the display area of the

14

graph, and paste the data with Ctrl⌣v. To enlarge or reduce part of a data set displayed in a graph, click on a corresponding line or data point (marker) in that graph, then either change its range description in the formula box, or move the cursor to the input data and drag the now colored frames around the *x*- and *y*-values by their handles in order to surround their new ranges. Make sure that the *x*- and *y*-ranges have the same lengths. No special action is needed when enlarging (or reducing) a data set by inserting new rows (or deleting old ones) *inside* existing columns, or for new columns inside already existing rows of data. But before you delete one or more rows or columns, carefully check (e.g., with the Trace Precedents and Trace Dependents auditing tools described in section 1.15.4) that no other data on the spreadsheet will be affected.

Exercise 1.3.1 (continued):

(6) To compute averages and standard deviations of pairs of nine successive data points, deposit in cell C5 the instruction =AVERAGE (B1:B9), and in cell D5 the command =STDEV(B1:B9). Highlight the block C1:D9, and double-click on its handle. You will see the averages and corresponding standard deviations appear on rows 5, 14, 23, 32, 41, etc.

(7) In order to plot C1:C1000 versus A1:A1000, copy the graph you made for Fig. 1.3.1, and in that copy click on a data point. The columns A1:A1000 and B1:B1000 will now be outlined with color. Go to the top of cell B1, grab its colored edge when the mouse pointer is an arrow, and move it over to cell C1. This will change the *y*-axis assignment of the graph to C1:C1000 vs. A1:A1000, see Fig. 1.3.2.

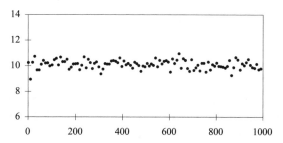

Fig. 1.3.2: Averages of groups of nine successive data points from the data shown in Fig. 1.3.1.

(8) To add error bars, click on a data point, right-click (on the Mac: Ctrl⌣click) to get the Format Data Series dialog box, and select the Y Error Bars tab. Highlight the Display: Both, select Custom:, and in both windows type =Sheet1! D1:D1000 (assuming that your spreadsheet is called Sheet1; otherwise, instead use whatever name shows on the tab below the working area of the spreadsheet). Compare with Fig. 1.3.3.

For error bars in **07**, **10** switch to the Layout ribbon of the Chart Tools, and select Error Bars in the Analysis group. This yields four fixed options plus, under More Error Bar Options, a Format Error Bars dialog box for Vertical error bars. You can short-circuit this entire procedure with AltJARM. For the corresponding horizontal error bar dialog box, click on those error bars in the figure.

(9) If you want to see a smaller fraction of these data, copy the graph, and in the copy right-click (on the Mac: Ctrl⌣click) on it to change the appropriate range, and in the resulting Format Axis dialog box, under the Scale tab, change the Minimum and Maximum values, as well as the Major and Minor units. Also change the *y* range, and the size of the markers.

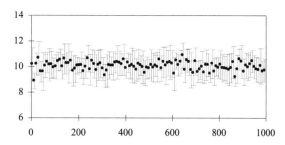

Fig. 1.3.3: The same data as in Fig. 1.3.2 with added (light gray) error bars.

(10) To enter text, click on the plot area of the graph so that the plot border (its inner framing) is highlighted. Type the text in the formula bar, then depress Enter (on the Mac: Return). The text will now appear in the graph in a text box, which you can move and shape with the mouse pointer. By passing over the text with the mouse key depressed, you can activate the text, then use Format ⇨ Text Box ⇨ Font to change its appearance. You can also insert chart titles and axis labels, or (often more flexible) text boxes.

Excel ⑰,⑩ has an ActiveX TextBox, accessible through the Developer ribbon ⇨ Insert by clicking on the Text Box (the fifth item on the first row) under the ActiveX Controls. Move the pointer, which is now a thin plus sign, to the graph, and use it to outline the box. Then right-click on the box, select TextBox Object ⇨ Edit, and enter your text.

(11) To highlight a particular point, double-click on it (the mouse pointer changes into crossed double-pointed arrows) to see the options in Format Data Point, where you can change its appearance. A few examples are shown in Fig. 1.3.4; color can also be used.

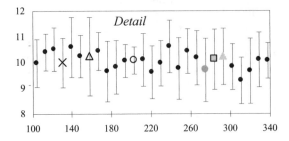

Fig. 1.3.4: Embellished detail from Fig. 1.3.3, with a few individual points highlighted with different markers (or, not shown here, colors).

When displaying more than one function in a single graph, it may be necessary to add a second ordinate (vertical axis) on the right-hand side of the plot. To do this, click on the particular data set in the graph that you want to associate with a second vertical axis, select its Format Data Series dialog box, and under the Axis tab select Secondary Axis.

Sometimes Excel places an axis somewhere in your graph (typically at $x = 0$ or $y = 0$) where you may not want it. If so, move it by selecting Format Axis and, under the Scale tab, change the Crosses at:. Note that you need to select the horizontal axis to move a vertical axis, and vice versa.

Some of these aspects are illustrated in exercise 1.3.2, which shows the use of two different axes by plotting the proton and hydroxyl ion concentrations as well as the pH as a function of the proton excess $\Delta = [H^+] - [OH^-]$. The plots for $[H^+]$ and $[OH^-]$ have two linear asymptotes, whereas that for pH has the typical shape of a titration curve. Instead of gray you may want to use a darker color.

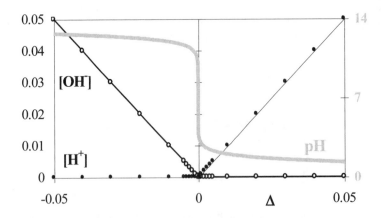

Fig. 1.3.5: Using two vertical axes. This rather complicated plot shows the values of $[H^+]$, $[OH^-]$, and pH = $-\log[H^+]$ as a function of the proton excess $\Delta = [H^+] - [OH^-]$. Gray is used here instead of color to identify the secondary (right-hand) scale and the corresponding curve.

16

Exercise 1.3.2:

(1) Here we illustrate the use of two different axes by plotting the proton and hydroxyl ion concentrations as well as the pH as a function of the proton excess $\Delta = [H^+] - [OH^-]$.

(2) Start a new spreadsheet, and in column A make a table of Δ with the values −0.05 (0.01) −0.01 (0.005) −0.005 (0.001) 0.005 (0.005) 0.01 (0.01) 0.05 where the numbers within brackets indicate the data spacing.

(3) In columns B, C, and D compute $[H^+] = \{\Delta + \sqrt{(\Delta^2 + 4 \times 10^{-14})}\}/2$ (assuming for convenience the value $K_w = 10^{-14}$), $[OH^-] = 10^{-14}/[H^+]$, and pH $= -\log[H^+]$.

(4) Highlight the data in columns A and B, and plot them in an XY graph. Select appropriate *x*- and *y*-scales.

(5) Highlight the data in column C, copy them with Ctrl⌣c, then highlight the plot border, and paste the data of column C into the graph with Ctrl⌣v. Select marker size and style, line thickness and/or colors to distinguish the two curves.

(6) Again highlight the plot border, type the text of appropriate function labels, use Enter (Mac: Return) to place them in the graph, maneuver the mouse pointer over the text to where the pointer takes the shape of a capital I, move it to highlight the text, then use Format ⇨ Text Box to modify the appearance of the text, and finally move the pointer to where it becomes a cross, at which point you can drag the label to its final place. Mmm

(7) Likewise, highlight the data in column D, copy them, highlight the plot border, and paste the copied data in the graph. Now click on these data, right-click (Mac: Ctrl⌣click), select Format Data Series, and under the Axis tab specify the plot series as Secondary Axis. In **07**, **10** the Format Data Series dialog box likewise has a Secondary Axis among its Series Options whenever the graph contains more than one data set.

(8) If, as in this example, the data in column D all fall outside the vertical range already established for the other data, replace one data point in column D by a temporary value (such as 0), and click on it to establish the secondary axis. Afterwards repair that point.

Use line width, marker type and size, and (if your final output can display it) color to emphasize important aspects, and to make your graph more intelligible. Resist the temptation to put too much information in a single graph: visual overload defeats the purpose of a graph. In fact, the information in Fig. 1.3.5 would be better illustrated in two separate graphs, one plotting $[H^+]$ and $[OH^-]$ vs. Δ, the other showing pH vs. Δ. The rule of thumb is: two is company, three is a crowd, unless the curves all belong to the same family. And do read the books by E. R. Tufte, especially *The Visual Display of Quantitative Information* (Graphics Press, P.O. Box 430, Cheshire CT, 1992) on the design of effective as well as visually pleasing graphical displays.

If you want to include details, use multiple panels or inserts; sometimes, a logarithmic scale will work. The Fourier transform of the tidal data shown in Fig. 5.10.2 are displayed there as three panels with different vertical scales in order to show both the major peaks and the harmonics. An alternative, logarithmic plot of the same data is illustrated in Fig. 1.3.6 and conveys the same information in a single frame.

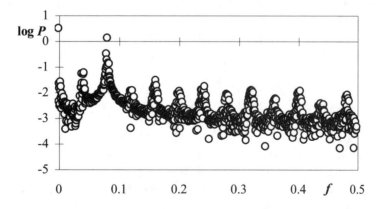

Fig. 1.3.6: The data in the three panels of Fig. 5.10.2 combined in a single, semi-logarithmic display, i.e., as the corresponding power spectrum.

It makes for a good-looking spreadsheet, and makes copying graphs into Word much easier, if you make sure that the graph is in register with the spreadsheet grid. To align, highlight the chart area (by clicking on the region between the right edges of the plot and chart areas), move the mouse to a corner of the chart area, grab the double-sided arrow, and drag it to a cell corner *while depressing the Alt key*. Doing this with two diagonally opposed corners will align the graph with the cell grid. When so aligned, a graph can be lifted off the spreadsheet for copying into Word, PowerPoint etc. by highlighting the underlying cell block, copying it to the Clipboard, and using Edit ⇨ Paste Special to move it to its new target.

Inserts are best made as independent graphs. After the insert is the way you want it, move it so that it is completely inside the area of the main graph, and adjust its scales, labels and symbols to fit with the main graph. By highlighting the cell block *underneath* the main graph you can then lift both off simultaneously and, e.g., transfer them to a Word or PowerPoint document. This book contains several examples of inserts, such as Figs. 4.5.2 and 4.5.3.

A figure is "worth a thousand words" because we can take in its main message through a primarily 'right-brain', intuitive, nonverbal action, absorbing 'at-a-glance' its overall, holistic impression. In his *Elements of Graphing Data* (Wadsworth 1985, Hobart Press 1994), W. S. Cleveland calls this graphical *perception*, whereas extracting specific, numerical information from the graph would be a *cognitive* (conscious, typically 'left-brain') task, like reading that information from a table, which is usually slower, especially when many data are involved. It is the first impression of a graph that should make its main, qualitative point, drawing the viewer's attention, and keeping it there long enough to absorb its quantitative message.

A good graph immediately conveys its main message. It should be unambiguous, and it should look good. Especially the latter requirement is highly subjective, something you should keep in mind while reading my recommendations. These are suggestions, not laws; follow your own taste and, above all, use your own good judgement. Unfortunately, not all of these suggestions are easily implemented in Excel, but most are, as you can judge for yourself from the illustrations in this book. So here goes.

* Always use an XY (scatter) plot rather than a line plot. A line plot tacitly assumes an equidistant horizontal scale; an XY plot treats both axes as fully flexible, with assignable scales.

* Directly conveying the main message of a graph requires both simplicity and clarity. The simpler the graph, the more immediate, visual impact it can have. Therefore, restrict the number of *points you want to make* (though not necessarily the number of *data points shown*) as much as possible.

* Don't overload the viewer with too much information, with too many (especially overlapping) data sets and/or curves. In general, only show multiple curves when they are either closely interrelated, or when discussing details, as in Figs. 1.3.5, 1.10.2 through 1.10.5, or 1.11.1. The sparser the graph, the more clearly it can emphasize its main features.

* Distinguish between the experimental data (with markers) and the assumed (or fitted) theoretical model expressions (as smooth curves), especially when the latter are continuous. (Discrete binomial and Poissonian statistics may require straight, possibly broken connecting lines.) Make the experimental points stand out from the fitted curves. When appropriate, emphasize individual points, as in Figs. 1.10.2 through 1.10.5.

* As much as possible, keep text out of graphs, and make them alternatives to (rather than mere extensions of) the text. Explanations and/or conclusions are best placed in the figure legend, and/or in the accompanying main text. Simple curve labels are often useful, but Excel's legend boxes (which refer to series numbers that in turn need an explanation) in my opinion are not.

* Preferably use simple, linear scales. If logarithmic scales must be used in order to compress the information (compare Figs. 1.3.6 and 5.10.2), label them clearly as such, in the graphs and/or in the accompanying legend. Ten-based logarithms are more familiar, and therefore more readily decoded, than logarithms based on either e (i.e., ln) or 2 ($\log_2$).

* Adjacent distances (lengths and heights) are more precisely read from a graph than angles; areas are worse, and volumes even more so. Therefore, stay away from pie charts, which exclusively rely on angles and on areas or volumes.

*It is best to use simple numbers to label axis tick marks. Using tick marks all around the graph (rather than only on its two main axes) makes it much easier to estimate data values in the top right-hand corner of a graph. Unfortunately, Excel still cannot create all-around tick marks. An alternative is to use gridlines, but these can be visually distracting. When they are needed, make them thin, in light gray or in another light color.

* When two axes are equivalent, as when they show the real and imaginary components of a function in a complex plane, make sure that they also have the same scales, so that angles are shown correctly. This applies to quantities such as the complex dielectric constant and the electrical impedance, see Figs. 4.20.1 and 4.20.2.

* When points and/or curves overlap, use color (or gray-scale), marker size and type, different line types (thin or thick, continuous or broken), etc., to keep different data sets visually distinct. Otherwise, split the graph into different (adjacent and/or stacked) panels with identical axes. When a graph takes time to grasp, it most likely misses its mark.

 * Show the origin unless doing so leads to a large, unused space. Deleting the origin in order to emphasize a relatively minor change can be outright misleading. If breaking the axes is necessary, it is best to show those breaks explicitly, in both the axes and in any corresponding curves (although Excel has as yet no facilities for doing so). Otherwise, mention the offset prominently in the figure legend.

* Simple curves are most pleasing, and their slopes most readily compared, when the aspect ratio is near 1, i.e., when dominant slopes are close to $\pm 45°$. But if this requires that the origin be deleted, make sure that this is clearly indicated, see above.

1.4 Making 3-D surface graphs

Since we live in a three-dimensional world, 3-D graphs or maps can often display the qualitative features of a function of two parameters far better than a table can, and will be discussed in sections 1.4 and 1.5. While the two-dimensional surface of a computer screen or a printed page cannot contain a truly three-dimensional image, it can give the *illusion* of a third dimension, just as a painting or photograph can. That is what is meant by a 3-D graph. Excel cannot make general 3-D graphs, with arbitrarily spaced functions for all three axes. For complicated three-dimensional shapes, programs such as Mathematica, Maple, or AutoCad should be used. However, for one single-valued variable a 3-D surface graph can be made. It is really a three-dimensional form of Excel's Line plot, i.e., it assumes that the *x*- and *y*-values are *equidistant*, so that only the *z*-variable (plotted vertically) can have arbitrary values. Moreover, you will have much less control over its appearance than Excel gives you for 2-D graphs. Still, such a graph will often make a reasonable 3-D plot as long as the independent coordinates (say, *x* and *y*) are both indeed equidistant and the plot does not contain so many data points that many individual lines fuse.

> **Exercise 1.4.1**:
>
> (1) Open a spreadsheet, and enter the sequence 0 (0.2) 10 in both A2:A52 and B1:AZ1. Deposit the instruction =(1+SIN($A2*SQRT(B$1)/PI()))/2 in cell B2, and copy this to the area B2:AZ52.
>
> (2) Highlight the block A1:Z52. Specifically include the *x*- and *y*-axes, which will be used automatically to calibrate the axes. Call the Chart Wizard with Insert ⇨ Chart, select Surface and its top-left Chart sub-type, then Finish. Click on the graph, drag it to where you want it on the spreadsheet, and align with the grid.
>
> (3) Click on the Category or Series graph axis, right-click (Mac: Ctrl˷click) on Format Axis, select the Scale tab, and set the Number of categories between tick mark labels at 10, and the Number of categories between tick marks at 5. Under the Number tab, use 0 Decimal places. Repeat for the other axis. For the vertical Value axis in Fig. 1.4.1 we have used 0 Decimal places under the Number tab, and 1 for both Major and Minor unit under Scale. (The latter choice gets rid of the multiple colors and horizontal contour lines, but that is a matter of taste.)
>
> (4) In fact, the color of the surface net is one of the few attributes of a 3-D graph you can change. But even that is not easy, so pay attention. Click inside the plot area (but avoiding any objects such as markers and lines+) to activate it, then click on the Legend box. (If it doesn't already show, Select Chart ⇨ Chart Options, under the Legend tab select Show Legend, and click OK.) Now click on one of the colored boxes in the Legend box, then right-click to get the Format Legend Key (or start in the Formatting toolbar with Format ⇨ Selected Legend Key), and click on the colored marker specifying an area color. (In Fig. 1.4.1 we could also have selected the color white. Selecting 'none' would have shown the surface as a transparent wire frame.) Changing the major unit on the vertical axis controls how many color bands are displayed. Exit with OK. Afterwards, you can click on the Legend box and delete the box; the selected color(s) will stay. Fi-

nally, move your pointer to find the Floor, right-click and select F̲ormat Floor, then modify it to your taste. Do the same with the Walls.

(5) Rotate the graph to select a different point of view. Click on a top corner of a vertical background panel when it shows the Corners label. Grab the little square at the top front corner, and drag it to rotate the graph until it suits you. Also activate the 3-D toolbar by clicking on 3-D Settings under T̲ools ⇨ C̲ustomize ⇨ Toolb̲ars, and see how it works.

(6) In cell B2 now deposit instead the instruction =EXP(-5*(($A2-3)^2))*EXP(-10*((B$1-6)^2))+0.7*EXP(-(($A2-7)^2))*EXP(-2*((B$1-4)^2))+0.5*EXP(-3*(($A2-2)^2))*EXP(-5*((B$1-3)^2)), and copy this to the area B2:AZ52. Your graph might look like Fig. 1.4.2. (⑦: Highlight your data as above, then use I̲nsert ⇨ O̲ther Charts or Alt‿NO, click on one of the Surface Charts shown, click on the graph, select 3-D R̲otation, etc.)

(7) A fun picture is that of the Mexican or cowboy hat $z = 0.5 [1 + \cos \sqrt{(x^2+y^2)}]$ illustrated in Fig. 1.4.3 for $-10 \le x \le 10$, $-10 \le y \le 10$ with all axes, legends, and borders colored white to make them invisible. The function is scaled to fit within the range $0 \le z \le 1$ in order to avoid lines where it crosses these boundaries. Make it, and play with it by moving the corner and thereby changing the point of view. Then, for precise control, use C̲hart ⇨ 3-D V̲iew, where you can numerically specify elevation, rotation, perspective, and height. In Fig. 1.4.3 we have removed all coordinate frames by clicking on them and either removing them or coloring them white.

To add shading to a 3-D chart, select one of the small boxes inside the chart legend box (which define specific colors of the various regions of z-values), right-click on it, select Format Legend Key, then the Options tab, and check the 3-D shading option box. This will apply shading to the entire graph. If you then rotate the graph, the shading rotates with it, which can make a more dramatic effect. This works in both color and gray-scale; a few examples are shown on my website.

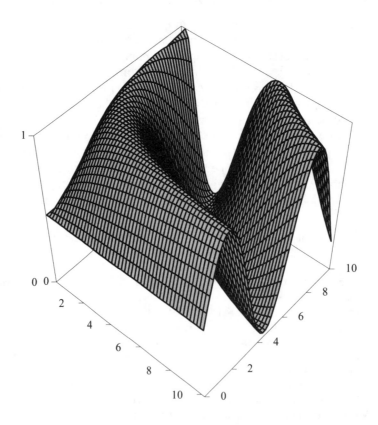

Fig. 1.4.1: A graph of the function $z = \frac{1}{2} + \frac{1}{2}\sin(x\sqrt{y}/\pi)$.

Because until Excel 2010 you could not control the line thickness of a 3-D line plot, it would become solid black when too many data are used. In that case it may be better to use several plots, e.g., one for an overview with a coarse grid and relatively few data points, and the other showing a specific detail with a finer grid. My excellaneous website shows how you can embellish these plots with color and/or shading.

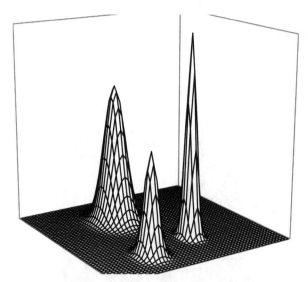

Fig. 1.4.2: A graph of three Gaussian peaks.

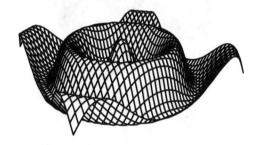

Fig. 1.4.3: The Mexican or cowboy hat, $z = \frac{1}{2}(1+\cos\sqrt{(x^2+y^2)})$, using the precise controls of
Chart ⇨ 3-D View. Top: Elevation 30, Rotation 70, Perspective 30, Height 100% of base.

Orienting 3-D graph by dragging one of its corners is more intuitive, but the digital controls provide the same resolution but make it much easier to come back to a given perspective. Tickmark labeling is best done after settling on a given orientation, so that tickmark labels don't overlap in, e.g., a strongly foreshortened axis. Axis labels do not move with the graph, and therefore must also be added afterwards.

Volpi has incorporated a 3-D plot in his Random_Plot.xls spreadsheet, which avoids some of the above-mentioned nuisances, such as that its labels don't move when the plot is rotated. It can be downloaded from my excellaneous website or from http://digilander.libero.it/foxes/RandomPlot.htm, and by then clicking on Random_Plot.xls at the bottom of the first downloaded page. Here we will merely illustrate its 3-D plot of the Rosenbrock function, *Comp. J.* 3 (1960) 175-183, a common test of optimization algorithms, with added shading as described above. In Random_Plot.xls the axis labels do follow the rotation.

In using Random_Plot.xls, make sure that the numbers listed in cells A7:D7 correspond with those you must enter in the domain box in C15:C18. In the present case, in cell A7 enter −2 for Xmin, and enter 2, -1, and 5 in B7 through D7. On the top line of the domain box, in cell C15, place x>=−2, and on the three lines below type x<=2, y>=−1, and y<=5 respectively. Highlight those four lines, i.e., cells C15:C18, and push the Plot button in the Domain selected box. Then, to the right, click on the Plot 3-D (stereo) button, and finally look at the result by selecting the plot 3D workbook tab. If necessary, click on one of the axis numbers, right-click on Format Axis, and adjust the axis scale, font, number, and alignment to your taste, then hover with the cursor near an edge, click when you see the Corners box, and move that corner (or any other corner, since they are now all highlighted) to rotate the graph to your liking

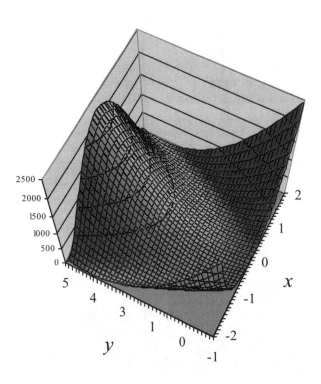

Fig. 1.4.4: The Rosenbrock function $z = 100\,(x^2 - y)^2 + (x - 1)^2$, plotted with Random_ Plot.xls over the range $-2 \le x \le +2$ and $-1 \le x \le +5$.

1.5 Making surface maps

Maps provide an alternative way to visualize a single-valued, three-dimensional surface, especially when that surface contains much detail. Maps are most satisfactory when one must display a large number of data points, precisely the situation where the grid of Excel's 3-D line plots may become too dense. 3-D line plots and maps are, therefore, largely complementary tools.

Traditionally, maps use color and/or contour lines to provide the impression of a third dimension. Color (or even gray-scale) maps are relatively easy to make as long as there are enough data to define each pixel. Excel has no built-in facilities for such maps, but here we will illustrate what can be done when we think a little 'outside the box'.

1.5.1 Color maps

As it turns out, it is possible to introduce color maps through a back door, because Excel has the option of using a picture as background for a graph. While that may have been intended for company logos, there is nothing to prevent us from using it for our maps. We therefore generate a picture based on the information we want to plot, i.e., with a gray scale or colors representing the values of the variable z in an *x,y* plot, and then mount this picture in the frame of that plot. The background picture then *is* the graph. The custom macro Mapper0 in the MacroBundle provides a continuous gray scale, while other versions of Mapper use various color schemes to represent height. Moreover, once you understand how to write code (see chapter 8) you can easily modify Mapper's color schemes to your own liking, or add your own versions. As implemented here, Mapper works only for equidistant *x*- and *y*-values.

Colors are coded in the RGB *additive* color scheme, in which all colors are represented in terms of three color components, *R*ed, *B*lue, and *G*reen, which roughly correspond to the maximum sensitivities of the three common types of cones in the human retina. (Some people have only two working types, a few have four.) The additive color scheme is used in light projection and in tv and computer monitors, which build the color sensation by adding light beams of different colors. In the additive system, red plus green yields yellow, while combining red, green, and blue colors in the right proportions leads to white. The alternative, *subtractive* color scheme is based on light absorption and reflection of the remainder, rather than on light emission. It is based on pigments and dyes, typically yellow, cyan, and magenta, and is used in color printing as well as in painting. Adding its three components leads to (a usually rather brownish or purplish) black rather than white.

Exercise 1.5.1:

(1) Open a spreadsheet, and enter the sequences –20 (0.4) 20 horizontally and vertically in, say, row 1 and column A.

(2) In cell B2 deposit the instruction for the modified Mexican hat, `=0.5*(1+COS(SQRT($A2*$A2+B$1*B$1)))/SQRT(100+$A2*$A2+B$1*B$1)`, and copy this to the area B2:CX101.

(3) Call the macro Mapper0 and see what you get. Then try colors (with Mapper1 through X), and other functions.

(4) Modify the axes to –50 (0.4) 50 horizontally and vertically, copy the same instruction to the area B2:IR251, and again call Mapper.

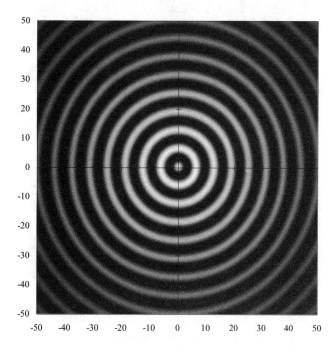

Fig. 1.5.1: The function $z = (1+\cos\sqrt{(x^2+y^2)}) / (100+x^2+y^2)$, a variation
on the cowboy hat, as represented (here in black and white) by Mapper.

Each RGB color is represented numerically by an integer with a value from 0 through 255. For example, black is (0, 0, 0), white is (255, 255, 255), pure red is (255, 0, 0), bright yellow is (0, 255, 255), while (180, 180, 180) yields a light neutral gray, etc. With three different colors to represent the single numerical value of each data point, there are many possible schemes to suggest height. Here we illustrate a gray

23

scale, for which the values for R, G, and B are the same. The colorful Mapper on the cover is described in section 6.10.

Just as Excel's 3-D graphs, Mapper can only display one surface per graph. Color maps lack the illusion of perspective obtainable by rotating 3-D graphs, but they can easily handle large data arrays, and can provide better scales and legends than Excel's 3-D graphs. They can be treated and modified like any other XY graph, and markers, curves, contour lines, and text boxes can all be added, see Fig. 1.5.2. However, keep in mind that these plots are made separately and then reimported into Excel, so that changing their axes does *not* alter the picture shown, only the displayed axis values.

In applying Mapper, place in the bottom right-hand corner whatever features you want to display in the bottom right-hand corner of the graph, etc. And make sure that the axis labels are *to the left* and *on top of* the data, and leave an empty space at the top left corner.

There is only one hitch in using Mapper, but that hitch is in Excel, not in the MacroBundle routines. When the X-axis runs from larger at left to smaller (i.e., less positive) at right, and/or the Y-axis from smaller at the top to larger at the bottom, Excel will invert the axis because it second-guesses that this is not what you had intended. Annoying, but not nearly as much as in the example at the end of section 1.8. Just right-click on the axis, and select <u>V</u>alue (..) Axis ⇨ F<u>o</u>rmat Axis ⇨ Scale ⇨ Values in <u>r</u>everse order to undo Excel's unwanted assistance.

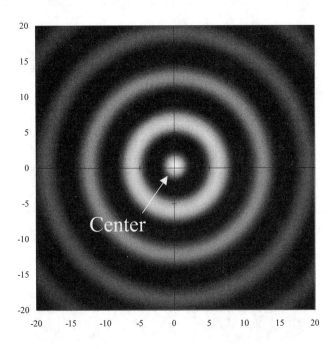

Fig. 1.5.2: The application of Mapper to the central part, BY109: FU209, of the data array used for Fig. 1.5.1, with superimposed (white) text, and with a (white) arrow from the drawing toolbar.

1.5.2 *Contour maps*

High-quality contour maps are more difficult and time-consuming to generate because they involve interpolation, but they can be made in Excel. Here we will highlight IsoL.xls (for *iso-livello*, Italian for iso-level or contour lines), a free, open-source custom macro written by Simonluca Santoro, which will generate an Excel contour diagram. If desired, it will even combine this with Mapper to color the resulting graph. It can be downloaded from Volpi's website http://digilander. libero.it/foxes/ SoftwareDownloads. htm as IsoL.zip, or from my website under ContourMap. Its operation and use are described in Volpi's "Plotting z = f(x,y) contour lines with Excel", which you can download from his foxes website under /documents.htm, and which is included in the Contour-Map download from my website. IsoL.xls takes a function defined on a rectangular grid, and interpolates in this grid by triangulation. It then draws contour diagrams using the interpolated data.

As input IsoL.xls takes either an Excel function, a rational function of the type $f(x,y)/g(x,y)$ where $f(x,y)$ and $g(x,y)$ are polynomials with positive integral powers of x and y of up to 4th order, or a look-up table, and generates the corresponding contour diagram, color map, or their combination. Just call the Excel spreadsheet IsoL.xls, specify the desired type of input and output, the data range (in terms of minimum and maximum values of x, y, and z), the number of data points per interval (i.e., the computational resolution), the number of contour lines, and the name and location of the output file. Then push Run; the macro will generate the plot as a free-standing graph in the specified output file. Afterwards you can treat that plot as any other fixed Excel plot, e.g., by changing its labels. In Fig. 1.5.3 we illustrate IsoL by showing a plot of the dimensionless van der Waals curve $z = (3/x^2+y)(3x-1)/8$, where $x = P/P_c$, $y = V/V_c$, and $z = T/T_c$. For reproduction in this book, the subroutine Mapper(xmin, xmax, ymin, ymax, Formula, Caso, Coeff, OutputFileName) was modified to yield a gray scale. (When in IsoL.xls, you can find this subroutine by clicking Alt‿F11, in the menu of the VBEditor module select View ⇨ Project Explorer, and then click on Modules, where you will find Mapper under Mapper_mod. That is also where you should go if you want to change its color scheme.

When you plot Mapper, you can use ScanF1 (also from the MacroBundle) to make a convenient data input listing for IsoL.xls. With a gradual Mapper scale you get a rough idea of what that contour diagram may look like, except for the contour lines themselves. Using the band diagrams of Mapper00, 000, or 000 and its colored equivalents will give you an even better idea, even though they still lack the neat resolution of IsoL.xls.

The detail available with IsoL is increased by using a denser grid (of up to 205 data points for x and/or y) selected in the top left-hand corner of the IsoL Input sheet, but this comes at the cost of slower execution, because the algorithm is fairly computer-intensive at about 100 operations per computed data point. It is therefore best to start with the contour diagram ('iso-level') and few contour lines, and to introduce additional lines and color only after you are satisfied that the result is otherwise just the way you want it. For large data arrays, Mapper's cruder band maps (as described in section 1.5.3) are much faster.

Exercise 1.5.2:

(1) Open IsoL.xls. It shows a special spreadsheet page, in-between a regular sheet and a dialog box. The first choices to be made are in blocks C8:E11, where you use the up arrow to select "3", an Excel function, and C14:C16, where you pick "1" for iso-level, i.e., contour lines.

(2) As your exercise function take an example from Volpi's "Plotting z = f(x,y) contour lines with Excel", and use a van der Waals curve made dimensionless by scaling the pressure P, volume V and absolute temperature T of a nonideal gas by its critical pressure P_c, critical volume V_c, and critical absolute temperature T_c, in which case the equation takes the simple form $z=(3/x^2+y)(3x-1)/8$ where $x=P/P_c$, $y=V/V_c$, and $z=T/T_c$.

(3) Go to cell O24 on the IsoL.xls sheet, where you enter the above formula as =(3/M24^2+N24)*(3*M24-1)/8, where M24 contains x and N24 holds y.

(4) Go to the table in B2:E5. In C3 enter the minimum value of 0.2 for x, and in D3 its maximum value, 3.2. (Letting x start at 0 would yield a run-time error as the first term in the expression for z, $3/x^2$, is computed for $x = 0$.) Likewise enter a 0 for y_{min} in C4, and the value 0.4 for y_{max} in D4. Set the corresponding resolutions in E3 and E4 to 20.

(5) In C5 place the value of 0.4 for z_{min}, and in D5 the value 2.0 for z_{max}. In E5 deposit the number of contour lines you want, in this case 9, for $z = 0.4 (0.2) 2.0$.

(6) Click on the New button in cells I2:J2, and specify a spreadsheet name, such as IsoTest1 in a folder of your choice. Click on the Parameters button in J9:K11 to preserve these settings, then press Run in J6:K8. After a short delay you should see the contour diagram.

(7) Verify that you indeed get the graph you want; it should have the main features of Fig. 1.5.3, but neither its resolution nor its background color. If the formula entered in O24 is incorrect, remedy it and run again. When you are satisfied that the plot is correct in principle, refine the settings as follows.

(8) In E3 and E4 select 200 instead of 20 to increase the computational resolution (and the corresponding time taken by the computation), and in E5 place the number 17 to create contour lines at $z = 0.4\ (0.1)\ 2.0$.

(9) In block C13:C17 select "3" for contour lines plus background coloring. Press Run once more.

(10) It will now take much longer to compute the contours, because the resolution of both x and y has been increased ten-fold, and there are twice as many contour lines to calculate, resulting in a 200-fold increase in computational effort.

(11) At this point you can leave well-enough alone, or further embellish the result. If you do the latter, and especially if you want to use it in a Word file or PowerPoint presentation, I suggest that your first action is to add a worksheet. Click on the Grafico tab, right-click and select Insert, and make a new Worksheet, most likely to be called Sheet1.

(12) Click on the Grafico tab to return to the graph, then move it from its fixed format as a separate sheet to a graph floating on a spreadsheet. This will allow you to shape it in any way you want without running into pixellation problems. So, click on the chart area (e.g., on the white band above the plot) to activate it (as indicated by the nine black handles that will appear on its corners and half-way its sides), right-click, select Location, and in the resulting Chart Location dialog box select As object in Sheet1.

(13) Again activate the Chart, and align it with the spreadsheet gridlines by pulling two opposite corners to grid corners while depressing the Alt key. Now you can apply any embellishments you want, and subsequently transfer the graph to Word or PowerPoint by merely activating the *underlying* spreadsheet cells, and using Paste Special to embed (or link) the graph.

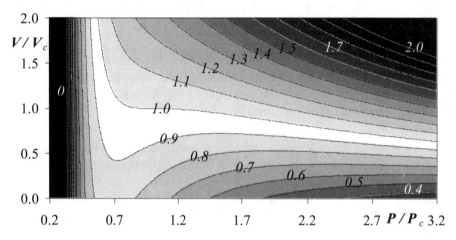

Fig. 1.5.3: A contour map drawn with Simonluca Santoro's IsoL.xls with background coloring (here shown in gray-scale), showing the dimensionless van der Waals equation $T/Tc = [3/(P/Pc)^2 + V/Vc] (3P/Pc - 1)/8$ where T is absolute temperature, P is pressure, V is volume, and the subscript c denotes the critical point. Array size 201×201; 21 contour lines. Values of T/T_c are indicated with the curves.

1.5.3 Band maps

In section 1.5.1 we saw that Mapper can make graduated color (or gray-scale) maps. This same routine can also display corresponding color bands, thereby making quick-and-dirty quasi-contour diagrams, e.g., at fixed percentage intervals. This works best for large arrays, because in that case the pixellation of the band edges is least noticeable, precisely those conditions where IsoL.xls is rather slow. Fig. 1.5.4 shows such a band map of the van der Waals equation displayed already with IsoL.xls in Fig. 1.5.3, and similarly annotated. We see that Mapper can indeed be used as a quick understudy for the more refined IsoL.xls. Here we placed the number one in the otherwise unused top-left-hand corner of the highlighted data block, which forces Mapper to set lower and upper limits, which were then specified as 0 and 2.1 to match the contours of Fig. 1.5.3.

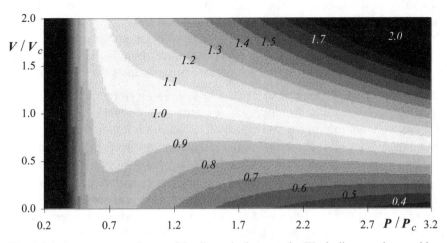

Fig. 1.5.4: A contour map drawn of the dimensionless van der Waals diagram, drawn with the 21-band gray-scale Mapper0000, with similar scale and annotation as in Fig. 1.5.3.

Figure 1.5.5 shows a map of the Rosenbrock function $z = 100 (x^2 - y)^2 + (x - 1)^2$, of which we already encountered a 3-D plot in Fig. 1.4.4. An array of 201×201 data points representing this function is displayed here with the 10-band Mapper00. This image shows the values of z calculated in a rectangular array of evenly spaced increments in the x- and y-coordinates. The parabolic valley of Fig. 1.4.4 is here seen as a black band, and does not indicate where the lowest point in that broad valley might be located.

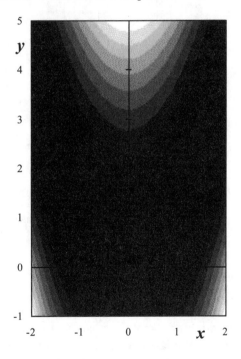

Fig. 1.5.5: A 2-D plot of the Rosenbrock function $z = 100 (x^2 - y)^2 + (x - 1)^2$ using Mapper00.

We now make a little excursion. Suppose that we want to localize that minimum value of this function. For that we can use the instruction Min(*array*) where *array* denotes the range of data in the table of z, say C5:GU205. In this case, place the instruction =MIN(C5:GU205) somewhere outside the data array. It will yield a value of 0.000 because the regular grid just happens to get you right on the proper spot. But where is that minimum located? On the scale of Fig. 1.4.4 you cannot tell, and Excel has no simple command to yield that address: its LookUp functions only work on either rows or columns that, moreover, must have been sorted first. We can, of course, write a function to do the search and produce the location of that minimum value, but here we will see how we can sometimes find it visually.

In this particular example, $z = 100 (x^2 - y)^2 + (x - 1)^2$ is the sum of two squares, and must therefore be positive for all real values of x and y. Moreover, the minimum value of z is apparently zero or very close to it. We might therefore want to plot log(z) instead of z, because a logarithmic scale tends to emphasize small values over larger ones. We therefore replace the formula used in the array, `=100*(E$4^2-$B6)^2+(E$4-1)^2`, by its logarithm, `=LOG(100*(E$4^2-$B6)^2+(E$4-1)^2)`, and call the higher-resolution 21-band Mapper0000. Now we obtain Fig. 1.5.6, with two white regions separated by a number of light-gray bands indicating that the minimum lies inside a narrow, lopsided gully, somewhere in the neighborhood of $x = 1$, $y = 1$. The picture obtained with the gradual Mapper0 closely resembles that found with Mapper000, because the contrast between adjacent gray-scale bands with only 5% differences in their darkness is too small in the absence of color. Figure 1.5.6 seems to suggest that the minimum may lie in a fairly narrow gully.

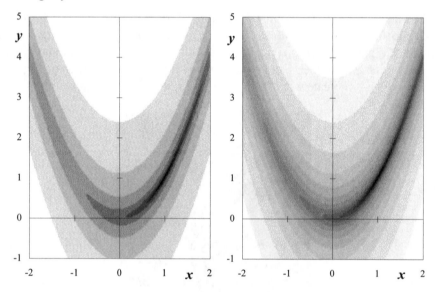

Fig. 1.5.6: Two band-plots of the logarithm of the Rosenbrock function, log(z) = log{100× $(x^2 - y)^2 + (x - 1)^2$}, using (left) 11-band Mappper00, and (right) 21-band Mapper 000.

Another available option is to use random values of x and y within the specified range, and then display those that fall inside alternate bands. Random_Plot.xls is set up to do this, as illustrated with the same Rosenbrock function in Fig. 1.5.7. Random_Plot also estimates the minimum and maximum values within its plotting range, which may provide a good starting estimate for subsequent refinement when you are, e.g., looking for the precise location of a minimum. As it turns out, the minimum in Fig. 1.5.7 lies within the wide band where no data points are shown, but the algorithm uses all of its data, including those that are not displayed, to estimate where the minimum and maximum might be located, and actually displays those two points. For better visibility the minimum estimated by Random_Plot.xls is shown in Fig. 1.5.7 as a white circle. Due to the stochastic nature of the samples taken by Random_Plot.xls, the estimated value of that minimum is off by a few percent, but at least it shows the neighborhood in which we might find it.

When we home in on that region we find that there is indeed a *very sharp* minimum at $x = 1$, $y = 1$, which is readily confirmed by substitution of these values into the Rosenbrock formula. The global minimum sits at the bottom of a narrow trench that Random_Plot happened to hit at some distance from the minimum. Note in Figs. 1.5.8 and 1.5.9 that the global minimum is quite narrow, making it difficult to find with the usual numerical search routines. The many graphical tools we now have available allow us to find such a hard-to-find minimum. If its entrance had been located on top of a ridge rather than at the bottom of a trench, it might have been impossible to find by the usual optimization programs.

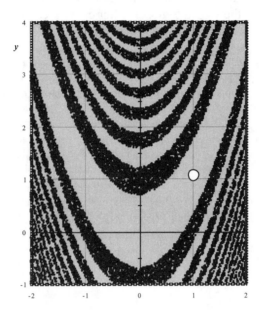

Fig. 1.5.7: A 2-D plot with Random_Plot.xls of the Rosenbrock function $z = 100\ (x^2 - y)^2 + (x - 1)^2$. The white circle indicates the estimated position of its minimum, at $x \approx 1.02703$, $y \approx 1.05704$, and the corresponding function value, $z \approx 0.001$, whereas the correct values are $x = y = 1$ with $z = 0$.

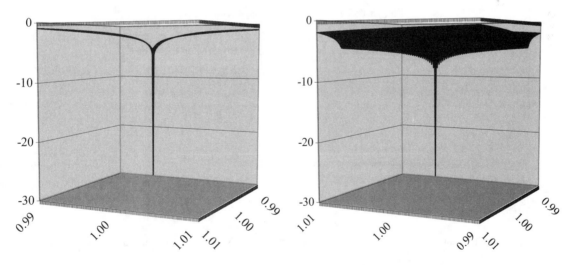

Fig. 1.5.8: Two close-up views in the region around $x = 1$, $y = 1$ of the minimum of the logarithm of the Rosenbrock function $z = 100\ (x^2 - y)^2 + (x - 1)^2$ with Excel's 3-D Surface Chart. The left-hand view is looking along the narrow trench in which the minimum sits, the right-hand view looks perpendicular to that trench. The minimum value of $\log(z)$ is at $-\infty$ which Excel represents as a large but finite negative number.

1.6 Making movies

Excel has a limited capability for making movies, which will not challenge Hollywood, but on occasion it may come in handy, if for no other reason than to break the monotony of a presentation. The MacroBundle contains a few demonstration macros (MovieDemo1 through 5) that illustrate how simple movements can be generated in an Excel graph. The trick is to make a computation that recalculates a number many times, and to force the screen to update after every recalculation.

Exercise 1.6.1:

(1) Open a spreadsheet, enter the number 0 in cells A1 and B1, and deposit the number 10 in A2. Highlight the area A1:B2, and use Insert ⇨ Chart to make a corresponding graph. Click on the axis (which may show the label Value (X) Axis or Value (Y) Axis), right-click (Mac: Ctrl click) to get Format Axis, and adjust both scales to have Minimum: 0 and Maximum: 10. Make sure that these values are not 'auto'matic (by turning off the top three check marks under Auto) because, in that case, the scale might change annoyingly as the movie plays. Moreover, for the duration of the show, turn off the spreadsheet gridlines (with Tools ⇨ Options, View tab, Gridlines).

⓿⓿-⓿⓿ : : Insert ⇨ Chart opens the Insert Chart dialog box. Select the category XY (Scatter), then double-click one of its five types. To make it your own, click just inside the outer edge and right-click on Format Chart Area, click inside the plot area and right-click to get to the Format Plot Area, click on an axis and right-click to find Format Axis, etc.

(2) Make sure that the graph displays A2:B2 vs. A1:B1 (for a square input array, Excel automatically plots rows vs. columns), and shows the individual point x,y (where the macro controls the x-value in cell A1, and the y-value in A2) prominently with an individual marker, with large size and striking color. Your starting graph should look like Fig. 1.6.1.

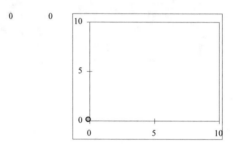

Fig. 1.6.1: The starting graph for MovieDemo1.

(3) Call the custom macro MovieDemo1, which is part of the MacroBundle, and enjoy the show. The instructions for this macro are shown below, and can be downloaded from the SampleMacros file on the website.

```
Sub MovieDemo1()

Range("A1") = 0
Range("A2") = 0

For i = 1 To 400
  Range("A1") = 10 - 0.05 * Abs(i - 200)
  Range("A2") = 10 * Exp(-0.001 * (i - 300) ^ 2)
  Application.ScreenUpdating = True
Next i

Range("A1") = 0
Range("A2") = 0

End Sub
```

(4) You should see the point trace a straight horizontal line on the way going, and a Gaussian peak on the way back.

Try the other MovieDemo macros of the MacroBundle. By clicking *once* on their name in the Macros dialog box, and then once on Edit, you will get to the VBA text used to code them. (To figure out how they work, you may have to read chapter 8 first, then make your own. Use different markers and colors to enliven the display.) Figures 1.6.2 through 1.6.5 illustrate the starting screens for these movie demos. Consult the heading comments of the MovieDemo macros for specific instructions on how to configure them, and where to place them. Have fun.

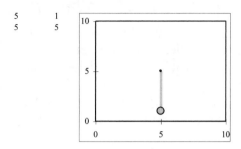

Fig. 1.6.2: The starting graph for MovieDemo2.

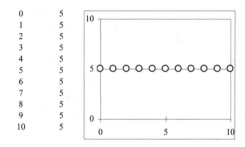

Fig. 1.6.3: The starting graph for MovieDemo3.

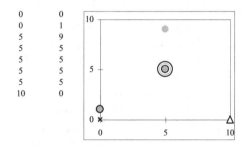

Fig. 1.6.4: The starting graph for MovieDemo4.

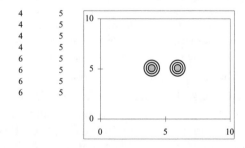

Fig. 1.6.5: The starting graph for MovieDemo5.

1.7 Printing, copying, linking & embedding

In order to print a spreadsheet, highlight the area you want to show, and print it. It may be helpful to add simulated spreadsheet axes (i.e., the letters A, B, C, etc. across, the numbers 1, 2, 3, etc. down), as was done in Fig. 1.1.1, because the grid parameters otherwise will not be shown. In some of our examples we also specify the instructions used, with the location where they are used first, and the cells to which they are copied. By placing the most important information at the top left-hand corner of the spreadsheet, perhaps even including one or more thumbnail graphs, it is often sufficient to show only that part of a large spreadsheet.

Exercise 1.7.1:

(1) To simulate a horizontal (letter) row atop a spreadsheet, color a cell in the top row (e.g., gray-25% of the Fill Color icon on the Formatting toolbar), accent it (with all-around thin border), copy it to the other cells in that row, and fill the cells with centered capitals such as A, B, C, etc. For the vertical (number) column, use the same approach (with numbers instead of letters), and set its Column Width to 3 points (after highlighting the entire column by clicking on its true column heading, followed by right-clicking or, on the Mac, Ctrl‿clicking).

Charts use absolute addressing, and therefore keep referring to their original input data even when moved around or copied. Note especially that this also applies to copying them to a new worksheet. To make compatible pictures it is often useful to make a copy, and then modify it. This can be done by highlighting each individual curve, and either changing its address in the formula bar, or clicking on the curve and dragging the identifying data frames to their new spreadsheet positions.

Copying a spreadsheet to another sheet in the same spreadsheet book is straightforward, except that embedded figures will still refer to the data series on their *original* sheet. To make the graphs reflect the values on the copied sheet, highlight each series in turn, and adjust its sheet name in the formula bar.

There are two different methods to import (part of) a spreadsheet into a Word document, *linking* and *embedding*. Embedding takes the part you select, and stores it permanently in the Word file. Linking instead establishes a connection ('link') between the spreadsheet and the Word document, so that any subsequent changes in the spreadsheet will be reflected in its image in Word. Not only does linking update the image in Word automatically when you subsequently make a change in the Excel file, but it is also much more efficient in terms of storage requirements. Unfortunately, in the experience of this author, linking has not always been reliable in Excel, and it may save you a lot of headaches to use embedding, provided that you can handle the resulting, huge data files. This is how you do it.

Exercise 1.7.2:

Highlight a block of cells in a spreadsheet, or an embedded graph. Store it in the clipboard with Ctrl‿c. Switch to the Word document, go to the place where you want to insert the graph, and make sure the corresponding line is formatted (Format ⇨ Paragraph) with the line spacing Single or At least, the only two formats that have self-adjusting heights and can therefore accommodate the picture. Then use Edit ⇨ Paste Special, click on Microsoft Excel Worksheet Object, deselect Float over text, and click OK. This is how all figures in this book were imported into the text.

Because embedding can require large amounts of space, it is not very suitable for use in, e.g., e-mail attachments, or for storage on what, not so long ago, were called high-density (1.2 MB) diskettes. In such cases it may be better to send (or store) text and spreadsheets containing graphs as separate items. Alternatively, if both sender and receiver can handle these, use CD's, USB flash memory sticks, or other high-capacity media, and/or use data compression, such as .zip or .pdf. Excel files that are either linked or embedded retain their vector nature, i.e., they are stored as equations, and can be resized afterwards without pixellation or loss of resolution. (Word allows many manipulations on embedded pictures, such as sizing, rotating, scaling, picture placement and text wrapping, cropping, and control over contrast and brightness. Just double-click on the image, and select Format Object.) All illustrations in this book were directly taken from Excel and embedded into Word, thereby preserving their original smoothness even if subsequently resized. This is the method of choice if publication-quality graphics are required.

There are other ways to paste Excel images into Word that require much less memory, such as by using the PrintScreen button to capture an image, which can then be pasted into Word (possibly after manipulation in Paint), or by using Save as Web Page to generate a GIF image to be inserted into Word. These methods are *not* recommended here because they store the image as a bitmap, a collection of pixels. Such graphs will show their discrete nature upon resizing, and the resulting *pixellation* has undeservedly given Excel graphics a bad name.

1.8 Entering & importing data

In general, data entry is made very easy in Excel, but there are a few details worth knowing. If you want to display a number as text, precede it with an apostrophe, or preformat the cell as Text with Format ⇨ Cells and, in the resulting Format Cells dialog box, select Text. (In ⓞⓩ, Home ⇨ Number or AltHFM will get you the Format Cells dialog box.) A green warning triangle may appear in the left-top corner of the cell, alerting you that the number is stored as text. When stored as text, leading zeros are retained. Note that you can still refer to the cell value in subsequent calculations.

When you want to show numbers as fractions, type them in the format *a b/c* where *a* is an integer, *b* the numerator, and *c* the denominator, e.g., enter 5/7 as 0 5/7, and 30/7 as either 4 2/7 or 0 30/7; typing 30/7 will display but will *not* be recognized as a value in subsequent calculations. Moreover, watch out for the automatic, irretrievable conversion of the typed fraction 3/16 into the date 16-March. And when you enter 3/16 in a cell after having selected its format as fraction, the result may show as 1/5 although the formula window shows it correctly as 0.1875. You avoid all such problems by using the equal sign, i.e., by typing =3/16, because the equal sign warns Excel that an equation is coming, in which case it interprets / as a divide instruction rather than a text character. However, in that case it will not display its value as a fraction unless you specifically format its cell as such.

Data copied directly from the web may fit directly into Excel, or may all squeeze into a single column (in which case they may *seem* to fit the spreadsheet columns, until you check what the formula bar shows for cells in the next column). You can avoid the latter situation by first converting them into a text format, e.g., by importing them into Notepad (which has the extension .txt rather than the Word extension .doc), and by saving them as such in a directory or on your Desktop. Then open Excel, select File ⇨ Open, make sure that the Open dialog box deals With files of type: All files (*.*) so that .txt files show, and select the Notepad file. Because the data are now presented to Excel as a text file, the Text Import Wizard will appear, in which you can specify how to treat the file. Usually the data are either separated by commas ('comma-delimited') or by empty spaces ('tab-delimited'), and after you tell the Wizard what you want it will execute your wishes.

When Excel encounters a cell containing what it considers a nonstandard date or number format, it will automatically, without asking, without leaving a trace, and *irretrievably* 'correct' it to what it thinks you must have meant. We already encountered a mildly annoying example of this at the end of section 1.5.1. Here is a much more serious one.

If you use Excel for genomic research, and want to represent, e.g., the tumor suppressor called Deleted in Esophageal Cancer 1, commonly abbreviated as DEC1, Excel will change DEC1 into 1-Dec automatically, and without warning. The standard abbreviations for septin proteins will likewise be changed from, e.g., Sept2 to 2-Sep. Even more troublesome than this presumed date conversion, Excel will perform a floating-point conversion by changing the RIKEN clone identifier 2310009E13 into 2.310009E+13 or even 2.31E+13, irreversibly! These problems are especially pernicious when large data files containing such abbreviations are imported into Excel, in which case you might not notice them. A possible workaround is to place a space or an apostrophe in front of all such names *before* they are imported into Excel. Alternatively, you can pre-label the receiving columns as text, see above, so that their contents will be considered as text strings. (This will not work with text imported directly as a Word .doc file; you should first use Notepad to convert the file to a .txt file before it into Excel.) For this problem see B. R. Zeeberg et al., *BMC Bioinformatics*, freely accessible at http://www.biomedcentral.com/1471-2105/5/80.

1.9 *Functions, subroutines & macros*

Excel is quite powerful, and comes with many functions, but it cannot be all things to all people. Fortunately, it has extra flexibility built in, allowing the user to personalize it by adding custom-made functions and macros to do things Excel might otherwise find difficult or impossible to do. The language used for these is VBA, an adaptation of Visual Basic, a modern and quite powerful computer language that is the user scripting language for in all parts of the Microsoft Office suite. Moreover, VBA will accept (with perhaps some minor modifications) earlier code written in modern versions of Basic, including TurboBasic and QuickBasic. In addition, VBA contains all the tools needed to communicate with the spreadsheet. Consequently there is no need to reinvent the wheel when writing your own functions and macros, because you can often find such material in the literature. And once you have your data on the spreadsheet, functions and macros can be made to read these directly. Chapter 8 will illustrate how to do this.

In this book we will use VBA as an interpreted (rather than as a compiled) language, which makes it easier to change but takes a large toll in execution speed. This is a major reason why VBA code becomes cumbersome to use for very large or complex programs.

Excel offers two custom-supplied VBA procedures: functions and subroutines. Of these, *functions* are somewhat restricted: they can only *display* (numerical and/or textual) *answers* in a single spreadsheet cell or cell block, but cannot also *take actions*, such as change the cell format and color, add comments, sound an alarm, reorganize the spreadsheet, open and close worksheets, etc. Within their restriction, though, functions can be quite powerful: they can use multiple inputs, write data arrays as their output, and can call other functions or subroutines as long as the end result only affects their own output.

Functions come in two flavors: public functions (the default) and private ones. Only the public functions show in the Insert Function box accessible via the icon f_x, whereas private functions can only be called from other functions or subroutines.

Excel's function LinEst and macro Regression illustrate some of the similarities and differences of functions and macros. Both use the very same algorithm, a quite powerful method based on matrix algebra that can solve both multivariate and polynomial linear least squares problems. But in order to use LinEst you will have to specify its output area whereas, for Regression, it is enough for you to indicate the top left-hand cell of its output. A function such as LinEst could also compute from its input how much output area it would need, but it cannot *act* on that knowledge.

An important advantage of functions over subroutines is that they respond automatically, and near-instantaneously, to changing input information, so that they need not be activated or called, but update themselves whenever a parameter affecting them is entered or modified. (By inserting the instruction `Application.Volatile True` you can even make them respond to any changes elsewhere on the spreadsheet, but this can slow you down quite noticeably in large spreadsheets.) Custom functions can be copied from one cell to another just as built-in Excel functions can, and are listed in the Insert Function dialog box you open by clicking on the f_x icon, in both the User Defined and All categories. Both custom functions and custom macros will be used throughout this book. Another advantage is that functions cannot be misused to introduce malicious software, because they cannot affect any other cells or objects beyond their assigned output.

Clicking on a particular function in the Insert Function dialog box helpfully displays the format of its argument, i.e., the information needed inside its brackets, and their order. It also allows you to enter that function in the previously highlighted spreadsheet cell, by clicking OK. However, do not click OK for so-called block (or array) functions that need more than one output cell, because OK will ignore that requirement even if you had highlighted an appropriate cell block.

Subroutines are not restricted to changing the output in a single spreadsheet cell, which makes them more powerful than functions, but also more difficult to write. In general, both functions and subroutines have input parameters that are specified in the function or subroutine call. (The argument list cannot contain output parameters, which are simply left in the subroutine or macro.) A subroutine without any input parameters is called a *macro*. Macros can be called directly from the spreadsheet, but they cannot be embedded in spreadsheet cells, nor do they update automatically. Instead, macros are stand-alone routines that must be called every time you want to use them. You will encounter many examples of custom macros in this book, and we will look at them in detail in chapter 8. You can use these specific examples as starting points for writing *your own* functions, macros, and subroutines. The latter work rather invisibly, upon being called either by a function, a macro, or another subroutine.

1.9.1 Custom functions

Functions can be placed in particular cells, in which case they can control the value displayed in those cells. The minimal function declaration in a cell contains its name followed by parentheses, as in =myOutput(). Inside the parentheses you may find one or more *arguments*, or none, as in the above example. If you type this instruction in a particular cell, without having defined its role, that cell will show the error message #NAME?.

You specify a function in a *module*. In Excel 5 and Excel 95, you open a module by clicking on the tab at the bottom of the spreadsheet, and then clicking on Module. After that, you can switch between module and spreadsheet by clicking on their tabs, just as you would move between different sheets in a workbook. In other words, the module is treated as a worksheet without a grid. In Excel 97 and more recent versions, the module is hidden from view in the Visual Basic Editor. To open the more recent type of module, use Tools ⇨ Macro ⇨ Visual Basic Editor, then in the Visual Basic toolbar click on Insert ⇨ Module. Once you have established a module, you can toggle between it and the spreadsheet with Alt⌣F11 (Mac: Opt⌣F11), where F11 is the function key labeled F11.

The arguments (the material within the brackets following the function name) comprise the input data; they can be either numerical values, addresses of individual cells, and/or of cell ranges where information can be found. They are defined in the function by the order in which they appear in the function argument, not by their names. You can even specify *optional* input arguments.

The output of a function is usually restricted to the output of a single cell and to a single value. The restriction to a single cell is not much of a restraint, because you can copy a function to any cell you want. Moreover, there is an important exception to the latter rule: it is possible to have a single function apply to a rectangular block of cells. You will encounter many such examples in chapter 10.

A module can contain one or more functions, subroutines, macros, or combinations thereof, and it is usually easiest to keep them all together in one module. A simple function might be defined as

```
Function myOutput()
myOutput = 8.3
End Function
```

which accomplishes the trivial task of setting the cell value to 8.3, but shows the general structure: a first line defining the function by its name, a last line specifying the end of the function, and in between one or more statements including at least one that specifies the function value, tying the function name (*without* its brackets) to the output. The output will most often be a value, but can also be a message (identified as such within quotation marks) as when the above statement line is replaced by myOutput = "abc".

The custom function will appear in the Paste Function dialog box (under Function category: User Defined, by Function name:) which you can access by clicking on the function icon f_x on the standard toolbar. (⑰,⑩: on the formula bar.) If you do not want such a listing, specify the function name in the module as Private, as in `Private Function myOutput()`. You will encounter useful custom functions throughout this book. A tricky but sometimes useful aspect of functions is that they can be *recursive*, i.e., they can call themselves. Here is an example of a recursive function to compute the factorial *n!*:

```
Function Factorial(n)
'Illustration of a recursive function
If n <= 1 Then
  Factorial = 1
Else
  Factorial = n * Factorial(n - 1)
End If
End Function
```

> **Exercise 1.9.1:**
> (1) Open a new spreadsheet, then open its VBEditor module with Alt⌣F11 (Mac: Opt⌣F11) followed by Insert ⇨ Module. In that module type the above function.
> (2) Switch back to the spreadsheet, type =`Factorial(5)` in, say, cell E3, and see what you get. Then change that number 5 to another positive integer.
> (3) Replace the number by a cell address, such as =`Factorial(C3)`, and place a positive integer in cell C3.
> (4) Compare your results with those of the Excel function =`Fact()`.

Functions can be copied from one cell to another. Section 1.10 will illustrate that functions can perform quite complex operations, such as a polynomial interpolation. Many more examples of the computational power of functions are provided by the Matrix and XN functions described in chapters 10 and 11.

1.9.2 Custom subroutines & macros

Subroutines are specified in the module by prefacing their name by Sub (instead of Function). You cannot enter a subroutine in a particular cell, but you can call it as a macro provided the subroutine has no arguments (i.e., has *empty* brackets in its name-defining statement), e.g., with Tools ⇨ Macro ⇨ Macros or, easier, with Alt⌣F8 (Mac: Opt⌣F8) and by using the resulting Macro dialog box. If a subroutine has arguments, it lives entirely out-of-sight in a module, and can only be called by other procedures, i.e., by functions, macros, or other subroutines.

Macros are a very useful sub-type of subroutines; they are essentially the public counterparts of the private non-macro subroutines. (Public and private subroutines would indeed be a more descriptive and less confusing nomenclature for macros and non-macro subroutines respectively.) As illustrated throughout this book, and described in chapters 8 through 11, they can be used for quite sophisticated mathematical operations. In general, they can perform all actions that functions can, and many more. A disadvantage is that they do not operate automatically, but must be called, and they therefore provide a snapshot that the spreadsheet may have outgrown since. Macros also require more complex coding, because their input and output must be specified. We will delay a detailed look at them until chapter 8. An important thing to remember about them here is that many scientific problems have already been solved, and that their computer solutions can often be found in the literature, so that you need not reinvent the wheel. If a computer solution happens to be available in Basic you are in luck, because Basic (especially in one of its more modern forms) can be incorporated readily in VBA which, after all, is a dialect of Basic, hence its middle initial. Even if the program is in Fortran77 it is often readily transcribed. When the program is listed in an early, Fortran-based edition of the *Numerical Recipes* by W. H. Press et al., Cambridge Univ. Press, (which can be read or copied free of charge from http://lib-www.lanl.gov/numerical/index.html or http://www.library.cornell.edu/nr/nr_index.cgi) you can find a corresponding Basic version in J. C. Sprott,

Numerical Recipes: Routines and Examples in Basic, Cambridge University Press, (1991). Often the only modification such code requires is making it operate in double rather than single precision. Of course you must supply the code for connecting the macro input(s) and output(s) with the spreadsheet, an aspect we will discuss in chapter 8.

When you call a macro, much of the real action may well be performed by subroutines and functions that are recruited by that macro. For example, when you call the basic linear least squares macros LS0 or LS1, these small macros merely set one number to 0 or 1 respectively, and then transfer the heavy lifting to a subroutine, which also calls several matrix functions. The Fourier transform macros ForwardFT and InverseFT similarly contain only a few lines of code, and then transfer the job to a subroutine which, in turn, leaves the real Fourier transformation to a second routine. It is just that you need a macro to start the process, because you cannot call any non-macro subroutines directly from the spreadsheet. Public functions and macros are always your entry points to behind-the-scenes VBA computations.

1.10 An example: Lagrange interpolation

In much of this book we will emphasize working with *experimental* data, i.e., with numbers that are not exact but that are to some extent uncertain, as a result of experimental 'noise' corrupting the underlying 'signal'. Such data require special methods to extract that signal, a problem addressed in the central chapters of this book. However, science is not about experimental numbers per se, but about comparing them with model theories, since this is how our ideas about nature are calibrated. Consequently we must also be able to handle theoretical expressions, where noise is absent, and where quite different methods can therefore be used.

In this section we will illustrate an approach for dealing with noise-free data. This will also give us a good(opportunity to practice with custom functions, and to illustrate what this book is all about: making the spreadsheet do the things *you* may want it to do. On the other hand, it may be more detailed than you care for at this point. In that case you will not miss anything by skipping this section for now, and coming back to it later. Or you may want to wait till chapter 9, where we will give a fuller account of interpolation methods.

*****

Interpolation is useful when we need to rescale a table of data, and even more so when we have a model theory that provides data $y = f(x)$ when, instead, we need those data in the form $x = g(y)$. The most common interpolation schemes use either polynomials or trigonometric functions. Below we will illustrate polynomial interpolation. For additional information, see section 9.1, as well as chapter 25 by P. J. Davis & I Polonsky in the *Handbook of Mathematical Functions*, M. Abramowitz & I. A. Stegun, eds., Dover (1965), and chapter 3 of the *Numerical Recipes* by W. H. Press et al., Cambridge Univ. Press (1986).

The prototype for polynomial interpolation of noise-free data is the Lagrange method. In order to find y for a given value of x by *linear* interpolation between the two adjacent points (x_1, y_1) and (x_2, y_2), where $x_1 \le x \le x_2$, we have

$$y = \frac{(x - x_2) y_1}{x_1 - x_2} + \frac{(x - x_1) y_2}{x_2 - x_1} \tag{1.10.1}$$

Cubic interpolation between four adjacent points (x_1, y_1) through (x_4, y_4), preferably with two points on either side, i.e., with $x_1 \le x_2 \le x \le x_3 \le x_4$, is given by

$$y = \frac{(x - x_2)(x - x_3)(x - x_4) y_1}{(x_1 - x_2)(x_1 - x_3)(x_1 - x_4)} + \frac{(x - x_1)(x - x_3)(x - x_4) y_2}{(x_2 - x_1)(x_2 - x_3)(x_2 - x_4)}$$
$$+ \frac{(x - x_1)(x - x_2)(x - x_4) y_3}{(x_3 - x_1)(x_3 - x_2)(x_3 - x_4)} + \frac{(x - x_1)(x - x_2)(x - x_3) y_4}{(x_4 - x_1)(x_4 - x_2)(x_4 - x_3)} \tag{1.10.2}$$

and so on. Such Lagrange interpolation is readily handled with a custom function; the one we will illustrate here is based on an elegant example from W. J. Orvis, *Excel for Scientists and Engineers*, Sybex (1993, 1996).

We should emphasize here that you can always fit n data points *exactly* to a polynomial of power $n-1$, but that there is no assurance that this will be a good approximation for the underlying curve through those n points, which may or may not resemble a power series in x. In this latter, more significant sense the interpolation is model-dependent and therefore not necessarily exact, even if it passes exactly through all n points. This is readily verified by observing that the result obtained with Lagrange interpolation in general depends on the polynomial order used.

As our example we will apply cubic Lagrange interpolation to an acid-base titration curve, i.e., to the relation between the pH of a solution containing a fixed initial amount of, say, an acid, as a function of the volume V_b of added base. The general theory of such curves (*Anal. Chem.* 68 (1996) 585; *Chem. Educ.* 6 (2001) 272) is quite straightforward when we *calculate* the volume V_b as a function of the proton concentration $[H^+]$, but not the other way around. In practice one does the opposite: one *measures* pH as a function of the added volume V_b of base. We therefore first calculate a table of V_b as a function of pH = $-\log[H^+]$, then interpolate this table in order to generate a second table of pH as a function of V_b. We will do so here for the simplest type of titration, viz., that of a single strong monoprotic acid (such as HCl) with a single strong monoprotic base (such as NaOH).

Exercise 1.10.1:

(1) Open a new spreadsheet, with 12 rows at the top for graphs. In cells A13:A16 place the labels for the constants, K_w, V_a, C_b, and C_a, and in A18:C18 enter the column headings pH, [H], and Vb.

(2) In B13:B16 deposit numerical constants for K_w, V_a, C_b, and C_a, such as 10^–14, 20, 0.1, and 0.1.

(3) In the column for pH, starting in cell A20, enter the values 1 (0.1) 12.9. In B20:B139 calculate $[H^+]$ as 10^–pH, and in C20:C139 the corresponding titrant volume as $V_b = V_a (C_a - [H^+] + K_w/[H^+]) / (C_b + [H^+] - K_w/[H^+])$. This completes the first stage, calculating a table of data in A20:C139.

(4) Plot the resulting titration curve as pH vs. V_b. Note that it shows many points in the transition region, since the points are computed for equal increments in pH which, in that region, is a very steep function of V_b.

(5) Now make a second table in which the pH is listed at given (not necessarily equidistant) values of V_b. In cells E18 and F18 place two more column headings, Vb and pH respectively. Below the Vb heading, in cells E20:E49, enter the values 1 (1) 30. In cell F20 of the corresponding pH column enter the instruction =Lagrange($C$20:$C$139, $A$20:$A$139,E20,3), and copy it down to F139. The ranges $C$20:$C$139 and $A$20:$A$139 specify the X- and Y-ranges in which to interpolate, E20 is the X-value for which the interpolation is requested, and 3 denotes the order of the Lagrange polynomial used, here a cubic.

(6) Although you have entered the function call, nothing will happen, because you have not yet specified that function.

(7) Open a Visual Basic module as described earlier. For instance, in Excel 97 or later, use <u>T</u>ools ⇨ <u>M</u>acro ⇨ <u>V</u>isual Basic Editor, and then (in the VB Editor toolbar) <u>I</u>nsert ⇨ <u>M</u>odule.

(8) In that module enter the following code (either by typing or by copying from the SampleMacro file):

```
Function Lagrange(XArray, YArray, X, m)

' m denotes the order of the polynomial used,
' and must be an integer between 1 and 14

Dim Row As Integer, i As Integer, j As Integer
Dim Term As Double, Y As Double

Row = Application.Match(X, XArray, 1)
If Row < (m + 1) / 2 Then Row = (m + 1) / 2
If Row > XArray.Count - (m + 1) / 2 Then Row = XArray.Count - (m + 1) / 2
For i = Row - (m - 1) / 2 To Row + (m + 1) / 2
  Term = 1
  For j = Row - (m - 1) / 2 To Row + (m + 1) / 2
    If i <> j Then Term = Term * _
      (X - XArray(j)) / (XArray(i) - XArray(j))
  Next j
  Y = Y + Term * YArray(i)
Next i
Lagrange = Y

End Function
```

(9) The =Match(*value, array, type*) function in Excel returns the relative position of the largest term in the specified array that is less than or equal to *value*. The array must be in ascending order, and the above definition is for *type* = 1. By preceding it with the instruction Application. we appropriate it as a VBA command. It works for many (but not all) Excel functions. You can find a listing of them by typing Application.WorksheetFunction. from which you can then select by clicking. Thereafter you can delete the superfluous instruction WorksheetFunction.

(10) The function will work without the dimensioning statements, which are included here as part of good housekeeping practice. The same applies to the two comment lines (preceded by apostrophe's), which are ignored by the computer but are intended for the benefit of the user.

(11) The two nested For...Next loops generate the terms in the numerators and denominators of the Lagrange expression, such as those in (1.10.2). Note that Y need not be initialized since the function starts afresh each time.

(12) Return to the spreadsheet with Alt‿F11 (Mac: Opt‿F11). There should now be data in F20:F49.

(13) Plot the pH (in F20:F49) as a function of V_b in (E20:E49). Note that there are now very few points in the transition region, for the same reason that the plot of V_b vs. pH has so many: near the equivalence point, the slope d(pH)/d(V_b) is quite high, and that of d(V_b)/d(pH) correspondingly low.

(14) The top of the completed spreadsheet is shown in Fig. 1.10.1.

We already mentioned that a cubic Lagrange interpolation will be a fairly good approximation for this curve as long as the spacing between adjacent, computed data points is sufficiently small. In this particular case a closed-form solution for the pH as a function of titrant volume V_b is available, so that we can check the interpolation procedure. It is always useful to 'calibrate' new software with a test for which the (exact) answer is known, because it provides an early indication of its reliability and, as a bonus, may alert you to possible problems.

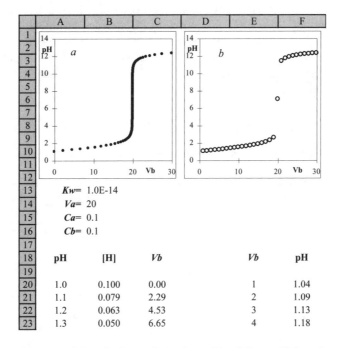

	A	B	C	D	E	F
13	*Kw*=	1.0E-14				
14	*Va*=	20				
15	*Ca*=	0.1				
16	*Cb*=	0.1				
17						
18	pH	[H]	*Vb*		*Vb*	pH
19						
20	1.0	0.100	0.00		1	1.04
21	1.1	0.079	2.29		2	1.09
22	1.2	0.063	4.53		3	1.13
23	1.3	0.050	6.65		4	1.18

Fig. 1.10.1: The top of the spreadsheet for interpolating in a table of V_b vs. pH (in columns C and A respectively) in order to generate a second table of pH as a function of V_b (in columns E and F). Note that the points in plot *a* are equidistant in pH (with ΔpH = 0.1) while those in plot *b* have constant increments ΔV_b = 1.

Inversion of the expression used under (3) in exercise 1.10, $V_b = V_a \times (C_a - [H^+] + K_w/[H^+]) / (C_b + [H^+] - K_w/[H^+])$, yields

$$pH = -\log[H^+] = -\log\left[\frac{C_aV_a - C_bV_b}{2(V_a + V_b)} + \sqrt{\frac{(C_aV_a - C_bV_b)^2}{4(V_a + V_b)^2} + K_w}\right] \tag{1.10.3}$$

which will now be used to check the results obtained from the Lagrange interpolation.

Exercise 1.10.1 (continued):

(15) You can calculate the pH from (1.10.3) in one operation, or even the difference between it and the pH computed by Lagrange interpolation. Here we will use three steps, which require simpler expressions but use more spreadsheet 'real estate'.

(16) In cell G20 calculate the quantity $(C_aV_a-C_bV_b)/(2(V_a+V_b))$ as `=($B$16*$B$14-$B$15*E20)/(2*($B$14+E20))`.

(17) In cell H20 compute the pH as `=-LOG(G20+SQRT(G20^2+$B$13))`.

(18) In cell I20 enter the instruction `=H20-F20`, and change the cell format to scientific with Format ⇨ Cells, Category: Scientific.

(19) Copy the instructions in cells G20:I20 down to row 49.

Notice that, in this case, the deviations are all less than $\pm4\times10^{-4}$, i.e., smaller than the resolution of a pH meter (typically ±0.01 pH unit, or at best ±0.001 pH unit), and therefore inconsequential. Verify that using a ten times smaller pH increment in column A (with a concomitant change in the ranges XArray and YArray in the function call) can reduce the errors by another three orders of magnitude. Increasing the polynomial order has a smaller effect, and can even be counter-effective, especially when the intervals are relatively large, in which case fitted curves of high order may swing wildly between adjacent points. Optimal results are usually obtained with a low-order polynomial interpolation of densely spaced data.

Now that we have converted a theoretical curve into one more like those encountered in the laboratory, we will make a short excursion to illustrate what we can do with it. First we will calculate the concentrations of the species of interest, [H$^+$] and [OH$^-$], and a useful, derived quantity, the proton excess $\Delta = $ [H$^+$] $-$ [OH$^-$]. Then we correct these for the mutual dilution of sample and titrant, and so obtain [H$^+$]', [OH$^-$]', and Δ'. Finally we will make the simulation more realistic by adding offset and random noise to the pH. In practical implementations, offset can usually be kept at bay by careful instrument calibration using standard buffers.

Exercise 1.10.1 (continued):

(20) In cell J18 place the heading [H], in cell J20 compute the proton concentration [H$^+$] as `=10^-E20`, and copy this instruction down to cell J49.

(21) In cell K18 deposit the label [OH], in cell K20 calculate [OH$^-$] as `=$B$13/F20`, and likewise extend this calculation downward to row 49.

(22) In L18 put the label Δ (type D, then highlight it and change the font to Symbol) for the *proton excess*, and in L20:L49 compute its value as $\Delta = $ [H$^+$] $-$ [OH$^-$]. Plot [H$^+$], [OH$^-$], and Δ as a function of V_b, see Fig. 1.10.2.

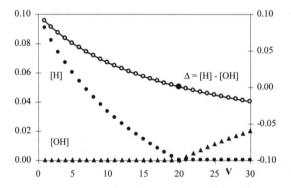

Fig. 1.10.2: The proton concentration [H$^+$], the hydroxyl ion concentration [OH$^-$] $= K_w/$[H$^+$], and (using the right-hand scale) the proton excess $\Delta = $ [H$^+$] $-$ [OH$^-$], all as a function of the titrant volume V_b.

(23) Adding titrant to sample clearly dilutes both. We can correct for this mutual dilution by multiplying [H$^-$], [OH$^-$], and Δ by $(V_a+V_b)/V_a$. Use three additional columns, M through O, one for [H$^+$]' $= $ [H$^+$] $(V_a+V_b)/V_a$, one for [OH$^-$]' $= $ [OH$^-$] $(V_a+V_b)/V_a$, and one for $\Delta' = $ [H$^+$]' $-$ [OH$^-$]', then plot these, as in Fig. 1.10.3. Note that the quantities [H$^+$]' and [OH$^-$]' are directly proportional to the Gran plots (G. Gran, *Analyst* 77 (1952) 661) for this type of titration.

(24) The above are purely *theoretical* plots. They suggest that the equivalence point of the titration can be found simply by looking for that value of V_b where Δ' is zero. You could do this, e.g., by linear interpolation in the table for Δ' as a function of V_b for $\Delta' = 0$.

(25) The above are purely *theoretical* plots. They suggest that the equivalence point of the titration can be found simply by looking for that value of V_b where Δ' is zero. You could do this, e.g., by linear interpolation in the table for Δ' as a function of V_b for $\Delta' = 0$.

(26) We now make the transition to *practical* data analysis. In cell D13 deposit the label *offset* =, in cell D14 the label *na* =, and in cell P18 the heading 'noise'.

(27) In cells E13 and E14 enter corresponding values (0 for zero offset or noise, 0.05 for offset or noise of 0.05 pH unit, etc.), and in P20:P49 deposit Gaussian ('normal') noise of zero mean and unit standard deviation, using the in Tools ⇨ Data Analysis ⇨ Random Number Generation, Distribution : Normal, Mean = 0, Standard Deviation = 1, Output Range: P19:P49, OK.

(28) To the instruction in cell F20 now add the terms +$E$13+$E$14*P20, and copy this down to F49. Experiment with non-zero values for offset and/or noise.

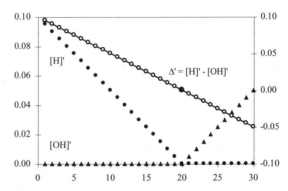

Fig. 1.10.3: The dilution-corrected proton concentration [H⁺]′, hydroxyl ion concentration [OH⁻]′, and proton excess Δ', all as a function of the titrant volume V_b. Note that Δ' is a linear function of V_b throughout the entire titration. The equivalence point, where $\Delta' = 0$, has been highlighted.

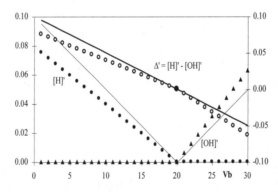

Fig. 1.10.4: The effect of a relatively small amount of pH offset (*offset* = 0.1) on the concentration parameters [H⁺]′, [OH⁻]′, and Δ'. Again, [H⁺]′ and [OH⁻]′ use the primary (left-hand) scale, while the secondary (right-hand) scale pertains to Δ'. For comparison, the lines are drawn for zero offset.

(29) The effect of an offset a is to multiply [H⁺]′ by $10^{(-a)}$, [OH⁻]′ by $10^{(+a)}$, and Δ' by $10^{(-a)}$ before the equivalence point, and by $10^{(+a)}$ beyond it, and therefore leads to the slope changes shown in Fig. 1.10.4.

(30) Even though the titration curve may barely show the added random noise, but the corresponding concentration terms [H⁺]′, [OH⁻]′, and Δ' and analysis procedures relying on them may be affected strongly, because the exponentiation in the conversion from pH to [H⁺] greatly accentuates the noise, see Fig. 1.10.5.

(29) The effect of an offset a is to multiply [H⁺]′ by $10^{(-a)}$, [OH⁻]′ by $10^{(+a)}$, and Δ' by $10^{(-a)}$ before the equivalence point, and by $10^{(+a)}$ beyond it, and therefore leads to the slope changes shown in Fig. 1.10.4.

(30) Even though the titration curve may barely show the added random noise, but the corresponding concentration terms $[H^+]'$, $[OH^-]'$, and Δ' and analysis procedures relying on them may be affected strongly, because the exponentiation in the conversion from pH to $[H^+]$ greatly accentuates the noise, see Fig. 1.10.5.

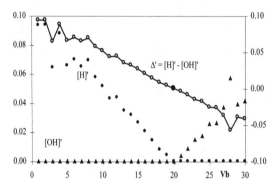

Fig. 1.10.5: The effect of a relatively small amount of random pH noise (with zero mean and standard deviation $s_n = 0.05$) on the concentration parameters $[H^+]'$, $[OH^-]'$, and Δ'.

It is straightforward to use formal mathematics to identify the zero crossing of Δ' in Fig. 1.10.3, but to do so in Fig. 1.10.5 is a different problem, because these data fit a straight line only approximately (even though most of the noise is at the extremes of the curve). How to deal with such more realistic data on a spreadsheet is one of the core problems discussed in this book. For now, the latter part of this example merely illustrates what we can do by *simulating* an experiment, e.g., by visualizing how sensitive a proposed analysis method will be to the effects of (systematic, deterministic) bias or offset, and (random, stochastic) noise. See section 4.4 for more robust data analysis methods.

1.11 Handling the math

One way in which Excel facilitates computations is through its extensive collection of functions, ranging from search tools to sophisticated mathematical and statistical tools. Some of the most useful of these are listed in appendices A.2 through A.4. Excel can also handle matrices and complex numbers, as illustrated below. The corresponding functions are listed in appendices A.5 and A.6 respectively. Much more information on applying matrix methods can be found in chapter 10, including many additional operations available through Matrix.xla.

1.11.1 Complex numbers

Excel operations on complex numbers use text strings to squeeze the two components of a complex number into one cell. In order to use the results of complex number operations, one must therefore first *extract* its real and imaginary components, using IMREAL() and IMAGINARY(). Instead of i you can use j to denote the square root of minus one (which must then be *specified* as such), but you *cannot* use the corresponding capitals, I or J. Appendix A.5 lists the complex number operations provided in Excel's Analysis ToolPak. VBA lacks a special data type for complex numbers, which are therefore best handled in terms of their separate, real and imaginary components, as in the Fourier transform macro described in section 8.17.

The Excel convention yields a compact display of complex numbers having integer real and imaginary components, but becomes rather unwieldy for general, non-integer values, because the displayed values are then shown in their full 15-digit lengths. Since they are text strings, number formatting cannot be used to trim them to shorter lengths.

The many Matrix and XN functions for complex quantities we will encounter in chapters 9 through 11 provide the same notation, but also an often more useful alternative option, viz. to use two (horizontally or vertically) adjacent cells, of which the left/top cell is for the real component, the other cell for its imaginary counterpart. The corresponding XN functions should then be treated as two-cell ranges, as in B3:C3 or B3:B4, in which case a complex output requires that the function be block-entered with the command Ctrl‿Shift‿Enter (Mac: Command‿Return).

1.11.2 Matrices

Excel has five built-in functions for matrix operations: {}, TRANSPOSE, INDEX, MINVERSE, and MMULT.

Curly brackets {} around a set of numbers separated by commas and/or semicolons can be used to deposit an array. Highlight a block of cells two cells wide and 3 cells high, then type the instruction ={2,3;4,5;6,7}, and deposit this instruction with Ctrl‿Shift‿Enter (on the Mac: Command‿Return). This will deposit the numbers 2 and 3 in the top row, 4 and 5 in the middle row, and 6 and 7 in the bottom row of the block. Here commas separate matrix elements in the same row, while semicolons separate successive rows. Remember the order: first rows, then columns. As a memory aid, think of the electrical RC (resistor-capacitor) circuit or its time constant: RC, first Row, then Column. The data are actually stored as a single, linear file, hence the requirement that rows precede columns in order to avoid ambiguity.

TRANSPOSE interchanges the row and column indices. Because transposing rows and columns is a common operation in, e.g., accounting, it is performed as part of the Edit ⇨ Paste Special operation. Select (i.e., highlight) the array to be transposed, and copy it to the clipboard (e.g., with Ctrl‿c). Then select the top left corner (or the left column, or the top row, or the entire area) of where you want its transpose to appear, and use the keystroke sequence Edit ⇨ Paste Special ⇨ Transpose ⇨ OK. (Depending on your software, you may have to specify Values or Formulas before Transpose, or the generic All may just work fine.)

INDEX(*array,row#,column#*) yields the individual matrix element in a given array. Say that C4:E8 contains the data

0	4	8
1	5	9
2	6	10
3	7	11

then =INDEX(C4:E8,2,3) yields the answer 9, since it specifies the array element in row 2, column 3 of block C4:E8. You can also incorporate the array elements in the instruction, as in =INDEX({0,4,8;1,5,9; 2,6,10; 3,7,11},2,3), where the array elements in each row are enumerated one at a time, from left to right, separated by commas, while different rows are separated by semicolons, and are read from top to bottom. This instruction likewise yields the answer 9.

MINVERSE (for matrix inversion) and MMULT (for matrix multiplication) work only on *data arrays*, i.e., on rectangular blocks of cells, but not on single cells. To enter these instructions, highlight the area where you want to place the result, type the instruction, and finally enter it with the block enter command Ctrl‿Shift‿Enter (Mac: Command‿Return). In the formula box, the instruction will show inside curly brackets to indicate that it is a matrix operation. Note that MINVERSE can only be used with *square* arrays, while for MMULT the number of columns in the first array must be equal to the number of rows in the second array. The terms first and second are important here, because the matrix product **A B** in general is not the same as the matrix product **B A**.

In VBA, parameters dimensioned As Variant (as well as all undimensioned parameters) can represent arrays, when their specific sizes (number of rows, number of columns) are specified using a Dim or ReDim statement. Manipulation of such matrices is best performed in subroutines, as illustrated in the weighted least squares macro of the MacroBundle.

Function	Description and example
MINVERSE(*array*)	The matrix inverse of a square array: when B3:C4 contains the data $\begin{matrix} 3 & 5 \\ 4 & 6 \end{matrix}$ then

$$\text{MINVERSE}(\{3,5; 4,6\}) = \{-3, 2.5; 2, -1.5\} = \begin{vmatrix} -3 & 2.5 \\ 2 & -1.5 \end{vmatrix}.$$

Instead of an *input array* such as {3,5; 4,6} we can also use an *input range* on the spreadsheet,

$$\text{MINVERSE(B3:C4)} = \begin{vmatrix} -3 & 2.5 \\ 2 & -1.5 \end{vmatrix}$$

MMULT(*array*)	The matrix product of two rectangular arrays, where the number of columns in the first array must be equal to the number of rows in the second array:

$$\text{MMULT}(\{3, 5; 4, 6\},\{-3, 25; 2, -1.5\}) = \begin{vmatrix} 1 & 0 \\ 0 & 1 \end{vmatrix},$$

and, likewise, MMULT(B3:C4,E6:F7) $= \begin{vmatrix} 1 & 0 \\ 0 & 1 \end{vmatrix}$ when B3:C4 and E6:F7 contain

the data $\begin{matrix} 3 & 5 \\ 4 & 6 \end{matrix}$ and $\begin{matrix} -3 & 2.5 \\ 2 & -1.5 \end{matrix}$ respectively.

1.12 Handling the funnies

With its many built-in functions, Excel makes it easy to compute many mathematical expressions. Even so, we may sometimes need to help it along, especially when our calculations involve some of the mathematical 'funnies', such as 0/0, $\infty-\infty$, ∞/∞, and $0\times\infty$. Below we will illustrate some of these; once you see the approach you will know how to deal with similar problems you may encounter.

As a simple example, the convolution of a sine wave and an impulse function yields the sinc function, $\text{sinc}(\omega t) = [\sin(\omega t)]/(\omega t)$. When ωt is zero, both the numerator and denominator are zero, suggesting that the value of $\text{sinc}(0)$ might be undefined. But this is not the case, as is most readily seen by expanding $\sin(x)$ for $|x| \ll 1$ as $x - x^3/3! + x^5/5! - x^7/7! + \ldots$ so that $\text{sinc}(x) = [\sin(x)]/x = 1 - x^2/3! + x^4/5! - x^6/7! + \ldots \rightarrow 1$ for $x \rightarrow 0$. If you encounter this problem in a spreadsheet, you can use the series expansion or, simpler, sidestep it by using a *very small* value instead of 0. Even if you take x as small as 10^{-300}, close to the smallest number Excel can represent, the spreadsheet will return 1 for $[\sin(x)]/x$. But for $x = 0$ you will get the error message #DIV/0! without a numerical result.

1.12.1 The binomial coefficient

There is an old birdwatcher's trick. When one person enters a blind, birds that have seen this will remember that someone went in until he or she comes out again. When two people enter, most birds will know that the blind is not yet empty after they see one of them emerge: $2 - 1 \neq 0$. But you can fool most birds by having three enter, and two leave: apparently, many birds count zero-one-infinity, i.e., they cannot distinguish between 2 and 3. Birds can count, but only up to a limited number.

The same applies to computers, even though they certainly are more numerate than birds: the typical personal computer can count a little beyond 10^{307}. But still, you may occasionally (though often unwittingly) ask a computer to calculate $\infty - \infty$, or ∞ / ∞, in which case it will come up short.

The binomial coefficient is most clearly associated with binomial statistics, and once in a while also crops up in seemingly unrelated scientific and engineering problems. For example, it occurs in the Gram functions used for equidistant least squares discussed in section 3.16.

The binomial coefficient is defined as

$$\binom{N}{n} = \frac{N!}{(N-n)!\,n!} \tag{1.12.1}$$

and should not give the spreadsheet any problems because Excel contains the factorial function (the instruction =FACT(3) will yield 6) and, at any rate, you can always evaluate a factorial from its definition, $N! = 1 \times 2 \times 3 \times 4 \times \cdots$. Perhaps so, but when you apply this to the binomial coefficient, you will quickly run out of luck.

Exercise 1.12.1:

(1) Start a spreadsheet with the label and value of n, two rows lower enter labels for N and the binomial coefficient, and in cell A5 start a column for $N = 0\ (1)\ 200$.

(2) In B5 start the column for the binomial coefficient where $N = n$, by calculating it as $N!\ /\ (N-n)!\ n!$. For $n = 10$ you will do fine till $N = 170$; thereafter, even though the binary coefficient is still smaller than 10^{16}, the computer fails.

(3) Make a temporary third column in which you calculate $N!$ for the same range of N-values. At $N = 171$, $N!$ exceeds the maximum number the computer can represent (of about 10^{207}), and this ruins the calculation of the much smaller binary coefficient.

Understanding what causes the problem is, of course, the most important part of fixing it. Obviously we should compute the binomial coefficient without explicitly calculating $N!$. Note that the definition of N! as a product makes it easy to compute it in logarithmic form, since

$$\ln(N!) = \ln(N) + \ln(N-1) + \ln(N-2) + \ln(N-3) + \ldots + \ln(2) + \ln(1)$$

will not so quickly exceed the numerical capacity of the computer.

Exercise 1.12.1 (continued):

(4) Re-label the third column as $\ln(N)$ and use it to compute $\ln(N!)$ by making cell C6 read =LN(A6), and by entering in cell C7 the instruction =C6+LN(A7). (We avoid cell C5 because $\ln(0)$ is not very useful.) Copy the instruction from cell C7 all the way down.

(5) In cells C1 and D1 enter the label and value respectively of $\ln(n!)$, which for $n < 170$ can be computed simply as =LN(FACT(B1)).

(6) Now use column D to compute the binomial coefficient. For example, for $n = 10$, deposit the instruction =EXP(C16-C6-$D$1) in row 16, and copy it all the way down. You now have the binomial coefficient for as far as the eye can see on the spreadsheet: for $N = 65531$ and $n = 10$ it has the value $4.02167227 \times 10^{41}$, a sizeable number but no problem whatsoever for Excel.

1.12.2 The exponential error function complement

A function that appears in, e.g., problems of statistics, heat transport, and diffusion is the calculation of the exponential error function complement, $y = \exp[x^2]\,\mathrm{erfc}[x]$. Excel provides both $\exp[x^2]$ and $\mathrm{erfc}[x]$, and we therefore start out by simply multiplying them, as illustrated in Exercise 1.12.2.

Exercise 1.12.2:

(1) In a spreadsheet enter columns for $x = 0\ (0.1)\ 10$ and $y = \exp[x^2]\,\mathrm{erfc}[x]$, the latter simply by calling the functions exp() and erfc() and multiplying them. Cell B3 might then read =EXP(A3^2)*ERFC(A3) when $x = 0$ is located in cell A3.

(2) Plot y versus x. There should be no problem as long as $x < 5$, while the computation obviously fails above $x = 6$. The open circles in Fig. 1.12.1 show what you should get.

Clearly we run into a problem for $x > 5$, where $\exp[x^2]$ becomes large while $\mathrm{erfc}[x]$ tends to zero. This is the digital analog of the product $\infty \times 0$, as can be recognized by plotting both functions separately. For large values of x we therefore use an asymptotic expansion instead, in this case

$$\exp[x^2]\,\mathrm{erfc}[x] \approx \frac{1}{x\sqrt{\pi}}\left\{1 + \sum_{m=1}^{\infty}(-1)^m\,\frac{1\cdot 3\cdot 5\cdots(2m-1)}{(2x^2)^m}\right\} \tag{1.12.2}$$

for $x \to \infty$. The problem therefore is twofold: how to incorporate a computation such as (1.12.2) into a cell, and (because the asymptotic expansion fails for small values of x) how to switch smoothly from one to the other. Below we will address the first problem by introducing a custom function.

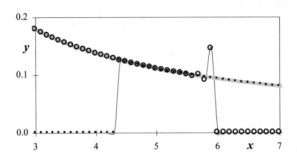

Fig. 1.12.1: Cobbling together a smooth function from two partially overlapping segments. Open circles: the product of $\exp(x^2)$ and $\mathrm{erfc}(x)$. Solid circles: the output of the asymptotic series. Gray band: the result of switching from one to the other at $x = 5$. Only the region of switch-over is shown.

Exercise 1.12.2 (continued):

(3) We first find a space in which to write the custom function. Either use Alt‿F11 (Mac: Opt‿F11) or <u>T</u>ools ⇨ <u>M</u>acro ⇨ <u>V</u>isual Basic Editor. If you find a gray space, there is no module yet, and you therefore make one with <u>I</u>nsert ⇨ <u>M</u>odule. If a module already exist, go to its top or its end.

(4) In the module, enter (by typing, or by copying from SampleMacros) the following lines. Below we will explain their function.

```
Function EE(x)

Dim m As Integer
Dim sum As Double
Dim oldterm As Double, newterm As Double
m = 1
sum = 1
oldterm = 1

Do
  newterm = -(2 * m - 1) * oldterm / (2 * x * x)
  sum = sum + newterm
  oldterm = newterm
  m = m + 1
Loop Until Abs(newterm) < 0.00000001

EE = sum / (x * Sqr([Pi()]))

End Function
```

(5) The first line specifies the function by name, and within brackets indicates the name of the parameter(s) on which the function operates. The last line identifies the end of the custom function.

(6) The next three lines contain the dimension statements, which specify the nature of the variables used in the custom function. Note that the variable x should not be dimensioned, since the spreadsheet already knows its dimension, which (through the first line) is imported into the function together with its value. You can operate the function without the dimension statements, except when your module starts with the line `Option Explicit`, in which case they are required. However, it is good general programming custom to include dimension statements, which is why we will do so here. Empty lines have no meaning for the computer, and are inserted merely for greater readability.

(7) The next three lines *initialize* the calculation, i.e., they assign the relevant parameters their initial values.

(8) The heart of this custom function is the part between `Do` and `Loop until`, which forms a so-called *do-loop*. This loop executes a set of commands until a termination criterion is reached; here we use as such a criterion the requirement

that the absolute value of the last-computed term is smaller than 10^{-8}. (The initial value of the function $\exp[x^2]\,\mathrm{erfc}[x]$, at $x = 0$, is 1.)

(9) Now we consider the terms summed in (1.12.2), which we can write as $T_1 = -1/2x^2$ for $m = 1$, $T_2 = -3T_1/2x^2$ for $m = 2$, $T_3 = -5T_2/2x^2$ for $m = 3$, and in general $T_m = -(2m-1)\,T_{m-1}/2x^2$. This is the logic behind starting with the parameter `oldterm` and using it to compute successive values of `newterm`.

(10) In the next line we then add the successive terms to sum, using the *assignment* symbol = to mean ⇐, i.e., to replace the left-hand expression (`sum`) by that on the right-hand side (`sum + newterm`). Note that, unlike the expression in (1.12.2), `sum` already incorporates the term 1.

(11) Then we update `oldterm`, and increment m.

(12) Finally, outside the loop, we assign the value of ee to `sum` divided by $x\sqrt{\pi}$. Visual Basic does not have the rich assortment of functions that Excel has, and doesn't know what π means. Therefore we can either write out the value of π, or simply use the spreadsheet function. In the latter case we must place that function, `Pi()`, between straight brackets: `[Pi()]`. Also note that the instruction for taking the square root in Visual Basic is `sqr`, not `sqrt`.

(13) Use Alt‿F11 (Mac: Opt‿F11) to switch back to the spreadsheet, and make a third column in which you use the custom function. For example, if your column containing the values of x starts in cell A3, in C3 deposit the instruction =EE(A3), and copy this down the length of columns A and B.

(14) Add the result obtained with this custom function to your graph.

Figure 1.12.1 illustrates what we have just calculated. Apparently, above $x = 5$ we are bitten by the dog, and below it scratched by the cat. So the final column takes the good parts of each calculation, and avoids their problems.

Exercise 1.12.2 (continued):

(15) In cell D3 deposit the instruction =IF(A3<5,EXP(A3^2)*ERFC(A3), EE(A3)). This reads as "if A3 < 5, then use EXP(A3^2)*ERFC(A3), otherwise use EE(A3)", and apparently solves both problems.

(16) Plot this result; it should look like Fig. 1.12.1.

1.13 Algorithmic accuracy

Excel can do many things, but how well does it do them? This question is increasingly being asked of many types of software, as benchmarks (such as the Statistical Reference Datasets from NIST, the National Institute of Science and Technology) have become available to test them. A number of software packages, including Excel, have been tested, and early tests of Excel were published by L. Knüsel, *Computational Statistics and Data Analysis* 26 (1998) 375, and B. D. McCullough & B. Wilson, *Computational Statistics and Data Analysis* 31 (1999) 27, and in broader comparisons such as given, e.g., by M. Altman & M. P. McDonald, *Political Science and Politics* 43 (2001) 68. More comprehensive studies have since been published on the web by, e.g., Cook et al., see http://www.npl.co.uk/ssfm/download/documents/cise27_99.pdf, and by D. A. Heiser, at http://www.daheiser.info.

A consensus has emerged that laments the fact that many of Excel's functions were sloppily written and, worse, were not upgraded until long after their deficiencies had been pointed out and, in many cases, confirmed by Microsoft in its KnowledgeBase. For this reason, many statisticians decided to stay away from Excel, despite its obvious appeal as a ubiquitous, easily learned and potentially quite powerful numerical software package with which many students and other potential users are already familiar.

In all fairness, Excel is primarily geared towards business applications, and has never marketed itself as statistical, scientific, or engineering software, but it could easily play those roles if it were more open to self-correction. If K. B. Oldham, J. C. Myland, and J. Spanier, two chemists and a mathematician, can produce an *Atlas of Functions* (Springer, 2nd ed. 2008) with *Equator* software look-up tables for a large number of highly complex mathematical functions, often to 14-decimal accuracy, produced entirely with standard, double-precision Visual Basic software, it is clear that a large organization such as Microsoft could easily make a similar effort if it wanted to. After all, most of the needed information is conveniently available in the now almost 50-year-old *Handbook of Mathematical Functions* edited by M. Abramowitz & I. A. Stegun. Perhaps only business considerations, such as increasing competition from more agile competitors, or a major numerical failure in a financial application, will make the managers of Excel pay more attention to its quality control.

A basic problem with all programs (including Excel) that use a fixed number of *binary units* ('bits') to represent data is that most nonintegers cannot be represented exactly as binary numbers. For example, the binary representation of 1/10 is 0.00011001100110011001... etc., and an error is therefore made wherever this infinite sequence of two ones followed by two zeroes is truncated. (The binary number shown, if truncated as 0.00011001100110011001, would only be good to fewer than five significant digits, since its decimal value is 0.0999994...) The resulting small errors can accumulate in complicated calculations, especially if those involve subtractions of large numbers of near-equal magnitudes. Good software design tries to minimize such errors, but that is an area of competence that most scientists will have to leave to the specialists. As a chemist, I certainly make no claim to such expertise, and my macros will no doubt confirm that.

There are several issues here. First and foremost one wants the final results of a calculation to be correct rather than wrong. We will call this *absolute accuracy*. I consider it optimal when software lets its user know when the computer cannot find the requested answer, rather than display the last result before the algorithm stops. Knüsel lists several examples where Excel cannot find a result, and then does not give one, but instead displays the error message #NUM!. I do not consider that a deficiency, even though one might wish that the algorithm could yield the requested answer. It is equivalent to a teacher, or a politician, honestly answering "I don't know" if that is the case, regardless of whether the answer is knowable.

Second, one would like only significant digits to be displayed, perhaps with one additional 'guard' digit or, better yet, to obtain and display a result accompanied by an estimated uncertainty.

Algorithms incorporated in standard software packages often reflect a compromise between accuracy and execution speed, although one would assume that, with the greatly increased memory and processing speed of modern computers, consistent accuracy by now would have become the sole determining factor. Algorithms chosen consciously for speed, to the detriment of accuracy, might have been justifiable in the days of 1 MB memories and 1 MHz processors, but are of questionable value now that personal computers have multi-gigabyte memories and clock speeds above 1 GHz. With Excel 2003 and Excel 2010, Microsoft finally has corrected some of its most glaring deficiencies, but in this respect much more work still needs to be done.

Since chapter 11 discusses accuracy in more detail, and shows specific approaches to improve it, we need not belabor the point here. It is prudent to assume, in the absence of contrary evidence, that not all digits displayed by Excel functions and macros (including the custom macros used in this book) are significant. Considering the uncertainties in the input data analyzed, this will often be unimportant, but it is still useful to keep in mind. When your results are of consequence, and depend critically on more than the first few non-zero digits of the result, it is time to check the numerical precision of the method used. Preferably it should be checked with nonintegers that cannot be represented exactly in binary notation, see S. D. Simon & J. P. Lesage, *Comp. Stat. Data Anal.* 7 (1988) 197. Testing with a number such as 0.375 would not be so useful, even though it is a noninteger, because $0.375 = 3/8$, so that it can be represented exactly in binary format as 0.011. As the ultimate test of round-off errors, use extended numberlength as described in chapter 11.

Here is another issue. In chapter 4 we describe many applications of the nonlinear least squares routine Solver, made by Frontline Systems Inc. and included in Excel as well as in Lotus 1-2-3 and in QuattroPro. While it is a well-designed and very powerful tool, it is a good general precaution always to apply Solver twice, in order to see whether its answer is stable. Not infrequently, a second run of Solver starting from the just-obtained answer will produce a slightly improved result. It is not clear why Solver doesn't incorporate such a simple check of its final-answer.

Algorithms are continually debugged, refined and made more robust, but available software packages may not always incorporate such improvements. In contrast to other makers of statistical software, Microsoft has been slow to improve its routines after its problems had been pointed out and acknowledged in its Knowledge Base, which makes for poor public relations. The only updates of computational accuracy in the past decade were in 2003 (e.g., with LinEst and StDev) and 2010 (including its statistical distributions and RAND, which is now based on the Mersenne twister, although VBA's Rnd was left unchanged). Custom-made functions and macros (including those in this book) are also likely to contain errors that crop up only when algorithms are put under some duress. (I will much appreciate your suggestions to improve my macros.) As with anything else, user beware! For most applications, as long as your data are relatively few, and the number of significant digits needed is small, Excel will be fine, and the same applies to the custom macros presented here. But if you deal with complex problems, and especially when the results you obtain may have serious, practical consequences, calibrate your procedure with similar, binary-incompatible data for which you know the exact answer, and independently verify them by using the extended numberlength method described in chapter 11, or with other software packages. This holds for Excel as well as for more specialized software programs. There are possible errors every step of the way: at sampling, at measuring, at data analysis, and at the final interpretation of the results, and it is best to be aware of them, and to keep the most influential of them as small as possible.

1.14 Mismatches between Excel and VBA

In this book we will first use macros, and then learn how to write them, at which point we will often switch back and forth between the spreadsheet and its macros. The language used in Excel macros is Visual Basic for Applications (VBA), an adaptation of Visual Basic which, itself, is an evolutionary development of Dartmouth Basic (an acronym for *Beginners All-purpose Symbolic Instruction Code*) via Borland's Turbo-Basic and Microsoft's QuickBasic. Along the way, Basic lost some of its less useful features, such as line numbers, and became more like Fortran77, which for some 15 years was the standard form of Fortran.

Visual Basic was combined with Excel in version 5 (Excel 95), when both were already mature products. As in any marriage, both partners brought in their own characteristics, and they did not always match. Unfortunately, Microsoft has done little to soften the resulting conflicts, a few of which we will illustrate below.

The order in which simple arithmetic operations are performed in Excel and VBA is not always the same. In Excel, negation comes before exponentiation, so that $-3^4 = 81$, whereas it is the other way around in VBA: $-3^4 = -81$. To avoid confusion and ambiguity it is therefore best *always* to use brackets when a minus sign is involved: $(-3)^4 = 81$ and $-(3^4) = -81$ in both Excel and VBA. Matters can get especially confusing when a negative sign is used all by itself, as in $=\exp[-(x-c)^2]$, which in Excel is therefore best coded as, e.g., =EXP(-((A3-$B$1)^2)) or =EXP(-1*(A3-$B$1)^2) because =EXP(-(A3-$B$1)^2) will square (and thereby cancel) the first minus sign.

Here are some more beauties: in Excel, $\sqrt{x}$ must be coded as sqrt(x), in VBA as sqr(x). In Excel the sign of x is obtained with sign(x), in VBA as sgn(x). Both are a consequence of the three-letter codes used in VBA. The VBA command Iff is equivalent to Excel's If. In the same category you will find rand(x) in Excel, and rnd(x) in VBA, for a random number, and atan(x) in Excel vs. atn(x) in VBA for the arc tangent. Moreover, Excel's atan(x) is good for $-\pi/2 \le x \le \pi/2$, VBA's atn for $-\pi < x < \pi$. VBA rounds 0.5 to the nearest even integer, i.e., Round (2.5,0) = 2 and Round(-2.5,0) = -2, while the Excel function rounds away from zero, i.e., it rounds up for $x > 0$ and down for $x < 0$, as in Round(2.5,0) = 3 and Round (-2.5,0) = -3.

The worst offender in this category is perhaps the logarithm. In VBA, log(x) represents the *natural*, e-based logarithm, which in Excel (and in almost everyone else's nomenclature) is written as ln(x). VBA does not even have a symbol for the ten-based logarithm, so that it must be calculated as log(x)/log(10), in what everyone else would write as log(x) or ln(x)/ln(10). Excel, on the other hand, has no fewer than *three* ways to represent the ten-based logarithm of x: log(x), log(x,10), and log10(x). In Excel, log(3) yields 0.47712, but in VBA we find log(3) = 1.0986. However, in VBA we can refer to the spreadsheet function, as in Application.log(3), in which case we obtain 0.47712, as illustrated in the function logarheads. Go figure!

```
Function logarheads(x)
MsgBox "Log(" & x & ") = " & Log(x) & " but" & Chr(13) & _
  "Application.Log(" & x & ") = " & Application.Log(x)
End Function
```

An additional set of problems is encountered outside the US, because Excel and VBA may provide different adaptations to languages other than American English. A case in point is the use of the decimal comma (rather than point) in most continental European languages. In the US versions of Excel and VBA, the comma is used as a general separator in both Excel and VBA, whereas a semicolon may be used as such in Europe. The macros described in this book may therefore have to be modified to run properly in such environments.

1.15 Good spreadsheet practice

The flexibility of Excel is one of its great strengths, but it also has some disadvantages. It is very easy to enter data without specifying where the numbers come from, what they mean, or what dimensions are used. The flow of information, from input via data manipulation to output, is left entirely to the user, and may not be obvious to someone other than its author or, a few months later, even to that author. Some useful spreadsheet operations, such as macros and subroutines, may not even leave a trace of their use on the spreadsheet other than the output data generated. And subsequent spreadsheet modifications may destroy the logical connections between some of its data. All of these aspects of flexibility can make spreadsheets extra error-prone and hard to validate.

There are many (often well-documented) anecdotes about spreadsheet errors with major financial consequences, sometimes in the millions of dollars. While the monetary stakes may not be quite so high in the physical sciences as they are in business and finance, the message should not be lost: spreadsheets of any consequence should be organized and documented carefully, operated transparently, and checked for errors. We will come back to this in chapter 11. But because these points are so important, we will briefly cover them here, before you immerse yourself in the detailed applications of Excel. Below, then, are a few suggestions, largely taken from those promulgated by the Statistical Services Centre of the University of Reading, which can be found on the web at http://www.rdg.ac.uk/ssc/publications/guides/ topsde.html.

1.15.1 Organization & documentation

An important aspect of spreadsheet readability, and hence usefulness, is its layout, which should clearly guide the user from input to output. This is best achieved when the information flows from left to right, and/or from top to bottom, as with text. Large data sets are usually placed in columns, because until 2007 Excel rows had only 256 cells. To guide the eye, one can use colored cell blocks. By using light cell colors, darkly colored and/or boldface fonts will remain available for highlighting problems and/or special data.

Because only the top of the spreadsheet will be displayed when it is first called up, it is good practice to reserve the first few rows of the sheet for a header, with a descriptive name and perhaps a few sentences elaborating on the purpose and operation of the spreadsheet, its date and the name or initials of its maker. Here you would also expect to find the date of its construction, and that of its last update. You may also want to reserve the first column of each spreadsheet for labels. For complicated spreadsheets it may be necessary to refer to a separate sheet containing the development history of the project, with dates, version numbers, and synopses of the various modifications made. However, in order to save space, we do not practice what we preach in the many sample spreadsheet snippets shown in this book.

Directly below the general spreadsheet header, place important graphs that summarize the results, and summaries of output results. The data should go below these, with clearly labeled column headings. In this way, the essentials of the spreadsheet are immediately visible, regardless of the lengths of the data columns used, or the complexity of the calculations. It will matter less what specific format is chosen than that it is used consistently throughout.

Clearly separate areas for input, computation, and output. Document long and/or complicated formulas by also describing their functions in words, either in an adjacent cell, with an attached cell comment, or on an added documentation sheet. Make provisions to protect against operations that can trip up the spreadsheet, such as division by zero, or taking the log or square root of negative numbers.

1.15.2 Data entry & validation

When you enter data by hand (rather than by importing data sets from, e.g., instruments), it is often helpful to keep the column headings in view. This can be done by highlighting the row or row number directly below the headings, and by then selecting Window ⇨ Freeze Panes or Window ⇨ Split. To undo, use Window ⇨ Unfreeze Panes or Window ⇨ Remove Split. (⊙⊘,⊙⊙: use the toggles Alt⌣WF and Alt⌣WS.)

In experiments using, say, different objects, species, etc. in a randomized order, the risk of typos in the repeatedly entered names can be reduced by first highlighting the column that will contain those names. Then call Data ⇨ Validation, under the Settings tab select Allow: ⇨ List, and in its Source refer to a block containing the allowed labels. Subsequently, in the highlighted list, names can be either typed or selected by clicking from that list, and unlisted names will be refused.

Numerical data will usually be expected to fall within a given range. Typos can often be caught by highlighting a range of entered data, and by then calling Data ⇨ Validation ⇨ Allow: ⇨ Decimal and specifying the allowed range. Suspicious data can be highlighted after selection of Tools ⇨ Auditing ⇨ Show Auditing Toolbar ⇨ Circle Invalid Data, and/or be labeled with a descriptive cell comment, using Insert ⇨ Comment. All cell comments can be displayed with View ⇨ Comments, while individual cell comments can be read more easily by placing the mouse pointer over the cell.

1.15.3 Spreadsheet calculation

Many errors are introduced when a spreadsheet is later modified. Since spreadsheets are often updated, it is good design practice to make them as foolproof as possible in this respect. Here are a few rules that tend to reduce the likelihood of subsequently introduced errors.

Do not hard-code numerical constants; instead, enter them in a separate cell or range, to which formulas refer either by absolute cell address (e.g., $B$15 or $B$15:$B$19) or by name.

Named cells and ranges can make formulas easier to read, but can also make spreadsheets more error-prone. It may be helpful to label named cells or ranges, e.g., by placing a border around them, and/or a cell label identifying the name used. Update the range name when the corresponding range is modified by, e.g., adding or deleting cells. Do not use named ranges in functions or macros, where they may be overlooked upon spreadsheet modification. Avoid copying formulas containing names to other spreadsheets, since this may create hidden links.

In general, avoid using circular references, unless you (1) have to, *and* (2) know what you are doing.

1.15.4 Auditing

The heart of spreadsheet use lies in its calculations. In Excel, the relations between cells can be visualized with Tools ⇨ Auditing, using Trace Precedents and/or Trace Dependents. (Trace Error can be used to visualize errors leading to error messages.) These auditing tools only works with one highlighted cell at a time, but because they do not erase their arrows unless specifically instructed to do so, one can accumulate networks of interdependencies by using them sequentially on different cells. A corresponding toolbar (selected with Tools ⇨ Auditing ⇨ Show Auditing Toolbar) provides a few more options, including the already mentioned Circle Invalid Data, which can be used in conjunction with Data Validation.

There are several more extensive tools available to help audit a spreadsheet. They range from relatively simple, free ones such as XLAnalyst, to more inclusive commercial ones, such as Spreadsheet Professional. Since these tools lack detailed information on what your spreadsheet is supposed to do, and on your style and layout, anticipate getting many false warnings, i.e., purported errors that are not.

Verifying that the spreadsheet does what you want it to do is usually first checked with one or more sets of trial input data, for which you know the answers. When the author is going to be the only user, this may often be enough. When the spreadsheet will also be used by others, it may be wise to test it against entering missing or incorrect input data, such as a number with a decimal comma rather than a decimal point (or, depending on where you live, the reverse), a 0, one or more letters, or a blank, when the spreadsheet expects an input number. If this produces serious problems, it may be necessary to use an input dialog box to reduce the likelihood of erroneous input, and /or to perform all computations in a macro.

1.15.5 Spreadsheet modification

Spreadsheet modifications are often unintended entry points for errors, and may also complicate subsequent auditing. This section lists some of these dangers. Note that, in this book, we only discuss unintentional errors. Preventing intentional fraud is an entirely different topic

Row or column insertions or deletions can play havoc with cells that refer to them. Especially before erasing cells, check with Tools ⇨ Auditing ⇨ Trace Dependents which cells would be affected, and take care of them. If there is space, it is usually safer to move part (say, about half) of a data block down or sideways to make space for more members. That way you will not inadvertently interfere with spreadsheet areas beyond what is shown on the monitor.

Sometimes it is necessary to copy numerical values. This can be done by referring to the source cells, as in =F17, or by copying the cell(s) involved, highlighting their destination, and then calling Edit ⇨ Paste Special ⇨ Values. The latter method has the advantage that the number(s) will not be updated (if that is what you wish), and the disadvantage that it leaves no auditing trace to identify the source of these data, or to verify that they were copied correctly. Even if one adds a cell comment documenting where these copied cells come from, subsequent spreadsheet changes may make such information obsolete. On the other hand, if the source data move or change, the direct references to them will automatically be modified as well.

1.15.6 Transparency

Excel is used for many commercial products, and therefore has extensive facilities to hide and/or password-protect formulas, columns, worksheets, macro codes, etc. Those approaches are inimical to verifiability, and therefore have no valid place in scientific data analysis.

Data manipulation on the spreadsheet occurs with formulas and functions, which are readily visualized with Tools ⇨ Options by selecting the View tab and checking Formulas. On the other hand, custom macros and subroutines can overwrite existing spreadsheet data or generate new ones without leaving an auditing trail. In this case, especially relevant to many examples given in this book, one can use cell comments to provide the necessary information. Moreover, such macros should not overwrite input or other valuable data. If macro operation requires that the input data be altered, the macro should restore not only the original data but also the underlying formulas.

This book empowers end-users, such as scientists, to write their own functions and macros, i.e., to sit on the programmer's chair. With that power comes the need to know the possibilities and limitations of the various available approaches, and the obligation to adopt the programmer's discipline of proper documentation and transparency.

1.16 Summary

Excel is a competent spreadsheet. It is primarily designed for business applications, and is marketed as such, which makes it both ubiquitous and affordable. Fortunately it also incorporates many features that make it very useful for science and engineering, and its ability to accommodate custom functions and macros using a relatively easy scripting language greatly extends its already considerable power to solve scientific data analysis problems. As you will see in the last few chapters of this book, Excel can be made into a numerical powerhouse by utilizing freely downloadable add-in functions and macros. Showing you how to utilize its power for solving your own problems is the main purpose of this book.

One of the reasons spreadsheets spread so quickly after their general introduction in 1979 as VisiCalc for the Apple II is their ease of making both calculations and graphs, a facility that used to be rather laborious in older numerical software such as FORTRAN. But with that convenience came an embarrassment of riches, an overabundance of colors, markers, and line shapes that can make graphs shout rather than sing, and a flexibility that can lead to chaos. In general, the simpler and clearer a graph is, the more convincing it can be, and the more impact it will have. For best effect, keep your graphs simple and clear, on-message, and use color sparingly: moderation marks the master.

That does not mean that you should try to do everything with Excel: just as no carpenter will go to the job with only one tool, no scientist should rely on just one type of data analysis software. For special problems, specialized software will often be required. For instance, Excel cannot efficiently handle computations on very large data arrays; it has limited capabilities for displaying three-dimensional objects; and it cannot do formal, closed-form mathematics. In all such cases, one should use more appropriate software. It also has some areas where it is still rather weak, such as in statistics. On the other hand, for many relatively small problems in science and engineering, including some fairly sophisticated ones, Excel is eminently suited, because it combines general availability and a low barrier to use with transparency, convenient graphics, and ready expandability. So, spread the sheet, and go for it.

1.17 For further reading

There are many introductory books on Excel, written primarily for a general (often: business-oriented) audience, of which those written by John Walkenbach (Excel 20xx Bible and Excel 20xx Power Programming with VBA) stand out for their clarity and completeness. There are also several books on Excel specifically written for scientists and/or engineers. In this latter category, first mention should go to D. M. Bourg, *Excel Scientific and Engineering Cookbook*, O'Reilly (2006), a fresh approach filled with practical hints. E. J. Billo wrote several books, *Excel for Scientists and Engineers*, Wiley (2007) and *Excel for Chemists* (3rd ed., Wiley 2011). Another Wiley book, *Excel for Engineers and Scientists* by S. C. Bloch (2nd ed. 2003) unfortunately has some of its most valuable chapters tucked away on an accompanying CD. Also useful is B. S. Gottfried, *Spreadsheet tools for engineers using Excel*, McGraw-Hill (latest edition 2009) even though, like Bloch's book, it hardly mentions custom functions and macros. The precursor of many of the above books, *Excel for Scientists and Engineers* by W. J. Orvis (2nd ed., Sybex 1996), was not shy of using VBA, and despite its age is still very worthwhile. All such books should of course be read in small installments, with the computer at hand; otherwise it is like trying to learn to swim without getting yourself wet.

The Microsoft manual provided with Excel is quite good; moreover, you have much information at your fingertips in the Help section. All Microsoft manuals can be consulted and searched on http://support. microsoft.com. For other books go to your local bookstore, public library, college library, or (if you can buy without browsing) to a web-based bookseller.

For the graphical presentation of data, consult the beautiful books by E. Tufte, such as *The Visual Display of Graphical Information* (1992) and *Visual Explanations* (1997), both from Graphics Press.

1.16 Summary

Excel is a competent spreadsheet. It is primarily designed for business applications, and is marketed as such, which makes it both ubiquitous and affordable. Fortunately it also incorporates many features that make it very useful for science and engineering, and its ability to accommodate custom functions and macros using a relatively easy scripting language greatly extends its already considerable power to solve scientific data analysis problems. As you will see in the last few chapters of this book, Excel can be made into a numerical powerhouse by utilizing freely downloadable add-in functions and macros. Showing you how to utilize its power for solving your own problems is the main purpose of this book.

One of the reasons spreadsheets spread so quickly after their general introduction in 1979 as VisiCalc for the Apple II is their ease of making both calculations and graphs, a facility that used to be rather laborious in older numerical software such as FORTRAN. But with that convenience came an embarrassment of riches, an overabundance of colors, markers, and line shapes that can make graphs shout rather than sing, and a flexibility that can lead to chaos. In general, the simpler and clearer a graph is, the more convincing it can be, and the more impact it will have. For best effect, keep your graphs simple and clear, on-message, and use color sparingly: moderation marks the master.

That does not mean that you should try to do everything with Excel: just as no carpenter will go to the job with only one tool, no scientist should rely on just one type of data analysis software. For special problems, specialized software will often be required. For instance, Excel cannot efficiently handle computations on very large data arrays; it has limited capabilities for displaying three-dimensional objects; and it cannot do formal, closed-form mathematics. In all such cases, one should use more appropriate software. It also has some areas where it is still rather weak, such as in statistics. On the other hand, for many relatively small problems in science and engineering, including some fairly sophisticated ones, Excel is eminently suited, because it combines general availability and a low barrier to use with transparency, convenient graphics, and ready expandability. So, spread the sheet, and go for it.

1.17 For further reading

There are many introductory books on Excel, written primarily for a general (often: business-oriented) audience, of which those written by John Walkenbach (Excel 20*xx* Bible and Excel 20*xx* Power Programming with VBA) stand out for their clarity and completeness. There are also several books on Excel specifically written for scientists and/or engineers. In this latter category, first mention should go to D. M. Bourg, *Excel Scientific and Engineering Cookbook*, O'Reilly (2006), a fresh approach filled with practical hints. E. J. Billo wrote several books, *Excel for Scientists and Engineers*, Wiley (2007) and *Excel for Chemists* (3rd. ed., Wiley 2011). Another Wiley book, *Excel for Engineers and Scientists* by S. C. Bloch (2nd ed. 2003) unfortunately has some of its most valuable chapters tucked away on an accompanying CD. Also useful is B. S. Gottfried, *Spreadsheet tools for engineers using Excel*, McGraw-Hill (latest edition 2009) even though, like Bloch's book, it hardly mentions custom functions and macros. The precursor of many of the above books, *Excel for Scientists and Engineers* by W. J. Orvis (2nd ed., Sybex 1996), was not shy of using VBA, and despite its age is still very worthwhile. All such books should of course be read in small installments, with the computer at hand; otherwise it is like trying to learn to swim without getting yourself wet.

The Microsoft manual provided with Excel is quite good; moreover, you have much information at your fingertips in the Help section. All Microsoft manuals can be consulted and searched on http://support.microsoft.com. For other books go to your local bookstore, public library, college library, or (if you can buy without browsing) to a web-based bookseller.

For the graphical presentation of data, consult the beautiful books by E. Tufte, such as *The Visual Display of Graphical Information* (1992) and *Visual Explanations* (1997), both from Graphics Press.

Chapter *2*
Simple linear least squares

All experimental observations are subject to experimental uncertainty. We can often distinguish two types of such uncertainty, which is sometimes called "error". Measurements may be distorted systematically by interfering phenomena, instrumental distortion, faulty calibration, or any number of factors that affect their *accuracy*, i.e., how far from true they are. (Since the truth is not known, the amount of inaccuracy can at best be guessed at the time, and can often only be estimated in retrospect.) Moreover, measurements may exhibit "noise", because most experiments leave wriggle room for a multitude of small, seemingly random fluctuations in experimental conditions: amplifiers may magnify the effects of thermal fluctuations, read-out instruments may have limited resolution, etc. Such noise affects the reproducibility of the measurements, i.e., its *precision*. Even assuming that all experimental artifacts could be removed, many measured properties are inherently *stochastic*, i.e., have a small amount of randomness because of the discrete nature of mass (atoms, molecules) and energy (quanta). We seldom have or take the time and tools to analyze the sources of such noise, and they are often of little interest as long as they can be removed without seriously affecting the underlying information. Only rarely do they make the evening news, as when the margin of error in vote counting machines in a crucial state exceeds the margin of votes for one presidential candidate over another.

In this and the next two chapters we will be mostly concerned with precision, i.e., with random fluctuations and their reduction or removal. This is no reflection on their relative importance vis-à-vis systematic sources of uncertainty, but merely of the fact that a useful theoretical framework exists for their treatment. Books can only teach what is known, a criterion that does not imply a value judgement regarding its relative importance. Chapter 6 will briefly discuss some of the known sources of systematic uncertainty, and their possible remedies.

Scientific experiments typically generate large volumes of observations, from which one tries to extract much smaller amounts of more meaningful numerical information, in a process often called *data reduction*. Ultimately, such information may lead to a quantitative understanding of the underlying phenomena. This chapter will illustrate the method of least squares, one of the most widely used techniques for the extraction of numerical information from an excess of experimental data. Excel provides convenient facilities for least squares analysis; where necessary we will use additional tools to facilitate the application of this method.

Least squares analysis is based on a single Gaussian distribution of errors. We do not explain the basis for this or other statistical techniques, since that would require a text all its own, and a large number of those have already been written. But, whenever necessary, we will explain some of the more practical features of least-squares methods, and highlight what choices the experimenter must make.

In order to keep the chapters within reasonable length, we have split the discussion of "linear" least squares into two parts. We put the word "linear" within quotation marks because it is generally used to distinguish it from "nonlinear" least squares described in chapter 4. However, those terms can be misleading, as they may suggest that the former is used only for fitting to a line. Names such as "direct" vs. "iterative" least squares might be better descriptors, but are not in common use.

In the present chapter we survey the simple applications of unweighted least squares methods to the proportionality $y = a_1 x$ and to the straight line $y = a_0 + a_1 x$. Chapter 3 will deal with its extensions to include polynomial, multi-parameter, and weighted linear least squares.

2.1 Repeat measurements

When we make a quantitative measurement, we obtain a number. When we repeat the measurement under what appear to be identical conditions, we will usually get a similar value, but not necessarily an identical one. Apart from major identifiable changes (the power just went out) or unintentional ones (we transposed two digits when noting down the result), this is most likely caused by possible fluctuations in some uncontrolled parameters: the temperature may have drifted somewhat between measurements, someone may have opened a door and let in a draft, there may have been a glitch on the power line because an instrument in an adjacent room was turned on or the elevator motor just started, or for any number of other, often not readily identifiable reasons. The question then arises: which is *the* correct result? There is no general answer to that question, and we usually deal with it by making several repeat observations, and averaging the result, on the assumption that any experimental errors tend to "average out". This can indeed be expected for many errors that are essentially random, although some experimental errors (such as might result from, e.g., the presence of an impurity, or a slow increase in room temperature during the morning hours) can introduce a bias, i.e., they are systematic rather than random.

The *sample average* or *sample mean*, y_{av} or $\bar{y}$, of N equivalent observations is defined as

$$y_{av} = \frac{1}{N} \sum_{i=1}^{N} y_i \tag{2.1.1}$$

where the index i, running from 1 to N, identifies the individual observations y_i. (In many fields of science and technology the superscript bar has a special, field-specific meaning, and it is also difficult to use in Excel. We will therefore use the more explicit notation y_{av}.) We can also get an estimate of the likely imprecision in that result, such as its *standard deviation*

$$s = \sqrt{\frac{\sum_{i=1}^{N}(y_i - y_{av})^2}{N-1}} \tag{2.1.2}$$

or the associated *variance*

$$v = s^2 = \frac{\sum_{i=1}^{N}(y_i - y_{av})^2}{N-1} = \frac{\sum_{i=1}^{N}\delta_i^2}{N-1} \tag{2.1.3}$$

where the difference between the individual observation and its average value, $\delta_i = (y_i - y_{av})$, is called the *residual*.

Exercise 2.1.1:

(1) We use the data generated in exercise 1.2.1. This is a large data set, which we cannot possibly display legibly on a typical computer screen. On a sheet of paper, totals are typically placed at the bottom of columns, and carried forward to the top of the next page when necessary. In a spreadsheet, the columns can be very long, making the bottom of a column rather hard to find. It is therefore convenient to place totals and related derived quantities at the *top* of the spreadsheet. If there is no room at the top, make it (which is much easier to do in a spreadsheet than in a job) by, e.g., highlighting the top two cells containing the row labels, right-clicking, and then selecting Insert.

(2) In order to calculate the average, you could use (2.1.1) and calculate the average of the data in column B with the instruction =SUM(B3: B1003)/1000, but it is more convenient to use instead =AVERAGE(B3: B1003). If you don't know how long the column is, just type =AVERAGE(and click on the top cell of the column (B3), then use Shift⌣End, Shift⌣↓ (where Ctrl is held down while keying Shift), then ↓ (or, in one command, Ctrl⌣Shift⌣↓), and Enter. You may not even need to enter the closing bracket.

(3) Likewise, in order to compute the standard deviation, you could use eq. (2.1.2), make a new column containing the squares of the residuals, add them up, and divide by N–1. But it is much easier to use the single command =STDEV(B3:B1003) instead.

The numbers we obtain for the average and standard deviation over a large number of data points are much closer to their "true" value (which in Exercise 2.1 we know to be 10 and 1 respectively, because these are synthetic rather than real data) than the averages and standard deviations for smaller subsets of these data. If we could take an infinite number of measurements, and the uncertainties would all be truly random, we would get their "correct" values. But for a small number of observations, we must make do with the sample average and sample standard deviation. For a sample of N observations, the *standard deviation of the mean* is $\sqrt{N}$ smaller than the standard deviation of the individual measurements,

$$s_{av} = s_i / \sqrt{N} \tag{2.1.4}$$

A sometimes more realistic measure of the imprecision in the mean is the *confidence interval* (or *confidence limit*), which is the standard deviation of the mean, y_{av} multiplied by a factor that reflects both the finite sample size and a specified "confidence level". The confidence interval is found with =CONFIDENCE(α,s,N) where α is the assumed uncertainty, in %: $\alpha = 0.05$ for 5% uncertainty, corresponding with a confidence of $1 - \alpha = 1 - 0.05 = 0.95$ or 95% ; $\alpha = 0.01$ for a confidence of 0.99 or 99%, etc. The second parameter, s, is the standard deviation, and N counts the number of data points analyzed.

Exercise 2.1 (continued):

(4) Calculate the 95% confidence limits of the first 9-point average of Exercise 1.3.1 using the instruction =CONFIDENCE(0.05,D7,9), or =CONFIDENCE (0.05,D5,9) in case you did not insert the two additional lines at the top.

Note that the confidence intervals delineate the likely range of the *reproducibility* of the data, and have nothing whatsoever to do with how true, reliable, or confidence-inspiring they are. The term "confidence" would appear to have been chosen deliberately to blur the distinction between accuracy (i.e., how reliable a number is) and precision (how reproducible that number is when the measurement is repeated under the very same experimental conditions). Confidence artists and confidence games have further tarnished the term.

2.2 Fitting data to a proportionality

Say that we apply a constant current I to a resistor, and measure the resulting voltage difference V across its terminals. We will assume that Ohm's law applies, as it has been shown to do over many orders of magnitude. We could make a single measurement, and calculate the resistance R of the resistor from Ohm's law as $R = V/I$. We can repeat the measurement, and then analyze the resulting data as in section 2.1. However, it is often more efficient to make measurements at several *different* currents, because we can then use the data also to test the applicability of the assumed proportionality. In this case we must fit the observations to a given *function*, here Ohm's law, $V = IR$.

In general, the resulting analysis is nontrivial, because the numerical values of *both* V and I will be subject to experimental uncertainties. Fortunately, one of them usually has a smaller uncertainty than the other, such as when one measures a variable as a function of time, because time can nowadays be measured to a very high degree of accuracy and precision, even in a lowly wristwatch. In such a case it is reasonable to focus on the more uncertain parameter, the so-called *dependent* (or *response*) variable, the other being called the *independent* (or *control*) variable, which we will then assume to be error-free. If the disparity between the uncertainties in the two variables is sufficiently large, this is often an acceptably small price to pay for a considerably simplified analysis. In section 4.19 we will see how this assumption can be avoided when fitting a proportionality or straight line to experimental data. -

Incidentally, neither terminology (dependent vs. independent, or response vs. control) is entirely satisfactory. In least squares analysis we typically deal with precision rather than accuracy, and *noisy* vs. *noise-free* or *assumedly noisier* vs. *assumedly less noisy* might be more appropriate distinctions. We will often use y for the dependent (response, noisy), and x for the independent (control, noise-free) variable.

Usually it will be clear from the type of measurements made which variable is the dependent one. In other situations, the choice is sometimes made merely for mathematical convenience. In any case, the experimenter must decide what *model* is the most appropriate to use in conjunction with the least squares method. Any least squares analysis *depends on a model*, and the choice of that model is always a judgement call.

Below we will assume that the measurement of V is the more uncertain one, so that I will be taken as the independent variable. When we plot V versus I we expect to see data that, apart from the noise, lie on a straight line with a slope R passing through the origin of the graph. In order to extract the value of the resistance R from such data, we need to use the expression

$$R = \sum_{i=1}^{N} I_i V_i \left/ \sum_{i=1}^{N} I_i^2 \right. \tag{2.2.1}$$

or, in general, for the proportionality $y = a_1 x$,

$$a_1 = \sum_{i=1}^{N} x_i y_i \left/ \sum_{i=1}^{N} x_i^2 \right. \tag{2.2.2}$$

where, by convention, y is the dependent variable, and the index 1 for the slope a_1 is given for the sake of consistency with subsequent extensions. Equation (2.2.2) can be derived by minimizing the sum of squares of the residuals δ_i, which in this case are defined as $\delta_i = (y_i - a_1 x_i)$.

We can now define *two* standard deviations, where s_f characterizes the stochastic uncertainty, i.e., the *imprecision*, in the over-all fit of the data to the theoretical model, and s_1 the resulting uncertainty in the derived slope a_1. The corresponding expressions are

$$s_f = \sqrt{\frac{\sum_{i=1}^{N} \delta_i^2}{N-1}} = \sqrt{\frac{\sum_{i=1}^{N} (y_i - a_1 x_i)^2}{N-1}} = \sqrt{\frac{\sum_{i=1}^{N} x_i^2 \sum_{i=1}^{N} y_i^2 - \left(\sum_{i=1}^{N} x_i y_i \right)^2}{(N-1) \sum_{i=1}^{N} x_i^2}} \tag{2.2.3}$$

and

$$s_1 = \frac{s_f}{\sqrt{\sum_{i=1}^{N} x_i^2}} = \sqrt{\frac{\sum_{i=1}^{N} x_i^2 \sum_{i=1}^{N} y_i^2 - \left(\sum_{i=1}^{N} x_i y_i \right)^2}{(N-1) \left(\sum_{i=1}^{N} x_i^2 \right)^2}} \tag{2.2.4}$$

Again, we could use the spreadsheet and eqs. (2.2.2) through (2.2.4) to compute a_1, s_f, and s_1 respectively, but Excel makes that unnecessary, because it has these operations already built-in.

2.3 LinEst

LinEst, for *lin*ear *est*imator, is the simplest (and most terse) least-squares fitting tool Excel provides.

Exercise 2.3.1:

(1) First we make a set of mock data on which to practice. In cell A1, deposit the label a1 =, and in cell C1 the label sn =, where s_n denotes the *s*tandard deviation of the *n*oise. In cells B1 and D1 place some associated values. (By left-justifying these, and right-justifying the associated labels, we make them easy to read as one unit.) In A3, B3 and N3 place labels for *y*, *x*, and noise respectively; why in this order will soon become clear. In B4:B10 deposit some *x*-values, such as 1 (1) 7, and in N4:N10 some Gaussian noise. (Use Tools ⇨ Data Analysis ⇨ Random Number Generation, select Distribution: Normal, activate Output Range, activate the corresponding window, enter N4:N10, then press OK or Enter. In order to keep the monitor screen uncluttered, we have put the noise out of sight, in column N.) In A4 place the instruction =$B$1*B4+$D$1*N4, and copy it to A5:A10. The spreadsheet should now resemble Fig. 2.3.1, except for the specific numbers.

	A	B	C	D	E		N
1	a1 = 2.3		sn = 0.2				
2							
3	*y*	*x*					*noise*
4	2.2400	1					-0.3002
5	4.3445	2					-1.2777
6	6.9489	3					0.2443
7	9.4553	4					1.2765
8	11.7397	5					1.1984
9	14.1466	6					1.7331
10	15.6633	7					-2.1836

Fig. 2.3.1: The spreadsheet with some test data. The instruction in cell A4, =$B$1*B4+$D$1*N4, was copied to cells A5:A10. The normally out-of-view cells N4:N10 contain Gaussian ('normal') noise with zero mean and unit standard deviation.

(2) Highlight an empty block, one cell wide and two cells high, such as E4:E5, type =LINEST(A4:A10,B4:B10, FALSE,TRUE) and enter this with the special instruction Ctrl⌣Shift⌣Enter, i.e., by holding down the Control and Shift keys before and while depressing the Enter key. This is necessary to let the computer know that you want to enter an instruction into a *block* of cells rather than in a single cell. The selected cell block will now contain, in its top cell, the value of the slope a_1, and directly below it the standard deviation s_1. Had you forgotten to hold down the Ctrl and Shift keys while depositing the LinEst instruction, you would only have obtained the top answer, a_1. The arguments of LinEst are the ranges of the *y*- and *x*-values respectively, then the absence (0 or false) or presence (1 or true) of an intercept, and whether you want the associated statistics (again 0 or 1, for false or true respectively).

(3) The value found for a_1 in cell D4 should be close to that in cell B1, but (because of the added noise) will usually not not quite match it. Check this by changing the value of s_n in D1 to 0. Then change s_n to a value larger than used earlier, and observe its effects.

(4) We will now, for once, verify that these numbers are indeed correct. In cells G3:I3 place the labels Σxx or Σx^2, Σxy, and Σyy or Σy^2 respectively, in cell G4 the instruction =B4^2, in H4 the command =A4*B4, and in I4 =A4^2. Copy these down to G5:I10. In G12 deposit =SUM(G4:G10), and copy this to H12 and I12, so that these cells now contain the sums Σx^2, Σxy, and Σy^2 respectively. In cell G14 compute the value of a_1 using (2.2.2), as =H12/G12, in H14 calculate s_f as =SQRT((G12*I12-H12^2)/(6*G12)), see (2.2.3), and in I14 find s_1 as =H14/SQRT(G12), see (2.2.4). To guard against the possibility of taking the square root of a negative quantity in the instruction in H14 you might instead want to use =SQRT(ABS((G12*I12-H12^2)/(6*G12))).

(5) If you have made no mistakes, the values for a_1 and s_1 will be the same as those generated by LinEst. But where is the value of s_y? Go to cell D4, now highlight block D4:E8, and again type =LINEST(A4:A10,B4:B10,FALSE,TRUE) or the equivalent but somewhat shorter =LINEST(A4:A10, B4:B10,0,1). (Excel uses 0 for false, 1 for true.) Pressing Ctrl⌣Shift⌣Enter will yield the answer, and your spreadsheet should now resemble that in Fig. 2.3.2. You will find the value of s_f in cell E6. The other information: D6 contains the square of the correlation coefficient, D7 the value of the F-test, and D8 the regression sum of squares; in column E you find, from top to bottom, the intercept (here zero by definition), its standard deviation (not applicable here, since there is no intercept), the value of s_f, that of the number of degrees of freedom $N–P$, and the residual sum of squares, SSR. Unfortunately, this output is rather cryptic since no labels are provided to tell you what is what. You can find that out by using Help ⇨ Contents and Index, by then typing LINEST, and by clicking on the LINEST worksheet function, or by consulting Fig. 2.3.3.

(6) In summary, LinEst is convenient, compact, and cryptic. It allows you to select what statistical information you want to display. It updates automatically when you change one of the y and/or x values, as long as they fall within the ranges specified for them, here A4:A10 and B4:B10 respectively. But don't forget to deposit the LinEst instruction in the entire block you want (e.g., if you want to see a_1, s_1, and s_f, select D4:E6), using Ctrl⌣Shift⌣Enter, otherwise you will only see the value of a_1. Note that one cannot *cut* and paste one or several numbers from the LinEst output, only the entire block, but that one can freely *copy* and paste the individual cells.

	A	B	C	D	E		N
1	a1 = 2.3		sn = 0.2				
2							
3	*y*	*x*					*noise*
4	2.2400	1		2.30584	0		-0.3002
5	4.3445	2		0.0244	#N/A		-1.2777
6	6.9489	3		0.99666	0.28868		0.2443
7	9.4553	4		1792.08	6		1.2765
8	11.7397	5		149.342	0.5		1.1984
9	14.1466	6					1.7331
10	15.6633	7					-2.1836

Fig. 2.3.2: The spreadsheet of Fig. 2.3.1 with the results of LinEst in block D4:E8.

a_1	a_0
s_1	s_0
R^2	s_f
F	$N–P$
SSE	SSR

Fig. 2.3.3: The layout of the LinEst output for fitting a proportionality or a straight line to data. The coefficients a_1 and a_0 occupy the top row, the corresponding standard deviations s_1 and s_0 the second row. Below s_0 is shown the standard deviation of the fit of the function, s_f, below s_f the number of degrees of freedom, $N–P$, and below that the residual sum of squares SSR, the quantity minimized in least squares analysis. The other, non- boldfaced parameters, are of less interest to us here: the square R^2 of the linear correlation coefficient between x and y, the F test, and the regression sums of squares SSE.

2.4 Regression

Regression is Excel's most extensive tool for least squares fitting of data. It yields a large (some might say excessive) amount of statistical information on the fit, as illustrated below. It can also generate useful auxiliary graphs.

Exercise 2.4.1:

(1) The Regression routine in the Analysis Toolpak is somewhat more user-friendly than LinEst, but may overload you with statistical information. You get it with Tools ⇨ Data Analysis. In the Data Analysis dialog box, use the scroll bar to the right of the list to see items too far down the alphabet to be displayed, and double-click on Regression. Another dialog box appears, in which you enter (by typing or pointing) the Input Y Range as A4:A10, and the Input X Range as B4:B10. Click on Constant is Zero (for the zero intercept), and select a cell for the Output Range next to or below your data, because the output block is large, and will overwrite and erase any data in its way. Click OK. You will now find three sets of data, as illustrated in Fig. 2.4.1. In the top set, labeled Regression Statistics, the correlation coefficient is listed as Multiple R, and s_f as Standard Error. In the second block, ANOVA, you will find the zero intercept and its non-applicable standard deviation, and as X Variable 1 the values of a_1 and s_1. The data at the bottom come with the two (optional) graphs discussed in step (2).

(2) Repeat the same analysis, but click on the square windows to the left of Line Fit Plots and Residual Plots. On pressing OK you will now see two graphs, illustrated in Fig. 2.4.2, which you can move around on the screen. You can also enlarge or reduce them, change their colors or other features, whatever, all by dragging and clicking. Figure 2.4.3 shows them after some adjustments to emphasize data rather than labels, and to distinguish more clearly between data *points* and fitted *line*.

(3) Note that the Regression routine in the Analysis Toolpak is a macro, and needs to be invoked every time the input information is changed. On the other hand, LinEst is a function, and updates automatically whenever the input changes.

SUMMARY OUTPUT

Regression Statistics	
Multiple R	0.998330163
R Square	0.996663115
Adjusted R Squa	0.829996448
Standard Error	0.288676399
Observations	7

ANOVA

	df	SS	MS	F	Significance F
Regression	1	149.3416561	149.3416561	1792.084172	1.38776E-07
Residual	6	0.500004381	0.083334063		
Total	7	149.8416605			

	Coefficients	Standard Error	t Stat	P-value	Lower 95%	Upper 95%	Lower 95.0%	Upper 95.0%
Intercept	0	#N/A	#N/A	#N/A	#N/A	#N/A	#N/A	#N/A
X Variable 1	2.30584072	0.024397609	94.5109313	9.45466E-11	2.246141878	2.365539561	2.246141878	2.365539561

RESIDUAL OUTPUT

Observation	Predicted Y	Residuals
1	2.30584072	-0.065887152
2	4.61168144	-0.267218073
3	6.917522159	0.031329302
4	9.223362879	0.231931829
5	11.5292036	0.210466445
6	13.83504432	0.311582302
7	16.14088504	-0.477602566

Fig. 2.4.1: The extensive output generated by Regression upon its application to the 7 data pairs in Fig. 2.3.1. As the intercept was set to zero, no corresponding statistical information for that intercept is available.

A note on nomenclature: least squares analysis was introduced in astronomy in 1805 by Legendre, who called it "la méthode des moindres carrés", literally "the method of least squares". Gauss, who had developed it earlier (in connection with predicting the orbit of the asteroid Ceres in 1801 from a very limited number of observations, just before Ceres disappeared behind the sun) but had not published his method, later called it the "theoria combinationis observationum erroribus minimis obnoxiae", i.e, the theory of combining observations to be subject to minimal errors. It is now often called "regression analysis" after Galton, an early statistician and the founder of the eugenics movement, who introduced the method into the humanities. However, the latter name is quite misleading, and will not be used here other than to refer to the Excel macro of that same name. To quote K. A. Brownlee, *Statistical Theory and Methodology in Science and Engineering*, 2nd ed., Wiley (1965) p. 409:

"Galton observed that on the average the sons of tall fathers are not as tall as their fathers, and similarly the sons of short fathers are not as short as their fathers; i.e., the second generation tended to regress towards the mean."

"But if we look at the data the other way round, we find that on average the fathers of tall sons are not as tall as their sons and the fathers of short sons are not as short as their sons, so the first generation tends to regress towards the mean. It seems implausible that both statements can be true simultaneously, so this phenomenon has been called the regression fallacy."

With Galton, let us assume that the variations in the heights of individuals between successive generations are largely random, within the range of variability determined by genetics. Moreover, we will assume that we can neglect external factors that change only little per generation, such as eating habits, sanitation, and health care. If we select the tallest individuals of one generation, then both their fathers and their adult sons on average will be smaller, as long as the average size remains constant. In other words, when we compare a highly biased (tallest) subset with a (preceding or subsequent) average, we should not be surprised that the two differ. The term 'regression' suggests that something 'regresses to the mean', a directionality that simply isn't there.

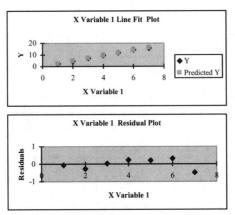

Fig. 2.4.2: Two plots produced by Regression upon its application to the data in Fig. 2.3.1.

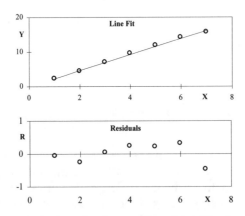

Fig. 2.4.3: The plots of Fig. 2.4.2, cleaned up by re-scaling, deleting background color, moving labels inside the graph, and representing measured data by points, the assumed function by a curve. Using the same area, Fig. 2.4.3 devotes more space to the data, and correspondingly less to empty framing.

2.5 LS

For reasons that will become clear later in this chapter, we also provide a *custom* least squares macro, LS, for *l*east *s*quares. It comes in two flavors: LS0 fits data to a line through the origin, while LS1 allows for an arbitrary intercept, and will therefore be discussed in section 2.7.

Starting with Excel 2003, LinEst and Regression have been improved, and are now equivalent to the singular value decomposition described in section 10.13. Both are, in general, superior to LS in their ability to handle so-called ill-conditioned matrices. However, for all but the most demanding applications, the difference in performance is usually insignificant. Moreover, in section 11.14 we will illustrate how LS can be transformed into a routine that is much more powerful than LinEst or Regression.

The input format of LS0 requires that the dependent data y and independent data x be placed in two *contiguous, adjacent* columns. The left-hand column must contain the dependent variable y, and the right-hand column the corresponding independent x-values. In order to use LS0, highlight the data in the two adjacent columns (without including their labels) and call the macro. This will provide the slope a_1 in bold italics in the column for x, directly below the data, underneath it the standard deviation s_1 in italics, and below that the standard deviation of the fit, s_f. If you have the MBToolbar installed, just click on LS ⇨ LS0. If not, use Tools ⇨ Macro ⇨ Macros, select LS0, and double-click on it or click on Run.

Exercise 2.5.1:

(1) Start again with the layout of Fig. 2.3.1. Highlight the two columns of data (in this example, block A4:B10) and then call LS0.

(2) If you want to display the standard deviation of the fit, s_y, answer the input box affirmatively. The spreadsheet should now look like Fig. 2.5.1.

(3) The non-intuitive order of using y in the left-most column is used here because it allows for easy expansion of the x-column into an x-block for the polynomial or multivariate models used in chapter 3. As a result, the order of presentation of the results in LS, from a_0 to a_1, is opposite of that used in LinEst, and the same applies to their standard deviations s.

	A	B	C	D	E		N	
1	a1 = 2.3		sn = 0.2					
2								
3	*y*	*x*					*noise*	
4	2.2400	1					-0.3002	
5	4.3445	2					-1.2777	
6	6.9489	3					0.2443	
7	9.4553	4					1.2765	
8	11.7397	5					1.1984	
9	14.1466	6					1.7331	
10	15.6633	7					-2.1836	
11	*Coeff.:*	*2.3058*						
12	*St.Dev.:*	*0.0244*						
13		*0.2887*						

Fig. 2.5.1: The spreadsheet of Fig. 2.3.1 after using LS0.

Whether we use LinEst, Regression, or LS0, it is usually good practice to make a plot of the experimental data (as points), and add to that graph the computed continuous line. For noisy data it is also advisable to calculate and plot the corresponding residuals, because a systematic trend in the deviations may reveal a flaw in the model used. Regression will make these plots automatically when you ask for them; with LinEst and LS0 you must make them yourself. In all cases the results should look like those in Figs. 2.4.2 and 2.4.3.

2.6 Trendline

When we already have made a graph of the data to be fitted, Trendline is a convenient tool to determine rough values of the unknown parameters, though without meaningful statistics. It is meant for predicting economic trends based on extrapolation (for whatever such forecasts are worth), but emphatically *not* for scientific use.

Exercise 2.6.1:

(1) Trendline is simpler to use, but also more limited, than LinEst, Regression, or LS. It requires that you have a *graph* of the data. Therefore, first make a graph of y vs. x on the spreadsheet, using Insert ⇨ Chart and the Chart Wizard. If you bypass step 2 of the Chart Wizard you will obtain a graph of x versus y. In that case, first exchange the positions of the x- and y-columns.

(2) Click on the data in the graph to highlight them, right-click, and select Add Trendline. (Alternatively, after highlighting the data, click on Chart ⇨ Add Trendline.) In the dialog box select Type Linear, and under Options activate both Set intercept = 0 and Display equation on chart. Click OK. The equation for y will now appear in the graph, together with a line representing it. You can click on the line and change its color, thickness, etc.; likewise, you can move the equation around and, e.g., change its font.

(3) Trendline is a function, just like LinEst, and automatically updates as you change any or all of the data in the graph. However, it cannot fit to part of a curve, nor does it provide any statistical estimates beyond the square of the correlation coefficient r_{xy}, which in this context is mostly a non-informative feel-good parameter. Compare your results with Fig. 2.6.1.

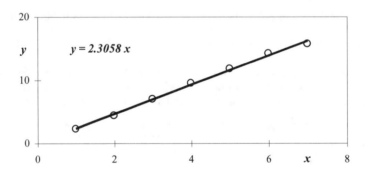

Fig. 2.6.1: Trendline automatically plots the computed curve through the data in Fig. 2.3.1 when these are presented graphically. Optionally it can also show the corresponding equation, but without useful uncertainty estimates.

When one considers a scientific quantity, one should not only know its numerical value, but also the inherent uncertainty of that value. LinEst, Regression, and LS can all provide uncertainty estimates of the individual parameter values they determine, but Trendline cannot. For that reason, the use of Trendline in quantitative scientific work should be discouraged.

Even though we have so far already described four least squares routines, we will encounter yet another, Solver, which will be introduced in section 4.1. Therefore you can rest assured that, with Excel, you will not need to evaluate the sums in eqs. (2.2.2) through (2.2.4) anymore!

2.7 Fitting data to a straight line

Often we deal with a function that can be expected to fit a straight line, as in $y = a_0 + a_1 x$, and with slope a_1 and intercepting the vertical axis at $x = a_0$. In that case (2.2.2) must be replaced by

$$a_0 = \left(\sum_{i=1}^{N} x_i^2 \sum_{i=1}^{N} y_i - \sum_{i=1}^{N} x_i \sum_{i=1}^{N} x_i y_i \right) \Big/ D \tag{2.7.1}$$

$$a_1 = \left(N\sum_{i=1}^{N} x_i y_i - \sum_{i=1}^{N} x_i \sum_{i=1}^{N} y_i \right) \Big/ D \qquad (2.7.2)$$

where

$$D = N\sum_{i=1}^{N} x_i^2 - \left(\sum_{i=1}^{N} x_i \right)^2 = N\sum_{i=1}^{N} (x_i - x_{av})^2 \qquad (2.7.3)$$

for the *intercept* a_0 and *slope* a_1 respectively. Likewise, instead of (2.2.3) and (2.2.4) we now should use

$$v_{ff} = s_f^2 = \frac{\sum_{i=1}^{N} \delta_i^2}{N-2} = \frac{\sum_{i=1}^{N} (y_i - a_0 - a_1 x_i)^2}{N-2} \qquad (2.7.4)$$

$$v_{00} = s_0^2 = v_{ff} \sum_{k=1}^{N} \left(\frac{\partial a_0}{\partial y_k} \right)^2 = v_{ff} \sum_{i=1}^{N} x_i^2 \Big/ D \qquad (2.7.5)$$

$$v_{11} = s_1^2 = v_{ff} \sum_{k=1}^{N} \left(\frac{\partial a_1}{\partial y_k} \right)^2 = v_{ff} N \Big/ D \qquad (2.7.6)$$

for the associated *variances* v, the squares of the standard deviations s_f, s_0 and s_1 respectively. (The doubling of the indices i on the variances v_{ii} anticipates the introduction of covariances v_{ij} in section 2.9.) As before, the residuals δ_i are the differences between the observed quantities y_i and their assumed, 'theoretical' expressions, $a_0 + a_1 x_i$, i.e., $\delta_i = (y_i - a_0 - a_1 x_i)$. Equations (2.7.1) and (2.7.2) can then be derived by minimizing the quantity $\Sigma\delta_i^2 = \Sigma(y_i - a_0 - a_1 x_i)^2$ with respect to a_0 and a_1 respectively. We will often abbreviate the sum as S, the residual δ_i as R, its square δ_i^2 as SR, and the corresponding sum $\Sigma\delta_i^2$ as SSR, the *S*um of *S*quares of the *R*esiduals.

While we could use the spreadsheet to make the above sums, the expressions are now becoming so complicated that spreadsheet help is welcome – and we have already seen that it is readily available. In LinEst, all we need to do is to specify its third argument as True or 1, signifying the presence of an intercept. In Regression, we do not activate Constant is Zero. For the custom least squares macro we select LS1 rather than LS0, because the latter forces the fitted line through the origin. And in Trendline, we do not activate Set intercept = 0. You might want to try them with a data set such as shown in Fig. 2.3.1, after addition of a constant to the expression for y.

In general, when fitting data to a straight line, the slope and intercept will *not* be independent quantities. This does not affect their values, or those of the corresponding standard deviations, but may complicate using these values in subsequent computations, specifically when we estimate how the experimental imprecision in the slope and intercept work their way (i.e., *propagate*) through a calculation to affect the imprecision of a result derived from them. We will therefore briefly discuss the propagation of experimental imprecision, and the new parameter involved, the *covariance*, before returning to least squares data fitting per se.

2.8. Simple propagation of imprecision

The parameters produced by a least squares fitting of experimental data may not be the final answers sought. Often, they need to be combined with other numbers or otherwise manipulated to generate the numerical end results of the experiment. We therefore consider how the standard deviations obtained in a least squares analysis propagate through any subsequent computation to affect the final numerical results.

First we will deal with the case in which the input data to such a calculation are mutually *in*dependent. On the other hand, when two or more data are derived from a single set of measurements, as is often the case with least squares analysis, the resulting parameter values are in general mutually *inter*dependent. The general treatment appropriate to that more general situation will be given in section 2.9.

Here we therefore consider a function F computed from one or more mutually *in*dependent experimental parameters a_j that have associated imprecision estimates (standard deviations, confidence limits, etc.), and ask what will be the resulting imprecision in the final result. For example, we might compute the volume V of a cylinder from its measured diameter d and height h as $\pi d^2 h/4$, and ask how the uncertainty in V is obtained from the experimental imprecisions in the measurements of d and h. (We specifically leave inaccuracy out of consideration because, for an object of previously unknown diameter, height, and volume, no analysis of mere sets of numbers d and h can determine whether, e.g., the cross section of the cylinder was truly circular, or the measuring tools used were properly calibrated. Those are relevant questions, but they are outside the realm of least squares analysis per se.)

In a few special cases (addition & subtraction, multiplication & division, exponentiation & log taking) we can formulate simple rules, but in general it is easier to use the general formula

$$v_{FF} = s_F^2 = \sum_j \left(\frac{\partial F}{\partial a_j} \right)^2 s_{a_j}^2 = \sum_j \left(\frac{\partial F}{\partial a_j} \right)^2 v_{a_j a_j} \tag{2.8.1}$$

which reduces to

$$s_F = \left| \frac{dF}{da} \right| s_a \tag{2.8.2}$$

when, for $j = 1$, F depends on a single parameter x. Excel does not provide a convenient tool to calculate the uncertainty in F given the known uncertainties in a (or in several a_j's), but the macro Propagation in the MacroBundle does. Below we will illustrate its application. Exactly how Propagation achieves its magic will be explained in section 8.18.

Exercise 2.8.1:

(1) Say that we want to compute the value of $F = \ln(4X+3/Y) + YZ^2$, and compute the associated uncertainty f given the uncertainties x, y, and z in X, Y, and Z respectively. We can use partial differentiation to find $\partial F/\partial X = 4/(4X+3/Y)$, $\partial F/\partial Y = (-3/Y^2)/(4X+3/Y)+Z^2$, and $\partial F/\partial Z = 2YZ$, so that $f^2 = \{4x/(4X+3/Y)\}^2 + \{-3y/[Y^2(4X+3/Y)]+yZ^2\}^2 + \{2zYZ\}^2$, from which the sought uncertainty f follows as its square root.

(2) When we use the spreadsheet, we will usually have numerical values for X, Y, and Z on that sheet, together with the values of their uncertainties x, y, and z, e.g., in the form of their standard deviations. In cells A1, A2, and A3 enter the labels X=, Y=, and Z= respectively, and place numerical values for them in cells B1 through B3. In cells C1 through C3 deposit the labels x=, y=, and z=, and in D1 through D3 their values. In cells A5 and A6 place the labels F= and f= respectively, in cell B5 deposit the instruction =LN(4*B1+3/B2)+B2*(B3^2), and in cell B6 compute f using the formula given above, i.e., =SQRT(((4*D1/(4*B1+3/B2))^2)+(-3*D2/((B2^2)*(4*B1+3/B2))+D2*B3^2)^2+ (2*D3*B2*B3)^2). The spreadsheet might now look like Fig. 2.8.1, except that you will of course have different values for the values X, Y, Z, x, y, and z, and therefore also different results for F and f.

(3) Call Propagation, and answer the input boxes. Specifically, for the example of Fig. 2.8.1, enter the location of the input parameters as B1:B3 (either by typing, or by pointing to that block with the mouse, followed by OK or Enter), that of the standard deviations as D1:D3, and that of the function as B5. Note that we left cell C5 free because that is where the macro will deposit its result. If C5 is used and cannot be overwritten, the answer will come as a message box, and you will need to write it down, busywork you can do without.

(4) Verify that you get the same result in C5 as that computed in B6 (usually to well within 0.001%), but without having to derive the expression for *f*, and without having to use that expression to find its numerical value. Try other input parameters, and other formulas. Because Propagation is a macro, it does not update automatically. Apart from that, it does it all for you, automatically.

	A	B	C	D	E
1	X = 30		x = 4		
2	Y = 20		y = 2		
3	Z = 10		z = 0.5		
4					
5	F = 2004.79				
6	f = 282.84				

B5 =LN(4*B1+3/B2)+B2*(B3^2)
B6 =SQRT(((4*D1/(4*B1+3/B2))^2)+(-3*D2/((B2^2)
$\qquad$ *(4*B1+3/B2))+D2*B3^2)^2+(2*D3*B2*B3)^2)

Fig. 2.8.1: The spreadsheet as it looks just before calling Propagation. The instructions shown below the screenshot merely serve as reminders of the formulas involved. Because the input data are organized column-wise, the answer from Propagate will automatically appear to the right of F, in cell C5, if empty.

2.9 Interdependent parameters

Equation (2.8.1) applies only when the various parameters a_j are linearly independent of each other (precisely what that means will be specified by definition (2.9.3) in terms of a non-zero covariance), but in the physical sciences such mutual independence is the exception rather than the rule. Say that we extrapolate data, using the slope a_1 and intercept a_0 of a straight line determined by a least-squares fit. Since a_0 and a_1 are obtained from the same data set in a single least squares minimization, a deviation in a_1 may be partially compensated by a corresponding change in a_0, in which case a_0 and a_1 may be linearly dependent on each other.

A brief clarification is needed here. Linear least squares analysis is a linear technique, and is therefore sensitive to linear dependencies. In chapter 3 we will see that it is quite common to fit a multivariate expression such as $y = a_0 + a_1 x_1 + a_2 x_2$ to data. In that case, relations between x_1 and x_2 such as $x_2 = x_1^2$ or $x_2 = \ln(x_1)$ are clearly mutually dependent, but not in a linear fashion. However, $x_2 = k + x_1/3$ has a (partial) linear dependency of x_2 on x_1, as does $x_2 = 2x_1 + x_1^2$. In these latter two examples, x_1 and x_2 are *partially linearly correlated*, even though the terms "partial" and "linear" may not always be included explicitly.

Multivariate problems may have more complicated interdependencies. For example, the house value and income level of a mortgagee may both depend on the general level of the economy. We will not consider such higher-order dependencies here, but they are very important in, e.g., risk assessment. Catastrophic accidents (Bhopal, Chernobyl, LTCM, Enron, AIG, Deepwater Horizon) often occur at the confluence of a number of by themselves rather improbable failures, each made more likely by some overarching attitude or policy.

When *F* is a function of two linearly *in*dependent parameters, say a_i and a_j, (2.8.1) reads

$$v_{FF} = \left(\frac{\partial F}{\partial a_i} \right)^2 v_{ii} + \left(\frac{\partial F}{\partial a_j} \right)^2 v_{jj} \tag{2.9.1}$$

but when a_i and a_j are linearly correlated parameters, (2.9.1) must be replaced by

67

$$v_{FF} = \left(\frac{\partial F}{\partial a_i}\right)^2 v_{ii} + 2\left(\frac{\partial F}{\partial a_i}\right)\left(\frac{\partial F}{\partial a_j}\right) v_{ij} + \left(\frac{\partial F}{\partial a_j}\right)^2 v_{jj} \tag{2.9.2}$$

where the *covariance* v_{ij} between the parameters a_i and a_j is defined as

$$v_{ij} = v_{ji} = v_{ff} \sum_{k=1}^{N}\left(\frac{\partial a_i}{\partial a_k}\right)\left(\frac{\partial a_j}{\partial a_k}\right) \tag{2.9.3}$$

which can be compared with (2.7.5) and (2.7.6).

The covariance has the dimension of a variance, but can be either positive or negative. The absolute value of the covariance is limited by

$$\left|v_{ij}\right| \le \sqrt{v_{ii}v_{jj}} = s_i s_j \tag{2.9.4}$$

so that (2.9.4) can have values between $\{(\partial F/\partial a_i)\,s_i - (\partial F/\partial a_j)\,s_j\}^2$ and $\{(\partial F/\partial a_i)\,s_i + (\partial F/\partial a_j)\,s_j\}^2$. When v_{ij} is zero, the two parameters a_i and a_j are not linearly correlated, and the middle term on the right-hand side of (2.9.2) vanishes. (We treat the variance v_{ii} as a covariance v_{ij} with $i = j$.)

For more than two input parameters the general relation for the variance v_{FF} of the function $F(a_1, a_2, \ldots a_i, \ldots a_P)$ is

$$v_{FF} = \sum_{i=1}^{P}\sum_{j=1}^{P}\left(\frac{\partial F}{\partial a_i}\right)\left(\frac{\partial F}{\partial a_j}\right) v_{ij} = \sum_{i=1}^{P}\left(\frac{\partial F}{\partial a_i}\right)^2 v_{ii} + 2\sum_{i=1}^{P}\sum_{j=1}^{i-1}\left(\frac{\partial F}{\partial a_i}\right)\left(\frac{\partial F}{\partial a_j}\right) v_{ij} \tag{2.9.5}$$

The variances and covariances are most conveniently arranged in a *covariance matrix* (also known by the unnecessarily long term *variance-covariance matrix*). For a function with P adjustable parameters, such a matrix is a square array of $P \times P$ terms that contains all P variances and $P(P–1)$ co-variances between these P parameters. For a straight line, with only two parameters, intercept a_0 and slope a_1, the covariance matrix is a 2×2 square containing four data, v_{00}, $v_{01} = v_{10}$, and v_{11}. In general, $v_{ij} = v_{ji}$, so that a $P \times P$ covariance matrix only contains $P(P+1)/2$ significant covariances $v_{i\ne j}$. The elements on its main diagonal are the variances v_{ii}.

Often the covariances between the various parameters will not be known, because many standard software routines (including Excel's LinEst, Regression, and Trendline) fail to provide them. This was one of the major reasons to write the custom macro LS, and Propagation can use the covariance matrix of LS to compute the correct precision estimate for any derived function F. Other reasons for writing LS will become clear once we start modifying LS to accommodate weighted least squares (see section 3.16), or to incorporate extended numberlength, see chapter 11.

How critical is the choice of dependent and independent variables, and how much difference will it make to neglect the covariances? As we will see shortly, it all depends on the computation used. To illustrate this we will use a century-old test data set from K. Pearson, *Phil. Mag.* 2 (1901) 559 which, as we will see in section 4.19, was used by Pearson for a quite different purpose. In exercise 2.9.1 we will analyze this data set, shown in Fig. 2.9.1, in two different ways: first we will assume that y is the dependent variable, and x the independent one, and write $y = a_0 + a_1 x$. Then we will invert these roles, and instead write $x = b_0 + b_1 y$.

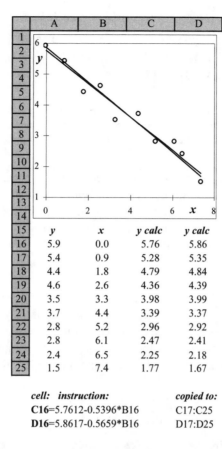

	y	x	y calc	y calc
16	5.9	0.0	5.76	5.86
17	5.4	0.9	5.28	5.35
18	4.4	1.8	4.79	4.84
19	4.6	2.6	4.36	4.39
20	3.5	3.3	3.98	3.99
21	3.7	4.4	3.39	3.37
22	2.8	5.2	2.96	2.92
23	2.8	6.1	2.47	2.41
24	2.4	6.5	2.25	2.18
25	1.5	7.4	1.77	1.67

cell:	instruction:	copied to:
C16	=5.7612-0.5396*B16	C17:C25
D16	=5.8617-0.5659*B16	D17:D25

Fig. 2.9.1: A data set from K. Pearson, *Phil. Mag.* 2
(1901) 559, analyzed either as *y* vs. *x* or as *x* vs. *y*.

Exercise 2.9.1:

(1) Enter the data shown in the first two columns of Fig. 2.9.1 in a spreadsheet, highlight them, and call LS1.

(2) Copy the columns for *y* and *x* to a different location, and change their order, so that the column for *x* is not to the left of that for *y*. Again highlight the data block, and call LS1. The covariance matrix will show in color, with the label CM.

(3) Go to the results obtained under (2), and below them calculate the values of $-b_0/b_1$ and $1/b_1$ respectively.

(4) Now call Propagation, and in response to its queries highlight the values for b_0 and b_1, the covariance matrix, and the cell in which you have just computed $-b_0/b_1$. Propagation will calculate the standard deviation of $-b_0/b_1$, and place this immediately below its value. Do the same for $1/b_1$.

In the first case we obtain $y = 5.7_6 \pm 0.1_9 - (0.54_0 \pm 0.04_2)\, x$, in the other $x = 10.3_6 \pm 0.5_4 - (1.7_7 \pm 0.1_4)$ *y*. How do these results compare? We rewrite the second set of results $x = b_0 + b_1 y$ as $y = -b_0/b_1 + x/b_1$. Combining the coefficients with their uncertainties, in terms of their standard deviations, we can then compare $a_0 = 5.7_6 \pm 0.1_9$ with $-b_0/b_1 = 5.8_6 \pm 0.2_0$, and $a_1 = 0.54_0 \pm 0.04_2$ with $1/b_1 = 0.56_6 \pm 0.04_4$.

The agreement between the two slopes and intercepts is close, though not perfect. The small differences in the coefficients are due to the different assumptions made about the sources of the experimental uncertainties in the two analyses. The same applies to the corresponding standard deviations, computed here with the macro Propagation using the covariance matrix.

However, if we use the standard deviations of b_0 and b_1 rather than the covariance matrix, we find a quite *different* standard deviation ($\pm 0.5_5$ instead of $\pm 0.2_0$) for $-b_0/b_1$, but the *same* answer for $1/b_1$. You have the data, and you can therefore verify this for yourself.

Exercise 2.9.1 (continued):

(5) Move the results just obtained one row lower (so as not to overwrite them), and again call Propagation. Repeat the procedure outlined in (4), except that, in response to the second input box, you now enter the standard deviations rather than the covariance matrix. Note that you find the same answer as under (4) for the standard deviation in $1/b_1$, but a quite different result for that in $-b_0/b_1$.

Why is this so? Because the calculation of the imprecision in $1/b_1$ requires only one imprecision estimate, whereas that of b_0/b_1 involves the imprecisions of *both* b_0 and b_1. Since b_0 and b_1 are highly correlated quantities, their interdependence must be taken into account. The actual uncertainty in $-b_0/b_1$ in this case is 2½ times smaller than one would compute by neglecting their mutual dependence. Much more dramatic examples of such effects will be encountered in sections 2.17 and 2.18.

2.10 Centering

When the covariances are not known, one often treats the input parameters as mutually independent ones, even though the resulting uncertainty estimate will then be uncertain, and may sometimes be quite far off. There are, of course, other ways in Excel to deal with the propagation of uncertainties in derived results, though none of them as convenient as the combined use of LS and Propagation. For example, for the straight line $y = a_0 + a_1 x$ the covariance v_{01} between the intercept and slope can be calculated from the variances v_{00} and v_{11} as

$$v_{01} = v_{10} = -v_{00} \frac{\sum x}{\sum x^2} = -v_{11} \frac{\sum x}{N} \qquad (2.10.1)$$

Consequently, for the straight line, we can make the covariance between slope a_1 and intercept a_0 vanish by making $\sum x$ equal to zero, i.e., by *centering* the data set around its average x-value, $x_{av} = (1/N) \sum x$. For a linear relationship we can therefore avoid covariances by proper *design* of the experiment, before any experimental data are collected, by selecting the x-values at which data will be taken in such a way that x_{av} will be zero. This can always be done by redefining the zero of the x-scale. Afterwards we then recalculate the intercept a_0 and its standard deviation s_0; the slope a_1 and its standard deviation s_1 are not affected. On the other hand, the more eccentric the x-values, the larger the resulting covariance.

Sometimes we are not so much interested in the absolute values of the covariances v_{ij} as in the corresponding *linear correlation coefficients* r_{ij}, which are defined as

$$r_{ij} = \frac{v_{ij}}{\sqrt{v_{ii} v_{jj}}} = \frac{v_{ij}}{s_i s_j} \qquad (2.10.2)$$

These show us immediately the *relative magnitude* of the linear correlation between the parameters a_i and a_j, i.e., $|r_{ij}| = 1$ signifies complete linear correlation between a_i and a_j, whereas $r_{ij} = 0$ indicates the absence of any linear correlation. From the linear correlation coefficients r_{ij} and the standard deviations s_i and s_j we can readily reconstruct the covariances as $v_{ij} = r_{ij} s_i s_j$, and LS provides these linear correlation coefficients as an option. For the Propagation macro, however, we must use the covariance matrix rather than the linear correlation matrix plus the standard deviations. Incidentally, when we use the covariance matrix as input for Propagation, there is no need to check first whether or not the data are mutually independent, since we treat them in general as mutually dependent. If they are not, the covariance matrix will contain zeros in the appropriate off-diagonal matrix elements. And when the mutual dependence is minor, as when $r_{ij} < 0.9$, it usually is of little or no consequence. In the most recent versions of LS, linear correlation coefficients that may need your attention are color-emphasized.

A short digression may be useful here. The term (*linear*) *correlation coefficient* can mean different things in different contexts, depending on which quantities are being correlated. In many least squares calculator and computer programs (including LinEst, Regression, and Trendline) a correlation coefficient r or R (or its square) reflects the correlation *between x and y*. This answers the question *whether* there is a linear correlation between these two *input variables*, x and y. Checking for a possible linear correlation between variables may be important in deciding, e.g., whether using a cordless phone increases the likelihood of brain cancer (apparently it doesn't), or whether unprotected sunbathing increases the chances for skin cancer (unfortunately it does). However, that question is usually irrelevant when, as in the examples used in this book, we apply least squares analysis to problems with well-established causality. In that case, the question is not whether there exists a correlation between the *input variables x* and y but what, if any, is the correlation between the *output parameters a* and b. The linear correlation coefficient r_{xy} in LinEst, Regression, or Trendline describe the correlation between the *input* variables x and y, using a formula just like (2.10.2) for r_{ab}, but its meaning is entirely different. The quantity r_{xy} should *not* be used as a measure of goodness-of-fit of the analysis, which it isn't. Incidentally, when the relation between x and y is strictly causal (i.e., free of random noise) but nonlinear, as with an exponential or a power law, r_{xy} will not be unity.

On the other hand, the linear correlation r_{ab} deals with the correlation *between the coefficients a and b*, and provides information useful for subsequent propagation of uncertainty when both a and b are involved in a derived quantity, a topic that will be amply illustrated in this chapter, starting with section 2.13. The moral of this digression is, therefore: when you see or hear the term correlation coefficient, ask yourself the question: correlation *between what and what*?

To return briefly to the title subject of this section: the use of centering to make slope and intercept mutually independent works for a straight line, but is not extendable as such to more complicated models. However, in sections 10.6 and 10.7 we will encounter another use of centering: to minimize truncation errors by keeping numbers as small as possible in multivariate and polynomial fits. And in section 3.11 we will see what can replace centering in order to find mutually independent model parameters.

2.11 Imprecision contours

When the result of a least squares fit to a straight line is plotted, it is sometimes useful to indicate in the graph not only the original points and the best-fitting line through them, but also some uncertainty estimate of that line. This is most readily done by drawing *imprecision contours* that enclose an *imprecision band* delineating the most probable region (within, e.g., plus or minus one standard deviation) where we might anticipate observing a next measurement of y at a given value of x. The construction of such contours is most readily appreciated when based on mutually independent variables.

The procedure is as follows. First we find the average x_{av}, calculate a column of values $x-x_{av}$, and fit the data to the line $y = a_0 + a_1(x-x_{av})$. This will yield the mutually independent coefficients a_0 and a_1 plus the standard deviations s_0, s_1, and s_y. We use the coefficients a_0 and a_1 to plot the line $y = a_0 + a_1(x-x_{av})$ together with the experimental data points. The vertical spacing between the line $y = a_0 + a_1(x-x_{av})$ and the uncertainty contours will then be given by

$$s = \sqrt{s_f^2 + s_0^2 + s_1^2(x-x_{av})^2} \qquad (2.11.1)$$

where s denotes the estimated standard deviation for the individual observations. This result is fully equivalent to equation (1.4.11) in N. R. Draper & H. Smith, *Applied Regression Analysis*, 2nd ed., Wiley (1981), but in a form that is easy to apply and to generalize. Exercise 2.11.1 illustrates this for data taken from Table 1.1 on p. 9 of that same book.

Exercise 2.11.1:

(1) The data are for y (pounds of steam used per month) as a function of x (temperature in $^\circ$F) but, for our purposes, they will be merely y vs. x. If you enter them from the Draper & Smith book, or from the MacroSamples file, they will not be ordered for increasing or decreasing values of x, which is inconvenient for making good graphs. Therefore first re-organize the data: move the column with x-values to the left of the column for y, highlight the data block of both columns, and click on the sort ascending icon on the standard toolbar. Your data should now look like those in columns A and B of Fig. 2.11.1.

(2) Somewhere on the sheet calculate the average value of x (with the function =AVERAGE) and use this to calculate in column C the corresponding values of $x-x_{av}$.

(3) Highlight the data in columns B and C, and call LS1. The covariance matrix should show (essentially) zero covariances.

(4) In column D calculate $y_{calc} = a_0 + a_1(x-x_{av})$ based on the just-computed values of a_0 and a_1.

(5) Plot the experimental data points and the computed line y_{calc} versus x (in column A).

(6) In column E calculate s using (2.11.1) as a function of $x-x_{av}$, and in columns F and G compute $y_{calc}-s$ and $y_{calc}+s$ respectively, then highlight the data in column F, copy them, and paste them into the figure. Do the same with the data in column G. Your plot should now resemble Fig. 2.11.2.

	A	B	C	D	E	F	G
1	Data from Draper & Smith, *Applied Regression Analysis*, Wiley 1981 p. 9.						
2			x_{av} = 52.6				
3							
4	x	y	$x - x_{av}$	y_{calc}	s	$y_{calc} - s$	$y_{calc} + s$
5							
6	28.1	11.88	-24.5	11.3798	0.9437	10.4361	12.3235
7	28.6	11.08	-24.0	11.3399	0.9422	10.3977	12.2821
8	28.9	12.19	-23.7	11.3159	0.9414	10.3745	12.2573
9	29.7	11.13	-22.9	11.2521	0.9392	10.3129	12.1913
10	30.8	12.51	-21.8	11.1643	0.9363	10.2280	12.1006
11	33.4	10.36	-19.2	10.9567	0.9300	10.0267	11.8867
12	35.3	10.98	-17.3	10.8050	0.9258	9.8792	11.7309
13	39.1	9.57	-13.5	10.5017	0.9188	9.5829	11.4205
14	44.6	8.86	-8.0	10.0626	0.9116	9.1510	10.9743
15	46.4	8.24	-6.2	9.9189	0.9101	9.0088	10.8290
16	46.8	10.94	-5.8	9.8870	0.9098	8.9772	10.7968
17	48.5	9.58	-4.1	9.7513	0.9088	8.8425	10.6601
18	57.5	9.14	4.9	9.0328	0.9092	8.1236	9.9421
19	58.1	8.47	5.5	8.9849	0.9096	8.0753	9.8945
20	58.8	8.40	6.2	8.9291	0.9101	8.0190	9.8392
21	59.3	10.09	6.7	8.8891	0.9105	7.9787	9.7996
22	61.4	9.27	8.8	8.7215	0.9125	7.8090	9.6340
23	70.0	8.11	17.4	8.0350	0.9260	7.1089	8.9610
24	70.0	6.83	17.4	8.0350	0.9260	7.1089	8.9610
25	70.7	7.82	18.1	7.9791	0.9275	7.0516	8.9066
26	71.3	8.73	18.7	7.9312	0.9288	7.0024	8.8600
27	72.1	7.68	19.5	7.8673	0.9307	6.9367	8.7980
28	74.4	6.36	21.8	7.6837	0.9363	6.7474	8.6200
29	74.5	8.88	21.9	7.6758	0.9366	6.7392	8.6123
30	76.7	8.50	24.1	7.5001	0.9425	6.5576	8.4426
31	*Coeff:*	*9.4240*	*-0.0798*				
32	*StDev:*	*0.1780*	*0.0105*	*CM:*	*0.0317*	*1.57E-19*	
33		*0.8901*			*1.57E-19*	*0.000111*	

Fig. 2.11.1: The data from Table 1.1 in Draper & Smith, analyzed as described in exercise 2.11.1.

(7) Alternatively you could use the data in column E to plot error bars of length s on the line depicting y_{calc}. This has the advantages that you need not order the data as was done here under point (1), and need not calculate the data in columns F and G either, and the disadvantage that it doesn't look as good, at least to me. But since tastes differ, try it, and judge for yourself.

Because of the term in $(x-x_{av})$ in the expression (2.11.1) for s, these contours are slightly curved, with a minimal vertical distance from the fitted line at $x = x_{av}$. Note that roughly 1 in 3 data points in Fig. 2.11.2 lie outside these contour lines, as one would expect for a single Gaussian distribution. If we were to draw them at $\pm 2s$, they would tend to encompass roughly 95% of all data; drawn at $\pm 3s$, they should include about 99.7% of all data, etc. But keep in mind that those numbers assume that the data can indeed be described by a Gaussian distribution.

We can also draw these imprecision contours without centering, in which case the covariances are needed. Specifically, for the straight line $y = a_0 + a_1 x$, instead of (2.11.1) we should then use

$$s = \sqrt{s_f^2 + v_{00} + 2v_{01}x + v_{11}x^2} \qquad (2.11.2)$$

The imprecision contours defined here pertain to the probability that a *single, individual* observation will fall within a given band around the least squares line. They therefore differ from those proposed by Working & Hotelling (*J. Am. Statist. Assoc.* 24 (1929) Suppl. p. 73), which pertain to the *mean* value, do not include the term s_f^2, and are therefore much more strongly curved.

If you prefer confidence contours and confidence bands instead, multiply s as defined in, e.g. (2.11.1) and (2.11.2), by $t(\alpha, N-P)$ or $\sqrt{F(\alpha, 1, N-P)}$, where $1-\alpha$ is the confidence level (i.e., $\alpha = 0.05$ corresponds to $1-\alpha = 0.95$ or a 95% confidence level), N is the number of data points, and P the number of model parameters. The Student t function $t(\alpha, N-P)$ for $\alpha = 0.05$ and $N-P = 12$ is obtained in Excel with `=TINV(0.05,12)`, the Fisher function $F(\alpha, 1, N-P)$ with `=FINV (0.05,1,12)`.

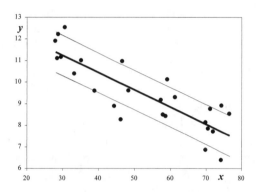

Fig. 2.11.2: The data from Table 1.1 in Draper & Smith, plotted as described in exercise 2.11.1.

2.12 How precise is the standard deviation?

The standard deviation provides an estimate of the precision of a number, i.e., of its reproducibility under near-identical experimental conditions. We now ask the next question: how precise is the standard deviation itself? Could we perhaps keep asking that question of the resulting answer, generating a never-ending series of questions and answers, such as "What is the imprecision of the imprecision of the imprecision, etc.?", much like a continued fraction, or the images of images of images in a hall of mirrors? Fortunately, the question asked in the heading of this section turns out to have a surprisingly simple, definitive answer.

Least squares analysis is based on the assumption that the data follow a Gaussian distribution, reflecting mutually independent, relatively small, random deviations from the average. The variance v (i.e., the square of the standard devation s) can then be shown to follow a so-called χ^2 ("chi-square") distribution. This distribution, as distinct from the Gaussian distribution, depends on only *one* parameter, in this case the number of degrees of freedom $N-P$, where N is the number of data points analyzed, and P the number of adjustable model parameters used, e.g., $P = 1$ for a proportionality, $P = 2$ for a straight line, etc. This χ^2 distribution representing the variance v has a mean $N-P$, a variance v_v of that variance of $2(N-P)$, and a standard deviation s_v of that variance of $\sqrt{2(N-P)}$.

However, we need the standard deviation of the standard deviation, s_s, not the standard deviation of the variance, s_v. (For comparison with the original quantities we need their standard deviations, because they have matching dimensions, which the variances do not.) How do we go from one to the other?

Let a quantity q have a variance v and a standard deviation $s = \sqrt{v}$, so that we can express the quantity together with its imprecision as $q \pm s = q \pm \sqrt{v}$. Likewise we formulate the variance v with its standard deviation s_v as $v \pm s_v$ and the standard deviation s with its standard deviation s_s as

$$s + s_s = \sqrt{v \pm s_v} = \sqrt{v}\sqrt{1 \pm s_v/v} \approx \sqrt{v}\left(1 \pm s_v/2v\right) = s\left(1 \pm s_v/2v\right) = s\left(1 \pm s_s/s\right) \tag{2.12.1}$$

where we have made the usual assumption that s_v/v is very much smaller than 1, so that we can use the general expansion $\sqrt{(1 \pm \delta)} \approx 1 \pm \delta/2$ for $\delta \ll 1$. From this we see that the relative standard deviation $s_s/s = s_v/2v$ of the standard deviation s of the quantity q is one-half of the relative standard deviation s_v/v of the variance, so that

$$s_s/s = s_v/2v = \sqrt{2(N - P)}/[2(N - P)] = 1/\sqrt{2(N - P)} \tag{2.12.2}$$

A rigorous derivation of this result, for the case of the population standard deviation (rather than the sample standard deviation, i.e., with N instead of $N–P$), can be found in, e.g., J. F. Kenney and E. S. Keeping, *Mathematics of Statistics*, 2nd ed., Van Nostrand, Princeton (1951), vol. 2 pp. 170-171.

Note that all the above properties of the χ^2 distribution depend only on the number of degrees of freedom, $N–P$, and are *independent* of the actual x and y values of the data set and their individual standard deviations. We can therefore estimate the imprecision of the standard deviation merely on the basis of the magnitude of $N–P$, as illustrated in Table 2.12.1.

Clearly, the standard deviation is often over-specified, i.e., reported with far more decimals than are significant. For example, performing a simple weighing in triplicate ($N = 3$, $P = 1$, hence $N – P = 2$) yields a standard deviation with a relative precision of $\pm50\%$, so that there is no need to insist on many decimal places for such a quantity. Minor differences in standard deviations are often statistically insignificant.

$N–P$	s_s/s	s_s/s in %
2	0.5000	50
5	0.3162	32
10	0.2236	22
20	0.1581	16
50	0.1000	10
100	0.0707	7.1
200	0.0500	5.0
500	0.0316	3.2
1,000	0.0224	2.2
10,000	0.0071	0.7

Table 2.12.1: The relative standard deviation of the standard deviation, as given by (2.12.2), as a function of the number of degrees of freedom, $N–P$.

In order to get a standard deviation with no more than 10% relative imprecision, we would need at least 50 observations, while at least 5 000 measurements would be required for a standard deviation with a 1% maximum imprecision. It is therefore wise to consider most standard deviations as imprecision *estimates*, and the same applies to quantities directly derived from the standard deviation, such as "confidence" measures.

2.13 Extrapolating the ideal gas law

In this and the next four sections we will consider several rather common applications of fitting experimental data to a straight line, including extrapolation, calibration, standard addition, finding the intersection of two straight lines, and a standard undergraduate physical chemistry lab experiment.

Kim et al. (*J. Chem. Educ.* 78 (2001) 238) recently described an elegantly simple high school experiment to determine the absolute zero on the centigrade temperature scale. Since it involves various elements of linear least squares fitting we will analyze those data here.

Kim et al. measured the volume V of air trapped in an inverted graduated cylinder immersed in water, as a function of temperature t, ranging between 0 and 75 °C. The specific set of measurements we will consider is shown in Table 2.13.1.

t	0.0	4.8	8.9	18.2	23.4	28.2	34.6	43.5	50.0	60.0	61.7	72.0
V	3.80	3.90	3.98	4.10	4.20	4.40	4.50	4.80	5.15	5.75	6.00	7.25

Table 2.13.1: The measured volumes V, in mL, as a function of temperature t, in °C.

The analysis consists of two parts. These air volumes V must be corrected for the volume occupied by water vapor. The corrected, dry air volumes V_d are found as $V_d = V (P_b - P_w) / P_b$ where P_w is the vapor pressure of water at temperature t, and P_b the barometric pressure. The resulting volumes V_d of dry air are a linear function of temperature t, as expected for an ideal gas, and can then be extrapolated to $V_d = 0$ to yield the zero of the absolute temperature scale.

First we must determine what type of least squares analysis to use, i.e., whether either V or t can be considered to be the dominant source of the experimental uncertainties. Analysis of the experimental data shows that the volume and temperature measurements have absolute uncertainties of about ±0.05 mL and ±0.1 °C respectively. Since V and t have different dimensions, we can compare these numbers no better than we can compare apples and oranges. After conversion into relative uncertainties, to about ±1% in volume and ±0.05% in absolute temperature T, it is clear that V is by far the more error-prone, and should be taken as the dependent variable. Note that the centigrade temperature scale t contains an arbitrary constant ($t = 0$ °C for $T = 273.16$ °K) that might be misleading in determining relative imprecisions. Since the data involve extrapolation to zero absolute temperature, the relative imprecision on the Kelvin scale is the one that counts here.

The vapor pressure P_w of water as a function of temperature t is a well-tabulated quantity that is readily parameterized, see section 3.21. These data are so much more precise than the reported volumes V that the correction does not add significantly to the experimental uncertainty in V_d, even though, at 72 °C, the correction amounts to almost 35% of the measured gas volume! Figure 2.13.1 shows the raw and corrected volumes, V and V_d respectively, as a function of temperature t. The remaining question is one of linear extrapolation.

Exercise 2.13.1:

(1) Copy the data from the paper of Kim et al. or from Fig. 2.13.1. Copy the values of V_d as listed, or compute them from the values for V minus the volume occupied by water vapor. The results will be similar, though not identical, because the computation results in additional digits for V_d not shown in Fig. 2.13.1. From the point of view of the exercise, the difference is rather immaterial. Make sure that the column with V_d is directly to the left of that with t.

(2) Call LS1. In making Fig. 2.13.1, we have used the option to display the linear correlation coefficients, and have moved it and the covariance matrix to save some space.

(3) Calculate $t_0 = -a_0 / a_1$, which yields $t_0 = -278.1$ °C.

(4) Call Propagation to find the associated standard deviation. Using the covariance matrix in Propagation produces the (correct) standard deviation of 9.6°C, so that the experiment yields $t_0 = -(278._1 \pm 9._6)$°C, where the lowered numbers are guard digits. This can be compared with the accepted value of –273.15 °C. The large inaccuracy and imprecision in the computed value for t_0 probably stems mostly from measuring volumes with a graduated cylinder, magnified by the long extrapolation.

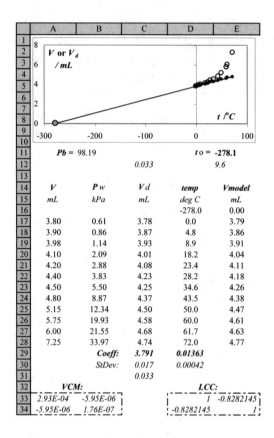

Fig. 2.13.1: Spreadsheet for the data of Exercise 2.13.1, after use of the LS1 and Propagation macros. Open circles: V; solid circles: V_d. The sought parameter, t_0, was computed in cell E11 as $= -\text{C29/D29}$. The (variance-) covariance matrix (VCM) has been moved, and the (linear) correlation coefficient matrix (LCC) labeled as such.

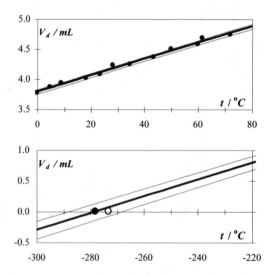

Fig. 2.13.2: The spreadsheet in the temperature range of the experimental data (top), and (bottom) the same near the absolute zero on the temperature scale. Both figures are drawn to the same (but shifted) scale. In the bottom panel, the closed circle shows the extrapolated point, and the open circle the true value of the absolute zero temperature, $-273.15\,^\circ\text{C}$.

(5) Using the standard deviations a_0 and a_1 would have given the incorrect value of 8.7 °C for the standard deviation, incorrect because the linear correlation coefficients show that a_0 and a_1 are strongly correlated. In this particular case, that actually has only a minor effect on the resulting precision.

(6) Use column E to compute $V_{model} = a_0 + a_1 t$, e.g., in cell E17 use = \$C\$29 + \$D\$29 * D17. Add the values for $t = t_0$ to show the extrapolated point and curve.

(7) Verify that you get the same result by centering the temperatures (see section 2.10), in which case there is no need to consider the covariance.

(8) Using the opposite assumption, namely that the temperature is the more error-prone measurement and should be used as the dependent variable, would have been incorrect, as shown by the data themselves. It also would have been rather impractical, because in that case correction for the water vapor pressure would have been much more complicated.

(9) Finally, in order to illustrate generating imprecision contours, add three columns to the spreadsheet, one in which you compute s according to (2.10.4), one in which you calculate $V_{model} - s$, and a third in which you do the same for $V_{model} + s$. Plot these contours next to the line through the points, both in the temperature range of the observations and near absolute zero temperature. As is clear from Fig. 2.13.2, the curvature of these imprecision contours is barely noticeable, but away from $x = x_{av}$ they gradually move apart, thereby providing a good indication of the problems inherent in a long extrapolation.

2.14 Calibration curves

A standard measurement procedure is to make a calibration curve of the variable y versus x, using a set of well-characterized, known samples, and to use this to find the best estimate for the x-value x_u corresponding to a measured *unknown* with observed response y_u. This is sometimes called an *inverse interpolation*: given a set of measurements y as a function of x, find the most likely x_u for a given value of y_u. We will here consider the simplest of calibration curves, namely those that consist of proportionalities or straight lines.

Typically, we first determine the dependent variable y for a number of values of the independent variable x under well-controlled circumstances, plot these data, and determine the best proportionality $y = a_1 x$ or straight line $y = a_0 + a_1 x$ through those points. Then we measure the y_u-value of an unknown, and use the calibration curve to compute the corresponding x-value, x_u. As our example we will use a synthetic data set from Table 5.1 in D. Harvey, *Modern Analytical Chemistry*, McGraw-Hill (2000). As our calibration curve we will first use a proportionality, then a straight line.

Exercise 2.14.1:
(1) In a new spreadsheet enter the data shown in cells A3:B8 of Fig. 2.14.1.
(2) Use LS0 (or LinEst or Regression) to find the slope a_1 and its standard deviation, s_1.

	A	B	C
1	*y*	*x*	*y*$_u$
2			
3	0.00	0.0	29.32
4	12.36	0.1	29.16
5	24.83	0.2	29.51
6	35.91	0.3	
7	48.79	0.4	
8	60.42	0.5	
9	*Coeff:*	*121.2745*	*29.330*
10	*StDev:*	*0.516507*	*0.175214*
11	*Sf:*	*0.383052*	
12		LS0	
13		*x*$_u$:	*0.2418*
14			*0.001774*

cell: instruction:

C9 = AVERAGE(C3:C5)
C10 = STDEV(C3:C5)
C13 = C9/B9

Fig. 2.14.1: A spreadsheet for reading data from a calibration line through the origin, using the LS0 and Propagation macros.

(3) Assume that we measure the response of an unknown three times, with the results shown in cells C3:C5. Enter those data, and in C9 and C10 compute the corresponding average and standard deviation respectively.

(4) In cell C13 compute the value of $x_u = y_u / a_1$, as done in Fig. 2.14.1.

(5) Finally, use Propagation to calculate the precision of this result, based on the input variables (in Fig. 2.14.1 these are located in B9:C9), their standard deviations (in B10:C10), and the function (in C13). It will appear just below C13.

(6) As shown in Fig. 2.14.1, we find $x_u = 0.241_8 \pm 0.001_8$.

Exercise 2.14.2:

(1) Use the next sheet of the same workbook, and copy the same data one column to the right, see Fig. 2.14.2.

(2) With LS1 find the intercept a_0 and slope a_1, their standard deviations s_0 and s_1, and the corresponding covariance matrix. Don't accept the matrix of linear correlation coefficients, or put them somewhere else.

(3) Again assume that we measure the response of an unknown three times, and compute the average of y_u in cell D9, and its standard deviation in D10.

(4) In cell D16 compute the value of $x_u = (y_{u,av} - a_0) / a_1$, as = (D9-B9) /C9.

(5) Using the Propagation macro is now somewhat more complicated, because the imprecision is now a mixed bag: for a_0 and a_1 we clearly need to use the covariance matrix (since they are correlated), whereas for y_u we only have the standard deviation. Propagation can handle either format, but not its mixture.

(6) Without loss of information we cannot reduce the imprecision in a_0 and a_1 to just two standard deviations, but we can add the variance of y_u to the covariance matrix. Since the imprecision in y_u is clearly unrelated to that in a_0 and a_1, we simply add the corresponding variance in y_u as an extension to the *main diagonal* (from top left to bottom right) of the covariance matrix. We therefore deposit in cell D14 the square of the standard deviation stored in D10, see Fig. 2.14.2. The covariance terms in cells B14:C14 and D12:D13 are zero, and need not be entered. So here is the procedure.

(7) In cell D14 calculate the square of the standard deviation s_u of y_u (located in D10). Leave cells B14, C14, D12, and D12 blank, or fill them with zeros.

(8) Call Propagation and, in reply to its queries, enter the locations of the input variables (B9:D9), of the covariance matrix (B12:D14), and of the function (in C16). This will yield $x_u = 0.241_3 \pm 0.002_0$, not significantly different from the value $x_u = 0.241_8 \pm 0.001_8$ obtained earlier.

(9) Verify that, by ignoring the correlation between a_0 and a_1, and therefore entering into Propagation the standard deviations in B10:D10 instead of the covariance matrix in B12:D14, you would have found the significantly larger (but incorrect) value of 0.003_4 for the standard deviation in x_u.

	A	B	C	D	
1		*y*	*x*	*y$_u$*	
2					
3		0.00	0.0	29.32	
4		12.36	0.1	29.16	*cell: instruction:*
5		24.83	0.2	29.51	
6		35.91	0.3		D9 = AVERAGE(D3:D5)
7		48.79	0.4		D10 = STDEV(D3:D5)
8		60.42	0.5		D14 = D10^2
9	*Coeff:*	0.208571	120.7057	29.330	D16 = (D9-B9)/C9
10	*StDev:*	0.291885	0.964065	0.1752	
11	*Sf:*	0.403297	LS1		
12	*CM:*	0.085197	-0.23236		
13		-0.23236	0.92942		
14				0.03070	
15					
16			*x$_u$:*	0.2413	
17				0.001993	

Fig. 2.14.2: A spreadsheet for reading data from a straight-line calibration curve, using LS1 and Propagation. The box around B13:D15 shows the enlarged covariance matrix.

Incidentally, the above result shows that there is no good reason to use a straight line rather than a proportionality in this case, because the absolute value of the intercept, $|a_0| = 0.2_1$, is smaller than its standard deviation, $s_0 = 0.2_9$. Consequently, the intercept is statistically indistinguishable from zero, and the result obtained in exercise 2.14.1 and illustrated in Fig. 2.14.1 is therefore preferable.

Alternatively, if we insist on using a straight-line calibration curve, we can center the calibration data to $y = a_0' + a_1 (x - x_{av})$ with $a_0' = a_0 + a_1 x_{av}$, and then compute any unknown x_u as $(y_{u,av} - a_0) / a_1 = (y_{u,av} - a_0' + a_1 x_{av}) / a_1$ where a_0' and a_1 are now mutually independent. This is illustrated in exercise 2.14.3 and Fig. 2.14.3, and of course yields the same result as that obtained in exercise 2.14.2. Or we can use non-linear least squares to accomplish the same, as described in chapter 4. Again, there are several ways of doing it right – although, as usual, there are still more ways of getting it wrong, such as by applying standard formulas thoughtlessly.

Exercise 2.14.3:

(1) Fig. 2.14.3 illustrates a possible lay-out of the spreadsheet for a centered calibration line. In column C we plot $x - x_{av}$ where $x_{av} = \Sigma x / N = 0.25$.

(2) Compute the average value of y_u, then copy its *value* to cell D9. And in cell D12 calculate x_u as $= (y_{u,av} - a_0' + a_1 x_{av}) / a_1$, i.e., with $= (\text{D9} - \text{B9} + \text{C9} * 0.25) / \text{C9}$.

(3) The standard deviation in cell D13 is now obtained with Propagation using the standard deviations in B10:D10.

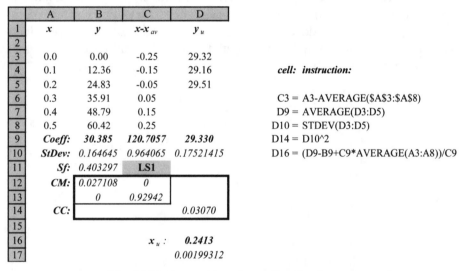

	A	B	C	D
1	*x*	*y*	*x-x$_{av}$*	*y$_u$*
2				
3	0.0	0.00	-0.25	29.32
4	0.1	12.36	-0.15	29.16
5	0.2	24.83	-0.05	29.51
6	0.3	35.91	0.05	
7	0.4	48.79	0.15	
8	0.5	60.42	0.25	
9	*Coeff:*	*30.385*	*120.7057*	*29.330*
10	*StDev:*	*0.164645*	*0.964065*	*0.17521415*
11	*Sf:*	*0.403297*	**LS1**	
12	*CM:*	0.027108	0	
13		0	0.92942	
14	*CC:*			*0.03070*
15				
16			*x$_u$:*	**0.2413**
17				*0.00199312*

cell: instruction:

C3 = A3-AVERAGE($A$3:$A$8)
D9 = AVERAGE(D3:D5)
D10 = STDEV(D3:D5)
D14 = D10^2
D16 = (D9-B9+C9*AVERAGE(A3:A8))/C9

Fig. 2.14.3: A spreadsheet for reading data from a centered straight-line calibration curve, using LS1 and Propagation.

If we had only a single measurement of y_u, we would not have a value for its standard deviation or variance. In that case the best we can do is to use s_f, the standard deviation in the fit of the standard curve, multiplied by $\sqrt{(N–P)}$. This quantity approximates the standard deviation of a single y-measurement, as long as the method used in making the standard curve and in determining the unknown are the same.

2.15 Standard addition

The standard addition method is sometimes used in, e.g., chemical analysis. This method usually assumes a proportionality between the concentration of the sample and the resulting, measured response, but does not presume a priori knowledge of the proportionality constant k. In its simplest form, a sample of known volume V_u and unknown concentration C_u yields a measured signal $y_u = kC_u$. One adds a known volume V_a of known concentration C_a to that sample, and measures the corresponding signal of that mixture, which should now be $y_a = k(C_a V_a + C_u V_u)/(V_a + V_u)$. Eliminating k then yields an explicit expression for the unknown concentration, $C_u = C_a V_a y_u / [(V_a + V_u) y_a - V_u y_u]$ in terms of measured quantities.

In a more sophisticated form, one prepares a series of solutions of constant total volume V_t by using a fixed, known volume V_u of a sample solution of unknown concentration C_u, adding to it known volumes V_i of a standard solution of known concentration C_a, and adding solvent (e.g., water) to give all solutions to be measured the same total volume V_t. One then measures the response of these solutions which, for an added volume V_i, will be $y_i = k (C_u V_u + C_a V_i) / V_t$. Least squares fitting of y_i vs. V_i then should yield a straight line of intercept $a_0 = k C_u V_u / V_t$ and slope $a_1 = k C_a / V_t$ from which we obtain $C_u = a_0 C_a / a_1 V_u$. This calculation involves the ratio a_0 / a_1, where both a_0 and a_1 are derived from the same set of measurements and therefore, in general, are mutually dependent. By centering the independent variable, we can make a_0 and a_1 mutually independent parameters, and thus avoid having to use the covariance.

As our experimental data we will use those reported by G. R. Bruce & P. S. Gill in *J. Chem. Educ.* 76 (1999) 805 (reproduced in A19:B24 of Fig. 2.15.1), in which they describe measurements on an aqueous sample containing an unknown lead concentration.

To a 25.0 mL sample was added 25.0 mL of an electrolyte solution (in order to give the sample sufficient conductivity for the electrochemical experiment) and 1.0 mL of 10.0 mg/L cadmium as an internal standard. The standard additive contained 10.0 mg/L of lead, and presumably the same electrolyte as the electrolyte solution, and apparently was added instead of an equal volume of electrolyte solution in order to keep the final volumes of the solutions to be measured at 51 mL. The ratio R of the peak currents due to lead and cadmium was then measured by stripping voltammetry.

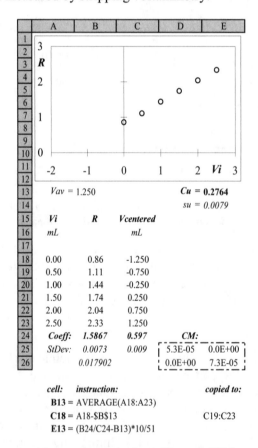

	A	B	C	D	E
13	*Vav* = 1.250			*Cu* = **0.2764**	
14				*su* = *0.0079*	
15	*Vi*	*R*	*Vcentered*		
16	*mL*		*mL*		
17					
18	0.00	0.86	-1.250		
19	0.50	1.11	-0.750		
20	1.00	1.44	-0.250		
21	1.50	1.74	0.250		
22	2.00	2.04	0.750		
23	2.50	2.33	1.250		
24	*Coeff:*	*1.5867*	*0.597*	*CM:*	
25	*StDev:*	*0.0073*	*0.009*	*5.3E-05*	*0.0E+00*
26		*0.017902*		*0.0E+00*	*7.3E-05*

cell:	instruction:	copied to:
B13 = AVERAGE(A18:A23)		
C18 = A18-$B$13		C19:C23
E13 = (B24/C24-B13)*10/51		

Fig. 2.15.1: The spreadsheet analyzing the data of Bruce & Gill *by centering* the data.

Exercise 2.15.1:

(1) Enter the data from Fig. 2.15.1 in a spreadsheet, then calculate the average value of V_i, and make a column for the centered volumes $V_c = V_i - V_{av}$.

(2) Treating R as the dependent variable, and V_c as the independent one, use LS1 to compute the slope and intercept of a straight line through these points. Display the covariance matrix, and note that the covariance terms are indeed zero, see Fig. 2.15.1.

(3) Calculate the unknown concentration as $C_u = a_0' C_a/a_1 V_u = (a_0/a_1 - V_{av}) \times (C_a/V_u)$ where $C_a = 10$ μg/mL of lead, and $V_u = 51$ mL, so that C_u is in μg/L.

(4) Use Propagation (with input parameters in B24:C24, standard deviations in B25:C25, and the function in E13) to calculate the standard deviation in c_u.

(5) Copy the input data to a different location on the same spreadsheet, and analyze the data from Fig.2.15.1 without centering.

(6) Note that, in this case, the covariance terms are not zero, and the covariance matrix must therefore be used as input to Propagation. Verify that, if this is not done, a slightly different (and incorrect) answer (0.0059 instead of 0.0079) is found for s_u. Figure 2.15.2 shows this addition to the spreadsheet.

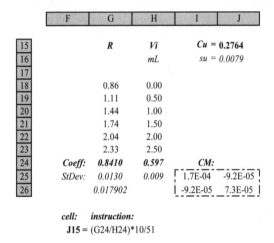

cell: instruction:

J15 = (G24/H24)*10/51

Fig. 2.15.2: The spreadsheet part directly analyzing the *uncentered* data of Bruce & Gill.

2.16 The intersection of two straight lines

Say that we need to determine the coordinates $x_\times$ and $y_\times$ of the intersection $\times$ between two straight lines, $y = a_0 + a_1 x$ and $z = b_0 + b_1 x$. The value of $x_\times$ follows from setting $y_\times$ equal to $z_\times$ as $x_\times = (b_0 - a_0)/(a_1 - b_1)$, and that of $y_\times = z_\times$ as $a_0 + a_1 x_\times = b_0 + b_1 x_\times = (a_1 b_0 - a_0 b_1)/(a_1 - b_1)$,

For the imprecision in $x_\times$ we assume that the least squares fits to the two line segments are mutually independent. We can therefore generate their combined covariance matrix by merely adding the two along a shared diagonal, as shown below, see block C44:F47 in Fig. 2.16.1. Then we can use Propagate to compute the standard deviation in $x_\times$.

For the imprecision in $y_\times$ we cannot use $y_\times = a_0 + a_1 x_\times$ because the imprecision in $x_\times$ is not independent of those in a_0 and a_1. To circumvent this problem, express $y_\times$ explicitly in terms of the four coefficients a_0 through b_1 as $y_\times = a_0 + a_1 x_\times = (a_1 b_0 - a_0 b_1)/(a_1 - b_1)$, and then use Propagation to calculate the standard deviation in $y_\times$.

Exercise 2.16.1:

(1) Arrange a spreadsheet for the calculation of the intersection between the two straight lines, $y = a_0 + a_1 x$ and $z = b_0 + b_1 x$, by entering labels and values for the coefficients a_0, a_1, b_0, b_1, and the noise 'amplitudes' s_{ny} and s_{nz}. Also make column headings for y, x, z, x, and for two columns of random noise, n_y and n_z. Then deposit values for x, and let the spreadsheet compute corresponding values for noisy straight lines y and z.

(2) Use LS1 to find approximate values for the coefficients a_0 and a_1, the standard deviations and covariance matrix, then do the same for b_0, b_1, etc.

(3) Use these coefficients to let the spreadsheet compute values of $x_\times = (b_0 - a_0)/(a_1 - b_1)$ and $y_\times = (a_1 b_0 - a_0 b_1)/(a_1 - b_1)$.

(4) Arrange the coefficients so that a_0, a_1, b_0, and b_1 are aligned in a single, contiguous row. Place the two covariance matrices such that the right-bottom corner of one touches the left-top corner of the other, so that they will form a single 4 × 4 matrix with a shared main diagonal, which should contain s_{a_0}, s_{a_1}, s_{b_0}, and s_{b_1}, in this order. Then call Propagation to find the standard deviations in $x_\times$ and $y_\times$. Figure 2.16.1 illustrates what you might get.

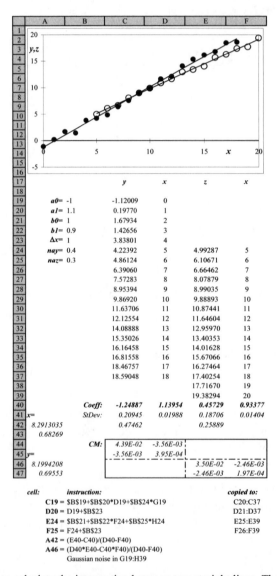

Fig. 2.16.1 A spreadsheet to calculate the intersection between two straight lines. The data in C40:F42 were obtained with LS1, those in A43 and A47 with Propagation. The noise in columns G and H is shown in Fig. 2.16.2. The lines drawn through the points were calculated from the coefficients in C40:D40 and E40:F40 respectively.

In the example shown in Fig. 2.16.1 we used a small angle of intersection between the two lines, and rather generous noise, to emphasize the difficulties one may face. We find $x_\times = 8.2_9 \pm 0.6_8$ and $y_\times = z_\times = 8.1_2 \pm 0.7_0$ whereas, in the absence of noise (i.e., for $s_{ny} = s_{nz} = 0$), the intersection would be at the point (10, 10). By using the standard deviations of a_0 through b_1 instead of the combined covariance matrix, we would have obtained a standard deviation in $x_\times$ of 1.6_8 instead of 0.6_8, and an (equally incorrect) standard deviation in $y_\times$ and $z_\times$ of 1.7_2 instead of 0.7_0.

Alternatively we can center the x-values to avoid having to deal with covariances. In this case we first compute the averages $x_{av,y}$ and $x_{av,z}$ of the two data sets $y(x)$ and $z(x)$, fit $y = a_0' + a_1 (x - x_{av,y})$ and $z = b_0' + b_1 (x - x_{av,z})$ where $a_0' = a_0 + a_1 x_{av,y}$ and $b_0' = b_0 + b_1 x_{av,z}$, and then calculate $x_\times = (b_0 - a_0) / (a_1 - b_1) = (b_0' - b_1 x_{av,z} - a_0' + a_1 x_{av,y}) / (a_1 - b_1)$, and $y_\times = (a_1 b_0 - a_0 b_1) / (a_1 - b_1) = [a_1 (b_0' - b_1 x_{av,z}) - (a_0' - a_1 x_{av,y}) b_1] / (a_1 - b_1)$.

	G	H	I	J	K	L
16			*x av,y =* 9		*x av,z =* 12.5	
17	*ny*	*nz*	*y*	*x*	*z*	*x*
18						
19	-0.3002	-1.2777	-1.1201	-9		
20	0.2443	1.2765	0.1977	-8		
21	1.1984	1.7331	1.6793	-7		
22	-2.1836	-0.2342	1.4266	-6		
23	1.0950	-1.0867	3.8380	-5		
24	-0.6902	-1.6904	4.2239	-4	4.9929	-7.5
25	-1.8469	-0.9776	4.8612	-3	6.1067	-6.5
26	-0.7735	-2.1179	6.3906	-2	6.6646	-5.5
27	-0.5679	-0.4040	7.5728	-1	8.0788	-4.5
28	0.1349	-0.3655	8.9539	0	8.9904	-3.5
29	-0.3270	-0.3702	9.8692	1	9.8889	-2.5
30	1.3426	-0.0853	11.6371	2	10.8744	-1.5
31	-0.1862	-0.5132	12.1255	3	11.6460	-0.5
32	1.9722	0.8657	14.0889	4	12.9597	0.5
33	2.3757	-0.6549	15.3503	5	13.4035	1.5
34	1.6615	-1.6124	16.1646	6	14.0163	2.5
35	0.5389	0.9022	16.8156	7	15.6707	3.5
36	1.9189	-0.0845	18.4676	8	16.2746	4.5
37	-0.5238	0.6751	18.5905	9	17.4025	5.5
38	-0.3002	-1.2777			17.7167	6.5
39	0.2443	1.2765			19.3829	7.5
40			*9.0070*	*1.1395*	*12.1294*	*0.9338*
41	*x=*		*0.1089*	*0.0199*	*0.0647*	*0.0140*
42	*8.29130*		*0.4746*		*0.2589*	
43	*0.68269*					
44		*CM:*	*1.19E-02*	*0.00E+00*		
45	*y=*		*0.00E+00*	*3.95E-04*		
46	*8.19942077*				*4.19E-03*	*0.00E+00*
47	*0.69553*				*0.00E+00*	*1.97E-04*

cell: *instruction:* *copied to:*

J16 = AVERAGE(J19:J39)

L16 = AVERAGE(L24:L39)

J19 = C19-$J$16   J20:J37

L24 = F24-$L$16   L25:L39

G42 = (K40-F40*L16-I40+C40*J16)/(J40-L40)

G46 = (J40*(K40-E40*L16)-(I40-C40*J16)*L40)/(J40-L40)

Fig. 2.16.2 Continuation of the spreadsheet of Fig. 2.16.1 showing the centered calculation as well as the noise columns G and H. The output in H40:L42 was obtained with LS1, and has again been aligned for subsequent use of the Propagation macro, resulting in the output in G43 and G47. The covariance matrices show zeros for all covariances, the off-diagonal terms.

The standard deviations in x_x and y_x are then calculated with Propagation, using the mutually independent standard deviations of a_0', a_1, b_0', and b_1. This alternative method is neither faster nor simpler, given the custom macros that generate and use covariance matrices, but confirms the earlier result obtained with the covariance matrix.

Finally we note that the computed coordinates are about three standard deviations away from their 'correct' values ($x_x = 10$, $y_x = 10$), again illustrating that standard deviations should not be considered as outer bounds, just as a first-order rate constant is not the time within which a first-order reaction runs to completion. Both are characteristic parameters, not delimiting ones.

2.17 Computing the boiling point of water

A rather dramatic example of the need to consider the covariance was reported by Meyer in *J. Chem. Educ.* 74 (1997) 1339, who described the determination of the boiling point of water from measurements of its vapor pressure as a function of temperature. In this example the pressure p (in torr) was determined with a mercury manometer, and the temperature t (in °C) with a thermistor. A set of such data, kindly provided by Prof. Meyer, is shown in Fig. 2.17.1, which also shows its analysis. The latter consists of converting p into $\ln p$, and t into $1/T$, where $T = t + 273.15$ is the absolute temperature. The quantity $\ln p$ was used as the dependent variable in fitting the data to the straight line

$$\ln p = a_0 + a_1/T \tag{2.17.1}$$

From the resulting values for a_0 and a_1 the boiling point t_b of water is then computed as

$$t_b = -273.15 + a_1 / [\ln(760) - a_0] \tag{2.17.2}$$

where we have substituted $p = 760$ torr. This is surely more complicated than directly measuring the temperature of water boiling at 760 torr, but is standard fare in undergraduate physical chemistry labs to illustrate the Clausius-Clapeyron equation.

The spreadsheet illustrated in Fig. 2.17.1, together with its included cell instructions, is rather self-explanatory, except for the need for the material in E13:G31, which is shown here because it will be used in Exercise 2.17.1. Use (2.17.2) to compute t_b in cell G32, and estimate the corresponding precision with the custom macro Propagation. This will place in cell G33 the result from using as inputs the coefficients C28:D28, the covariance matrix C31:D32, and the temperature in G32. Then move that result to C34, to make space in C33 for the output of Propagation based on the inputs C28:D28, the standard deviations in C29:D29, and G32 respectively. The results in G33 and G34 differ by a factor of about 29. Note the strong *collinearity* (i.e., mutual linear dependence) between the coefficients a_0 and a_1 in C28:D28, as evidenced by the linear correlation coefficients in C34 and D33 of –0.9995, i.e., very close to 1. The standard deviation in G33 is therefore clearly incorrect. Its value of about 2 °K for the boiling point of water is absurd anyway for temperature measurements made very close to 100 °C, with uncertainties of only about 0.05 °C.

In this case it is instructive to visualize the *error surface* or *pit map*, as it was called by Dyrssen, Ingri & Sillén in *Acta Chem. Scand.* 15 (1961) 694. Such a map displays log SSR as a function of the coefficients, here a_0 and a_1. We anticipate finding the minimum value of SSR at the bottom of a cone of elliptical cross-section, rounded at its bottom since experimental noise will prevent SSR from reaching zero. The ellipticity is primarily caused by the different dimensionalities and arbitrary scales of a_0 and a_1 in such a map. To display an error surface, plot $\ln p_{calc}$ in E16:E27 as a function of a_0 and a_1, and then SSR in cell G31. Thereafter, use the macro ScanF0 of the MacroBundle, which you can find on the MBToolbar under miscellany, whereupon Mapper will yield the error surface. Exercise 2.17.1 lists the steps to be taken.

Exercise 2.17.1:

(1) In cell J2 place the number 15.00, and in cell K2 the instruction =J2+0.05. (Start in row 2 to leave space for the macro name on row 1.)

(2) Copy the instruction of cell K2 to L2:HB2.

(3) In cell I3 place the number –3000, in cell I4 the instruction =I3–10, and copy the latter to I5:I403.

(4) Call the macro ScanF0. Answer Yes to the first dialog box, then specify the input data block as I2:HB403, X as C28, Y as D28, and F as G31, the location of SSR. (Had you highlighted I2:HB403 first, then you might have had to use Ctrl‿Home or the scroll bars to get back to the left top of the spreadsheet.)

(5) Computing the answer takes its time, because there are 201×401 = 80601 data to calculate, each requiring 3 invasive spreadsheet operations, a relatively slow process for a total of almost a quarter million of them, see section 8.14.1.

(6) Now call Mapper; its output with the black-and-white Mapper0 is shown in Fig. 2.17.2.

Figure 2.17.2 doesn't show a typical pit; instead, the surface looks more like a trench! If this is an elliptical cone, that ellipse surely has a huge ratio of its long and short axis. Centering can remove this collinearity in fitting a straight line to a data set, see section 2.10. When that is done, the discrepancy disappears, i.e., the covariances become zero (within the resolution of Excel), and Propagation yields identical results for the standard deviation of the boiling point t_b of 0.0071, whether we use the standard deviations or the covariance matrix. In summary: the boiling point of water at 760 torr is obtained as $t_b = 99.83_0 \pm 0.07_1$ °C, which is within three standard deviations of the accepted value of 100 °C.

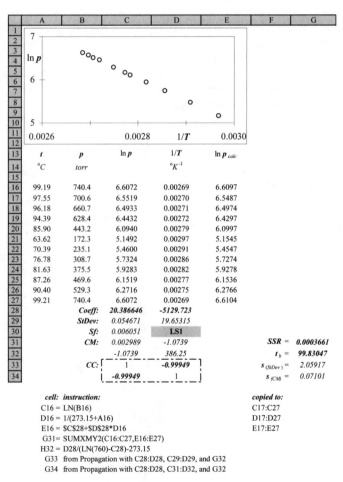

cell: instruction:
C16 = LN(B16)   copied to:
D16 = 1/(273.15+A16)   C17:C27
E16 = $C$28+$D$28*D16   D17:D27
G31= SUMXMY2(C16:C27,E16:E27)   E17:E27
H32 = D28/(LN(760)-C28)-273.15
  G33 from Propagation with C28:D28, C29:D29, and G32
  G34 from Propagation with C28:D28, C31:D32, and G32

Fig. 2.17.1: The spreadsheet for fitting data to eq.(2.17.1).

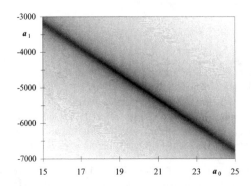

Fig. 2.17.2: The error surface for the <u>un</u>weighted data analysis.

However, the above computation is still sub-optimal, because it minimizes the sum of squares of $\ln p$, whereas the experimental data used as the dependent variable are the pressures p, not their natural logarithms. We therefore use *centered and weighted* least squares, with averaged global weights w', where

$$w = \frac{1}{\left(d\ln p/dp\right)^2} = \frac{1}{\left(1/p\right)^2} = p^2 \qquad \text{and} \qquad w' = w/w_{av} \tag{2.17.3}$$

Note that centering weighted least squares requires that the *weighted* sum $\Sigma\, w_i x_i$ of the dependent variable x be made equal to zero. When this is done, you will indeed find zero covariance terms. The boiling temperature of water should now be calculated with

$$t_b = a_1 / [\ln(760) - a_0 + a_1(w'/T)_{av}] - 273.15 \tag{2.17.4}$$

Exercise 2.17.2:

(1) Make the properly centered and weighted least squares analysis spreadsheet, as illustrated in Fig. 2.17.3.

(2) Then make the error surface for this centered & weighted least squares analysis of the Meyer data, the same way as outlined in steps (1) through (6) of exercise 2.17.1. That map should look like Fig. 2.17.4.

The result is not much different from that obtained in Fig. 2.17.1; t_b is now found to be $99.83_9 \pm 0.06_4$ °C instead of the earlier $99.83_0 \pm 0.07_1$ °C. However, thanks to the centering, the error surface in Fig. 2.17.4 now looks quite different from that in Fig. 2.17.2. In this case, weighting does not change our main conclusion regarding the need to use the covariance, but merely accentuates it.

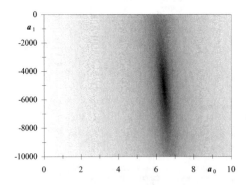

Fig. 2.17.4: The error surface for the weighted data analysis.

	A	B	C	D	E	F	G
43	t	p	$\ln p$	w'	$1/T - (w'/T)_{av}$	w'/T	$\ln p_{calc}$
44	°C	torr			°K^{-1}		
45							
46	99.19	740.4	6.6072	1.91	-0.00004	0.00514	6.6094
47	97.55	700.6	6.5519	1.71	-0.00003	0.00462	6.5485
48	96.18	660.7	6.4933	1.52	-0.00002	0.00413	6.4972
49	94.39	628.4	6.4432	1.38	-0.00001	0.00375	6.4296
50	85.90	443.2	6.0940	0.69	0.00006	0.00191	6.0999
51	63.62	172.3	5.1492	0.10	0.00024	0.00031	5.1557
52	70.39	235.1	5.4600	0.19	0.00018	0.00056	5.4556
53	76.78	308.7	5.7324	0.33	0.00013	0.00095	5.7280
54	81.63	375.5	5.9283	0.49	0.00009	0.00139	5.9282
55	87.26	469.6	6.1519	0.77	0.00005	0.00214	6.1538
56	90.40	529.3	6.2716	0.98	0.00002	0.00269	6.2766
57	99.21	740.4	6.6072	1.91	-0.00004	0.00514	6.6101
58		Coeff:	6.3969412		-5124.62		
59		StDev:	0.0017995		32.9922		
60		Sf:	0.0062335			$(w'/T)_{av}$ =	0.00273
61		CM:	3.238E-06		7.06E-16	SSR =	0.0003691
62			7.056E-16		1088.48	t_b =	99.83863
63		CC:	1		0.00000		0.06398
64			0.00000		1		0.06398

cell:	instruction:	copied to:
C46 =	LN(B46)	C47:C57
D46 =	12*(B46^2)/SUMSQ(B46:B57)	D47:D57
E46 =	1/(273.15+A46)-$G$60	E47:E57
F46 =	D46/(A46+273.15)	F47:F57
G46 =	$D$58+$E$58*E46	G47:G57
G60 =	AVERAGE(F46:F57)	
G61 =	SUMXMY2(C46:C57,G46:G57)	
G62 =	E58/(LN(760)-D58+E58*G60)-273.15	

Fig. 2.17.3: The spreadsheet for the weighted data analysis.

2.18 Phantom relations

In using least squares it is tacitly assumed that the input data represent *independent* measurements. If that is not the case, quite misleading results may be obtained, as illustrated by the following problem (#9 on page 383) of K. Connors, *Chemical Kinetics, the Study of Reaction Rates in Solution* (VCH, 1990):

"From the last four digits from the office telephone numbers of the faculty in your department, systematically construct pairs of "rate constants" as two-digit numbers times 10^{-5} s^{-1} at temperatures 300 K and 315 K (obviously the larger rate constant of each pair to be associated with the higher temperature). Make a two-point Arrhenius plot for each faculty member, evaluating $\Delta H^{\ddagger}$ and $\Delta S^{\ddagger}$. Examine the plot of $\Delta H^{\ddagger}$ against $\Delta S^{\ddagger}$ for evidence of an isokinetic relationship."

Essentially, the reader is asked to take two arbitrary two-digit y-values y_1 and y_2, assign them to pre-selected x-values x_1 and x_2 respectively, compute the resulting slope a_1 and intercept a_0, repeat this for a number of arbitrary input pairs y (for the same two x-values), and then plot the resulting a_1-values versus a_0, or vice versa. The actual procedure is somewhat less transparent, since it also involves sorting the input data, a logarithmic transformation, and giving the slopes and intercepts thermodynamic names, all steps that tend to obscure the true nature of the problem. Moreover, the above assignment uses only positive input numbers. Below we will simply take pairs of random two-digit integer values for y, associate them with two fixed x-values such as $x_1 = 300$ and $x_2 = 320$, compute the resulting slopes and intercepts, and then plot these against each other.

Exercise 2.18.1:

(1) In cells B2 and C2 place the labels y1 and y2 respectively. Do the same in cells E2:F2, and in cells H2:I2 deposit the labels a0 and a1 respectively.

(2) In cells B4 and C4 deposit the instruction =INT(200*(RAND()-0.5)), which will generate random two-digit integers between -100 and $+100$. Copy these instructions down to row 23.

(3) The numbers in B4:C23 will change every time you change something on the spreadsheet. In order to have a fixed set of random numbers, highlight B4:C23, copy it with Ctrl∪c, highlight cell E4, and use Edit ⇨ Paste Special ⇨ Values to copy the *values* of y_1 and y_2 so obtained. After that, use the data in block E4:F23 as your random input data, while ignoring those in B4:C23 that keep changing while you work the spreadsheet.

(4) Based on the data in E4:F23, compute in column H the slope of each pair of data points (x_1, y_1), (x_2, y_2) as $(y_2-y_1)/(x_2-x_1)$, and in column I the corresponding intercepts as $(x_2 y_1 - x_1 y_2)/(x_2-x_1)$.

The data in Fig. 2.18.1 seem to fall on or near a straight line, for which Trendline yields the formula $y = -311.18\,x - 0.8877$, with $R^2 = 0.9983$. Is this what you would have expected for having used random input numbers for y? You *see* a straight line, how can that possibly be *random*? What happens here?

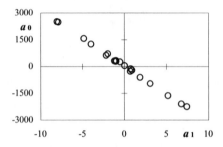

Fig. 2.18.1: An example of a phantom line you might find with $x_1 = 300$ and $x_2 = 320$.

Because each pair of input numbers y of this graph is completely determined by the calculated slope and intercept for given input values of x, the graph uses strongly *linearly correlated* pairs of input data. We already encountered the formula for that correlation, (2.10.1). The sign of (2.10.1) explains the negative correlation (causing the negative slope da_0/da_1 in Fig. 2.18.1), and the effect is the more pronounced the larger is Σx, i.e., the more eccentric are the x-values used. Plotting such slopes and intercepts against each other will then lead to a convincingly linear but physically meaningless relationship, approximating the proportionality $y = -x_{av}x$. This merely verifies the correlation (2.10.1) between slope and intercept, as is perhaps more evident after we rewrite $y = -x_{av}x$ using more appropriate symbols as $a_0 = -x_{av}a_1$.

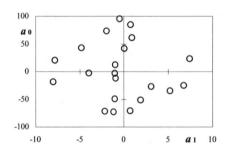

Fig. 2.18.2: The same y-values as in Fig. 2.18.1 analyzed with $x_1 = -10$ and $x_2 = +10$.

This is the origin of the "isokinetic relationship" of J. E. Leffler, *J. Org. Chem.* 20 (1955) 1202, and illustrates how neglecting the covariance can trick you. An extensive discussion of this problem, as well as a suggested solution, was given by Krug et al. in *J. Phys. Chem.* 80 (1976) 2335, 2341. For an interesting (and only seemingly alternative) explanation see G. C. McBane, *J. Chem. Educ.* 75 (1998) 919.

(6) Use the same *y*-values collected in columns H and I, but now analyze them for a pair of *x*-values *centered* around the average $x_{av} = 310$, so that $x_1 = -10$ and $x_2 = +10$. Does this support the above explanation?

Given that the input data were random, what are the parameters that determine the 'line' in Fig. 2.18.1? There is no significant intercept, just a slope, and the latter is simply $-(\Sigma x)/N$, i.e., minus the average value of *x*. In the above example we have $-(\Sigma x)/N = -(300+320) / 2 = -310$, so that we would expect $y = -310\,x$, which compares well with the result of Trendline, $y = -311.18\,x - 0.8877$, as illustrated in Fig. 2.18.3, not only in terms of its slope but also for the positions of its individual points, which each computed dot neatly nested within the corresponding larger circle of the data. Indeed, as already noticed by Leffler, in many cases the absolute values of the reported slopes of isokinetic plots were close to the average absolute temperatures of the data sets considered. In such cases the isokinetic effect is nothing more than an artifact of incorrectly applied statistics.

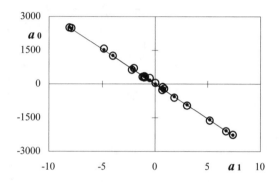

Fig. 2.18.3: The data from Fig. 2.18.1 (large open circles) and, for comparison, those computed as $a_0 = -x_{av}\,a_1$ (small filled circles connected by a thin line).

2.19 Summary

Typical experimental data are occasional samples of some underlying continuous feature, corrupted by scatter. Linear least squares methods often allow the experimenter to recover the underlying trend from the sporadic, noisy data. Note that this underlying, noise-free trend can contain systematic errors, and that the uncertainty estimates generated by least squares methods only deal with precision, not with accuracy.

Because least squares methods have become so easy to apply, they have become ubiquitous in many fields of science and technology. Keep in mind, however, that the method and the results obtained with it presume that the noise is random and can be described adequately by a single Gaussian distribution. We seldom either have or take the time to verify those assumptions, and therefore should take the results with one or more proverbial grains of salt.

In fact, the often-quoted need for outlier rejection suggests that assuming a Gaussian distribution often oversimplifies the actual problem considered. If instead we were to assume, e.g., a Lorentzian (Cauchy) distribution, which has a larger fraction of its data in its tails, then the entire analysis method would have to be revised, since this distribution doesn't even have a standard deviation! That clearly would be undesirable, but begs the question which distribution is more descriptive of actual experiments. The standard choice of a Gaussian ("normal") distribution contains a fair amount of wishful thinking.

In this chapter we have focused our attention on fitting data to a straight line, because this problem is so common in applied science. It is often assumed that the parameters obtained by least squares fitting to a straight line are mutually independent, but this is usually *not* the case (another case of wishful thinking). Consequently, quite misleading results may be obtained, as illustrated in section 2.18, where the culprit was the (easily overlooked) covariance of those input data. Working backwards, it shows how to convert perfectly random data from the 'scatter' plot of Fig. 2.18.2 into the convincingly linear relationship of Fig. 2.18.1 (with an R^2 factor of more than 0.998), an object lesson in 'how to lie with statistics'. Beware, it is all too easy to fool oneself! With appropriate software, getting the correct result is not particularly difficult, but attention must be paid.

Fitting data to a proportionality generates only one coefficient, the slope, and therefore seldom involves problems of covariance. Fitting a straight line yields two adjustable parameters, a_0 and a_1, which in general will be mutually dependent. The macro LS provides the corresponding covariance (and, as we will see in chapter 3, does the same for polynomial and multivariate fits as well) and the macro Propagation can subsequently account for their covariance(s). In the examples shown in sections 2.17 and 2.18, centering could avoid this problem, because it leads to mutually independent coefficients a_0 and a_1, thereby making the covariances $v_{01} = v_{10}$ zero. Unfortunately, this only works for fitting to a straight line. In section 3.11 we will encounter orthogonal transformation as the (much more complicated) equivalent of centering for polynomial and multivariate fits. In general, using the covariance matrix is by far the simpler and more efficient solution.

Data analysis starts with data acquisition. Then, if one does not want to hold on to the original data, the covariance v_{01} should be recorded and preserved, or the data analyzed in their centered form, and the result stored together with the value(s) of x_{av}. If only the fitting parameters a_0 and a_1 and their standard deviations s_0 and s_1 are available, one will in general *not* be able to compute the correct precision of any subsequently derived results requiring both a_0 and a_1, because there is no way to determine, retroactively, the value of their covariance. Unfortunately, such careless and misleading use of least squares occurs far more often than one would hope. Of course, one should not get carried away with this: uncertainty estimates are just that, *estimates*, a point vividly illustrated in section 2.12. Still, if time and effort are spent on making those estimates, it might as well be done correctly.

In this book the focus is on data analysis, i.e., on an after-the-fact look at what the experiments might reveal. Mostly between the lines, however, there is a second message: now that statistics have become so easy to apply, do involve them early, *during the execution* of the experiment. The reason is simple: by analyzing intermediate data, we are often alerted to unexpected behavior, such as an intercept that should not be there and thus might point to improper calibration, or a curvature that might reflect some nonlinear instrumental response we might be able to avoid. Those might still be corrected at this stage, saving us from having to redo the entire experiment or, worse, from drawing incorrect conclusions from a poorly designed experiment.

Better yet, involve statistical concepts *during the design* of an experiment, before a single measurement is taken. All too often, faulty design will doom an experiment from the start, just as a questionnaire with leading questions will not yield a valid, unbiased sampling of public opinion. Unfortunately, there is no statistical or other magic that, afterwards, can then put Humpty Dumpty together again.

In the next chapter we will extend linear least squares analysis to polynomials and multivariate functions. We will see that we can further broaden the application of least squares methods by transforming data that do not fit that mold into a polynomial form. That still leaves many functions out; for those, chapter 4 will describe nonlinear least squares.

2.20 For further reading

Excellent, highly readable starting points for linear least squares methods are *An Introduction to Error Analysis* by J. R. Taylor (University Science Books, 1982, 1997), and the classic *Data Reduction and Error Analysis for the Physical Sciences* by P. R. Bevington (McGraw-Hill, 1969, 1992). These books (and many others) clearly explain the underlying assumptions, and show many examples of practical applications. For the lighter side, take a look at L. Gonick & L. Smith, *The Cartoon Guide to Statistics* (Harper Perennial, 1994), or its predecessor, D. Hill's *How to Lie with Statistics* (Norton, 1982).

Chapter *3*

Further linear least squares

In this chapter we apply least squares methods to polynomials in the independent variable x, and to multivariable functions. We also describe weighted least squares, and show how least squares methods can be simplified when the x-values are spaced equidistantly.

3.1 Fitting data to a polynomial

Excel makes it easy to extend the procedures discussed in chapter 2 to fitting data to a power series of the general form $y = a_0 + a_1x + a_2x^2 + a_3x^3 + a_4x^4 + \ldots + a_mx^m = \Sigma\, a_j x^j$, where $j = 0\,(1)\,m$, again assuming that y contains all the experimental imprecisions, and that these follow a single Gaussian distribution. For either LinEst, Regression, LS0 or LS1, we merely have to arrange m adjacent, contiguous columns, for x, $x^2, x^3, \ldots, x^m$ instead of one for x, so that they can be entered *as a block*. For LS0 or LS1, the first two columns should still contain the values of y_i and x_i, but the highlighted block should now include one or more adjacent columns for, say, x_i^2, x_i^3, etc. There is neither a requirement that consecutive orders of x be used (you need not include columns for powers you do not need), nor that they be in any particular order (although that is usually easier to work with). LS1 fits data to a general polynomial, while LS0 sets the value of a_0 equal to zero, thereby forcing the fitted curve to go through the origin. With LinEst(*y-range*, *x-range*, *type*, *statistics*) the equivalent choice is made by setting *type* to 0 or false in order to force a_0 to zero; with Regression the same is achieved by activating Constant is Ζero in the dialog box.

When you use LinEst to fit data to a polynomial, make sure that you highlight a block *of sufficient width* (and 5 rows in height) and, of course, use the block enter command Ctrl◡Shift◡Enter. If you use just two columns, you would see only two coefficients, viz. those for the two highest powers of x, without labeling them as such or warning you that some output data are missing. You will need a block that is as many columns wide as there are adjustable parameters in your model, e.g., two for a straight line: intercept and slope. (If you also forgot the block enter, you would get a one-cell output, but in that case you would notice that something went awry.) When in doubt, it is therefore better to use too many columns, since any unused cells will merely be filled with N/A. Regression and LS internally determine the size of the needed output block, and therefore will give you no such problems.

With Trendline you do not need to make any new columns for higher orders of x, but merely select the power series and specify its order (between 2 and 6). In order to display its numerical results, click on the Options tab, then select Display equation on chart. Trendline yields the individual coefficients a_i, but neither the corresponding standard deviations s_i nor the standard deviation s_f of the fit. It can only provide the rather uninformative r^2, the square of the multiple correlation coefficient, with Options, Display R-squared value on chart. A convenient Forecast feature of Trendline Options allows you to extrapolate the curve on the basis of the calculated parameters, but without any indications of the resulting imprecisions.

Sections 3.2 through 3.4 illustrate fitting data to a polynomial.

3.2 Fitting data to a parabola

Exercise 3.2.1:

(1) Start a new spreadsheet, make up a data set from a quadratic expression plus some noise, and fit it with each of the above methods. For Linest, Regression, or LS use columns for y, x, and x^2 in this order. For Trendline the data placement doesn't matter, as long as the data are plotted in a graph.

(2) Figure 3.2.1 shows an example, in which we have used the instruction =LINEST(A15:A27,B15:C27,1,1) to find the coefficients a_i used in computing $y_{calc} = a_0 + a_0 x + a_0 x^2$ in column D, which is then plotted as a line through the points. (The second range is now a block, for both x and x^2. Since there are three coefficients to be calculated, use three columns for the result, and enter the array instruction with Ctrl$\cup$Shift$\cup$Enter.)

(3) The LinEst output is

-0.793484	9.0412407	-11.9781
0.051121	0.7355022	2.23884
0.974976	2.2873408	#N/A
194.8118	10	#N/A
2038.483	52.319277	#N/A

(4) These results in the top two lines, $a_0 = -12._0 \pm 2._2$, $a_1 = 9.0_4 \pm 0.7_4$, and $a_2 = -0.79_3 \pm 0.05_1$, can be compared with the values used in generating the synthetic data, $a_0 = -10$, $a_1 = 8$, and $a_2 = -0.7$. While the fitted quadratic is noise-free, the presence of noise in the parent data results in rather uncertain coefficients: the relative standard deviation $|s_0/a_0|$ is more than 18%.

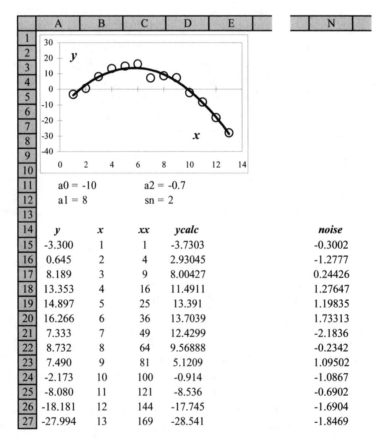

	A	B	C	D	E		N
11	a0 = -10		a2 = -0.7				
12	a1 = 8		sn = 2				
13							
14	*y*	*x*	*xx*	*ycalc*			*noise*
15	-3.300	1	1	-3.7303			-0.3002
16	0.645	2	4	2.93045			-1.2777
17	8.189	3	9	8.00427			0.24426
18	13.353	4	16	11.4911			1.27647
19	14.897	5	25	13.391			1.19835
20	16.266	6	36	13.7039			1.73313
21	7.333	7	49	12.4299			-2.1836
22	8.732	8	64	9.56888			-0.2342
23	7.490	9	81	5.1209			1.09502
24	-2.173	10	100	-0.914			-1.0867
25	-8.080	11	121	-8.536			-0.6902
26	-18.181	12	144	-17.745			-1.6904
27	-27.994	13	169	-28.541			-1.8469

Fig. 3.2.1: A spreadsheet to fit noisy data to a parabola. Cell A15 contains the instruction =$B$11+ $B$12*B15+$D$11*C15+$D$12*N15, and is copied to A16:A27, while the instruction =B15^2 in cell C15 is copied to C16:C27. Cells N15:N27 contain Gaussian noise with zero mean and unit standard deviation.

(5) For a_1 and a_2 the correct results lie beyond one standard deviation. As we already saw in chapter 2, standard deviations should not be interpreted as indicating the likely range of deviations; for that purpose, confidence intervals (which depend on the standard deviation s, the number N of data points used, and a selected probability, such as 95% or 99%) are more appropriate.

(6) The coefficients a_j obtained from a single least squares operation are of course mutually dependent. If they are to be used in subsequent computations, you will need the corresponding covariance matrix, which can be displayed by the custom macros LS.

(7) Save the data for use in exercise 3.11.1.

For polynomials of second and higher order, centering no longer suffices, and orthogonal polynomials are needed to make the covariance(s) zero. We will discuss a particular set of such orthogonal polynomials in section 3.11, but (except for equidistant data) it is often easier to use LS0 or LS1 to find a straightforward polynomial fit and, if the results require further mathematical manipulation, to use the covariance matrix with Propagation to compute the precision of the resulting answers.

3.3 The iodine vapor spectrum

As our next example we consider the visible absorption spectrum of iodine vapor, I_2, a homonuclear diatomic molecule. Because of its symmetry, I_2 has no dipole moment in any of its vibrational or rotational modes. It therefore does not absorb light in the infrared and microwave regions of the spectrum, where one usually observes vibrational and rotational transitions respectively. In the visible part of the spectrum, however, I_2 can be excited from its electronic ground state to an (at room temperature essentially unoccupied) electronically excited state.

In both the ground state (here indicated with $\circ$) and the electronically excited state (labeled with $'$), the molecules exist in discrete vibrational and rotational states, defined by the quantum numbers v and J respectively. The electronic transition is associated with a change in dipole moment, and can therefore lead to light absorption. There are no quantum-mechanical restrictions (selection rules) that govern the changes in vibrational levels during this electronic transition. When, as in the experiments used here, the vapor phase absorption spectrum is observed with relatively low resolution ($\Delta\lambda \approx 0.5$ nm), the rotational states are not resolved. Several series of spectral absorption lines can be observed, each originating from a different vibrational level (such as $v^\circ = 0, 1, 2$, etc.) in the electronic ground state, and leading to various vibrational levels (with their quantum numbers v') in the electronically excited state. The data we will analyze here reflect transitions between the vibrational and electronic ground state ($v^\circ = 0$) and different vibrational states (with vibrational quantum numbers v') in the electronically excited state.

As our experimental data we will use a set of measurements discussed in C. J. Pursell & L. Doezema, *J. Chem. Educ.* 76 (1999) 839; the actual data used were kindly provided by Dr. Pursell and are listed in Fig. 3.3.1. This same data set has also been reproduced by Ogren, Davis & Guy in *J. Chem. Educ.* 78 (2001) 827, Table 1.

In the simplest model, that of the harmonic oscillator, the energy $E(v)$ of a particular vibrational state can be described as $E(v)/hc = \overline{\omega_e}\,(v+\frac{1}{2})$, where h is Planck's constant, c the vacuum speed of light, and $\overline{\omega_e}$ the fundamental vibrational 'frequency' in units of wavenumbers (cm^{-1}), as indicated by the superscripted bar. The latter can be expressed in terms of the force constant k and the reduced mass μ (here half the atomic mass of iodine) as $\overline{\omega_e} = \left[1/(2\pi c)\right]\sqrt{k/\mu}$. A more realistic description includes a second-order term, as in

$$E(v)/hc = \overline{\omega_e}(v+1/2) - \overline{\omega_e x_e}(v+1/2)^2 \tag{3.3.1}$$

where $\overline{\omega_e x_e}$ is called the anharmonicity constant. The optically observable transition energy $\overline{v}$ from the vibrational and electronic ground state $v^\circ = 0$ to the electronically excited state at various vibrational quantum states v' is then given by

$$\overline{v} = [E(v') - E(v^\circ)]/hc = E_{el} + \overline{\omega_e}'(v'+1/2) - \overline{\omega_e^\circ}/2 - \overline{\omega_e'x_e'}(v'+1/2)^2 + \overline{\omega_e^\circ x_e^\circ}/4 \qquad (3.3.2)$$

	A	B	C	D	E
1	vibrational	wave-	v+1/2	(v+1/2)^2	wave-
2	quantum	number			number
3	number	(obs)			(calc)
4					
5	18	17702	18.5	342.25	17703
6	19	17797	19.5	380.25	17797
7	20	17889	20.5	420.25	17888
8	21	17979	21.5	462.25	17978
9	22	18064	22.5	506.25	18065
10	23	18149	23.5	552.25	18150
11	24	18235	24.5	600.25	18234
12	25	18318	25.5	650.25	18315
13	26	18396	26.5	702.25	18394
14	27	18471	27.5	756.25	18471
15	28	18546	28.5	812.25	18546
16	29	18618	29.5	870.25	18619
17	30	18688	30.5	930.25	18691
18	31	18755	31.5	992.25	18759
19	32	18825	32.5	1056.25	18826
20	33	18889	33.5	1122.25	18891
21	34	18954	34.5	1190.25	18954
22	35	19019	35.5	1260.25	19015
23	36	19077	36.5	1332.25	19074
24	37	19131	37.5	1406.25	19130
25	38	19186	38.5	1482.25	19185
26	39	19238	39.5	1560.25	19238
27	40	19286	40.5	1640.25	19288
28	41	19339	41.5	1722.25	19337
29	42	19384	42.5	1806.25	19383
30	43	19429	43.5	1892.25	19428
31	44	19467	44.5	1980.25	19470
32	45	19512	45.5	2070.25	19510
33	46	19546	46.5	2162.25	19549
34	47	19585	47.5	2256.25	19585
35	Coeff.:	*15603.7*	*132.42*	*-1.0232*	
36	St.Dev.:	*6.0*	*0.38*	*0.0057*	
37		*2.092*			
38			35.740	-2.243	0.033
39	*CM:*		-2.243	0.144	-0.002
40			0.033	-0.002	0.000
41			1	-0.990	0.968
42	*LCC:*		-0.990	1	-0.993
43			0.968	-0.993	1

Fig. 3.3.1: The spectroscopic data for I_2 vapor from Pursell & Doezema.

which is a quadratic function of $(v'+1/2)$, as is more readily seen after rewriting it as

$$\overline{\nu} = \left(E_{el} - \overline{\omega_e^\circ}/2 + \overline{\omega_e^\circ x_e^\circ}/4 \right) + \overline{\omega_e}'(v'+1/2) - \overline{\omega_e' x_e}' (v'+1/2)^2 \tag{3.3.3}$$

where E_{el} is the (theoretical) energy difference between the minima for the electronic ground state and excited state in the diagrams of potential energy vs. bond length.

Exercise 3.3.1:

(1) In a new spreadsheet, enter the vibrational quantum numbers v' and the corresponding wavenumbers in columns A and B respectively.

(2) In column C calculate $v'+\frac{1}{2}$, and in column D the quantity $(v'+\frac{1}{2})^2$.

(3) Highlight the data in columns B through D, call LS1, and find the corresponding values for $\left(E_{el} - \overline{\omega_e^\circ}/2 + \overline{\omega_e^\circ x_e^\circ}/4 \right)$, $\overline{\omega_e}'$, and $\overline{\omega_e' x_e}'$, and the associated imprecision estimates. Figures 3.3.1 and 3.3.2 illustrate how well a quadratic fits these experimental data.

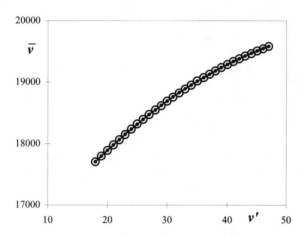

Fig. 3.3.2: A quadratic fit of the observed spectral lines, in wavenumbers, as a function of the assigned vibrational quantum numbers v' of the electronically excited state, for the iodine vapor spectral data of Pursell & Doezema, *J. Chem. Educ.* 76 (1999) 839. Open circles: experimental data; line and small solid points: fitted data.

(4) Compute the quantity $\overline{x_e}'$ from $\overline{\omega_e}'$ and $\overline{\omega_e' x_e}'$, using the covariance matrix and the Propagation macro. When the data are organized as in Fig. 3.3.1 and $\overline{x_e}'$ is computed in cell B41 as $\overline{\omega_e x_e}/\overline{\omega_e}$ or = –D35/C35, for Propagation specify the location of the input parameters as B35:D35, that of the covariance matrix as C38:E40, and the address of the function as B41. This will yield $\overline{x_e}' = 0.007727 \pm 0.000021$ cm^{-1}, whereas specifying the standard deviations in B36:D36 would have led to 0.007727 ± 0.000048 cm^{-1} instead, i.e., to a standard deviation more than twice as large. This should not be surprising, since $\overline{\omega_e}'$ and $\overline{\omega_e' x_e}'$ are clearly mutually dependent quantities. This is also clear from the linear correlation coefficients shown in Fig. 3.3.1, which are close to ± 1.

(5) Apart from the calculation of the standard deviation of $\overline{x_e}'$ you could also have obtained the same results with LinEst or Regression. However, when such numbers are used for further calculations, as illustrated by Pursell & Doezema and also by, e.g., Long et al., *J. Chem. Educ.* 76 (1999) 841, the covariance matrix may again have to be taken into account.

3.4 The intersection of two parabolas

Say that we need to determine the coordinates of an intersection of two parabolas, or of curves that, in the neighborhood of their intersection, can be approximated as parabolas. We fit the first curve (or curve fragment) to $y = a_0 + a_1 x + a_2 x^2$, and the second to $z = b_0 + b_1 x + b_2 x^2$, in order to determine the coefficients a_i and b_i. We then compute the x-value at their intersection by setting y equal to z, so that $(a_2 - b_2) x^2$

$+ (a_1–b_1) x + (a_0–b_0) = 0$ or $x_\times = \{-(a_1–b_1) \pm \sqrt{[(a_1–b_1)^2 – 4(a_0–b_0)(a_2–b_2)]}\} / \{2(a_2–b_2)\}$, where the choice of sign before the square root depends on the numerical values used. The corresponding values $y_\times$ and $z_\times$ then follow from substitution of $x_\times$ into $y = a_0 + a_1x + a_2x^2$ or $z = b_0 + b_1x + b_2x^2$.

Exercise 3.4.1:

(1) In cells A1:A3 of a new spreadsheet enter labels for a_0 through a_2, and in cells A4:A6 labels for b_0 through b_2. In cells B1:B6 deposit their numerical values.

(2) In cells A10:H10 place column headings for y_n, x, xx (or $x{\wedge}2$), z_n, x, xx, n_y, and n_z respectively, in cells E7 and E8 place labels for the noise standard deviations s_{ny} and s_{nz}, and in cells F7 and F8 deposit their numerical values.

(3) In B12 and E12 start duplicate columns with x-values, and do the same in C12 and F12 for x^2.

(4) In columns G and H, starting from row 12 down, deposit Gaussian ('normal') noise of zero mean and unit standard deviation.

(5) In A12 compute y_n as =$B$1+$B$2*$B12+$B$3*$C12+$F$7*G12, and copy this down. Likewise, starting with cell D12, compute z_n as =$B$4+ $B$5*$E12+$B$6*$F12+$F$8*H12. Extend all columns down to the same row as the x-values in columns B and E.

(6) Plot the resulting parabolas, and adjust the parameters in B1:B6 to yield intersecting curves.

(7) Call LS1 and fit the data in columns A, B, and C. Place the covariance matrix in E1:G3. Using Edit ⇨ Paste Special ⇨ Transpose, copy the resulting coefficients a_0 through a_2 to cells C1:C3, and their standard deviations to D1:D3.

(8) Now call LS1 for the data in columns D through F, and place the covariance matrix in (no, this is no misprint) H4:J6. Again using Edit ⇨ Paste Special ⇨ Transpose, copy the resulting coefficients b_0 through b_2 to C4:C6. Copy the corresponding standard deviations to D4:D6.

(9) For the coordinates of the intersection, compute the value of $x_\times$ in cell C7 from the formula given above, and in cell C9 calculate the associated value of $y_\times = z_\times$ as $z_\times = b_0 + b_1x_\times + b_2x_\times^2$.

(10) Call Propagation to calculate the standard deviation in $x_\times$. For input parameters use the data in C1:C6, for their imprecisions the combined covariance matrix in E1:J6, and for the function cell C7.

(11) If we use the values in D1:D6 instead of those in E1:J6 as the imprecision estimates, we will obtain a quite different (but incorrect) result, just as we saw earlier in sections 2.12 and 2.14. For the data in Fig. 3.4.1 the resulting standard deviation in $x_\times$ is then found as 3.61, whereas the correct answer is only 0.21.

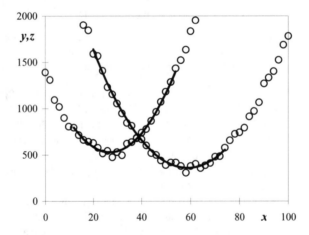

Fig. 3.4.1: Determining the coordinates of the intersection of two parabolas. The solid lines show the least-squares parabolas used in the computation.

So far this is not much different from exercise 3.2.1. What is new here is the estimate of the resulting standard deviations in $x_\times$ and $y_\times$. The value of $x_\times$ depends on six parameters, a_0 through a_2 and b_0 through b_2, of which the a_j are a mutually dependent set, as are the b_j. As long as the two parabolas are mutually independent, we can handle this by combining the covariance matrices of their fits, i.e., by placing the two matrices such that their main diagonals are joined, see Fig. 2.14.2. This is why we put the second matrix in H4:J6, because the first was located in E1:G3. The resulting 6×6 matrix E1:J6, with the six variances on its main diagonal, see Fig. 3.4.3, can then serve as the input for the custom macro Propagation. The latter will interpret the empty spaces in E1:J6 as zeroes.

For the standard deviation of y_x the procedure is similar, except that we must first convert the expression for y_x explicitly in terms of the coefficients a_0 through a_2 and b_0 through b_2, e.g., as $y_x = a_0 + a_1 \{-(a_1-b_1) \pm \sqrt{[(a_1-b_1)^2 - 4(a_0-b_0)(a_2-b_2)]}\} / \{2(a_2-b_2)\} + a_2 \{-(a_1-b_1) \pm \sqrt{[(a_1-b_1)^2 - 4(a_0-b_0)(a_2-b_2)]}\} / \{2(a_2-b_2)\}^2$.

Exercise 3.4.1 (continued):

(12) In cell C8 calculate y_x as just indicated, then use Propagation to find its standard deviation.

(13) Again check the difference between using the covariance matrix or merely the individual standard deviations of the coefficients. In our numerical example we find $y_x = 691.5 \pm 6.4$ using the covariance matrix, and $y_x = 691.5 \pm 105.7$ when the covariances are ignored.

	A	B	C	D
1	*a0*=	1400	1397	*35*
2	*a1*=	-65	-64.5	*2.1*
3	*a2*=	1.2	1.195	*0.029*
4	*b0*=	3300	3332	*81*
5	*b1*=	-100	-102.4	*4.3*
6	*b2*=	0.85	0.883	*0.053*
7		*x inters* =	38.68	*0.21*
8		*z inters* =	691.49	*6.44*

Fig. 3.4.2: The left top corner of the spreadsheet of exercise 3.4.1.

	E	F	G	H	I	J
1	1228.2	-72.26	0.9326			
2	-72.26	4.586	-0.0617			
3	0.9326	-0.0617	0.00086			
4				6507.02	-339.8	4.08377
5				-339.8	18.311	-0.2248
6				4.08377	-0.2248	0.00281
7	*sn y* =	30				
8	*sn z* =	30				

Fig. 3.4.3: The section of the spreadsheet showing the combined covariance matrix.

3.5 Multivariate fitting

We can also use LinEst, Regression, and LS (but *not* Trendline) to fit data as a linear function of several variables, say x, x^3, $\sqrt{z}$ and log t, as long as all the experimental imprecision is concentrated in y, and can be assumed to follow a single Gaussian distribution. Just make columns for the variables to which y is to be fitted. The various variables need not be independent; in fact, fitting to a polynomial can be considered as a special case of a multivariate (i.e., multi-variable) fit. LinEst, Regression, and LS all will accept multivariate fits in the same way as polynomial fits. Trendline cannot handle them since the graph has only one horizontal axis, and it therefore cannot to determine what the independent variables might be. As in all applications of least squares methods, the number of adjustable parameters should preferably be much smaller than the number of data points. Sections 3.6, 3.7 and 3.15 will illustrate such multivariate data fitting.

When using LinEst to fit data to a multivariate function (as with fitting data with LinEst to a polynomial, see section 3.1), make sure that you start with highlighting a block of sufficient width and, of course, use the block command Ctrl∪Shift∪Enter. Using two columns and five rows, as you would for fitting data to a proportionality or a straight line, will only display two coefficients. And since LinEst displays its coefficients in reverse order, fitting data to, e.g., $y = a_0 + a_1x_1 + a_2x_2 + a_3x_3$ and reserving a block of 5 rows and 2 columns would only show you the values for a_3 and a_2, without labeling them as such, or even warning you that this is not the whole story. There are no such problems with Regression and LS.

3.6 The infrared spectrum of $H^{35}Cl$

As our first example of multivariate least squares fitting we will use a set of frequencies of the infrared absorption spectrum of $H^{35}Cl$ vapor between 2500 and 3100 cm^{-1} (for the fundamental) and between 5400 and about 5800 cm^{-1} (for the first harmonic or overtone) as published by R. W. Schwenz & W. F. Polik in *J. Chem. Educ.* 76 (1999) 1302. The actual spectrum of HCl vapor consists of a set of doublets, due to the presence of about 24.5% naturally occurring ^{37}Cl; the corresponding lines are easily recognized by their lower intensities. These data can be fitted at two levels: that of the usual first-order approximations of a rigid rotor and a harmonic oscillator, and that of a more complete theory. We will here use the second approach since there is no good reason to oversimplify the mathematics when the spreadsheet can just as easily apply the more complete theoretical model.

Rotational-vibrational transitions are usually observable in the infrared part of the spectrum. The corresponding frequencies $E(v, J) / hc$ of a heteronuclear diatomic molecule such as HCl, which has a permanent dipole moment, are given by

$$E(v,J)/hc = \omega_e(v+1/2) + B_e J(J+1) - \omega_e x_e(v+1/2)^2$$
$$- D_e J^2(J+1)^2 - \alpha_e(v+1/2)J(J+1) \tag{3.6.1}$$

where $E(v, J)$ is the energy, v is the vibrational quantum number, J the rotational quantum number, h is Planck's constant, and c the speed of light in vacuum. The harmonic vibrational frequency $\overline{\omega_e}$ can again be expressed in terms of the force constant k and the reduced mass $\mu = 1 / (1/m_1 + 1/m_2)$ as $\overline{\omega_e} = (1/2\pi c)\sqrt{k/\mu}$, and the rotational constant $\overline{B_e}$ as $\overline{B_e} = h/8\pi^2 cI_e$ where $I_e = \mu r^2$ is the moment of inertia, r the bond distance, and m_1 and m_2 are the atomic mass of H and ^{35}Cl respectively. Finally, $\overline{\omega_e x_e}$ is the anharmonicity constant, and $\overline{D_e}$ the centrifugal distortion constant, while $\overline{\alpha_e}$ describes rotational-vibrational interactions. As in section 3.3, the bar indicates that the quantities involved are energies expressed in wavenumbers, so that, e.g., $\overline{\omega_e}$ is not misinterpreted as an angular frequency.

The lines in the absorption spectrum correspond to transitions between these energy states, i.e., to differences between the energy levels given by (3.6.1). In this case the observation does not involve an electronic transition (as in the preceding example of iodine vapor), and light absorption is now restricted by the selection rule $\Delta J = \pm 1$ (except for diatomic molecules with an odd number of electrons, such as NO). Moreover, room temperature observations are mostly restricted to transitions from the vibrational ground state $v = 0$ either to $v = 1$ (producing the fundamental) or to $v = 2$ (yielding the overtone).

The experimentally observed frequencies are listed in Table 1 of the paper by Schwenz & Polik, and can also be downloaded from their web site at http://www.chem.hope.edu/~polik/doc/hcl.xls. We will fit them to the expression

$$\overline{v} = [E(v',J') - E(v^\circ,J^\circ)]/hc = \overline{\omega_e}\left[(v'+1/2) - (v^\circ+1/2)\right] + \overline{B_e}\left[J'(J'+1) - J^\circ(J^\circ+1)\right]$$
$$- \overline{\omega_e x_e}\left[(v'+1/2)^2 - (v^\circ+1/2)^2\right] - \overline{D_e}\left[J'^2(J'+1)^2 - J^{\circ 2}(J^\circ+1)^2\right]$$
$$- \overline{\alpha_e}\left[(v'+1/2)J'(J'+1) - (v^\circ+1/2)J^\circ(J^\circ+1)\right] \tag{3.6.2}$$

where the zero and prime denote the lower-energy and higher-energy states of the particular transition respectively.

	A	B	C	D	E	F	G	H	I	J
1	v^o	v'	J^o	J'	nu	z1	z2	z3	z4	z5
2	0	1	0	1	2905.995	1	2	-2	-4	-3
3	0	1	1	2	2925.581	1	4	-2	-32	-8
4	0	1	2	3	2944.577	1	6	-2	-108	-15
5	0	1	3	4	2962.955	1	8	-2	-256	-24
6	0	1	4	5	2980.689	1	10	-2	-500	-35
7	0	1	5	6	2997.788	1	12	-2	-864	-48
8	0	1	6	7	3014.202	1	14	-2	-1372	-63
9	0	1	7	8	3029.941	1	16	-2	-2048	-80
10	0	1	8	9	3044.965	1	18	-2	-2916	-99
11	0	1	9	10	3059.234	1	20	-2	-4000	-120
12	0	1	10	11	3072.771	1	22	-2	-5324	-143
13	0	1	11	12	3085.600	1	24	-2	-6912	-168
14	0	1	12	13	3097.550	1	26	-2	-8788	-195
15	0	1	13	14	3108.914	1	28	-2	-10976	-224
16	0	1	14	15	3119.418	1	30	-2	-13500	-255
17	0	1	15	16	3129.099	1	32	-2	-16384	-288
18	0	1	1	0	2864.834	1	-2	-2	4	1
19	0	1	2	1	2843.315	1	-4	-2	32	0
20	0	1	3	2	2821.249	1	-6	-2	108	-3
21	0	1	4	3	2798.641	1	-8	-2	256	-8
22	0	1	5	4	2775.499	1	-10	-2	500	-15
23	0	1	6	5	2751.817	1	-12	-2	864	-24
24	0	1	7	6	2727.624	1	-14	-2	1372	-35
25	0	1	8	7	2702.907	1	-16	-2	2048	-48
26	0	1	9	8	2677.697	1	-18	-2	2916	-63
27	0	1	10	9	2651.932	1	-20	-2	4000	-80
28	0	1	11	10	2625.689	1	-22	-2	5324	-99
29	0	1	12	11	2598.979	1	-24	-2	6912	-120
30	0	1	13	12	2571.861	1	-26	-2	8788	-143
31	0	1	14	13	2544.220	1	-28	-2	10976	-168
32	0	1	15	14	2516.141	1	-30	-2	13500	-195
33	0	2	0	1	5687.494	2	2	-6	-4	-5
34	0	2	1	2	5705.926	2	4	-6	-32	-14
35	0	2	2	3	5723.158	2	6	-6	-108	-27
36	0	2	3	4	5739.109	2	8	-6	-256	-44
37	0	2	4	5	5753.793	2	10	-6	-500	-65
38	0	2	5	6	5767.262	2	12	-6	-864	-90

Fig. 3.6.1: The top part of a spreadsheet with the infrared spectral data on $H^{35}Cl$ vapor of Schwenz & Polik (columns A through E), containing the fundamental band. In order to display the calculation, some column widths have been adjusted.

#										
39	0	2	6	7	5779.441	2	14	-6	-1372	-119
40	0	2	7	8	5790.312	2	16	-6	-2048	-152
41	0	2	8	9	5799.833	2	18	-6	-2916	-189
42	0	2	9	10	5808.141	2	20	-6	-4000	-230
43	0	2	1	0	5646.969	2	-2	-6	4	1
44	0	2	2	1	5624.896	2	-4	-6	32	-2
45	0	2	3	2	5601.612	2	-6	-6	108	-9
46	0	2	4	3	5577.185	2	-8	-6	256	-20
47	0	2	5	4	5551.571	2	-10	-6	500	-35
48	0	2	6	5	5524.865	2	-12	-6	864	-54
49	0	2	7	6	5496.971	2	-14	-6	1372	-77
50	0	2	8	7	5467.968	2	-16	-6	2048	-104
51	0	2	9	8	5437.895	2	-18	-6	2916	-135
52			Coeff:	2989.281	10.58919	51.796	0.0005206	0.30167		
53			StDev:	0.034	0.00089	0.012	0.0000029	0.00010		
54			0.048							
55			CM:	0.0011548	2.975E-06	0.000384	9.23475E-10	1.83E-06		
56				2.975E-06	7.871E-07	9.58E-07	2.21736E-09	7.84E-09		
57				0.000384	9.578E-07	0.000132	7.74469E-10	4.96E-07		
58				9.235E-10	2.217E-09	7.74E-10	8.3649E-12	-3.09E-11		
59				1.827E-06	7.842E-09	4.96E-07	-3.0883E-11	9.63E-09		

Fig. 3.6.2: The bottom part of a spreadsheet with the infrared spectral data on $H^{35}Cl$ vapor of Schwenz & Polik (columns A through E), containing the overtone data as well as the results obtained with the macro LS0.

Equation (3.6.2) can be rewritten in a compact form suitable for multivariate least squares as

$$\overline{y} = \overline{\omega_e} z_1 + \overline{B_e} z_2 + \overline{\omega_e x_e} z_3 + \overline{D_e} z_4 + \overline{\alpha_e} z_5 \tag{3.6.3}$$

where

$$\overline{y} = [E(v',J') - E(v^\circ, J^\circ)]/hc \tag{3.6.4}$$

and

$$z_1 = (v'+1/2) - (v^\circ + 1/2) \tag{3.6.5}$$

$$z_2 = J'(J'+1) - J^\circ(J^\circ + 1) \tag{3.6.6}$$

$$z_3 = -(v'+1/2)^2 + (v^\circ + 1/2)^2 \tag{3.6.7}$$

$$z_4 = -J'^2(J'+1)^2 + J^{\circ 2}(J^\circ + 1)^2 \tag{3.6.8}$$

$$z_5 = -(v'+1/2)J'(J'+1) + (v^\circ + 1/2)J^\circ(J^\circ + 1) \tag{3.6.9}$$

The experimental data for $\overline{y} = [E(v',J') - E(v^\circ, J^\circ)]/hc$ are given as a function of the (readily assigned) quantum numbers v°, v', J°, and J', so that the functions z_i are all known. The problem therefore reduces to finding the five unknown parameters $\overline{\omega_e}$, $\overline{B_e}$, $\overline{\omega_e x_e}$, $\overline{D_e}$, and $\overline{\alpha_e}$, a situation tailor-made for fitting with a multivariate linear least squares routine. Note that we must treat the product $\omega_e x_e$ as an independent parameter, otherwise the problem is no longer linear in the fitting parameters.

Exercise 3.6.1:

(1) In a spreadsheet, enter the data as provided in the above-mentioned paper or web site, in five adjacent columns for v^ρ, v', J°, J', and $(E' - E^\circ)/hc$ respectively.

(2) Enter five more columns, for z_1 through z_5 respectively, in which you calculate these functions using the relations given in (3.6.5) through (3.6.9).

(3) Highlight the columns for $(E'-E°)/hc$ and z_1 through z_5, and call LS0. This will provide you with the values and standard deviations in ω_e, B_e, $\omega_e x_e$, D_e, and α_e. Also display the covariance matrix, which you will need in order to compute x_e as $\omega_e x_e / \omega_e$, which are of course strongly correlated (with, in this case, a linear correlation coefficient of 0.982). Your spreadsheet should now resemble Figs. 3.6.1 and 3.6.2.

These results can of course be used to compute the bond distance $r = \sqrt{(h/8\pi^2 B_e c\mu)}$ and to fit a potential-energy surface. They can also be compared, e.g., with similar data (from the same source) for $D^{35}Cl$, as reported in table 1 of P. Ogren, B. Davis & N. Guy, *J. Chem. Educ.* 78 (2001) 827. By relegating the mechanics of curve fitting to the spreadsheet, the researcher can focus on the interpretation and further uses of the extracted information.

3.7 Spectral mixture analysis

Figure 3.7 illustrates the absorption spectra of four fantasy species, made of one or more Gaussian peaks, and of an imaginary mixture made of these species. The spectral peaks were simulated as $a \exp[-(x-c)^2/(2b^2)]$; instead of the exponential part you can also use the instruction =NormDist(x, *mean*, *stdev*, *false*) to generate Gaussian curves $\left(1/\sigma\sqrt{2\pi}\right)\exp\left[-(x-\bar{x})^2/2\sigma^2\right]$ where $\bar{x}$ is the mean (locating the position of the peak center), σ the standard deviation (defining its width), and where 'false' specifies the Gaussian curve rather than its integral. In exercise 3.7.1 we simulate such spectra, compute the spectrum of a mixture of these components (assuming their additivity, as in Beer's law, and the absence of other light-absorbing species), add different noise to each simulated data point, then use multivariate analysis to reconstruct the composition of that mixture.

Exercise 3.7.1:

(1) In column A deposit wavelengths, and in columns B through E calculate four fantasy spectra, each with one or more Gaussian peaks. Each Gaussian peak requires three constants: an amplitude a, a standard deviation b or σ, and a center frequency c or mean $\bar{x}$.

(2) In columns M through Q generate random Gaussian ('normal') noise, and in columns H through K make somewhat noisy single-component spectra by adding some noise from column N to the spectrum of column B, etc., in order to create more realistic single-species spectra.

(3) Near the top of the spreadsheet enter four concentrations, and use these in column G to make a synthetic 'mixture spectrum' of the four single-component spectra, each multiplied by its assigned concentration, plus added noise from column M. (You could do without columns B through E by adding noise directly to the data in columns B through E, and then subtracting that same noise from the mixture spectrum. Noise in the single-component spectra and in the spectrum of the simulated mixture should of course be independent.)

(4) Plot the spectra of columns G through K, which might now look like those in Fig. 3.7.1. Note that the resulting curve does not show distinct features easily identifiable with any of its constituent spectra. In this particular example we have used the data of Table 3.7.1, together with noise standard deviations of 0.005 for all components as well as for the synthetic mixture. You should of course use your own data to convince yourself that this is no stacked deck.

(5) Highlight the data block in columns G through K, and call LS0 for a multivariate analysis of the mixture spectrum in terms of its four component spectra.

The results of that analysis are shown in Table 3.7.2. Despite the added noise, the absence of stark features, and considerable overlap between the various single-component spectra, the composition of the mixture is recovered quite well.

It is sometimes advocated to analyze mixtures of a few components by taking one dominant point per component, typically its absorption at λ_{max}, and solving the resulting matrix expression. That method cannot discriminate between signal and noise, and has no mechanism to assign statistical estimates for its numerical results either, and its use should therefore be discouraged.

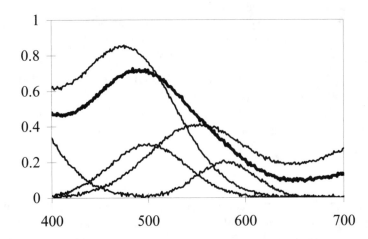

Fig. 3.7.1: The simulated single-component spectra (thin lines) and the spectrum of their mixture (heavy line). The simulation parameters used, as well as the composition of the mixture and the results of its analysis, are listed in Tables 3.7.1 and 3.7.2. Independent Gaussian noise (mean 0, st. dev. 0.005) has been added to all curves.

	ampl:	*mean:*	*st.dev.:*		*ampl:*	*mean:*	*st.dev.:*
curve 1:	300	270	80	*curve 3*:	30	500	40
	100	480	50	*curve 4*:	200	300	60
curve 2:	50	550	50		15	580	30
	70	760	80				

Table 3.7.1: The constants for the Gaussian peaks used in generating Fig. 3.7.1 with the function `NormDist()`.

	curve 1	*curve 2*	*curve 3*	*curve 4*
mixture composition:	0.650	0.500	0.300	0.200
recovered:	0.648±0.003	0.496±0.003	0.305±0.011	0.207±0.007

Table 3.7.2: The assumed and recovered composition of the synthetic mixture.

The above method is simple and quite general, as long as spectra of all mixture constituents are available. In the analysis you can include spectra of species that do not participate in the mixture: for those species, the calculation will simply yield near-zero contributions. However, a missing constituent spectrum will cause the method to fail if its contribution to the mixture spectrum is significant.

A final note: the numbers obtained for the recovered composition are mutually dependent. When a subsequent result depends on more than one concentration, the covariance matrix should be used in its computation, rather than the individual standard deviations.

3.8 How many adjustable parameters?

Now that it has become so easy to fit data to a polynomial, such as a power series in x, one might be tempted to throw in more terms, on the (mistaken) assumption that 'the more terms, the better the fit'. Ultimately this will defeat the noise-reducing purpose of least squares, since we can fit N data points *exactly* (including all noise) to a polynomial of order $N-1$ (with its N coefficients a_0 through a_{N-1}). Moreover, we would then have replaced N experimental y-values with the same number N of fitting parameters, defeating the data-reduction purpose of least squares as well.

Long before we reach such an extreme situation, we may already include statistically meaningless terms. We therefore ask whether there is an optimal polynomial degree, and if so, how it can be determined. And because the least squares method is about data reduction while simultaneously filtering out as much noise as possible, the answer cannot be based solely on the exactitude of the fit. Ideally, theory should be our guide in selecting the model to which to fit the data. Often, however, we lack sufficient theoretical guidance, in which case decisions such as the optimal length of a power series must be made on the basis of statistical information inherent in the data. In sections 3.9 through 3.14 we will address that problem.

In many cases we do have theoretical models to guide us in deciding what function to use in fitting experimental data. We did just that with the vapor-phase spectra of I_2 (section 3.3) and $H^{35}Cl$ (section 3.6). However, even when a reliable theory is available, matters are not always that simple. For instance, Ohm's law requires that we use $V = IR$ without a constant, because (short of making a perpetual motion machine) we cannot have a current I without a driving force V. But the *measurement* might still show a non-zero intercept if the meter had not been zeroed properly, in which case we might indeed want to fit the data to the line $V = V_{offset} + IR$. Such possible sources of systematic error are best avoided at the time of measurement, through careful calibration, rather than corrected later, but that is of little help once the experiment has been performed.

Back to the main question of this section: what do we do when we have no theory to guide us? In that case we may want to use a polynomial such as the power series $y = a_0 + a_1x + a_2x^2 + a_3x^3 + \ldots + a_mx^m$ as a rather general-purpose fitting function, but then we will need some criterion to help us decide what the order m of that polynomial should be. (It is sometimes claimed that, with enough high-order terms, one could draw an elephant, but that is bull.) There are several such criteria, none infallible, of which we will here illustrate three. While such criteria can guide us, they do not always yield identical answers. Consequently, individual judgment is still called for.

Before we use a power series in x without theoretical guidance, we must first mention two caveats. (1) The over-all trend of the experimental data should be representable in terms of the model used. For many functions, such as sine waves, an expansion in terms of a power series in x would be rather inefficient; for others, e.g., for points that lie approximately on a circle, such a power series would be totally inadequate. (2) Absent theoretical guidance, the information on the optimal order of the polynomial must be extracted from the data themselves. Since random noise can be of no help in this respect, we can only hope for reasonable success when the signal-to-noise ratio is sufficiently large. When the signal-to-noise ratio is too small, such methods must fail. (There are methods available to pull a small signal from a large amount of noise, such as synchronous detection ("lock-in" amplification) or boxcar amplification, but these require additional information on the nature of the signal, and typically must be built into the instrumentation used. These methods therefore cannot be used afterwards with already existing experimental data.)

3.9 Criteria based on the standard deviation

Least squares analysis produces two different types of standard deviations: one standard deviation s_i for each of the i parameters a_i of the model used, and one standard deviation, s_f, for the overall fit of that model to the data. These are useful quantities, which can be exploited to help us decide whether a particular, empirical model is inappropriate.

First we look at the standard deviations s_i of the individual coefficients a_i. Since s_i is always positive, regardless of the sign of a_i, we consider the absolute value of their ratio $|a_i/s_i|$. When $|a_i/s_i| \leq 1$, the signal is drowned out by its random noise, and a_i must be considered statistically insignificant. Even when $|a_i/s_i|$ is less than, say, 2 or 3, a_i might be of rather dubious statistical significance. (For a small sample size, you might want to multiply s_i by the Student t, which would make the criterion more restrictive.) This simple and readily available criterion is often our best first line of defense against an excess of model parameters, and recent versions of LS use color coding to alert the user to such possible signs of trouble.

A second criterion to judge the entire model can be based on the standard deviation s_f of the fit of the function to the data, or its square, the variance v_{ff}, by selecting that polynomial for which s_f (or v_{ff}) is minimal. Because $v_{ff} = (\Sigma\Delta^2)/(N-P)$, where the residual Δ is given by $y-y_{model}$, and P denotes the number of model parameters used to describe y_{model}, v_{ff} (and likewise s_f) should continually decrease with increasing polynomial order P, even when the added parameters are useless, since at worst $\Sigma\Delta^2$ remains constant, while $N-P$ increases. But if unnecessary higher-order terms are included in a polynomial model, the corresponding matrices increase in size, and so do the numerical errors in manipulating those matrices. This often results in the appearance of one or more minima in a plot of s_f vs. polynomial order. Assuming that the polynomial represents a rapidly converging series expansion, we might then want to truncate it at the first local minimum in a plot of s_f vs. m. This criterion should be used with care, because it applies to the overall fit, and is therefore not very selective. Moreover, it is easy to find examples where it might lead us astray, e.g., when the underlying function is odd or even, so that its series expansion contains only alternate powers of x.

In order to find the minimal value of s_f we can use LinEst, Regression, or LS repeatedly, gradually increasing the order of the polynomial, each time extracting the corresponding value of s_f. Collecting those values, we can then make our choice of polynomial if s_f indeed goes through a minimum. This would be a rather tedious process, but since we have a computer at our fingertips, and the above protocol is eminently suitable for automation, we will use a custom macro, LSPoly, for that purpose. It yields s_f-values together with the individual fitting coefficients a_i and their standard deviations s_i, see sections 3.13 and 3.14. For multivariate models a similar approach, based on the custom macro GradeBySf, will be illustrated in section 3.15. And if you want to modify any of these custom macros to your own liking (e.g., by incorporating the Student t in the color-coding of the output of LS), go ahead – these macros are open access for the very reason of allowing you to adapt them to your needs.

3.10 The F-test

A second, closely related approach is based on the *F*-test, named after one of its originators, R. A. Fisher. It likewise considers the variance v_{yy} of the entire fit. In the power series $y = a_0 + a_1x + a_2x^2 + a_3x^3 + \ldots + a_px^p$ the number of parameters used to define the polynomial is $p+1$, because there are $p+1$ terms, from a_0x^0 through a_px^p, so that the number of degrees of freedom is $N-p-1$. (If we were to leave out the constant term a_0, we would instead have $N-p$ degrees of freedom.)

The *F*-test, which in Excel can be computed with the function =FINV(criterion,df1,df2), requires the user to select a *criterion* for the acceptable probability α (expressed as a decimal fraction, such as 0.05 for 5%), while *df1* and *df2* denote the degrees of freedom of the two fitting functions that are being compared. The most commonly used α-values are 0.05 (i.e., 5%) and 0.01 (1%).

An application of the *F*-test to evaluate the usefulness of extending a polynomial fit of N data points from order p to order q (with $q > p$) involves comparing the ratio

$$F_{q,p} = \frac{(\Sigma\Delta_p^2 - \Sigma\Delta_q^2)/(q-p)}{\Sigma\Delta_q^2/(N-q-1)} = \frac{(N-p-1)(v_{pp}/v_{qq})-(N-q-1)}{(q-p)} \tag{3.10.1}$$

where $v_{pp} = \Sigma\Delta_p^2/(N-p-1)$ and $v_{qq} = \Sigma\Delta_q^2/(N-q-1)$, with the *F*-test $F(\alpha, q-p, N-q-1)$ in

$$FR\alpha = \frac{F_{q,p}}{F(\alpha,q-p,N-q-1)} = \frac{(N-p-1)(\Sigma\Delta_p^2/\Sigma\Delta_q^2-1)}{(q-p)\,F(\alpha,q-p,N-q-1)}$$

$$= \frac{(N-p-1)(v_{pp}/v_{qq})-(N-q-1)}{(q-p)\,F(\alpha,q-p,N-q-1)} \tag{3.10.2}$$

If *FR*α is substantially larger than 1, the additional terms up to q can be considered to be statistically significant *at the chosen value of α*. Note that $q–p$ is the *difference* between the degrees of freedom of the two fits, and that this method can only be applied for $q < N–1$. We typically apply (3.10.1) with $q = p+1$ although, especially when dealing with symmetrical functions, it may be useful to consider $q = p+2$ as well. The above result applies to the general polynomial $y = a_0 + a_1x + a_2x^2 + a_3x^3 + \ldots + a_px^p$. For the polynomial $y = a_1x + a_2x^2 + a_3x^3 + \ldots + a_px^p$ through the origin we have instead

$$FR\alpha = \frac{F_{q,p}}{F(\alpha, q-p, N-q)} = \frac{(N-p)\,(v_{pp}/v_{qq}) - (N-q)}{(q-p)\,F(\alpha, q-p, N-q)}$$

(3.10.3)

where $v_{pp} = \Sigma\Delta_p^2/(N-p)$ and $v_{qq} = \Sigma\Delta_q^2/(N-q)$.

The custom macro LSPoly1 displays both s_f and two values of $FR\alpha$ as defined in (3.10.2), for $q = p+1$ with $\alpha = 0.05$ and 0.01 respectively. Likewise, LSPoly0 incorporates s_f and two $FR\alpha$-values based on (3.10.3). For an added term to be included within a given probability (5% for $FR5$, 1% for $FR1$), its F-ratio should be larger than 1, preferably by at least a factor of 3. If desired, $FR\alpha$-values for $q = p+2$ can also be incorporated in those custom macros.

3.11 Orthogonal polynomials

In fitting data to a straight line, the covariance can be made to disappear by fitting to $y = a_0' + a_1(x–x_{av})$ instead of to $y = a_0 + a_1x$, i.e., by using a function of x (in this case $x–x_{av}$) rather than x itself. This principle can be extended to least-squares fitting to a power series such as $y = a_0 + a_1x + a_2x^2 + a_3x^3 + \ldots + a_mx^m$, or to multivariate fitting as in $y = a_0 + a_xx + a_zz + \ldots$, and requires that we use *orthogonal polynomials*. Making the covariances zero makes the fitting coefficients mutually independent, so that they can be computed one at a time, and can then be evaluated individually for statistical significance. In principle this would seem to be the optimal way to determine at what term to terminate a power series. In practice there are several constraints.

(1) In general, finding orthogonal polynomials can be rather laborious, because such polynomials must be constructed anew for every data set, on the basis of its individual x-values. We already encountered this in centering: the quantity $(x–x_{av})$ depends on all x-values in the data set. For equidistant data this complication is relatively minor, because the sought polynomials then are the readily computed *Gram polynomials*, which depend only on the number N of data points in the set, on the order j of the polynomial, and on the average x-value x_{av}. At any rate, being laborious is no valid excuse when macros can take care of the busywork. We therefore provide two custom macros, Ortho0 and Ortho1, to compute orthogonal polynomials for finite sets of x-values. Ortho0 should be used for curves that go through the origin, whereas the intercept of curves fitted by Ortho1 is not constrained. The x-values need not be equidistant.

(2) A particular set of orthogonal polynomials corresponds to a particular power series or other parametric expression, e.g., the orthogonal polynomials of order j considered below will be linear combinations of x^0, x^1, x^2, x^3, …, x^j. Note that the data fit obtained with orthogonal polynomials is no better than that obtained with the corresponding power series or parametric expression, and in fact is entirely equivalent. The advantage of using orthogonal polynomials is that they provide mutually independent fitting coefficients, which can be tested for statistical relevance. Since the coefficients are mutually independent, their covariances are zero, which may be convenient to simplify the propagation of experimental imprecision through subsequent calculations.

(3) The method indeed works beautifully for noise-free data but, as with any other statistical method, can be overwhelmed by too much noise. This is, of course, nothing new: statistical data analysis always labors under the constraint that the validity of the analysis is questionable when the quality of the input data is insufficient. This is summarized succinctly in the expression "garbage in, garbage out".

(4) The orthogonal polynomials found can be used directly to represent the analyzed data, but their conversion back to, say, a power series in x is not quite so straightforward.

(5) The orthogonal polynomials discussed here are constructed one column at a time, moving from left to right. Because the order of the various columns can affect the output, all its positional permutations must be considered when it is used as a rejection criterion.

But enough provisos already. *Orthogonal* polynomials are defined as polynomials that have mutually independent (i.e., uncorrelated) coefficients. Specifically, a set of polynomials $P_j(x)$ is orthogonal if

$$\sum_i P_j(x_i)\,P_k(x_i) = 0 \quad \text{for } j \neq k \tag{3.11.1}$$

$$\sum_i P_j(x_i)\,P_k(x_i) \neq 0 \quad \text{for } j = k \tag{3.11.2}$$

Expressing an unknown function in terms of orthogonal polynomials $y = p_0 + p_1 P_1(x) + p_2 P_2(x) + p_3 P_3(x) + \ldots + p_m P_m(x)$ instead of as a power series $y = a_0 + a_1 x + a_2 x^2 + a_3 x^3 + \ldots + a_m x^m$ involves the same number $m+1$ of terms, with the polynomial $P_j(x)$ containing terms in x up to and including x^j. As already indicated, an advantage of expressing y in terms of orthogonal polynomials $P_j(x)$ instead of as a direct power series in x is that the resulting coefficients p_j are mutually independent. In going from, say, a quadratic to a cubic, we need not recalculate the coefficients p_0 through p_2 because these remain the same, so that we only have to compute the added coefficient p_3. Moreover, we can test whether p_3 is statistically significant by comparing its absolute magnitude with, e.g., its standard deviation and/or the numerical imprecision of the computation. If p_3 passes that test, we can increase the order of the polynomial by 1, repeat the procedure by testing p_4, etc. In other words, orthogonal polynomials allow us to approach data fitting as a problem of successive approximation, including a termination criterion. This method therefore satisfies the intuitive notion of testing each added term for its statistically significance.

Fitting a set of data to the function $y = p_0 + p_1 P_1(x) + p_2 P_2(x) + p_3 P_3(x) + \ldots + p_m P_m(x)$ yields the various coefficients p_j. Because these p_j are mutually independent, multiplying a given term $P_j(x)$ by a constant λ_j will only affect the corresponding coefficient p_j, because $(p_j/\lambda_j) \times \lambda_j P_j(x) = p_j P_j(x)$. Consequently, orthogonal polynomials can be defined with arbitrary scale factors λ_j. This has led to various normalizing schemes. The resulting multitude of equivalent expressions, differing only by order-dependent constants λ_j, can be quite confusing to the novice.

The custom macro Ortho works for all situations to which LS can be applied, since it does not rely on a fixed formula for the orthogonal polynomials but, instead, computes these for any data set by Gram-Schmidt orthogonalization.

In order to illustrate how orthogonal polynomials work we will here illustrate them for data that are equidistant in the independent variable x, in which case the resulting *Gram polynomials* (J. P. Gram, *J. reine angew. Math.* 94 (1883) 21) take on a rather simple form. As our example we will consider fitting data to the power series $y = a_0 + a_1 x + a_2 x^2 + a_3 x^3 + \ldots + a_m x^m$, which can be represented by the corresponding set of Gram polynomials $G_j(x)$, i.e., $y = g_0 + g_1 G_1(x) + g_2 G_2(x) + g_3 G_3(x) + \ldots + g_m G_m(x)$ with coefficients g_j. The first two Gram polynomials are

$$G_0(x)/\lambda_0 = 1 \tag{3.11.3}$$

$$G_1(x)/\lambda_1 = \xi \tag{3.11.4}$$

with the compact notation $\xi = (x - x_{av})/d$, where $d = \Delta x$ is the distance between adjacent x-values, and λ_j is an arbitrary constant for the Gram polynomial G_j. Typically, both λ_0 and λ_1 are set equal to 1, but no dominant convention has yet emerged for $\lambda_{j>1}$. For a set of N data points, additional polynomials G_j can then be computed with the recursion formula

$$G_{j+1}(x) = \xi\, G_j(x) - \frac{j^2\,(N^2 - j^2)}{4\,(4j^2 - 1)}\, G_{j-1}(x) \tag{3.11.5}$$

so that (for $\lambda_0 = \lambda_1 = 1$) the next few terms are

$$G_2(x)/\lambda_2 = \xi^2 - \frac{(N^2 - 1)}{12} \tag{3.11.6}$$

$$G_3(x)/\lambda_3 = \xi^3 - \frac{(3N^2 - 7)}{20}\,\xi \tag{3.11.7}$$

$$G_4(x)/\lambda_4 = \xi^4 - \frac{(3N^2 - 13)}{14}\,\xi^2 + \frac{3\,(N^2 - 1)\,(N^2 - 9)}{560} \tag{3.11.8}$$

$$G_5(x)/\lambda_5 = \xi^5 - \frac{5\,(N^2 - 7)}{18}\,\xi^3 + \frac{(15N^4 - 230N^2 + 407)}{1008}\,\xi \tag{3.11.9}$$

$$G_6(x)/\lambda_6 = \xi^6 - \frac{5\,(3N^2 - 31)}{44}\,\xi^4 + \frac{(5N^4 - 110N^2 - 329)}{176}\,\xi^2$$
$$- \frac{5\,(N^2 - 1)\,(N^2 - 9)\,(N^2 - 25)}{14784} \tag{3.11.10}$$

We note that $G_1(x) = \xi = (x - x_{av})/d$, so that centering is indeed equivalent to fitting data to a Gram polynomial of order 1. Since $G_0(x) = 1$, the above polynomials pertain to a power series with arbitrary intercept. For a curve through the origin a different set of Gram functions is obtained, as is readily verified with the custom macro Ortho0.

3.12 Imprecision contours, once more

In section 2.11 we saw how to draw imprecision contours around a straight line, providing the graph with some visual imprecision estimates. With the tools now at hand we can extend this approach to power series of the type $y = a_0 + a_1 x + a_2 x^2 + a_3 x^3 + \ldots + a_m x^m$. Upon their transformation into the orthogonal power series $y = p_0 + p_1 P_1(x) + p_2 P_2(x) + p_3 P_3(x) + \ldots + p_m P_m(x)$ these can be fitted by least squares to find the coefficients p_j and the corresponding standard deviations s_j. We now generalize (2.11.1) to

$$s_c = \sqrt{s_f^2 + s_0^2 P_0^2 + s_1^2 P_1^2 + \ldots + s_m^2 P_m^2} = \sqrt{s_f^2 + \sum_{j=0}^{m} s_j^2 P_j^2} \tag{3.12.1}$$

For a straight line, $j = 1$, $P_0 = 1$ and $P_1 = x - x_{av}$, so that (3.12.1) indeed reduces to (2.11.1). Since the custom macro Ortho1 provides both P_j and s_j, application of (3.12.1) is rather straightforward, as illustrated in exercise 3.12.1 for the data shown in Fig. 3.2.1. For curves through the origin, j in (3.12.1) should run from 1 to m.

Exercise 3.12.1:

(1) Return to exercise 3.2.1, or make a new data set along similar lines. The instructions below will assume the format of Fig. 3.2.1, and may need modification if you make your own data set.

(2) Highlight the data block A15:C27, and call Ortho1, which skips one column and will therefore leave the data in D15:D27 intact. Label the data in columns E through G with headings for y, P_1, and P_2 respectively.

(3) Because the increments in x are constant, the input data are equidistant, so that Ortho1 generates Gram polynomials. Verify that column F indeed shows $\xi = (x - x_{av})/d$ with $d = 1$ for the increment Δx, and that column G contains $\xi^2 - (N^2 - 1)/12$ where $N = 13$, the number of data points used, see (3.11.6).

(4) In column H, under a second label y_{calc}, verify that you obtain the very same answers as in column D when using the coefficients p_0, p_1, and p_2 shown in E28:G28. In other words, the instruction =$E$28+$F$28*F15+$G$28*G15 in cell H15 will reproduce the value in cell D15, etc.

(5) In column I calculate s_c according to (3.12.1), and in columns J and K compute $y_{calc}-s_c$ and $y_{calc}+s_c$ respectively. The value of s_f can be found in cell E31, those of s_0, s_1, and s_2 in cells E29 through G29 respectively.

(6) Plot the data in columns H, J, and K vs. those in column B, together with the individual data points, see Fig. 3.12.1.

(7) To keep matters in perspective (and keep you humble), also calculate and plot (in a different color) the function $y = -10 + 8x - 0.7x^2$ that was the starting point for the data in Fig. 3.2.1.

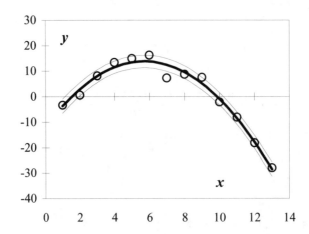

Fig. 3.12.1: The data of Fig. 3.2.1 with imprecision contours at ± one standard deviation s_c.

We can also find the imprecision contours from the usual series expression for y, as long as we have access to the corresponding covariance matrix. In that case we must use

$$s_c = \sqrt{s_f^2 + \sum_{j=0}^{m} \sum_{k=0}^{m} v_{jk} x_i^j x_i^k} \tag{3.12.2}$$

instead of (3.12.1) or, for a multivariate analysis,

$$s_c = \sqrt{s_f^2 + \sum_{j=0}^{m} \sum_{k=0}^{m} v_{jk} x_{ji} x_{ki}} \tag{3.12.3}$$

where x_{ji} denotes the value of x_j for observation i. For curves where $a_0 \equiv 0$, the indices j and k should start at 1. Again, for confidence contours, multiply s_c in expressions such as (3.12.1) through (3.12.3) by $\sqrt{\{F(\alpha, 1, N-P)\}}$. For $N-P \geq 10$, $F(1/3, 1, N-P) \approx 1$, i.e., ± one standard deviation corresponds roughly with a confidence level $1-\alpha$ of 2/3.

3.13 Gas-chromatographic analysis of ethanol

As our first example we will use a small data set provided by Leary & Messick, *Anal. Chem.* 57 (1985) 956, who reported the observations listed in Table 3.13.1 for the peak area fraction in a gas chromatogram due to ethanol, as a function of the ethanol content (in volume %) of an injected ethanol-water mixture.

$x =$	10	20	30	40	50	60	70	80	90	*vol%*
$y =$	8.16	15.9	22.7	31.5	39.8	49.4	59.7	70.6	83.6	*area%*

Table 3.13.1: The relative peak area y due to ethanol, in area%, as a function of the volume fraction x of the injected sample, in volume%.

Theoretically these data should fit a straight line that, if extended, would pass through the points (0,0) and (100,100). (How to force a least squares program to do that will be illustrated in section 4.9.) Unfortunately, a plot of y vs. x will show that the data exhibit a clearly nonlinear trend. We do not know what causes this trend, nor do we know whether a power series would be an appropriate model. The following exercise is simply that: an exercise in finding the optimal fit of these data *assuming* that they can be represented meaningfully by a power series. We use this example because it contains equidistant data points, so that we can illustrate the application of orthogonal polynomials at its simplest level, with closed-form solutions of the type shown in section 3.11. We will use Gram polynomials to check the data for nonlinearity.

Exercise 3.13.1:

(1) In a spreadsheet deposit the values for x and y respectively from Table 3.12.1. In column A deposit x, and in column B the corresponding values of y. In column C calculate $G_1 = \xi = (x-x_{av})/d$, i.e., -4 (1) 4 ($= -4, -3, -2, -1, 0, 1, 2, 3, 4$) because $x_{av} = 50$ and $d = 10$. Finally, in columns D through G calculate the polynomials G_2, G_3, G_4, and G_5 using (3.11.6) through (3.11.8), as in Fig. 3.13.1.

(2) Highlight the data in columns B and C, and call LS1, which will calculate the fit to a first-order Gram polynomial. Condense the output by overwriting the label *st. dev.:* with s_f, then save the results by moving them at least three rows down. Repeat LS1, each time including one more column to the right as input to LS1, and arrange the results in tabular form, as in Fig. 3.13.2.

(3) For each application of LS1, display the corresponding covariance matrix, and verify that it only contains significant values on its main diagonal; all off-diagonal terms should be zero except for computer round-off errors.

	A	B	C	D	E	F	G
1	x	y	$G1/\lambda 1$	$G2/\lambda 2$	$G3/\lambda 3$	$G4/\lambda 4$	$G5/\lambda 5$
2							
3	10	8.16	-4	9.333	-16.800	24.000	-26.667
4	20	15.9	-3	2.333	8.400	-36.000	73.333
5	30	22.7	-2	-2.667	15.600	-18.857	-26.667
6	40	31.5	-1	-5.667	10.800	15.429	-60.000
7	50	39.8	0	-6.667	0.000	30.857	0.000
8	60	49.4	1	-5.667	-10.800	15.429	60.000
9	70	59.7	2	-2.667	-15.600	-18.857	26.667
10	80	70.6	3	2.333	-8.400	-36.000	-73.333
11	90	83.6	4	9.333	16.800	24.000	26.667

Fig. 3.13.1: The analysis of the data in Table 3.13.1 in terms of Gram polynomials.

(4) The most significant aspect of Fig. 3.13.2 is that the coefficients g_j obtained at lower polynomial order are not changed when higher-order polynomials are included in the data analysis. For G_0 through G_3 the (absolute magnitudes of the) corresponding coefficients g_j clearly exceed the corresponding standard deviations s_i, i.e., they are statistically significant. However, this is not the case for the next coefficients, 0.018 and 0.0029, and we can use this as a criterion for determining the optimal polynomial order. In terms of an integer power series in x, the data in Table 3.13.1 are therefore best represented by a third-order polynomial.

(5) Because G_1 is simply the average value of x, the data in Fig. 3.13.2 do *not* indicate whether they are best represented with or without a term a_0. For this we now use LSPoly0 and LSPoly1, see Figs. 3.13.3 and 3.13.4. (Note that this requires interchanging the columns for x and y.)

(6) We first note that the values for s_f in Figs. 3.13.2 and 3.13.4 are the same. These s_f values show a first minimum at order 3, as does LSPoly0 in Fig. 3.13.3. For LSPoly0, both F-ratios ($FR5$ and $FR1$, representing $\alpha = 0.05$ and 0.01 respectively) clearly exceed unity for the second and third orders, and drop to well below 1 at order 4. For LSPoly1, the result for the third-order F-ratios is more ambiguous, and depends on the value of α, with $FR5 > 1$, $FR1 < 1$. Note that s_f, $FR5$, or $FR1$ are all non-monotonic functions of polynomial order.

(7) Where does all this lead us? The orthogonal polynomials suggest that we use terms up to and including x^3; at higher polynomial order, the standard deviations s_i are of the same order of magnitude as the corresponding coefficients a_i.

(8) Representing the data of Table 3.13.1 as a cubic power series through the origin, $y = a_1x + a_2x^2 + a_3x^3$ with $a_1 = 0.79_9 \pm 0.02_2$, $a_2 = (-1.8_2 \pm 0.7_2) \times 10^{-3}$, and $a_3 = (3.6_1 \pm 0.5_6) \times 10^{-5}$, is clearly supported by all the above criteria, and leads to coefficients a_i that are all much larger than the corresponding imprecisions s_i.

	term 0	term 1	term 2	term 3	term 4	term 5
Coeff.:	**42.37**	**9.296**				
2.52	*0.84*	*0.325*				
Coeff.:	**42.37**	**9.296**	**0.373**			
0.51	*0.17*	*0.066*	*0.029*			
Coeff.:	**42.37**	**9.296**	**0.373**	**0.0262**		
0.34	*0.11*	*0.044*	*0.019*	*0.0090*		
Coeff.:	**42.37**	**9.296**	**0.373**	**0.0262**	**0.0018**	
0.37	*0.12*	*0.048*	*0.021*	*0.0099*	*0.0049*	
Coeff.:	**42.37**	**9.296**	**0.373**	**0.0262**	**0.0018**	**0.0029**
0.35	*0.12*	*0.046*	*0.020*	*0.0094*	*0.0046*	*0.0025*

Fig. 3.13.2: The results of applying LS1 to the data in Fig. 3.13.1. The bold numbers directly below the *Coeff.* labels are the standard deviations of the fit, s_f.

(9) On the other hand, a fit of the same data in terms of the general cubic expression $y = a_0 + a_1 x + a_2 x^2 + a_3 x^3$ is much less successful, as is best seen when we consider the resulting coefficients, $a_0 = 0.9_9 \pm 0.7_3$, $a_1 = 0.72_3 \pm 0.06_0$, $a_2 = (-0.2_1 \pm 1.3_6) \times 10^{-3}$, and $a_3 = (2.6_2 \pm 0.9_0) \times 10^{-5}$, where a_0 is only marginally significant, and a_2 is not significant at all.

(10) Incidentally, this conclusion differs from that reached by L. M. Schwartz, *Anal. Chem.* 58 (1986) 246, who considered neither the ratios of the individual coefficients and their standard deviations, nor the possibility of a curve through the origin.

(11) For equidistant data, the orthogonal polynomials can be written in terms of simple integers. Verify that this is indeed the case in the spreadsheet of Fig. 3.13.1 by multiplying G_2 by 3, G_3 by 5 (or, if you want to make these integers as small as possible, by 5/6), G_4 by 7 (or 7/12), and G_5 by 3 (or 3/20). Another common way to standardize these polynomials is to divide all polynomials of given order j by the value of that polynomial at its last data point, at $i = N$. In that case all polynomials will alternately start (for $i = 1$) with either 1 (for even values of j) or –1 (for odd j).

(12) The above illustrates both the advantages and limitations of fitting data to a power series. The method does *not* tell us whether a power series expansion is appropriate, but if it is, we can use orthogonal polynomials to determine how many terms to include. Whether that power series should include a constant term $a0$ is a separate question that we have here answered using LSPoly0 and LSPoly1.

Order 1 *term 1*					*Sf:* 3.088	
Coeff.: 8.648					*FR5:* N/A	
St.Dev.: 0.183					*FR1:* N/A	
Order 2 *term 1*	*term 2*				*Sf:* 0.936	
Coeff.: 6.712	0.272				*FR5:* 14.301	
St.Dev.: 0.223	0.030				*FR1:* 6.530	
Order 3 *term 1*	*term 2*	*term 3*			*Sf:* 0.362	
Coeff.: 7.994	-0.181	0.036			*FR5:* 6.833	
St.Dev.: 0.218	0.072	0.006			*FR1:* 2.976	
Order 4 *term 1*	*term 2*	*term 3*	*term 4*		*Sf:* 0.373	
Coeff.: 8.317	-0.389	0.075	-0.002		*FR5:* 0.100	
St.Dev.: 0.458	0.266	0.048	0.003		*FR1:* 0.041	
Order 5 *term 1*	*term 2*	*term 3*	*term 4*	*term 5*	*Sf:* 0.319	
Coeff.: 9.322	-1.394	0.399	-0.044	0.002	*FR5:* 0.366	
St.Dev.: 0.715	0.641	0.197	0.025	0.001	*FR1:* 0.133	

Fig. 3.13.3: Analysis of the data of Table 3.13.1 with LSPoly0.

	term 0	term 1						
Order 1	*term 0*	*term 1*			*Sf:*	2.52E+00		
Coeff.:	-4.107	0.930			*FR5:*	N/A		
St.Dev.:	1.828	0.032			*FR1:*	N/A		
Order 2	*term 0*	*term 1*	*term 2*			*Sf:*	5.09E-01	
Coeff.:	2.724	0.557	3.73E-03			*FR5:*	2.76E+01	
St.Dev.:	0.648	0.030	2.90E-04			*FR1:*	1.20E+01	
Order 3	*term 0*	*term 1*	*term 2*	*term 3*			*Sf:*	3.39E-01
Coeff.:	0.993	0.723	-2.08E-04	2.62E-05			*FR5:*	1.29E+00
St.Dev.:	0.733	0.060	1.36E-03	8.98E-06			*FR1:*	5.25E-01
Order 4	*term 0*	*term 1*	*term 2*	*term 3*	*term 4*			*Sf:* 3.72E-01
Coeff.:	1.439	0.662	2.22E-03	-1.01E-05	1.82E-07			*FR5:* 1.82E-02
St.Dev.:	1.437	0.176	6.66E-03	9.76E-05	4.86E-07			*FR1:* 6.62E-03
Order 5	*term 0*	*term 1*	*term 2*	*term 3*	*term 4*	*term 5*		*Sf:* 3.54E-01
Coeff.:	-1.360	1.150	-2.54E-02	6.63E-04	-7.16E-06	2.94E-08		*FR5:* 1.41E-01
St.Dev.:	2.708	0.441	2.39E-02	5.70E-04	6.15E-06	2.45E-08		*FR1:* 4.20E-02

Fig. 3.13.4: Analysis of the data of Table 3.13.1 with LSPoly1.

3.14 Raman spectrometric analysis of ethanol

In a recent paper, Sanford, Mantooth & Jones (*J. Chem. Educ.* 78 (2001) 1221) used laser spectrometry to determine the ethanol content of ethanol-water mixtures. They reduced random noise by integrating the signal in the area of the Raman peak, between -2825 and -3096 cm^{-1} over a one-minute period, and they applied a baseline correction using the average of the signals at -2815 and -3106 cm^{-1}. The resulting low-noise calibration data (kindly provided by Prof. Sanford) are listed in Table 3.14.1 and illustrated in Fig. 3.14.1, where y is the integrated, baseline-corrected peak area, and x the ethanol percentage. These data were reported to fit the straight line $y = -181.82 + 101.40x$ with a squared linear correlation coefficient r_{xy}^2 of 0.9978 or, better-looking yet, $r_{xy} = \pm0.9989$. In section 2.10 we already commented on r_{xy}^2 or r_{xy}, feel-good parameters provided by many software packages, including Excel's LinEst and Regression.

x	0	1	2.5	5	7.5	10	15	20	25	30	35
y	0.0	100.7	194.8	420.7	667.2	874.6	1359.1	1764.9	2287.9	2769.2	3230.1

x	37.5	40	42.5	45	47.5	50	60	70	80	90	100
y	3532.1	3708.1	3998.2	4295.9	4526.1	4799.8	5763.9	6817.4	7974.0	9048.7	10352.6

Table 3.14.1: The measured Raman intensities y (in arbitrary units) as a function of the percentage of ethanol x in the ethanol-water mixtures.

However, visual inspection of Fig. 3.14.1 suggests some curvature: the reported points at the extremes of the curve tend to lie above the fitted straight line, while those in the middle region lie below it. We therefore calculate and plot the residuals, as shown in Fig. 3.14.2. The magnitudes of those residuals are rather small, considering that the signal range is about 10000, i.e., these integrated data show relatively little *random* scatter. That makes it easier to distinguish their *systematic* trend.

Exercise 3.14.1:

(1) Make a spreadsheet with the data from Table 3.14.1, plot them, and calculate and plot their residuals.

(2) Apply LSPoly0 and LSPoly1 to those data, as well as Ortho0 and Ortho1. Verify that you obtain the results shown.

(3) Calculate and plot the data of Table 3.14.1 to the equation $y = a_1x + a_2x^2$, and also compute and plot the corresponding residuals.

(4) Do the same using the equation $y = a_1x + a_2x^2 + a_4x^4$.

Figs. 3.14.3 and 3.14.4 show the resulting outputs. The value of *sf* exhibits a big drop in going from 1st to 2nd order, and thereafter shows only minor changes. Likewise, the *F* ratios are much larger than 1 for first and second order, and just barely exceed 1 for 4th order.

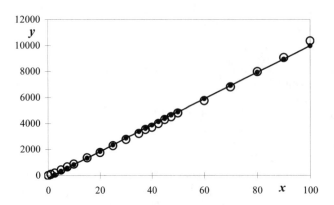

Fig. 3.14.1: The measured Raman intensities y as a function of the percentage of ethanol x in the ethanol-water mixture (open circles). The line shows $y = -181.82 + 101.40\,x$, and the small solid points the resulting y-values at the x-values of the data.

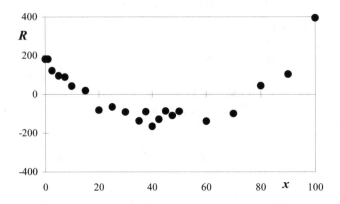

Fig. 3.14.2: The corresponding residuals R clearly show a systematic trend.

Figs. 3.14.3 and 3.14.4 show the resulting outputs. The value of s_f exhibits a big drop in going from 1st to 2nd order, and thereafter shows only minor changes. Likewise, the F ratios are much larger than 1 for first and second order, and just barely exceed 1 for 4th order.

Fits to LSPoly1 (see Fig. 3.14.4) yield rather large relative standard deviations for a_0. This is not surprising, because the data had already been baseline-corrected. Moreover, for all but the 1st order, the absolute magnitudes of the corresponding coefficients a_0 are either smaller than their standard deviations s_0, or only marginally larger, instilling little confidence in their statistical significance.

Figures 3.14.5 and 3.14.6 show the results obtained with orthogonal polynomials. Because the data are not equidistant, we use the custom macros Ortho0 and Ortho1 to generate the necessary orthogonal polynomials. The ratios $|a_i/s_i|$ from the orthogonal polynomials are above 20 for the linear and quadratic terms, and at or below 3 for terms of order 3 or higher, for both Ortho0 and Ortho1.

Guided by the parsimony principle (and resisting the temptation to include 3rd and 4th order terms to correct the remaining, slight increase in the residuals at larger x-values), we opt for the simplest of the 2nd-order fits, the function $y = a_1x + a_2x^2$, which has no more parameters than the linear function $y = a_0 + a_1x$ it replaces. This fit, and the corresponding residuals, are shown in Figs. 3.14.7 and 3.14.8 respectively.

Order 1	*term 1*					*Sf:* 1.81E+02	
Coeff:	9.83E+01					*FR5:* N/A	
StDev:	8.24E-01					*FR1:* N/A	
Order 2	*term 1*	*term 2*				*Sf:* 3.58E+01	
Coeff:	8.73E+01	1.55E-01				*FR5:* 1.18E+02	
StDev:	5.11E-01	6.83E-03				*FR1:* 6.36E+01	
Order 3	*term 1*	*term 2*	*term 3*			*Sf:* 3.54E+01	
Coeff:	8.88E+01	1.02E-01	3.98E-04			*FR5:* 3.49E-01	
StDev:	1.33E+00	4.34E-02	3.22E-04			*FR1:* 1.87E-01	
Order 4	*term 1*	*term 2*	*term 3*	*term 4*		*Sf:* 2.85E+01	
Coeff:	8.31E+01	4.48E-01	-5.68E-03	3.24E-05		*FR5:* 2.55E+00	
StDev:	2.03E+00	1.09E-01	1.83E-03	9.66E-06		*FR1:* 1.36E+00	
Order 5	*term 1*	*term 2*	*term 3*	*term 4*	*term 5*	*Sf:* 2.87E+01	
Coeff:	8.53E+01	2.26E-01	1.26E-03	-5.29E-05	3.58E-07	*FR5:* 1.61E-01	
StDev:	3.33E+00	2.84E-01	8.40E-03	1.01E-04	4.23E-07	*FR1:* 8.54E-02	
Order 6	*term 1*	*term 2*	*term 3*	*term 4*	*term 5*	*term 6*	*Sf:* 2.96E+01
Coeff:	8.54E+01	2.15E-01	1.77E-03	-6.33E-05	4.55E-07	-3.34E-10	*FR5:* 3.25E-05
StDev:	5.23E+00	6.40E-01	2.81E-02	5.57E-04	5.12E-06	1.76E-08	*FR1:* 1.71E-05

Fig. 3.14.3: The output of LSPoly0 for the first 6 orders.

Order 1	*term 0*	*term 1*					*Sf:* 1.44E+02	
Coeff:	-1.82E+02	1.01E+02					*FR5:* N/A	
StDev:	5.01E+01	1.07E+00					*FR1:* N/A	
Order 2	*term 0*	*term 1*	*term 2*				*Sf:* 3.67E+01	
Coeff:	-4.53E+00	8.75E+01	1.54E-01				*FR5:* 6.59E+01	
StDev:	1.65E+01	8.62E-01	9.04E-03				*FR1:* 3.53E+01	
Order 3	*term 0*	*term 1*	*term 2*	*term 3*			*Sf:* 3.52E+01	
Coeff:	-2.02E+01	9.05E+01	6.69E-02	6.11E-04			*FR5:* 6.01E-01	
StDev:	1.85E+01	2.01E+00	5.39E-02	3.75E-04			*FR1:* 3.20E-01	
Order 4	*term 0*	*term 1*	*term 2*	*term 3*	*term 4*		*Sf:* 2.92E+01	
Coeff:	6.18E+00	8.22E+01	4.80E-01	-6.11E-03	3.43E-05		*FR5:* 2.04E+00	
StDev:	1.77E+01	3.22E+00	1.44E-01	2.25E-03	1.14E-05		*FR1:* 1.08E+00	
Order 5	*term 0*	*term 1*	*term 2*	*term 3*	*term 4*	*term 5*	*Sf:* 2.96E+01	
Coeff:	-9.34E-02	8.53E+01	2.25E-01	1.29E-03	-5.31E-05	3.59E-07	*FR5:* 1.24E-01	
StDev:	1.98E+01	5.28E+00	3.71E-01	1.02E-02	1.18E-04	4.82E-07	*FR1:* 6.52E-02	
Order 6	*term 0*	*term 1*	*term 2*	*term 3*	*term 4*	*term 5*	*term 6*	*Sf:* 3.06E+01
Coeff:	-2.82E-01	8.54E+01	2.09E-01	1.99E-03	-6.71E-05	4.86E-07	-4.32E-10	*FR5:* -6.95E-06
StDev:	2.22E+01	8.24E+00	8.31E-01	3.39E-02	6.49E-04	5.82E-06	1.97E-08	*FR1:* -3.63E-06

Fig. 3.14.4: The output of LSPoly1 for the first 6 orders.

	term 1	*term 2*	*term 3*	*term 4*	*term 5*
Coeff.:	98.3250	0.15511	3.98E-04	3.24E-05	3.58E-07
st.dev.:	0.1310	0.00548	2.62E-04	9.73E-06	4.23E-07
ratio:	750.58	28.30	1.52	3.33	0.85

Fig. 3.14.5: The output of Ortho0 for the first 5 orders.

	term 0	*term 1*	*term 2*	*term 3*	*term 4*	*term 5*
Coeff.:	3567.55	101.396	0.1535	6.11E-04	3.43E-05	3.59E-07
st. dev.:	6.32	0.220	0.0073	3.16E-04	1.15E-05	4.82E-07
ratio:	564.69	460.05	21.04	1.93	2.97	0.75

Fig. 3.14.6: The output of Ortho1 for the first 5 orders.

The above example illustrates the benefits of plotting residuals, and of subjecting the data to statistical tests that can indicate whether higher-order polynomials would yield a statistically better fit. The above tests do not reveal what specific form, if any, would best fit the data, nor do they clarify the reason for the nonlinearity in the above results. The latter may be an artifact from the integration procedure used, or reflect a more basic nonlinear feature in the data.

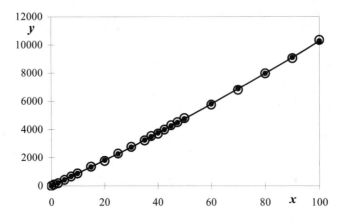

Fig. 3.14.7: The same data analyzed as a quadratic through the origin, $y = a_1x + a_2x^2$. The line is drawn with $a_1 = 87.325$, $a_2 = 0.155$.

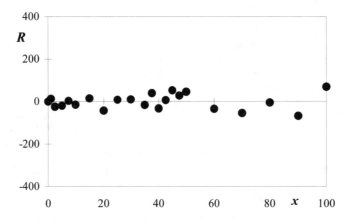

Fig. 3.14.8: The residuals of the quadratic fit in Fig. 3.14.7 exhibit only a slight trend towards larger-amplitude residuals at larger x-values. The scale is the same as that in Fig. 3.14.2.

For the purpose of chemical analysis, the quadratic calibration curve should yield more accurate results than a straight line, assuming of course that all other experimental conditions are kept constant, including the integration procedure. We will now illustrate how to use such a quadratic calibration curve for that purpose. Say that we make three replicate measurements on an ethanol-water mixture of unknown composition that, on the same equipment and under the same experimental conditions, yield Raman intensities of 4000, 4050, and 3980. We now wish to determine the corresponding ethanol percentage x_u, and its imprecision. With the expression $y = a_1x + a_2x^2$ we have $x_u = [-a_1 \pm \sqrt{(a_1{}^2 + 4a_2y_u)}] / [2a_2]$ where y_u is the average Raman intensity of the unknown.

Exercise 3.14.1 (continued):
(5) Use LS0 to fit the data of Table 3.14.1 to $y = a_1x + a_2x^2$. Display the covariance matrix.
(6) In another column, place the three observations of the Raman intensity of the sample of unknown composition (4000, 4050, and 3980) and compute its average y_u with =AVERAGE(), and its variance v_u with =VAR().

116

(7) Use Cut and Paste to move the average y_u-value into alignment with the values for a_1, a_2, so that they form on one contiguous row, or one contiguous column. Likewise align the variance v_{uu} so that the covariance matrix and the standard deviation s_u in y_u share a diagonal, with the variances v_{11}, v_{22}, and v_{uu} in the same order as a_1, a_2, and y_u, cf. Fig. 3.14.9. Calculate x_u with the equation shown above, $x_u = [-a_1 \pm \sqrt{(a_1{}^2+4a_2y_u)}] / [2a_2]$.

4295.9	45	2025	
4526.1	47.5	2256.25	
4799.8	50	2500	4000
5763.9	60	3600	4050
6817.4	70	4900	3980
7974.0	80	6400	
9048.7	90	8100	*4010*
10352.6	100	10000	
Coeff:	*87.325*	*0.1551*	*4010*
StDev:	*0.511*	*0.0068*	*36.06*
	35.84173		
CM:	0.262	-0.003312	
	-0.003312	4.67E-05	
			1300
xu=	*42.684*		
su=	*0.374*		

Fig. 3.14.9: Spreadsheet detail showing the bottom of the columns for the calculation of a_1, a_2, and y_u, and the subsequent computation of x_u. The variance $v_{uu} = s_u{}^2$ is entered in the covariance matrix.

(8) Call the custom macro Propagation and find the standard deviation s_u. For this example, the correct answer for the unknown ethanol concentration is $x_u = 42.6_8 \pm 0.3_7$ vol%, i.e., with a relative standard deviation of less than 1%, a quite respectable result.

(9) If you had used the standard deviations s_1, s_2, and s_u instead of the covariance matrix, the answer would have been $42.6_8 \pm 0.4_4$ vol%, quite close to the answer under (8). If you had used the straight-line fit $y = a_0 + a_1x$ you would have found $x_u = 41.3_4 \pm 0.3_1$ with the covariance matrix (or with centering), or $x_u = 41.3_4 \pm 0.6_6$ without it. Unfortunately, there are many ways to get incorrect answers even from quite good data.

We now ask a practical question: given these calibration data, is it worthwhile to make more repeat measurements of y_u in order to obtain a result with higher precision? For the answer we go to the part of the spreadsheet shown in Fig. 3.14.9, substitute 0 (instead of 1300) for the variance of the measurement, and use Propagation, which now yields a standard deviation of 0.11. In other words, the major part of the imprecision in the answer indeed comes from the imprecision in y_u. That is encouraging.

However, a completely precise measurement is not a realistic goal, and we therefore ask what the result would be if we quadrupled the number of observations, from 3 to 12, assuming that the average would stay the same, and that their individual deviations would be similar. In that case $\Sigma\Delta^2$ would increase four times, $N-1$ would increase from $3-1=2$ to $12-1=11$, so that the variance v_{uu} would be reduced by a factor $4 / (11/2) = 8/11$ to $8\times1300/11=945.45$. Substituting this into the covariance matrix and again using Propagation we find that the standard deviation in x_u would go down from 0.3_7 to 0.3_2, a rather minor improvement for four times as many measurements. Depending on the subsequent uses of the result of the analysis, it may or may not be worth your while to spend so much extra effort on a relatively minor improvement in the precision of the answer. Establishing why the calibration data do not quite fit a straight line might be a more efficient use of your time.

The method used here and illustrated in Fig. 3.14.9 is similar to that of section 3.4, except that we here deal with the intersection of a parabola and a horizontal line, $y = y_u$. If the curvature of the calibration curve is so severe that terms of higher than second order are required, the above method cannot be used, because it relies on having a closed-form solution for y_u. However, in that case it may still be possible to approximate the calibration curve in the limited region around x_u by a parabola.

3.15 Heat evolution during cement hardening

A much-quoted example of a multivariate fit can be found in the measurements of H. Woods, H. H. Steinour & H. R. Starke (*Ind. Eng. Chem.* 24 (1932) 1207) on the heat evolved during the first 180 days of hardening of Portland cement, studied as a function of the amounts (in weight percentages) of its dry ingredients: tricalcium aluminate, tricalcium silicate, tricalcium aluminoferrate, and β-dicalcium silicate. All measurements were made after adding 3.2% gypsum, a hardening retardant. Because the sum of the four weight percentages must add to 100%, the four weight percentages can be anticipated to be mutually dependent. If so, we face the question: which variables should we include in the analysis as significant, and which (if any) could possibly be left out? The experimental data are shown in Fig. 3.15.1.

	A	B	C	D	E	F
1		y	$x1$	$x2$	$x3$	$x4$
2						
3		78.5	7	26	6	60
4		74.2	1	29	15	52
5		104.3	11	56	8	20
6		87.6	11	31	8	47
7		95.9	7	52	6	33
8		109.2	11	55	9	22
9		102.7	3	71	17	6
10		72.5	1	31	22	44
11		93.1	2	54	18	22
12		115.9	21	47	4	26
13		83.8	1	40	23	34
14		113.3	11	66	9	12
15		109.4	10	68	8	12

Fig. 3.15.1: The experimental data of Woods, Steinour & Starke, *Ind. Eng. Chem.* 24 (1932) 1207, for the heat evolution y (in calories per gram of cement) as a function of the weight percentages x of the clinkers used in making the cement, where x_1 refers to the chemical composition $Al_2Ca_3O_6$, x_2 to Ca_3SiO_5, x_3 to $Al_2Ca_4Fe_2O_{10}$, and x_4 to β-Ca_2SiO_4.

We note that the weight percentages are rounded, and add up to numbers ranging from 95 to 99%. It is not clear from the original paper what causes these discrepancies, but they may keep the problem from being overspecified. Perhaps we need not worry about having too many variables, in which case the only question is whether to use a multivariate analysis with or without an adjustable intercept.

Analyzing this data set with LS0 (or with LinEst or Regression with zero intercept), we find no particular problems with the ratios $|a_i/s_i|$ of the individual coefficients, or with the covariance terms, see Fig. 3.15.2. Apparently, the collinearity (i.e., the mutual dependencies between the adjustable parameters a_1 through a_4) is insufficient to affect the analysis.

However, when the same data set is analyzed with LS1, i.e., with an arbitrary intercept, we obtain values for a_0, a_2, a_3, and a_4 for which $|a_i/s_i|$ is smaller than 1. This latter set is, therefore, not acceptable. And a good thing it is: what would a significant non-zero intercept mean? Could there be heat evolution independent of any of the chemical constituents of cement? Given the care the authors have shown in obtaining their data, a non-zero intercept is unlikely to be due to calibration error, or to some unexpected instrumental offset. The above data clearly do not support such a model.

Why is this not the end of the story? Why has this example been quoted repeatedly in statistical texts? It is possible that the answer lies in a cursory reading of the problem, which suggests that it should be an overdetermined system. In that case, the question would be how to decide which of the four constituents to leave out of the analysis. Below we will consider the problem in that light, as an example of how it might be addressed if it were germane to this particular example.

	Coeff:	2.194809	1.153154	0.759162	0.485647
16					
17	StDev:	0.184584	0.047764	0.158919	0.041254
18		2.408722			
19	CM:	0.034071	-0.007636	0.022144	-0.004751
20		-0.007636	0.002281	-0.00651	0.000945
21		0.022144	-0.00651	0.025255	-0.004809
22		-0.004751	0.000945	-0.004809	0.001702
23					
24	LCC:	1	-0.866155	0.754908	-0.62393
25		-0.866155	1	-0.857707	0.479507
26		0.754908	-0.857707	1	-0.733495
27		-0.62393	0.479507	-0.733495	1

Fig. 3.15.2: The results obtained with LS0 for the data shown in Fig. 3.15.1

In that case we face a number of alternatives: if we delete one of the four species as superfluous, which one of the four do we leave out? If two are deleted, there are six such combinations, and four more if three species are eliminated from the analysis. That yields a total of 14 possibilities. Do we then force the fit through the origin, or let it find its own y-intercept? That question doubles the number of choices to 28. And what criterion should we use to compare them?

With so many options, the most practical solution is to use a single criterion. The custom macro GradeBySf uses the same algorithm as LS0 and LS1 to compute the standard deviation of the overall fit of the function to the data, s_f, for all possible permutations, for up to six independent variables (or more, if you care to extend it in its open-access VBA code), and can thereby save much tedious work. Its output is illustrated in Fig. 3.15.3.

Judging by this criterion, several combinations seem to provide a fair fit to the data. Apart from 1,2,3,4 with zero offset, we find that 1,2, 1,4, 1,2,3, 1,2,4, 1,3,4, 2,3,4, and 1,2,3,4 all yield s_f-values between 2.3 and 2.8 when analyzed with a non-zero offset; the closest remaining competitors have s_f-values larger than 4.

Now that GradeBySf has narrowed down our choices from 30 to 8 (or, excluding the analysis of the entire data set, from 28 to 6), we examine the latter individually. Among the truncated data sets, only those retaining columns 1,2,4 or 2,3,4, show coefficients with fairly strong collinearities, with linear correlation coefficients larger than 0.99 in absolute value. The four remaining combinations, 1,2, 1,4, 1,2,3, and 1,3,4, show no such problems. By the combined criteria of a low value of s_f, coefficients for which $|a_i/s_i|$ exceeds 1, and with no linear correlation coefficients of the a_i larger than 0.99 or smaller than −0.99 we therefore find four plausibly truncated multivariate analyses listed in Table 3.15.1, together with two more questionable answers.

Another way to consider the above questions would be to use orthogonal transformation, in order to make the various 'independent' variables truly independent, see section 3.11. When we test, e.g., the full data set of Fig. 3.15.1 with Ortho0, the results are fine, see Fig. 3.15.4.

And when we use Ortho1 instead, we find that the last coefficient is clearly statistically insignificant, and the penultimate one nearly so, see Fig. 3.15.5. This corroborates what we found for this same data set with LS0 and LS1 respectively.

However, the application of orthogonal transformation to multivariate least squares has a practical problem. Unlike s_f, which is independent of the particular *order* in which the independent variables are presented, orthogonal transformation yields different answers for, say, the permutations 1,2,3, 1,3,2, 2,1,3, 2,3,1, 3,1,2, and 3,2,1, because the method works sequentially, column by column. This makes its use in this case rather laborious, and we will therefore not pursue it here.

	A	B	C	D	E	F
17			Standard deviation of fit			
18		Indices:	Thru 0	General		
19			**GradeBySf**			
20		1	52.214217	10.734416		
21		2	19.729791	9.083181		
22		3	54.650211	13.289855		
23		4	58.453311	8.968893		
24						
25		1,2	16.828668	2.402125		
26		1,3	17.669594	11.084383		
27		1,4	40.101196	2.728218		
28		2,3	19.934872	6.451528		
29		2,4	10.047144	9.326902		
30		3,4	50.836282	4.195315		
31						
32		1,2,3	9.253363	2.304482		

Fig. 3.15.3: The output of the custom macro GradeBySf applies to the data of Fig. 3.15.1. The first column lists the indices of the independent variables used, the second the s_f-values for fitting without offset, and the right column the s_f-values obtained by allowing an arbitrary offset.

indices	$a_0 \pm s_0$	$a_1 \pm s_1$	$a_2 \pm s_2$	$a_3 \pm s_3$	$a_4 \pm s_4$	s_f
1,2	$52._5 \pm 2._3$	$1.4_7 \pm 0.1_2$	$0.66_3 \pm 0.04_6$			2.40
1,4	$103._1 \pm 2._1$	$1.4_4 \pm 0.1_4$			$-0.61_5 \pm 0.04_9$	2.73
1,2,3	$48._1 \pm 3._9$	$1.7_0 \pm 0.2_0$	$0.65_7 \pm 0.04_4$	$0.2_5 \pm 0.1_8$		2.30
1,2,4	$7._1 \pm 1._4$	$1.4_5 \pm 0.1_2$	$0.4_2 \pm 0.1_9$		$-0.2_4 \pm 0.1_7$	2.30
1,3,4	$111_7 \pm 4_6$	$1.0_5 \pm 0.2_2$		$-0.4_1 \pm 0.2_0$	$-0.64_3 \pm 0.04_4$	2.37
2,3,4	$20_4 \pm 2_1$		$-0.9_2 \pm 0.2_6$	$-1.4_5 \pm 0.1_5$	$-1.5_6 \pm 0.2_4$	2.86
1,2,3,4	$6_2 \pm 7_0$	$1.5_6 \pm 0.7_4$	$0.5_2 \pm 0.7_2$	$0.1_1 \pm 0.7_5$	$-0.1_4 \pm 0.7_1$	2.44
1,2,3,4		$2.1_9 \pm 0.1_8$	$1.15_3 \pm 0.04_8$	$0.7_6 \pm 0.1_6$	$0.48_6 \pm 0.04_1$	2.40

Table 3.15.1: The results obtained for the eight permutations with the lowest values of s_f. For reasons given in the text, the results shown in gray are considered less plausible.

Where does this leave us? When we analyze the data as containing at least one dependent variable, we can drop one or two columns, resulting in three or four coefficients respectively. On the basis of the parsimony principle, we might select one of the two three-parameter solutions (either 1,2 or 1,4 with arbitrary intercept) over any of the other four-parameter solutions (1,2,3, and 1,3,4 with LS1). Note that the difference in s_f between, say, 1,2 analyzed with LS1 and the full data set analyzed with LS0, is only in the fourth digit. In view of section 2.12, it is statistically insignificant.

Our conclusion so far must therefore be somewhat ambiguous. Fitting the heat data to either $y = a_0 + a_1 x_1 + a_2 x_2$ or $y = a_0 + a_1 x_1 + a_4 x_4$ provides the *most compact* description, and is therefore 'best' if mere data compression is our goal. But as far as an *interpretation* of these results is concerned, i.e., for a chemical understanding of the hardening of cement, a description as $y = a_1 x_1 + a_2 x_2 + a_3 x_3 + a_4 x_4$ in terms of the four constituents would seem to be the more appropriate. What constitutes the 'best' description is here seen to depend on the intended purpose of the data analysis, because a non-zero value for a_0 requires an explanation.

H	I	J	K	L
y	*X1*	*X2*	*X3*	*X4*
78.5	7	-4.249342	2.672732	37.93956
74.2	1	24.67867	6.201072	22.92501
104.3	11	8.46532	-2.213322	-2.223176
87.6	11	-16.53468	6.01623	10.89775
95.9	7	21.75066	-5.886002	25.37379
109.2	11	7.46532	-0.88414	-3.603877
102.7	3	58.036	-4.129871	-10.9925
72.5	1	26.67867	12.54271	-3.743438
93.1	2	45.35733	1.718872	-4.464174
115.9	21	-43.74802	4.222839	-17.83383
83.8	1	35.67867	10.58007	-11.57251
113.3	11	18.46532	-4.505143	-7.497086
109.4	10	24.78665	-6.910859	-0.769587
Coeff:	*8.807638*	*1.585151*	*2.131376*	*0.485647*
StDev:	*0.071371*	*0.022193*	*0.108016*	*0.041254*
Ratio:	*123.4056*	*71.42726*	*19.73201*	*11.77198*
	2.408722			

Fig. 3.15.4: The results produced by Ortho0. The columns for X1 through X4 display the orthogonal polynomials for the data in C3:F15, while the three bottom lines show the corresponding coefficients *a*, their standard deviations *s*, and the ratios *a/s*.

Incidentally, the answer we obtain with 1,2, viz. $y = (52._5 \pm 2._3) + (1.4_7 \pm 0.1_2) x_1 + (0.66_3 \pm 0.04_6) x_2$, see Table 3.15.1, agrees with the result obtained via a much more laborious route by N. R. Draper & H. Smith, *Applied Regression Analysis*, 2nd ed., Wiley (1981), who devote most of their chapter 6 to this problem. This problem had earlier been discussed by A. Hald in his *Statistical Theory with Engineering Applications*, Wiley (1952) pp. 635-649, and it is still being tossed around, as in M. A. Golberg & H. A. Cho, *Introduction to Regression Analysis*, WIT Press (2004) pp. 204, 369, and 383-384. In this particular instance, statistics may leave us with several choices (with often quite different parameter values, see Table 3.15.1) rather than with a single, objective solution.

Finally, there is the question of the appropriateness of the model used. Cement hardening is clearly not a simple precipitation-dehydration reaction, but the formation of an intricate molecular network. The concrete dome of the Parthenon in Rome was completed in 126 AD; nearly 19 centuries later it still stands, as the largest non-reinforced concrete dome in the world. The Hoover dam contains 2.5 million m^3 of concrete, and was certainly built to last. Such large, enduring concrete structures use cement as their binder, which implies aggregation through extensive bond formation. It would be rather surprising if the exothermic heat of those *chemical reactions* would merely be an *additive* function of the concentrations of the chemicals mixed to make the clinker, rather than a function of, say, appropriate *products* of those concentrations, possibly raised to some powers, and most likely a composite of several of such processes. Indeed, simply replacing the four concentration terms x_1 through x_4 by, e.g., the four product terms $x_1 x_2$, $x_2 x_3$, $x_2 x_4$, and $x_3 x_4$, and analyzing those data with LS1, yields $s_f = 1.54$, considerably smaller than any s_f-value listed in Fig. 3.15.3! Much more detailed chemical experiments may therefore be needed, changing only one or two concentrations at a time, in order to extract the principal concentration dependencies, before a *meaningful* data analysis can be undertaken. What we have so far is merely a compact numerical representation of this specific data set. If, as is possibly the case here, this problem is formulated in terms of incorrectly chosen 'independent' parameters, no amount of statistical treatment of this data set can get the answer right.

G	H	I	J	K	L
	y	*X1*	*X2*	*X3*	*X4*
	78.5	-0.461538	-21.87477	-5.716573	1.037882
	74.2	-6.461538	-15.24676	-2.242237	-0.683594
	104.3	3.538462	5.706558	-0.715707	-2.326357
	87.6	3.538462	-19.29344	-0.182183	-0.792525
	95.9	-0.461538	4.125232	-6.271438	0.522698
	109.2	3.538462	4.706558	0.305634	-0.31691
	102.7	-4.461538	25.54391	0.68199	0.165842
	72.5	-6.461538	-13.24676	4.715081	0.550354
	93.1	-5.461538	9.148574	1.134513	-1.128102
	115.9	13.53846	-9.340126	4.579097	0.443878
	83.8	-6.461538	-4.246758	5.523012	0.746268
	113.3	3.538462	15.70656	0.070883	0.888204
	109.4	2.538462	18.31123	-1.882072	0.892361
Coeff.:	95.41538	1.870304	0.662804	0.251449	-0.13832
St.Dev.:	0.676303	0.119665	0.046467	0.194808	0.706859
Ratio:	**141.0839**	**15.62947**	**14.2641**	**1.290753**	**0.195678**

Fig. 3.15.5: The results produced by Ortho1 when applied to the data set in Fig. 3.15.1. Note that the orthogonal polynomials differ from those shown in Fig. 3.15.4.

3.16 Least squares for equidistant data

Equidistant data sets are collections of data for which the *independent* variable is equidistant, i.e., for which all successive increments Δx in the independent variable x are equal. Such data sets are quite common in science, because many instruments produce data at constant increments in time, voltage, magnetic field, wavelength, wavenumber, etc. Least squares analysis can be simplified significantly when the data are equidistant, in which case they can be represented conveniently in terms of Gram polynomials. This has led to new applications of least squares methods, which are readily implemented on a spreadsheet. The use of Gram polynomials for moving polynomial fits was developed by Sheppard in *Proc. London Math. Soc.* (2) 13 (1914) 97, Gram in *Mitt. Ver. Schweiz. Versicherungsmath.* (1915) 3, and Sherriff in *Proc. Roy. Soc. Edinburgh* 40 (1920) 112, who all provided tables of so-called convoluting integers. This approach was further popularized by Whittaker & Robinson in *The Calculus of Observations*, their well-known 1924 treatise on numerical analysis that was still reprinted in the 1960s, as well as in other textbooks, such as Milne's *Numerical Calculus* (1949) and Wylie's *Advanced Engineering Mathematics* (1951, 1960). In chemistry it is often associated with the names of Savitzky and Golay, who in a paper in *Anal. Chem.* 36 (1964) 1627 reminded analytical chemists of this by then 50-years-old method when computers became more generally available. Unfortunately, Savitzky & Golay confused their readers with tables of convoluting integers containing an unusually large number of errors, subsequently corrected by Steiner, Termonia & Deltour in *Anal. Chem.* 44 (1972) 1906.

Here we will explore how the moving polynomial method can be used to fit a small, contiguous sample section of the data with a relatively low-order "moving" polynomial of a small, typically odd number of data points. From this fit we compute and store the resulting, smoothed value at the midpoint of the sample. The polynomial is then moved up by one point along the data set (by dropping the extreme point on one side, and adding a new data point on the other side), whereupon the process is repeated. By doing this until the moving polynomial has slithered along the entire data set, we can compute a smoothed replica thereof, except near the ends of the data set, where a slightly modified algorithm is needed. An advantage of this method is that we need not know the precise mathematical description of the curve. As long as the data density is sufficiently large with respect to the shape-defining features of that curve, any small subset of the data can usually be fitted reasonably well with a low-order polynomial.

For an odd number of equidistant data points, the moving polynomial method is very easy to implement on a spreadsheet, because the least squares analysis can then be performed with a set of fixed, tabulated *convoluting integers*. The macro ELSfixed makes it even simpler, by computing those convoluting integers, and subsequently applying them in the analysis. You specify the data set, and the length and order of the moving polynomial. As illustrated in exercise 3.15.1, the length of the moving data sample should not exceed the characteristic width of the smallest features you want to be resolved without appreciable distortion. The length of the polynomial must be a compromise: as high as possible for maximum smoothing, and as low as possible for minimal data distortion. A variant, ELSauto, automatically selects the order each time the polynomial is moved, using an *F*-test, so that the order varies throughout the curve. Since it uses Gram polynomials, it can readily be modified to use the ratio of the highest-order orthogonal coefficient and its standard deviation as an alternative criterion. The ELS macro was contributed by P. Barak, and is based on his paper in *Anal. Chem.* 67 (1995) 2758.

It is sometimes necessary to compute the first or higher derivative of a function represented by experimental data points. It is obviously impossible to determine the derivative of a set of individual data points, but that is not what is meant here. Instead, we desire the derivative of the *reconstructed, continuous* curve on which the individual, experimental data points are assumed to lie in the absence of noise. In this case, smoothing is usually necessary because differentiation is highly sensitive to noise. The moving polynomial method fits the bill, because it provides smoothing to a noise-free algebraic expression, which can then be differentiated. For example, when we smooth a data segment by fitting it to the quadratic expression $y = a_0 + a_1x + a_2x^2$, its first derivative is immediately available as $dy/dx = a_1 + 2a_2x$. ELS can therefore be used on equidistant data to determine not only the smoothed values of the sample, but also the corresponding first and second derivatives. Again, you can modify ELS to provide higher derivatives.

Exercise 3.16.1:

(1) As test set we will use a set of four Lorentzian peaks, such as occur in, e.g., nuclear magnetic resonance spectra. In order to illustrate the effects of distortion, we will use peaks of unit height but of gradually diminishing half-widths. In A4:A1403 deposit 1 (1) 1400, in cell B4 the instruction =10/(0.001*(A4-550)^2+10)+10/(0.01*(A4-900)^2+10)+10/(0.1*(A4-1100)^2 +10)+10/((A4-1200)^2+10), and copy this instruction down (e.g., by clicking on its handle). Plot these data; you should see a graph such as Fig. 3.16.1, which will represent our idealized (i.e., noise-free) data set.

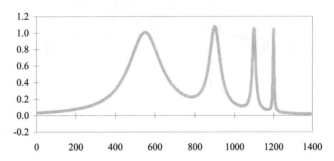

Fig. 3.16.1: A set of four Lorentzian peaks of diminishing widths.

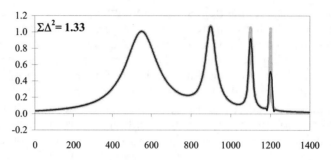

Fig. 3.16.2: The noise-free data set of Fig. 3.16.1 after smoothing with a 35-point cubic.

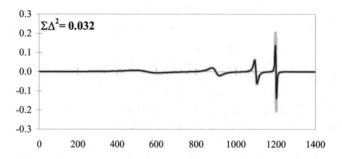

Fig. 3.16.3: The first derivative of the data of Fig. 3.16.1, obtained with a seven-point moving quadratic (thin line) and, for comparison, the separately computed true first derivative of the function. The few data points around the fourth peak contribute virtually all of $\Sigma\Delta^2$.

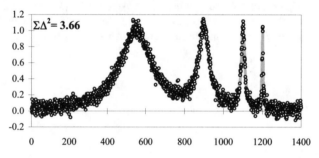

Fig. 3.16.4: The data of Fig. 3.16.1 with added Gaussian noise, $s_n = 0.05$. The signal amplitude is 1, so that the resulting signal-to-noise ratio is $1 / 0.05 = 20$.

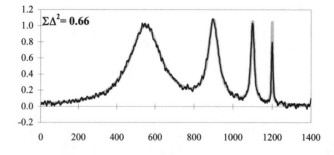

Fig. 3.16.5: The data of Fig. 3.16.4 smoothed with a seven-point moving line.

124

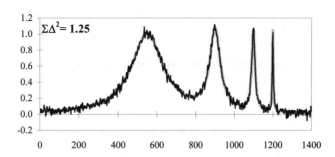

Fig. 3.16.6: The data of Fig. 3.16.4 smoothed with a seven-point moving quadratic.

(2) First we will do the analysis manually, to get an idea of how it works. We use a sliding five-point parabola, $y = a_0 + a_1 x + a_2 x^2$, for which the convoluting integers are –3, 12, 17, 12, and –3, with their algebraic sum 35 as common divisor.

(3) In cell G6 place the instruction = (-3*B4+12*B5+17*B6+12*B7-3*B8)/35 and copy this instruction down through cell G1401. Column G will now contain the smoothed values, except for the first and last two points. There are ways to fill in those missing ends, but we will not worry about such details.

(4) Having to look up the convoluting integers for a given polynomial length and order can be a bother. The custom macro ELSfixed will compute these integers, and then apply them to the data. Call Tools ⇨ Macro ⇨ Macros, select ELSfixed, and click on Run or Enter. In the input boxes enter the location of the data set (B4:B1403), the length of the polynomial (say, 35), its order (e.g., 3), and the order of the derivative (0 for smoothing). You should get a result such as in Fig. 3.15.2, where the moving cubic is too long to represent the sharpest peaks in the graph. To quantify the distortion, compute $\Sigma\Delta^2$ with =SUMXMY2(B4:B1403,C4:C1403), and place the resulting value in the graph. Verify that you find less distortion with a shorter moving polynomial of, e.g., only seven data points.

(5) You can also use ELS to fid the first derivative of the curve, as illustrated in Fig. 3.15.3, where the gray curve represents the computed derivative, and the thinner black line the computed one. As in Fig. 3.15.2 the imposed filter causes distortion, which is most pronounced in the sharper peaks. Consequently, the few data points around the fourth peak contribute virtually all of $\Sigma\Delta^2$.

(6) Now make the data set more realistic by adding Gaussian noise, see Fig. 3.16.4, and repeat these analyses. Figures 3.16.5 and 3.16.6 illustrate what you might obtain with ELSfixed, while Fig. 3.16.7 show results obtained with ELS-optimized.

The above examples illustrate several points:

(1) When the sample length exceeds the characteristic width of the smallest feature you want to resolve, distortion will result, even in the absence of any noise.

(2) Comparison of, e.g., Figs. 3.16.5 and 3.16.6 illustrates that the lower the order of the smoothing polynomial, the more noise is removed, but the more the signal is distorted (see the line at $x = 1200$). The self-optimizing ELSauto can negotiate a useful compromise between these two, as illustrated in Fig. 3.16.7, but you still must tell it what polynomial length to use. As can be seen in Fig. 3.16.8, you can also use ELSauto (or ELSfixed) for differentiation.

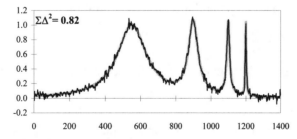

Fig. 3.16.7: The data of Fig. 3.16.4 smoothed with a seven-point moving polynomial of variable order, between 1 and 5.

125

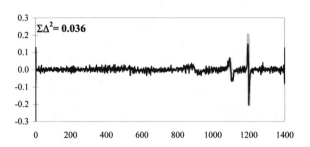

Fig. 3.16.8: The first derivative of the data of Fig. 3.16.4 computed with a seven-point moving polynomial of variable order, between 1 and 5.

3.17 Weighted least squares

Sometimes we know that an instrument is noisier in one region of its range than in another. In that case we can assign more weight to data from the less noisy region than to data obtained elsewhere. This is not unlike listening to witnesses in a court of law, and giving more credence to those that appear to be trustworthier. (A difference is, of course, that courts supposedly consider accuracy, while least squares only deal with precision, i.e., with the effects of random noise.)

Assigning weights to data requires that we know how much (relative) weight to allot to each measurement, and how to handle such individual weights or weighting factors w_i in an analysis. If we have sufficient replicates of each observation, we might, e.g., assign each measurement its proper *individual* weight, equal to the reciprocal of its variance, $w_i = 1/v_{ii} = 1/s_i{}^2$. Unfortunately, such information is seldom available. However, for a scanning instrument we might, e.g., determine its baseline noise as a function of its scanning parameter, and base weights w_i on the variance of that noise.

A second need for weighting arises when we use a *transformation* to make experimental data suitable for least squares analysis. For instance, data involving radioactive decay, first-order chemical kinetics, or the electrical current following a stepwise voltage change in a resistor-capacitor circuit, all follow an exponential decay of the type $y = a\,e^{-bt}$ where t denotes time. It is usual to 'rectify' such an expression by taking (natural) logarithms, so that $\ln y = \ln a - bt$, which is the expression for a straight line of $\ln y$ vs. t. If we then fit the transformed data using least squares, we minimize the sum of the residuals in $\ln y$ rather than those in y. In some cases that may well be correct, namely when the errors in y are *relative* ones, proportional to the magnitude of the signal y. But when the experimental errors are *absolute*, the resulting fit will overemphasize the tail end of the data set. This problem can be accommodated by using weighting, which in this case simply follows from

$$\frac{\Delta \ln y}{\Delta y} \approx \frac{d \ln y}{dy} \tag{3.17.1}$$

and is valid as long as Δy is sufficiently small, because by definition

$$\frac{d \ln y}{dy} \equiv \lim_{\Delta y \to 0} \frac{\ln(y + \Delta y) - \ln y}{\Delta y} = \lim_{\Delta y \to 0} \frac{\Delta \ln y}{\Delta y} \tag{3.17.2}$$

Consequently we can assign each point of the transformed data set a *global* weight

$$w_i = \frac{1}{(d \ln y / dy)^2} = \frac{1}{(1/y)^2} = y^2 \tag{3.17.3}$$

or, in general, upon transforming the dependent variable y into Y,

$$w_i = \frac{1}{(dY / dy)^2} \tag{3.17.4}$$

The total weight will then be the product of the individual and global weights, i.e.,

$$w_i = \frac{1}{s_i^2 \, (dY/dy)^2} \qquad\qquad (3.17.5)$$

where it is customary to normalize the global weights, i.e., to use only their relative values.

There may be additional problems with a transformation. For example, when an exponential decays to zero, the experimental data will be scattered around zero, so that some of them will be negative. Because the spreadsheet cannot take the logarithms of negative numbers, the data set must be truncated before the data become negative. We would *bias* the result if we merely left out the logarithms of the negative data.

	A	B	C	D
1	*y*	*w*	*x*	*s(y)*
2				
3	0	2500	0	0.02
4	12.36	2500	0.1	0.02
5	24.83	204.0816	0.2	0.07
6	35.91	59.1716	0.3	0.13
7	48.79	20.66116	0.4	0.22
8	60.42	9.182736	0.5	0.33
9		*Coeff:*	*122.9652*	
10		*StDev:*	*0.645729*	
11			*0.144358*	

	A	B	C	D
1	*y*	*w*	*x*	*s(y)*
2				
3	0	2500	0	0.02
4	12.36	2500	0.1	0.02
5	24.83	204.0816	0.2	0.07
6	35.91	59.1716	0.3	0.13
7	48.79	20.66116	0.4	0.22
8	60.42	9.182736	0.5	0.33
9	*Coeff:*	*0.044459*	*122.6411*	
10	*StDev:*	*0.085417*	*0.935897*	
11		*0.156195*		
12	*CM:*	*0.007296*	*-0.05319*	
13		*-0.05319*	*0.875904*	

Fig. 3.17.1: Fitting a set of data with standard deviations s_i of the individual y_i-values to a proportionality with WLS0 (top panel) or to a straight line with WLS1 (bottom panel).

Excel provides no built-in facility to handle weighted least squares. We therefore provide a custom macro for weighted least squares, WLS, that is similar to LS but has an additional column (between the columns for the dependent and independent variables) for the weights w_i. By either leaving the second column empty or filling it with ones, WLS reverts to yielding results for unweighted least squares. Note that WLS normalizes the weights, i.e., it only considers *relative* weights. And one more thing: centering weighted least squares requires that $\Sigma w_i x_i$ rather than Σx_i be made equal to zero.

Exercise 3.17.1:

(1) As a first illustration of a weighted least squares analysis we again use the data set from D. Harvey, see exercise 2.13.1, with the added standard deviations s_i shown in column D of Fig. 3.17.1. Enter the y-values in column A, the x-values in column C (leaving the B column free for the weights w), and the standard deviations s_i of the individual y_i-values in column D.

(2) In column B calculate the weights $1/s_i^2$ according to (3.17.15) without a global transformation, i.e., with $Y = y$ so that $dY/dy = 1$.

(3) Highlight the data in columns A through C and call WLS0. Then copy your data and now call WLS1. The results are shown in Fig. 3.17.1.

(4) As in exercise 2.12.1, and absent any contra-indication, these data are best fitted to a proportionality rather than to a general line, as in the latter case the standard deviation in the intercept is larger than the absolute value of the intercept.

As with LS, WLS comes in two flavors, WLS0 for curves that should go through the origin, and WLS1 for curves that need not do so. WLS provides the best-fitting coefficients a_i, the associated sample standard deviations s_i, and the covariance matrix. Tables 3.17.1 and 3.17.2 list several functions that can be transformed into linear or quadratic form respectively, and the associated global weights. To repeat: centering weighted least squares requires that $\Sigma\, w_i\, x_i$ rather than $\Sigma\, x_i$ be set to zero.

Sections 3.18 through 3.20 will illustrate the application of WLS to (1) an exponential decay of the form $y = a\, e^{-bx}$; (2) fitting enzyme kinetic data; and (3) fitting data to a Lorentzian curve.

equation	Y	X	a_0	a_1	w	comments
$y = a + b/x$	y	$1/x$	a	b	1	$x \neq 0$
$y = a + bx^p$	y	x^p	a	b	1	$x > 0$ for non-integer p
$y = a + b \ln x$	y	$\ln x$	a	b	1	$x > 0$
$y = ax^p + bx^q$	yx^{-p}	x^{q-p}	a	b	x^{2q}	$x > 0$ for non-integer p or q
$y = ab^x$	$\ln y$	x	$\ln a$	$\ln b$	y^2	$y > 0$
$y = ab^{1/x}$	$\ln y$	$1/x$	$\ln a$	$\ln b$	y^2	$x > 0, y > 0$
$y = ae^{bx}$	$\ln y$	x	a	$\ln b$	y^2	$y > 0$
$y = ae^{b/x}$	$\ln y$	$1/x$	a	$\ln b$	y^2	$x \neq 0, y > 0$
$y = ax^b$	$\ln y$	$\ln x$	a	$\ln b$	y^2	$x > 0, y > 0$
$y = ax^{bx}$	$\ln y$	$x \ln x$	a	$\ln b$	y^2	$x > 0, y > 0$
$y = ax^{b/x}$	$\ln y$	$(\ln x)/x$	a	$\ln b$	y^2	$x > 0, y > 0$
$y = e^{b/(x+a)}$	$1/\ln y$	x	a/b	$1/b$	$y^2 (\ln y)^4$	$x \neq -a, y > 0 (\ln y)^4$
$y = \dfrac{1}{a+bx}$	$1/y$	x	a	b	y^4	$y \neq 0$
$y = \dfrac{x}{ax+b}$	$1/y$	$1/x$	a	b	y^4	$x \neq 0, y \neq 0$

Table 3.17.1: Some equations that can be transformed into the linear form $Y = a_0 + a_1 X$, with the associated global weights w as given by (3.17.4). The values of p and q must be known.

equation	Y	X	a_0	a_1	a_2	w	comments
$y = a + b/x + cx$	xy	x	b	a	c	x^{-2}	van Deemter eqn., $x \neq 0$
$y = ae^{(x-b)^2/c}$	$\ln y$	x	$\ln a + b^2/c$	$-2b/c$	$1/c$	y^2	Gauss distribution, $y > 0$
$y = ae^{(\ln x - b)^2/c}$	$\ln y$	$\ln x$	$\ln a + b^2/c$	$-2b/c$	$1/c$	y^2	lognormal distribution, $x > 0, y > 0$
$y = \dfrac{a}{(x-b)^2 + c}$	$1/y$	x	$(b^2 + c)/a$	$-2b/a$	$1/a$	y^4	Lorentz distribution, $y > 0$
$y = \dfrac{a}{(x+b)^2 + c}$	$1/y$	x	$(b^2 + c)/a$	$2b/a$	$1/a$	y^4	Cauchy distribution, $y > 0$

Table 3.17.2: Some equations that can be transformed into the quadratic form $Y = a_0 + a_1 X + a_2 X^2$.

There is one problem with weighted least squares, which will be illustrated in section 4.15, viz. that (3.17.4) always squares, and therefore yields positive numbers. With random noise with zero average this leads to systematic bias, especially in regions where the function studied is near-zero. When the signal-to-noise ratio is small, nonlinear least squares may therefore the preferred method.

The above is reminiscent of the conversion of absorbance and fluorescence measurements from a wavelength (λ) to a wavenumber (ν) scale. Since spectroscopic measurements integrate over the slit width used, any automatic slit width change should be incorporated. Moreover, since these are measured areas A, they are directly proportional to the scales used, and scale conversion from λ to $\nu = 1/\lambda$ must therefore involve the factor $\partial A/\partial \nu = \partial A/\partial \lambda\ \partial \lambda/\partial \nu = \lambda^2\ \partial A/\partial \lambda$.

3.18 An exponential decay

Exercise 3.18.1:

(1) Start by making a test set. Deposit 'normal' (i.e., Gaussian) noise in column N, using <u>T</u>ools ⇨ <u>D</u>ata Analysis ⇨ Random Number Generation. In column D deposit some *x*-values, and in column A compute $y = a_0 \exp[-a_1 x]$ + noise, using noise from column N multiplied by some noise 'amplitude' s_n. In column B calculate the transformed quantity $Y = \ln y$, and in column C the weights y^2, see the entry for $y = b\,e^{ax}$ in Table 3.17.1. Include a plot of your data. Your spreadsheet might now resemble Fig. 3.18.1. As the exponential function $y = a_0 \exp[-a_1 x]$ approaches zero, but the added noise can bring the signal below zero, and interfere with taking logarithms, as can be seen in cells B21 and B25 of Fig. 3.18.1.

(2) Highlight the data in columns B through D, range B12:D25 in Fig. 3.18.1, and call the weighted least squares macro WLS1. If the dependent variable, ln *y*, contains error messages, the macro will tell you so, and sign off. Try again, in the above example by highlighting range B12:D20 instead. The custom macro will now provide values for both ln a_0 and a_1, with their standard deviations, either by overwriting cells B21:D22, or with message boxes.

(3) Compare the values of $a_0 = \exp[\ln a_0]$ and a_1 obtained with those used in the calculation of *y*. For our example we find ln a_0 = 2.250975 ± 0.031581 and a_1 = 0.415494 ± 0.023354, i.e., $a_0 = 9.5_0 \pm 0.3_0$ and $a_1 = 0.41_5 \pm 0.02_3$, which can be compared with the assumed values of 10 and 0.5 respectively. No resounding success, but what can you expect from only seven data points in the presence of considerable noise?

(4) By changing the standard deviation s_n of the noise, verify that the difference indeed vanishes in the absence of noise. Save the spreadsheet for later use.

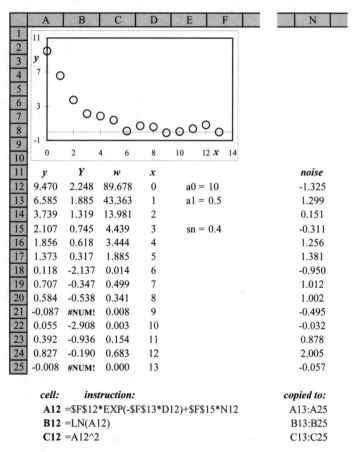

cell:	instruction:	copied to:
A12	=$F$12*EXP(-$F$13*D12)+$F$15*N12	A13:A25
B12	=LN(A12)	B13:B25
C12	=A12^2	C13:C25

Fig. 3.18.1: Fitting a synthetic exponential decay with Gaussian noise using weighted least squares. The text below the screenshot shows some of the instructions used. Cells N14:N27 contain Gaussian ('normal') noise with zero mean and unit standard deviation.

The Excel function LogEst (for *log*arithmic *est*imator) is the logarithmic analog of LinEst. It automatically takes the logarithm of y, and can therefore be used to fit an exponential. However, LogEst does not include any facilities for weighting.

3.19 Enzyme kinetics

The simplest kinetic relation in enzyme kinetics, first derived by Henri, *Compt. Rend.* 135 (1902) 916, but usually associated with the names of Michaelis and Menten, *Biochem. Z.* 49 (1913) 333, is

$$v = \frac{s\, v_m}{K + s} \tag{3.19.1}$$

where v is the initial rate of the enzymatic conversion of the substrate S with concentration s, v_m is the maximum rate, and K is a constant.

Traditionally, experimental data have been fitted to this equation after linearizing it. Hanes, *Biochem. J.* 26 (1932) 1406, rewrote (3.19.1) as

$$\frac{s}{v} = \frac{K}{v_m} + \frac{s}{v_m} \tag{3.19.2}$$

which suggests a linear plot of s/v vs. s, with slope $1/v_m$ and intercept K/v_m. In a similar vein, Lineweaver & Burk, *J. Am. Chem. Soc.* 56 (1934) 658, inverted (3.19.1) to

$$\frac{1}{v} = \frac{K}{s\, v_m} + \frac{1}{v_m} \tag{3.19.3}$$

so that a plot of $1/v$ vs. $1/s$ would be linear, with slope K/v_m and intercept $1/v_m$. The usual experimental imprecisions are such that the initial reaction velocity v should be the dependent variable. The two methods therefore yield somewhat *different* results for the very same experimental input data, because the transformations from v to either s/v or $1/v$ introduce a different bias to the residuals. We will use the data in Table 3.19.1 to illustrate this in exercise 3.19.1.

One final comment before we are ready for this exercise. Both (3.19.2) and (3.19.3) will yield $1/v_m$ and K/v_m, so that K must subsequently be computed as $K = (K/v_m) / (1/v_m)$. Since $1/v_m$ and K/v_m are obtained from the same data analysis, they will be correlated, and we will therefore need the covariance matrices to estimate the resulting precision of K. These are included in Fig. 3.19.1.

Here, then, are the experimental data:

s / mM	0.138	0.220	0.291	0.560	0.766	1.460
v *	0.148	0.171	0.234	0.324	0.390	0.493

Table 3.19.1: The initial rate v (*: in μM / 3 min / mg enzyme) of formation of nicotinamide adenine dinucleotide at pH = 4.95 as a function of the concentration s of the corresponding mononucleotide. Data from Atkinson et al., *Biochem. J.* 80 (1961) 318, as reported by Wilkinson in *Biochem. J.* 80 (1961) 324.

Exercise 3.19.1:

(1) Open a new spreadsheet, with columns for s, v, s/v, and s, and enter the data from Table 3.19.1 in the first two columns. Use LS1 to analyze these data according to (3.19.2), and determine v_m from the slope $a_1 = 1/v_m$, and K from the ratio of the intercept $a_0 = K/v_m$ and the slope $1/v_m$. Then use Propagation to find the standard deviations for v_m and K respectively.

(2) Extend the spreadsheet by adding columns for $1/v$ and $1/s$, and use these to analyze the data according to (3.19.3). In this case, compute v_m and K from the intercept $a_0 = 1/v_m$ and the slope $a_1 = K/v_m$ respectively, and use Propagation to find their standard deviations.

(3) For the weighted least squares analysis, insert a column for the weights w between the dependent and the independent variables. Enter their appropriate values: for the Lineweaver-Burk method, which uses $1/v$ as its dependent variable, $d(1/v)/dv = -1/v^2$, so that (3.17.4) leads to $w = v^4$. Call WLS1 to perform the analysis. Repeat for the Hanes method, where the independent variable is s/v, so that we have instead $w = v^4/s^2$.

(4) Compute v_m and K as for the unweighted cases, then call Propagation to calculate the corresponding standard deviations. For comparison do this in two ways: first correctly, using the covariance matrix (with results as shown in Fig.

130

3.19.1), then incorrectly, just using the standard deviations. It makes no difference for the precision estimate of v_m, which depends on only one coefficient, but does affect the standard deviation of K, which depends on both intercept and slope.

(5) Your spreadsheet might now look like Fig. 3.19.1. Save it, because we will return to it in section 4.14.

The results for the properly weighted analyses are identical, as well they should, since they are based on the same data and the same mathematical model of Henri and Michaelis & Menten, and only differ in the way that model is linearized. In the absence of weighting, however, the results differ significantly. In this particular example, the unweighted Lineweaver-Burk analysis is noticeably off, especially for K, as can be seen in Fig. 3.19.1: $K = 0.4_4 \pm 0.1_2$ for the unweighted Lineweaver-Burk analysis, vs. $0.58_2 \pm 0.06_9$ for unweighted Hanes analysis, and $0.57_1 \pm 0.06_4$ for both models when properly weighted. However, the rather common failure to weigh the Lineweaver-Burk analysis is not their fault: Lineweaver, Burk & Deming in *J. Am. Chem. Soc.* 56 (1934) 225 strongly emphasized the need for proper weighting. But then, who reads the original papers any more?

	A	B	C	D	E	F	G	H
1	*unweighted*			*Hanes*			*Lineweaver-Burk*	
2	*s*	*v*		*s/v*	*s*		*1/v*	*1/s*
3								
4	0.138	0.148		0.93243	0.138		6.75676	7.24638
5	0.220	0.171		1.28655	0.220		5.84795	4.54545
6	0.291	0.234		1.24359	0.291		4.27350	3.43643
7	0.560	0.324		1.72840	0.560		3.08642	1.78571
8	0.766	0.390		1.96410	0.766		2.56410	1.30548
9	1.460	0.493		2.96146	1.460		2.02840	0.68493
10			*Coeff:*	*0.85005*	*1.460337*	*Coeff:*	*1.70846*	*0.75279*
11			*StDev:*	*0.05958*	*0.081784*	*StDev:*	*0.30327*	*0.07815*
12			*Sf:*	*0.09024*		*Sf:*	*0.42912*	
13			*CM:*	*0.00355*	*-0.00383*	*CM:*	*0.09197*	*-0.01935*
14				*-0.00383*	*0.00669*		*-0.01935*	*0.00611*
15			*LCC:*	1	-0.78589	*LCC:*	1	-0.81627
16				-0.78589	1		-0.81627	1
17				*v max:*	*K:*		*v max:*	*K:*
18				*0.68477*	*0.58209*		*0.58532*	*0.44063*
19				*0.03835*	*0.06941*		*0.10390*	*0.11854*
20								
21	*weighted*			*Hanes*			*Lineweaver-Burk*	
22	*s*	*v*	*s/v*	*w*	*s*	*1/v*	*w*	*1/s*
23								
24	0.138	0.148	0.93243	0.02519	0.138	6.75676	0.00048	7.24638
25	0.220	0.171	1.28655	0.01767	0.220	5.84795	0.00086	4.54545
26	0.291	0.234	1.24359	0.03541	0.291	4.27350	0.00300	3.43643
27	0.560	0.324	1.72840	0.03514	0.560	3.08642	0.01102	1.78571
28	0.766	0.390	1.96410	0.03943	0.766	2.56410	0.02313	1.30548
29	1.460	0.493	2.96146	0.02771	1.460	2.02840	0.05907	0.68493
30			*Coeff:*	*0.83984*	*1.47089*	*Coeff:*	*1.47089*	*0.83984*
31			*StDev:*	*0.05590*	*0.07605*	*StDev:*	*0.07605*	*0.05590*
32			*Sf:*	*0.07958*		*Sf:*	*0.10826*	
33			*CM:*	*0.00313*	*-0.00346*	*CM:*	*0.00578*	*-0.00346*
34				*-0.00346*	*0.00578*		*-0.00346*	*0.00313*
35			*LCC:*	1	-0.81381	*LCC:*	1	-0.81381
36				-0.81381	1		-0.81381	1
37				*v max:*	*K:*		*v max:*	*K:*
38				*0.67986*	*0.57097*		*0.67986*	*0.57097*
39				*0.03515*	*0.06436*		*0.03515*	*0.06436*

Fig. 3.19.1: The spreadsheet analyzing the enzyme kinetic data of Atkinson et al., *Biochem. J.* 80 (1961) 318 with unweighted and weighted linear least squares.

In the above discussion we have not considered two other well-known linearizations of (3.19.1), viz. those of Eadie-Hofstee, $v = v_m - K v / s$, and of Scatchard, $v / s = v_m / K - v / K$, because they contain the independent variable v on both sides of the equal sign, and are therefore unsuitable for linear least squares analysis.

3.20 Fitting data to a Lorentzian

The inherent shape of many optical absorption peaks is Lorentzian, i.e., it is described by an equation of the form

$$y = \frac{a}{(x-b)^2 + c} \qquad (3.20.1)$$

with a maximum at $x = b$. For the same peak height, half-width, and area, a Lorentzian peak is much broader at its base than a Gaussian. As a three-parameter curve, it cannot be linearized, but (3.20.1) can be converted into a quadratic with the transformation $Y = 1/y = (b^2 + c)/a - 2bx/a + x^2/a$. According to (3.17.4) this transformation must be given the weight $w = y^4$, compare Table 3.17.2.

Exercise 3.20.1:

(1) Open a new spreadsheet, with space at the top for a graph and for four constants, a, b, c, and s_n. Below those, enter column labels for Y, w, x, x^2, and y in A through E respectively. Also place a label for noise at the same row in column N.

(2) Enter numerical constants for a, b, and c next to their labels. The value for b should be well within the range of x-values you will use. For s_n enter the numerical value 0.

(3) In column N enter Gaussian ('normal') noise of unit amplitude and zero mean.

(4) Enter x-values in column C, then calculate the corresponding y-values in column E using (3.20.1) plus noise, and the numerical constants for a, b, c, and s_n. For noise use s_n times the value in column N.

(5) Now complete the columns: calculate $Y = 1/y$ in column A, $w = y^4$ in column B, and x^2 in column D.

(6) In column F compute the resulting, fitted curve for $y_{reconstructed}$ as $1/(a_0 + a_1 x + a_2 x^2)$ with the coefficients a_0, a_1, and a_2 computed by WLS1.

(7) Plot y and $y_{reconstructed}$ as a function of x, and compare with Fig. 3.20.1.

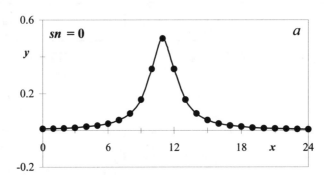

Fig. 3.20.1: Points calculated for a noise-free Lorentzian (filled circles) with $a = 1$, $b = 11$, and $c = 2$, and the curve fitted through them using the coefficients computed by using the macro WLS with appropriate weights.

(8) Now change the value of s_n from 0 to a more realistic value (but still much smaller than 1), highlight the data block in columns A through D, and call WLS1 again (because macros do not update automatically). You might now get something like Fig. 3.20.2. When in column B you use unit weights instead, equivalent to an unweighted fit, you would have found a correct answer in the absence of noise, but nonsense even with a relatively low amount such as shown in Fig. 3.20.2. This is because y is maximal near the peak center, for $x \approx b$, where the signal/noise ratio is maximal, whereas the transform $Y = 1/y$ is maximal *away* from the peak center, where the signal is much smaller than the noise.

(9) Keep pushing the envelope, by increasing the standard deviation s_n of the noise. Figure 3.20.3 illustrates what will eventually happen: the fitted function $y_{reconstructed}$ will broaden and no longer serve any useful purpose, as in Fig. 3.20.3.

(10) Save your spreadsheet.

132

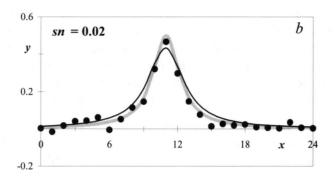

Fig. 3.20.2: Points calculated for the same Lorentzian as in Fig. 3.20.1 (gray background band) plus Gaussian noise (filled circles), and the curve fitted through them using the coefficients computed with the least squares macro WLS.

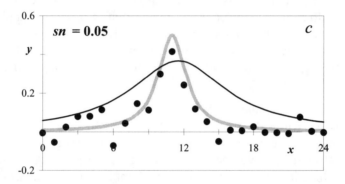

Fig. 3.20.3: The same as in Fig. 3.20.2 but with a larger noise amplitude. The fitted curve no longer provides a useful representation of the data.

The above illustrates the usefulness of testing realistic (i.e., noisy) data. The transform looks fine on paper, but a small amount of added noise disrupts it unless we use the proper weighting. That helps for weak noise, see Fig. 3.20.2, but is still not very robust, as illustrated in Fig. 3.20.3.

What went wrong in Fig. 3.20.3? The weights $w = y^4$ are indeed appropriate for the Lorentzian curve, but are wholly *in*appropriate for noise, which they emphasize by converting noise that averages to zero into an always positive contribution. Here, then, we clearly see the limit of usefulness of weighted least squares, because we cannot find weights that would be appropriate for *both* signal *and* noise. This is why, in Fig. 3.20.3, the analysis can only handle a small amount of noise.

But don't give up, and hold on to the spreadsheet: a more noise-resistant solution to this problem will be described in section 4.15.

3.21 The boiling point & vapor pressure of water

After so many worked-out examples here are two that we just mention, without much handholding. By now you will know your way around the spreadsheet in order to solve such problems. In section 2.15 we indicated that a proper analysis of the data shown in Fig. 2.15.1 requires weighting, since the measured quantity is pressure p while the fitted quantity is its natural logarithm, $\ln p$. Use weighted least squares to analyze these data, and compare your results with those listed at the end of section 2.15.

In section 2.11 we used an algebraic expression for the temperature dependence of the vapor pressure P_w of water between 0 to 75°C. Use tabulated values for P_w as a function of temperature t from the 1984 *NBS/NRC Steam Tables*, as reproduced in, e.g., the *CRC Handbook of Chemistry and Physics*, (81st edition, D. R. Lide, ed., Chemical Rubber Co. 2000/2001, p. 6-10). These already smoothed data clearly don't fit a straight line, but are readily represented in terms of a power series in t. Use LSPoly1 to find the optimal order of such a series, determine its coefficients, and plot the resulting residuals.

Since $\ln P_w$ is a more linear function of temperature t, the vapor pressure of water can also be represented as a lower-order polynomial of the type $P_w = \exp[a_0 + a_1 t + a_2 t^2 + \dots]$. Compute $\ln P_w$ and express it as a power series in t, then calculate $P_w = \exp[\ln P_w]$ and display the resulting residuals.

3.22 The power of simple statistics

This chapter should neither leave you with the impression that least squares analysis is very complicated, nor that it is mere frosting on the cake, something you do *after* the experiment has run, when you are ready to report the final results. To the contrary, more often than not, the application of least squares analysis is quite straightforward, especially when using the ready-made tools provided by Excel and its add-ins. Moreover, when used *during* rather than after the experimental stage of a study, it can often help you identify (and remedy) experimental problems early on, thereby saving you from having to redo the experiment.

First, a caveat: the following example involves a small set of absorption measurements reported by M. S. Kim, M. Burkart & M.-H. Kim in *J. Chem. Educ.* 83 (2006) 1884, as reproduced in Table 3.22.1. In that communication, these data were not shown for their scientific implications, but only to illustrate how to visualize the process of least squares. Therefore they should not be judged as more than a demo data set, and we will use them here in that vein, merely to highlight how least squares can and should be used. Incidentally, the point listed at the origin was not really measured, but apparently was added subsequently as a mere "dummy data point", and for that reason is not included in Table 3.22.1. We therefore have just five observations, and the question is: how should they be analyzed?

concentration c (M)	absorbance A
0.025	0.097
0.050	0.216
0.100	0.434
0.150	0.620
0.200	0.796

Table 3.22.1: The absorbance data listed by Kim et al.

The simplest answer is to follow the theory, i.e., to use Beer's law, $A = abc$, which for a single absorbing species in a non-absorbing medium predicts a proportionality of the form $y = a_1 x$, where y is the measured absorbance A, x is the known absorbate concentration c, while the slope a_1 is the product of the molar absorptivity a and the optical path length b through the light-absorbing solution. A sometimes recommended alternative is the straight line $y = a_0 + a_1 x$, justified by assuming the possible presence of an absorbing background species (absent in this case, where the solutions were prepared in the lab from reagent-grade components) or a constant instrumental offset. The latter is, of course, entirely avoidable by proper prior calibration.

Exercise 3.22.1:

(1) Enter the data for the absorbance A in one spreadsheet column, and the corresponding concentration c in the column to its immediate right. Label the columns, and make a copy of them elsewhere on the spreadsheet.

(2) Analyze one data set with LS0, the other with LS1. (You can, of course, use LinEst or Regression instead, once with and once without zero y-intercept.) For the proportionality, each of these routines will yield a slope of $4.08_4 \pm 0.06_6$, and a standard deviation s_f of the overall fit of the model function to the data of 0.018; for the straight line with arbitrary intercept, the corresponding results are a slope of $3.99 \pm 0.1_3$, an intercept of $0.01_4 \pm 0.01_6$, and $s_f = 0.019$.

Clearly, these data do not support the second model, because the intercept a_0 is smaller than its standard deviation s_0. Nor is there any other valid justification for using that model with these data: the test solutions were made by weighing and/or diluting a known, pure chemical in a high-purity, non-absorbing solvent (water), so that there was nothing to cause a constant background absorption. Arguments of instrumental drift should not be used, because such drift affects not only the origin but all measured data points. (It is, of course, most readily *observable* at the origin.) Instrumental drift is often, to a first approximation, a linear function of time, in which case one could make multiple series of measurements as a function of time, and apply a bivariate analysis with concentration and time as the independent variables. Preferably, though, once such drift is observed, it is minimized by proper instrument warm-up, using a constant-temperature lab, and by likewise controlling all its other causative factors. Prevention is always better than subsequent remediation.

Exercise 3.22.1 (continued):

(3) Now plot the data, or use the graph in Kim et al., *J. Chem. Educ.* 83 (2006) 1884, and look along its minor diagonal, i.e., from its origin at the bottom left to its top right corner. In such a foreshortened view, the data show a clear curvature. You will see the same by computing and plotting the residuals to either model curve: the first and last points are too low, the middle point too high for a straight line. Clearly, these data display some curvature not represented by a straight line.

(4) Make two more copies of the original data set, each with an extra column for c^2, and fit the parabolas $y = a_1 x + a_2 x^2$ and $y = a_0 + a_1 x + a_2 x^2$ to the data. For the two-parameter model you will find $a_1 = 4.5_3 \pm 0.1_4$, $a_2 = -2.6_7 \pm 0.8_3$, and $s_f = 0.01_0$; for the three-parameter model $a_0 = -0.024_0 \pm 0.005_9$, $a_1 = 5.0_1 \pm 0.1_3$, $a_2 = -4.5_8 \pm 0.5_7$, and $s_f = 0.004_0$.

Both parabolas yield plausible parameter values. Assuming for the sake of the exercise that these few observations really reflect a trend in the data rather than mere statistical fluctuations, we find at least three acceptable ways to represent these five data points, as $A = (4.08_4 \pm 0.06_6) \, c$ with $s_f = 0.01_8$, as $A = (4.5_3 \pm 0.1_4) \, c + (-2.6_7 \pm 0.8_3) \, c^2$ with $s_f = 0.01_0$, or as $A = -0.024_0 \pm 0.005_9 + (5.0_1 \pm 0.1_3) \, c + (-4.5_8 \pm 0.5_7) \, c^2$ with $s_f = 0.004_0$; however, the general straight line $y = a_0 + a_1 x$ is not among them. Incidentally, this latter conclusion also applies at concentrations below 0.1 M, where there are only two available measurements, because the necessarily exact fit of a two-parameter expression to just two data points has no predictive statistical value.

We see that some very simple considerations using readily available spreadsheet tools allow us to find plausible fits to these data, and to exclude an often advocated but in this case clearly inappropriate model, as indicated *by the data themselves*. However, to reach these conclusions we do need to look not only at the parameter values, but *also* at their imprecision estimates. (Incidentally, using Trendline should be discouraged in the physical sciences precisely because it does not provide such estimates.) And in order to select an appropriate model, once we look for an essentially empirical model describing the data, it is helpful to consider trends in the residuals. If this were a real experiment, it should of course be checked whether such nonlinearity is reproducible and, if it is, whether it is caused by some avoidable instrumental artifact, such as stray light or slits that are too wide, or (much less likely) by an actual deviation from Beer's law. In this way, by fully integrating least squares analysis during the measurement process rather than as an after-the-fact embellishment, we can derive maximal benefits from its use. Properly used statistics can be very helpful at the experimental stage, because they can reveal problems that may need to be addressed and fixed *at that time*.

3.23 Summary

In this chapter we have applied linear least squares methods to functions far beyond a proportionality or a straight line. Once the computer takes care of the mathematical manipulations, the least squares method is very easy to apply, and has therefore become ubiquitous in many fields of science and technology. It provides a convenient way to fit data to a polynomial or a multivariate function, or to any other function that can be transformed into one of these. In the latter case, weighting may be required to correct for the bias introduced by the transformation.

The least squares method furnishes estimates of the precision of its results, based on the (usually tacit) assumptions that the noise is random and can be described adequately by a single Gaussian distribution. The latter is a useful working assumption, which often can only be verified or falsified with large data sets. For that same reason, the likely errors resulting from incorrectly assuming a single Gaussian distribution for small data sets will usually be rather inconsequential. It is therefore customary to assume a single Gaussian distribution of errors, unless there is evidence to the contrary. Such evidence may be in the form of 'outliers' that may, e.g., indicate the presence of more than one distribution, or point to the need for another, more appropriate distribution.

An example of the presence of more than one distribution is the weight of US pennies, which typically have a mass of about 2.5 g. But if our sample includes pennies from before 1982, when they were still made of copper rather than of zinc with a copper coating, we will encounter two distinct Gaussian distributions, around 3 g for the older, solid copper pennies, and around 2.5 g for the zinc ones. If our measurements include only few measurements, among which one old penny, it would distort the average for post-1982 pennies. On the other hand, if the heavy penny were considered an outlier, and therefore be disregarded, we would create a semblance of orderliness where none exists. Outliers are often the canaries in the coal mine, warning us of potential problems.

The least squares algorithm can be simplified greatly when applied to equidistant data, thereby making them practical for use in 'sliding' polynomials for smoothing, interpolation, and differentiation, even if the data set has no known theoretical description and, in its entirety, does not fit a polynomial at all. Of course, the convenience of least squares methods should not lead to carelessness. The example of enzyme kinetics summarized in Fig. 3.19.1 illustrates but one of the many ways in which incorrect answers can be obtained by thoughtless application of least squares. And they are often not quite as obvious as those described by Darrell Hill in his delightful book on *How to Lie with Statistics*, Norton (1982).

When theoretical guidance is absent, there are ways to determine whether higher-order terms are statistically significant. Even though we have not illustrated this here, you can readily prove to yourself (by trying it out on a spreadsheet) that use of terms higher than necessary can lead to problems, such as oscillations between the points used for determining the model parameters. The probability of such oscillatory behavior between data points increases with higher polynomial order and with larger data spacing, and they can be particularly troublesome for interpolation or differentiation. This, as well as maximal noise reduction, are good reasons to favor the lowest possible polynomial order in fitting experimental data. On the other hand, low-order polynomials can introduce systematic distortion if the underlying signal has sharp features. The optimal solution to this dilemma is to collect a sufficiently large number of closely spaced data, and to analyze them with a relatively short, low-order moving polynomial. In this case the working assumption is that, in the limit of infinitesimally small spacing, everything is linear, and that, for slightly larger spacing, a quadratic or cubic fit will do.

In this and the previous chapter we encountered the covariance and its companion, the linear correlation coefficient, which specify the interrelatedness of specific parameters obtained by least squares, such as the slope and intercept of a straight line. There is another, more prevalent but often incorrect application of the linear correlation coefficient r_{xy}, in which it is used as a measure of goodness of a least-squares fit. We already commented on this in section 2.10, but the point bears repeating.

In the usual application of the linear correlation coefficient as a measure of goodness of fit for, say, a straight line, that correlation is between a straight line $y = a_0 + a_1x$ and a straight line $x = b_0 + b_1y$, and therefore answers the question whether there is a linear correlation between the *input* parameters x and y. This assumes that we are not yet concerned with any details of the specific numerical relation between x and y, but ask the more basic question whether x and y are (linearly) correlated at all. That can be a valid question when we need to answer whether cigarette smoking causes lung cancer (as it clearly does), or whether living close to power lines causes leukemia (which it apparently does not). However, in the type of data analysis we emphasize in this book, the existence of a causal relationship can usually be assumed, and we seek to answer a different question: not *whether* a (linear) relation exists, but specifically *what* that (not necessarily linear) relationship is. For such applications, the linear correlation coefficient r_{xy} or its square are poorly suited, inappropriate measures.

It is sometimes assumed that least squares methods are inherently objective. This is true insofar as their number-crunching aspects are concerned (compared with, say, eyeballing a best-fitting curve), but is *not* true in terms of the underlying assumptions about the nature of the experimental fluctuations (random or biased, following a single or multiple distribution, assumed to be either Gaussian or other) or in terms of the various choices made by the analyst (which variable to take as the dependent one, or what equation, polynomial order, and/or weighting factors to use in fitting the data). Least squares analysis can be mis-applied just as easily as any other method. Remember that all that glitters isn't necessarily gold, and that fool's gold, FeS_2, is far more abundant than the precious commodity, Au.

For the many functions that cannot be fitted to a polynomial or be transformed into one, a nonlinear least squares analysis is possible as long as we have an analytical expression (or find an approximate one) to which the experimental data can be fitted. Nonlinear least squares may sometimes even be preferable in cases where one has a choice between linear and nonlinear least squares, as will be illustrated in section 4.15. Nonlinear least squares will be described in the next chapter.

3.24 For further reading

There are many books on linear least squares methods and on multivariate analysis, although not that many that bridge the gap between the introductory texts and the specialist books written for statisticians. A very good text, more advanced than the ones already listed in section 2.20, is *Applied Regression Analysis* by N. R. Draper & H. Smith, Wiley (1966, 1981, 1998). It uses the powerful (but initially perhaps somewhat forbidding) matrix formalism now standard among statisticians, and used in most computer-based least squares computer routines, including those in section 10.5 and in the least squares macros of the MacroBundle.

Chapter *4*

Nonlinear least squares

In the previous chapters we have encountered the *linear* least squares method, so called because it fits data to equations that are linear functions *of their adjustable coefficients* a_i. Note that the equations themselves can be highly nonlinear in the dependent and independent *parameters*, as in $y^3 = a_0 + a_1 x^2 + a_2 \log(x) + a_3 \exp(z^5)$, as long as they are linear *in the coefficients* a_i, as in this example. This is readily seen by substituting $Y = y^3$, $X_1 = x^2$, $X_2 = \log(x)$, and $X_3 = \exp(z^5)$, which converts the above expression into the standard form of multi-parameter linear least squares, $Y = a_0 + a_1 X_1 + a_2 X_2 + a_3 X_3$. Linear least squares methods use algorithms that lead to singular, usually well-defined results.

Unfortunately, there are many problems to which linear least squares analysis cannot be applied, e.g., when the term $a_1 x^2$ in the above expression for y^3 is replaced by $a_1 xz$. The only least squares methods then applicable are *nonlinear* ones, which will be discussed in the present chapter. We will also encounter a few examples (e.g., in section 4.15) in which it may be preferable to use nonlinear least squares analysis even though a linear least squares analysis is feasible.

In a nonlinear least squares method, one compares a given data set (which we will call the experimental one, even though in some of our exercises we may simulate it, either for simplicity or for lack of real experimental data) with a model expression that depends on one or more numerical parameters. We compute the sum of squares of the residuals, SSR, or some other appropriate single-valued criterion, then minimize that criterion by adjusting the numerical coefficients used in the model. If the model is appropriate, and the noise is not too large, we can usually find a set of coefficients to provide a reasonably close fit to the experimental data. Unlike the case of linear least squares, there is no guarantee that we will necessarily find the 'best' fit for the model assumptions made. Where a direct comparison with linear least squares is possible, we usually end up with a quite similar answer, as long as the initial (guessed) values of the coefficients are fairly close to their final values. Again, one of the best checks on the reasonableness of a fit is to plot the residuals, because that graph can often reveal the presence of systematic deviations.

The sophistication of a nonlinear least squares method lies in how efficiently it adjusts the model parameters. For nonlinear least squares methods, Excel provides Solver, a powerful and convenient add-in based on the generalized reduced gradient algorithm of Leon Lasdon, Allan Waren, John Watson and Dan Fylstra. It can be found in the Tools submenu (**07**, **10**: Data ribbon, Analysis group), and apart from its basic function has several useful Options, such as Use Automatic Scaling and Show Iteration Results. These options are explained in the Excel Help files, and some of them are illustrated in exercise 4.0.1.

Microsoft includes Solver in Excel, but its code, provided by Frontline Systems (http://www.frontsys. com), may still have to be installed in case a minimal version of the software was installed originally.

As provided by Excel, Solver has one major deficiency: it yields results without any associated uncertainty estimates. This can be remedied by subsequently running a custom macro, SolverAid, see *J. Chem. Educ.* 76 (1999) 1594, which will reconstruct the standard deviations based on (2.8.1), (2.9.1) or (2.9.2), and deposit them next to the parameters found by Solver if that space is available. SolverAid can also furnish the covariance matrix and its scaled version, the linear correlation coefficient matrix.

The first group of examples, in sections 4.1 through 4.6, will illustrate the power of Solver to fit data to expressions for which there are no easy or known transformations into polynomials with integer powers. In section 4.1 we will analyze data from the cosmic microwave background radiation detector aboard the COBE (*Co*smic *B*ackground *E*xplorer) satellite. This satellite measured the so-called black body radiation in interstellar space, radiation believed to be a relic of the big bang. Black body radiation is described by the Planck equation, famous because its formulation is often associated with the birth of quantum theory. There is no known transformation of the Planck equation to allow a linear least squares analysis of these data, but fortunately that is no requirement for nonlinear least squares. Our next, more down-to-earth examples will involve fitting a profile of molecular potential energy versus distance, acid-base titrations, and phosphorescence decay. Sections 4.6 and 4.7 will then deal with curves that contain several peaks, as often occur in, e.g., spectra and chromatograms.

As an introduction to using Solver we will first use it in a simple example of reverse-engineering a complex mathematical operation. Imagine that you know how to multiply, and therefore how to compute $b = a^3 = a \times a \times a$, but that you do not know how to perform its reverse operation, taking the cube root $\sqrt[3]{b}$ to find a. Several approaches come to mind: (1) learn about cube roots and how to calculate them, (2) get a machine or algorithm that will do the trick, or (3) use a trial-and-error method based on Solver. Here is how you might use the latter approach: take b and some reasonable estimate of a, calculate a^3, then let Solver adjust the value of a in order to minimize the difference between b and a^3. Inelegant, perhaps, but it works!

Exercise 4.0.1:

(1) In a new spreadsheet, deposit in cells A1:A4 the labels b=, a=, aaa= or a^3=, and SR= where SR stands for Square of the Residual, i.e., $(b-a^3)^2$.

(2) In cell B1 deposit the number 3, in cell B2 the number 1, in cell B3 the instruction =B2*B2*B2 or =B2^3, and in cell B4 the instruction =(B1-B3)*(B1-B3).

(3) Call Solver, Set Target Cell to B4, Equal To Min, By Changing Cells B2, and press OK. Bingo: the cube root of 3 will appear in cell B2, correct to eight significant digits. As you can see, it works indeed. (We use this merely to illustrate the approach, but do not advocate this as your method of choice for cube-rooting: the instruction =B2^(1/3) is easier, faster, and much more accurate.)

(4) This gives us an opportunity to digress about Solver's Options. Max Time and Iterations are self-explanatory and, anyway, inconsequential because, for serious computations with Solver, you should always try Solver again, starting from its last result, to make sure it gave you its best, final answer. Change the value of b to the cube of an integer number, say, 8, so that you can more readily see how good the answer is. Then play with Precision to establish that it defines how tightly your condition must be met. You may have to reset the value of a, otherwise Solver may just nod and leave well enough alone. For many scientific applications, a Precision of 10^{-10} to 10^{-12} is often more appropriate than its default setting.

(5) Tolerance only works when you use integer constraints. It might better be called 'Integer tolerance'.

(6) Convergence determines the amount of relative change in the last five iterations; if that is less than the set amount, Solver will stop and consider its job done. Try various values to see how it works. For most scientific applications, decrease the Convergence setting significantly, typically to 10^{-8} or 10^{-9}.

(7) Assume Linear Model is seldom useful, but Assume Non-Negative can be. See what happens when you start with $b = 9$, $a = -3.1$ and in cell B3 the modified instruction =B2*B2, with or without Assume Non-Negative. Then try it with $a = 3.1$. It may remind you of the need to have good initial estimates.

(8) Use Automatic Scaling is useful when the adjustable parameters are of rather different orders of magnitude. This is equivalent to taking their logarithms, as will be done in sections 4.3 and 4.4, where we use equations that feature equilibrium constants K but let Solver adjust their negative logarithms, pK, which are all of a similar order of magnitude.

(9) Show Iteration Results can be instructive, because it shows snapshots of what happens during the iterations.

(10) Estimates, Derivatives, and Search are usually best left alone.

(11) In conclusion: when Solver yields invalid or suspect results with reasonable initial estimates, decrease Precision and Convergence, select Use Automatic Scaling, and try again, allowing more iterations when it needs them.

4.1 Cosmic microwave background radiation

We will use the spectral data given by S. Bluestone in *J. Chem. Educ.* 78 (2001) 215, and reproduced here in Table 4.1.1, then fit these data to Planck's expression for black body radiation,

$$B = \frac{2h\nu^3}{c^2(e^{h\nu/kT}-1)} \tag{4.1.1}$$

where B denotes the optical brightness, h is Planck's constant, ν is the frequency of the light, c is the speed of light in vacuum, and T is the absolute temperature. In terms of fitting experimental brightness B as a function of wavenumber $\bar{\nu} = \nu/c$ we can rewrite (4.1.1) as

$$B = \frac{a\bar{\nu}^3}{e^{b\bar{\nu}}-1} \tag{4.1.2}$$

where a and b are adjustable parameters.

$\bar{\nu}$ /cm^{-1}	B_{exp} /10^{-18}	w /10^{-3}	$\bar{\nu}$ /cm^{-1}	B_{exp} /10^{-18}	w /10^{-3}	$\bar{\nu}$ /cm^{-1}	B_{exp} /10^{-18}	w /10^{-3}	$\bar{\nu}$ /cm^{-1}	B_{exp} /10^{-18}	w /10^{-3}
2.27	2.0110	5.10	7.26	3.3773	6.94	12.25	1.1438	1.89	17.24	0.2287	1.28
2.72	2.5003	2.77	7.71	3.1752	8.26	12.71	1.0019	1.89	17.70	0.1945	1.11
3.18	2.9369	1.60	8.17	2.9535	10.00	13.16	0.8771	2.07	18.15	0.1657	0.98
3.63	3.2858	1.89	8.62	2.7281	8.26	13.61	0.7648	2.27	18.61	0.1396	0.92
4.08	3.5503	2.07	9.08	2.4957	6.94	14.07	0.6631	2.50	19.06	0.1185	0.82
4.54	3.7316	2.27	9.53	2.2721	5.10	14.52	0.5749	2.77	19.51	0.1003	0.59
4.99	3.8269	3.09	9.98	2.0552	3.91	14.97	0.4965	2.77	19.97	0.0846	0.33
5.45	3.8477	3.09	10.44	1.8438	3.09	15.43	0.4265	2.77	20.42	0.0717	0.13
5.90	3.8027	3.91	10.89	1.6488	2.07	15.88	0.3669	2.27	20.87	0.0587	0.04
6.35	3.7025	5.10	11.34	1.4672	2.07	16.34	0.3136	1.89	21.33	0.0459	0.01
6.81	3.5551	5.92	11.80	1.2973	1.89	16.79	0.2684	1.48			

Table 4.1.1: The cosmic background radiation data from COBE as summarized by S. Bluestone in *J. Chem. Educ.* 78 (2001) 215.

Exercise 4.1.1:

(1) Open a spreadsheet, leave room at its top for a graph, and enter the wave-number $\bar{\nu}$ and brightness B_{exp} in columns A and B, e.g., starting in row 18.

(2) In column C compute B_{model} according to (4.1.2), using assumed values for a and b located in. e.g., cells G3 and G4 respectively.

(3) Plot both B_{exp} and B_{model} vs. $\bar{\nu}$, and adjust the values of a and b so that both curves are visible in the same plot, such as $a = 1$ and $b = 1$.

(4) In cell G5 compute the sum of the squares of the residuals $R = \Delta = (B_{exp}-B_{model})$, i.e., SSR (for the *S*um of *S*quares of the *R*esiduals) $= \Sigma \Delta^2 = \Sigma (B_{exp}-B_{model})^2$. This is most readily done with the command =SUMXMY2(), where the argument contains the address ranges for B_{exp} and B_{model} respectively.

(5) Call Solver with <u>T</u>ools ⇨ Sol<u>v</u>er. In the window to Set target cell enter the address of SSR, specify Equal to Mi<u>n</u>, and in the window <u>B</u>y Changing Cells enter the addresses of the parameters a and b, then press Solve or Enter. Accept the answer by checking the <u>K</u>eep Solver solution and press OK. Look at the fit in the graph. If it is poor, repeat Solver with the new values for a and b. If that doesn't work, use different starting values for a and b to get Solver past what may be a 'false' (i.e., local rather than global) minimum.

(6) Now call the macro SolverAid to get estimates of the precision of your results. In the example of Fig. 4.1.1, the parameters determined by Solver are located in G3:G4, the sum of squares of the residuals in G5, and the column containing Y_{calc} is C18:C60. Do request to see the covariance matrix, and specify its space as G6:H7.

(7) Your spreadsheet may now look like that shown in Fig. 4.1.1. Notice that SolverAid places the standard deviations in a and b to the right of these parameters, and the standard deviation of the over-all fit to the right of the sum of squares of the residuals, here labeled SSR.

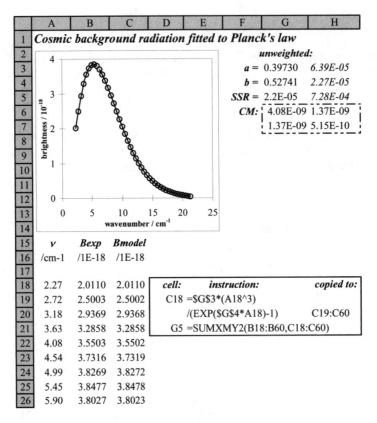

	A	B	C	D	E	F	G	H
1	*Cosmic background radiation fitted to Planck's law*							
2							unweighted:	
3						$a =$	0.39730	6.39E-05
4						$b =$	0.52741	2.27E-05
5						$SSR =$	2.2E-05	7.28E-04
6						$CM:$	4.08E-09	1.37E-09
7							1.37E-09	5.15E-10

	v	$Bexp$	$Bmodel$
15	v	$Bexp$	$Bmodel$
16	/cm-1	/1E-18	/1E-18
17			
18	2.27	2.0110	2.0110
19	2.72	2.5003	2.5002
20	3.18	2.9369	2.9368
21	3.63	3.2858	3.2858
22	4.08	3.5503	3.5502
23	4.54	3.7316	3.7319
24	4.99	3.8269	3.8272
25	5.45	3.8477	3.8478
26	5.90	3.8027	3.8023

cell:	instruction:	copied to:
C18	=$G$3*(A18^3)	
	/(EXP($G$4*A18)-1)	C19:C60
G5	=SUMXMY2(B18:B60,C18:C60)	

Fig. 4.1.1: The top of the spreadsheet of exercise 4.1.1 after using Solver and SolverAid for an unweighted nonlinear least squares analysis of the COBE data. Note that v should read $\bar{v}$, which Excel cannot display.

(8) The covariance matrix in G6:H7 contains the variances v_{aa} and v_{bb} on its (top-left to bottom-right) diagonal, and the covariances $v_{ab} = v_{ba}$ in the off-diagonal locations. Verify that, indeed, $v_{aa} = s_a^2$ (v_a is found in cell G6, s_a in cell H3) and, likewise, $v_{bb} = s_b^2$, but that v_{ab} (in cell G7) is not given by (2.10.1), which applies specifically to a straight line.

(9) Also verify that v_{ab}^2 has almost the same value as the product $v_{aa}v_{bb}$, indicating that a and b are highly correlated, see (2.9.4). What this means is readily illustrated by setting a to a different value, and then using Solver to adjust only b, showing that an error in a causes a corresponding error in b, and vice versa.

In this initial data fitting attempt to fit these data we have neglected the information in the third column of Table 4.1.1, which lists the relative weights w_i that should be assigned to each individual brightness B_i. We now modify the spreadsheet in order to accommodate these weights.

The appropriate criterion to be minimized is now $\Sigma w(B_{exp} - B_{model})^2$. Because Excel does not have a conveniently compact function (analogous to SUMXMY2 (*range1, range2*)) to compute such a weighted sum of squares of residuals, we use an additional column to compute it. Moreover, for the sake of comparing the results obtained with unweighted and weighted nonlinear least squares, we will normalize the relative weights used in $\Sigma w\Delta^2$ (denoted on the spreadsheet by *SwSR*) through division by the normalizing factor $(\Sigma w)/N$, which is here displayed separately on the spreadsheet, but could have been included directly in the formula used for *SwSR*.

Exercise 4.1.1 (continued):

(10) Enter the weights w listed in Table 4.1.1 in column D, and in column E calculate w times the square of the residuals, i.e., $w \Delta^2 = w (B_{exp} - B_{model})^2$, or *wSR* for short. In cell G14 calculate $(\Sigma w)/N$, and in cell G11 compute the weighted sum of squares of the residuals, *SwSR*, as $N \Sigma w(B_{exp} - B_{model})^2/\Sigma w$, so that cells G14 and G11 will contain the instructions =AVERAGE(D18:D60) and =SUM(E18: E60)/G14 respectively.

(11) Let the expressions now refer to a and b in cells G9 and G10 respectively. Engage Solver again (now using G11 as the target cell, and G9:G10 as the adjustable parameters), and recalculate the values for a and b. In this particular case, where the data clearly fit the model very well and are relatively noise-free, weighting makes only a relatively minor improvement, mostly on the uncertainty.

(12) Comparison of (4.1.1) and (4.1.2) shows that $a = 2h/c$ and $b = hc/kT$. You can use this to calculate the background temperature T of the universe! With the numerical values $h = (6.6260687_6 \pm 0.0000005_2) \times 10^{-34}$ J · s, $c = 2.99792458 \times 10^8$ m · s^{-1}, and $k = (1.380650_3 \pm 0.000002_4) \times 10^{-23}$ J · °K^{-1} we find $T = (2.72831_2 \pm 0.00003_2)$ °K for the temperature of interstellar space. Here we have used the Propagation macro to estimate the propagated imprecision in $T = hc/kb$, after division of b by 100 to convert it from measuring cm (i.e., inverse wave numbers) to m. Note that this computation only requires b, so that there is no need to use the covariance matrix.

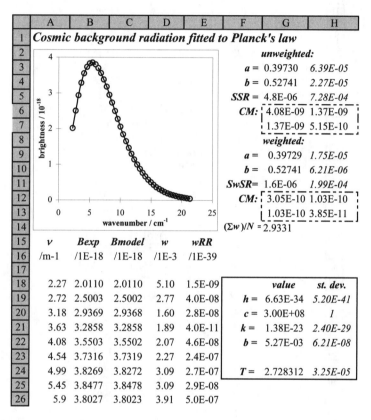

Fig. 4.1.2: The top of the final form of the spreadsheet of exercise 4.1.1, after using Solver and SolverAid for a weighted nonlinear least squares analysis of the COBE data. Again please read $\bar{v}$ for the column heading v.

Because these measurements allowed determining the temperature of interstellar space with a precision of the order of at least 10^{-4} °K, the spatial fine structure of the cosmic background radiation could now be observed. This was indeed done by the Microwave Anisotropy Probe that was subsequently launched by NASA.

4.2 The I_2 potential energy vs. distance profile

Spectroscopic measurements such as those described in sections 3.3 and 3.6 can be used to determine the potential energy – distance profile (often called the potential energy curve) of a diatomic molecule. This can then be used to test various model expressions for such a profile, and to estimate the equilibrium distance r_e and the dissociation energy D_e. As our example we will use a set of data reported by R. D. Verma in *J. Chem. Phys.* 32 (1960) 738, Table VII, for the ground state of iodine, I_2. We reproduce these data in Fig. 4.2.1, and analyze them in Exercise 4.2.1.

	A	B	C	D	E	F
1	Data from R.D.Verma, JPC 32 (1960) 738.					
2						
3	*Morse:*			*Lennard-Jones:*		
4	$a =$	12666.6	*67.7*	$a =$	12385	*150*
5	$b =$	0.019899	*0.000162*	$b =$	229.14	*0.157*
6	$r\,eq =$	236.342	*0.237*	$r\,eq =$	257.2	*0.176*
7	$SSR =$	4.14E+06	*252.4*	$SSR =$	3.34E+07	*771.6*
8						
9	v	$U(r)$	r	$U(M)$	$U(LJ)$	
10		*/cm*	*pm*	*pm*	*pm*	
11						
12	112	12547.52	228.8	12375.58	12826.54	
13	107	12532.22	228.8	12375.58	12826.54	
14	105	12522.32	228.8	12375.58	12826.54	
15	103	12509.82	228.8	12375.58	12826.54	
16	101	12495.02	228.8	12375.58	12826.54	
17	99	12476.92	228.8	12375.58	12826.54	
18	97	12454.62	228.9	12276.80	12693.71	
19	95	12427.12	228.9	12276.80	12693.71	
20	93	12393.42	228.9	12276.80	12693.71	
21	91	12352.32	229.0	12178.61	12561.98	
22	89	12302.32	229.0	12178.61	12561.98	
23	85	12170.52	229.1	12081.00	12431.33	
24	82	12039.72	229.2	11983.98	12301.77	
25	78	11824.50	229.4	11791.69	12045.83	
26	74	11562.11	229.6	11601.71	11794.13	
27	70	11251.24	229.8	11414.02	11546.58	
28	66	10893.54	230.1	11136.72	11182.94	
29	62	10490.72	230.5	10774.81	10712.12	
30	58	10045.19	230.9	10421.67	10256.93	
31	54	9559.11	231.5	9908.06	9602.49	
32	50	9034.45	232.1	9413.30	8980.82	
33	46	8474.73	232.8	8859.19	8295.11	
34	42	7882.80	233.6	8255.42	7561.13	
35	38	7260.45	234.6	7543.24	6713.89	
36	34	6608.93	235.8	6748.11	5793.17	
37	30	5930.54	237.1	5955.98	4904.44	

Fig. 4.2.1a: The top of the spreadsheet of exercise 4.2.1, with the distances r in pm, and the results of Solver and SolverAid. Also shown is the value of the equilibrium distance calculated for the Lennard-Jones model as $r_{eq} = b\sqrt[6]{2}$, and the associated precision computed with Propagation.

Exercise 4.2.1:

(1) Enter the data of Table VII of R. D. Verma, *J. Chem. Phys.* 32 (1960) 738 in a spreadsheet, as an increasing function of r. Use three columns: one for the vibrational quantum number v, one for the energy $U(r)$, and one for the distance r. Note that the values for v, $U(r)$, and r will appear twice, once for r_{min} and once for r_{max}. Plot the data as $U(r)$ vs. r.

(2) Enter labels and initial guess values for fitting $U(r)$ to the Morse function $U(r) = a\{1-\exp[-b(r-r_e)]\}^2$, add a column in which you compute U_{Morse} on the basis of these data, and plot the resulting curve. Adjust the guessed values to achieve a crude fit with the experimental data. Such visually adjusted initial guess values might be $a = 12000$, $b = 0.02$, and $r_e = 250$ when (as in Fig. 4.2.1) r has been entered in pm. For r in Ångstrom units, use $r_e = 2.5$ instead.

(3) Compute SSR using the function SUMXMY2(), then call Solver to adjust the values of a, b, and r_e, and call SolverAid to compute the precision.

38	26	5226.63	238.6	5125.97	4006.76
39	22	4498.49	240.3	4286.43	3138.03
40	18	3747.28	242.3	3425.21	2294.54
41	14	2973.82	244.6	2587.99	1531.05
42	10	2179.06	247.4	1765.36	852.58
43	6	1363.60	251.0	981.65	307.46
44	2	527.44	256.4	277.98	4.37
45	0	102.08	262.1	7.94	142.16
46	0	102.08	271.7	297.35	974.25
47	2	527.44	279.0	907.76	1848.12
48	6	1363.60	287.4	1833.15	2929.52
49	10	2179.06	294.0	2641.68	3770.59
50	14	2973.82	300.1	3409.03	4514.22
51	18	3747.28	305.6	4096.19	5146.75
52	22	4498.49	311.1	4765.69	5738.77
53	26	5226.63	316.4	5385.98	6269.43
54	30	5930.54	321.7	5976.61	6761.07
55	34	6608.93	327.3	6564.94	7239.36
56	38	7260.45	332.9	7114.63	7677.34
57	42	7882.80	338.9	7660.05	8104.65
58	46	8474.73	345.1	8176.90	8504.03
59	50	9034.45	351.7	8676.66	8886.13
60	54	9559.11	359.1	9178.51	9267.03
61	58	10045.19	367.1	9656.67	9628.65
62	62	10490.72	376.0	10117.48	9977.58
63	66	10893.54	386.1	10560.30	10315.26
64	70	11251.24	397.3	10965.80	10629.02
65	74	11562.11	410.8	11355.44	10938.05
66	78	11824.50	426.3	11696.45	11219.20
67	82	12039.72	444.8	11991.12	11476.48
68	85	12170.52	462.8	12192.54	11666.03
69	89	12302.32	494.2	12411.70	11897.73
70	91	12352.32	513.3	12492.03	11996.09
71	93	12393.42	535.4	12554.02	12082.46
72	95	12427.12	556.3	12592.28	12144.26
73	97	12454.62	577.8	12618.13	12193.06
74	99	12476.92	601.0	12636.06	12233.31
75	101	12495.02	626.3	12648.15	12266.47
76	103	12509.82	652.2	12655.59	12292.01
77	105	12522.32	682.3	12660.57	12314.03
78	107	12532.22	723.6	12663.97	12335.09
79	112	12547.52	881.4	12666.52	12369.70

Fig. 4.2.1b: The rest of that spreadsheet.

(4) Another often used fitting function is that of Lennard-Jones, which has the form $U(r) = a + 4a\{(b/r)^{12} - (b/r)^6\}$. Enter the labels and guess values for a and b, compute $U(r)$ according to the Lennard-Jones formula in the next column, add these data to the plot, and calculate the corresponding sum of squares of the residuals. Then call Solver to optimize the fit, and SolverAid for uncertainty estimates. Your spreadsheet might now look like Fig. 4.2.1.

(5) For both the Morse equation and the Lennard-Jones expression, the parameter a denotes the dissociation energy $\overline{D_e}$ in units of wavenumbers. The Morse curve fits the data better in Fig. 4.2.2 than the Lennard-Jones curve, although the residuals show considerable systematic deviations for both. The two analyses yield different results for both the dissociation energy and the equilibrium distance r_e, and this difference persists if we only analyze, say, the 12 data points surrounding the curve minimum, as shown in the inset to Fig. 4.2.2.

(6) Fitting the Morse function to all data yields $r_e = 263.3_4 \pm 0.2_4$ pm, while fitting the 12 points nearest to the curve minimum curve leads to $r_e = 266.74_7 \pm 0.04_4$ pm. Even within a given model, the result can therefore depend markedly on the number of data points used.

(7) The uncertainty in the dissociation energy is even larger, and clearly depends on the model used. It should be realized in this context that r_e and $\overline{D}_e$ are truly model parameters, because they both refer to a physically non-realizable, vibrationless "basement" state below the ground state at $v = 0$.

(8) We might be tempted to use linear least squares to fit the data to a Lennard-Jones function, with $U(r) = a_0 + a_1 r^{-6} + a_2 (r^{-6})^2$. So analyzed, the data yield $U(r) = (1.23_7 \pm 0.01_6) \times 10^4 - (7.1_0 \pm 0.1_6) \times 10^{18}\, r^{-6} + (1.02_8 \pm 0.02_3) \times 10^{33}\, r^{-12}$, from which we find $a = a_0 = (1.23_7 \pm 0.01_6) \times 10^4$, $b = (-a_2/a_1)^{1/6} = 229._1 \pm 1._2$, and $r_{eq} = 2^{1/6} b = 257.2_0 \pm 0.1_8$ pm, in full agreement with the results obtained with Solver and SolverAid. Note, however, that by (erroneously) using the standard deviations s_1 and s_2 rather than the covariance matrix, we would again obtain $b = 229._1 \pm 1._2$, but now find $r_{eq} = 257._2 \pm 1._4$ pm instead.

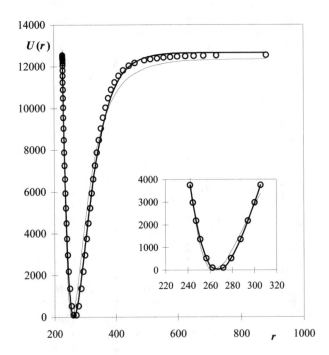

Fig. 4.2.2: The data of Verma (open circles) and two fitting functions: a Morse curve (heavy line) and a Lennard-Jones curve (thin line). The inset shows the 12 data around the minimum, fitted (as sets of 12 data) to these two model functions.

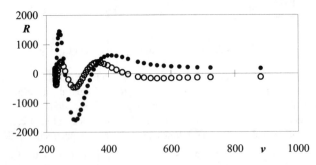

Fig. 4.2.3: The residuals of fitting Verma's data to the Morse equation (open circles) are about three times smaller than those for the Lennard-Jones formula (solid circles). Both show systematic rather than random trends.

146

4.3 Ionic equilibrium in aqueous solution

The computation of ionic equilibria in aqueous solutions has long been performed either with the help of large, non-transparent programs, or by using simplifying assumptions of often dubious justification. Nonlinear least squares analysis provides a third alternative, based on the numerical solution of exact, general formulas. Here we briefly summarize a spreadsheet-friendly formalism that can be applied to aqueous acid-base equilibrium problems. A similar approach can be used with substitution-labile metal-ligand equilibria, with reversible electrochemical equilibria, or even with their combinations, as illustrated in, e.g., *J. Chem. Educ.* 84 (2007) 136.

The acid-base formalism is based on the *proton condition*, a concept introduced by Sillén and coworkers in the 1950s, see, e.g., L. G. Sillén in *Treatise on Analytical Chemistry*, vol.1 part 1, I. M. Kolthoff, P. J. Elving & E. B. Sandell, eds., Wiley (1959) p. 227, and popularized by J. N. Butler in his *Ionic Equilibrium, a Mathematical Approach*, Addison-Wesley (1964). The proton condition counts solution species that gain and lose one or more protons upon dissolution or chemical reaction. By bringing all chemical terms in the proton condition to the side with a positive term $[H^+]$ and then deleting the "= 0" this can be converted into a *proton function*, ^HF. Using conservation of mass and charge, it can be shown (*Chem. Educ.* 6 (2001) 272) that the general condition for proton equilibrium is

$$^HF = 0 \tag{4.3.1}$$

and that the acid-base buffer strength B of that solution is given by

$$B = \frac{d\,^HF}{d\ln[H^+]} = [H^+]\frac{d\,^HF}{d[H^+]} \tag{4.3.2}$$

Other acid-base expressions are likewise simplified, as will be illustrated below.

4.3.1 The proton function

When pure water dissociates into H^+ and OH^-, equal numbers of each ion are formed, and their concentrations in a given solution volume must therefore also be equal. The autodissociation equilibrium between H_2O, H^+ and OH^- can be described in terms of the ion product of water, $[H^+]\,[OH^-] = K_w$, with a numerical value of about 10^{-14} M^2 at 25°C.

Electroneutrality in pure water requires that $[H^+] = [OH^-]$, so that $[H^+] = [OH^-] = \sqrt{K_w} \approx 10^{-7}$ M or pH $= -\log[H^+] \approx 7$. The proton condition is $[H^+] = [OH^-]$, and the proton function $^HF = [H^+] - [OH^-]$ is indeed zero, see (4.3.1). In view of the autodissociation of water, we can also write this as

$$^HF = [H^+] - K_w / [H^+] \qquad \text{for water} \tag{4.3.3}$$

When NaCl is dissolved in water, the Na^+ and Cl^- ions of the salt crystal become hydrated, but there is no net change in the proton function: as far as protons (i.e., hydrogen ions, H^+) are involved, Na^+ and Cl^- are just *spectator* ions. When HCl is added to water, to a final concentration of C_a M (= moles per liter), there are two sources of protons: the original water, and the added strong acid. The electroneutrality condition yields the charge balance $[H^+] = [Cl^-] + [OH^-]$. Because the hydrochloric acid is the only source of chloride ions, and the chloride mass balance is $[Cl^-] = C_a$, the proton function reads $^HF = [H^+] - C_a - [OH^-]$, which is again zero. After substituting $K_w / [H^+]$ for $[OH^-]$, we obtain its desired form in terms of the single variable $[H^+]$, viz.,

$$^HF = [H^+] - C_a - K_w / [H^+] \qquad \text{for } C_a \text{ M HCl} \tag{4.3.4}$$

When, instead, we add a *weak* monoprotic acid HA, where weak implies that it is not necessarily fully dissociated in water, then the electroneutrality requirement applies only to that fraction α_0 of the acid that is ionized, and therefore has lost its proton, hence the notation α_0. The proton function then reads $^HF = [H^+] - \alpha_0 C_a - [OH^-]$. We can express α_0 in terms of the acid dissociation constant $K_a = [H^+]\,[A^-] / [HA]$ as $\alpha_0 = [A^-] / C_a = [A^-] / \{[HA] + [A^-]\} = K_a / ([H^+] + K_a)$, so that the proton function can now be written as

147

$$^HF = [H^+] - C_a K_a / ([H^+] + K_a) - K_w / [H^+] \qquad \text{for } C_a \text{ M HA} \qquad (4.3.5)$$

For a diprotic acid H_2A we similarly find

$$^HF = [H^+] - (\alpha_1 + 2\alpha_0) C_a - K_w / [H^+]$$

$$= [H^+] - \frac{([H^+]K_{a1} + 2K_{a1}K_{a2})C_a}{[H^+]^2 + [H^+]K_{a1} + K_{a1}K_{a2}} - \frac{K_w}{[H^+]} \qquad \text{for } C_a \text{ M } H_2A \qquad (4.3.6)$$

and for C_a M H_3A of a triprotic acid H_3A

$$^HF = [H^+] - (\alpha_2 + 2\alpha_1 + 3\alpha_0) C_a - K_w / [H^+]$$

$$= [H^+] - \frac{([H^+]^2 K_{a1} + 2[H^+]K_{a1}K_{a2} + 3K_{a1}K_{a2}K_{a3})C_a}{[H^+]^3 + [H^+]^2 K_{a1} + [H^+]K_{a1}K_{a2} + K_{a1}K_{a2}K_{a3}} - \frac{K_w}{[H^+]} \qquad (4.3.7)$$

For a solution containing C_a M HA + C_a' M H_3A we then have

$$^HF = [H^+] - \alpha_0 C_a - (\alpha_2' + 2\alpha_1' + 3\alpha_0')C_a' - [OH^-] = [H^+] - \frac{C_a K_a}{[H^+] + K_a}$$

$$- \frac{([H^+]^2 K_{a1} + 2[H^+]K_{a1}K_{a2} + 3K_{a1}K_{a2}K_{a3})C_a'}{[H^+]^3 + [H^+]^2 K_{a1} + [H^+]K_{a1}K_{a2} + K_{a1}K_{a2}K_{a3}} - \frac{K_w}{[H^+]} \qquad (4.3.8)$$

and so on.

The complexity of the explicit expression for ^HF merely reflects that of the solution composition. However, the contributions of its individual components remain readily identifiable as the added contributions of water, $[H^+] - [OH^-]$, the monoprotic acid $-[A^-] = -\alpha_0 C_a$, the triprotic acid $-\{[H_2A^-] + 2[HA^{2-}] + 3[A^{3-}]\} = -(\alpha_2' + 2\alpha_1' + 3\alpha_0') C_a'$, etc. Just as the mass and charge balance expressions from which it hails, the proton function ^HF is always an *additive* function of components of the solution.

For bases, the same reasoning applies. Here we will merely use the proton function of a C_b M strong monoprotic base, such as NaOH, for which we have

$$^HF = [H^+] + C_b - K_w / [H^+] \qquad \text{for } C_b \text{ M NaOH} \qquad (4.3.9)$$

The above relations are exact when written in terms of the concentrations of their chemical constituents. However, when they are expressed in terms of equilibrium constants, we may have to consider activity effects, a consequence of the mutual interactions between dissolved species, i.e., of their energetics. Activity effects also enter the picture when *electrometric* pH measurements are used to calculate proton concentrations, $[H^+]$. When needed, activity effects can best be considered subsequently, as corrections to the above computations, as described in section 4.4.2.

4.3.2 Calculating the pH

Exercise 4.3.1 illustrates how to use the proton function to compute the pH of an aqueous solution of a strong monoprotic acid or base, and in exercise 4.3.2 the same is done for a weak monoprotic acid HA, a triprotic acid H_3A, and a mixture thereof. In exercise 4.3.3 we will find their buffer strengths.

Exercise 4.3.1:

(1) Find the pH of 0.12 M aqueous HCl, with $pK_w = 14.00$.

(2) For HCl we use (4.3.4), i.e., $[H^+] - C_a - K_w/[H^+] = [H^+] - 0.12 - 10^{-14}/[H^+] = 0$ which we can, of course, solve directly as $[H^+] = \{C_a \pm \sqrt{(C_a^2 + 4K_w)}\}/2 = \{0.12 \pm \sqrt{(0.12^2 + 4 \times 10^{-14})}\}/2 \approx 0.12$. In general, however, such a closed-form solution cannot be found, and we will therefore illustrate how Solver can be used instead, starting with a problem with an easily verifiable solution.

(3) Open a new spreadsheet, and in cells B2 through G2 enter column headings for pH, $[H^+]$, ^HF, B, C_a, and C_a'.

(4) In cell H4 enter a label for K_w, and in I4 the corresponding value, 1E-14 (or =10^-14). In cell F4 enter the chosen value for C_a, 0.12.

(5) In B4 enter an arbitrary guess value for pH, say 2.

(6) In C4 compute [H$^+$] as =10^-pH, and in D4 calculate the proton function ^HF from (4.3.4), using [H$^+$], C_a and K_w, in cells C4, F4 and I4 respectively.

(7) Just to check, in cell C10 compute [H$^+$] as =(F4+SQRT(F4^2+4*I4))/2, and in cell B10 calculate the pH as =−LOG(C10). Note that the alternate root, $\{C_a - \sqrt{(C_a^2+4K_w)}\}/2$, would lead to a negative (and therefore physically unrealizable) value for [H$^+$], because $\sqrt{(C_a^2+4K_w)} > \sqrt{(C_a^2)} = C_a$.

(8) Now call Solver, Set the Target Cell as D4 (which computes ^HF), Equal to the Value of: 0, By Changing Cells: B4 (which contains the pH).

(9) Bingo, the answer almost immediately shows in B4 as pH = 0.92, and in C4 as [H$^+$] = 0.12. The number in cell D4 indicates how closely Solver came to making ^HF zero.

(10) Compare the answer for the pH in cell B4 with that calculated directly in B10, and likewise the answers for [H$^+$] in cells C4 and C10.

(11) Now try this for C_a = 1.2 mM by changing the value in F4 to, e.g., 1.2E-3, and again calling Solver. You will now find pH = 2.92. And, just to make sure, try it also for, say, C_a = 1.2 μM, and 1.2 nM. Each time you change the value of C_a in cell F4, the results in cells B10 and C10 will appear immediately, whereas those in B4 and C4 require that you call Solver for each new value of C_a in cell F4. But that disadvantage in speed and convenience will disappear with a more complex chemical system, for which no closed-form solution is available.

(12) A more serious restriction is the following. It is always possible to make Solver miss its goal by using far-off initial estimates. If you look for the solution for C_a = 0.12 M by starting from pH = 7, you will not find it. In other words, after finding the correct answer for C_a = 1.2 nM, changing the value of C_a in cell F4 back to 0.12 and just calling Solver will *not* do: you will also have to change the guessed, initial pH to a more "reasonable" value, such as −5, 0, or +4, but not −6 or +5. A trial-and-error method, even one as sophisticated as Solver, cannot be put on automatic!

(13) As a slight excursion, now consider a strong base at various concentrations C_b. To do this, copy cells B4:D4 to B5:D5, place the value of C_b in G5 (even though column G is mislabeled for this particular purpose), and change the formula in D5 to =C5+G5−I4/C5 to bring it in line with (4.3.9). Call Solver, and now let D5 approach zero by adjusting B5.

(14) Assuming that you started from a reasonable initial value, you should now find pH = 13.08. Again, test it with other values for C_b. For comparison you may want to copy B10:C10 to B11:C11, then change the formula in C11 to (G5−SQRT(G5^2−4*I4))/2. Keep the spreadsheet for use in the next exercises.

Note that this approach is somewhat analogous to finding the cube root in exercise 4.0.1. It is also quite general: you provide the appropriate formula for ^HF (in column D), the requisite constants (in columns F, G, and I), and close starting values for the pH (in column B), whereupon Solver can do the rest. In this case, the answers can be compared with their algebraic solutions, and are usually seen to agree within the specified precision, see item (4) of exercise 4.0.1.

Exercise 4.3.2:

(1) Extend the spreadsheet of exercise 4.3.1 to find the pH of 0.34 M HA with pK_a = 4.00, 0.56 M H$_3$A with pK_{a1} = 2.00, pK_{a2} = 3.00, and pK_{a3} = 6.00, and the pH of the mixture of 0.78 M HA with 0.90 M H$_3$A with the above acid dissociation constants and pK_w = 14.00.

(2) In cell B6 place an initial pH value, say 2; in C6 the corresponding pH computed as =10^-B6; in D6 code (4.3.5) as =C6−I5*F6/(C6+I5)−I4/C6. In F6 deposit the value 0.34; in H5 place a label for K_a and in I5 its value, 1E-4. Call Solver, and specify D6 as its target, and B6 as the variable to be adjusted. You should find pH = 2.24. Check that you find the same result with other initial pH values, such as 0 or 5.

(3) In cell B7 again place a plausible initial pH value, in C7 compute its proton concentration, and in D7 use (4.3.7). Use G7 for the concentration, 0.56 M. Place labels for K_{a1} through K_{a3} in H6:H8, and the corresponding values in I6:I8: $K_{a1} = 10^{-2}$ M^2, $K_{a2} = 10^{-3}$ M^2, $K_{a3} = 10^{-6}$ M^2. In cell D7 place the appropriate formula for the proton function, =C7−(C7^2*I6+2*C7*I6*I7+3*I6*I7*I8)*G7 / (C7^3+C7^2*I6+C7*I6*I7+I6*I7*I8)−I4/C7, see (4.3.7). Use Solver to make ^HF approach zero by changing the pH. You should now find pH = 1.15. Again, verify your answer with a few neighboring values as initial pH.

(4) In cell D8 code for the acid mixture, using (4.3.8), with C_a = 0.78 in F8, and C_a' = 0.90 in G8. The resulting pH is 1.02. Verify this result different for starting pH values, then play around by changing the concentrations and/or pK values. When your curiosity is satisfied, hold on to the spreadsheet, because we will use it again.

Exercises 4.3.1 and 4.3.2 illustrate how we can find the pH of any aqueous solution, given the concentrations and equilibrium constants of the solution components. Beyond neglecting activity effects (which, when necessary, can always be introduced afterwards, see section 4.4.2), no approximations are used. Moreover, we can freely change the input parameters, i.e., their concentrations and equilibrium constants, and find the associated pH values. The same applies to bases, acid or basic salts, and their mixtures, e.g., (4.4.1) specifies the formula for $^H F$ for the acid salt KH_2PO_4. As long as you can specify what's in the soup, in terms of concentrations and equilibrium constants of proton donors and proton acceptors, Solver can give you its pH, usually to a much higher precision than that of the pH measurements themselves.

4.3.3 Computing the buffer strength

The buffer *strength* is related to the buffer *value* β introduced by van Slyke, *J. Biol. Chem.* 52 (1922) 525, through the factor $\ln(10) \approx 2.3026$, i.e., $B \approx \beta /2.3$ or $\beta \approx 2.3\ B$. Omitting this factor simplifies the math, as already shown by Henderson in his appendix to van Slyke's 1922 paper. It also makes B essentially equal to C_a for a concentrated single, monoprotic strong acid, or to C_b for a concentrated single, strong monoprotic base, and usually makes the buffer strength follow concentration profiles in logarithmic concentration diagrams. Simply multiply B by 2.3 to get the original van Slyke buffer value β.

For the buffer strength, we need to differentiate, see (4.3.2). Since we can readily derive explicit expressions for $^H F$ in terms of $[H^+]$, we can always differentiate them analytically. Here, however, we will also use the spreadsheet for that purpose, by replacing a mathematical differentiation by a numerical one. Although there are more sophisticated algorithms available, as described in section 9.2 and illustrated in the CentralDifferencing MacroMorsel, it will suffice here to use a simple first-order central differencing formula, in which the derivative is replaced by the approximation

$$\frac{dF}{dx} = \lim_{\Delta x \to 0} \frac{F(x+\Delta x) - F(x-\Delta x)}{2\Delta x} \approx \frac{F(x+\Delta x) - F(x-\Delta x)}{2\Delta x} \quad \text{for } |\Delta x| \ll |x| \qquad (4.3.10)$$

which we will apply here specifically to (4.3.2) by implementing it with a custom macro, BufferStrength. The VBA code of BufferStrength is shown here in case you want to see how it is done, although for now you need not be concerned with such details.

```
Sub BufferStrength()

' Computes the buffer strength B
' using first-order differencing.
' F is the proton function,
' H is the proton concentration, [H+].

Dim B As Double, Delta As Double
Dim vH As Double, vHm As Double, vHp As Double
Dim vF As Double, vFm As Double, vFp As Double
Dim rgH As Range, rgF As Range
Dim fA

Delta = 0.0000001

' Read F and H

Set rgF = Application.InputBox(Prompt:= _
  "The proton function F is located in ", Type:=8)
rgF.Select
vF = rgF.Value

Set rgH = Application.InputBox(Prompt:= _
  "The proton concentration is located in ", Type:=8)
rgH.Select
vH = rgHA.Value
fH = rgH.Formula
```

150

```
' Modify vH and read the corresponding values of vF

vHm = vH * (1 - Delta)
rgH.Select
Selection.Value = vHm
rgF.Select
vFm = rgF.Value

vHp = vH * (1 + Delta)
rgH.Select
Selection.Value = vHp
rgF.Select
vFp = rgF.Value

' Restore H

rgH.Select
Selection.Formula = fH

' Compute B = H*(dF/dH)

B = (vFp - vFm) / (2 * Delta)

' Write the result next to F

rgF.Select
Selection.Offset(0, 1).Select
Selection.Value = B
Selection.Offset(0, -1).Select

End Sub
```

Exercise 4.3.3*:*

(1) If you have not already done so for the entire SampleMacros file (which can be downloaded from my web site), at least copy the BufferStrength macro from it, and paste it into a VBEditor module, e.g., at the end of the MacroBundle.

(2) In the spreadsheet of exercises 4.3.1 and 4.3.2, call BufferStrength, enter or drag D4 into its first input box, C4 into its second input box, and see the buffer strength appear in cell E4.

(3) Call BufferStrength again, enter D5 and C5 respectively, to obtain B in E5. Continue down to fill out the B-values through row 8.

(4) Compare your spreadsheet with that shown in Fig. 4.3.1, where we only have added some labels in column A to identify the various solutes.

Again, the values obtained for the buffer strength B in column E are general, except for the absence of activity corrections. Such corrections are seldom applied to quantities such as B or β, but if they are needed, you can add them afterwards, as illustrated in section 4.4.2.

	A	B	C	D	E	F	G	H	I
1									
2		pH	[H$^+$]	$^H F$	B	Ca	Ca'		
3									
4	HCl	0.92	1.20E-01	-9.5E-10	0.12	0.12		Kw = 1.0E-14	
5	NaOH	13.08	8.33E-14	3.0E-11	0.12		0.12	Ka = 1.0E-04	
6	HA	2.24	5.78E-03	-7.7E-10	0.0115	0.34		Ka1 = 1.0E-02	
7	H3A	1.15	7.10E-02	-4.8E-11	0.13		0.56	Ka2 = 1.0E-03	
8	HA+H3A	1.02	9.52E-02	2.4E-10	0.37	0.78	0.90	Ka3 = 1.0E-06	
9									
10	HCl	0.92	1.20E-01						
11	NaOH	13.08	8.33E-14						

Fig. 4.3.1: The spreadsheet used in exercises 4.3.1 through 4.3.3.

4.4 Acid-base titrations

Apart from a few notable exceptions, aqueous acid-base equilibria are established very quickly, on a time scale of microseconds or less. Acid-base titrations, on the other hand, typically take many seconds, because the usual pH-measuring glass electrode has a high internal resistance which, together with the cable capacitance, often leads to a slow response. Making sure that the solution is homogeneous may also slow down the process, even when the titration mixture is stirred vigorously. Consequently, most acid-base titrations can be described in terms of a gradually changing equilibrium.

On the basis of chemical equilibrium, plus the conservation of mass and charge, the titration of any acid(s) with any base(s) is fully described by the deceptively simple expression

$$^{H}F_a\, V_a = -\,^{H}F_b\, V_b \tag{4.4.1}$$

where $^{H}F_a$ is the proton function of the original acid sample of volume V_a, and $^{H}F_b$ the proton function of the titrant base(s), see *Chem. Educ.* 6 (2001) 272. Here V_b is the added titrant volume at any time during the titration, and therefore varies as the titration progresses. In (4.4.1) we use the *formula* for $^{H}F_a$ of the original acid sample, and the *formula* for $^{H}F_b$ of the pure titrant, both expressed as explicit functions of [H$^+$], but during the titration we will treat the proton concentration [H$^+$] in $^{H}F_a$ and $^{H}F_b$ as a *variable*. Under those conditions, eq. (4.4.1) provides a direct relationship between the two principal variables in an acid-base titration, V_b and [H$^+$]. When we know the nature of all chemicals present in a solution, their concentrations C, and the corresponding equilibrium constants K, then we can always formulate the proton function of that solution, regardless of its chemical complexity.

A second aspect of this approach, when applied to titrations, is that it is much easier to consider V_b as a function of [H$^+$] rather than the other way around. This is so because the proton function is readily written as an explicit function of [H$^+$], while the reverse is seldom true. We will call a plot of titrant volume vs. pH a *progress* curve, in order to distinguish it from the traditional *titration* curve of pH vs. titrant volume.

Progress curves were first introduced by G. Hägg (*Kemisk Reaktionsläre*, Geber, Uppsala 1940). Both Waser (*J. Chem. Educ.* 44 (1967) 274) and Willis (*J. Chem. Educ.* 58 (1981) 659) have emphasized that, in a least squares sense, titrations are best treated by using the titrant volume, an extensive quantity, as the dependent variable, and pH, an intensive quantity, as the independent variable. During a typical titration one adds titrant, and measures the resulting pH, but there is no need to follow the *measurement* procedure in the *analysis* protocol. In Fourier-transform infrared (FTIR) measurements, i.e., an interferogram is measured as a function of mirror travel distance, and in Fourier-transform nuclear magnetic resonance (FTNMR) a free induction decay is monitored as a function of time, but in both cases the data are interpreted in the frequency domain, after a Fourier transformation. In the present case the situation is far simpler: the transformation from titration curve to progress curve merely involves an interchange of axes, i.e., a simple transposition.

4.4.1 Simulating progress and titration curves

Here we will first describe how to simulate an acid-base progress curve and the corresponding titration curve, in this example the progress curve of a single triprotic acid, such as citric acid or orthophosphoric acid, with a single strong base, such as NaOH. We have already encountered the proton function $^{H}F_a$ for a triprotic acid, (4.3.7), and the proton function $^{H}F_b$ for a monoprotic strong base, (4.3.9), and in exercise 4.4.1 we will now compute $V_b = -\,^{H}F_a\, V_a\, /\,^{H}F_b$ for a given sample volume V_a and a known titrant concentration C_b.

Exercise 4.4.1:

(1) On a spreadsheet, deposit column headings for pH, [H$^+$], and V_b.

(2) In another column, enter labels for C_b, V_a, C_a, K_w, K_{a1}, K_{a2}, and K_{a3}, and in the next column deposit values for these parameters, say 0.01, 25, 0.01, 1E–14, 1E–2, 1E–7, 1E–12.

(3) Deposit the numbers 0 (0.1) 14 in the column with the heading pH, in the second column compute the corresponding proton concentrations as =10^{-pH}, and in the third column compute $V_b = -\,^H F_a\, V_a\, /\,^H F_b$ for the proton concentrations computed in the column for [H$^+$], and with the parameter values listed for C_b through K_{a3}.

(4) Make two plots: one of pH vs. V_b, the other of V_b vs. pH. If you wish, you can make one graph, copy it, then highlight the curve and, in the formula box, interchange the column names. Or in making each graph you can specify the two variables. These graphs should resemble those in Figs. 4.4.1 and 4.4.2.

(5) A few comments are in order. First, we see that the computed curve in Fig. 4.4.1 starts at negative volumes V_b. This is an artifact of the computation, in that one cannot achieve pH = 0 with an 0.01 M acid. The actual titration starts where $V_b = 0$, i.e., where the curve crosses the pH axis, at a pH of about 2.05.

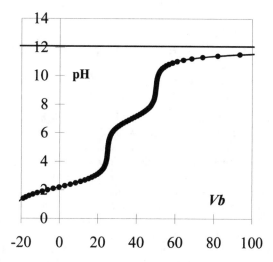

Fig. 4.4.1: The titration curve for the titration, with 0.01 M NaOH, of a 25 mL sample of a 10 mM aqueous triprotic acid with p$K_w = 14$, p$K_{a1} = 2$, p$K_{a2} = 7$, and p$K_{a3} = 12$, roughly corresponding with the pK_a's of H$_3$PO$_4$.

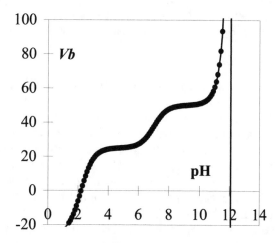

Fig. 4.4.2: The progress curve for the same titration as shown in Fig. 4.4.1 differs from its titration curve only by the interchange of its *x*- and *y*-axes.

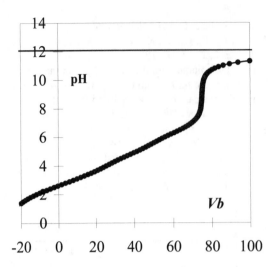

Fig. 4.4.3: The titration curve for the titration, with 0.01 M NaOH, of a 25 mL sample of a 10 mM aqueous citric acid with $pK_w = 14$, $pK_{a1} = 3.13$, $pK_{a2} = 4.76$, and $pK_{a3} = 6.40$.

(6) There is a similar section near pH = 12, where the calculation goes through a discontinuity, with the pH rising very steeply to $+\infty$, then continuing from $-\infty$ onwards. You can verify this in your spreadsheet; in the titration curve of Fig. 4.4.1 it shows as a near-horizontal line as the pH abruptly goes from $+\infty$ to $-\infty$; in the progress curve shown in Fig. 4.4.2 the corresponding line is near-vertical. Again, this discontinuity in the pH merely reflects the fact that it is impossible to make the solution pH higher than 12 with 0.01 M NaOH. It just can't be done with the chemicals specified, and the calculation tries to tell us that, in the only language numbers can speak.

(7) If these non-materializable sections bother you, just plot the curve only over the range where V_b is positive; in this case, for pH values from 2.1 to about 11.5. But leave the calculations alone: these limits will change when you modify the parameters, or even when you apply activity corrections, as we will do in the next section.

(8) The sample acid (which resembles H_3PO_4) has three dissociation constants, but you see only two steps, one near V_b = 25 mL, the second at twice as large a titrant volume. The absence of a third step, near V_b = 75 mL, is due to the masking effect already hinted at in section 4.3.2, resulting from the close proximity of pK_{a3} and pK_w.

(9) Now change the parameters, and see what happens. You might, e.g., want to change the pK_a-values to match, e.g., those of citric acid, in which case the titration curve would look like that in Fig. 4.4.3, which shows only one clear step, at the third equivalence point (i.e., at V_b = 75 mL), after a very gradual increase in the so-called buffer region, just the opposite of the behavior of orthophosphoric acid. Also change either one or both of the concentrations, and see what happens.

4.4.2 Applying activity corrections

In sections 4.3.1, 4.3.2, and 4.4.1 we mentioned activity effects, but gave few details. We now illustrate how to incorporate them. It is useful to distinguish two different types of activity corrections: the thermodynamic ones that apply to equilibrium constants, and the hypothetical (because in principle unknowable) ones that are applied according to the current IUPAC recommendation, which defines pH as the negative logarithm of the hydrogen ion activity rather than of its concentration. (Ionic concentrations are thermodynamically well-defined quantities, *ionic* activities and *ionic* activity coefficients are not, because the activity coefficient of an *individual ionic species* is not experimentally accessible, and its models are not experimentally verifiable, except in very dilute solution, where the Debye-Hückel limiting law is experimentally well-established.) While the IUPAC definition of pH is based on the Debye-Hückel theory, it was combined with an extra-thermodynamic assumption about the chloride ion activity that is incompatible with thermodynamic data. Moreover, it assumes the constancy of liquid junction potentials when measuring the pH of the sample and of those of the two reference standards.

At ionic strengths above about 0.1 M, most salt activities reverse the trend predicted by the Debye-Hückel theory, and this is usually taken into account by an added, empirical term, as first proposed by

Hückel. Here we will use the Davies model, which has the practical advantage of requiring no ion-specific parameters beyond their valencies. (This is also its Achilles heel, as the individual salt activities clearly show differences when either their cations or their anions are exchanged for others with identical valencies. The IUPAC recommendation is specifically restricted to low ionic strengths, and does not recognize higher-order models such as those of Hückel, Davies, and others.) Fortunately, one can often get away with rather large uncertainties in activity corrections because, especially in dilute aqueous solution, such corrections are usually relatively minor and therefore rather inconsequential.

In the Debye-Hückel model, and in all of its elaborations, including the Davies formula, the characteristic parameter for ion-ion interaction is the ionic strength I, defined as

$$I = \frac{1}{2} \sum_i z_i^2 C_i \tag{4.4.2}$$

where z_i denotes the valency of the ionic species i and concentration C_i. Since the ionic strength changes continuously during the titration, and the resulting adjustments are small, activity corrections are best applied as an afterthought.

Incidentally, the Debye-Hückel theory includes a second parameter, the distance of closest approach of cations and anions. In a solution containing only one kind of each, that distance can be considered as the sum of their ionic radii, but the model explicitly does *not* contain the ionic radii of individual ions. Moreover, the concept of a distance of closest cation-anion approach becomes poorly defined when the solution contains more than two kinds of ions, as it invariably does the case in a titration. The distance of closest approach is therefore often approximated by a factor 1 multiplying $\sqrt{I}$ in the term $(1 + \sqrt{I})$ in the exponent of the Davies equation (4.4.3), although a somewhat larger value, of about 2, often yields a slightly better fit for the activities of many common salts.

The Davies equation can be written as

$$f_i = 10^{-0.5 z_i^2 \{[\sqrt{I}/(1+\sqrt{I})]-0.3I\}} = f^{z_i^2} \tag{4.4.3}$$

where the (common) ionic activity coefficient of all monovalent ions is then assumed to be

$$f = 10^{-0.5\{[\sqrt{I}/(1+\sqrt{I})]-0.3I\}} \tag{4.4.4}$$

which is only a function of the ionic strength I. The activity coefficients of neutral species are ignored in the Davies expression, just as they are in the Debye-Hückel model, but salting-in and salting-out effects are included, and supposedly represented by a constant term $-0.3\,I$, even though salting-*in* and salting-*out* obviously require different signs. The Davies expression approximates an "average" salt solution but exactly fits none, while exhibiting the correct limiting behavior for $I \to 0$. We should only use it as long as the resulting correction is relatively small.

In our example of the titration of H_3A with NaOH we then compute the ionic strength from (4.4.2) as

$$I = \frac{1}{2} \left\{ [H^+] + [Na^+] + [OH^-] + [H_2A^-] + 4\,[HA^{2-}] + 9\,[A^{3-}] \right\}$$

$$= \frac{1}{2} \left\{ \begin{array}{l} [H^+] + \dfrac{C_b V_b}{V_a + V_b} + \dfrac{K_w}{[H^+]} \\[2mm] + \dfrac{[H^+]^2 K_{a1} + 4[H^+] K_{a1} K_{a2} + 9 K_{a1} K_{a2} K_{a3}}{[H^+]^3 + [H^+]^2 K_{a1} + [H^+] K_{a1} K_{a2} + K_{a1} K_{a2} K_{a3}} \dfrac{C_a V_a}{V_a + V_b} \end{array} \right\} \tag{4.4.5}$$

where the factors $V_a/(V_a+V_b)$ and $V_b/(V_a+V_b)$ represent the mutual dilution of sample and titrant. The spectator ion Na^+ doesn't figure in the proton function, but does contribute to the ionic strength.

The effect of ionic activity coefficients on equilibrium "constants" is to make them only approximately constant. Denoting their "*true*" (or "*thermodynamic*") equilibrium values by K', we have, for the ions involved in the titration of exercise 4.4.1,

$$K_w^t = [H^+]f_{+1}[OH^-]f_{-1} = f^2 K_w \tag{4.4.6}$$

$$K_{a1}^t = \frac{[H^+]f_{+1}[H_2A^-]f_{-1}}{[H_3A]} = f^2 K_{a1} \tag{4.4.7}$$

$$K_{a2}^t = \frac{[H^+]f_{+1}[HA^{2-}]f_{-2}}{[H_2A^-]f_{-1}} = f^4 K_{a2} \tag{4.4.8}$$

$$K_{a3}^t = \frac{[H^+]f_{+1}[A^{3-}]f_{-3}}{[HA^{2-}]f_{-2}} = f^6 K_{a3} \tag{4.4.9}$$

so that $K_w = f^{-2} K_w^t$, $K_{a1} = f^{-2} K_{a1}^t$, $K_{a2} = f^{-4} K_{a2}^t$, and $K_{a3} = f^{-6} K_{a3}^t$.

Finally, if we follow the IUPAC recommendation (which yours truly does *not* recommend), we should also correct the pH, because IUPAC has defined pH as

$$pH_{corr} = -\log\{[H^+]f\} = pH - \log f \tag{4.4.10}$$

We now have all the necessary pieces in place, and therefore proceed with exercise 4.4.2.

Exercise 4.4.2:

(1) Expand the spreadsheet used in exercise 4.4.1 by inserting eight columns to the right of the column for V_b.

(2) In the first of these columns, compute the ionic strength I from (4.4.5).

(3) In the next column, calculate the monovalent activity coefficient f from (4.4.4).

(4) In subsequent columns compute K_w, K_{a1}, K_{a2}, and K_{a3}, using their fixed values as K^t-values. For example, compute $K_w = f^{-2} K_w^t$.

(5) Now calculate $V_{b,corr}$ based on the corrected (rather than the earlier, fixed) values of K, as listed in the four preceding columns.

(6) Finally find the corrected values of pH_{corr} using (4.4.10).

(7) Below the very first column of pH values, leave one blank row, and in the next cell refer to the first (top) value you have just computed for the corrected pH. Do the same for the corrected V_b at the bottom of the third column. Then copy these two instructions down 140 rows.

(8) Now return to one of the graphs you made earlier, click on the curve, and in the formula box extend the data ranges of the variables used, pH and V_b, to row 140. Now you will see two curves, one for the uncorrected data, the other after activity correction. For the titration of 0.1 M citric acid with 0.1 M NaOH the titration curve will now look similar to that shown in Fig. 4.4.4. The progress curve will resemble that in Fig. 4.4.5. The concentrations C_a and C_b were increased tenfold in order to emphasize the activity effect.

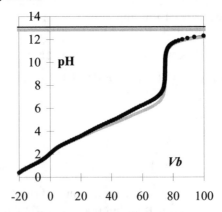

Fig. 4.4.4: The titration curve for the titration, with 0.1 M NaOH, of a 25 mL sample of a 0.1 M aqueous citric acid with $pK_w^t = 14$, $pK_{a1}^t = 3.13$, $pK_{a2}^t = 4.76$, and $pK_{a3}^t = 6.40$. The solid black circles show the curve computed without activity corrections. The gray curve is obtained after application of activity corrections based on the Davies expression.

The above example features trivalent ions and fairly concentrated solutions, which both tend to enhance the magnitude of activity effects, yet the corresponding corrections in the titration and progress curves are relatively minor. Moreover, the location of the near-vertical step in Fig. 4.4.4, or of the corresponding plateau in Fig. 4.4.5, is hardly affected by activity corrections. This is the region around the third equivalence point, i.e., the point where $V_b = 3C_aV_a/C_b$, a quantity that is purely based on counting species, and is therefore unaffected by activity corrections. We see that activity corrections are of minor importance when the titration is used to measure solution concentrations, although they can be significant when the purpose of the titration is to determine equilibrium constants.

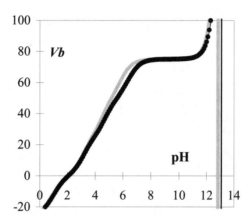

Fig. 4.4.5: The progress curve for the titration, with 0.1 M NaOH, of a 25 mL sample of a 0.1 M aqueous citric acid with $pK_w{}' = 14$, $pK_{a1}{}' = 3.13$, $pK_{a2}{}' = 4.76$, and $pK_{a3}{}' = 6.40$. As in Fig. 4.4.4, the solid black circles show the curve computed without activity corrections; the gray curve is obtained after activity correction based on the Davies expression.

Exercise 4.4.3:

(1) Expand the spreadsheet used in exercise 4.4.2 by adding three more columns, one for H_{corr}, one for $V_{b,solver}$, and one for residuals.

(2) Also make a second set of labels and spaces for C_b, V_a, C_a, K_w, K_{a1}, K_{a2}, and K_{a3}, and a separate set for pC_a, pK_w, pK_{a1}, pK_{a2}, and pK_{a3}.

(3) Set $pC_a = 1$, $pK_w = 14$, $pK_{a1} = 3.13$, $pK_{a2} = 4.70$, and $pK_{a3} = 6.40$, then use these to compute the corresponding values for C_a, K_w, K_{a1}, K_{a2}, and K_{a3}. Also enter $C_b = 0.1$ and $V_a = 25$.

(4) In the column for H_{corr} compute $[H^+]$ as $10^{-pH_{corr}}$.

(5) In the column for $V_{b,solver}$ compute the volume of added titrant using the same relation as in the column for V_b in exercise 4.4.1, but now using the values for H_{corr} for $[H^+]$, and the constants in the new data set for C_b through K_{a3} introduced in instructions (2) and (3).

(6) Make a label for SSR, and a corresponding cell where you calculate, using the function SUMXMY2, the sum of squares of the differences between $V_{b,corr}$ and $V_{b,solver}$.

(7) Call Solver, and let it minimize SSR by adjusting the values for pC_a, pK_w, pK_{a1}, pK_{a2}, and pK_{a3} that control those of C_a, K_w, K_{a1}, K_{a2}, and K_{a3}.

(8) In the residuals column calculate and plot the differences between $V_{b,solver}$ and $V_{b,corr}$. Then plot $V_{b,solver}$ in the same graph as $V_{b,corr}$, and in a separate graph display the differences between them.

The values found by Solver, $C_a = 0.1002$, $pK_w = 13.89$, $pK_{a1} = 3.08$, $pK_{a2} = 4.49$, and $pK_{a3} = 5.86$ (instead of 0.1000, 14.00, 3.13, 4.70, and 6.40 respectively), support the above contention that the value of C_a is not affected significantly by ignoring activity effects, whereas the pK values are, especially those involving high-valency ions, such as pK_{a2} and pK_{a3}. A plot of $V_{b,solver}$ and $V_{b,corr}$ vs. pH_{corr} yields two visually indistinguishable curves, and the column for the residuals, as well as a corresponding graph, show that their differences are smaller than ± 0.15 mL (about 3 drops) except at the very beginning of the titration, when the analysis ignores the simulated activity effects.

Before we leave this example, please note that K-values were used in computing the volumes $V_{b,solver}$, but that Solver adjusted the corresponding pK values instead. This was done on purpose, because the disparity between, e.g., K_w and K_{a1} is so large that Solver otherwise would not get to adjust K_w. (You can also use the Solver Option Use Automatic Scaling to achieve an equivalent result.) Taking logarithms is a great equalizer: while K_w and K_{a1} differ by almost eleven *orders* of magnitude, the difference between pK_w and pK_{a1} is less than a factor of 11. This is analogous to using $[H^+]$ in the calculations, but plotting the results on the more compact pH scale.

4.4.3 The titration of an acid salt with a strong base

We now consider a set of experimental data. As our example we use a recent report by A. L. Soli in *Chem. Educ.* 9 (2004) 42, which lists data observed for the titration of the acid salt KH_2PO_4 with NaOH. We use (4.3.3) where V_a is now the original volume of the titrated acid salt, and ^HF_a is the proton function

$$^HF_a = [H^+] + [H_3PO_4] - [HPO_4^{2-}] - 2[PO_4^{3-}] - [OH^-]$$

$$= [H^+] + (\alpha_3 - \alpha_1 - 2\alpha_0)\,C_a - [OH^-]$$

$$= [H^+] + \frac{([H^+]^3 - [H^+]K_{a1}K_{a2} - 2K_{a1}K_{a2}K_{a3})\,C_a}{[H^+]^3 + [H^+]^2 K_{a1} + [H^+]K_{a1}K_{a2} + K_{a1}K_{a2}K_{a3}} - \frac{K_w}{[H^+]} \qquad (4.4.11)$$

where the alphas are the concentration fractions, labeled with the number of attached protons. Meanwhile we have (4.3.9) for the strong base NaOH. Consequently, the progress of the titration is described by

$$V_b = \frac{-[H^+] - \dfrac{([H^+]^3 - [H^+]K_{a1}K_{a2} - 2K_{a1}K_{a2}K_{a3})\,C_a}{[H^+]^3 + [H^+]^2 K_{a1} + [H^+]K_{a1}K_{a2} + K_{a1}K_{a2}K_{a3}} + \dfrac{K_w}{[H^+]}}{[H^+] + C_b - \dfrac{K_w}{[H^+]}} V_a \qquad (4.4.12)$$

Equation (4.4.12) has two variables, $[H^+]$ and V_b, which both change continuously during the titration, and seven parameters: the two concentrations C_a and C_b, the original sample volume V_a, the three acid dissociation constants K_{a1}, K_{a2}, and K_{a3} of the triprotic acid H_3PO_4, and the ion product K_w of water. Of these, the volume V_a of the original sample is known from Soli's paper as $V_a = 25$ mL, and the titrant concentration as $C_b = 0.1049$ M. The experimental observations are listed in Table 4.4.1, and cover the entire titration curve, from beginning to way past its equivalence point.

V_b	pH	V_b	pH	V_b	pH	V_b	pH	V_b	pH
0.00	4.41	10.10	6.50	21.00	7.20	27.70	8.43	30.80	10.60
0.49	5.06	11.00	6.55	22.00	7.28	27.90	8.61	31.48	10.71
1.00	5.36	12.00	6.61	23.00	7.38	28.03	8.81	32.51	10.85
2.00	5.65	13.00	6.68	23.96	7.48	28.18	9.11	33.41	10.94
2.90	5.78	14.02	6.73	25.00	7.62	28.30	9.30	34.51	11.04
4.10	5.98	14.98	6.79	26.00	7.79	28.50	9.64	35.00	11.07
4.95	6.08	16.00	6.86	26.50	7.92	28.70	9.90	36.02	11.14
6.02	6.19	17.00	6.92	26.75	8.00	28.93	10.05	37.00	11.21
7.30	6.29	18.00	6.98	26.97	8.07	29.20	10.18	38.00	11.26
8.00	6.34	19.01	7.05	27.35	8.22	29.51	10.31	39.11	11.32
9.00	6.42	20.00	7.12	27.51	8.30	30.01	10.44		

Table 4.4.1: The experimental data of Soli for the titration of 25.00 mL aqueous KH_2PO_4 with 0.1049 M NaOH. The volume V_b of added NaOH is in mL.

These 54 data pairs should amply suffice to determine the five remaining unknowns: C_a, K_{a1}, K_{a2}, K_{a3}, and K_w. We will use Solver to assign numerical values to these five unknown parameters (or, more presisely, to their negative logarithms), and SolverAid to estimate the corresponding imprecisions.

158

Exercise 4.4.4:

(1) Set up the spreadsheet with columns for pH, [H$^+$], V_b, $V_{b,calc}$, $V_{b,guess}$, and R, or some other abbreviation for residual.

(2) Also make a column with the labels, and a column with the corresponding numerical values, for the known parameters V_a and C_b, as well as for the unknowns C_a, pK_{a1}, pK_{a2}, pK_{a3}, and pK_w, for K_{a1}, K_{a2}, K_{a3}, and K_w, and for SSR, the sum of squares of the residuals. It is convenient for subsequent use to group these as V_a and C_b, C_a through pK_w, K_{a1} through K_w, and SSR, separated by empty cells.

(3) The duplication of K's and their negative logarithms pK is intentional: the K-values are most convenient for using (4.4.12) in computing $V_{b,calc}$, but the corresponding pK's must be used in Solver, which otherwise may ignore the smaller K-values. Alternatively use Sol<u>v</u>er ⇨ <u>O</u>ptions ⇨ <u>U</u>se Automatic Scaling

(4) For V_a deposit the value 25, and for C_b the value 0.1049.

(5) For C_a, pK_{a1}, pK_{a2}, pK_{a3}, and pK_w, use guess values; in Fig. 4.4.6 we have used $C_a = 0.08$, p$K_{a1} = 3$, p$K_{a2} = 6$, p$K_{a3} = 11$, and p$K_{a1} = 14$, but feel free to select others, especially ones that show a better initial fit.

(6) Compute K_{a1} as $10^{-pK_{a1}}$, and do similarly for the other K-values.

(7) Place the values of V_b and pH in their columns, compute [H$^+$] as $=10^{-pH}$, and in the column for $V_{b,calc}$ compute V_b based on (4.4.12) and the known and guessed parameter values. Copy the resulting values (but not their formulas) to the next column, under the heading $V_{b,guess}$, using <u>E</u>dit ⇨ Paste <u>S</u>pecial ⇨ <u>V</u>alues.

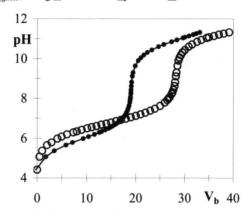

Fig. 4.4.6: The progress curve for the titration of 25.00 mL aqueous KH$_2$PO$_4$ with 0.1049 M NaOH. Open circles are the experimental data of Soli, see Table 4.4.1; the curve with small filled circles is computed with the assumed parameter values, *before* Solver is used.

(8) Plot $V_{b,calc}$ vs. pH. The corresponding plot of $V_{b,guess}$ vs. pH keeps a record of the difference Solver makes.

(9) Calculate SSR with the SUMXMY2 function, using the data under V_b and $V_{b,calc}$.

(10) Call Solver, and minimize SSR by letting it adjust the values of the five unknowns: C_a, pK_{a1}, pK_{a2}, pK_{a3}, and pK_{a1}. This will affect the values of $V_{b,calc}$ but not those under $V_{b,guess}$.

(11) Call SolverAid to find the standard deviations of C_a, pK_{a1}, pK_{a2}, pK_{a3}, and pK_{a1}, and their covariance matrix. Also plot the corresponding array of linear correlation coefficients.

(12) Compute the residuals $V_{b,calc} - V_b$, and plot them as a function of pH.

The so-called *equivalence volume* V_{eq} is defined as the volume V_b at which an equivalent amount of base has been added to the acid, i.e., the value of V_b for which $C_a V_a = C_b V_b$. Traditionally, V_{eq} is determined from the titration curve, and then used to compute C_a as $C_b V_{eq}/V_a$, where one introduces the standard deviations of V_a and C_b, and propagates the associated uncertainties to find that of C_a. In this case we find $V_{eq} = C_a V_a / C_b = (0.11859_2 \pm 0.00008_2) \times 25 / 0.1049 = 28.26_3 \pm 0.01_9$ mL. The approach used here simply bypasses V_{eq}, and directly yields the sought quantity C_a and its standard deviation,

For a comparison with Soli's empirical approach we restrict the analysis to 17 data points (from $V_b = 26.00$ to 30.01 mL) around V_{eq}. When these are analyzed in the above way we find $C_a = 0.11846_7 \pm 0.00006_5$. Again neglecting the standard deviations in V_a and C_b, this yields $V_b = 28.23_3 \pm 0.01_5$ mL, which can be compared directly with $V_{eq} = 28.22 \pm 0.026\sqrt{17} = 28.22 \pm 0.11$ mL obtained by Soli. We see that the theory-based analysis of these 17 data is some seven times more precise than Soli's strictly empirical approach. In the analysis of high-grade data, the caliber of the model used typically determines the quality of the results.

We now consider these numerical results.

(1) The values obtained for both C_a and K_{a2} are quite satisfactory. This is to be expected: C_a is computed directly, without the intermediary of an equivalence point. The value of C_a is essentially independent of (in this example: neglected) activity corrections, but this does not apply to value of K_{a2}.

(2) The value for K_{a1} obtained is not very precise, because the titration of KH_2PO_4 with NaOH only provides experimental data in the region where pH > pK_{a1}. To obtain a better value for K_{a1} one would have to either titrate H_3PO_4 instead of KH_2PO_4 with NaOH, or titrate the acid salt with a strong acid.

(3) The values obtained for K_{a3} and K_w are not very precise either. As can be seen from their linear correlation coefficient, these two numbers are strongly correlated, i.e., mutually dependent, and consequently neither of them can be determined very well from this type of experiment.

(4) Although these were experimental data, their analysis with a model that neglects activity effects is quite satisfactory in terms of determining the unknown concentration C_a, compare exercise 4.4.3. Of course, the values obtained for the equilibrium constants K_{a1} through K_{a3} and K_w do not agree too well with their literature values, since the latter have been corrected for activity effects by, in effect, extrapolating them to 'infinite' dilution.

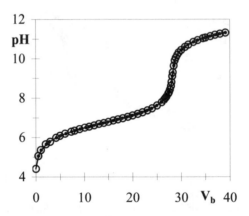

Fig. 4.4.7: The progress curve for the titration of 25.00 mL aqueous KH_2PO_4 with 0.1049 M NaOH. Open circles are the experimental data of Soli, see Table 4.4.1; the small filled circles are computed with the parameter values found by Solver. Note how the individual, computed points nest in the open circles representing the experimental data: they don't merely fit the curve, but their specific locations on it.

4.5 Fitting a luminescence decay

Glow-in-the-dark toys based on copper-doped zinc sulfide can be excited with visible light, and then placed in a light-tight box with a photodetector. Prof. Carl Salter of Moravian College lets his students in physical chemistry lab do this experiment, and has kindly provided a set of such data. Copy them from here, or download them from the web site.

Often, kinetic processes are of first order, i.e., they follow an equation of the form $I = I_0 e^{-k_1 t}$ where t is time, I_0 is the amplitude of the signal I at $t = 0$, and k_1 is the first-order rate constant. A plot of the experimental data, see Table 4.5.1 and Fig. 4.5.1, suggests that there may be a significant background signal, see Fig. 4.5.2a. The box may not have been light-tight after all, or perhaps it had not been closed properly. We therefore fit the data to $I = I_0 e^{-k_1 t} + I_b$, where I_b is a constant representing an unspecified, constant background signal. The resulting fit is fair, but the systematic trends in the residuals plotted in Fig. 4.5.2b suggest that the model used is still inadequate.

Because the photo excitation generates equal numbers of electrons and ions (electron 'holes'), which subsequently recombine to cause the observed luminescence, we actually should expect second-order kinetics in this case. We therefore fit the data to the corresponding rate expression $I = I_0 / (1 + I_0\, k_2\, t) + I_b$, where k_2 is a second-order rate constant.

t	I_{exp}	t	I_{exp}	t	I_{exp}	t	I_{exp}	t	I_{exp}	t	I_{exp}	t	I_{exp}
0	0.2006	15	0.0959	30	0.0762	45	0.0726	60	0.0695	75	0.0660	90	0.0644
1	0.1798	16	0.0964	31	0.0794	46	0.0730	61	0.0675	76	0.0668	91	0.0646
2	0.1550	17	0.0897	32	0.0823	47	0.0727	62	0.0670	77	0.0661	92	0.0646
3	0.1504	18	0.0904	33	0.0766	48	0.0741	63	0.0694	78	0.0668	93	0.0641
4	0.1431	19	0.0916	34	0.0785	49	0.0727	64	0.0771	79	0.0669	94	0.0641
5	0.1325	20	0.0898	35	0.0776	50	0.0715	65	0.0677	80	0.0664	95	0.0645
6	0.1234	21	0.0908	36	0.0773	51	0.0715	66	0.0665	81	0.0660	96	0.0638
7	0.1174	22	0.0852	37	0.0765	52	0.0709	67	0.0678	82	0.0653	97	0.0634
8	0.1171	23	0.0843	38	0.0767	53	0.0705	68	0.0640	83	0.0663	98	0.0638
9	0.1126	24	0.0857	39	0.0750	54	0.0713	69	0.0675	84	0.0583	99	0.0605
10	0.1079	25	0.0834	40	0.0752	55	0.0709	70	0.0672	85	0.0662	100	0.0619
11	0.1056	26	0.0865	41	0.0743	56	0.0695	71	0.0673	86	0.0659	101	0.0632
12	0.1048	27	0.0871	42	0.0739	57	0.0703	72	0.0670	87	0.0638	102	0.0635
13	0.1024	28	0.0836	43	0.0740	58	0.0714	73	0.0665	88	0.0635	103	0.0626
14	0.0857	29	0.0825	44	0.0739	59	0.0696	74	0.0667	89	0.0649	104	0.0635

Table 4.5.1: The luminescence decay data used in Figs. 4.5.1 through 4.5.3.

	A	B	C	D	E	F
1		$I_0=$	0.1121	*0.0027*	0.1418	*0.0017*
2		$k=$	0.0904	*0.0038*	1.2128	*0.0356*
3		$I_b=$	0.0679	*0.0006*	0.0565	*0.0005*
4		$SSR=$	0.0018	*0.0049*	0.0004	*0.0024*
5						
6	t	$I\ exp$	$I\ calc$	R	$I\ calc$	R
7			*1st order*		*2nd order*	
8	0	0.2006	0.1801	0.0205	0.1983	0.0023
9	1	0.1798	0.1704	0.0094	0.1775	0.0023
10	2	0.1550	0.1615	-0.0065	0.1620	-0.0070
11	3	0.1504	0.1534	-0.0030	0.1500	0.0004
12	4	0.1431	0.1461	-0.0030	0.1405	0.0026
13	5	0.1325	0.1393	-0.0068	0.1327	-0.0002

Fig. 4.5.1: The top of the spreadsheet used for the data in Table 4.5.1. The results of Solver are shown in C1:C3 and E1:E3 for the 1st-order and 2nd-order fits, while D1:D3 and F1:F3 contain the corresponding results of SolverAid.

Figure 4.5.3 shows both the resulting fit and the corresponding residuals, and Fig. 4.5.1 the top of the corresponding spreadsheet. It is clear from Fig. 4.5.3*b* that this simple second-order model satisfactorily represents the data, without obvious systematic bias. Note that the obvious "outliers" need not be removed in order to get this result.

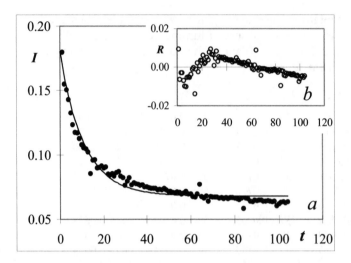

Fig. 4.5.2: (*a*) The measured phosphorescent light intensity (solid circles), in arbitrary units, vs. time *t* in seconds, and its analysis (drawn line) in terms of a *first*-order decay with offset, and (*b*) the resulting residuals.

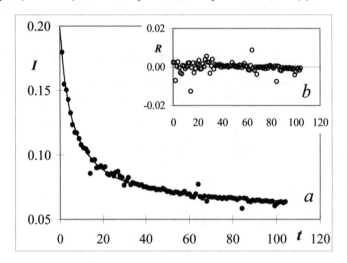

Fig. 4.5.3: (*a*) The measured phosphorescent light intensity (solid circles), in arbitrary units, vs. time *t* in seconds, and its analysis (drawn line) in terms of a *second*-order decay with offset, and (*b*) the resulting residuals.

4.6 *Fitting a curve with multiple peaks*

Our next example of Solver as a rather general curve-fitting tool will illustrate the principle of a spectrum analyzer, sometimes used to decompose spectra or chromatograms into their assumedly additive, substituent components. (Note: decomposition and deconvolution are quite different processes. Deconvolution is discussed in chapter 6.) For the purpose of our illustration we will assume that all peaks conform to a given general shape, which we will here take to be Gaussian. We will first generate a noisy 'experimental' curve, then analyze this curve in terms of a number of Gaussian peaks of the general form $y = a \exp[-(x-b)^2/c^2]$. The method is primarily visual, based on the assumed number and approximate positions of the spectral components. Peaks with considerable overlap can often be resolved, provided that the assumed model expressions for their peak shapes are correct.

Exercise 4.6.1:

(1) Open a spreadsheet. At its top leave space for two graphs, and below that for labels and constants, specifically for the peak amplitudes, center positions, and widths in the experimental and calculated function. Also enter labels for the standard deviation s_n of the noise, and for the sum of the squares *SSR* of the residuals.

(2) Below these parameter labels, enter a row of column labels for X, noise, Y_{exp}, Y_{calc}, and R.

(3) The values for X can be arbitrary: they represent sample number, wavelength or wavenumber, elution time, magnetic field shift, or whatever appropriate independent variable. In the example of Fig. 4.6.1 we use $X = 1$ (1) 1000, a sufficiently large data array to ensure that random noise will average out. One cannot expect to get similar results with small data sets.

(4) Fill the noise column with Gaussian noise of unit standard deviation and zero average.

(5) For Y_{exp} assume the sum of, say, three Gaussians, plus added noise. The instruction in cell C21 of Fig. 4.6.1 might then read `=$A$15*EXP(-1*((A21-$B$15)/$C$15)^2)+$A$16*EXP(-1*((A21-$B$16)/$C$16)^2)+$A$17* EXP (-1*((A21-$B$17)/$C$17)^2)+$H$15*B21`. We use `-1*` instead of `-` in view of Excel's precedence of negation over exponentiation, see section 1.16.

(6) For Y_{calc} we will first assume two peaks, so that the instruction in cell D21 might then read `=$D$15*EXP(-1* ((A21-$E$15)/$F$15)^2)+$D$16*EXP(-1*((A21-$E$16)/$F$16)^2)`.

(7) The residual R is simply the difference between Y_{exp} and Y_{calc}.

(8) Plot Y_{exp} and Y_{calc} vs. X and, in a separate graph, R vs. X.

(9) Try some parameter values for a fit. By playing with the parameters in block D16:F17 you will quickly home in on a visually reasonable fit, such as peak centers at about 270 and 675 nm, amplitudes of about 3 and 3.8, and base widths of about 100 and 115.

(10) Calculate SSR as `=SUMSQ(E21:E1020)`, then optimize the parameters in D16:F17 with Solver. Figure 4.6.1 shows an example.

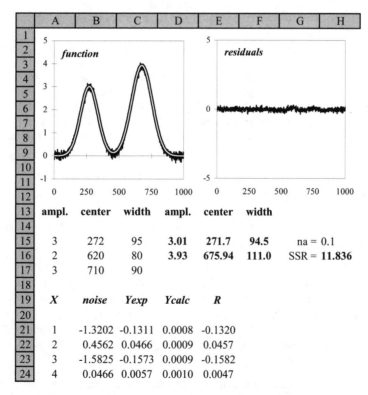

Fig. 4.6.1: The top of the spreadsheet, showing the noisy combination of three Gaussian peaks, and their analysis in terms of two Gaussians (double black line).

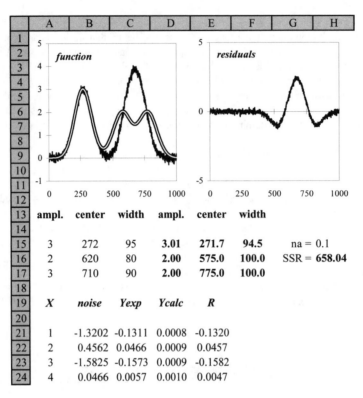

	A	B	C	D	E	F	G	H
13	ampl.	center	width	ampl.	center	width		
15	3	272	95	3.01	271.7	94.5	na = 0.1	
16	2	620	80	2.00	575.0	100.0	SSR = 658.04	
17	3	710	90	2.00	775.0	100.0		
19	X	noise	Yexp	Ycalc	R			
21	1	-1.3202	-0.1311	0.0008	-0.1320			
22	2	0.4562	0.0466	0.0009	0.0457			
23	3	-1.5825	-0.1573	0.0009	-0.1582			
24	4	0.0466	0.0057	0.0010	0.0047			

Fig. 4.6.2: The top of the spreadsheet just before adjusting the curve with Solver to three Gaussians.

(11) Comparison with the initially assumed values is quite good for the peak centered around $X = 270$, but only fair for the second peak. In fact, the residuals give a (very slight) hint of a systematic deviation. We therefore test whether this peak can be resolved into two parts, by extending the expression for V_{calc} in column D with a third Gaussian, and introducing the corresponding parameters in D18:F18, as in Fig. 4.6.2. Run Solver again; you can save computer time by only adjusting D17:F18, i.e., by keeping the first peak as is, leaving good enough alone. Fig. 4.6.3 shows what you may obtain.

How do we know whether the extra peak is significant? In general this question cannot be answered: the peak in the experimental set might be a Lorentzian or have another shape sufficiently different from a Gaussian to require more than one Gaussian to represent it. Only if we *know* that the peaks are all Gaussian, as is the case here (because we use made-up peaks), can we use the F-test described in section 3.10 to estimate the likelihood that the third Gaussian is statistically significant.

In this case the variance ratio is 11.836 / (1000 – 6) divided by 9.8788 / (1000 – 9) or 1.1945, where 11.836 and 9.8788 are the values of SSR, $N = 1000$ is the number of data points, and $P = 6$ or 9 is the number of variables used to describe them in Figs. 4.6.1 and 4.6.3 respectively. Some playing with the Excel function =FINV(*criterion, df1, df2*) will show that this variance ratio is approximately equal to FINV(0.003, 994, 991), i.e., it corresponds with a probability of 0.00258 or about 0.3% of being a coincidence. By this criterion, the third peak is surely significant, even though the positions, heights, and widths of the second and third peak are rather inaccurate.

We cannot emphasize enough that the usefulness of the above fitting procedure depends on the appropriateness of the model used. We may instead need to use Lorentzians, asymmetric peak shapes, or any mixture thereof. The above procedure can easily be automated in a custom macro. The point made here is not any specific peak shape used, but the flexibility of Solver as a general curve-fitting tool. Choosing the specific model to be used for fitting is the responsibility of the user, who should know the source of the

164

data and the purpose of the curve fitting. Note also that significant noise reduction is achieved when the number of fitting parameters used, P, is much smaller than the number of experimental data points N. On the other hand, fitting to an incorrect model may lead to significant distortion of the underlying curve.

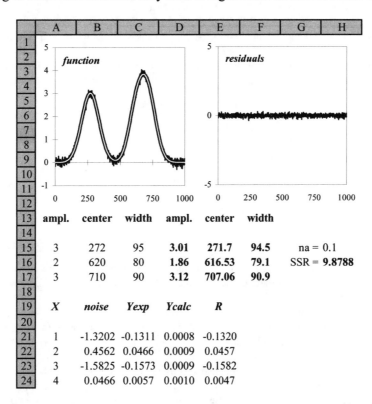

Fig. 4.6.3: The top of the spreadsheet after adjusting the curve with Solver to three Gaussians.

4.7 *Fitting a multi-component spectrum with wavelength shifts*

In section 3.7 we saw how to use linear least squares to resolve the composite spectrum of a mixture when the (additive) constituent spectra are known. Spectra in a mixture can usually be considered to be mutually independent, in which case that approach is all that is required. However, matters might be more complicated because the component spectra were taken in a different medium, in which case they may be subject to shifts to longer or shorter wavelengths due to the interaction with the solvent. In that case the simple method illustrated in section 3.7 does not work, and we will need to parameterize the spectra so that they can be shifted smoothly. For the sake of the exercise we will assume here that the spectra merely shift along the energy (rather than wavelength) axis but otherwise retain their shape, a somewhat idealized situation but often the best we can do without much more specific information. We then have a two-dimensional problem with adjustable parameters for both x (wave-number shifts) and y (amplitudes).

As our specific example we will use a preliminary analysis of the spectrum of CP29, a light-harvesting pigment-protein complex, in terms of its dominant constituent pigments: chlorophyll a, chlorophyll b, and xanthophyll (lutein). The data for this exercise were kindly provided by Prof. Harry Frank of the University of Connecticut. The spectra of the three main constituents shown in Fig. 4.7.1 are sufficiently broad that they can each be represented quite satisfactorily with six Gaussians. Once that is done, we construct a linear combination of the spectra of these three components, and adjust the resulting six parameters (three for amplitude, three for wavenumber shift) in order to minimize the sum of the squares of the difference between this combination and the spectrum of CP29. Although it is not strictly necessary, we will use a custom spectral function S to give the problem a more compact notation.

Exercise 4.7.1:

(1) The spectra can be downloaded from the SampleData on my web site, where they can be found in file CP29, and should be entered into a spreadsheet. Plot the individual spectra, as illustrated in Fig. 4.7.1. Convert the wavelength scale into one of wavenumbers, since the spectral shifts are in terms of energy.

(2) Use the keystroke combination Alt‿F11 (Mac: Opt‿F11) to go to the <u>V</u>isual Basic Editor, then (in the Visual Basic Editor menu bar) select Insert ⇨ Module, which will give you a blank sheet in which you type the instructions for the function.

(3) In that module, type or copy (from SampleMacros) the text shown below. You need not enter the spaces between the symbols, as the Visual Basic editor will insert them. The spacer lines and indents are used for easy readability.

```
Function S(x, amplitude, shift, a1, b1, c1, a2, b2, c2, _
  a3, b3, c3, a4, b4, c4, a5, b5, c5, a6, b6, c6)

Dim T1 As Double, T2 As Double, T3 As Double
Dim T4 As Double, T5 As Double, T6 As Double

T1 = a1 / Exp(((x - c1 - shift) / b1) ^ 2)
T2 = a2 / Exp(((x - c2 - shift) / b2) ^ 2)
T3 = a3 / Exp(((x - c3 - shift) / b3) ^ 2)
T4 = a4 / Exp(((x - c4 - shift) / b4) ^ 2)
T5 = a5 / Exp(((x - c5 - shift) / b5) ^ 2)
T6 = a6 / Exp(((x - c6 - shift) / b6) ^ 2)

S = amplitude * (T1 + T2 + T3 + T4 + T5 + T6)

End Function
```

(4) The first long line (wrap around for better visibility on the monitor screen, by typing a space followed by an underscore) specifies the name of the function (here called S) and its 21 input parameters (within parentheses). The last line specifies the end of the function.

(5) Then there are two lines that specify the parameters T1 through T6 as having double precision. All other parameters come from the spreadsheet, and are therefore already in double precision. This may seem (and is) strange, but Visual Basic was developed independently and, unlike Excel, does not automatically use double precision. So we must insist on it, with those dimension statements.

(6) The lines of code specifying T1 through T6, and that specifying S, are the heart of S, because they instruct the function what to do: to calculate S as the sum of Gaussians. We can use more elaborate expressions for Gaussians, or even use the Excel-provided function NORMDIST, but these are not as convenient because their amplitudes vary with their standard deviations, whereas no such interactions between the parameters occur in the simple-minded definitions of T used here.

(7) Go back to the spreadsheet with Alt‿F11 (Mac: Opt‿F11), which acts as a toggle switch between the module and the spreadsheet, and deposit labels and values for the 18 constants a_1, b_1, c_1, a_2, b_2, etc.

(8) Make a column for the calculated spectrum of, say, chlorophyll a, and in its top row deposit the instruction =S($B27,1,0,P$4,P$5,P$6,P$7,P$8, P$9,P$10,P$11,P$12,P$13,P$14,P$15,P$16,P$17,P$18,P$19,P$20,P$21) if you have, say, placed the wavelengths λ (typically in nm = 10^{-9} m) in A27:A227, the corresponding wavenumbers v (in cm^{-1} = 10^2 m^{-1}, so that $v = 10^7/\lambda$) in B27:B227 and the constants a_1 through c_6 in, e.g., P4:P21. Copy this instruction down 200 rows, i.e., the same length as the spectrum. Here $B27 refers to the top of the column with the wavenumber scale, 1 sets the amplitude to one, 0 makes the shift zero, and the rest refer to the locations of the 18 fitting parameters. The optional dollar signs following the column identifier (P) facilitates copying this expression to another row for the next component.

(9) The function only changes the contents of the cell in which it resides, just as standard instructions such as sqrt() or exp() would. Each cell in the column must therefore contain the function statement.

(10) Highlight the column containing the calculated data, copy it, and paste it into the graph for chlorophyll a. Select wavenumbers at the centers of visible peaks, such as at 23,000, 24,000 and 26,000 cm^{-1} and corresponding amplitudes, such as 0.8, 0.7, and 0.4 respectively, and play with the corresponding values of b to get the peak widths approximately right. Then add minor peaks at different wave numbers to fit the extremes of the curve. Play with these parameters (since they are independent, this is easier than it sounds) to get as tight a visual fit to the experimental data as you can.

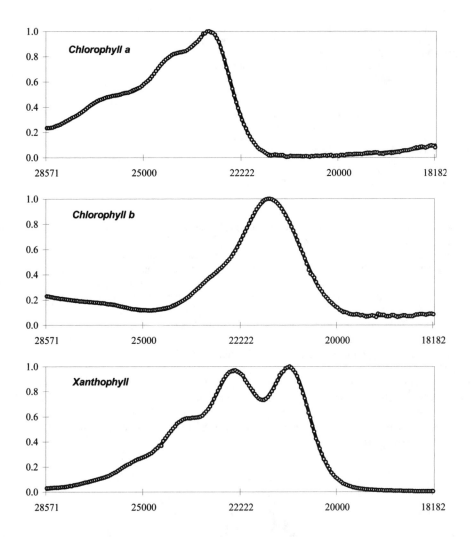

Fig. 4.7.1: The experimental spectra of chlorophyll a, chlorophyll b, and xanthophyll (open circles) and their parameterizations in terms of six Gaussian peaks (solid curve, almost entirely hidden by the points). Horizontal scale: energy in wavenumbers; vertical scale: arbitrary absorbance units.

(11) Enter a label and formula for the sum of squares of the residuals. Then call Solver, and let it minimize SSR by adjusting, say, the three parameters defining the major peak near 23,000 cm^{-1}. Then do the same for a, b, and c for the peak at 24,000 cm^{-1}, and repeat for each of the six peaks.

(12) Now increase your range and fit, say, the six parameters describing the peaks at both 23,000 and 24,000 cm^{-1}. Gradually widen your net, until you finally fit all 18 parameters simultaneously. You may have to reduce Solver parameters such as P̲recision, Tol̲erance, and Conv̲ergence, that you will find under O̲ptions, by adding zeros behind their decimal points.

(13) You may encounter trouble with the computed values, showing the error #NUM!. This most likely reflects a numerical *underflow*, in which a number becomes too small for Excel to represent, while it is too dumb to replace it by 0. That can easily happen with an expression such as $1/\exp[x^2]$ which for $x = 27$ is already smaller than about 10^{-306}, the approximate numerical limit for Excel. To prevent this from happening we change the instructions for function S, as illustrated below, where we merely repeat the coding with, in bold, the changes to be made to guard against underflow.

```
Function S(x, amplitude, shift, a1, b1, c1, a2, b2, c2, _
  a3, b3, c3, a4, b4, c4, a5, b5, c5, a6, b6, c6)

Dim T1 As Double, T2 As Double, T3 As Double
Dim T4 As Double, T5 As Double, T6 As Double
```

```
If ((x - c1 - aa) / b1) < 25 Then _
   T1 = a1 / Exp(((x - c1 - aa) / b1) ^ 2) Else T1 = 0
If ((x - c2 - aa) / b2) < 25 Then _
   T2 = a2 / Exp(((x - c2 - aa) / b2) ^ 2) Else T2 = 0
If ((x - c3 - aa) / b3) < 25 Then _
   T3 = a3 / Exp(((x - c3 - aa) / b3) ^ 2) Else T3 = 0
If ((x - c4 - aa) / b4) < 25 Then _
   T4 = a4 / Exp(((x - c4 - aa) / b4) ^ 2) Else T4 = 0
If ((x - c5 - aa) / b5) < 25 Then _
   T5 = a5 / Exp(((x - c5 - aa) / b5) ^ 2) Else T5 = 0
If ((x - c6 - aa) / b6) < 25 Then _
   T6 = a6 / Exp(((x - c6 - aa) / b6) ^ 2) Else T6 = 0

S = amplitude * (T1 + T2 + T3 + T4 + T5 + T6)

End Function
```

(14) By now you should have a well-fitting curve through the experimental data for chlorophyll a. Repeat the same procedure for the two other pigments, chlorophyll b and xanthophyll.

(15) With the three constituent spectra parameterized, you are ready for the final fitting of these spectra to the data for CP29. In order to keep the equations relatively simple, we make three additional rows, one for each constituent, in which we compute the spectrum with two additional adjustable parameters, amplitude and shift. For example, when these two parameters are stored in cells P2 and P3 respectively, we would use in the new column for chlorophyll a the command =S($B27, **P$2,P$3**,P$4,P$5,P$6,P$7,P$8,P$9,P$10,P$11,P$12,P$13,P$14,P$15,P$16,P$17,P$18,P$19,P$20, P$21), where we have bold-faced the difference. (Don't worry: the Visual Basic editor will not recognize boldfacing even if you try.) Do the same for the other two species.

(16) Make a column where you calculate the algebraic sum of the three last-made columns, and display this in the graph for CP29.

(17) Now play with the three amplitudes and the three shifts, without altering any of the other parameters. First try to fit the dominant peak by adjusting the amplitude and shift for chlorophyll a, then do the same for chlorophyll b, and finally for xanthophyll. After you get as close by manual adjustment as you can, call Solver and repeat the same approach, first fitting single components, then fitting all six parameters together. You are now refining the last 6 of a system with a total of $6 + 3 \times 18 = 60$ adjustable parameters!

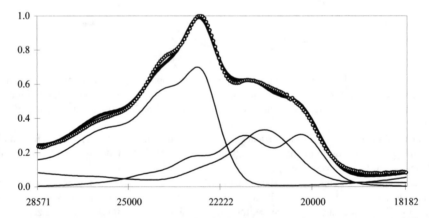

Fig. 4.7.2: The spectrum of CP29 (open circles) and that for its three major pigments, scaled and shifted for optimal fit (heavy drawn line). Also shown (as thin lines) are the three individual components, properly scaled and shifted.

The result, displayed in Fig. 4.7.2, shows an imperfect fit, with systematic deviations around, e.g., 27000, 24000, 22000, 21000 and 19000 cm^{-1}. Yet, like the cup that is either half empty or half full depending on what you want to see, the fit is quite good, considering the limitations inherent in the underlying model. There are two additional known pigments in CP29, violaxanthine and neoxanthine, with spectra that resemble shifted spectra of xanthophyll. Furthermore, CP29 contains multiple copies of the various pigment molecules, which may find themselves in different molecular surroundings. Since these sur-

168

roundings cause the spectral shifts, it is unrealistic to assume, as done here, that these multiple copies of the same pigments will exhibit the same wavenumber shifts. Moreover, the assumption that the spectra merely shift (while retaining their exact shapes) is only a first approximation. That we nonetheless achieve a quite reasonable fit with such simplifying assumptions is, in a way, quite encouraging, and clearly illustrates what can be done with parameterization.

4.8   Constraints

Constraining the parameter space searched by Solver may be needed when it would otherwise find, e.g., a negative answer for a quantity that, for physical reasons, cannot be negative. Solver has provisions for limiting its search of particular parameter values (in the Solver Parameter dialog box, under the heading Subject to the Constraints) or, in this particular example, as a general constraint (in Solver ⇨ Options with Assume Non-Negative). Here we will not discuss these in detail, although they will occasionally come up in particular examples. Instead we will focus on constraints that involve the functions rather than their specific parameters.

When data are to be fitted to several related curves, Solver may be required to maintain one or more mutual relations between them, thereby constraining the fit. Several types of constraints will be illustrated in this and the next five sections. Below we will fit data to two separate but parallel lines; in section 4.9 to a curve through two fixed points; and in section 4.10 to three lines with a common intersection. In section 4.11 we will illustrate how to fit results for chemical kinetics at various temperatures, in section 4.12 we will fit data to a discontinuous curve, while section 4.13 will demonstrate a piecewise fit. Clearly, the possibilities are endless, and we can merely give you a sense for what can be done.

Say that we want to fit two sets of data to straight lines, the first set to $y_p = a_{p0} + a_{p1}x$, the second to $y_q = a_{q0} + a_{q1}x$. This is readily accomplished by separately fitting the two data sets with linear least squares. In that case, the slopes a_{p1} and a_{q1} as well as the intercepts a_{p0} and a_{q0} will in general be different. If there are theoretical or other good reasons to expect the slopes to be the same, then the two sets should be fitted simultaneously, with a common value for a_1, i.e., the first to $y_p = a_{p0} + a_1x$, the second to $y_q = a_{q0} + a_1x$. Below we illustrate how to do this.

Exercise 4.8.1:

(1) Open a spreadsheet, and enter two small sets of linear functions of x with different intercepts but identical slopes, such as (in the example given in Fig. 4.8.1) $y_p = 2 + 1.5x$ and $y_q = 13.5 + 1.5x$. Then add a generous amount of noise.

(2) Using a linear least squares routine, fit the first and second data sets individually, and plot the corresponding lines through these data.

(3) Then deposit guess values for a_{p0}, a_{q0}, and a_1, fit the first data set to $y_p = a_{p0} + a_1x$, the second to $y_q = a_{q0} + a_1x$, compute the sum of the squares of the residuals for *both*, and use Solver to minimize this sum by adjusting a_{p0}, a_{q0}, and a_1, and plot the results, as in Fig. 4.8.1. You can of course add uncertainty estimates for the coefficients found.

4.9   Fitting a curve through fixed points

Once more we consider the data of Leary & Messick, *Anal. Chem.* 57 (1985) 956, displayed in Table 3.13.1. Since *in theory* the detector response at 0 and 100% ethanol should be 0 and 100% of the measured area, they fixed these values. This assumes the absence of any offset or baseline drift, or any other unanticipated phenomenon. By similar reasoning we might then anticipate a strictly linear rather than a quadratic relationship, but Leary & Messick instead elected to fit their data to a quadratic. We will first focus on the mechanics of fitting the data of Table 3.12 to $y = a_0 + a_1x + a_2x^2$ while this expression is forced to go through the points (0,0) and (100,100). The requirement that $y = 0$ for $x = 0$ leads directly to $a_0 = 0$, while $y = 100$ for $x = 100$ then yields the relation $100 = 100 a_1 + 10000 a_2$ or $a_2 = (1-a_1)/100$.

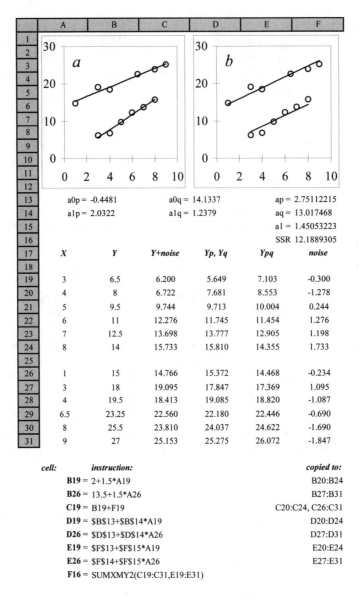

a0p = -0.4481		a0q = 14.1337		ap = 2.75112215	
a1p = 2.0322		a1q = 1.2379		aq = 13.017468	
				a1 = 1.45053223	
				SSR 12.1889305	

X	Y	Y+noise	Yp, Yq	Ypq	noise
3	6.5	6.200	5.649	7.103	-0.300
4	8	6.722	7.681	8.553	-1.278
5	9.5	9.744	9.713	10.004	0.244
6	11	12.276	11.745	11.454	1.276
7	12.5	13.698	13.777	12.905	1.198
8	14	15.733	15.810	14.355	1.733
1	15	14.766	15.372	14.468	-0.234
3	18	19.095	17.847	17.369	1.095
4	19.5	18.413	19.085	18.820	-1.087
6.5	23.25	22.560	22.180	22.446	-0.690
8	25.5	23.810	24.037	24.622	-1.690
9	27	25.153	25.275	26.072	-1.847

cell:	instruction:	copied to:
B19 =	2+1.5*A19	B20:B24
B26 =	13.5+1.5*A26	B27:B31
C19 =	B19+F19	C20:C24, C26:C31
D19 =	$B$13+$B$14*A19	D20:D24
D26 =	$D$13+$D$14*A26	D27:D31
E19 =	$F$13+$F$15*A19	E20:E24
E26 =	$F$14+$F$15*A26	E27:E31
F16 =	SUMXMY2(C19:C31,E19:E31)	

Fig. 4.8.1: The spreadsheet for exercise 4.8.1.

We therefore use Solver to fit the data of Table 3.12.1 to $y = a_1 x + (1-a_1) x^2/100$, as illustrated in Fig. 4.9.1, which also shows how these constraints skew the fit. Note that this approach can include as many constraints as the fitting equation allows.

It is interesting to take a second look at these data (now that the mechanics of their fitting are relegated to the computer) because they illustrate some of the real difficulties involved in data fitting: what fitting function should we use, and what constraints.

The question is only answerable within a given context: do we use the experiment (1) to extract model coefficients, (2) to verify or falsify a particular model, or (3) to find a representation of the experimental data for subsequent use in, e.g., a calibration? Leary & Messick did not specify any specific model, but they must have had one in mind in order to justify their constrained quadratic fit. What if we consider these data for calibration purposes only?

170

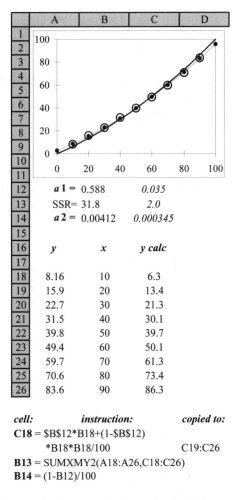

cell:	instruction:	copied to:
C18 = $B$12*B18+(1-$B$12)		
	*B18*B18/100	C19:C26
B13 = SUMXMY2(A18:A26,C18:C26)		
B14 = (1-B12)/100		

Fig. 4.9.1: A spreadsheet using Solver to find a quadratic (thick curve) through the points (0,0) and (100,100) that best fits the data of Table 3.13.1 (large open circles). SolverAid was used to find the corresponding standard deviation s_1 of a_1 in cell C12, and Propagation to calculate the resulting standard deviation s_2 of a_2 in cell C14. The small closed circles (including those for $x = 0$ and $x = 100$) connected by a thin curve show the unconstrained quadratic $y = 2.7 + 0.56x + 0.0037x^2$, which fits the data of Table 3.13.1 much better.

If we let the data speak for themselves, without any theoretical guidance, we conclude that, by all three of the criteria (minimal s_y, FR5 and FR1 > 1, and all coefficient-to-standard-deviation ratios $|a_i/s_i| > 1$) these data are best represented by an unconstrained quadratic, see section 3.13. But if, for some reason, one has good reasons to constrain the curve, the above illustrates how this can be done, and the thick curve in Fig. 4.9.1 shows the result.

4.10 Fitting lines through a common point

This is a simple variation on the same theme of section 4.8. When we require the line $y = a_0 + a_1x$ to pass through the same, as yet undetermined point (X,Y), we have $Y = a_0 + a_1X$ or $a_0 = Y - a_1X$, so that the expression for the line becomes $y = Y + a_1(x - X)$. Fitting several sets of data to lines all intersecting at point (X,Y) therefore requires that the first set be fitted to $y_1 = Y + a_1(x - X)$, the second to $y_2 = Y + a_2(x - X)$, etc. Again, the constraint that all lines go through the point (X,Y) is readily handled by Solver, which will find the coordinates X and Y of the common point as well as the coefficients a_1, a_2, etc.

171

Exercise 4.10.1:

(1) Open a spreadsheet, provide space for graphs and labels, then make columns for *x*, *y*, *n*, and *y+n*, where *n* represents noise. In the column for *n* deposit Gaussian noise using the Random Noise Generator.

(2) Split the columns in three parts by inserting two empty rows, as in Fig. 4.10.1. Assume values for the coordinates *X* and *Y* of the point of intersection of the three lines. Then take some values for *x*, and compute corresponding values for *y* as $y = Y + a_i(x–X)$, where a_i assumes different values for the three segments.

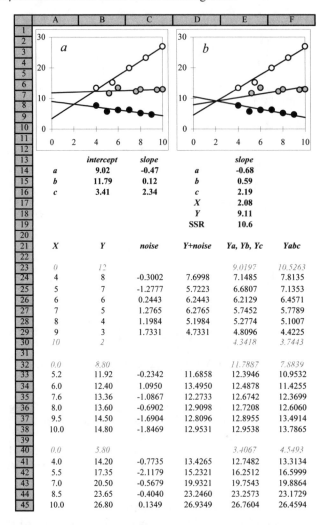

Fig. 4.10.1: A spreadsheet for exercise 4.10.1 showing three sets of straight lines intersecting in a common point (2,10) in column B, and the same with Gaussian noise of unit standard deviation in column D, (*a*) analyzed separately, and (*b*): forced to go through one common point. The data printed in gray italics are used for the graph but not in the analysis.

(3) Calculate the corresponding values of *y+n*, then use linear least squares to compute separate, straight lines through the three noisy data sets, and plot these as well as the noisy data.

(4) Somewhere near the top of the spreadsheet, insert spaces for three slopes a_1 through a_3, as well as for the coordinates *X* and *Y*, and enter guess values for all of these. As guess values for a_1 through a_3 you can use the slopes obtained under (3) by linear least squares.

(5) Make a column in which you calculate $y = Y + a_i(x - X)$, using the guess values and, in each segment, the appropriate value of the slope a_i.

(6) Compute the sum of squares of the residuals by comparing the data in the just-made column with those in the column for *y+n*.

172

(7) Call Solver to minimize that sum of squares of the residuals, by letting it adjust the three slopes and the two coordinates of the intersection point.

(8) Plot the resulting lines. Compare your spreadsheet with that in Fig. 4.10.1.

In Fig. 4.10.1 we have used few points and rather generous noise in order to illustrate the effect of the constraint. The individual straight line segments start out intersecting at the point X,Y before noise is added to them. After noise has been added, they no longer pass through a common point. Because of the paucity of data and the large noise amplitudes used, the lines drawn are of course quite uncertain, as can best be seen from their standard deviations, which have been collected in table 4.10.1.

Incidentally, in order to draw the lines across the entire width of the graph, points for $x = 0$ and $x = 10$ were added, though of course not included in the analysis. These have been printed in italics in Fig. 4.10.1; one could make them disappear from a print-out by coloring them white. Forcing the three data sets through a common point of course makes the resulting parameter values interdependent, so that their covariances may have to be considered in subsequent computations.

Assumed:		Found for three separate lines:	Found for three lines through a common point:
intercept 1	12	$a_0 = 9.0_2 \pm 0.9_9$	
slope 1	−1	$a_1 = -0.4_7 \pm 0.1_5$	$-0.6_7 \pm 0.1_0$
intercept 2	8.8	$b_0 = 11._8 \pm 1._2$	
slope 2	0.6	$b_1 = 0.1_2 \pm 0.1_5$	$0.59_0 \pm 0.06_7$
intercept 3	5.8	$c_0 = 3._4 \pm 1._1$	
slope 3	2.1	$c_1 = 2.3_4 \pm 0.1_5$	$2.19_1 \pm 0.09_3$
X	2		$2.0_8 \pm 0.2_3$
Y	10		$9.1_1 \pm 0.3_2$

Table 4.10.1: The results obtained in Fig. 4.10.1, analyzed as three independent straight lines, or as three straight lines through a common point.

Alternatively, if the coordinates of the point of intersection are fixed at $x = X$ and $y = Y$, such as at $X = 2$ and $Y = 10$, one can use Solver to adjust the values of a, b, and c, either separately or simultaneously, while keeping the values of X and Y constant. In this case, separate linear least squares fits of $y–Y = a_1(x–X)$ would also work.

Whenever two or more curves must be fitted with mutually dependent parameters, Solver is a convenient tool to use; the corresponding uncertainties can then be obtained from SolverAid. The above approach is quite general, as will be illustrated in the next example.

4.11 Fitting a set of curves

We now consider a set of data representing the progress of a first-order chemical reaction at various temperatures and times, taken from p. 124 of Y. Bard, *Nonlinear Parameter Estimation*, Academic Press (1974). The dependent variable f is the fraction of the initial reagent remaining after a reaction time t at an absolute temperature T. The assignment is to analyze these numbers in terms of the rate expression $f = \exp(–kt)$ where the rate constant k has the temperature dependence $k = a \exp(–b/T)$, so that $f = \exp[–at \exp(–b/T)]$. Exercise 4.11.1 illustrates such an analysis using Solver and SolverAid.

Exercise 4.11.1:

(1) Open a spreadsheet, and enter the labels, parameter values, column headings, and data. For subsequent plotting of the calculated curves, it is convenient to keep empty rows between the data for different temperatures, so that the graph will show the solution as three unconnected line segments. (And leave more rows free if you want to extend the calculated curves from $t = 0$ to $t = 0.5$ hrs.) Plot the data.

(2) Compute f as $f = \exp[–at \exp(–b/T)]$ based on initial guess values for a and b, and show the resulting curve. Also calculate SSR, the sum of the squares of the residuals.

(3) Use Solver and SolverAid to find a solution. Figure 4.11.1 shows what you will get when you start with, e.g., $a = b = 1$, and ask SolverAid to display the correlation coefficients.

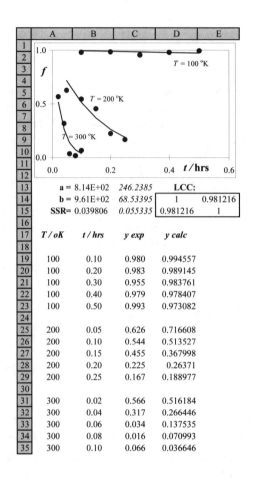

a = 8.14E+02	*246.2385*	**LCC:**	
b = 9.61E+02	*68.53395*	1	0.981216
SSR= 0.039806	*0.055335*	0.981216	1

T / oK	*t / hrs*	*y exp*	*y calc*
100	0.10	0.980	0.994557
100	0.20	0.983	0.989145
100	0.30	0.955	0.983761
100	0.40	0.979	0.978407
100	0.50	0.993	0.973082
200	0.05	0.626	0.716608
200	0.10	0.544	0.513527
200	0.15	0.455	0.367998
200	0.20	0.225	0.26371
200	0.25	0.167	0.188977
300	0.02	0.566	0.516184
300	0.04	0.317	0.266446
300	0.06	0.034	0.137535
300	0.08	0.016	0.070993
300	0.10	0.066	0.036646

Fig. 4.11.1: The remaining concentration fraction f of a species undergoing a first-order chemical reaction, as a function of time t, at different temperatures T. Lines calculated with Solver-determined parameters.

If you have no clue what to use for plausible starting guesses for the data of Fig. 4.11.1, you might start with separate parts of the data set, say, with those for 200 and 300°K. You fit each of these to $f = \exp(-kt)$, either with Solver or with any of the linear least squares programs in Excel. You will find k-values of about 6.7 and 33 hr^{-1}. Now fit these two values to the temperature dependence $k = a \exp(-b/T)$, and you find $a = 810$ and $b = 960$. With these as guess values you are virtually guaranteed to home in on the final answer when you subsequently analyze the complete data set, especially since the data at 100°K don't contribute much information.

The data used in Fig. 4.11.1 are clearly hypothetical, made up by a non-experimentalist: the data at 100°K show virtually no reaction, and there are only two data points at 300°K that are significantly different from zero. Moreover, with more realistic data the noise in the data should also be smaller, and hence the standard deviations for a and b shown in cells C13 and C14 respectively. Yet, even with such poor data, Solver finds a plausible solution. As can be seen from the correlation coefficient r_{12} of about 0.98, the values for a and b are quite interdependent. Note, however, that we were lucky that $a = 1$ and $b = 1$ led to a plausible answer. It does not always work that way: $a = 8000$ and $b = 8000$ might not get you anywhere, even though your initial guess values are now within a factor of 10 of their 'best' values. In this case the calculated values of y are all very close to 1, so that SSR, the sum of the squares of the residuals, doesn't change perceptibly, making it difficult or impossible for Solver to locate its minimum. This trouble is easily spotted by the fact that the initial guess values are not changed.

Had you started with $a = -100$ and $b = -100$, you would have run into the same problem, albeit for a different reason: now some of the y-values are so large that they essentially mask any changes in SSR, and again get Solver stuck. In this case, you can find the correct answer with Solver $\Rightarrow$ Options $\Rightarrow$ Assume Non-Negative, which prevents it from accepting negative values for any of the adjustable parameters for which you have not specified any particular constraints.

A more interesting case occurs with, e.g., $a = -10$ and $b = -10$, which quickly leads to a local minimum that is not the global one. In this case, simply engaging Solver once more will get you to the correct answer: apparently, the initial iteration step differs from subsequent ones. This trick sometimes works: if you don't trust the answer Solver provides, accept that result, then use it as the starting point for a second try with Solver and see whether it gets Solver unstuck. In this particular example, Options $\Rightarrow$ Assume Non-Negative would have avoided the problem.

This illustrates, again, that Solver may not always work when the initial guess values are far off. This typically occurs when you know little or nothing about the context of the data, something that should not happen with real experimental data, but occasionally does. Even so, in such a case one might try Solver once or twice with wild guess values, on the off chance that these just might work. If not, use a fraction of the data for which the analysis is simpler, assemble estimates for most or all of the parameters that way, then use these as guess values in the final nonlinear fit of the entire data set.

How will you know whether you have hit the jackpot? Look at the resulting fit of the calculated model curve to the data points, as in Fig. 4.21.1. Plot the residuals, as in Fig. 4.21.2, and see whether they show a trend, although in the present example there are too few data points to make this a meaningful criterion. Check whether a subsequent application of Solver modifies the result: sometimes a second application of Solver does change its results, and it is good practice to repeat Solver at least once to see whether it has reached a steady answer. And, most of all, remain skeptical: nonlinear least squares do not come with any guarantees, a problem that we will take up again in section 4.17. Fortunately, you will typically know what order of magnitude to expect for your data, and you should preferably have more and better data points than in Fig. 4.11.1. In practice, Solver often works surprisingly well.

4.12 Fitting a discontinuous curve

One sometimes encounters experimental data sets that exhibit a discontinuity, as may occur, e.g., with phase transitions. We can treat its constituent parts as separate segments, but often the coordinates of the transition are also subject to experimental uncertainty, in which case it may be preferable to fit the entire data set. As always, the best description starts with the appropriate model describing the phenomenon. Here we will merely illustrate the method for a simulated, discontinuous data set.

Say that we have a set of data that can be described by $y = a_0 + a_1 x$ for $x \le c$, and by $y = b_0 + b_1 x + b_2 x^2$ for $x > c$. We now express that behavior in a single equation with six unknowns, a_0, a_1, b_0, b_1, b_2, and c, and then use Solver to find their optimum values. The single equation will contain an IF statement. If the curve contains a change in slope (a "knee") rather than a discontinuity (a "break"), one of the unknowns can be eliminated since continuity at $x = c$ requires that $a_0 + a_1 c = b_0 + b_1 c + b_2 c^2$.

Exercise 4.12.1:

(1) Set up a spreadsheet similar to that shown in Fig. 4.12.1, with (at the top of the spreadsheet) the model and adjustable parameters, and below it the corresponding columns for x, y, and y_{calc}. Include a column of random noise, and add s_n times this noise to the data for y. Also compute the sum of the squares of the residuals.

(2) Plot both y and y_{calc} vs. x, and adjust the parameters in C1:C6 so that the calculated line roughly fits the (in this case simulated) experimental data. Such a first-order fit is shown in Fig. 4.12.2.

(3) Call Solver and let it minimize SSR by adjusting the parameters in C1:C6.

(4) Call SolverAid and let it determine the corresponding uncertainties. Note that SolverAid *cannot* find the uncertainty in c, $\pm \Delta x/2$, which it indicates (while displaying an appropriate warning message) as 0. This uncertainty depends on the data density of x; in this example, with $\Delta x = 0.1$, it is ± 0.05. Note that this uncertainty represents an absolute limit rather than a standard deviation.

(5) Figure 4.12.3 illustrates the resulting graph. Perhaps more telling is the covariance matrix obtained with SolverAid, which shows a_0 and a_1 to be independent of b_0, b_1, and b_2, as they should be, as well as the (incorrect) zeros for the uncertainty in c.

	A	B	C
1	*a0* =	3	2
2	*a1* =	1	1.5
3	*b0* =	25	30
4	*b1* =	-1	-0.9
5	*b2* =	-0.2	-0.3
6	*c* =	5	4.5
7	*sn*=	0.5	
8	*SSR*=	924.15	
9			
10	*x*	*y*	*y calc*
11			
12	0	2.849884	2
13	0.1	2.461158	2.15
14	0.2	3.322129	2.3

Fig. 4.12.1: The top of the spreadsheet of exercise 4.12.1. Cell B12 contains the instruction `=IF(A12<$B$6,$B$1+$B$2*A12,$B$3+$B$4*A12+$B$5*A12*A12)+$B$7*N12`, while cell C12 contains `=IF(A12< $C$6,$C$1+$C$2*A12,$C$3+$C$4*A12+$C$5*A12*A12)`.

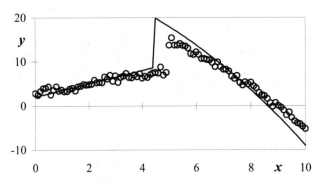

Fig. 4.12.2: The simulated data (open circles) and an unadjusted, crudely fitted curve through them.

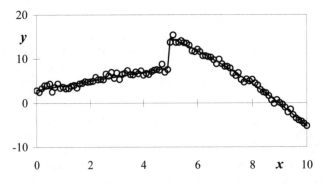

Fig. 4.12.3: The simulated data (open circles) and the adjusted curve through them.

4.13 Piecewise fitting a continuous curve

Sometimes it may be desirable to represent data by a smooth-looking curve, perhaps even in the absence of a theoretical justification for such a piecemeal approach. A smooth appearance usually requires that the segments and their first derivatives be continuous. This can readily be achieved with splines (e.g., with the Smoothed line option in Excel XY graphs; see also section 9.6.2 for further details) but will here be illustrated with least squares.

A study of E. S. Eppright, H. M. Fox, B. A. Fryer, G. H. Lamkin, V. M. Vivian & E. S. Fuller published in *World Rev. Nutrition Dietetics* 14 (1972) 269 (Karger, Basel) reported the weight/height ratios (weights in pounds, heights in inches) of preschool boys in the north-central region of the US as a function of their age (in months). These data were subsequently analyzed by A. R. Gallant et al., *J. Am. Stat. Assoc.* 68 (1973) 144; 72 (1977) 523, in terms of two connected sections. For the sake of the exercise we will do the same here, first fitting them to two straight-line sections with a knee, and subsequently fitting them with the smooth combination of a parabola and a straight line. The experimental observations can also be found in G. A. Seber & C. J. Wild, *Nonlinear Regression*, Wiley (1989) p. 461.

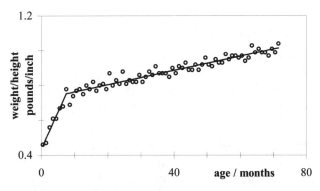

Fig. 4.13.1: The data of Eppright et al. fitted with two connected straight-line segments.

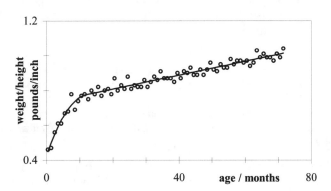

Fig. 4.13.2: The data of Eppright et al. fitted with a parabola plus a straight line, with both the function and its slope continuous at the joint.

Exercise 4.13.1:

(1) Copy the data into your spreadsheet, with the weight-to-height ratio as the dependent variable y, and age as the independent variable x. Plot these data; neither the beginning nor the end fits a line or higher-order power series in x through the origin, and we will therefore use straight lines with arbitrary intercepts. Continuity of a fit with $y = a_0 + a_1 x$ for $x < c$, and $y = b_0 + b_1 x$ for $x > c$, requires that $a_0 + a_1 c = b_0 + b_1 c$ so that $b_0 = a_0 + (a_1 - b_1)c$.

177

(2) Enter labels and values for a_0, a_1, b_1, and c, then compute y_{calc} with an instruction containing an IF statement, as $a_0 + a_1x$ for $x < c$, and $y = a_0 + (a_1 - b_1)c + b_1x$ for $x > c$. Plot the resulting curve for y_{calc} in the above graph, and adjust the values of a_0, a_1, b_1, and c to provide an approximate fit with the experimental data.

(3) Compute SSR using the SUMXMY2 function, call Solver to minimize SSR, then call SolverAid to find the associated uncertainties. Keep in mind that the uncertainty estimate of c derives exclusively from its role in defining the slope of the longer straight-line segment. The resulting curve is shown in Fig. 4.13.1.

(4) There is no known reason to assume that something suddenly happens at $x = c$ to render the slope dy/dx discontinuous at that age. As long as we are merely looking for a smooth-looking mathematical description of these data in terms of relatively few parameters, a curve without a knee would seem preferable. We therefore fit these same data to $y = a_0 + a_1x + a_2x^2$ for $x < c$, and $y = b_0 + b_1x$ for $x > c$, with the constraints that both y and dy/dx are continuous at $x = c$.

(5) Calculate $b_0 = a_0 + (a_1 - b_1)c$.

(6) Since this exercise already provided reasonable guess values for $b_0 = a_0 + (a_1 - b_1)c$ and b_1, we now express a_0 and a_1 in terms of b_0 and b_1, i.e., $a_1 = b_1 - 2a_2c$ and $a_0 = b_0 + (b_1 - a_1)c - a_2c^2 = b_0 + a_2c^2$. We therefore calculate y_{calc} in an IF statement as $(b_0 + a_2c^2) + (b_1 - 2a_2c)x + a_2x^2$ for $x < c$, otherwise $b_0 + b_1x$.

(7) Using the graph displaying y and y_{calc} as a guide, set a_2 and c to some plausible guess values, such as -0.001 and 20, compute SSR, and call Solver to adjust a_2, b_1, b_2, and c. (In case you encounter trouble, do this in steps, first adjusting only a_2 and c.) Finally, find the corresponding uncertainty estimates with SolverAid. Figure 4.13.2 shows the resulting fit of the curve to the data.

4.14 Enzyme kinetics, once more

Nonlinear least squares can be used for convenience, in order to avoid the complications of weighting and/or error propagation. We will illustrate how Solver can bypass the need for weighted linear least squares, by revisiting enzyme kinetics. In a second example, in section 4.15, we will see how Solver can sometimes be used when weighted least squares yield unsatisfactory results. In section 4.16 we will then reconsider linear extrapolation.

In section 3.19 we encountered a set of data on enzyme kinetics that, after some rearrangement, could be analyzed with linear least squares as Hanes or Lineweaver-Burk plots. Using unweighted least squares we found answers that depended on the rearrangement used, whereas properly weighted linear least squares gave consistent results. Still, the procedure was rather laborious, because it required us to determine the appropriate weights, to apply weighted least squares, and finally to propagate the uncertainty. Below we will show that similar results can be obtained more simply by using Solver, without the need for weights or special error propagation.

Exercise 4.14.1:

(1) Extend the spreadsheet of exercise 3.17.1 or enter the data of Table 3.19.1 into a new spreadsheet, as in Fig. 4.14.1. Also enter labels and initial values for the two parameters to be determined, K and v_m, and use these to compute v as a function of s according to eq. (3.17.1).

(2) Compute SSR, then call Solver to adjust the values of K and v_m.

(3) Call SolverAid to calculate the associated uncertainties, and to provide the covariance matrix in case subsequent computations will use both K and v_m. Figure 4.14.1 shows it all.

Comparison of the above results ($K = 0.059_7 \pm 0.06_8$, $v_m = 0.69_0 \pm 0.03_7$) with those of the weighted least squares method ($K = 0.0571 \pm 0.064$, $v_m = 0.68_0 \pm 0.035$) shows them to be similar but not identical. And when the values for K and v_{max} found earlier with weighted least squares in section 3.17 are substituted into cells F3 and G3 of the spreadsheet of Fig. 4.14.1, a slightly higher value for SSR results. What went wrong here?

The answer lies in the approximation (3.17.1) used to determine the appropriate weights, which is only valid when the relative deviations $\Delta y/y$ are much smaller than 1. This is not quite the case in the present example, thereby making Solver not only more convenient (because it homes in directly on the quantities of interest) but also slightly superior in terms of its numerical results.

	A	B	C	D	E	F	G
1	**s**	**v** exp	**v** model		**Solver + SolverAid**		
2	/mM	/μM	/μM			**K**	**v** m
3					**Value:**	0.597	0.690
4	0.138	0.148	0.130		*St.Dev.:*	*0.068*	*0.037*
5	0.220	0.171	0.186				
6	0.291	0.234	0.226		*SSR:*	0.0007	*0.014*
7	0.560	0.324	0.334				
8	0.766	0.390	0.388		*CM:*	0.0047	0.0024
9	1.460	0.493	0.490			0.0024	0.0014

C4 = A4*$G$3/($F$3+A4)   copied to C5:C9

Fig. 4.14.1: A spreadsheet for analyzing enzyme kinetics with Solver plus SolverAid.

4.15 The Lorentzian revisited

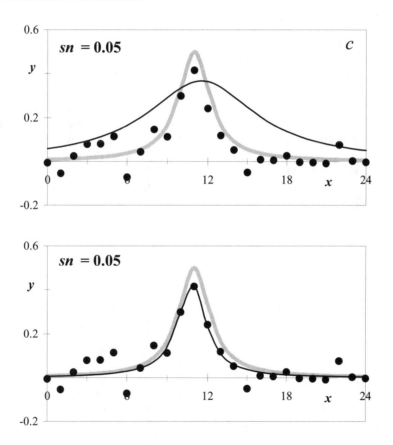

Fig. 4.15.1: The results of exercise 4.15.1 (bottom panel) and, for comparison, the weighted least squares results obtained in exercise 3.20.3 (top panel) for the very same data. Solid circles: data points; gray band: noise-free curve used in generating the data; thin black line: fitted curve.

In section 3.20 we used a weighted least squares routine to fit data to a Lorentzian. There was no problem as long as the signal did not contain much noise, but the method failed miserably when the signal-to-noise ratio was too small. Here we will revisit this problem with Solver.

Exercise 4.15.1:

(1) Extend the spreadsheet of exercise 3.20.1, by entering labels and initial values for the parameters *a*, *b*, and *c* of (3.20.1). Use these to compute *y* as a function of *x* according to (3.20.1) for the data used in Fig. 3.20.3.

(2) Calculate SSR, and let Solver minimize SSR by changing *a*, *b*, and *c*.

(3) Figure 4.15.1 shows the result, and repeats Fig. 3.20.3 for comparison.

In this example, Solver is much more impervious to noise than a weighted least squares analysis. As already indicated in section 3.20, this is because weighting (based on the needs of a Lorentzian) converts zero-average noise into a positive bias, which distorts the resulting fit, whereas nonlinear least squares doesn't because it need not use weights. For this reason, Solver is often more robust than weighted least squares. In other words, the very same weighting that transforms the Lorentzian into a quadratic converts random, zero-average noise into a positive bias, and the more so the larger is the stretch of near-baseline signal included in the analysis. Eventually, though, the Lorentzian (or any other signal) can be over-whelmed by noise no matter what algorithm is used. In that case, different experimental methods, such as signal averaging or synchronous detection, must be used, but these must be designed into the experiment, and cannot be used after-the-fact.

4.16 Linear extrapolation

We now briefly revisit the problem of linear extrapolation addressed in section 2.13. Here, Solver will allow us to home in directly on the parameter of interest. In the experimental determination of absolute zero temperature, we want to know the intercept t_0 of a straight line $V = a_0 + a_1 t$ with the horizontal axis, where $V_0 = 0$ so that $a_0 = -a_1 t_0$. We reformulate the problem as $V_{model} = V - V_0 = a_1(t - t_0)$, use Solver to find the best-fitting values for a_1 and t_0, and SolverAid to determine the corresponding uncertainties. In Fig. 2.13.1 we displayed the linear correlation coefficients showing a correlated slope and intercept, thus requiring the use of the covariance matrix. By using Solver plus SolverAid, we can avoid this complication.

11	*Pb* = 98.19			*t₀* = **-278.0**	*9.6*
12	*SSR*= 0.011	*0.033*		*a₁* = 0.01364	*0.00042*
13					
14	*V*	*Pw*	*Vd*	*temp*	*Vmodel*
15	*mL*	*kPa*	*mL*	*deg C*	*mL*
16				-278.0	0.00
17	3.80	0.61	3.78	0.0	3.79
18	3.90	0.86	3.87	4.8	3.86
19	3.98	1.14	3.93	8.9	3.91
20	4.10	2.09	4.01	18.2	4.04
21	4.20	2.88	4.08	23.4	4.11
22	4.40	3.83	4.23	28.2	4.18
23	4.50	5.50	4.25	34.6	4.26
24	4.80	8.87	4.37	43.5	4.38
25	5.15	12.34	4.50	50.0	4.47
26	5.75	19.93	4.58	60.0	4.61
27	6.00	21.55	4.68	61.7	4.63
28	7.25	33.97	4.74	72.0	4.77

Fig. 4.16.1: The spreadsheet computation of Fig. 2.13.1 as modified for use with Solver and SolverAid.

Exercise 4.16.1:

(1) Extend the spreadsheet of exercise 2.13.1, where *V* is assumed to have the dominant experimental uncertainties, see Fig. 2.13.1. Enter labels and initial values for the parameters a_1 and t_0, and use these to compute *V* as a function of *t* according to $V = a_1 (t - t_0)$.

180

(2) Calculate SSR, call Solver, and let it minimize SSR by changing $a1$ and $t0$, then call SolverAid to get the associated uncertainties. Figure 4.16.1 shows what such a spreadsheet computation might look like. The results are substantially the same as those of Fig. 2.13.1. Linear correlation coefficients with absolute values smaller than 0.9 are seldom consequential.

4.17 Guarding against false minima

The convenience of Solver must be balanced against the possibility that it produces an incorrect answer. This is the consequence of the method by which the generalized reduced gradient algorithm finds its way to the lowest value of the minimization criterion. That method, an elaboration of an approach proposed by K. Levenberg, *Q. Appl. Math.* 2 (1944) 164, and first implemented by D. W. Marquardt, *J. SIAM* 11 (1963) 431, is analogous to the flow of rainwater that, after haven fallen on land, usually finds its way to the ocean, which we will here take as its lowest level. But sometimes the rainwater flows into a mountain lake high above sea level, with no outlet, and then can go no lower.

As with any analogy, the above image is only partially applicable, because water can also run into a lake below sea level, such as the Dead Sea. This would only be avoided if all non-moving water could freely communicate. Fortunately, it doesn't, or my coastal well water would be as salty as ocean water.

In general, finding a minimum does not guarantee that it is the lowest possible one. How can we guard against getting stuck in a *local* minimum rather than in the *global* minimum within a given range? There is no foolproof way to find this global minimum, or even a local minimum. Just imagine a golf ball rolling on a golf course; its chances of finding a hole by itself, just under the influence of gravity, are minuscule. (In section 1.5.3 we already encountered a seemingly simple, continuous function with a very deep and narrow minimum, like a dug water well.) Fortunately, most minima are not so narrowly confined, and we can often reduce our chances of ending in a local minimum by starting Solver from different initial values that cover most of the likely parameter space, i.e., the range of parameter values within which we expect the global minimum to occur.

The following exercise illustrates the problem. Say that we have a curve with two well-separated peaks, one Gaussian, the other Lorentzian, which we want to fit with Solver. In order to simplify the problem, we select the same height and width parameters for both curves, so that they differ only in their peak positions. We must now assign two initial values to Solver, one each for the guessed peak positions of the Gaussian and the Lorentzian. We will call the initial guess value for the peak center of the Gaussian G, and that for the Lorentzian L, and will try Solver for various values of G and L. Thus we will probe a two-dimensional parameter space, varying both G and L.

Exercise 4.17.1:

(1) In cell A16 place the value 300, in A17 the value 700, in B16 and B17 the number 4, and in C16:C17 the value 50.

(2) In A19:E19 put the labels *x*, *noise*, y_{exp}, y_{calc}, and *residuals*.

(3) In A21:A1029 construct the series 1 (1) 1000.

(4) In B21:B1020 deposit Gaussian noise using <u>T</u>ools (⑰,⑱: Data) ⇨ <u>D</u>ata Analysis ⇨ Random Number Generation with <u>D</u>istribution Normal, M<u>e</u>an = 0, <u>S</u>tandard Deviation = 0.1, activate <u>O</u>utput Range and specify B21:B1020, then press OK.

(5) In cell C21 place the instruction =4*EXP(-1*(B22-300)^2/(2*50^2))+3000*4/((B22-700)^2+60*50)+C22, and copy down to C2010.

(6) In cell D21 place =$B$16*EXP(-1*(A21-$A$16)^2/(2*$C$16^2))+3000*$B$17/((A21-$A$17)^2+60*$C$17), and again copy this down to C2010.

(7) In E21 compute =E22-D22 and copy this down also.

(8) Make a graph of C21:C1020 vs A21:A1020, then add D21:D1020.

(9) Also make a (separate) graph of E21:E1020 vs. A21:A1020.

(10) Finally, place the label SSR= in cell E16, and the formula =SUMXMY2(C21:C1020,D21:D1020) in cell F16.

(11) Your spreadsheet should now resemble Fig. 4.17.1.

(12) Now interchange the values in A16 and A17, and see what you get. You should find something like Fig. 4.17.2, with a crude fit. You can improve on it by letting Solver adjust the values in B16:C17, in which SSR would decrease somewhat, although the fit would hardly look much better. Try it.

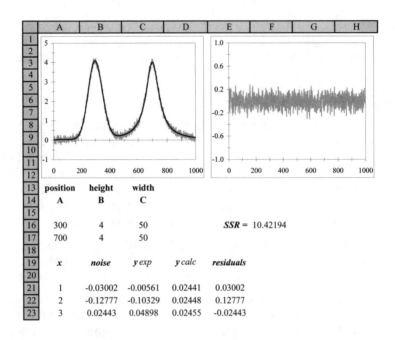

Fig. 4.17.1: The top of a spreadsheet containing 1000 data points, showing a Gaussian peak $B \exp[-(x-A)^2/2C^2]$ centered at $A = 300$ plus a Lorentzian peak $3000B / [(x-A)^2 + 60C]$ at $A = 700$ plus Gaussian noise of zero mean and amplitude $s_n = 0.1$.

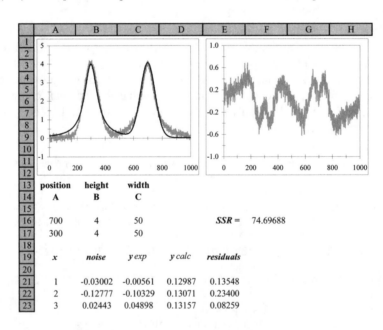

Fig. 4.17.2: The same as Fig. 4.17.1, but obtained with Solver upon assuming the Lorentzian to be centered at $x = 300$, and the Gaussian at $x = 700$.

Here, then, we have a case where we might expect to see a *false minimum*. We could test this by using Solver for several combinations of numbers in cells A16 and A17, but it is impractical to perform such a search manually. We can automate the process with the macro SolverScan, inspired by a paper by P. Nikitas & A. Pappa-Louisi in *Chromatographia* 52 (2000) 477. There are several ways to conduct such a search. The simplest is to use a regular grid, where the initial guess values for the two peak positions are each given one of, say, 10 equidistant values. That will force the macro to apply Solver $10 \times 10 = 100$ times. Even if Solver takes only 5 seconds on your computer, 100×5 s will consume more than 8 minutes. If we insist on an n times higher resolution, we need to apply Solver n^2 times as often. Except for a very simple calculation performed on a very fast computer, this will quickly become too time-consuming.

The same speed limitation applies when, instead of using constant steps in the x- and y-directions, we randomize the initially assumed values for the peak positions in such a way that they cover the same parameter space. Unfortunately, such a scheme often produces a rather uneven coverage of that parameter space for practical (i.e., fairly small) numbers of trials. An intermediate solution is to use a regular grid to divide the parameter space in equal-sized cells, and then to assign the initial parameter values inside each of those cells with random numbers. This leads to a so-called pseudo-random search, which is somewhat less likely to cluster. Figure 4.17.3 illustrates these three options.

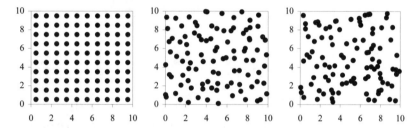

Fig. 4.17.3: Three different grids for searching an area. Left panel: a regular grid, here with points at $G = i + 0.5$, $L = j + 0.5$, where $i = 0$ (1) 9 and $j = 0$ (1) 9. Central panel: a pseudo-random grid, with $G = i +$ RAND(), $L = j +$ RAND(), where RAND() yields a random number between 0 and 1. Right panel: $G = 10*$RAND(), $L = 10*$RAND().

Unfortunately, results obtained with the second and third option are more difficult to plot in Excel, because it can only handle 3-D plots of equidistant data, and the same restriction applies to the macro Mapper. Moreover, the result is probably substantially the same. If the minimum is broad (compared with the average distance between adjacent test points), it will make little difference. And if the minimum is very narrow, it will be a hit-or-miss proposition no matter how we distribute the points. Our best bet may therefore be to use Random_Plot.xls, as already illustrated in Fig. 1.5.7, which makes it very easy to increase the number of random points. Here we will use a regular (equidistant) grid.

A simple way to search quickly for false minima is to compute log SSR for various values of G and L, which we can do with the custom macro ScanF, thereby bypassing Solver, whereupon we use Mapper to plot the resulting SSR values in an *error surface* or, as Sillén et al. in *Acta Chem. Scand.* 15 (1961) 694, called it, a pit map, see section 2.17. This is indeed much faster. Exercise 4.17.2 illustrates how this is done.

Exercise 4.17.2:

(1) Select a large, rectangular array that comfortably fits, say, a 100×100 array. Here we will use J16:DG117.

(2) In cell K16 place the value 0, in cell L16 deposit the instruction =K16+10, and copy the latter to M16:DG16. This will be the horizontal axis for our plot, which for Mapper must be placed *above* the data.

(3) In cell J17 put the value 1000, in cell J18 the instruction =K16+10, and copy the latter down to J117. This will make the vertical axis for our plot.

(4) Highlight J16:DG117, and call ScanF0. The 0 indicates that the rectangular array of SSR values is all you want; ScanF1 would also make a listing suitable for importation into IsoL.xla.

(5) Answer the three input boxes, the first with the location of X (A16), the second with that of Y (A17), the third with that of the function F, here SSR (F16).

(6) After ScanF has finished (it takes some time to compute the 10,000 SSR-values) again highlight J16:DG117, and now call your favorite version of Mapper. (Cell J16 should remain empty, as here, or contain a 1. The latter tells Mapper that you want to define the scale used, in which case you will be asked for its minimum and maximum values.)

(7) Figure 4.17.4 shows the resulting error surface as drawn with Mapper0, which now clearly shows two minima, the global minimum for $G = 300$ and $L = 700$, and a false one for $G = 700$ and $L = 300$.

(8) Alternatively you can make a 3-D plot of the error surface, as illustrated in Fig. 4.17.5. This can be rotated on your monitor screen, though not on this page, for a fuller view. The undulations in the error surface at the top of Fig. 4.17.5 (which are only dimly visible in Fig. 4.17.4) also reveals the presence of quite shallow local minima where Solver can get trapped. Dots on the bottom (dark gray) plane of the 3-D plot indicate the approximate projections of the two major minima, and were added subsequently, as were the two horizontal axes. These do not move when you rotate the picture.

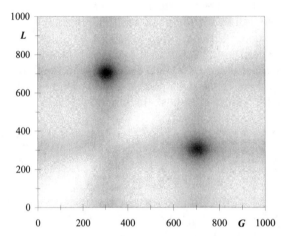

Fig. 4.17.4: The error surface shows two distinct minima, at $G = 300$ and $L = 700$, and at $G = 700$ and $L = 300$, in an otherwise rumpled surface.

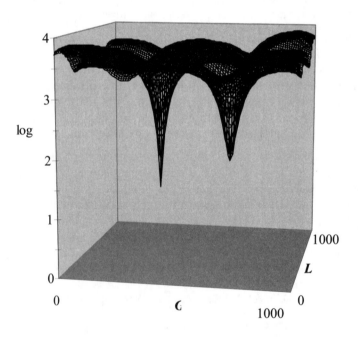

Fig. 4.17.5: The same error surface as in Fig. 4.17.4 but in 3-D. Note that the deeper pit lies closer to the back walls of the graph.

184

Figures 4.17.4 and 4.17.5 illustrate the usefulness of looking at the error surface when there is the possibility of false minima. Granted, this example was concocted, and one seldom encounters such stark examples, but it is good to be alert to their possible presence and have some tools to find them. And it is not only the two deep minima, but also the undulations at the top of the error surface that can trap Solver into a false minimum. When we use SolverScan for G = 0 (100) 1000 and L = 0 (100) 1000 we find the results shown in Table 4.17.1.

	G = *0*	*100*	*200*	*300*	*400*	*500*	*600*	*700*	*800*	*900*	*1000*
L = 1000	1275	1281	**10**	**10**	**10**	1272	**58**	**58**	**58**	1281	1255
900	1412	**10**	**10**	**10**	**10**	**10**	1270	**58**	1412	1255	694
800	1412	**10**	**10**	**10**	**10**	475	694	**58**	694	694	694
700	1412	**10**	**10**	**10**	**10**	475	475	694	694	1233	694
600	1412	**10**	**10**	**10**	**10**	475	**58**	694	694	694	694
500	1157	**10**	1157	**10**	**10**	475	**58**	**58**	**58**	694	1235
400	469	469	469	**10**	475	475	**58**	**58**	**58**	**58**	**58**
300	469	469	469	469	475	**58**	**58**	**58**	**58**	**58**	**58**
200	469	469	469	**10**	469	475	**58**	**58**	**58**	**58**	**58**
100	469	1149	**10**	**10**	1220	**58**	**58**	**58**	1220	**58**	**58**
0	1149	1590	893	891	893	1220	1003	**58**	**58**	1270	356

Table 4.17.1: The values for the sum of the squares of the residuals, SSR, for Solver solutions starting from various initial values for the peak centers x_1 and x_2 respectively. The correct result, SSR = 10, and the incorrect, interchanged result, SSR = 58, are both displayed in bold, and the axes in bold italics.

Among its $11 \times 11 = 121$ samples, only 27 combinations of the initial values for *G* and *L* lead to the correct minimum (SSR = 10), and 32 combinations to reverse the peak positions as in Fig. 4.17.2 (with SSR = 58). On the other hand, 62 initial guesses yield other, *completely false* results (that do not even appear to represent the two prominent minima) with much higher SSR-values. In other words, *more than half* of the initial guesses lead to completely unacceptable 'solutions', and fewer than a quarter find the correct answer. Note that Gaussian noise is not the main culprit here: when we repeat the analysis with zero noise, the values obtained for SSR are all smaller by about 10, but the over-all pattern remains the same. In a tricky situation such as considered here, we clearly cannot start with just any parameter estimates and expect Solver to do the rest! That is also why a graphical display of the fit, before and after Solver, is important. The message is clear: nonlinear least squares need reasonably close initial estimates to work reliably, and the resulting fit and its residuals should always be displayed and inspected before the answer is accepted as correct.

4.18 Inverse interpolation with Solver

We now revisit the problem of section 1.10, inverse interpolation, as another example of using a macro to control Solver. Lagrange interpolation assumes that the function to be interpolated can be approximated as a polynomial, and the result will therefore depend on the assumed polynomial order. When the function has a closed-form analytical description, as in the spreadsheet of exercise 1.10.1, Solver can be used instead, without the need to make any polynomial approximations.

Say that, in the titration of C_{a1} M HCl + C_{a2} M HAc with C_b M NaOH, one needs to compute the pH as a function of the volume V_b of added base. The approach of section 4.3 readily provides V_b as a function of [H$^+$], and one can therefore use Solver to evaluate the pH for individual titrant volumes V_b as illustrated below.

Exercise 4.18.1:

(1) In cells A13:A15 enter labels for C_{a1}, C_{a2}, and C_b, and in C13:C15 those for V_a, K_a, and K_w. In B13:B15 place some corresponding values, such as 0.1, 0.1, and 0.1, and in D13:D15 the values 10, $10^{-4.76}$, and 10^{-14}. The value for K_a must be coded with an equal sign, as =10^–4.76; the value of K_w can either be specified as =10^–14 or (because the exponent is integer) as E^–14.

(2) In cell A19 enter a specific pH value, say 5, and in cell B19 calculate the corresponding value of [H$^+$] = 10^{-pH}. In cell C19 then compute $V_b = V_a\{C_{a1}+ C_{a2}K_a/([H^+]+K_a) - [H^+] + K_w/[H^+]\} / \{C_b + [H^+] - K_w/[H^+]\}$, which for pH 5 should yield a base volume V_b of 16.43.

(3) Now say that one needs to compute the pH for V_b = 16.273. Call Solver, Set Target Cell C19 to the <u>V</u>alue of 13.27 <u>B</u>y Changing Cells A19, and go; it will yield pH = 4.448.

The above works well for a single point, but becomes tedious when a whole set of data is needed to generate a curve. It is here that the custom macro ColumnSolver can be helpful.

Exercise 4.18.1 (continued):

(4) In cells A17:D17 place column labels for pH, [H$^+$], V_b, and $V_{b,calc}$.

(5) If one wants, say, data for V_b from 0 to 30 at increments of 1, place the values 0 (1) 30 in cells D19:D49. Then copy cells A19:C19 down to row 49.

(6) Make sure that Excel has access to the Solver object library, as described in section 4.17, otherwise ColumnSolver will not run.

(7) Call ColumnSolver, and select ColumnSolverValue. Specify the target cells as C19:C49, the wanted target values as D19:D49, and the adjustable parameters as located in A19:A49.

(8) Plot the results in A1:D12, which will now compute the titration curve for the specified titrant volumes.

4.19 *General least squares fit to a straight line*

So far we have assumed that we can assign one variable to be *the* dependent one. Often that is indeed possible, in which case it greatly simplifies the analysis. However, there are situations where it makes no physical sense to assign all the uncertainty to only one variable, as if loading the sins of all the data on the back of a single black sheep. Treating both x and y as equivalent parameters will in general require a special macro. Here we will merely illustrate the approach for the relatively simple case of a straight line, for which no special macro is needed, since the spreadsheet solution using Solver and SolverAid is fairly straightforward. In section 4.20 we will do the same for a semi-circle.

In chapter 2 we fitted data to the line $y = a_0 + a_1 x$ by minimizing the sum of squares of the deviation Δy. Instead, if we want to minimize the sum of squares of the distance d_i between the points x_i, y_i and the line $y = a_0 + a_1 x$, we use a simple trigonometric argument illustrated in Fig. 4.19.1, i.e., $d_i = \Delta y_i \cos\alpha$ and $\tan\alpha = dy/dx = a_1$, which can be combined with the trigonometric relation $\cos\alpha = 1/\sqrt{(1+\tan^2\alpha)} = 1/\sqrt{(1+a_1^2)}$ to $d_i^2 = \Delta y_i^2/(1+a_1^2)$. Consequently we minimize $\Sigma d_i^2 = \Sigma\Delta y_i^2/(1+a_1^2)$ instead of $\Sigma\Delta y_i^2$. (Even though we here fit data to a line, this approach is not suitable for a linear least squares algorithm, since the term $(1+a_1^2)$ makes the expressions nonlinear in the coefficients a_i.) Similarly, we can fit data to a plane $y = a + bx + cz$ by minimizing $\Sigma d_i^2 = \Sigma\Delta y_i^2 / (1+b^2+c^2)$, etc.

The above expression $d_i^2 = \Delta y_i^2/(1+a_1^2)$ can be converted into $d_i^2 = \Delta y_i^2/(1+\Delta y_i^2/\Delta x_i^2) = \Delta y_i^2 \Delta x_i^2/(\Delta x_i^2+ \Delta y_i^2)$ or $1/d_i^2=1/\Delta x_i^2+1/\Delta y_i^2$, an expression symmetrical in x and y that is convenient for the introduction of individual weights. Likewise, $\Sigma d_i^2 = \Sigma\Delta y_i^2 / (1+b^2+c^2)$ can be rewritten as $1/d_i^2 = 1/\Delta x_i^2+1/\Delta y_i^2+1/\Delta z_i^2$.

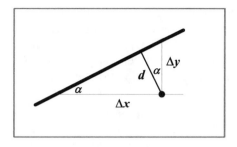

Fig. 4.19.1: The shortest distance d between the point (x,y) (solid circle) and the line $y = a_0 + a_1 x$.

Exercise 4.19.1:

(1) Use the data set from Fig. 2.9.1. Make labels and cells for the (initially assumed) parameter values a_0 and a_1, and a column in which you calculate the squares of the residuals, $1/\{1/[(y_i - a_0 - a_1 x_i)^2] + 1/[(x_i + a_0/a_1 - y_i/a_1)^2]\}$ for each row. Compute the sum of these squares of residuals, minimize it by using Solver, compute the properly scaled value of SSR, i.e., SSR $\times (1 + a_1^2)$ since $d^2 = \Delta y^2 / (1 + a_1^2)$, and finally use the latter to find the associated uncertainties with SolverAid.

(2) You will obtain the correct values for a_0 and a_1 regardless of whether the sum of the squares of the residuals is properly scaled, but in order to get correct uncertainty estimates with SolverAid, that sum should be scaled through multiplication by $(1 + a_1^2)$. This is why the spreadsheet in Fig. 4.19.2 contains SSR (to be used for Solver) and its scaled version, sSSR (to be used subsequently with SolverAid). You will obtain $y = 5.7_8 \pm 0.1_9 - (0.54_6 \pm 0.04_2)\,x$, the same result as obtained by Pearson.

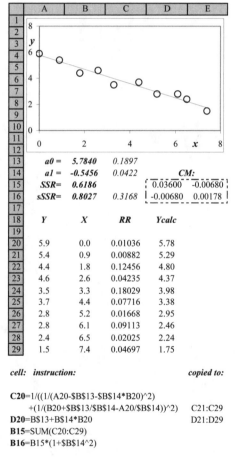

	A	B	C	D	E
13	a0 =	5.7840	0.1897		CM:
14	a1 =	-0.5456	0.0422		
15	SSR=	0.6186		0.03600	-0.00680
16	sSSR=	0.8027	0.3168	-0.00680	0.00178
17					
18	Y	X	RR	Ycalc	
19					
20	5.9	0.0	0.01036	5.78	
21	5.4	0.9	0.00882	5.29	
22	4.4	1.8	0.12456	4.80	
23	4.6	2.6	0.04235	4.37	
24	3.5	3.3	0.18029	3.98	
25	3.7	4.4	0.07716	3.38	
26	2.8	5.2	0.01668	2.95	
27	2.8	6.1	0.09113	2.46	
28	2.4	6.5	0.02025	2.24	
29	1.5	7.4	0.04697	1.75	

cell: *instruction:*   *copied to:*

C20=1/((1/(A20-$B$13-$B$14*B20)^2)
      +(1/(B20+$B$13/$B$14-A20/$B$14))^2)   C21:C29
D20=B$13+B$14*B20   D21:D29
B15=SUM(C20:C29)
B16=B15*(1+$B$14^2)

Fig. 4.19.2: A spreadsheet for general unweighted data fitting to a straight line.

In section 3.17 we introduced global weights w_i as multipliers of Δy_i^2 in the least squares minimization procedure, and we can do likewise in the present context. If certain data points must be emphasized more than others, we can minimize $\Sigma w_i d_i^2 = \Sigma w_i \Delta y_i^2/(1+a_1^2) = \Sigma 1/[1/(w_i \Delta x_i^2) + 1/(w_i \Delta y_i^2)]$; if the x_i- and y_i-values of individual points should be assigned separate weights, we instead minimize $\Sigma 1/[1/(w_{xi} \Delta x_i^2) + 1/(w_{yi} \Delta y_i^2)]$. We will illustrate this more general situation below.

Exercise 4.19.1 (continued):

(3) Insert two new columns, one each for w_x and w_y. Modify the column label from SR to wSR, and the corresponding instructions to $1/\{1/[w_{yi} (y_i - a_0 - a_1 x_i)^2)] + 1/[w_{xi} (x_i + a_0/a_1 - y_i/a_1)^2]\}$. Also make a column for the weights $1/(1/w_{yi} + a_1^2/w_{xi})$. And for SolverAid again use the scaled sum sSwSR, which is equal to SwSR divided by the average value of the terms $1/(1/w_{yi} + a_1^2/w_{xi})$.

(4) First verify that you obtain the same result as under (1) and (2) by setting all w_x and w_y equal to 1. Then make all w_x equal to 1000000, in which case you will recover the result for y as the dependent parameter, $a_0 = 5.7612 \pm 0.1895$, $a_1 = -0.5396 \pm 0.0421$. Also check that for, say, all $w_y = 1000$ and all $w_x = 0.001$, you get the result for x as the dependent parameter, $a_0 = 5.8617 \pm 0.1941$, $a_1 = -0.5659 \pm 0.0431$.

(5) Now try some arbitrary individual weights. Often the resulting differences will be small, although you can find examples where weighting really makes a difference, e.g., by emphasizing a small subset of the data. This is illustrated in Fig. 4.19.3, where the lowest points of the graph dominate the fit through a rather extreme choice of individual weights.

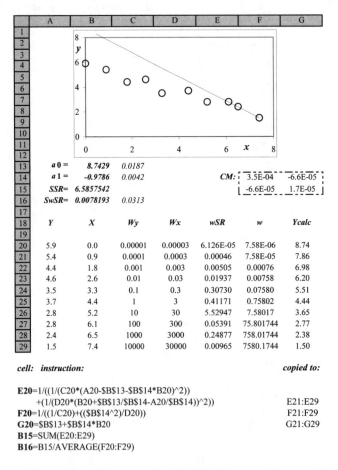

	A	B	C	D	E	F	G
13	$a0 =$	8.7429	0.0187				
14	$a1 =$	-0.9786	0.0042		CM:	3.5E-04	-6.6E-05
15	SSR=	6.5857542				-6.6E-05	1.7E-05
16	SwSR=	0.0078193	0.0313				
17							
18	Y	X	Wy	Wx	wSR	w	Ycalc
19							
20	5.9	0.0	0.00001	0.00003	6.126E-05	7.58E-06	8.74
21	5.4	0.9	0.0001	0.0003	0.00046	7.58E-05	7.86
22	4.4	1.8	0.001	0.003	0.00505	0.00076	6.98
23	4.6	2.6	0.01	0.03	0.01937	0.00758	6.20
24	3.5	3.3	0.1	0.3	0.30730	0.07580	5.51
25	3.7	4.4	1	3	0.41171	0.75802	4.44
26	2.8	5.2	10	30	5.52947	7.58017	3.65
27	2.8	6.1	100	300	0.05391	75.801744	2.77
28	2.4	6.5	1000	3000	0.24877	758.01744	2.38
29	1.5	7.4	10000	30000	0.00965	7580.1744	1.50

cell: instruction: copied to:

E20=1/((1/(C20*(A20-$B$13-$B$14*B20)^2))
    +(1/(D20*(B20+$B$13/$B$14-A20/$B$14))^2))   E21:E29
F20=1/((1/C20)+(($B$14^2)/D20))   F21:F29
G20=$B$13+$B$14*B20   G21:G29
B15=SUM(E20:E29)
B16=B15/AVERAGE(F20:F29)

Fig. 4.19.3: The spreadsheet for a general weighted least squares fit to a straight line for an arbitrarily chosen set of weights $w_{x,i}$ and $w_{y,i}$ that greatly emphasize the lowest points.

The above approach is readily extendable to those cases for which $y = F(x)$ can be inverted to an algebraic solution $x = G(y)$, such as the proportionality $y = a_1 x$ and the quadratic $y = a_0 + a_1 x + a_2 x^2$, so that Δx can be evaluated for a given Δy.

Clearly, the spreadsheet presents no problem to a weighted general least squares fit to a straight line. The difficulty of such use does not lie in its mechanics, but rather in the assignment of appropriate weights. If the standard deviations s_x and s_y are known, weights $w_x = s_x^{-2}$ and $w_y = s_y^{-2}$ may be appropriate for individual data points, unless transformations add global weights. A more detailed discussion of this topic lies beyond our current, necessarily limited purview.

4.20 General least squares fit to a complex quantity

Consider an impedance plot, in which we make a graph of the imaginary component $-Z''$ of the impedance versus its real component Z'. Both of these quantities are typically measured at the same time, using the same instrument, as a function of frequency. When we plot the magnitude $\sqrt{\{(Z')^2+(Z'')^2\}}$ and the phase angle $\arctan(Z'/Z'')$ as a function of frequency, we can consider the frequency (especially when derived from a quartz oscillator) as the independent variable. However, in a typical impedance plot of $-Z''$ vs. Z' the frequency is *implicit*, and both Z' and $-Z''$ are subject to similar experimental uncertainties, so that it will not do to assign all experimental uncertainty to either the real or the imaginary component of the measured impedance. Below we will use as our model the electrical circuit formed by resistance R_s in series with the parallel combination of a resistance R_p and a capacitance C, which yields a semicircular impedance plot. Similar graphs occur, e.g., in Cole plots of the dielectric constant, or in electrochemical impedance plots. Note that the method is generally applicable, regardless of the complexity of the equivalent circuit used, as long as the coordinates of both the real and imaginary component are given.

The impedance of the above-mentioned circuit is given by

$$Z = R_s + \frac{1}{j\omega C + 1/R_p} = R_s + \frac{R_p(1 - j\omega R_p C)}{1 + (\omega R_p C)^2} \qquad (4.20.1)$$

with the in-phase (real) and quadrature (imaginary) components

$$Z' = R_s + \frac{R_p}{1 + (\omega R_p C)^2}, \qquad Z'' = \frac{-\omega R_p^2 C}{1 + (\omega R_p C)^2} \qquad (4.20.2)$$

We simply minimize the square of the distance d between the experimental and calculated points, where $d^2 = (Z'_{exp} - Z'_{calc})^2 + (Z''_{exp} - Z''_{calc})^2$.

Exercise 4.20.1:

(1) In a new spreadsheet, in block A15:B18, deposit the labels and values of the constants R_s, R_p, C, and s_n, and in block C15:D18 for the constants R_s, R_p, C, and SSR. Below these make column labels for ω, $-Z''$, Z', $-Z''_{calc}$, Z'_{calc}, and SR.

(2) As the first cell in column A deposit, say, 0.01, and in the next a number that is a factor of $10^{0.1}$ (i.e., about 26%) larger. Do this for a total of 41 points, ending at a value of 100. (The same could of course be achieved with two columns, one for log ω and the other for ω, where log $\omega = -2$ (0.1) 2, while the second column calculates its antilog.) In columns M and N deposit Gaussian noise of zero mean and unit standard deviation.

(3) In columns B and C compute $-Z''$ and Z' respectively, based on (4.20.2) with added noise, using the constants in B15:B18 plus the values of ω in column A. These will serve as our stand-in for experimental data. In columns D and E again calculate $-Z''$ and Z' respectively, again based on eq. (4.20.2) but without noise, and now using the guessed constants listed in D15:D17 instead.

(4) In column F compute the squares of the residuals, $SR = (Z' - Z'_{calc})^2 + (Z'' - Z''_{calc})^2$, and in cell D18 place the instruction =SUM() to calculate SSR.

(5) Call Solver and let it minimize D18 by adjusting D15:D17, which will yield the required values for R_p, R_s, and C. Then call SolverAid for estimates of the precision of the found parameters. Figures 4.20.1 and 4.20.2 illustrate this approach for a rather noisy data set; by varying the value of s_n you can see how the parameters found depend on the noise level. For $s_n = 0$ you will of course recover the parameter values in B15:B17 exactly.

This example shows the flexibility of the above approach. The model can be quite complicated, with many adjustable parameters, as long as both its real and imaginary component are measurable. It allows for the introduction of individual weights, by including them in column F. In this way, quite complicated equivalent circuits can be accommodated.

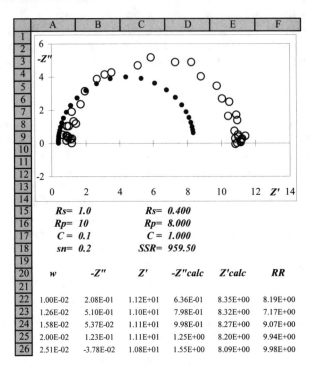

Rs= 1.0		Rs= 0.400			
Rp= 10		Rp= 8.000			
C = 0.1		C = 1.000			
sn= 0.2		SSR= 959.50			
w	-Z"	Z'	-Z"calc	Z'calc	RR
1.00E-02	2.08E-01	1.12E+01	6.36E-01	8.35E+00	8.19E+00
1.26E-02	5.10E-01	1.10E+01	7.98E-01	8.32E+00	7.17E+00
1.58E-02	5.37E-02	1.11E+01	9.98E-01	8.27E+00	9.07E+00
2.00E-02	1.23E-01	1.11E+01	1.25E+00	8.20E+00	9.94E+00
2.51E-02	-3.78E-02	1.08E+01	1.55E+00	8.09E+00	9.98E+00

Fig. 4.20.1: The top of the spreadsheet of Exercise 4.20.1, before using Solver. Open circles: simulated noisy ("experimental") data; closed circles: calculated using the rough estimates for R_s, R_p, and C shown

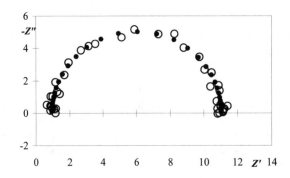

Fig. 4.20.2: The result after Solver has adjusted the parameter values, and SolverAid has determined the associated uncertainties. For the data shown in Fig. 4.20.1 this results in $R_s = 0.96_5 \pm 0.04_6$, $R_p = 10.0_7 \pm 0.06_2$, and $C = 0.098_1 \pm 0.001_6$, with SSR = 3.077 and a standard deviation of the fit of 0.28. Note that SolverAid can accommodate two adjacent columns for Y_{calc}, and also yields the corresponding covariance matrix (not shown) which, in this case, shows only a weak mutual dependency.

4.21 Analyzing reaction rates

As a capstone case for these three chapters on least squares methods we will now consider in some detail a small set of data from chemical kinetics. T. C. Bruice and G. L. Schmir in *J. Am. Chem. Soc.* 79 (1957) 1663 reported the rate constants k for the spontaneous hydrolysis of *p*-nitrophenolacetate in a 28.5% (vol/vol) ethanol/water mixture with 5.4 mM phosphate buffer of pH 8.0 at various temperatures, and analyzed them to extract the activation energy E of the reaction. We will do likewise here, using the Arrhenius equation

$$k_T = k' \exp[-E/RT] \tag{4.21.1}$$

in its logarithmic form,

$$\ln k = \ln k' - E/RT \tag{4.21.2}$$

where k' is a rate constant, and the gas constant R has the value 1.9858775×10^{-3} kcal mol^{-1} K^{-1}. The reported data are shown in Fig. 4.21.1. To find the rate constant k_{25} at 25 °C we combine (4.21.2) with $\ln k_{25}$ $= \ln k' - E/RT_{25}$ (where T_{25} is the absolute temperature at 25 °C, i.e., $T_{25} = 273.15 + 25 = 298.15$ K) to

$$\ln k = \ln k_{25} + \frac{E}{R}\left(\frac{1}{T_{25}} - \frac{1}{T}\right) \tag{4.21.3}$$

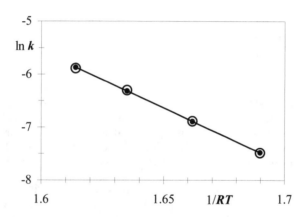

Fig. 4.21.1: Open circles: the natural logarithm of the experimental rate constants k versus $1/RT$, where R is the gas constant and T the absolute temperature, for the hydrolysis of *p*-nitrophenolacetate according to Bruice & Schmir. The line and small closed circles were calculated from the least-squares-fitted straight line through these points.

Equation (4.21.2) suggests a linear relationship between $\ln k$ and E, which Fig. 4.21.1 confirms for these data. In order to find both $\ln k_{25}$ and E we therefore proceed with the straightforward analysis shown in Fig. 4.21.2 which, together with its listed cell instructions, will be mostly self-explanatory by now. The only noteworthy aspect of Fig. 4.21.2 is that the standard deviation of k_{25} was computed with Propagation in two different ways. It was first obtained in cell G5 from the standard deviations in C9:D9, i.e., by neglecting the covariance $v_{i \neq j}$. This answer was moved down to cell G6, whereupon Propagation was used again in the now empty cell G5, but this time based on the covariance data of C13:D14. The two values for s_{25} in G5 and G6 differ by a factor of about 50. Moreover, the value computed in G6 is more than 50% of the value of k_{25} itself. This is surprising because the straight line fitted to the original data had an R^2-value of 0.99973, as found with LinEst, see cell F12 in Fig. 4.21.2, and the experimental data were given to three digits, with one of them, at 298 K, quite close to 25 °C = 298.15 K. How can this be possible?

	A	B	C	D	E	F	G
1	*T*	*k*	ln *k*	−1/*RT*	(ln *k*)calc	*R* =	*1.9859E-03*
2	K	min⁻¹		mol kcal⁻¹			
3						*E* =	*21.21004910*
4	298	5.60E-04	-7.487573774	-1.68978434	-7.481892271	k_{25} =	*7.47150E+27*
5	303	1.02E-03	-6.887952652	-1.66190011	-6.890466384	st.dev.=	*6.78841E-06*
6	308	1.83E-03	-6.303439312	-1.63492121	-6.318242635	st.dev.=	*3.32990E-04*
7	312	2.78E-03	-5.885304351	-1.61396068	-5.873668800	*SSR* =	*0.000393123*
8		*Coeff:*	*28.35851653*	*21.2100491*			
9		*StDev:*	*0.40584306*	*0.24590769*		*LinEst:*	
10		*Sf:*	*0.01402003*	LS1		*21.2100491*	*28.35851653*
11		*CM:*	*0.164708588*	*0.099785042*		*0.2459077*	*0.405843058*
12			*0.099785042*	*0.060470594*		*9.99731E-01*	*0.014020035*
13		*CC:*	*1*	*0.999850815*		*7.43942E+03*	*2*
14			*0.999850815*	*1*		*1.46230E+00*	*0.000393123*
15							
16		*cell:*	*instruction:*				*copied to:*
17		C4 = LN(B4)					C5:C7
18		D4 = 1/($G$1*A4)					D5:D7
19		G3 = D8					
20		G4 = EXP(C8+D8/(G1*298.15))					
21		F10:G14 = LINEST(C4:C7,D4:D7,1,1)					
22		E4 = $C$8+$D$8*D4					E5:E7
23		G7 = SUMXMY2(C4:C7,E4:E7)					

Fig. 4.21.2: An Excel spreadsheet illustrating the analysis. The experimental data are listed in cells A4:B7, their transformed values in C4:D7, the resulting least squares parameters in C8:D8 and G10:F10 for LS1 and LinEst respectively, the corresponding standard deviations in C9:D9 and G11:F11, and the standard deviation of the over-all fit in C10 and G12. The covariance matrix CM is given by LS1 in C11:D12, and the corresponding matrix of linear correlation coefficients CC in C13:D14.

The spreadsheet provides the answer: the values of ln k' (in cell C8) and E (in cell D8) are strongly correlated, so that neglecting their covariances (in cells D13 and C14) leads to a large error in the standard deviation of k_{25} in cell G6. LS even alerts you by displaying the contents of cells C14 and D13 in bold (and, on the monitor screen, vivid red) numerals. It is ironic that the precision of the standard deviation is usually overrated (see section 2.12) while, by neglecting the covariance, its reported accuracy is often so poor.

It is helpful to consider the error surface introduced in sections 1.5.3 and 4.17, i.e., a map of log SSR as a function of its two main variables, here E and ln k. Make two numerical axes: one row for E from 10 to 30 in increments of 0.1, say in I4:DE4, and one column for ln k' = 40 (−0.1) 20 in H5:H205, and then compute log SSR in I5:DE205. Highlight block H4:DE205, use the scroll bars to move the pointer back to the top left-hand corner of the spreadsheet, and call ScanF0. Assign X to cell D8, Y to C8, and F to G7. Finally, use Mapper to display the results, which you might have expected to show a narrow pit around the minimum value of log SSR. Instead, in Fig. 4.21.3a,b we find what looks more like a trench!

A more vivid view of this result is obtained with a 3-D surface graph, which we can rotate to see the error surface from various angles. When we look along the length of the trench we get Fig. 4.21.4, and a more detailed look along and perpendicular to the direction of that trench is shown in Fig. 4.21.5a,b. The minimum in SSR is quite narrow in one direction, but very gradual in the other. This makes the coordinates of E and ln k extremely vulnerable to small amounts of systematic errors (bias) in the data.

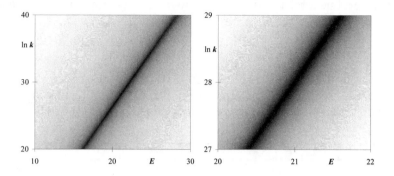

Fig. 4.21.3: Two 200 × 200 cell error surfaces of the spreadsheet of Fig. 4.21.2, at different scales.

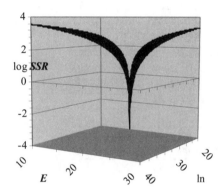

Fig. 4.21.4a: A 3-D surface graph of log SSR, looking along the trench in Fig. 4.21.3.

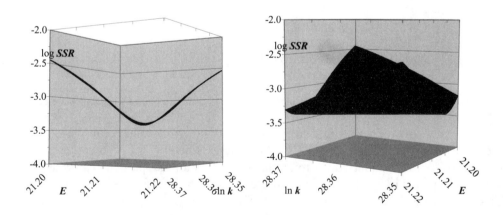

Fig. 4.21.4b: Two views of the same 3-D surface graph, looking (left) along and (right) perpendicular to that trench.

193

Because we analyze a linear relationship, we can avoid collinearity through centering, i.e., by using

$$\ln k = \ln k'' + E\left(\left(\frac{1}{RT}\right)_{av} - \frac{1}{RT}\right)$$ (4.21.4)

where $\ln k = \ln k''$ when $1/T = (1/T)_{av}$, here about 32.01 °C. As can be seen in Fig. 4.21.5, this solves the problem of collinearity (see cells C29 & D28 or C31 & D30) and results in equal answers in cells G22 and G23. Moreover, the error surface shows a better defined minimum, see Figs. 4.21.6 and 4.21.7.

	A	B	C	D	E	F	G
18	T	k	$\ln k$	$1/RT - (1/RT)_{av}$	$(\ln k)_{calc}$	$R =$	*1.9859E-03*
19	°K	min^{-1}		mol kcal^{-1}		$(1/RT)_{av} =$	*1.65014159*
20						$E =$	*21.2100*
21	298	5.60E-04	-7.487573774	0.03964275	-7.481892271	$k_{25} =$	*2.9727E-03*
22	303	1.02E-03	-6.887952652	0.01175852	-6.890466384	CC	*6.7884E-06*
23	308	1.83E-03	-6.303439312	-0.01522037	-6.318242635	st.dev.	*6.7884E-06*
24	312	2.78E-03	-5.885304351	-0.03618090	-5.873668800	$SSR =$	*0.00039312*
25		*Coeff:*	*-6.641067522*	*-21.2100491*			
26		*StDev:*	*0.007010017*	*0.245907694*		*LinEst:*	
27		*Sf:*	*0.014020035*	LS1		*-21.2100491*	*-6.641067522*
28		*CM:*	*4.9140E-05*	*0*		*0.2459077*	*0.007010017*
29			*0*	*0.060470594*		*9.99731E-01*	*0.014020035*
30		*CC:*	*1*	*0.0000000*		*7.43942E+03*	*2*
31			*0.0000000*	*1*		*1.46230E+00*	*0.000393123*

cell: instruction: copied to:
C21 = LN(B21)   C22:C24
D21 = D4-$G$19   D22:D24
E21 = $C$25+$D$25*D21   E22:E24
G19 = AVERAGE(D4:D7)
G20 = -D25
G21 = EXP(C25-D25*(1/(G18*298.15)-G19)
G24 = SUMXMY2(C21:C24,E21:E24)
F27:G31 = LINEST(C21:C24,D21:D24,1,1)

Fig. 4.21.5: A centered analysis of the same input data; the covariances in cells C31 and D30 are now zero.

Now that we know how to avoid collinearity and its telltale error surface, can we explain the peculiar shape of the latter? The spreadsheet of Fig. 4.21.2 can help us here: cell G7 computes SSR, and we now change the value of E in D8 and let Solver minimize $\ln k$ in C8 for that particular E-value, so that we find some coordinates of points in that trench. Their subsequent analysis is shown in Table 4.21.1. We see that the trench indeed has a well-defined minimum (not evident in Figs. 4.21.3 and 4.21.4 which only covered a small area), and is fitted well by a straight line, as can also be seen from the superposition in Fig. 4.21.8.

194

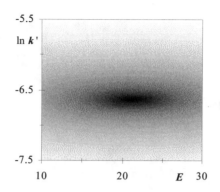

Fig. 4.21.6: The error surface of the centered approach.

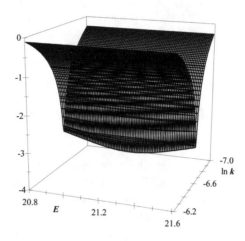

Fig. 4.21.7: A 3-D view of a detail of the same error surface.

	a_0	a_1	SSR	log SSR
	21.4113394	17	0.0580072	-1.2365184
	28.3585165	21.2100491	0.0003931	-3.4054718
	33.7874013	24.5	0.0355761	-1.4488415
	39.5628969	28	0.1502536	-0.8231750
Coeff:	-6.64106752	1.650141585		
StDev:	1.68708E-09	7.32284E-11		
Sf:	5.95081E-10	LS1		

Table 4.21.1: A few values for the coordinates $a_0 = \ln k$ and $a_1 = E$ of the trench in Figs. 4.21.3 and 4.21.4.

195

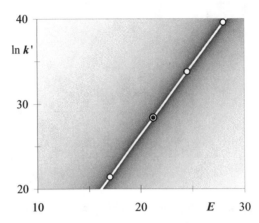

Fig. 4.21.8: The error surface of Fig. 4.21.3 with the discrete points and (white) straight line of Table 4.21.1 The minimum value of log SSR found in the spreadsheet analysis of Fig. 4.21.2 is emphasized as a larger point with a central dot.

What is the physical meaning of such a linear trench, i.e., what determines its intercept and slope? For its intercept $a_0 = -6.64106752$, compare this value with that of $\ln k$ for the centered approach in cell C25 of Fig. 4.21.5, and for its slope $a_1 = 1.650141585$, consider the value of $(1/RT)_{av}$ in cell G19 of that same spreadsheet. The trench-like error surface of the non-centered approach already contains the essential elements of its centered counterpart!

$$*****$$

There is still a problem with the analysis so far, because it minimizes the sum of squares of the residuals in $\ln k$ whereas the experimental data were k-values. Bruice & Schmir did not give individual uncertainty estimates, and we should therefore use weighted least squares by inserting in the spreadsheet a column, between those for $\ln k$ and $1/RT$, for the global weights w, see section 3.17. We then use WLS instead of LS for the least squares analysis, in which case we have, see (3.17.3),

$$w \equiv \frac{1}{\left(d\ln k/dk\right)^2} = \frac{1}{\left(1/k\right)^2} = k^2 \tag{4.21.5}$$

The resulting weighted, centered spreadsheet analysis is shown in Fig. 4.21.9, and has (apart from round-off errors) zero covariance between $\ln k$ and E. Of course, the values of $\ln k$ and E now obtained are slightly different from those found with an unweighted analysis. Which set of results should we use? In the absence of more specific experimental data than provided by Bruice & Schmir, the best we can do is to use the following, plausible argument.

In a typical study of chemical reaction rates, a concentration c is measured as a function of time t. A hydrolysis reaction typically follows the rate expression

$$\frac{dc}{dt} = -kc \qquad \text{or} \qquad c = c_0 e^{-kt} \tag{4.21.6}$$

which is first-order in the concentration of the hydrolyzing species. The water concentration is so large as to be essentially constant, and therefore need not enter the rate law. Extracting k-values from such data is usually done by least squares analysis of the linear relationship $\ln c = \ln c_0 - kt$, which yields $-k$ as its slope, in which case it is appropriate to analyze the results as having uncertainties in k rather than in $\ln k$.

	A	B	C	D	E	F	G	H
18	T	k	$\ln k$	w	$1/RT$-$(1/RT)_{av}$	$(\ln k)_{calc}$	$R =$	$1.9859E$-03
19	°K	min^{-1}			mol kcal^{-1}		$w/(RTw_{av}) =$	1.62553221
20							$E =$	20.838456
21	298	5.60E-04	-7.487574	3.14E-07	0.06425212	-7.46120	$k_{25}=$	$5.8525E$-04
22	303	1.02E-03	-6.887953	1.04E-06	0.03636789	-6.88013	CC	$1.4420E$-05
23	308	1.83E-03	-6.303439	3.35E-06	0.00938900	-6.31793	st.dev.	$1.4420E$-05
24	312	2.78E-03	-5.885304	7.73E-06	-0.01157153	-5.88115	$SSR =$	$9.8433E$-04
25			*Coeff:*	*-6.122280303*	*-20.83845629*			
26			*StDev:*	*0.006708296*	*0.373937906*		$w_{av} =$	3.1078E-06
27			*Sf:*	*0.013416592*	WLS1		w/w_{av}	$w/(RTw_{av})$
28			*CM:*	*4.50012E-05*	*-2.30437E-18*		0.1009	0.170510363
29				*-2.30437E-18*	*0.139829557*		0.3348	0.556350783
30			*CC:*	*1*	*-9.18631E-16*		1.0776	1.761742583
31				*-9.18631E-16*	*1*		2.4868	4.013525130

cell:	instruction:		copied to:
C21 = LN(B21)			C22:C24
D21 = B21^2			D22:D24
E21 = E4-$H$19			E22:E24
F21 = $D$25+$E$25*E21			F22:F24
G28 = D21/$H$26			G29:G31
H19 = AVERAGE(E4:E7)			
H20 = -E25			
H21 = EXP(D25+E25*(1/(H18*298.15)-H19))			
H24 = SUMXMY2(C21:C24,F21:F24)			
H26 = AVERAGE(D21:D24)			
H28 = G28/E4			H29:H31

Fig. 4.21.9: The spreadsheet showing a weighted, centered analysis of the Bruice & Schmir data.

In the above spreadsheets, the difficulty with the non-weighted approach was that the analysis didn't directly yield the sought parameter k_{25}, and linearizing the Arrhenius equation (4.21.1) required use of $\ln k$ instead of k. We can avoid this problem by using nonlinear least squares instead, as illustrated in the spreadsheet of Figs. 4.21.10a and 4.21.10b, where we first use Solver to obtain E and k_{25}, and then SolverAid to find the associated uncertainty estimates. This is often the simplest and fastest approach, although we have seen that it is not without possible pitfalls, see section 4.17.

Table 4.21.2 presents an overview of the results obtained in this example. The bold-printed, fully equivalent results can be obtained with weighted linear least squares (WLS) and with nonlinear least squares (Solver + SolverAid), even though the latter uses an entirely different algorithm. On the other hand, it is impossible to find these results with LinEst or Regression, because these routines neither allow weights nor provide the covariances. You have to pick your tools carefully, especially in cases involving exponential relations, as we already saw in section 2.18.

	A	B	C	D	E	F
1	*T*	*k*	*k*$_{calc}$	*R* =	*1.9859E-03*	
2	°K	min^{-1}				
3						
4	298	5.60E-04	0.000099153	*SSR* =	*1.0349E-05*	
5	303	1.02E-03	0.000131041	*E* =	*10.0000*	
6	308	1.83E-03	0.000171623	*k*$_{25}$ =	*1.0000E-04*	
7	312	2.78E-03	0.000211644			
8						
9						
10						

cell: instruction: *copied to:*

C4 = $E$6*EXP(($E$5/$E$1)*(1/298.15-1/A4))   C5:C7

E4 = SUMXMY2(B4:B7,C4:C7)

Fig. 4.21.10*a*: The spreadsheet ready for analyzing the Bruice & Schmir data by nonlinear least squares.

	A	B	C	D	E	F
1	*T*	*k*	*k*$_{calc}$	*R* =	*1.9859E-03*	
2	°K	min^{-1}				
3					**SolverAid**	
4	298	5.60E-04	0.000574602	*SSR* =	*1.1152E-09*	*2.36131E-05*
5	303	1.02E-03	0.001027578	*E* =	*20.8463*	*0.369240958*
6	308	1.83E-03	0.001803293	*k*$_{25}$ =	*5.8488E-04*	*1.4242E-05*
7	312	2.78E-03	0.002791458	*CM:*	*0.136338885*	*-5.05589E-06*
8					*-5.05589E-06*	*2.02834E-10*
9				*CC:*	*1*	*-0.961430484*
10					*-0.961430484*	*1*

cell: instruction: *copied to:*

C4 = $E$6*EXP(($E$5/$E$1)*(1/298.15-1/A4))   C5:C7

E4 = SUMXMY2(B4:B7,C4:C7)

Fig. 4.21.10*b*: The final spreadsheet after using Solver and SolverAid.

Method	tool	*E* / kcal mol^{-1}	$10^4\,k_{25}$ / min^{-1} from st. dev.	from CM
Simple linear least squares	LS1	$21.2_1 \pm 0.2_5$	$5._7 \pm 3._3$	$5.73_4 \pm 0.06_8$
Centered linear least squares	LS1	$21.2_1 \pm 0.2_5$	$5.73_4 \pm 0.06_8$	$5.73_4 \pm 0.06_8$
Weighted linear least squares	WLS	$\mathbf{20.8_4 \pm 0.3_7}$	$5._8 \pm 5._1$	$\mathbf{5.8_5 \pm 0.1_4}$
Centered & weighted linear LS	WLS1	$\mathbf{20.8_4 \pm 0.3_7}$	$\mathbf{5.8_5 \pm 0.1_1}$	$\mathbf{5.8_5 \pm 0.1_4}$
Nonlinear least squares	Solver + SolverAid	$\mathbf{20.8_5 \pm 0.4_0}$	$\mathbf{5.8_5 \pm 0.1_4}$	

Table 4.21.2: The least squares results obtained with the small data set of Bruice & Schmir.

4.22 Miscellany

This section contains a rather random collection of further examples of using Solver for data analysis. At this point you will have enough experience and self-confidence to tackle these problems without step-by-step instructions. The primary purpose of this section is to illustrate the wide range of problems that can be addressed efficiently by nonlinear least squares, and to provide some exercises for self-testing.

4.22.1 Viscosity vs. temperature & pressure

As an example of fitting a set of high-quality experimental data to an equation with several adjustable parameters, use measurements from T. Witt (Ph.D. thesis, Technological University Eindhoven, 1974) on the pressure dependence of the kinematic viscosity of a lubricant at four different temperatures, as listed by D. M. Bates & D. G. Watts, *Nonlinear Regression Analysis and Its Applications*, Wiley (1988), Table A1.8, p. 275, as well as in the DataSamples. Here the dependent variable, y, is the natural logarithm of the measured kinematic viscosity v_{kin} (in Stokes), and is to be fitted to the empirical expression

$$y = \frac{a_1}{a_2 + t} + a_3 p + a_4 p^2 + a_5 p^3 + (a_6 + a_7 p^2) \, p \exp\left[\frac{-t}{a_8 + a_9 p^2}\right] \qquad (4.22.1)$$

where t is temperature, in $^\circ$C, and p is pressure, in kAtm.

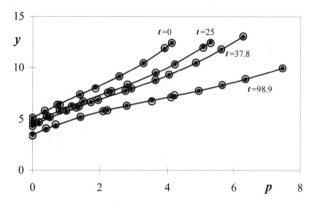

Fig. 4.22.1: Comparison of the experimental data (open circles) and those calculated with Solver (line plus small solid points) by fitting the data to eq.(4.22.1).

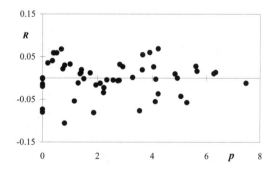

Fig. 4.22.2: The residuals of the fit shown in Fig. 4.22.1.

Use Solver, with the initial values $a_1 = a_2 = \ldots = a_9 = 1$, then SolverAid, compare your results with those listed on p. 89 of Bates & Watts, and find the significant typo in one of their listed constants. Plot your results and the corresponding residuals, and compare these with Figs. 4.22.1 and 4.22.2.

4.22.2 *Potentiometric titration of a diprotic base*

In *Technometrics* 18 (1975) 161, W. H. Sachs reported data for a potentiometric titration of 20.000 mL 0.043051 M N,N-dimethylaminoethylamine + 0.09658 M NaCl with 0.09975 M HCl, see Table 4.22.1, and its analysis assuming that the volume of titrant added was the independent variable, and pH the dependent one. In this case it is not clear which parameter carries more experimental uncertainty, and no arguments are offered one way or the other. Because the analysis is more straightforward when it is assumed that the titrant volume is the dependent variable instead, we will take that approach here.

Va	pH	Va	pH	Va	pH	Va	pH
1.695	10.002	6.790	8.830	10.410	6.889	15.221	5.837
2.402	9.820	7.090	8.731	10.840	6.777	15.720	5.686
2.743	9.739	7.294	8.660	11.280	6.675	16.220	5.489
3.195	9.643	7.660	8.497	11.730	6.578	16.634	5.249
3.599	9.559	8.097	8.230	12.230	6.474	16.859	5.045
4.104	9.457	8.386	7.991	12.725	6.378	17.000	4.852
4.678	9.339	8.671	7.735	13.229	6.280	17.101	4.656
4.990	9.276	9.070	7.430	13.726	6.184	17.140	4.552
5.589	9.145	9.531	7.194	14.225	6.078	17.170	4.453
6.190	8.994	9.980	7.026	14.727	5.959	17.228	4.220

Table 4.22.1: The titration data from W. H. Sachs, *Technometrics* 18 (1975) 161.

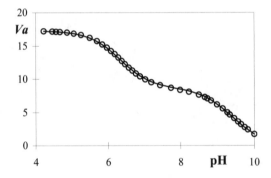

Fig. 4.22.3: Open circles: experimental data; line: the theoretical progress curve for the titration calculated by Solver with $pK_{a1} = 6.33$ and $pK_{a1} = 9.40$.

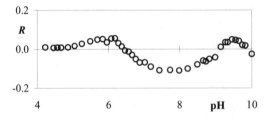

Fig. 4.22.4: The corresponding residuals.

Analyze these data in terms of the expression for the titration of a diprotic base with a strong monoprotic acid, using K_{a1}, K_{a2}, K_w, and V_b as adjustable parameters, by making columns for V_a, pH, $[H^+]$, and $V_{a,calc}$, and calculating SSR from the differences between the entries for V_a and $V_{a,calc}$.

For $V_{a,calc}$ use the theoretical expression

$$V_a = \cfrac{\cfrac{2[\text{H}^+]^2 + [\text{H}^+]K_{a1}}{[\text{H}^+]^2 + [\text{H}^+]K_{a1} + K_{a1}K_{a2}}C_b + [\text{H}^+] - K_w/[\text{H}^+]}{C_a - [\text{H}^+] + K_w/[\text{H}^+]} \qquad (4.22.2)$$

Assume that $pK_{a1} = 6$ and $pK_{a2} = 10$, set pK_w to 14, and from these calculate $K_{a1} = 10^{\wedge}(-pK_{a1})$ and $K_{a2} = 10^{\wedge}(-pK_{a2})$. It is these pK_a values (rather than the far smaller K_a values themselves) that Solver should optimize. You should get a result similar to that shown in Fig. 4.22.3. A residual plot of $R = V_a - V_{a,calc}$ vs. pH shows that systematic rather than random deviations control the standard deviation, see Fig. 4.22.4. Similar systematic deviations are also apparent in Fig. 1 of the Sachs paper, and from the data listed for $\hat{\varepsilon}_{i1}$ in its Table 1, which are the corresponding residuals in pH. The above fit neglects activity corrections, which we will now apply. These require that we calculate the ionic strength $I = \frac{1}{2} \Sigma z^2 c$, and we will then estimate the activity corrections with the approximation $f = 10^{\wedge}\{-0.5 [(\sqrt{I})/(1+\sqrt{I}) - 0.3I]\}$ due to C. W. Davies, *Ion Association*, Butterworth (1962), and $K'_{a1} = K_{a1}/f^2$, $K'_{a2} = K_{a1}$, and $K'_w = f^2 K_w$. (Sachs used an earlier form of the Davies equation, with a coefficient -0.2 instead of -0.3.) The ionic strength, buffered by the presence of 0.09658 M NaCl incorporated in the sample, is given by

$$I = 0.5 \left([\text{H}^+] + [\text{OH}^-] + 4[\text{H}_2\text{B}^{2+}] + [\text{HB}^+] + [\text{Na}^+] + [\text{Cl}^-]\right) = 0.5 \left([\text{H}^+] + \frac{K_w}{[\text{H}^+]}\right)$$

$$+ \frac{V_b}{V_a + V_b}\left(\frac{(2[\text{H}^+]^2 + 0.5[\text{H}^+]K_{a1})C_b}{[\text{H}^+]^2 + [\text{H}^+]K_{a1} + K_{a1}K_{a2}} + 0.09658\right) + \left(\frac{0.5\,C_a V_a}{V_a + V_b}\right) \qquad (4.22.3)$$

Following this procedure, already illustrated in section 4.4.2, we obtain $pK'_{a1} = 6.55$ and $pK'_{a2} = 9.40$, changes that hardly justify the additional effort.

Strictly speaking, we should now repeat this procedure by using the new pK_a estimates to recalculate I, then f, and again $V_{a,calc}$, until the results no longer change, but that is obviously not necessary here since it will not lead to substantial further changes. Because of the presence of added NaCl in the sample, the ionic strength does not change much during the titration, so that the result is only slightly different from that obtained without activity corrections. Re-plotting the residuals R shows that the systematic deviations illustrated in Fig. 4.22.4 likewise persist after activity correction, so that the absence of such a correction did not cause the systematic deviations in R.

Sachs reported similar systematic trends in the residuals $\hat{\varepsilon}_{i1}$, but somewhat different numerical values for the equilibrium constants: $pK'_{a1} = 5.97$ (rather than 6.55) and $pK'_{a2} = 9.28$ (instead of 9.40). This is not unexpected, because Sachs used a quite different mathematical approach, from the early days of nonlinear least squares analysis. Since insufficient chemical information is available about the titration (such as the chemical purity of the sample used), the origin(s) of the systematic deviations in both fitting procedures cannot be ascertained.

4.22.3 Analyzing light from a variable star

In their influential book *The Calculus of Observations*, Blackie & Sons, 4th ed. (1944) pp. 349-352, E. Whittaker & G. Robinson list the brightness of a variable star supposedly recorded during 600 successive cloudless midnights, and rounded to integer values. These data can also be downloaded from http://www. york.ac.uk/depts/ maths/data/ts/ts.26.dat, and are shown as open circles in Fig. 4.22.5. They exhibit an interference pattern implying at least two sinusoids, plus a constant offset. Counting maxima, one quickly finds that the frequency of one of these sinusoids must be approximately $20\frac{1}{2}/600 \approx 0.029$ day^{-1}, while the beat pattern indicates that their periods $1/f$ must differ by about 5 days. Therefore use Solver to fit these data to an equation of the form $y = a_0 + a_1 \sin(2\pi f_1 + b_1) + a_2 \sin(2\pi f_2 + b_2)$ with initial guess values for f_1 and f_2 of 0.03 and $1/(29-5) \approx 0.04$ respectively.

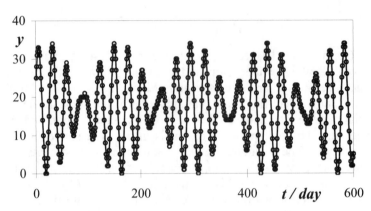

Fig. 4.22.5: The intensities of the variable star (open circles) observed on 600 successive midnights, and their analysis (line) in terms of a constant plus two sinusoids.

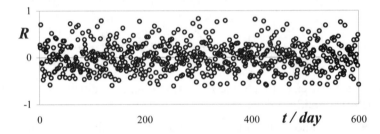

Fig. 4.22.6: The residuals for the fit of Fig. 4.22.5 show no discernable trend, just a standard deviation of 0.302. This is roughly what one would expect on the basis of merely rounding the data to integer values, suggesting that this was a made-up data set.

Using these data, you should find $a_0 = 17.08_6 \pm 0.01_2$, $a_1 = 10.03_1 \pm 0.01_8$, $f_1 = 0.034482_4 \pm 0.000001_7$, $b_1 = 0.650_4 \pm 0.003_6$, $a_2 = 7.08_4 \pm 0.01_8$, $f_2 = 0.041666_5 \pm 0.000002_3$, and $b_2 = -0.261_6 \pm 0.005_0$. Figures 4.22.5 and 4.22.6 indicate how close a fit you can obtain. (The corresponding periods $1/f$ are 29.000 and 24.000 respectively!) The analysis used here is both much faster and easier that that discussed by Whittaker & Robinson (before nonlinear least squares were readily available), which yielded $a_0 = 17$, $a_1 = 10$, $f_1 = 1/29$, $b_1 = 6\pi/29 \approx 0.6500$, $a_2 = 7$, $f_2 = 1/24$, and $b_2 = -2\pi/24 \approx -0.6218$.

The above data lack any indication of a possible experimental source, and their noise is certainly compatible with a made-up set rounded to integer values. You may therefore want to add some Gaussian noise, and delete some data points (to represent missing observations on overcast pre-satellite-era nights) to make the data seem more realistic. Solver has no problems with missing data.

Incidentally, the above-mentioned web site contains 74 interesting time series, listed in http://www.york.ac.uk/depts/maths/data/ts/welcome.

4.22.4 The growth of a bacterial colony

In his book on *Elements of Mathematical Biology*, Williams & Wilkins (1924), Dover (1956), A. J. Lotka listed data by Thornton on the area A occupied by a growing colony of Bacillus dendroides in a growth medium containing 0.2% KNO_3, and reproduced here in Table 4.22.2. Fit these data to the equation $A = a / (b + e^{-ct})$ where a, b, and c are adjustable parameters, and t is age, in days. Give the best-fitting values for a, b, and c, together with their uncertainty estimates, and plot your results.

time t, in days:	0	1	2	3	4	5
area A, in cm^2:	0.24	2.78	13.53	36.3	47.5	49.4

Table 4.22.2: The area A occupied by the bacterial colony at age t, in days. For experimental details see H. G. Thornton, *Ann. Appl. Biol.* 9 (1922) 265.

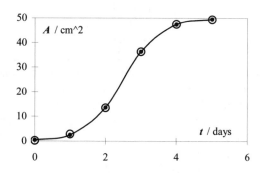

Fig. 4.22.7: The area A occupied by the bacterial colony at age t, as described by Solver and SolverAid with $a = 0.37_0 \pm 0.02_5$, $b = 0.0074_2 \pm 0.0005_0$, $c = 1.96_2 \pm 0.02_8$.

Incidentally, the fit shown in Fig. 4.22.7 has a ten times lower value for SSR than that given by Lotka. However, one should consider both sets of numerical results with skepticism, because all three adjustable parameters are strongly correlated, especially a and b, which in our solution exhibit a linear correlation coefficient of 0.9987.

4.23 How good is Solver?

With linear least squares we found in chapters 2 and 3 that some problems were more difficult to solve than others, and the same applies to nonlinear least squares. In discussing this question it is helpful to use an objective set of test data, for which we will here use those of the NIST Statistical Reference Datasets or StRD. This collection of 27 nonlinear least squares test data sets, of varying difficulty, can be downloaded freely from http://www.itl.nist.gov/div898/strd/nls/nls_info.shtml.

But there is more to it: whether we find a solution also depends on how we use Solver. We have emphasized before that, for scientific uses, we should not use Solver as provided, but exploit its Options. Specifically, we recommended to lower the Precision criterion significantly, by several orders of magnitude (such as from 0.000 001 to 0.000 000 000 001), to do likewise for the Tolerance (from 5% to, e.g., 0.000 005%), to select Use Automatic Scaling, and to move the Derivatives from Forward to Central. In this section we will see that it indeed matters whether we use Solver "as is", or with such "optimized" settings. Solver provides these options precisely because, unlike with linear least squares, there is no generally applicable "optimal" setting, a designation we therefore use loosely here to indicate a reasonable set of initial settings for scientific applications of Solver. Note: For Excel 2010, Frontline Systems has updated its Solver, which now also includes two alternative optimizing routines, but which we have not yet tested. The following comments therefore apply only to pre-2010 versions of Excel.

We have emphasized that, for optimal results, it may be useful to run Solver twice, in order to check whether it has indeed converged. Again, this is no hard-and-fast rule: sometimes, additional repeats are necessary, or no reasonable number of them seems to converge on a final answer, in which case Solver clearly cannot find a solution. The need for repeats is clearly a design fault in Solver. Since no new information is entered in doing so, the user shouldn't have to repeat Solver to find out whether or not it has converged on its solution.

Here we will use Misra 1 and Lanczos, two NIST Standard Reference Data sets that have multiple uses. Misra 1 comes in four flavors, distinguished by the suffixes a through d, which fit four different models to the same data set. Lanczos 3 fits a simple model to y-values specified to 11 digits, while Lanczos 1 and 2 use shorter versions of the same input data. All of these fit the NIST categories of "lower" or "average" level of difficulty.

The common data set used for Misra $1a$ through Misra $1d$ can be downloaded from the SampleData file on my website. These data are then analyzed in terms of four different two-parameter model expressions, which all happen to yield fairly close agreement with the proper parameters. The four model expressions are shown in Table 4.23.1. Since the NIST data sets come with certified parameter values, we can readily compute how close the results obtained with Solver are to those reference values in terms of the parameter pE defined in section 9.1, which shows the relative precision of the answer obtained, a quantity closely related to the number of significant figures in that answer. Since two parameters are involved, we merely list the lowest of their pE-values to get a single identifier for the quality of our answer. For practical purposes, pE for double-precision data is restricted to the range from 0 to 14, and in Table 4.23.1 is rounded to the nearest integer. In that table they are listed for using Solver either "as is" or "optimized", after a first application of Solver, and after that answer is used for a second use of Solver. We see that, on its first try, Solver does poorly when used "as is", even when used as "optimized". On a retry, however, using the earlier result as its starting estimate, Solver can yield quite respectable results (good to at least 1 in 10^9).

In the case of Misra 1, you can easily determine which of the optimizing changes are essential, by applying them one at a time or in small combinations. In this case you will find that it is necessary to Use Automatic Scaling, which (certainly in retrospect) makes eminent sense when you consider that the two parameters b_1 and b_2 differ by about six orders of magnitude. Table 4.23.1 also illustrates the need for repeated use of Solver for difficult problems. If Solver converges, a second repeat often makes only a small improvement; if Solver fails to converge, the answers obtained may keep changing.

An aspect to savor in this example is that the four quite different model expressions shown in Table 4.23.1 each can yield visually perfect fits, with values of SSR of 0.12 or less, which is not bad considering that the y-values range from 10 to 82. The take-home lesson here is that a good fit does not prove the validity of a particular model. A poor fit, however, should ring an alarm about the model chosen, at least for noise-poor data.

test	model expression	try	pE as is	pE optimized
Misra $1a$	$y = b_1\,(1-\exp(-b_2 x))$	1	2	2
		2	2	9
Misra $1b$	$y = b_1\,(1-(1+b_2 x/2)^{\wedge}(-2))$	1	0	2
		2	1	10
Misra $1c$	$y = b_1\,(1-(1+b_2 x)^{\wedge}(-0.5))$	1	2	5
		2	3	10
Misra $1d$	$y = b_1\,b_2\,(1+b_2 x)^{\wedge}(-1))$	1	1	2
		2	1	10

Table 4.23.1: The approximate number of significant figures obtained with the above NIST test data sets, using Solver as is or optimized as described in the text, after a first try and, then, after that result is used in a second try.

What merits these Misra data a place in the NIST StRD? What makes them difficult enough that Solver, even after scaling its input, cannot find a good fit on its first try? The answer is suggested by Fig. 4.23.2 for Misra $1a$; the corresponding error surfaces for Misra $1b$ through Misra $1d$ all look quite similar. All four data sets show a high collinearity between the two adjustable parameters, b_1 and b_2. Combine this with the large disparity in the magnitudes of b_1 and b_2 and you have a non-trivial problem

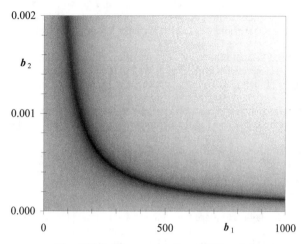

Fig. 4.23.2: The error surface of Misra 1a.

The three Lanczos test sets, also downloadable from the SampleData file, use the single model, $y = b_1 \exp(-b_2 x) + b_3 \exp(-b_4 x) + b_5 \exp(-b_6 x)$, and differ only in the number of decimals used as input data. Solver performs poorly on all three Lanczos tests regardless of optimization and repeats: none of these tests score above $pE = 0$ for the lowest parameter found, and not a single parameter in all these tries has a pE above 2.

4.24 An alternative: the Levenberg-Marquardt routine

As already indicated at the end of section 4.11, Solver is a well-rounded general-purpose nonlinear least squares program. Moreover, it can handle a large number of adjustable parameters, and allows constraints on these adjustable parameters. Frontline Systems, its provider, also sells several more powerful versions of Solver. However, the version incorporated in Excel is relatively weak in terms of accuracy, and there are other algorithms that in this respect may be preferable. Among these, the Levenberg-Marquardt method is the most prominent. An implementation of this algorithm in VBA by Luis Isaac Ramon García is incorporated in Volpi's Optimiz.xla at http :// digilander . libero . it / foxes / Software-Downloads.htm, and can also be downloaded from my excellaneous web site.

In many cases it makes little difference whether we use Solver or Levenberg-Marquardt, because the accuracy of the result obtained is limited by experimental noise. However, a direct comparison of Solver and Levenberg-Marquardt using the NIST StRD test data sets shows that the latter consistently outperforms Solver, on every one of its 27 tests. Granted, StRD contains rather small data sets with relatively few adjustable parameters, which do not require constraints, and therefore do not fully utilize some of the major advantages of Solver. In exercise 4.24.1 we will the use the Misra 1a data set to illustrate the use of this alternative to Solver, and in exercise 4.24.2 we will do the same with Lanczos.

Exercise 4.24.1:

(1) If you have not yet installed Optimiz.xla yet, do so now, using the procedure outlined in section 1.2.5.

(2) First, organize your experimental data from left to right as follows: one or more columns for x, then the corresponding column for y. In the spreadsheet of Fig. 4.24.1 we use B3 and C3 for labels, place the x-values in data in B5:B18, and the y-values in C5:C18. You can copy these data from the SampleData file and paste them directly into the spreadsheet, unless you enjoy typing and proofreading them.

(3) In, say, E22 and E23 deposit some initial values, with corresponding labels in D20:D21. We will use the "Start 1" data of the Misra 1 data set, 500 and 0.0001 respectively, stored here in A22:A23.

(4) Using these values and the model expression used, make a column containing y_{calc}. In our example, use the model equation $y = b_1 (1-\exp(-b_2 x))$ of Misra 1a in, say, column E, in which case cell E5 might contain the instruction =\$E\$22* (1-EXP(-\$E\$23*B5)). Copy this down to E18, and label the column.

(5) Even though it is not required, it is often useful to compute SSR in, e.g.,cell E25, as =SUMXMY2(C5:C18,E5:E18).

(6) After these preliminaries, call Optimiz with Tools ⇨ Optimiz ⇨ NL-Regression ⇨ Levenberg-Marquardt. This will bring up the Non Linear Regression dialog box, which has four large windows on its left-hand side, and four smaller ones on its right.

(7) In the top left window, labeled "Data to fit: *(x, y)*", enter the combined *x,y* data block, here B5:C18, and click Enter. You can download the data from the SampleData file if you don't particularly enjoy typing and proofreading them.

(8) In the second large window, Model: *f(x,a,b,c...)*, likewise enter E4:E17. And in the third wide window, Parameters: *a,b,c...* enter E20:E21.

(9) Leave the bottom window (Derivatives: *df/da, df/db ...*) open, and click on Run.

(10) The answer will appear on the spreadsheet in the parameter block, here E22:E23, just as it does with Solver. Click on the red close button

(11) If you want to find the corresponding number of significant figures, you might want to place the NIST reference values for b_1 and b_2 in, say, cells C22:C23. In this particular case, a direct comparison of the results obtained in E22:E23 and the reference values in C22:C23 will show you good agreement, to about 1 in 10^{11}, not bad considering that the certified answers contain only eleven digits.

(12) You may want to use the simplified instruction =-LOG(ABS((B22-E22)/E22)) in, e.g., cell C22, and copy this down to C23. You don't need to display p*E* to more than one or two decimal places. You will find p*E*-values of about 11, i.e., the results have a relative precision of about 1 in 10^{11}. Note that repeated application of this Levenberg-Marquardt routine, using the previous result as its starting values, will keep changing somewhat, though always at similar p*E*-values.

(13) Your spreadsheet might now look like Fig. 4.24.1.

	A	B	C	D	E	F	G
1		Misra 1a as analyzed with LM using numerical derivatives					
2							
3		*x*	*y*		*y calc*		
4							
5		77.6	10.07		9.98627		
6		114.9	14.73		14.63675		
7		141.1	17.94		17.84672		
8		190.8	23.93		23.81018		
9		239.9	29.61		29.54369		
10		289.0	35.18		35.12439		
11		332.8	40.02		39.97705		
12		378.4	44.82		44.90642		
13		434.8	50.76		50.83467		
14		477.3	55.05		55.18192		
15		536.8	61.01		61.09979		
16		593.1	66.40		66.52381		
17		689.1	75.47		75.39379		
18		760.0	81.78		81.65036		
19							
20	*init.:*	*reference:*	p*E*		*parameters:*		
21							
22	500	238.9421	11.49		b_1 = 238.9421		
23	0.0001	0.00055	11.42		b_2 = 0.00055		
24							
25					*SSR* = 0.124551		

cell: instruction: *copy to:*

E5 = \$E\$22*(1-EXP(-\$E\$23*B5))   E6:E18

C22 = IF(E22=B22,"!",-LOG(ABS((E22-B22)/B22)))   C23

E25 = SUMXMY2(C5:C18,E5:E18)

Fig. 4.24.1: The spreadsheet for the analysis of the Misra 1a data set using the Levenberg-Marquardt routine with numerical differentiation.

Because NIST specifies its reference parameters for nonlinear least squares to eleven digits, getting them to agree to better than 1 in 10^{11} is right-on. Just like Solver, this Levenberg-Marquardt routine does not provide standard deviations of the individual parameters, but you can use SolverAid to provide them. That was the reason to include SSR in the above exercise; it might also come in handy if you want to plot, e.g., an error surface, but we already did that in Fig. 4.23.2. Such a plot neither depends on nor uses any particular least squares method, and shows that the NIST reference data are incomplete: in a case with strong collinearity, the covariance is as much needed as the variance (or its square root, the standard deviation) when more than one of the adjusted parameters is used in a subsequent calculation.

Exercise 4.24.1 (continued):

(14) Call SolverAid, and specify E20:E21 as the location of the adjustable parameters. The location of the target is E23, and the column containing y_{calc} is E4:E17. Finally, specify a place to deposit the covariance matrix and the corresponding linear correlation coefficients on the spreadsheet, and let SolverAid loose. Your spreadsheet should now resemble Fig. 4.24.2, with standard deviations on b_1 and b_2 in F20:F21, the standard deviation of the fit of the model to the data in F23, and the CM and CC in the locations you specified. In view of the collinearity shown in Fig. 4.23.2 you should not be surprised by the linear correlation coefficient of almost -0.999 between b_1 and b_2.

	A	B	C	D	E	F	G
1		Misra 1a as analyzed with LM plus supplied derivatives					
2							
3		x	y		y calc	dy/db_1	dy/db_2
4							
5		77.6	10.07		9.98627	0.041794	17766.97
6		114.9	14.73		14.63675	0.061256	25772.69
7		141.1	17.94		17.84672	0.074691	31196.56
8		190.8	23.93		23.81018	0.099648	41047.18
9		239.9	29.61		29.54369	0.123644	50234.69
10		289.0	35.18		35.12439	0.147	58903.33
11		332.8	40.02		39.97705	0.167309	66215.58
12		378.4	44.82		44.90642	0.187938	73423.11
13		434.8	50.76		50.83467	0.212749	81789.12
14		477.3	55.05		55.18192	0.230943	87708.75
15		536.8	61.01		61.09979	0.25571	95465.77
16		593.1	66.40		66.52381	0.27841	102261.3
17		689.1	75.47		75.39379	0.315532	112701.2
18		760.0	81.78		81.65036	0.341716	119541.7
19							
20	*init.:*	*reference:*	pE	*parameters:*			
21							
22	500	238.9421	!	$b_1 =$	238.9421		
23	0.0001	0.00055	!	$b_2 =$	0.00055		
24							
25				*SSR =*	0.124551		

cell:	instruction:	copy to:
E5 =	\$E\$22*(1-EXP(-\$E\$23*B5))	E6:E18
F5 =	1-EXP(-\$E\$23*B5)	F6:F18
G5=	\$E\$22*B5*EXP(-\$E\$23*B5)	G6:G18
C22 =	IF(E22=B22,"!",-LOG(ABS((E22-B22)/B22)))	C23
E25 =	SUMXMY2(C5:C18,E5:E18)	

Fig. 2.24.2: The spreadsheet for analyzing Misra 1a with analytical derivatives.

In order to find the direction of search for the sought optimum, Solver uses first-order forward or central differencing which both, as described in more detail in section 9.2, yield rather crude approximations of the first derivative. The Levenberg-Marquardt routine similarly uses first-order forward differencing as its default, but provides the alternative of using algebraic solutions for these derivatives. For the latter you enter separate columns for the partial derivatives of the model function, in such a way that they automatically track the changing values of the adjusting parameters. Here is how that is done.

Misra 1*a* uses the model function $y = b_1 (1 - \exp(-b_2 x))$, so that the partial derivatives are $\partial y/\partial b_1 = 1 - \exp(-b_2 x)$, and $\partial y/\partial b_2 = b_1 x \exp(-b_2 x)$. As indicated in the specific instructions in Fig. 4.24.2, these expressions are then used to make spreadsheet columns representing those derivatives, which are updated every time the routine updates its parameter estimates. There is no need to use VBA.

Exercise 4.24.2:

(1) Either remove the answers, and modify the spreadsheet by adding the partial derivatives in F5:F18 and G5:G18, or start a new data analysis somewhere else on the spreadsheet.

(2) Again call the LM routine, but now in its fourth window enter the block F5:F28, and push Run. The resulting spreadsheet should resemble Fig. 2.24.2.

(3) Finally, call Call SolverAid.

From the resulting exclamation marks in the expressions for p*E* in cells C22 and C23 you can see that the Levenberg-Marquardt routine with analytical derivatives nails Misra 1*a*, including the four extra zeroes beyond the eleven digits specified by NIST! By clicking on cells C22 and E22, or C23 and E23, and looking at their numerical values in the formula toolbar, or by copying their values to sufficiently wide cells to the right of column G, you can verify that this is indeed the case.

In Fig. 2.24.2, the definition of p*E* has been extended to avoid the "problem" when the answer is an exact fit, viz. that log(0) is not defined. (The expression for p*E* is still slightly simplified, because it does not confront the situation where the reference value is zero, as the complete definition in section 9.1 does.) Considering that p*E* = 14 allows for a difference of only one unit in the least significant digit, which is quite acceptable in a complicated calculation, you might want to incorporate the condition pE_{max} = 14 of equation (9.1.1), by modifying the instruction in cell C22 to =IF(ABS((E22-B22)/B22)< 0.00000000000001, "!",-log(ABS((E22-B22)?B22))), and by copying this to cell C23.

In exercise 4.24.3 we consider Lanczos 1, the most challenging of the Lanczos tests. The spreadsheet of Fig. 2.24.3 and its accompanying instructions should be sufficient for you to reproduce this problem on your spreadsheet; the input data come from the NIST website or from the SampleData file.

Exercise 4.24.3:

(1) On a new spreadsheet, place the *x*-values of Lanczos 1 in B5:B28, and the *y*-values in C5:C28. Put the starting values labeled start 1 in A32:A37, and the reference values in E32:E37. If you want to play a bit with this problem, place a spare set of starting values in B32:B37. Label these input data.

(2) In E5 compute $y_{calc} = b_1 \exp(-b_2 x) + b_3 \exp(-b_4 x) + b_5 \exp(-b_6 x)$, using the values of b_1 through b_6 in E32:E37. Copy this instruction down to E28.

(3) In C32 compute p*E*, and copy this to C37.

(4) Call <u>T</u>ools ⇨ Optimiz ⇨ NL-Regression ⇨ Levenberg-Marquardt, and enter the data as follows: the input *x*- and *y*-data B5:C28 as *(x, y)*, the model values ycalc in E5:E28 as *f(x,a,b,c...)*, the adjustable parameters in E32:E37 as *a,b,c...* , and push Run.

(5) The results will replace the starting parameters in E32:E37, and C32:C37 will show their p*E*-values, which typically will be around 11.

(6) Call SolverAid, and enter the parameters as E32:E37, the SSR-value as E39, and the values of y_{calc} as E5:E28. Find an appropriate place for the covariance matrix and the matrix of linear correlation coefficients, which both occupy 6×6 cells. Fig. 4.24.3 shows the complete spreadsheet.

Exercise 4.24.3.describes the analysis of the same data set with LM using analytical derivatives, and is illustrated in Fig. 4.24.3. With either numerical or analytical derivatives, the Levenberg-Marquardt routine gets all six parameter values correct to about 1 in 10^{11}, even though this problem exhibits very strong collinearity between its output parameters, as is clear from the linear correlation coefficients. Unfortunately, there is no hope of visualizing the error surface, which in this case is seven-dimensional.

These examples will suffice to illustrate the power and convenience of the Levenberg-Marquardt routine. David Heiser (http://www.daheiser.info) has tested this algorithm with all 27 NIST nonlinear least squares routines, and using analytical derivatives obtained results of p*E* ≥ 10 for all of them. With numerical derivatives, the Levenberg-Marquardt method often yields results that are less accurate by up to 2 decimal places, but that will still be sufficient for most problems. By comparison, Solver scored p$E \leq 0$ on fully half of these same tests, and on none reached a pE score of 6 or higher.

	A	B	C	D	E	F	G	H	I	J	K	L
1		**Lanczos 1**	as analyzed with LM and numerical derivatives									
2												
3		*x*	*y*		*y calc*							
4												
5		0.00	2.5134		2.5134	*CM:*	*2.84E-21*	*1.46E-20*	*7.06E-21*	*1.77E-20*	*-9.91E-21*	*5.77E-21*
6		0.05	2.0443		2.0443		*1.46E-20*	*7.54E-20*	*3.61E-20*	*9.07E-20*	*-5.07E-20*	*2.95E-20*
7		0.10	1.6684		1.6684		*7.06E-21*	*3.61E-20*	*1.84E-20*	*4.48E-20*	*-2.55E-20*	*1.50E-20*
8		0.15	1.3664		1.3664		*1.77E-20*	*9.07E-20*	*4.48E-20*	*1.11E-19*	*-6.25E-20*	*3.66E-20*
9		0.20	1.1232		1.1232		*-9.91E-21*	*-5.07E-20*	*-2.55E-20*	*-6.25E-20*	*3.54E-20*	*-2.1E-20*
10		0.25	0.9269		0.9269		*5.77E-21*	*2.95E-20*	*1.50E-20*	*3.66E-20*	*-2.08E-20*	*1.22E-20*
11		0.30	0.7679		0.7679	*CC:*	*1.00000*	***9.99E-01***	*9.76E-01*	***9.96E-01***	*-9.88E-01*	*9.79E-01*
12		0.35	0.6389		0.6389		***0.99948***	*1.00E+00*	*9.69E-01*	***9.92E-01***	*-9.82E-01*	*9.73E-01*
13		0.40	0.5338		0.5338		*0.97587*	*9.69E-01*	*1.00E+00*	***9.92E-01***	*-9.98E-01*	***1.0E+00***
14		0.45	0.4479		0.4479		***0.99560***	***9.92E-01***	***9.92E-01***	*1.00E+00*	*-9.98E-01*	*9.94E-01*
15		0.50	0.3776		0.3776		*-0.98753*	*-9.82E-01*	***-9.98E-01***	*-9.98E-01*	*1.00E+00*	***-1.0E+00***
16		0.55	0.3197		0.3197		*0.97924*	*9.73E-01*	***1.00E+00***	***9.94E-01***	***-9.99E-01***	*1.00E+00*
17		0.60	0.2720		0.2720							
18		0.65	0.2325		0.2325							
19		0.70	0.1997		0.1997							
20		0.75	0.1723		0.1723							
21		0.80	0.1493		0.1493							
22		0.85	0.1301		0.1301							
23		0.90	0.1138		0.1138							
24		0.95	0.1000		0.1000							
25		1.00	0.0883		0.0883							
26		1.05	0.0783		0.0783							
27		1.10	0.0698		0.0698							
28		1.15	0.0624		0.0624							
29												
30	*init.:*	*reference:*	pE		*parameters:*	*st. dev.:*						
31												
32	1.2	9.51E-02	11.37		$b_1 =$ 0.0951	*5.33E-11*						
33	0.3	1.00E+00	10.56		$b_2 =$ 1	*2.75E-10*						
34	5.6	8.61E-01	11.29		$b_3 =$ 0.8607	*1.36E-10*						
35	5.5	3.00E+00	10.94		$b_4 =$ 3	*3.33E-10*						
36	6.5	1.56E+00	10.61		$b_5 =$ 1.5576	*1.88E-10*						
37	7.6	5.00E+00	11.64		$b_6 =$ 5	*1.11E-10*						
38					**SolverAid**							
39		1.43E-25		*SSR =*	1E-25	*8.91E-14*						

cell: instruction: copy to:

E5 = \$E\$32*EXP(-\$E\$33*C5)+\$E\$34*EXP(-\$E\$35*C5)+\$E\$36*EXP(-\$E\$37*C5)   E6:E28
C32 = IF(ABS((E22-B22)/B22)<0.00000000000001, "!",-log(ABS((E22-B22)?B22)))   C33:C37
E39 = SUMXMY2(C5:C28,E5:E28)

Fig. 4.24.3: The completed spreadsheet analysis of Lanczos 1 using LM and numerical derivatives.

Exercise 4.24.3:

(1) On a new spreadsheet, place the *x*-values of Lanczos 1 in B5:B28, and the *y*-values in C5:C28. Put the starting values labeled start 1 in A32:A37, and the reference values in E32:E37. If you want to play a bit with this problem, place a spare set of starting values in B32:B37. Label these input data.

(2) In E5 compute $y_{calc} = b_1 \exp(-b_2 x) + b_3 \exp(-b_4 x) + b_5 \exp(-b_6 x)$, using the values of b_1 through b_6 in E32:E37. Copy this instruction down to E28. In C32 compute pE, and copy this to C37.

(3) Call Tools ⇨ Optimiz ⇨ NL-Regression ⇨ Levenberg-Marquardt, and enter the data as follows: the input *x*- and *y*-data B5:C28 as *(x, y)*, the model values ycalc in E5:E28 as *f(x,a,b,c...)*, the adjustable parameters in E32:E37 as *a,b,c...* , and push Run. The results will replace the starting parameters in E32:E37, and C32:C37 will show their pE-values, which typically will be around 11.

209

(3) Call <u>T</u>ools ⇨ Optimiz ⇨ NL-Regression ⇨ Levenberg-Marquardt, and enter the data as follows: the input *x*- and *y*-data B5:C28 as *(x, y)*, the model values ycalc in E5:E28 as *f(x,a,b,c...)*, the adjustable parameters in E32:E37 as *a,b,c...* , and push Run. The results will replace the starting parameters in E32:E37, and C32:C37 will show their pE-values, which typically will be around 11.

(4) Call SolverAid, and enter the parameters as E32:E37, the SSR-value as E39, and the values of y_{calc} as E5:E28. Find an appropriate place for the covariance matrix and the matrix of linear correlation coefficients, which both occupy 6 × 6 cells. Fig. 4.24.3 shows the complete spreadsheet.

	A	B	C	D	E	F	G	H	I	J	K	L	M
1		**Lanczos 1**	as analyzed with LM and user-supplied analytical derivatives										
2													
3		*x*	*y*		*y calc*			dy/db_1	dy/db_2	dy/db_3	dy/db_4	dy/db_5	dy/db_6
4													
5		0.00	2.5134		2.5134			1.00E+00	0.00E+00	1.00E+00	0.00E+00	1.00E+00	0.00E+00
6		0.05	2.0443		2.0443			9.51E-01	-4.52E-03	8.61E-01	-3.70E-02	7.79E-01	-6.07E-02
7		0.10	1.6684		1.6684			9.05E-01	-8.61E-03	7.41E-01	-6.38E-02	6.07E-01	-9.45E-02
8		0.15	1.3664		1.3664			8.61E-01	-1.23E-02	6.38E-01	-8.23E-02	4.72E-01	-1.10E-01
9		0.20	1.1232		1.1232			8.19E-01	-1.56E-02	5.49E-01	-9.45E-02	3.68E-01	-1.15E-01
10		0.25	0.9269		0.9269			7.79E-01	-1.85E-02	4.72E-01	-1.02E-01	2.87E-01	-1.12E-01
11		0.30	0.7679		0.7679			7.41E-01	-2.11E-02	4.07E-01	-1.05E-01	2.23E-01	-1.04E-01
12		0.35	0.6389		0.6389			7.05E-01	-2.35E-02	3.50E-01	-1.05E-01	1.74E-01	-9.47E-02
13		0.40	0.5338		0.5338			6.70E-01	-2.55E-02	3.01E-01	-1.04E-01	1.35E-01	-8.43E-02
14		0.45	0.4479		0.4479			6.38E-01	-2.73E-02	2.59E-01	-1.00E-01	1.05E-01	-7.39E-02
15		0.50	0.3776		0.3776			6.07E-01	-2.88E-02	2.23E-01	-9.60E-02	8.21E-02	-6.39E-02
16		0.55	0.3197		0.3197			5.77E-01	-3.02E-02	1.92E-01	-9.09E-02	6.39E-02	-5.48E-02
17		0.60	0.2720		0.2720			5.49E-01	-3.13E-02	1.65E-01	-8.54E-02	4.98E-02	-4.65E-02
18		0.65	0.2325		0.2325			5.22E-01	-3.23E-02	1.42E-01	-7.96E-02	3.88E-02	-3.93E-02
19		0.70	0.1997		0.1997			4.97E-01	-3.31E-02	1.22E-01	-7.38E-02	3.02E-02	-3.29E-02
20		0.75	0.1723		0.1723			4.72E-01	-3.37E-02	1.05E-01	-6.80E-02	2.35E-02	-2.75E-02
21		0.80	0.1493		0.1493			4.49E-01	-3.42E-02	9.07E-02	-6.25E-02	1.83E-02	-2.28E-02
22		0.85	0.1301		0.1301			4.27E-01	-3.46E-02	7.81E-02	-5.71E-02	1.43E-02	-1.89E-02
23		0.90	0.1138		0.1138			4.07E-01	-3.48E-02	6.72E-02	-5.21E-02	1.11E-02	-1.56E-02
24		0.95	0.1000		0.1000			3.87E-01	-3.49E-02	5.78E-02	-4.73E-02	8.65E-03	-1.28E-02
25		1.00	0.0883		0.0883			3.68E-01	-3.50E-02	4.98E-02	-4.29E-02	6.74E-03	-1.05E-02
26		1.05	0.0783		0.0783			3.50E-01	-3.49E-02	4.29E-02	-3.87E-02	5.25E-03	-8.58E-03
27		1.10	0.0698		0.0698			3.33E-01	-3.48E-02	3.69E-02	-3.49E-02	4.09E-03	-7.00E-03
28		1.15	0.0624		0.0624			3.17E-01	-3.46E-02	3.17E-02	-3.14E-02	3.18E-03	-5.70E-03
29													
30	*init.:*	*reference:*	pE		*parameters: st. dev.:*		**CM:**	2.8449E-21	1.4643E-20	7.0651E-21	1.7684E-20	-9.909E-21	5.774E-21
31								1.4643E-20	7.5449E-20	3.6115E-20	9.0756E-20	-5.075E-20	2.954E-20
32	1.2	9.51E-02	11.34		b_1 = 0.0951	5.33E-11		7.0651E-21	3.6115E-20	1.8424E-20	4.4841E-20	-2.549E-20	1.5E-20
33	0.3	1.00E+00	10.56		b_2 = 1	2.75E-10		1.7684E-20	9.0756E-20	4.4841E-20	1.109E-19	-6.252E-20	3.659E-20
34	5.6	8.61E-01	11.29		b_3 = 0.8607	1.36E-10		-9.909E-21	-5.075E-20	-2.549E-20	-6.252E-20	3.539E-20	-2.08E-20
35	5.5	3.00E+00	10.94		b_4 = 3	3.33E-10		5.7743E-21	2.9536E-20	1.5003E-20	3.6587E-20	-2.077E-20	1.222E-20
36	6.5	1.56E+00	10.61		b_5 = 1.5576	1.88E-10	**CC:**	1	*0.99948181*	0.97586819	*0.99559712*	-0.9875343	0.979235
37	7.6	5.00E+00	11.64		b_6 = 5	1.11E-10		*0.99948181*	1	0.9686353	*0.99214741*	-0.9821722	0.9726118
38			SolverAid					0.97586819	0.9686353	1	*0.99199944*	*-0.998074*	0.999759
39		1.43E-25	*SSR* =		1E-25	8.91E-14		*0.99559712*	*0.99214741*	*0.99199944*	1	*-0.9979125*	0.9937591
40								-0.9875343	-0.9821722	*-0.998074*	*-0.9979125*	1	*-0.998854*
41								0.97923505	0.97261179	*0.99975899*	0.99375908	-0.9988536	1

cell: instruction: *copy to:*

E5 = \$E\$32*EXP(-\$E\$33*C5)+\$E\$34*EXP(-\$E\$35*C5)+\$E\$36*EXP(-\$E\$37*C5)   E6:E28
H5 = EXP(-B5*\$E\$33)
I5 = -\$E\$32*B5*EXP(-\$E\$33*B5)
J5 = EXP(-B5*\$E\$35)
K5 = -\$E\$34*B5*EXP(-\$E\$35*B5)
L5 = EXP(-B5*\$E\$37)
M5 = -\$E\$36*B5*EXP(-\$E\$37*B5)
C32 = IF(ABS((E22-B22)/B22)<0.00000000000001, "!",-log(ABS((E22-B22)?B22)))   C33:C37
E39 = SUMXMY2(C5:C28,E5:E28)

Fig. 4.24.4: The completed spreadsheet analysis of Lanczos 1 using LM and analytical derivatives.

These examples will suffice to illustrate the power and convenience of the Levenberg-Marquardt routine. David Heiser (http://www.daheiser.info) has tested this algorithm with all 27 NIST nonlinear least squares routines, and using analytical derivatives obtained results of $pE \geq 10$ for all of them. With numerical derivatives, the Levenberg-Marquardt method often yields results that are less accurate by up to 2 decimal places, but that will still be sufficient for most problems. By comparison, Solver (non-optimized, and on a single try) scored $pE \leq 0$ on fully half of these same tests, and on none reached a pE score of 6 or higher.

4.25 Summary

As with linear least squares, there are two complementary questions: how appropriate is the model used, and how good is the fit between the data and that model? Again, there are no absolute answers, although looking for systematic trends in a plot of residuals can usually smoke out some inappropriate or incomplete models, while the standard deviation s_f can give some indication of the quality of fit between model and data. With nonlinear methods there is always the risk of ending up in a local minimum; visualizing the error surface can usually alert us to the presence of such traps. For consequential results, the following hints may be helpful: (1) try both Solver and Levenberg-Marquardt on the same data set; (2) rerun Solver for all consequential results, using its earlier estimates as starting values; and (3) for up to two adjustable parameters, use the error surface as your guide in choosing starting parameter values.

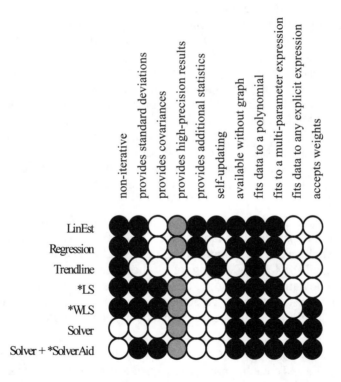

Fig. 4.23.1. Comparison of the various least-squares methods available in Excel. Closed circles show availability of listed option, open circles show lack thereof. Gray circles denote approximately single precision: even though the results can be displayed to fifteen figures, usually no more than the first six or seven of these are significant. The methods labeled with an asterisk use the special custom macros of the MacroBundle. Extended numberlength versions of LS and WLS are available in the xMacroBundle. In terms of this diagram, the Levenberg-Marquardt method in Optimiz.xla is equivalent to Solver, except that the current version of LM does not yet accept weights.

Solver is not tied to the least-squares criterion, but can also be used, e.g., with more robust algorithms, where in this context 'robust' usually means less sensitive to the effects of outliers. (We can consider outlier rejection an extreme, binary case of weighting, using all-or-none weights of 1 or 0 only.) Solver can also be incorporated into custom functions and macros since they can call it, as illustrated by SolverScan. Consequently Solver can be used to solve nonlinear problems as they might occur in, e.g., implicit numerical simulations. However, it is a complex and therefore rather time-consuming program that may cause noticeable delays when used repeatedly inside a loop.

In this chapter we have not used Goal Seek, Excel's implementation of the Newton-Raphson method, because it is limited to just one variable, and this implementation leaves much to be desired. You can improve the latter somewhat by decreasing the numerical value in Tools ⇨ Options, Calculations tab, Maximum change, but that doesn't always help, and may even destabilize it. Because Goal Seek doesn't seem to have any obvious advantages over Solver or the Levenberg-Marquardt method, and doesn't appear to be as carefully crafted either, my advice is to stay away from it. You will never miss it.

4.26 A sobering perspective

It is sometimes healthy to step away from a method and see what it can achieve in practice, because all too often we are swayed by its intended purpose, and may not clearly see its actual results. A dose of detached skepticism is therefore a necessary antidote.

IMEP, an International Measurement Evaluation Programme run by the Institute for Reference Materials and Measurements of the European Commission, has published a series of reports on a systematic comparison of chemical analyses of carefully prepared test samples by a number of professional analytical laboratories. This collaborative, voluntary testing program is focused on answers rather than procedures, and publishes its results while safeguarding the identities of the individual participating laboratories. Its goal is not to test those labs (although they will of course know their own scores), but to evaluate the limits of the actual knowledge derivable from chemical measurements made in well-reputed laboratories by trained personnel under non-hurried, non-threatening circumstances. It encompasses measurements on sub-samples of carefully homogenized test samples, thereby eliminating discrepancies in sampling methods, and the resulting sampling errors. It uses test samples of relevant concentrations of elements and/or compounds, especially those that can affect human health and well-being. Its results are available on the web; for IMEP-20 use http://irmm.jrc.ec.europa.eu/interlaboratory_comparisons/imep/imep20/eur21018en.pdf

Here we will briefly consider a typical example: the analysis of mercury in tuna fish, as reported in 2004 by IMEP-20 by all 204 participating laboratories. For mercury (Hg) in tuna fish, the European Commission has set a threshold value of 1 mg per kg dry weight. The test sample had an independently determined mercury content of 4.32 ± 0.16 mg kg^{-1}, where the uncertainty in the IMEP document is defined as $\pm$ *two* standard deviations. Of course, the laboratories participating in the test did not know this reference value. Beyond the fact that the reference value indeed lies within the relevant concentration range, its actual value is irrelevant to the general conclusions that can be drawn from this and many similar IMEP studies.

The measurements shown in Fig. 4.26.1 are arranged in order of their reported average value, as shown by individual markers. To each marker is attached a vertical line indicating the corresponding imprecision, as $\pm$ two standard deviations, again as reported by the contributing laboratory. The gray horizontal band specifies the reference value determined by a few selected, generally well-regarded and fully qualified laboratories, using methods considered the best ones available. The sample was freeze-dried muscle tissue from a batch of tuna fish, caught in the Mediterranean Sea near Messina, which had been taken off the market because of its elevated mercury level. It was homogenized, and its homogeneity was tested on ten sub-samples by Zeeman atomic absorption spectrometry, and on three sub-samples by isotope dilution mass spectrometry. The reference value was found by an analysis of variance of these results.

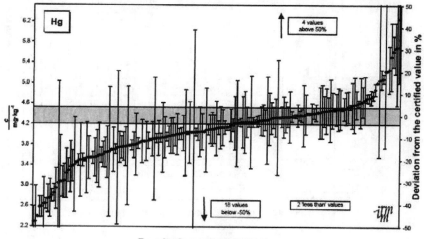

IMEP- 20: Trace elements in Tuna Fish
Certified value : 4.32 ± 0.16 mg·kg⁻¹ [U=k·u_c (k=2)]

Results from all participants

Fig. 4.26.1: The 204 results of the IMEP-20 collaborative international study of total mercury in tuna fish (solid black diamonds), shown as a function of ascending average value reported. The individual error bars have lengths of ± two standard deviations. The gray horizontal bar represents the reference value with its reported ± 2s imprecision. Shown are all results reported by more than 200 participating laboratories, except for 18 reported values below half the reference value, and 4 values larger than 1½ times that reference value, which 22 points therefore lie outside the picture frame shown. Two laboratories only reported "less than" values. This and the following graphs are from http://www.irmm.jrc.be/interlaboratory_comparisons/imep/imep20/eur21018en.pdf.

What is striking in Fig. 4.26.1 is that accuracy (the positions of the solid markers) and precision (the length of the corresponding vertical lines) do *not* appear to be correlated in any obvious way, and that both are *all over the map*. This might possibly derive from the use of different measurement methods by the various labs (which each selected their own best method), but Fig. 4.26.2 clearly belies this. Nor was there an obvious correlation between whether or not the lab was located in an EC member or candidate-member state, was a governmental, university, or private laboratory, or with other such easy explanations.

Likewise, there were no obvious correlations with prior experience of the labs with this particular analysis (and they could choose whether to participate and with what method), how many of such samples the labs analyzed per year, time spent on the measurement, the calibration strategy used, use of certified reference materials, participation in proficiency testing schemes, whether the lab was accredited and/or authorized, whether the lab reports uncertainties to its customers, or whether it used ISO1995 or EURACHEM/CITAC guidelines to calculate their reported uncertainties, see IMEP Figs. 27 (4) 59. From the aggregate of this and many other IMEP studies, of diverse samples, testing various elements and compounds of environmental and safety importance, using different methods and with differing participating laboratories, we can only conclude that this type of professional chemical analysis shows *no correlation* between precision and accuracy, and that both vary from lab to lab over much wider ranges than one might hope. Some accurate results have large associated error bars; some clearly far-off results are reported with quite small imprecisions. Fewer than 4% of all answers were fully (including their error estimates) within the reference value ± 2s. These results are not reassuring concerning the usefulness of data produced by some of the world's best chemical analysis labs on significant health issues.

213

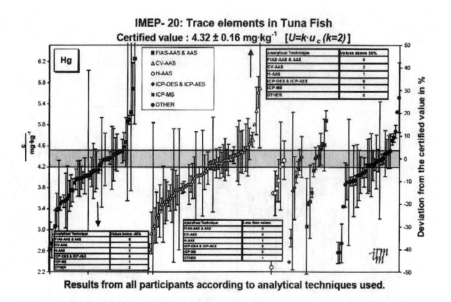

Fig. 4.26.2: The same 204 results as shown in Fig. 1.26.1, but now arranged by analysis method used. From left to right: solid squares: atomic absorption spectrometry (AAS) with or without flow injection analysis; open triangles: cold-vapor AAS; open circles: hydride AAS; solid diamonds: inductively coupled plasma AAS; solid squares: inductively coupled plasma mass spectrometry; solid circles: other.

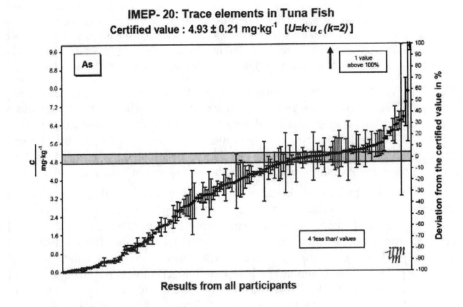

Fig. 4.26.3: The 169 results of the IMEP-20 collaborative international study for total arsenic (As) in the same tuna fish sample.

That these are not isolated results is even more clearly illustrated by the results shown in Fig. 4.26.3 for arsenic in the same sample. Note that the EC threshold level for that element is 0.2 mg kg^{-1}, and that the reference value was about 24 times higher. Also note that the vertical scale in Fig. 4.26.3 is twice as large as those in Figs. 4.26.1 and 4.26.2, now covering from 0 to 200% of the reference value. Again, these are not confidence-inspiring results.

Few such systematic, wide-ranging interlaboratory comparisons are available in the public domain, but there is little reason to believe that results in other scientific areas would be qualitatively different. Not all numbers are what they seem to be. Caveat emptor.

4.27 For further reading

An extensive treatment of nonlinear least squares is provided by D. M. Bates & D. G. Watts, *Nonlinear Regression Analysis and Its Applications*, Wiley (1988). It contains many fine examples of nonlinear curve fitting in the physical sciences, including their original data, and therefore provides excellent practice material for the present chapter. Volpi's *Tutorial on numerical analysis with Optimiz.xla*, included with Optimiz.xla downloaded from my excellaneous web site, is highly recommended reading. Additional applications are described in J. F. Russling & T. F. Kumosinski, *Nonlinear Computer Modeling of Chemical and Biochemical Data*, Academic Press (1996), and in H. Motulsky & A. Christopoulos, *Fitting Models to Biological Data Using Linear and Nonlinear Regression*, Oxford University Press (2004).

Chapter *5*

Fourier transformation

5.1 Sines & cosines

This chapter deals with the application of Fourier transformation in numerical data analysis rather than in instrumentation, where it is often built in. We are all familiar with manipulating functions of a number, or of a single variable representing such a number, as in $\sqrt{3}$, $\log x$, or $\sin \alpha$. In a Fourier transform we operate instead on a whole *set* of numbers, such as a spectrum or a transient. The methods for dealing with entire data sets are somewhat more involved, but are perfectly suited to spreadsheets.

Fourier transformation is a method designed to determine the *frequency* content of a *time*-dependent signal. Since it is a mathematical operation, 'frequency' f (in Hz) and 'time' t (in s) are symbols that can just as easily represent another pair of physical variables whose product is dimensionless, such as wavelength or distance (in cm) and wavenumber (in cm^{-1}). The Fourier transformation $G(f)$ of a continuous, time-dependent function $g(t)$ can be defined as

$$G(f) = \int_{-\infty}^{+\infty} g(t)\, e^{-2\pi j f t} dt = \int_{-\infty}^{+\infty} g(t)\, e^{-j\omega t} dt = \int_{-\infty}^{+\infty} g(t) \cos(2\pi f t) dt - j \int_{-\infty}^{+\infty} g(t) \sin(2\pi f t) dt$$

$$= \int_{-\infty}^{+\infty} g(t) \cos(\omega t)\, dt - j \int_{-\infty}^{+\infty} g(t) \sin(\omega t)\, dt \qquad (5.1.1)$$

where we have used Euler's rule, $e^{\pm jx} = \cos(x) \pm j \sin(x)$, with $j = \sqrt{-1}$ and $\omega = 2\pi f$, in radians per second (rad s^{-1}). If we count time t in seconds, f should be counted in Hertz; for t measured in days, f has the dimension day^{-1}, i.e., 'per day'. Likewise, if t represents wavelength, f stands for wavenumber; if t is voltage, f has the dimension of V^{-1}, etc. (Because the symbols F and f are commonly used for function and frequency respectively, we here use the symbols G and g.) The corresponding inverse Fourier transformation is then

$$g(t) = \int_{-\infty}^{+\infty} G(f)\, e^{+2\pi j f t} df \qquad (5.1.2)$$

In experimental science we often deal with a *sampled* function, i.e., with a *finite* number of *discrete*, *equidistant* data points, in which case the definition corresponding to (5.1.1) is

$$G(f) = \sum_{k=1}^{N} g(t) \cos(2\pi\, k/N) - j \sum_{k=1}^{N} g(t) \sin(2\pi\, k/N) \qquad (5.1.3)$$

where N denotes the number of data points, and $k = 1, 2, \ldots, N$. Efficient, fast-executing methods exist for computing (5.1.3) and its inverse, especially when N is an integer power of 2, i.e., $N = 2, 4, 8, 16, 32, 64, 128, 256, 512, 1024$, etc. The application of such *fast* Fourier transform algorithms to discrete, equidistant data is the central subject of this chapter.

Excel provides a tool for Fourier transformation in its Data Analysis Toolpak. Unfortunately it has a rather awkward input and output format, in the form of labels. In this chapter we will therefore use two custom macros, ForwardFT and InverseFT respectively, which are somewhat easier to apply. They require that the input data be organized in three contiguous columns of 2^n data, where n is a positive (non-zero) integer.

For forward Fourier transformation the first (left-most) column should contain time t, in equidistant intervals, while the next two columns should hold the real and imaginary components of the function $g(t)$ respectively. The data for time t should either start at $t = 0$ or, preferably, be 'centered' around $t = 0$, with 2^{n-1} data at $t < 0$, one point at $t = 0$, and the remaining $2^{n-1}-1$ data at $t > 0$. When $g(t)$ is a real function, the third column can either be left blank or be filled with zeros. Similarly, if $g(t)$ is imaginary, the second column should be left blank or be filled with zeros.

In order to initiate the transformation, highlight the data in the three columns (including the third column, even if it only contains blanks) and call the custom macro ForwardFT. Its output, i.e., the result of the forward Fourier transformation, will be written in the three columns immediately to the right of the block of input data, displaying from left to right the frequency, the real (in-phase) component, and the imaginary (quadrature, or $90°$ out-of-phase) component of the transformed data $G(f)$.

The macro InverseFT converts the transformed data back from the frequency domain to the time domain. It uses the same three-column format for input and output, with the positions of the time and frequency columns interchanged. Its frequency scale must be centered around $f = 0$, with 2^{n-1} data at $f < 0$, and the remaining 2^{n-1} data at $f \geq 0$. (In case you wonder what might be the physical meaning of a negative frequency, just consider it a mathematical consequence of the Nyquist theorem, to be described in section 5.3.) The format of ForwardFT and InverseFT is such that you can easily transform data sets back and forth. Exercise 5.1 will familiarize you with the operation of these custom macros.

Exercise 5.1:

(1) Open a spreadsheet, and enter column headings such as time, Re, Im, freq, Re, and Im, or (if you prefer to denote real and imaginary components with ' and " respectively) t, g', g", f, G', and G".

(2) In its first column enter the numbers –8 (1) 7.

(3) In its second column compute a cosine wave such as $a \cos(2\pi b\, t / N)$, where b is a positive integer specifying the number of repeat periods, t is time as given here in the first column, and N is the number of data points, here 16.

(4) Fill the third column with zeros, so that the graph will show them.

(5) Highlight the data in these three columns, and call ForwardFT. (Use FT ⇨ ForwardFT on the MacroBundle toolbar or the Custom-Macros menu, otherwise Tools ⇨ Macro ⇨ Macros to get the Macro dialog box.)

(6) Plot the resulting transform, see Fig. 5.1.1, and verify that it shows two non-zero points of amplitude $a/2$ at $f = \pm b/N$.

(7) Replace the cosine wave in column A by a sine wave of, say, double the frequency, and repeat the process. Note that the Fourier transform of a sine wave has only imaginary components, one positive, the other negative, see Fig. 5.1.2.

(8) Replace the signal in column A by the sum of a sine wave and a cosine wave, of different amplitudes so that you can more readily identify their transforms. Then add another sine or cosine wave, and identify the transforms of each. In order to see the effect of a larger number of input signals, you may have to extend the range from 16 to, e.g., 32, 64 or 128 data points.

The discrete Fourier transform operates on a limited data set, but tacitly assumes that this is *one repeat unit* of an infinitely long, self-repeating signal. Section 5.4 will discuss what happens when this is not the case.

The Fourier transform accepts complex input data, i.e., with real and/or imaginary components, and likewise produces complex output. However, experimental data are often real, and we will therefore focus briefly on real functions. The cosine function has the property that $\cos(-x) = \cos(x)$, and is therefore called an *even* function. On the other hand, the sine is an *odd* function, because $\sin(-x) = -\sin(x)$. Figure 5.1.1

218

illustrates that the Fourier transform of a real, even function is real, whereas Fig. 5.1.2 suggests that the Fourier transform of a real, odd function is imaginary. This turns out to be true in general for any real function $g(t)$.

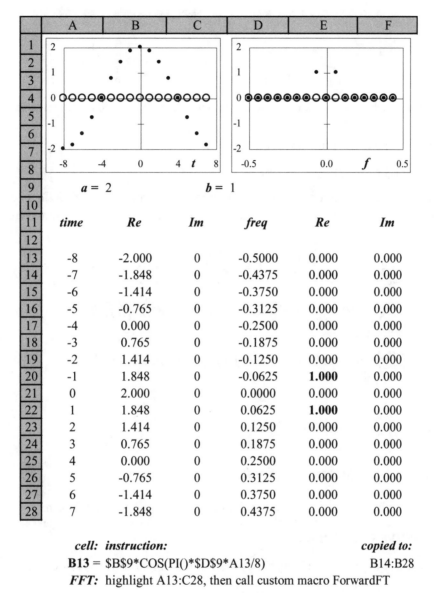

	time	Re	Im	freq	Re	Im
	-8	-2.000	0	-0.5000	0.000	0.000
	-7	-1.848	0	-0.4375	0.000	0.000
	-6	-1.414	0	-0.3750	0.000	0.000
	-5	-0.765	0	-0.3125	0.000	0.000
	-4	0.000	0	-0.2500	0.000	0.000
	-3	0.765	0	-0.1875	0.000	0.000
	-2	1.414	0	-0.1250	0.000	0.000
	-1	1.848	0	-0.0625	**1.000**	0.000
	0	2.000	0	0.0000	0.000	0.000
	1	1.848	0	0.0625	**1.000**	0.000
	2	1.414	0	0.1250	0.000	0.000
	3	0.765	0	0.1875	0.000	0.000
	4	0.000	0	0.2500	0.000	0.000
	5	-0.765	0	0.3125	0.000	0.000
	6	-1.414	0	0.3750	0.000	0.000
	7	-1.848	0	0.4375	0.000	0.000

cell: *instruction:*   *copied to:*

B13 = \$B\$9*COS(PI()*\$D\$9*A13/8)   B14:B28

FFT: highlight A13:C28, then call custom macro ForwardFT

Fig. 5.1.1: The spreadsheet showing a *cosine* wave and its Fourier transform. Solid circles: real components; open circles: imaginary components. In column E the two non-zero points in the transform are shown in boldface for emphasis.

We can always write a real function as the sum of an even and an odd real function:

$$g_{real}(t) = g_{even}(t) + g_{odd}(t) \tag{5.1.4}$$

219

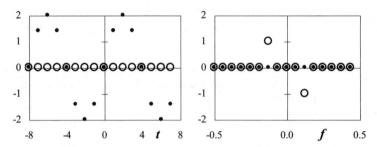

Fig. 5.1.2: The spreadsheet showing a *sine* wave and its Fourier trans-form. Solid circles: real components; open circles: imaginary components.

Likewise we can write (5.1.1) in compact notation as

$$G(f) = G'(f) - j\,G''(f) \qquad\qquad (5.1.5)$$

where the superscripts $'$ and $''$ denote the real and imaginary components of $G(f)$. Since multiplying an even and an odd function produces an odd function which yields zero when integrated from $-\infty$ to $+\infty$, we have

$$G(f) = \int_{-\infty}^{+\infty} g_{real}(t)\,e^{-2\pi j f t}dt = \int_{-\infty}^{+\infty} [g_{even}(t) + g_{odd}(t)]\,e^{-2\pi j f t}dt$$

$$= \int_{-\infty}^{+\infty} [g_{even}(t) + g_{odd}(t)][\cos(2\pi f t) - j\sin(2\pi f t)]\,dt$$

$$= \int_{-\infty}^{+\infty} g_{even}(t)\cos(2\pi f t)\,dt - j\int_{-\infty}^{+\infty} g_{odd}(t)\sin(2\pi f t)\,dt \qquad (5.1.6)$$

so that

$$G'(f) = \int_{-\infty}^{+\infty} g_{even}(t)\cos(2\pi f t)\,dt \qquad\qquad (5.1.7)$$

$$G''(f) = -\int_{-\infty}^{+\infty} g_{odd}(t)\sin(2\pi f t)\,dt \qquad\qquad (5.1.8)$$

Equivalent rules apply to the discrete (rather than continuous) Fourier transform.

5.2 Square waves & pulses

We will now use a square wave, which can be considered as an infinite set of cosines,

$$sqw(\omega t) = \frac{4}{\pi}\sum_{n=0}^{\infty}\frac{(-1)^n \cos[(2n+1)\omega t]}{2n+1}$$

$$= \frac{4}{\pi}\left\{\cos(\omega t) - \frac{1}{3}\cos(3\omega t) + \frac{1}{5}\cos(5\omega t) - \frac{1}{7}\cos(7\omega t) + \cdots\right\} \qquad (5.2.1)$$

In a discrete Fourier transformation, with only a limited number of input data and an equally limited number of frequencies, the square wave is represented by a truncated series, which therefore has somewhat different coefficients. When we follow the Fourier transform by its inverse, we recover the original input data. However, if we were to use the coefficients of the forward Fourier transform to reconstruct the input data, we find a curve that indeed passes through all input data, but is a caricature of a square wave.

220

But then, we did not enter a square wave, but only the discrete data points. Whatever curve we want to see in those discrete data is our prerogative, like seeing images in groupings of unrelated stars and calling them constellations.

Exercise 5.2.1:

(1) Modify the spreadsheet by replacing the input signal by that of a square wave, as in Fig. 5.2.1. Note that the zero-crossings of the square wave must be entered explicitly, as the *average* of the function values just before and after the change.

(2) Transform these, and immediately follow this by an inverse transform. In this 16-point analysis you will find only four components of the series (5.1.3), with coefficients slightly different from $4/\pi$, $-4/3\pi$, $4/5\pi$, and $-4/7\pi$, i.e., 1.273, -0.424, 0.255, and -0.182 instead of the found values of 1.257, -0.374, 0.167, and -0.050 respectively. Note that the inverse transform only approximates the presumed underlying square wave, but will reconstruct the discrete input data exactly.

(3) This is more readily seen by computing values of (5.2.1) at intermediate values of t (e.g., at intervals of 0.1) and by plotting the resulting curve in the same thumbnail sketch.

(4) For this, extend the second time scale, starting e.g. in cell G30 with $t = -8$, and proceeding downwards with increments of 0.1 till cell G180. In cell J30 then deposit the instruction =E\$21+2*(E\$22*COS(2*PI()*D\$22*G30)+E\$23 *COS(2*PI()*D\$23*G30)+...+E\$28*COS(2*PI()*D\$28*G30)), and copy this all the way to cell J180. You can speed up the computation by calculating the term 2*PI() in a separate cell and referring to that numerical value rather than repeating the calculation of 2π in every cell.

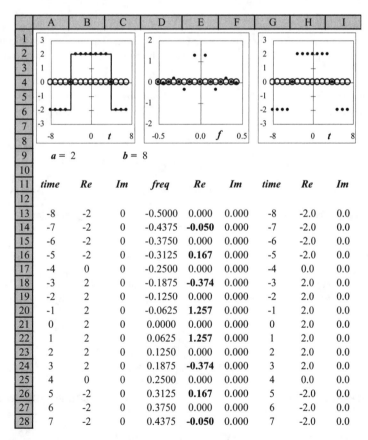

Fig. 5.2.1: The spreadsheet of a square wave and its Fourier transform. Solid circles: real components; open circles: imaginary components. The drawn line in the leftmost panel, computed also for intermediate, noninteger values of t, illustrates that the (boldfaced) coefficients define a curve through all input data but do *not* trace a square wave.

221

(5) Highlight the real data set in the third thumbnail sketch, and in the formula box extend its time scale from G13:G28 to G13:G180, and its function reach from H13:H28 to H13:H180.

(6) Highlight the column J13:J180, copy it to the clipboard (with Ctrl∪c), highlight the plot area of the third thumbnail sketch, and paste the data in with Ctrl∪v.

(7) Do the same for the input function. If necessary, sharpen its corners by changing, e.g., $t = -4.1$ and -3.9 to $t = -4.001$ and -3.999 respectively. For better visibility, offset this new curve by adding 0.5 to its y-values.

Exercise 5.2.2:

(1) Modify the spreadsheet by replacing the input signal by that of a narrow pulse, as in Fig. 5.2.2. Again, the zero-crossings of the pulse should be entered explicitly as the average of the values before and after the change.

(2) Transform these, apply the inverse transformation, and display the results.

(3) Again use the coefficients in the output of the forward FFT to construct the function at intermediate values of t.

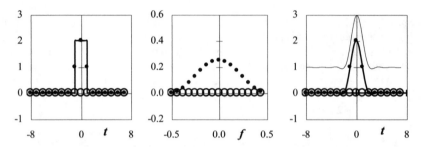

Fig. 5.2.2: A rectangular pulse, its FFT, and the inverse FFT of the latter. The thin line represents the reconstructed curve shifted up by 1 for better visibility, and clearly shows the oscillatory nature of that reconstruction.

Exercise 5.2.3:

(1) Move the pulse in time so that it is no longer symmetrical with respect to $t = 0$, see Fig. 5.2.3. Again, the zero-crossings of the pulse should be entered explicitly as the average of the values before and after the change.

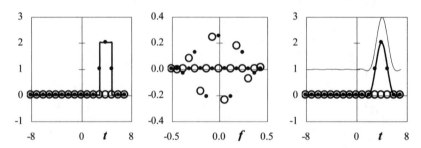

Fig. 5.2.3: The same for a rectangular pulse shifted in time. The recovered function is also shown as a thin line offset by 1.

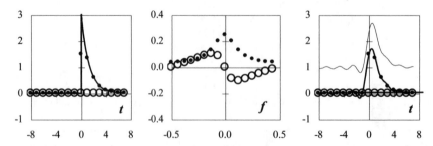

Fig. 5.2.4: The exponential $y = 0$ for $t < 0$, $y = 3e^{-0.8t}$ for $t > 0$, its FFT, and the inverse FFT of the latter. The recovered function is also shown offset by +1.

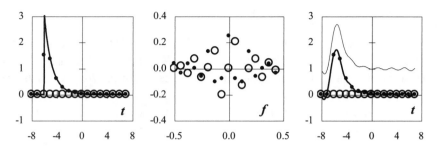

Fig. 5.2.5: The same for the function $y = 0$ for $t < -6$, $y = 3e^{-0.8(t+6)}$ for $t > -6$.

Exercise 5.2.4:

(1) Use an exponential function, such as $y = 0$ for $t < 0$, and $y = ae^{-bt}$ for $t > 0$, as in Fig. 5.2.4. Again, the zero-crossings of the pulse should be entered explicitly as the average of the values before and after the change: $y = a/2$ for $t = 0$.

Exercise 5.2.5:

(1) Shift the exponential function in time to, e.g., $y = 0$ for $t < -6$, $y = 3/2$ for $t = -6$, and $y = 3e^{-0.8(t+6)}$ for $t > -6$, as in Fig. 5.2.5.

The input signal is by no means restricted to sines and cosines; we only started with these because they yield the simplest transforms. These examples illustrate the following aspects of Fourier transformation:

(1) For an input signal that is symmetrical with respect to $t = 0$, so that $g(-t) = g(t)$, the Fourier transform is real, see Figs. 5.1.1, 5.2.1 and 5.2.2. When we write $g(t)$ and $G(f)$ explicitly in terms of their real and imaginary components as $g(t) = g'(t) + j\, g''(t)$ and $G(f) = G'(f) + jG''(f)$ respectively, a so-called *even* input function $g(-t) = g(t)$ yields a real Fourier transform, i.e., $G''(f) = 0$.

(2) When the input signal has mirror symmetry with respect to $t = 0$, so that $g(-t) = -g(t)$, it is called *odd*, as for the sine wave in Fig. 5.1.2. In that case its Fourier transform is imaginary, hence $G'(f) = 0$.

(3) If the input signal lacks either of the above symmetries, its Fourier transform will be complex, i.e., it will have both real and imaginary components, as illustrated in Figs. 5.2.3 through 5.2.5.

(4) All the above examples have a real input, i.e., $g''(t) = 0$, and consequently their Fourier transforms all have an even real part, i.e., $G'(-f) = G'(f)$, and an odd imaginary part, $G''(-f) = -G''(f)$. Likewise, when $g(t)$ is imaginary, $G'(f)$ is odd and $G''(-f)$ is even. Because the Fourier transform of a sum $g(t) = g'(t) + j\, g''(t)$ is the sum of the Fourier transforms of its components, the entire information content of any Fourier transform can in principle be repackaged in terms of non-negative frequencies f, although this is not customary. However, it does imply that the Fourier transform of N input data contains information on only $(\frac{1}{2}N + 1)$ frequencies, a conclusion that is related to the sampling theorem of section 5.3. The one 'extra' frequency beyond $\frac{1}{2}N$ is the zero frequency, $f = 0$, which represents the average value of the function.

(5) Forward Fourier transformation followed by inverse Fourier transformation recovers the original data points exactly (within the round-off errors of the computation, i.e., in Excel usually well within 1 in 10^{15}). While we may have *meant* the input data to represent a particular, underlying function, such as a square pulse in Figs. 5.2.1 through 5.2.3, or a single exponential in Figs. 5.2.4 and 5.2.5, in a discrete Fourier transform algorithm there is no way to specify such a function other than through the discrete input points used. We cannot expect the algorithm to guess what we mean; it can only respond to the specific input data provided. Therefore, especially when we furnish relatively few points of a continuous function, its discrete Fourier transformation will only approximate the continuous Fourier transform of that function. This can be seen clearly in the continuous curves calculated in Figs. 5.2.1 through 5.2.5. And because the input function is only specified *at* those N points, it often cannot be reconstructed reliably *between* them, just as one cannot count on getting a reliable interpolation from a Lagrange polynomial for an arbitrary input function.

5.3 Aliasing & sampling

One of the most amazing aspects of the continuous Fourier transform, and the one that delayed its initial publication for many years at the hand of some of Fourier's great French contemporaries, is that it can even express a *discontinuous* function in terms of an infinite series of *continuous* sines and cosines, as in (5.2.1). That is clearly not possible with a *finite* set of sines and cosines, and consequently this property does not carry over to the discrete Fourier transform, which only uses a finite sample of the function, and likewise has only a finite number of frequencies with which to represent it.

In the present section we will consider aliasing and the related sampling theorem, while section 5.4 will discuss leakage. Both are artifacts of the *discrete* Fourier transformation, and are without counterparts in the continuous transform. Finally, in section 5.5, we will encounter an uncertainty relationship similar to that of Heisenberg, although in a strictly classical context.

Aliasing results when the signal frequencies fall *outside* the frequency range covered, while leakage occurs with signal frequencies that lie *inside* that range but fall *in between* the limited set of frequencies provided by the discrete Fourier transformation. Aliasing is easily understood with a series of examples, such as those of exercise 5.3.1.

Exercise 5.3.1:

(1) Return to (or recreate) the spreadsheet shown in Fig. 5.1.1.

(2) Leaving row 29 empty, extend column A with cells A30:A190 containing the times −8 (0.1) 8, and in cells G30:G190 enter the corresponding values of the cosine wave. Show these data in the graph as a thin line.

(3) Change the value of b from 1 to 2, and Fourier transform the data, which will now exhibit contributions at $f = \pm 0.125$ instead of $f = \pm 0.0625$.

(4) Increment the value of b by 1 to $b = 3$, and Fourier transform A13:C28. Observe that the non-zero points in the transform hop over to the next-higher (absolute) frequency.

(5) Continue this for the next few integer values of b. It works fine up to and including $b = 8$, but at $b = 9$ you have obviously run out of the frequency scale. What happens then is shown in Fig. 5.3.1: the Fourier transformation yields the same result as for $b = 7$.

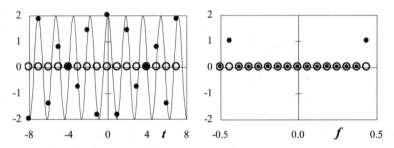

Fig. 5.3.1: The function $y = 2 \cos (9 \pi t / 8)$ and its Fourier transform.

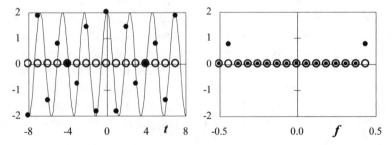

Fig. 5.3.2: The function $y = 2 \cos (7 \pi t / 8)$ and its Fourier transform.

224

(6) Comparison with the earlier result, for $b = 7$, shows why: the input data for both cases are identical, as illustrated in Fig. 5.3.2. No wonder we get the same transform when the input *data* are the same. The only difference between the two left panels is in the *line drawn through them*. The Fourier transform merely sees the input data, whereas the line indicates what we *intend* the data to represent. The Fourier transform only finds the lowest possible frequency that fit these data. The same Fourier transform would be obtained with 16 equally spaced data calculated with $y = 2 \cos (b\pi t / 8)$ for $b = 23$, 25, 39, 41, etc.

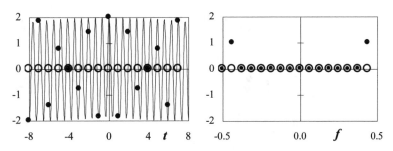

Fig. 5.3.3: The function $y = 2 \cos (\mathbf{23}\pi t / 8)$ and its Fourier transform.

(7) What we see here is called aliasing, as if these higher frequencies masquerade under an alias. But it really is a problem of sampling, because we give the Fourier transformation insufficient information. That this is so is perhaps even more clearly seen when we select $b = 15$ or $b = 17$, as illustrated in Figs. 5.3.4 and 5.3.5, which should be compared with Fig. 5.1.1.

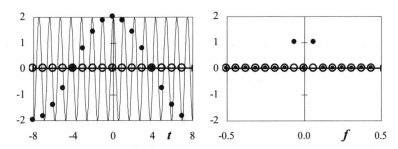

Fig. 5.3.4: The function $y = 2 \cos (\mathbf{15}\pi t / 8)$ and its Fourier transform.

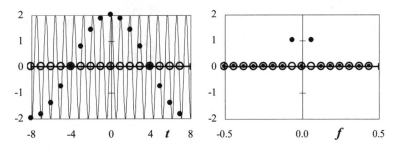

Fig. 5.3.5: The function $y = 2 \cos (\mathbf{17} \; \pi t / 8)$ and its Fourier transform.

The above examples suggest that we can put an infinity of cosine waves through 16 points. The Fourier transform yields the lowest possible of these, i.e., it uses the *parsimony principle*. Clearly, the problem lies with the input data rather than with the Fourier transformation. This is where the *Nyquist* or *sampling theorem* comes in. It states that, in order to define a periodic signal *unambiguously*, we must sample it more than twice per period. The assumed infinite periodicity of the sampled signal fragment then fills in the rest. Aliasing results when the signal is undersampled, as it was in Figs. 5.3.1 through 5.3.5.

225

Please note that aliasing is *not* a special property of Fourier transformation, as the following example of Volpi demonstrates. Imagine that you want to plot the function $f(t) = e^{-t} \sin(\omega t)$ with $\omega = 316$ for x between 0 and 6, and therefore compute and plot it for $t = 0$ (0.1) 6. You will obtain the plot shown in Fig. 5.3.6, showing a function with a first maximum at $t \approx 0.6$, a first zero crossing beyond the origin at $t \approx 1.7$, a first minimum at $t \approx 2.3$ and, as expected for an oscillatory function damped by e^{-t}, approaching 0 as $t \rightarrow s \infty$.

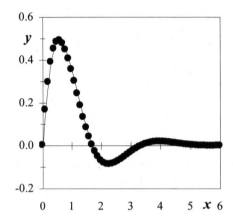

Fig. 3.5.6: The function $f(t) = e^{-t} \sin(\omega t)$ for $\omega = 316$, calculated and plotted for $x = 0$ (0.1) 6.

Unfortunately, this picture is wrong, as you can see when you change the intervals Δx used to, e.g., 1.1, as illustrated in Fig. 5.3.7a. When you let Excel connect the dots by a smooth curve, by changing Δx to 0.01, as in Fig. 5.3.7b, you get a quite different picture.

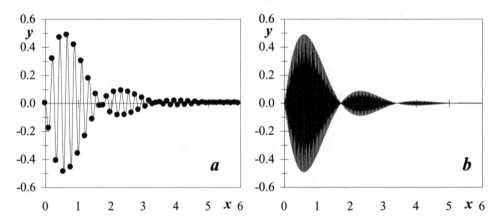

Fig. 3.5.7: The function $f(t) = e^{-t} \sin(316\ t)$, calculated and plotted (*a*) for $x = 0$ (0.11) 6.05, and (*b*) for $x = 0$ (0.01) 6.05.

Unfortunately, this is still incorrect. What is happening here? We have a function that uses two quite different time scales: the time constant τ of the exponent is 1, whereas that of the sinewave is $2\pi/\omega \approx 0.02$. To resolve the latter time constant we need to use a data spacing smaller than $\frac{1}{2} \times 0.02 = 0.01$, as in Fig. 5.3.8a, where we have used $\Delta x = 0.001$ over $0 \le t \le 0.2$. When we then lengthen the scale to encompass the range $0 \le t \le 6$ and plot the result we find Fig. 5.3.8b or, using uniformly random numbers between 0 and 5, those in Fig. 5.3.9. The latter approach is optimal when we suspect aliasing, because it avoids taking equidistant data points, even though it may not always be practical for experimental data.

226

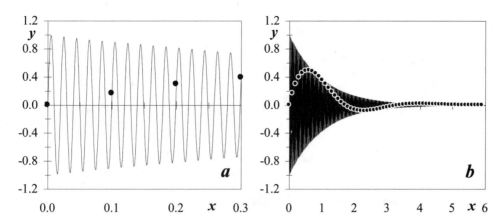

Fig. 3.5.8: The function $f(t) = e^{-t} \sin(316\,t)$, calculated and plotted (*a*) for $x = 0\,(0.001)\,0.3$, with the first four points for $x = 0\,(0.1)\,0.3$ superimposed as solid black circles, and (*b*) for $x = 0\,(0.001)\,6$, with the same data for $x = 0\,(0.1)\,6$ superimposed as white circles with a black core, compare Fig. 3.5.6.

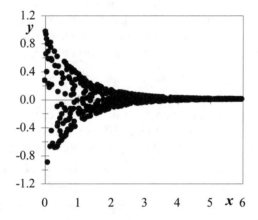

Fig. 3.5.9: The same function $f(t) = e^{-t} \sin(316\,t)$, calculated and plotted for $x = 6*\text{Rand}()$.

Clearly, aliasing has nothing to do with Fourier transformation per se, but everything with the ratio of the data spacing and any repeat frequencies in the signal. However, given that we so often use equidistant points to plot functions, it is most likely to come up when we deal with repetitive signals such as the sines and cosines that are the basis functions of Fourier transformation.

5.4 Leakage

Another problem specific to the discrete Fourier transform is leakage. Again, it is most readily demonstrated with a sine or cosine wave. It occurs when the signal is amply sampled according to the Nyquist criterion, but contains frequencies in between those used in the Fourier transformation. This is illustrated in exercise 5.4.1, where we consider a sine wave with frequency 2.1. The transform shows the dominant frequency as 2, but it needs contributions from the other, adjacent frequencies to make the fit, because it cannot represent the frequency 2.1 directly, just as integers cannot represent numbers such as e or π. It is, therefore, as if the frequency 'leaks out' into the adjacent frequencies. Another way of looking at it is that, when the signal is repeated (as is implied in Fourier transformation), it exhibits discontinuities that can only be represented with higher frequencies.

227

Exercise 5.4:

(1) On the same spreadsheet, now use $b = 2.1$. Figure 5.4.1 shows the result.

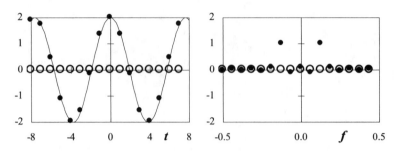

Fig. 5.4.1: The function $y = 2 \cos (\mathbf{2.1}\, \pi t / 8)$ and its Fourier transform.

Leakage often occurs when data are acquired at rates that are not exact (sub)multiples of the power line frequency (60 Hz in the US, 50 Hz elsewhere) because many signals are contaminated by that ubiquitous signal. In such cases the problem is readily avoided by synchronizing the data acquisition rate to that of the power line frequency. Once that is done, and the noise contribution is isolated at those specific frequencies, it can be filtered out after Fourier transformation by removing the contribution at that specific frequency, e.g., by setting it to zero or, better yet, by using its nearest neighbors to interpolate the removed value. The same may have to be done also for its prominent harmonics.

5.5 *Uncertainty*

When we hear a sustained note we can recognize its pitch and, if we have perfect pitch, identify its name and therefore (at least in principle) its frequency. If that same note is sounded only very briefly, we cannot do this; apparently we need several complete cycles of the sinusoid involved to define its pitch.

A continuous sine wave supposedly lasts indefinitely, and is specified by a precise frequency f, i.e., within an infinitely narrow spread. In this case the product of the time interval (∞) and the corresponding frequency spread (0), is $\infty \times 0$, which is ill-defined. But as soon as we restrict the sine wave to a finite interval τ, its frequency is no longer so precisely defined, as can be seen by Fourier transformation when we select one or a small number of cycles of that sine wave, setting its remainder to zero.

Exercise 5.5.1:

(1) Generate a sine wave and its Fourier transform, as in Fig. 5.5.1a.

(2) Delete most of the sine wave, leaving first three, then only one of its central cycles. Avoid generating a break (which would generate spurious high frequencies) by setting the signal to zero up to a point where the sine wave itself is zero.

(3) Apply the Fourier transform. Figures 5.5.1b and 5.5.1c illustrate what you may get: a broadened set of frequencies centered *around* the frequency value of the left panel in Fig. 5.5.1a. This is the trick used in nuclear magnetic resonance spectroscopy to generate a narrow *range* of frequencies to encompass any chemical shifts.

In this example the time period is well-defined, but the range of frequencies is not. However, when we just take the width of the frequency peak at its base as a crude measure, we find that it is 5×0.0078125 wide in Fig. 5.5.2, and 15×0.0078125 wide in Fig. 5.5.3, i.e., it is inversely proportional to the length of the signal burst. The number 0.0078125 is the unit of f, equal to 1/128 for a 128-point signal. This suggests a constant product of the time interval and the associated frequency spread.

Thus, even when we use a pure sine wave, its brevity converts its single frequency into a frequency *distribution*. It is not a deficiency of our ears that we cannot identify the pitch of a very brief note played on a double bass; it simply does not *have* a well-defined pitch. (This property is exploited in pulsed NMR to excite a narrow *range* of frequencies of interest by gating a short section of a purely sinusoidal signal.) The shorter a signal, the fuzzier its frequency.

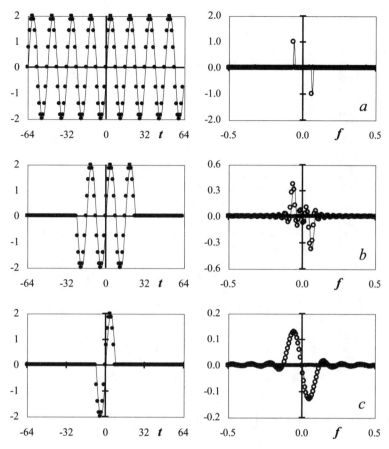

Fig. 5.5.1*a,b,c*: The transform of a continuous sine wave and of two bursts of the same, lasting only three cycles and one cycle respectively. For the sake of clarity only the imaginary part of the transform is shown; in all these cases its real part is zero. Note the changing vertical scales of the right-hand panels.

For features for which the characteristic widths in time and frequency can be defined in terms of standard deviations, the above can be formulated mathematically by stating that the product $s_\tau s_f$ of the standard deviation s_τ of the time interval τ over which the signal is observed, times the standard deviation s_f of its frequency f, cannot be determined to better than $1/(2\pi)$. Or, even simpler: the product of the standard deviation in time t and that in angular frequency $\omega = 2\pi f$ is at least 1. Below we will illustrate this uncertainty principle with a Gaussian curve, because (a) its width is expressed in terms of its standard deviation, and (b) the Fourier transform of a Gaussian is again a Gaussian. Here we have an analog, in Newtonian physics, of the Heisenberg uncertainty principle of quantum mechanics!

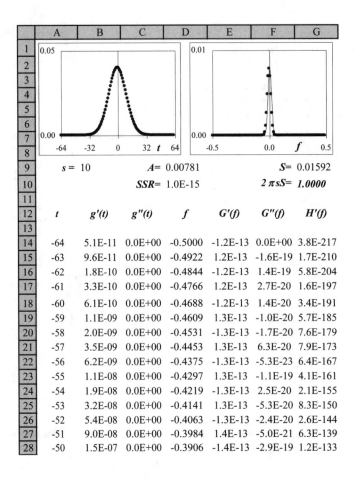

	A	B	C	D	E	F	G
9	$s =$	10		$A =$ 0.00781		$S =$	0.01592
10			$SSR =$ 1.0E-15			$2\pi sS =$	**1.0000**
11							
12	t	$g'(t)$	$g''(t)$	f	$G'(f)$	$G''(f)$	$H'(f)$
13							
14	-64	5.1E-11	0.0E+00	-0.5000	-1.2E-13	0.0E+00	3.8E-217
15	-63	9.6E-11	0.0E+00	-0.4922	1.2E-13	-1.6E-19	1.7E-210
16	-62	1.8E-10	0.0E+00	-0.4844	-1.2E-13	1.4E-19	5.8E-204
17	-61	3.3E-10	0.0E+00	-0.4766	1.2E-13	2.7E-20	1.6E-197
18	-60	6.1E-10	0.0E+00	-0.4688	-1.2E-13	1.4E-20	3.4E-191
19	-59	1.1E-09	0.0E+00	-0.4609	1.3E-13	-1.0E-20	5.7E-185
20	-58	2.0E-09	0.0E+00	-0.4531	-1.3E-13	-1.7E-20	7.6E-179
21	-57	3.5E-09	0.0E+00	-0.4453	1.3E-13	6.3E-20	7.9E-173
22	-56	6.2E-09	0.0E+00	-0.4375	-1.3E-13	-5.3E-23	6.4E-167
23	-55	1.1E-08	0.0E+00	-0.4297	1.3E-13	-1.1E-19	4.1E-161
24	-54	1.9E-08	0.0E+00	-0.4219	-1.3E-13	2.5E-20	2.1E-155
25	-53	3.2E-08	0.0E+00	-0.4141	1.3E-13	-5.3E-20	8.3E-150
26	-52	5.4E-08	0.0E+00	-0.4063	-1.3E-13	-2.4E-20	2.6E-144
27	-51	9.0E-08	0.0E+00	-0.3984	1.4E-13	-5.0E-21	6.3E-139
28	-50	1.5E-07	0.0E+00	-0.3906	-1.4E-13	-2.9E-19	1.2E-133

Fig. 5.5.2: The top of the spreadsheet for exercise 5.5.3 illustrating the uncertainty principle.

Exercise 5.5.2:

(1) Make a spreadsheet in which you compute $2N$ points of a Gaussian, such as for $t = -64$ (1) 63, the function $g(t) = (s\sqrt{2\pi})^{-1} \exp[-t^2/(2s^2)]$ where you refer to the value of s as stored in a separate location (such as cell B9 in Fig. 5.5.2. Start with, say, $s = 10$. Plot the Gaussian input curve.

(2) Apply the Fourier transform, and again plot the resulting Gaussian peak.

(3) In a seventh column calculate a Gaussian in terms of frequency f, $H'(f) = A \exp[-f^2/(2S^2)]$, using externally stored values for A and S.

(4) Now use Solver to match this Gaussian, $H'(f)$, with the result of the Fourier transformation, $G'(f)$. This will verify that, indeed, the Fourier transform $G'(f)$ fits a Gaussian, and will yield a numerical value for its standard deviation S.

(5) Compute the product of $2\pi s$ and the just-found value of S. If s times S is $1/(2\pi)$, this product should be close to 1.

(6) Change the value of s from 10 to, say, 5 or 3, and repeat steps (2), (4), and (5). Qualitatively, the more the signal extends in the time domain, the more tightly it is restricted in the frequency domain, and vice versa. Quantitatively, you should find close adherence of the product of the standard deviations s and S to the value of $1/(2\pi)$. The above is illustrated in Fig. 5.5.2.

5.6 Filtering

So far we have dealt with mathematical functions rather than with experimental data, i.e., we have not yet considered the effects of random noise on the input signal. In this and the next few sections we will include noise, and we will transform noisy (time-domain) data into the frequency domain, manipulate them there, and return the modified data to the time domain. Below we will consider filtering, while sections 5.7 through 5.9 will deal with differentiation, interpolation, and data compression respectively.

230

We can distinguish two types of filtering, equivalent to their analog equivalents: tuned, and general. A *tuned filter* either enhances or rejects signals in a narrow frequency band. Fourier transformation allows for the ideal tuned filter, because it can be as narrow as one single frequency. If we want to filter out a particular frequency from a signal, we Fourier-transform the signal (after making sure that the frequency to be filtered is part of the frequencies used in the Fourier transform so as to avoid leakage), set the real and imaginary contributions at that frequency to zero, and inverse transform the resulting data set. If you want to remove all frequencies other than a particular one, we Fourier-transform, set the contributions at all other frequencies to zero, and transform back. Of course, the narrower the tuned filter, the smaller the margin of error in matching that frequency with the desired signal frequency we want to single out for enhancement or rejection, otherwise we will encounter leakage. When a tuned filter for a particular frequency is desired, Fourier transformation, frequency-domain filtering, and inverse Fourier transformation often provide an optimal software solution.

A more complicated problem is that of general filtering, with has a less clearly defined purpose, and often a correspondingly more tentative solution. General filtering is essentially a statistical process, and we will therefore assume that we have collected a sufficiently large number of data points. Part of its noise will occur at frequencies higher than those of the signal. A crude approach to removing high-frequency noise is to Fourier transform the data, to set a number of highest-frequency contributions to zero, and to transform the result back into the time domain. However, the sharp transition between the frequencies that are included and those that are excluded can lead to oscillations in the filtered output.

A way to avoid such artificial oscillations is to use a more gradual filter, typically again applied in the frequency domain (i.e., after Fourier transformation) to reduce the highest-frequency contributions to zero, while leaving intact most of the frequencies carrying the signal.

Many different *window functions* have been proposed for that purpose, often based on either trigonometric functions or exponentials. For an extensive listing see F. J. Harris, *Proc. IEEE* 66 (1978) 51, or chapter 6 in D. F. Elliott & K. R. Rao, *Fast Transforms: Algorithms, Analyses, Applications*, Academic Press (1982).

In our context perhaps the most generally useful window is the cosine window apparently first proposed by Julius von Hann (and sometimes called the Hanning window, a confusing name since a different window function was proposed by R. W. Hamming and is therefore called the Hamming window). In its simplest form, the von Hann window function is

$$W(n) = \cos^2\left(\frac{\pi n}{N}\right) = 0.5 + 0.5 \cos\left(\frac{2\pi n}{N}\right) \tag{5.6.1}$$

where N is the total number of data points used in a centered data set (i.e., $n = -N/2$, $-N/2+1$, $-N/2+2$, ... , -1, 0, 1, ... , $N/2-2$, $N/2-1$), and $n = t$ when the windowing is applied in the time domain, or $n = f$ when used in the frequency domain. At its extremes (i.e., at $n = -N/2$ and $n = +N/2$), $\cos^2(\pi n/N) = \cos^2(\pm\pi/2) = 0$, as are all its derivatives $d^p\cos^2(\pi n/N)/dn^p$.

For more variable filtering we can extend the von Hann filter with a single adjustable parameter s (for *s*tenosis, Greek for narrowness)

$$W(n) = \cos^{2s}\left(\frac{\pi n}{N}\right) = \left[0.5 + 0.5 \cos\left(\frac{2\pi n}{N}\right)\right]^s \tag{5.6.2}.$$

and $-N/2 \leq n \leq N/2 - 1$. Exercise 5.6.1 and Fig. 5.6.1 illustrate this highly adjustable filter.

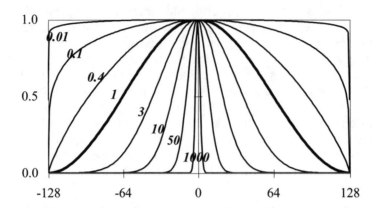

Fig. 5.6.1: The adjustable von Hann window for various values of s as indicated with the curves. The thick curve for $s = 1$ is the original von Hann filter.

An alternative window function introduced by Tukey uses the two halves of the von Hann filter to remove some of the abruptness of an otherwise sharp cut-off filter. This filter has two adjustable parameters, a and b, where $0 \le a \le b \le 1$, and is described (again, for a centered set with $n = -N/2, -N/2+1, -N/2+2, \ldots, -1, 0, 1, \ldots, N/2-2, N/2-1$) by

$$W(n) = 1 \qquad\qquad\qquad\qquad\qquad\qquad\qquad\qquad \text{for } 0 \le 2|n|/N \le a$$

$$W(n) = \cos^2\left[\frac{\pi}{b-a}\left(\frac{|n|}{N} - \frac{a}{2}\right)\right] = 0.5 + 0.5\cos\left[\frac{2\pi}{b-a}\left(\frac{|n|}{N} - \frac{a}{2}\right)\right] \quad \text{for } a \le 2|n|/N \le b \quad (5.6.3)$$

$$W(n) = 0 \qquad\qquad\qquad\qquad\qquad\qquad\qquad\qquad \text{for } b \le 2|n|/N \le 1$$

The Tukey window compresses the gradual cosine function within the region between a and b; it is identical to the von Hann window (5.6.1) for $a = 0$ and $b = 1$, whereas it becomes a rectangular window for $a = b$. A combination of the von Hann filter for $s \ge 1$ and a Tukey filter with $a = 1 - s$ and $b = 0$ for $s < 1$ is shown in Fig. 5.6.2 for various values of s.

When a von Hann or Tukey window is used to filter (by multiplication) a *time* sequence, it can gradually reduce the value of the function and of its derivatives near the extremes of its range. In the *frequency* domain, such a window predominantly attenuates the highest frequencies, which usually contain mostly noise. Fourier transform instruments often incorporate so-called *apodizing* window functions that somewhat resemble a raised von Hann filter of the form $W(n) \approx a + (1 - a)\cos(2\pi n/N)$ where $0.5 \le a \le 1$, see R. N. Norton & R. Beer, *J. Opt. Soc. Am.* 60 (1976) 259, 67 (1977) 418.

Exercise 5.6.1:
(1) For $N = 256$ and $n = -128$ (1) 127, compute and plot (5.6.2) for various values of s, and compare your results with Fig. 5.6.1.
(2) For $N = 256$ and $n = -128$ (1) 127, compute and plot (5.6.3) for various values of a and b, and compare your results with Fig. 5.6.1. Note that this requires two nested IF statements, as in (symbolically) `=IF(ABS(n)< a*128, 1,IF(ABS(n)> b*128,0,0.5+0.5*COS(2*π*(ABS(n)/256-a/2)/ (b-a))))`. Compare with Fig. 5.6.2.

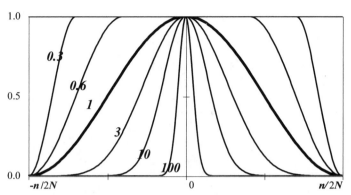

Fig. 5.6.2: A combined von Hann-Tukey window for various values of *s* as indicated with the curves.

Both the von Hann and Tukey windows allow for a more gradual filtering action than the simple high-frequency cut-off method, and are usually preferable to a sharp cut-off. Still, as long as they do not take into account any specific information of the data set used, they are at best shots in the dark. Fortunately, we can let the data themselves guide us in the choice of filter.

The simplest way to do this is to Fourier-transform the data, and to display the corresponding *power spectrum*. This is a logarithmic plot of the magnitude M (i.e., the square root of the sum of squares of its real and imaginary components) of the transformed data as a function of frequency f. For a real input signal, the power spectrum has mirror symmetry along $f = 0$, i.e., $M(-f) = M(f)$. Therefore the power spectrum is often plotted only for $f \geq 0$, although it may be helpful to display the entire (positive and negative) frequency range as a reminder of that symmetry, i.e., of the need to use the absolute values $|f|$ of all odd powers of f. For our present purpose it is actually easier to plot $\log M^2 = 2 \log M$.

Since the power spectrum omits all phase information, it has a simpler appearance than the frequency spectrum: as a real (rather than a complex) function it is easier to visualize and to plot. The wider a feature is in the time domain, the narrower it will be in the frequency domain, and hence in the power spectrum. The position of a single feature in the time domain is represented in the frequency domain by a phase shift, and is therefore lost in the power spectrum.

As an example, Fig. 5.6.3 shows a collection of Gaussian curves with added random noise, and Fig. 5.6.4 illustrates the corresponding power spectrum. Note that we have extended the data set with zeros to the nearest integer power of 2 in order to facilitate its 'fast' Fourier transformation. We can readily distinguish the contributions of signal and noise by their different frequency dependences. In this simple example the noise is 'white', i.e., it is essentially independent of frequency, and therefore shows in the power spectrum as a horizontal band. It can also have a non-constant frequency dependence, as in, e.g., so-called $1/f$ or 'pink' noise.

Exercise 5.6.2:

(1) First generate a sample data set. The data shown in Fig. 5.6.3 were created with five Gaussians plus Gaussian noise, but you are of course welcome to use other functions.

(2) If the curves are all well contained within the original data set, extend the data set with zeros at both ends; otherwise, extrapolate the data to taper off smoothly to zero in the added 'wings'.

(3) Fourier-transform the extended set.

(4) Calculate and plot $\log M$ or $2 \log M$, where M is the sum of the squares of the real and imaginary components of the Fourier-transformed data. Such a plot is shown in Fig. 5.6.4, and often exhibits two distinct regions: one (typically at lower values of $|f|$) in which the signal dominates, the other (at the high-frequency end) in which noise is the determining

233

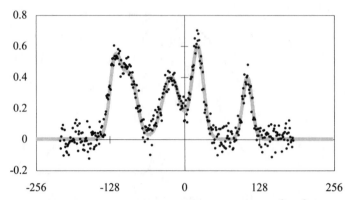

Fig. 5.6.3a: A test function composed of five Gaussian peaks $a \exp[-(x-c)^2/(2b^2)]$ (thick gray curve) and the same plus Gaussian noise of zero mean and standard deviation 0.05 (dots). The constants used for the Gaussian peaks were $a = 0.5, 0.4, 0.4, 0.6, 0.4$, $b = 10, 12, 15, 10, 8$, and $c = -117, -92, -22, 23$, and 108 respectively. The original data set of 401 points was extended to 512 to facilitate Fourier transformation.

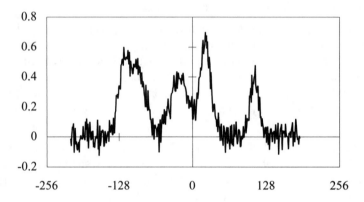

Fig. 5.6.3b: Another representation of the same noisy data (the points in Fig. 5.6.3a), here drawn as a 'continuous' curve.

At its simplest we can use the power spectrum (see Fig. 5.6.4) to conclude that, in this example, the signal predominates at $|f|$–values smaller than about 0.055, while noise is the most important factor at higher frequencies. We can then filter the data by zeroing all frequency components above 0.055 before inverse transformation. Figure 5.6.5 illustrates such smoothing. A Tukey filter with a narrow transition range (e.g., $a = 3/32$, $b = 1/8$) yields an essentially similar result.

Exercise 5.6.2 (continued):
(5) Estimate by eye at what frequency f_0 the two regions intersect. Then copy the Fourier transform obtained under (3), and in that copy replace all values of the transform by zero whenever $|f| > f_0$.
(6) Inverse Fourier-transform these data back into the time domain, and plot the result. Also compute and plot the residuals, and calculate the sum of the squares of these residuals. Figure 5.6.5 illustrates such results.

Wiener showed that one can use the power spectrum to obtain *optimal* least-squares filtering, by considering the signal and noise components of $M^2(f)$ as the algebraic sum of two smooth functions, $S^2(f)$ and $N^2(f)$, where $S^2(f)$ approximates the contribution of the *s*ignal to $M^2(f)$, and $N^2(f)$ that of the *n*oise. We can usually estimate $S^2(f)$ and $N^2(f)$ only in those regions of the frequency spectrum where they dominate. However, in the absence of better information, we will typically extrapolate them to the other regions of the spectrum. The resulting *Wiener filter* then is $S^2(f) / [S^2(f) + N^2(f)]$, and attenuates the data more strongly the smaller is the value of $S^2(f) / N^2(f)$, the square of the *signal-to-noise ratio*. As long as the noise is not overwhelming the signal, Wiener filtering tends to affect the peak signal amplitudes only weakly because, at the frequencies describing those peaks, $S^2(f) \gg N^2(f)$, so that $S^2(f) / [S^2(f) + N^2(f)] \approx 1$.

234

On the other hand, contributions from frequency regions where noise predominates are much more strongly attenuated, because there $S^2(f) / [S^2(f) + N^2(f)] \ll 1$.

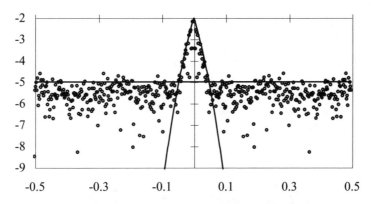

Fig. 5.6.4: A plot of 2 log $M(f)$ as a function of frequency f for the data of Fig. 5.6.3. The lines drawn are 2 log $M(f) = -2 - 50\,|f| - 300\,f^2$ and 2 log $M(f) = -5$ respectively.

Exercise 5.6.2 (continued):

(7) Fit simple polynomials to the two parts of the plot of 2 log $M(f)$ vs. f. Do not use unweighted least squares, since the top points should carry more weight than the lower points. For a visual estimate use a curve near the top of the data, but disregarding a few high points which are most likely due to noise. The parameters for the two lines shown in Fig. 5.6.4 were guessed in this way.

(8) Multiply the Fourier transform obtained under (3) with the Wiener function $S^2(f)/[S^2(f)+N^2(f)]$, then call the inverse transform to convert the data back to the time domain. Plot the resulting, filtered data, and compare with Fig. 5.6.6. Also compute and plot the residuals, calculate the sum of the squares of these residuals, and compare this with SSR obtained under (6).

Because the Wiener method requires only a crude approximation of the signal and noise components in the data set, we can fit the data in the logarithmic plot (of log $M^2(f)$ vs. f) to obtain, e.g., low-order polynomial expressions for log $S^2(f)$ and log $N^2(f)$, then exponentiate these to obtain $S^2(f)$ and $N^2(f)$, as illustrated in exercise 5.6.6. Wiener showed that use of his filter yields the smallest value of SSR, the sum of squares of the residuals, which makes it 'optimal' in a least-squares sense. Table 5.6 lists a few simple expressions for Wiener filters.

The noise reduction achieved by the Wiener filter is perhaps best illustrated by Fig. 5.6.7, where we plot the random noise originally added to the Gaussian peaks of Fig. 5.6.3, and the noise remaining after filtering. Note the absence of perceptible bias.

If we knew the functional form of S, we could fit the data to that form directly, e.g., with Solver, and obtain a completely smooth result. While the Wiener method removes only part of the noise, it is rather general, requires no a priori information on the nature of the signal, and derives its information directly from the data set to be filtered. It does assume that the contributions of signal and noise can be identified separately, and can be extrapolated validly. Provided that the noise can be described as following a single Gaussian distribution and is additive to the signal, Wiener filtering is optimal in a least-squares sense.

235

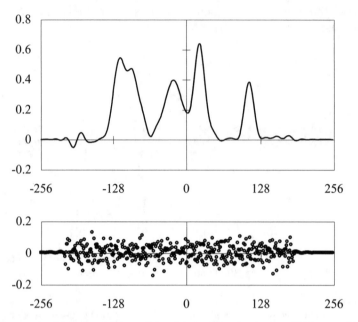

Fig. 5.6.5: The result of filtering the data of Fig. 5.6.3 with a simple cut-off filter at $|f/f_{max}| = 0.11$ in the frequency domain. Top: the filtered curve; bottom: the residuals, i.e., the differences between the original, noisy data set and the filtered one. The sum of the squares of the 401 residuals is 0.918.

function	approximation for log $S^2(f)$	
Lorentzian	$a_0 + a_1 \|f\|$	
Gaussian	$a_0 + a_1 \|f\| + a_2 f^2$	
exponential	$a_0 + a_1 \log[(\|f\|+a_2)/(f_{max}+a_2-\|f\|)]$	$0 < a_2 \ll 1$

Table 5.6: Useful approximations for log $S^2(f)$ for some prototypical signals $s(t)$.

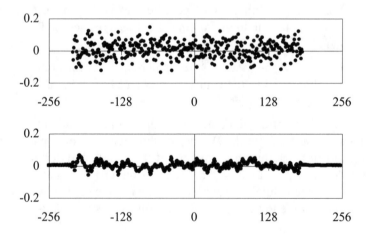

Fig. 5.6.7: The noise originally added to the Gaussian peaks in the model signal used (top panel), and the remaining noise after Wiener filtering (bottom panel). The standard deviations are 0.051 (top panel) and 0.022 (bottom panel) respectively.

236

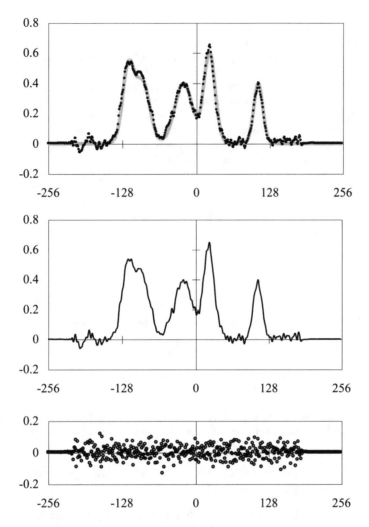

Fig. 5.6.6: The result of filtering the data of Fig. 5.6.3 with the Wiener filter $10^{\wedge}(-2-50|f|-300f^2)/$ $[10^{\wedge}(-2$ $-50|f|-300f^2)+10^{\wedge}(-5)]$. Top panel: the filtered data (dots) and the initially assumed, noise-free data (thick gray curve); middle panel: the filtered data represented as a line; bottom panel: the residuals between the unfiltered noisy data, and the filtered curve. The sum of the squares of the 401 residuals is 0.688.

5.7 Differentiation

In principle, differentiation is readily performed using Fourier transformation because differentiation with respect to time t in the time domain is equivalent to multiplication by $j\omega = 2\pi j f$ in the frequency domain, where $j = \sqrt{(-1)}$. One can therefore differentiate a function by transforming it into the frequency domain, multiplying it by $j\omega$, and transforming the resulting product back to the time domain. Since the Fourier transform is in general a complex quantity, say $a+jb$, multiplication by $j\omega$ yields $j\omega(a+jb) = -b\omega+j\omega a$. Below we illustrate the procedure with three examples. (Double differentiation can be obtained in a single operation through multiplication in the frequency domain by $(j\omega)^2 = -\omega^2$, triple differentiation through multiplication by $(j\omega)^3 = -j\omega^3$, etc., though noise enhancement at high ω-values often makes the one-step approach inadvisable.)

Exercise 5.7.1:

(1) In column A of a new spreadsheet enter $x = -16$ (1) 15 and, separated by one empty row, $x = -16$ (0.0625) 15.9375. In column B calculate, for $x = -16$ (1) 15, the corresponding values for $y = 0.7 \exp[-0.3(x+0.4)^2]$. In column C compute the same y for $x = -16$ (0.0625) 15.9375. Plot both series, with markers and with a line respectively, as in Fig. 5.7.1.

(2) Highlight the data for $x = -16$ (1) 15 in column A, the corresponding y-values in column B, and the associated empty spaces in column C, and call ForwardFT to generate the transform in columns D through F.

(3) In column G copy the data from column D. In column H calculate -2π times the corresponding frequency (in column G) times the corresponding imaginary component (in column F). It is most efficient to pre-calculate the value of 2π and then refer to its address, rather than have the spreadsheet compute PI() each time. Likewise, in column I, calculate 2π times f (from column G) times the real component (from column E).

(4) Highlight the data in columns G:I, call InverseFT, and plot the resulting real component of column K.

(5) For $x = -16$ (0.0625) 15.9375 calculate the derivative $dy/dx = -0.6 (x + 0.4) y$, and plot these results in Fig. 5.7.1.

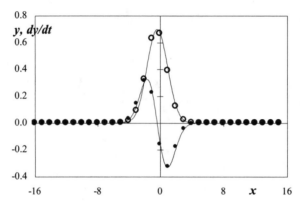

Fig. 5.7.1: The Gaussian $y = 0.7 \exp[-0.3(x+0.4)^2]$ (open circles and thin line through them) and its derivative as calculated by Fourier transformation (closed circles) and by calculation (thin line).

The result of this differentiation is very satisfactory: the fit in Fig. 5.7.1 between the derivative computed by Fourier transformation (solid circles) and those calculated algebraically for the Gaussian peak (line) is very good, with errors smaller than ±0.1%.

Now that we have established the principle of differentiation by Fourier transformation, we examine how it holds up under strain, such as caused either by noise or by discontinuities.

Exercise 5.7.1 (continued):

(6) Since it is more instructive (and more fun) to illustrate what works than what does not, we will here use the second data set, for $x = -16$ (0.0625) 15.9375.

(7) Add a column of Gaussian noise of zero mean and unit standard deviation, a label for a noise amplitude *na*, and a place for its numerical value.

(8) Add s_n times noise from the column made under (7) to your Gaussian curve in order to make it noisy.

(9) Fourier-transform the noisy Gaussian, then (to the right of that transform) insert three columns. In the first of these, calculate the logarithm of the sum of the squares of the real and imaginary components of the transform. Plot these data for positive frequencies, in order to make a Wiener filter.

(10) Use the two remaining, empty columns to generate simple functions (such as a parabola and a horizontal line) to approximate the contributions of signal and noise, $\log S^2(f)$ and $\log N^2(f)$ respectively. The resulting plot of $\log M^2(f)$ vs. f might now look like Fig. 5.7.2.

(11) Perform the cross-multiplication as under (3) but, in addition, incorporate in all terms the Wiener filter $S^2(f) / [S^2(f)+N^2(f)]$. Then inverse Fourier-transform to get the derivative, and plot your result, as in Fig. 5.7.3. The fit is not perfect, but differentiation of noisy data does not get any better than this.

(12) Now that you know what filter to use, you can actually mimic it with a Tukey filter in the frequency domain. Use Solver to adjust a and b of the Tukey filter, (5.6.3) with $n = f$ and $N = 2f_{max}$, to match the Wiener filter. You can indeed approximate the Wiener filter in this case by a Tukey filter with $a \approx 0.023$ and $b \approx 0.043$, which indicates how 'narrow' this Wiener filter is.

(13) Follow the same procedure with the smaller data set for $x = -16$ (1) 15. Even if you use the Wiener filter you found earlier (which is cheating, but it is difficult to define $S^2(f)$ and $N^2(f)$ with only a few noisy data points) the result is unsatisfactory: you simply have too few data points to pull it off.

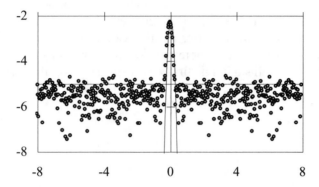

Fig. 5.7.2: Plot of log $M^2(f)$ vs. f for a simulated, noisy Gaussian curve. The lines are drawn with log $S^2(f) = -2.2 + |f| - 40\,f^2$ and log $N^2(f) = -5$.

Noise requires filtering before differentiation, and efficient filtering requires a sufficient number of data points so that noise can be averaged out. The moral: if you want to differentiate a set of data for which you have no good model, get as many data points as possible to define the curve. This applies to differentiation by Fourier transformation, just as much as it does to differentiation with least squares, such as with equidistant least squares, see section 3.15.

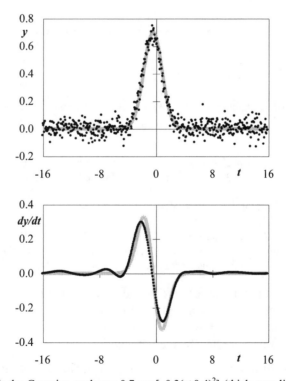

Fig. 5.7.3: Top panel: the Gaussian peak $y = 0.7\,\exp[-0.3(t+0.4)^2]$ (thick gray line) and the same with Gaussian noise with zero mean and standard deviation 0.05 (dots). Bottom panel: the first derivative of the noise-free curve (thick light-gray line) and that of the experimental data (dots) after Wiener filtering.

You can get away with differentiating relatively few data points when you know the precise mathematical formula to which the data can be fitted, in which case you find the fitting parameters with Solver, then use these parameters to calculate the derivative algebraically. However, if you need to differentiate data without an a priori model, make sure you have enough of them, because you will then have to rely on statistical methods, which do not work well for small data sets.

Noise is not the only source of trouble: differentiation can also run into difficulties when the data include one or more discontinuities, because there the derivative would be infinite, beyond the reach of digital representation. Below we will study this first with a square wave, then with an exponential.

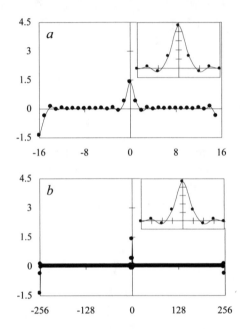

Fig. 5.7.4: The derivative of a square wave of (*a*) 32 points and (*b*) 512 points. The inserts show the central regions of both plots, with (in both cases) a horizontal range from –4 to +4, and a vertical range from –0.2 to +1.5.

Exercise 5.7.2:

(1) Generate one cycle of a square wave as follows. Generate the numbers $x = -16$ (1) 15 in cells A16:A47. In cells B16 and B32 place a zero, in cells B17:B31 a minus one (–1), and in cells B33 through B47 a one (1). Leave C16:C47 blank.

(2) Fourier-transform A16:C47, and use the result in D16:F47 to generate, in G16:I47, the same quantity multiplied by $j\omega$, as already done in exercise 5.7.1.

(3) Inverse Fourier-transform G16:I47, then plot the result, I16:I47 vs. G16:G47, see Fig. 5.7.4*a*.

(4) Repeat the same, but now for $x = -16$ (0.0625) 15.9375. For *y* now use one zero, followed by 255 terms –1, another 0, and the remaining 255 terms 1. Use Fourier transformation to generate its derivative, and plot it, as in Fig. 5.7.4*b*.

In Fig. 5.7.4*a* a relatively large number of points is affected by the discontinuities in the middle and at the edges of the range, whereas this is much less apparent in Fig. 5.7.4*b*. However, as the inserts show, the derivatives at the discontinuities are the same, and affect the same number of adjacent points. In the larger data set there are just many more unaffected numbers!

Because the input consists of discrete, evenly spaced points, we cannot really represent a truly sudden parameter change; at best we can make a change over one interval Δx. In fact, so far we have made that change over *two* intervals Δx. The next exercise illustrates the effect of making the transition less abrupt. (Even the continuous Fourier transform has a known problem, the Gibbs phenomenon, with a step function.)

Exercise 5.7.3:

(1) Use the block A19:L47 of the previous exercise, or make a similar new one.

(2) Modify the input sequence from 0, –1 (fifteen times), 0, 1 (fifteen times), to sixteen terms –1 followed by sixteen terms 1, and repeat the analysis.

(3) Now make changes in the other direction, by performing the differentiation on the following input sequences: 0, –0.5, –1 (×13), –0.5, 0, 0.5, 1 (×13), 0.5, then 0, –1/3, –2/3, –1 (×11), –2/3, –1/3, 0, 1/3, 2/3, 1 (×11), 2/3, 1/3, and finally 0, –0.25, –0.5, –0.75, –1 (×9), –0.75, –0.5, –0.25, 0, 0.25, 0.5, 0.75, 1 (×9), 0.75, 0.5, 0.25.

(4) Figure 5.7.5 illustrates the results. Clearly, the more sudden the transition, the more oscillations we get. And the shorter the data array, the less space there is for these oscillations to die down.

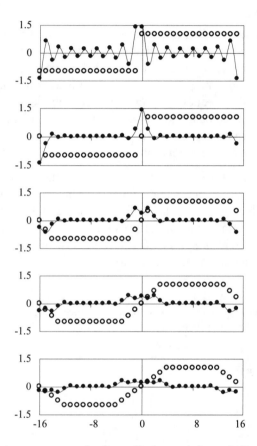

Fig. 5.7.5: A set of 32-point square waves of unit amplitudes, and slopes $\Delta y/\Delta x = 1, 1/2, 1/3$, etc. (open circles), and their Fourier-transform derivatives (solid circles connected by straight-line segments) illustrating that the severity of the oscillations in the computed derivative decreases as the transition is made more gradual.

Figure 5.7.5 illustrates that the differentiation of sharp transitions by Fourier transformation can cause oscillations, and is therefore only practical when the data set is sufficiently large so that the oscillations can taper off long before the signal has done so.

The message is clear: in order to use Fourier transformation to differentiate a function with one or more discontinuities, you need many data points in order to restrict the inevitable oscillations to a relatively narrow range. If you can describe the function in terms of an appropriate model, especially if that model describes sections of the data set that do not contain discontinuities, fit that model piecemeal, and use Fourier transformation to differentiate its parts. If you absolutely must use Fourier transformation to differentiate a small set of data without an appropriate model but with discontinuities and including much noise, consult your almanac or palm reader.

5.8 Interpolation

Often, data sets need to be interpolated. If the shape of the function is known, say, as a Gaussian or Lorentzian peak, nonlinear least squares can of course be used to fit the data to that function. If the data cannot be described mathematically but can be represented reasonably well in terms of polynomials, Lagrange interpolation may be indicated. Likewise, if the data can be fitted in terms of sines and cosines, Fourier transformation might be considered, especially when, inside the measuring instrument, the data are already available in Fourier-transformed format. Below we will discuss how Fourier transformation can be used for data interpolation.

In interpolation we use the existing data to construct intermediate values for which no direct evidence is available. This can only be done by assuming that no significant features of the signal are missing, despite the limited data set. In the present context this means that we assume the absence of signals at frequencies higher than those sampled. The procedure therefore is as follows: take the existing data points, Fourier-transform them, extend the frequency range with contributions of zero amplitude at the added higher frequencies, then transform the data back. Such *zero filling* results in a larger data set without added information, i.e., in a smooth interpolation. If still higher resolution is necessary, the few data near the maximum can then be fitted to a low-order polynomial in order to find the precise peak maximum.

For example, in mass spectrometry it is common to acquire the fragmentation pattern as equidistant points on an m/z scale, where m denotes mass and z valency. The chemical identity of a fragment can usually be identified unambiguously when the peak maximum can be specified to within 10^{-4} mass units, but it may be impractical to acquire data at such a high resolution, either in terms of acquisition rate or storage requirements. The question therefore arises: can one reconstruct the position of the peak maximum from a small number of measurements in the peak region?

Exercise 5.8:

(1) In a new spreadsheet, make up a signal by, e.g., computing a Gaussian peak of which only few data points have been sampled, such as that shown in Fig. 5.8.1, where we have computed 32 data points for $x = -16$ (1) 15 with $y = 0.7$ $\exp[-0.3 (x+0.4)^2]$, and have plotted this function for $x = -16$ (0.0625) 15.

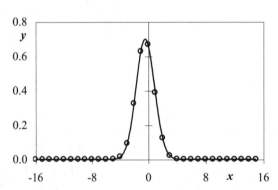

Fig. 5.8.1: The test function $y = 0.7 \exp[-0.3 (x+0.4)^2]$ plotted for just 32 points (open circles) and with 16 times smaller increments, i.e., 512 points (drawn curve).

(2) Taking the Fourier transform of the 32 data yields a transform for $f = -0.5$ (0.03125) 0.46875.

(3) Make a table with $f = -8$ (0.03125) 7.96875, i.e., 16 times as long. For the real and imaginary components enter zeros, then copy the data for $f = -0.5$ (0.03125) 0.46875 in the appropriate place in that data set. Repeat the y- value for $x = -0.5$ at $x = +0.5$.

(4) Upon inverse transformation you will obtain 16 times more data, i.e., 15 data points will have been interpolated between every two original points. Plot these together with the original data, as in Fig. 5.8.2 where we have focused on the peak region.

242

(5) Estimate the position of the maximum by fitting the points around the peak maximum to a low-order polynomial, such as a quadratic. Use the fitted parameters to calculate the sought x-value, see the inset to Fig. 5.8.2. By using least squares, say, from $t = -0.6875$ to -0.125, to fit the top ten interpolated data to a parabola $y = a_0 + a_1 x + a_2 x^2$, and then computing the maximum as $x_{max} = -a_1/(2a_2)$, we find $x = 0.3998 \pm 0.0001$ and $y_{max} = 0.69991 \pm 0.00001$, quite close to the correct values of $x_{max} = -0.4$ and $y_{max} = 0.7$.

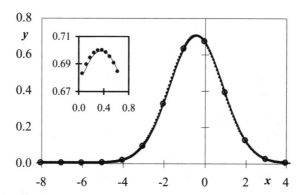

Fig. 5.8.2: The result of Fourier transform interpolation of the test function of Fig. 5.8.1 (small solid circles) in the region of the peak. Inset: the top ten points of the interpolated data with a linear least squares parabola fitted through them.

However, when the function is asymmetric, the above method can lead to systematic distortion. For the function $y = 1/\{\exp[-0.5\,(x+0.1)] + 1/\exp[4\,(x+0.1)]\}$ we find $x_{max} = -0.843 \pm 0.001$ and $y_{max} = 0.6346 \pm 0.0002$, whereas the correct values are $x_{max} = -0.5621$ and $y_{max} = 0.70551$, see Figs. 5.8.3 and 5.8.4. The interpolated function passes exactly through all data points, but doesn't fit the function. Note that, in this case, the differences in x_{max} and y_{max} far exceed their standard deviations, illustrating the danger of interpreting the standard deviation as a measure of accuracy.

What caused the above failure to obtain a closer estimate of the position of the peak maximum? The interpolation reconstructs the function in terms of the sines and cosines of the original Fourier transform, which can lead to systematic distortion. By going to a less symmetrical curve, as in the next example, the problem is exacerbated and, therefore, more readily visible.

Exercise 5.8 (continued):

(6) Replace the Gaussian test function by the asymmetrical function $y = 1/\{\exp[-0.5(x+0.1)]+\exp[4(x+0.1)]\}$, while otherwise treating the data in the same way as before. Figure 5.8.3 shows the function, and Fig. 5.8.4 its interpolation. Now the distortion is obvious, and no least-squares fitting to a parabola is needed to bring it out.

It is clear from Fig. 5.8.4 that Fourier transform interpolation, like any other interpolation, introduces distortion when the implied basis set (here: sine and cosine waves) poorly fits the interpolated shape. The paucity of data only makes the distortion worse.

Another problem with interpolation is its extreme sensitivity to noise when only few data points are available, because the interpolated curve will tend to go as closely as possible through those points, even if they contain noise.

In general, interpolation is a poor substitute for making more closely spaced measurements, and the spreadsheet is a convenient tool to visualize its consequences. If the functionality involved is known, it is preferable to fit sparse data to that function using nonlinear least squares, because this can avoid the above-illustrated systematic distortion. You can readily verify that, given the functional forms (though not the particular parameter values) of the equations used, Solver can recover the peak position and height exactly (i.e., to within its numerical precision of about $\pm 10^{-14}$) from the above, sparse but noise-free data sets. Solver is also much less sensitive to noise, because it does not try to fit all data points exactly.

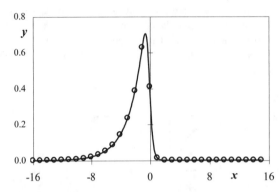

Fig. 5.8.3: The test function $y = 1/\{\exp[-0.5(x+0.1)]+\exp[4(x+0.1)]\}$ plotted for just 32 points (open circles) and with 16 times smaller increments (drawn curve).

Another problem with interpolation is its extreme sensitivity to noise when only few data points are available, because the interpolated curve will tend to go as closely as possible through those points, even if they contain noise. In general, interpolation is a poor substitute for making more closely spaced measurements, and the spreadsheet is a convenient tool to visualize its consequences. If the functionality involved is known, it is preferable to fit sparse data to that function using nonlinear least squares, because this can avoid the above-illustrated systematic distortion. You can readily verify that, given the functional forms (though not the particular parameter values) of the equations used, Solver can recover the peak position and height exactly (i.e., to within its numerical precision of about $\pm 10^{-14}$) from the above, sparse but noise-free data sets. Solver is also much less sensitive to noise, because it does not try to fit all data points exactly. However, when we don't know the correct functionality, the Fourier transform may well provide as good a guess as other convenient methods. And in some applications, where we look specifically for periodic phenomena, and where finer detail is largely illusory anyway, as in scanning tunneling microscopy, Fourier transform smoothing is clearly the preferred method.

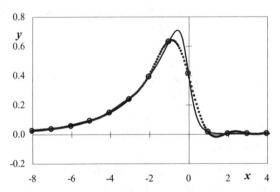

Fig. 5.8.4: The result of Fourier transform interpolation (small solid circles) of 32 samples (large open circles) of the test function $y = 1/\{\exp[-0.5(x+0.1)] +\exp[4(x+0.1)]\}$ (thin black curve) of Fig. 5.8.3 in the region of the peak.

5.9 Data compression

Least squares can be used to extract the essential data from, say, a noisy but otherwise linear calibration curve. Likewise we can use Fourier transformation to extract some essential features from an arbitrary signal. For example, a common chromatographic detector uses ultraviolet light to illuminate the effluent, and monitors the resulting fluorescence. This can give both qualitative and quantitative information on the eluted sample components. We will here focus on the qualitative aspect, i.e., on how to use

244

the spectral information to identify the chemical identity of the eluting sample, assuming that we have a computer 'library' of reference spectra that can be consulted.

A fluorescence spectrum can cover a fairly wide spectral range, but often contains only a relatively small number of identifiable features. A library search can therefore be simplified considerably by compressing the data, even if such compression leads to some distortion. Fourier transform filtering can often serve this purpose, as described, e.g., by Yim et al. in *Anal. Chem.* 49 (1977) 2069. We will illustrate the method here with spectral data available on the web from the Oregon Medical Laser Center of the Oregon Graduate Institute at http://omlc.ogi.edu/spectra/PhotochemCAD/html/index.html.

Exercise 5.9:

(1) Go to the above website, and select a compound. At the bottom of its page, below its fluorescence spectrum (assuming it has one), click on Original Data, then highlight and copy those data. Below we will use tryptophan as an example; feel free to select instead any other fluorescence spectrum, from this or any other source. Some of these fluorescence spectra exhibit less fine-structure, some have more. Obviously, the more details one can measure and compare, the more reliable the identification can be.

(2) Leave the web page, open Notepad, and paste the spectral data there; Notepad is a convenient intermediary between external data and Excel. Save the file.

(3) Open a spreadsheet, select File ⇨ Open, and in the resulting Open dialog box specify where to look for the data file, the file name, and the file type (in this case: Text Files). In the Text Import Wizard specify Delimited, and the spectral data will appear in your spreadsheet.

(4) Graph both the fluorescence intensity FI and its logarithm. The logarithmic representation will be used here as it shows more characteristic features.

(5) Since these data were not intended for use with Fourier transformation, the number of data points, 441, is not an integer power of 2. We now have two options: reducing the data set to the nearest smaller suitable number, 256, or 'padding' the data to 512, the next-higher integer power of 2. Here we illustrate how to accomplish the latter.

(6) Perusal of the graph of log(FI) vs. wavelength shows that, at long wave-lengths λ, it exhibits an essentially linear dependence on λ. We therefore extrapolate this linear relationship to $\lambda = 535.5$ nm by fitting the data from, e.g., 380 to 400 nm to a line, and then using the computed intercept and slope to calculate values for $400 < \lambda < 540$ nm. Plot these to make sure that the extrapolated data are indeed continuous with the measured ones.

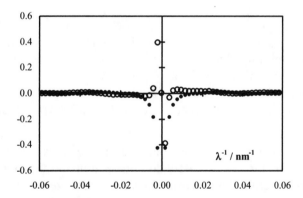

Fig. 5.9.1: The 61 low-frequency components of the Fourier transform of the tryptophan fluorescence spectrum (for excitation at 270 nm) after its extrapolation to 512 data points. The zero-frequency point is far off-scale in this plot.

(7) Fourier-transform this extended data set, and plot the result. Most of the signal will be concentrated in the few lowest frequencies, see Fig. 5.9.1.

(8) In a copy, set the higher-frequency contributions to zero, inverse transform the data, and again plot the result. By repeating this while retaining, say, the 10, 20, 30, and 40 lowest frequencies, you will get a sense of how few low-frequency data are needed to represent the over-all shape of the curve, and how many more must be kept to show the minor shoulder near 300 nm.

(9) Figure 5.9.1 shows that retaining only 30 of the 256 frequencies is sufficient to exhibit the general shape of the fluorescence peak, without noticeable loss of information. On the other hand, the main fluorescence peak can be represented with fewer than 10 (positive and negative) frequencies.

(10) The small 'hook' at the lowest wavelengths is an artifact resulting from the requirement that the Fourier-transformed signal be a repeatable unit. In this example we were lucky; had the signal levels at the two extremes of the wavelength scale been very different, the consequent change would have led to undesirable oscillations, which can only be avoided with additional effort.

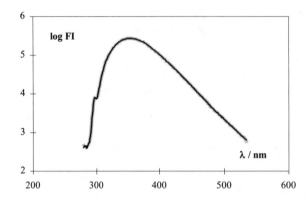

Fig. 5.9.2: The original data set extrapolated to 535.5 nm (thin black line) and its representation in terms of only 30 frequencies (broad gray band).

By Fourier transformation, a fluorescence spectrum can be represented by a relatively small number of frequency terms, thereby greatly facilitating library search routines for computer-based identification. In the present example, 61 data (the real and imaginary components at the lowest 30 frequencies plus the zero-frequency term) can be used to replace the original 441 data points. A further reduction to 31 points can be achieved through symmetry, because the data at negative frequencies can be reconstituted from those at the corresponding positive frequencies: since the input function $g(t)$ is real, $G(-f)$ must be the complex conjugate of $G(f)$.

In section 4.6 we already encountered examples of spectral fitting, and we therefore ask here how the Fourier transform and least squares methods compare. In principle, nonlinear least-squares methods are more flexible, since they are not limited to a basis set of sines and cosines. Relatively simple spectra can often be described to the same accuracy with far fewer parameters than required for Fourier transformation. But this strongly depends on the number of features to be represented: with more peaks the balance shifts in favor of the Fourier transform method, as it does with typical nuclear magnetic resonance, infrared, and mass spectra.

Then there are practical constraints: fitting by nonlinear least squares may require personal judgement, and may therefore be more difficult to automate than Fourier transformation. On the other hand, Fourier transformation may need some help if the spectrum does not tend to zero at its extremes. The choice may also depend on whether the spectral information already exists in Fourier-transformed format inside a measuring instrument. For cataloguing and data searching, the Fourier transform method may be the more convenient, because it expresses all data sets in terms of the same, limited set of fixed frequencies, which greatly facilitates their intercomparison.

5.10 Analysis of the tides

So far in this chapter we have seen that Fourier transformation can be competitive with least squares analysis in, say, differentiation and integration. Below we will give an extensive analysis of a particular data set to illustrate how we can often *combine* Fourier transformation and least squares analysis for efficient data fitting of periodic phenomena. Each method has its own strengths and weaknesses: Fourier transformation can show us many simultaneous frequency components, but has limited frequency resolution, which may lead to leakage. Least squares fitting is more flexible in what it can fit, but needs more extensive guidance. Because the two methods often *complement* each other, their combined use can make a very powerful data analysis tool.

The tides have been understood quantitatively through the work of such scientific giants as Newton, Euler, Daniel Bernoulli, Laplace, and Kelvin as due to the combined effects of lunar and solar attraction. What we experience as tides is the differential effect of the attractive forces on the solid earth and those on the more mobile surface water, modulated by the shape (size and depth profile) of the particular body of water and by the cohesive forces that produce drag to water movement, and further modified by wind, barometric pressure, and local currents (as where rivers meet oceans). We need not look here into its detailed mathematical description, but merely consider the tidal record as a signal that should have as its principal frequency components the lunar and solar periods, and take it from there. Fortunately, tidal records are readily available on the web from NOAA, and we will use one such record. You are of course welcome to select a record from another location, and/or pick a different time period. Since arbitrarily chosen data sets seldom contain precisely $2n$ data points, we will deliberately take a record that does not fit that restriction, and then select a subset of it whenever we need to use Fourier transformation.

Exercise 5.10:

(1) Go to the website co-ops.nos.noaa.gov/, and under Observations select Verified/Historical Water Level Data: U.S. and Global Coastal Stations.

(2) Select a station; in the example given below we have used 8410140 Eastport, Passamaquoddy Bay, ME, but you can of course pick another.

(3) Specify a time interval (we have used W2, hourly heights), a Begin Data (here: 20010601 for 2001, June 1) and an End Data (here: 20010831, for August 31 of that same year, yielding a 2208-hour period).

(4) Take a preview of the data in ViewPlot.

(5) Select the data with View Data, highlight them all with Edit ⇨ Select All, and copy them to the clipboard with Ctrl∪c. Minimize or close the web site.

(6) Start Word, then click Open, Look in: Windows, select Notepad.exe, and paste the file into it with Ctrl∪v. Save the file as a Notepad file using any name that suits your fancy. As you will see in the next few steps, Notepad triggers Excel to open its Text Import Wizard, which is useful to format the data properly.

(7) Open Excel, Select Open, then specify Files of type: as All Files (*.*) so that you will see the just-saved Notepad .txt file, and select it.

(8) You will now see Step 1 of the Text Import Wizard, in which you specify that the data are of Fixed width, i.e., they are tab-delimited. Preview the file to see where the file header (containing all the explanatory text) ends, and then specify the row at which to start importing the data. (In our example, that would be at row 23.) Move to the next Step.

(9) In the Data preview of Step 2 of the Text Import Wizard, enter lines to define the columns you want (in our example, at lines 8, 12, 13, 15, 16, 19, 21, 27, 32, 35, and 40. You can use fewer columns, but then you will have more cleanup to do. Click Finish.

(10) You will now have all the data in your spreadsheet, in columns, starting in cell A1. In the first column replace the station number (8410140) by a row counter: 0 in the top row, 1 in the next row, etc. Delete all peripheral columns, such as the one containing the year (2001), a slant (/), minutes (:00).

(11) You can also delete the right-most columns, except the column between 35 and 40 that had been labeled Sigma, which you may want to save for the end of the exercise. Regardless of whether or not you save this column, first place the instruction =STDEV(F3:F2210) (or whatever appropriate range) at its top to compute the standard deviation of the fit

between the observations and the predicted data. In our example it is only 0.006 m, or 6 mm, out of an average tidal swing of several meters!

(12) Insert two rows at the top, and use the higher one of these to enter the labels time, month, data, hour, and height (after having made sure that these labels are indeed appropriate). Also label the next two columns Hcalc and residuals. These labels and data will occupy columns A through G.

(13) Plot the water heights versus time t, in hours.

Figure 5.10.1 illustrates the 2208 data points so imported, as a function of time. It clearly shows a periodic oscillation, with a somewhat variable amplitude that is slightly more pronounced and alternating at its tops than at its bottom values.

For Fourier analysis we take the last 2048 data points, thereby leaving some space near the top of the spreadsheet. After their Fourier transformation we calculate and plot the magnitude of the response as a function of frequency.

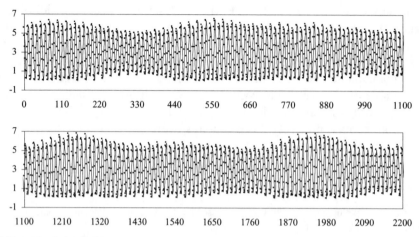

Fig. 5.10.1: The height of the water (as measured in meters vs. the 'average lowest low water level') at Eastport, ME, as a function of time (in hours) during the period from June 1 through Aug. 3, 2001.

Exercise 5.10 (continued):

(14) In row 163 (or wherever you find $t = 160$) copy the water level in, say, column J, and in column I enter the shifted time $t - 160$. Copy both down to the end of the data file. You should now have 2048 data in columns I and J. Highlight these, extend the highlighted area to include column K, and call the forward Fourier transform macro.

(15) In column O calculate the square root of the sum of the squares of the real and imaginary components so obtained, and plot these versus the frequency (in column L).

The result is illustrated in Fig. 5.10.2 at three different vertical scales. The top panel shows a large contribution, of value 2.991, at zero frequency. This component merely reflects the average value of the signal, which is measured versus a 'average lowest low level' in order to make most data values positive quantities. Indeed, by using the function =AVERAGE(*range*) to calculate the average we likewise obtain 2.991.

The largest peak at a non-zero frequency is found at $f = 0.0806$ h^{-1}, a value that roughly corresponds with half a moon day of 24 h 50 min 28.32 s or $1/12.4206$ h^{-1} = 0.0805114 h^{-1}. This peak has a rather wide base, suggesting that it may be broadened by multiple components and/or leakage. In addition, there are two series of minor peaks, one at integer multiples of 0.08 h^{-1}, i.e., at 0.16, 0.32, 0.40 and 0.48 h^{-1}, the other at half-integer multiples of the same value, at 0.04, 0.12, 0.20, 0.28, 0.36, and 0.44 h^{-1}. Neither series has quite died out at $f = 0.5$, and one can therefore assume that there will be higher-order terms as well, which can only be observed using longer data records.

We can either fit these data on a purely empirical basis, or try to identify signals with known astronomical time constants, as we did in the above paragraph. The latter approach, which introduces independently obtainable information into the data analysis, is usually the more powerful, and will be pursued here. We therefore fit the data to an adjustable constant a_0 plus a sine wave of adjustable amplitude a_1 and phase shift p_1 but with a fixed frequency f_1 of 0.0805114 h^{-1}, i.e., to $h = a_0 + a_1 \sin(2\pi f_1 t + p_1)$ where t is

248

time in hours, starting with 0 at the first data point. We then calculate the residuals, and Fourier-transform them in order to find the next-largest term(s), etc.

Exercise 5.10 (continued):

(16) Arrange labels and values for the adjustable parameters a_0, a_1, and p_1, in one column, and in another (leaving at least one space in-between) the fixed parameter f_1. Specify a_0, a_1, and p_1 as zero, and f_1 as 0.0805114.

(17) In column F compute the water height h_{calc} using the assumed parameters a_0, a_1, and p_1, and in column G calculate the difference between the measured and calculated water heights.

(18) Also deposit a label and cell for the computation of SSR as =SUMXMY2 (E3:E2210,F3:F2210) or for whatever the appropriate ranges are.

(19) Call Solver to minimize SSR by changing the values of a_0, a_1, and p_1.

(20) In cell R163 repeat the count of $t - 160$ that you already used in cell I163, and in cell S163 copy the residual from G163. Copy these down to row 2210. Highlight R163:T2210, apply the forward Fourier transformation, in row X calculate the corresponding magnitude (i.e., the square root of the sum of squares of the real and imaginary components) of the Fourier transform, and plot these.

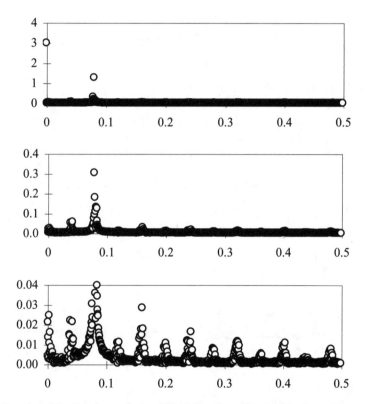

Fig. 5.10.2: Results of the Fourier analysis of 2048 data from Fig. 5.10.1, shown here as the magnitudes of the resulting frequency components, at three different vertical scales, in m. The horizontal scale shows the frequency, in h^{-1}. For a more compact representation of these data see Fig. 1.3.6.

The next most important term, clearly visible in Fig. 5.10.3, is at 0.079 h^{-1}, and is due to the ellipticity of the lunar orbit, which has a period of 27.55 days. As the moon travels from its perigee (at the shortest moon-earth distance) to its apogee (farthest away) and back, the gravitational attraction changes, and in our linear analysis this translates as a difference frequency. Indeed, the corresponding first-order correction term has a frequency of $0.0805114 - 1 / (24 \times 27.55) = 0.0805114 - 0.0015124 = 0.078999 \, h^{-1}$.

(21) Extend the parameter lists to accommodate a_2, and p_2 as well as $f_2 = 0.078999$, and add a corresponding, second sine wave to the instructions in column F. In order to facilitate later use of SolverAid, place all adjustable coefficients (i.e., the amplitudes and phase shifts) in a single, contiguous column, one below the other.

(22) Rerun Solver, now simultaneously adjusting the five coefficients a_0, a_1, p_1, a_2, and p_2.

(23) Rerun the Fourier transform of the residuals, and look at the updated plot of these residuals.

(24) The next-highest peak in the residual plot is at 0.083 h^{-1}, close to the frequency of $2/24 = 0.083333$ h^{-1} associated with half the solar day.

(25) After you include this frequency and repeat the protocol sketched in points (18) through (20) you will find that there is yet another frequency near 0.08 h^{-1}, viz. at about 0.082 h^{-1}, which can be identified with the *sum* frequency $0.0805114 + 1 / (24 \times 27.55) = 0.0805114 + 0.0015124 = 0.082024$ h^{-1}.

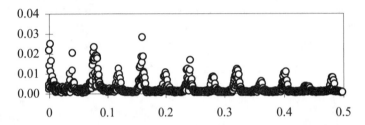

Fig. 5.10.3: The magnitudes of the residual frequency components, after accounting for the average and the leading sinusoidal component at $f_1 = 0.0805114$ h^{-1}.

(26) Also incorporate this frequency, call Solver to adjust the nine resulting coefficients a_0 through a_4 and p_1 through p_4, Fourier-transform the residuals, and plot them.

(27) Extend the parameter lists to accommodate four new frequencies, amplitudes, and phase angles, and include them in the instruction for the calculated heights in column F.

(28) Set the frequencies at $f_1/2$, $f_2/2$, $f_3/2$, and $f_4/2$, and subsequently let Solver adjust the amplitudes a_0 through a_8 and p_1 through p_8.

(29) After you have done this, run SolverAid (which requires that a_0 through a_8 and p_1 through p_8 form one contiguous column) to calculate the standard deviations of the coefficients.

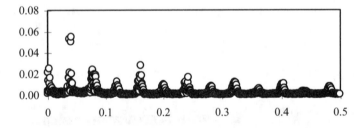

Fig. 5.10.4: The magnitudes of the residual frequency components, after accounting for the average and four sinusoidal component near 0.08 h^{-1}.

The resulting Fig. 5.10.4 shows that we finally have accounted for the *four* major frequency components near 0.08 h^{-1}. Even though the Fourier analysis showed only one peak around 0.08 h^{-1}, we used astronomical information to resolve this into four different signals, exploiting least squares analysis to find their amplitudes and phase angles. The *combination* of different methods is often more powerful than each method by itself.

The next-largest contributions are around 0.04 h^{-1}. We therefore extend the analysis with four more frequencies, each one-half of the corresponding values near 0.08 h^{-1}, and subsequently use Solver to adjust the coefficients, which now number 17. As can be seen in Fig. 5.10.5, with the four frequencies we have found so far we can indeed represent the general envelope of the tidal curve, but not its alternating amplitudes or other details.

Table 10.5.1 lists the results so obtained for the (absolute values of the) various amplitudes; the phase angles are needed for the analysis but have no physical meaning because they are tied to the particular starting time chosen. We see that we can represent most of the signal in terms of predictable periodic functions, so that tide tables can indeed anticipate the tides. Such tables are, of course, based on much longer data sets (so as to include the length of the moon's *node*, a period of about 18.6 years) and on using more frequencies.

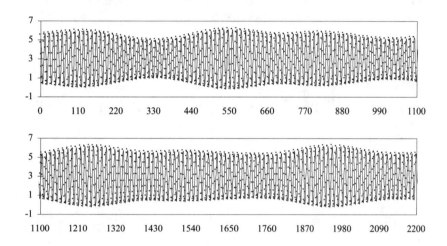

Fig. 5.10.5: The tides recalculated using the four principal frequency components near 0.08 h^{-1}. Comparison with Fig. 5.10.1 shows that this indeed represents the dominant longer-term features of the experimental data.

frequency	amplitude	frequency	amplitude
0	2.993 ± 0.004	standard deviation of the fit: 0.19	
0.03950	0.023 ± 0.006	0.078999	0.568 ± 0.006
0.040256	0.034 ± 0.006	0.080511	2.620 ± 0.006
0.041012	0.006 ± 0.006	0.082024	0.215 ± 0.006
0.041667	0.158 ± 0.006	0.083333	0.286 ± 0.006

Table 5.10.1: The amplitudes found, with their standard deviations as provided by SolverAid, for the nine frequencies considered so far.

We see that only one of the four half-frequency components is important, and that (using three times the standard deviation as our criterion) one of them is not even statistically significant. However, the Fourier transform shows that not all frequency components around 0.04 h^{-1} have been accounted for, since there is a remaining signal at about 0.0386 h^{-1}, which we can tentatively associate with the difference frequency 0.0805114 / 2 − 0.0015128 = 0.038743 h^{-1}. Indeed, if we replace the non-significant frequency 0.041012 by 0.038743, run Solver again, and then Fourier-transform the residuals, we find that that all remaining components have amplitudes smaller than 0.03 m, see Fig. 5.10.6.

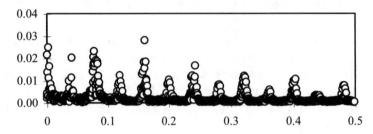

Fig. 5.10.6: The magnitudes of the residual frequency components, after accounting for the average and eight sinusoidal components near 0.08 and 0.04 h^{-1}.

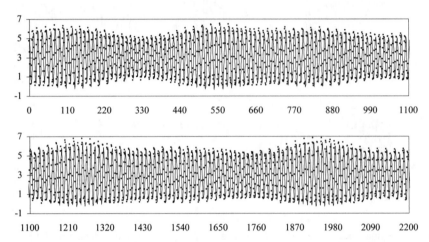

Fig. 5.10.7: The original data (solid points) and the fitted curve (drawn line) based on the average and eight sinusoidal components near 0.08 and 0.04 h^{-1}.

frequency	amplitude	frequency	amplitude
0	2.994 ± 0.004	standard deviation of the fit: 0.17	
0.03950	0.007 ± 0.005	0.078999	0.568 ± 0.005
0.040256	0.020 ± 0.005	0.080511	2.620 ± 0.005
0.038743	0.114 ± 0.005	0.082024	0.216 ± 0.005
0.041667	0.156 ± 0.005	0.083333	0.286 ± 0.005

Table 5.10.2: The same results after one frequency near 0.04 h^{-1} has been redefined.

By comparing the data in Tables 5.10.1 and 5.10.2 we see that changing one frequency can alter the amplitudes of the neighboring frequencies, and we therefore look into the mutual dependence of these results. SolverAid can provide the corresponding array of linear correlation coefficients, in this case an array of 17 by 17 = 289 numbers. Below we show how we can quickly screen them for significant correlations.

Exercise 5.10 (continued):

(30) Run SolverAid (again) and let it provide the matrix of linear correlation coefficients. Say that you have placed it in AA1:AQ17. Deposit in cell AS1 the instruction =IF(ABS(AA1)>0.9,ABS(AA1)," "), and copy this instruction to the entire block AS1:BI17. Any linear correlation coefficient with an absolute value larger than 0.9 will show, whereas all other cells will remain empty because they will contain the 'empty' string between the two quotation marks in the IF statement. You can of course set the bar lower, at 0.8 or wherever, since in this particular case none of the 17 adjusted parameters has a very pronounced dependence on any other. In fact, the largest linear correlation coefficients (apart from the 1's on the main diagonal) are smaller than 0.2!

252

(31) To get an idea of how well you can represent the observed tidal data with just eight frequencies, plot the original and calculated curves in one graph, using different symbols and/or colors, as in Fig. 5.10.7. If you want to see how far you still would have to go, plot the residuals, as in Fig. 5.10.8. And if you want to see what is possible by harmonic analysis (using a longer database and many more harmonic terms), plot the data in the 'Sigma' column you may have set aside under point (11). This plot is shown in Fig. 5.10.9, and indicates that there is very little 'noise' on this signal. Such 'noise' may still be deterministic, when caused by, e.g., effects of earthquakes or storms, but could only be recognized as such in retrospect, by comparison with geological and meteorological records, and certainly would not be predictable.

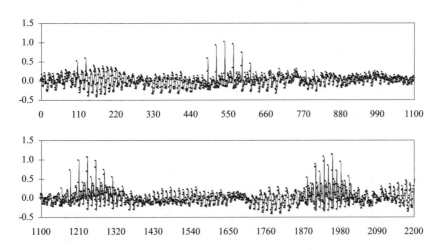

Fig. 5.10.8: The residuals after accounting for the average and eight sinusoidal components near 0.08 and 0.04 h^{-1}.

It is clear that we can continue this process and, by including more and more frequencies, make the fit better and better. This is indeed how tidal tables are made. Remember that the standard deviation between the observed and the predicted heights listed in the NOS-NOAA table was a mere 6 mm, see under step (11) in the exercise. The corresponding value for our fit so far is 174 mm, more than 30 times larger. Still, you get the idea; in this case, with a large signal and apparently relatively little 'noise' from earthquakes, storms etc., the prediction can be extremely reliable, and the more so the longer the experimental record on which it is based.

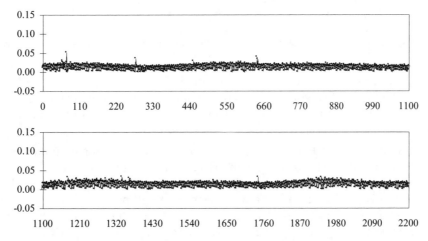

Fig. 5.10.9: The residuals in the NOS/NOAA harmonic analysis of the same data set. Note the ten times enlarged vertical scale.

5.11 Additional software

So far we have exclusively used macros in this chapter, but XN contains an equivalent set of functions, called FFT and FFT_INV, which have the advantage of automatically self-updating. Their use is illustrated in Fig. 5.11.1. (Don't use the box you get by clicking on f_x and selecting FFT, but enter the instruction directly as an array instruction with Ctrl∪Shift∪Enter.) More interesting are the functions DFT and DFT_INV, which use the discrete (rather than fast) Fourier transformation, and are based directly on (5.1.3) and its counterpart. With discrete Fourier transformation, the number N of data points need not be an integer power of 2, but the function is still assumed to be periodic. The algorithm is slower, but you will not notice a speed difference for a small data set, such as that in Fig. 5.11.2.

	A	B	C	D	E	F	G	H	I	J
1										
2		*FFT of 16-point sine and cosine:*								
3		*time*	*Re*	*Im*		*Re*	*Im*		*Re*	*Im*
4										
5		0	3	0		0	0		3	0
6		1	3.771639	0		1.5	0		3.771639	0
7		2	2.12132	0		0	0		2.12132	0
8		3	0.14805	0		0	0		0.14805	0
9		4	-6.13E-17	0		0	-0.5		0	0
10		5	-0.14805	0		0	0		-0.14805	0
11		6	-2.12132	0		0	0		-2.12132	0
12		7	-3.771639	0		0	0		-3.771639	0
13		8	-3	0		0	0		-3	0
14		9	-1.771639	0		0	0		-1.771639	0
15		10	-2.12132	0		0	0		-2.12132	0
16		11	-2.14805	0		0	0		-2.14805	0
17		12	-1.29E-15	0		0	0.5		0	0
18		13	2.14805	0		0	0		2.14805	0
19		14	2.12132	0		0	0		2.12132	0
20		15	1.771639	0		1.5	0		1.771639	0

cell:	instruction:	copied to:
C5=	SIN(2*PI()*B5/4)+3*COS(2*PI()*B5/16)	C6:C20
F5:G20 =	FFT(C5:D20)	
I5:J20 =	FFT_INV(F5:G20)	

Fig. 5.11.1: The fast Fourier transform of a 16-point sine wave with the XN function FFT.

When you are interested in the magnitude and phase angle of the transform rather than its real and imaginary components, you can of course compute the former from the latter, but it will be faster to use the functions DFSP and DSSP_INV. These can display the amplitude (the default) or the power spectrum in db, i.e., 20 log(amplitude), and the angle can be shown in radians ($1/(2\pi)$ of a full circle, the default), grads ($1/400^{th}$ of a circle), or degrees ($1/360^{th}$ of a circle). Try them.

There are many applications of Fourier transformation to two-dimensional digital objects, e.g., for filtering STM results or satellite pictures. For such applications, use the XN.xla(m) functions FFT2D and FFT2D_INV for two-dimensional fast Fourier transformation, as illustrated in Fig. 5.11.3 for Gaussian noise as its real input in B2:I5. XN also contains a macro that will perform one- or two-dimensional discrete Fourier transformation unless the data set contains 2^n data (n integer), in which case it will automatically switch to the corresponding fast Fourier transformation algorithm. To activate this macro, click on the XN icon, a purple book with a question mark on its cover, to install the XN Toolbar, which displays three items: Macros, X-Edit, and Help. Click on Macros, select Fourier Analysis, then 2DFT. And don't forget to browse the other Macro options, under the self-explanatory names Matrix,Vector..., Integral, Numbers, Polynomials, Function min/max, Regression, and ODE.

254

	A	B	C	D	E	F	G	H	I	J
1										
2		*DFT of 15-point sine:*								
3		*time*	*Re*	*Im*		*Re*	*Im*		*Re*	*Im*
4										
5		0	3	0		0	0		3	0
6		1	3.735158	0		**1.5**	0		3.735158	0
7		2	1.79948	0		0	0		1.79948	0
8		3	-0.024006	0		0	0		-0.024006	0
9		4	0.093151	0		0	**-0.5**		0.093151	0
10		5	-0.633975	0		0	0		-0.633975	0
11		6	-3.014836	0		0	0		-3.014836	0
12		7	-3.677588	0		0	0		-3.677588	0
13		8	-2.191298	0		0	0		-2.191298	0
14		9	-1.839266	0		0	0		-1.839266	0
15		10	-2.366025	0		0	0		-2.366025	0
16		11	-0.720322	0		0	**0.5**		-0.720322	0
17		12	1.878107	0		0	0		1.878107	0
18		13	2.215304	0		0	0		2.215304	0
19		14	1.746114	0		**1.5**	0		1.746114	0

cell: instruction:　　　　　　　　　　　　　　　　　*copied to:*
C5= SIN(2*PI()*B5/3.75)+3*COS(2*PI()*B5/1. C6:C19
F5:G19 = DFT(C5:D19)
I5:J19 = DFT_INV(F5:G19)

Fig. 5.11.2: The discrete Fourier transform application of a 15-point sine wave with the XN function DFT.

	A	B	C	D	E	F	G	H	I
1									
2		-0.061505	0.4845299	0.2553861	0.0834416	-0.650646	-0.352113	-0.897605	1.2661758
3		1.673748	0.0260502	-0.667949	0.0556042	0.0327088	0.7627182	1.0548092	0.7586323
4		0.733471	-0.332807	0.7622066	0.2039349	0.2864954	-1.15479	-0.106957	-0.558066
5		0.008606	0.3378238	0.6134678	-1.516478	-0.17302	1.6968534	0.8821462	0.1659578
6									
7		0.177276	0.1416877	-0.001426	0.0369862	0.0568092	0.0369862	-0.001426	0.1416877
8		0.009193	0.0577851	0.0930006	-0.119689	-0.198542	0.0419802	-0.120166	0.037694
9		-0.179704	0.0149652	0.0198505	-0.064124	-0.014275	-0.064124	0.0198505	0.0149652
10		0.009193	0.037694	-0.120166	0.0419802	-0.198542	-0.119689	0.0930006	0.0577851
11		0	0.0707068	-0.031533	0.0726267	0	-0.072627	0.0315332	-0.070707
12		-0.05253	-0.003938	-0.090497	-0.001978	0.0048978	-0.105015	-0.09573	-0.071496
13		0	-0.251799	0.1784499	-0.00095	0	0.0009497	-0.17845	0.2517992
14		0.05253	0.0714964	0.09573	0.105015	-0.004898	0.0019777	0.0904965	0.0039376
15									
16		-0.061505	0.4845299	0.2553861	0.0834416	-0.650646	-0.352113	-0.897605	1.2661758
17		1.673748	0.0260502	-0.667949	0.0556042	0.0327088	0.7627182	1.0548092	0.7586323
18		0.733471	-0.332807	0.7622066	0.2039349	0.2864954	-1.15479	-0.106957	-0.558066
19		0.008606	0.3378238	0.6134678	-1.516478	-0.17302	1.6968534	0.8821462	0.1659578
20		0	0	0	0	0	0	0	0
21		0	0	0	0	0	0	0	0
22		0	0	0	0	0	0	0	0
23		0	0	0	0	0	0	0	0

cell: instruction:　　　　　　　　　　　　　　　　　*copied to:*
B2:I5 = filled with random Gaussian noise
B7:I14 = FFT2D(B2:I5)
B16:I23 = FFT2D_INV(B7:I14)

Fig. 5.11.3: An example of the application of the XN function FFT2D to Gaussian noise.

5.12 Summary

For determining the frequency content of a repetitive signal, or a circuit, Fourier transformation is often the method of choice. It can also be used to manipulate data, as in filtering, differentiation, and interpolation. In all those areas, it tends to compete with least squares analysis. With Wiener filtering, the transform method can be combined with least squares curve fitting to get an optimal least-squares filter. As illustrated in the example of tidal analysis, the combined use of Fourier transformation and least squares methods can exploit the best features of both approaches, especially when supplemented by other (in this case: astronomical) information.

Because Fourier transformation uses trigonometric functions as its basis set rather than the polynomials at the heart of least squares analysis, equivalent operations of the two approaches on the same data will yield somewhat different results. As in instrumentation, the advantages of Fourier transformation are most pronounced with large, information-rich data sets. Fourier transformation of a data set and rejection of its high-frequency components can yield a compact set of descriptors of the main (low-frequency) components of that signal, which can then be used for cataloguing and searching.

A minor nuisance in using Fourier transforms is the confusion between different conventions used in the literature: which transform to call forward, and what to use as normalizing factor. Here we have used the mathematical/physical sign convention, and we have shifted the burden of the normalization factor $1/(2\pi)$ entirely on the inverse transform in order to have a simple relation between the amplitude of a sine or cosine wave and that of its Fourier transform. This makes the frequency f (in Hz or cps) rather than the angular frequency $\omega = 2\pi f$ (in rad s^{-1}) the primary frequency parameter. This convention was advocated, among others, by R. B. Blackman & J. W. Tukey in *The Measurement of Power Spectra*, Dover (1958), and by R. N. Bracewell in *The Fourier Transform and Its Applications*, McGraw-Hill (1965), because it makes Fourier and Laplace transforms compatible (i.e., we use the negative exponent for the forward transform). Alternative arguments can be advanced for a more equitable distribution of the normalization factors $\sqrt{(1/2\pi)}$, which do for a square wave what the definition used here does for a sine and cosine. There is also the factor $1/N$, which is here bundled with the inverse transform but can also be shared more equitably by both forward and inverse transforms.

Ultimately, some consensus will be reached, just as it will be for keeping either right or left in traffic, a similar problem that has no inherently good or bad solution but would benefit from a globally accepted choice. But forging such a consensus may take a longer time than we have available, and occasionally there may still be relapses, as when log is used in VBA where ln, the natural logarithm, is meant, see section 1.14. But then, this is the price we pay for using the same concepts in different disciplines, with different purposes and different traditions. (As an analytical chemist I have often marveled at how my own professional tribe has been able to stick with liters, a volume measure that fits neither the cm-g-s nor the m-kg-s system. It has even managed to get the symbol changed to a capital L, presumably in honor of a mythical Dr. Liter (first name Milli?), even though its real etymological root, the Greek litra, denoted a rather ordinary *weight*, as did its Latin relative, libra, which spawned both the weight unit lbs and the monetary unit £. Go figure!)

This short chapter is a mere teaser as far as Fourier transformation is concerned; for more complete coverage the reader should consult entire books devoted to this single topic. We have not even mentioned here the possibility of performing frequency analysis without imaginary terms, as demonstrated by Hartley in 1942, or the existence of the Hadamard transform, the digital equivalent to Fourier transformation. In short, this chapter should be considered as an appetizer rather than a main dish. Its primary purpose is, of course, to illustrate that the spreadsheet can be a useful aid in teaching, visualizing, and applying Fourier transformation.

Fourier transformation can be used to predict the distortion (convolution) of experimental information by a measuring instrument, or by a complicating physical phenomenon. Conversely, it can contribute to the correction of such distortion (deconvolution). It can also be applied to analyze the frequency components of time-dependent phenomena. The next chapter will describe several such applications, and show how Excel can be used in those contexts.

5.13 For further reading

An excellent introduction to the discrete Fourier transform is E. O. Brigham's book on *The Fast Fourier Transform*, Prentice Hall (1974, 1997). A classic reference for the (closely related) continuous Fourier transformation is R. N. Bracewell, *The Fourier Transform and Its Applications*, McGraw-Hill (1978). For the Hartley transform the reader is referred to Hartley's paper in *Proc. IRE* 30 (1942) 144, or to Bracewell's book *The Hartley Transform*, Oxford Univ. Press (1986).

Chapter *6*

Convolution, deconvolution, and time-frequency analysis

In this chapter we will consider time-dependent signals. In principle these are different from stationary data sets, such as spectra, because *evolving* time has an inherent directionality, at least until the entire signal has been recorded, at which time it becomes just another set of numbers. We will see the consequences of this in convolution and its undo operation, deconvolution. These techniques will be discussed first as independent methods. Subsequently we will illustrate how they can sometimes be performed more efficiently with the help of Fourier transformation. Finally, we will examine time-frequency analysis or Gabor transformation, a direct application of Fourier transformation.

6.1 Time-dependent filtering

We first consider the well-known example of a so-called *RC*-filter, the combination of a series resistor and capacitor that has a characteristic rate constant $k = 1/RC$, where R is the resistance of the resistor, typically in Ω (the symbol for Ohms), and C is the capacitance of the capacitor, in F (for Farads). When we pass a step-wise signal change through such a filter, it will respond by exponentially approaching the new steady state. A characteristic property of such a filter is its memory, through the charge stored in its capacitor, which only slowly leaks out through its resistor. Below we will illustrate how we can use a spreadsheet to simulate the behavior of such a filter and, eventually, of much more complicated filters and other signal distortions.

Exercise 6.1:

(1) Start a new spreadsheet, leaving the top 12 rows for graphs, and with column headings for time, input, filter, and output in, say, A15:D15.

(2) Start time at negative values, say at $t = -20$ in cell A17, then extend the column down to as far in the positive domain as desired, say, to $t = 100$ with increments Δt of 1.

(3) Place a signal in the signal column, e.g., a unit step starting at $t = 30$ and returning to zero at $t = 65$. Don't worry about such a bland signal: you can soon make it as fancy as your heart desires.

(4) Place a time constant k somewhere at the top of the spreadsheet, say in cell B13, with its label in A13. A value for k between about 0.2 and 0.5 is convenient for the scale and unit step-size used here: if k is too large, there are only a few points that significantly differ from 0; if k is too small, the exponential hardly approaches 0 at $t = -20$.

(5) In the filter column, for non-positive values of time t only (i.e., in C17:C37), calculate the exponential e^{kt}.

(6) Place the label norm= in cell C13, and the instruction =SUM(C17: C37) in cell D13.

(7) In cell D37 place the instruction =(B37*\$C\$37+B36*\$C\$36+ ... +B18*\$C\$18+B17*\$C\$17)/\$D\$13, where the dots indicate 17 terms of similar form. Copy this instruction down to row 137.

(8) Make another column in which you compute the functions $1-e^{-k(t-\tau_1)}$ and $e^{-k(t-\tau_2)}$, where τ_1 and τ_2 are the times at which the signal jumps from 0 to 1 and from 1 to 0 respectively. In other words, in cell E66 deposit the instruction =1-EXP(-\$B\$13*(A66-\$A\$66)) and copy this down to cell E101, where you replace it with =EXP(-\$B\$13*(A101-\$A\$101)), and copy that down to row 137.

(9) Plot both the signal (in column B), its filtered form (in column D), and its calculated form (in column E) as a function of time (in column A), and compare with Fig. 6.1.1. The thin vertical lines shown there were drawn separately, and with Smoothed line turned off, in order to avoid the trapezoidal look you get by just connecting successive points, or the rounded corners and overshoot from using interpolating cubic splines.

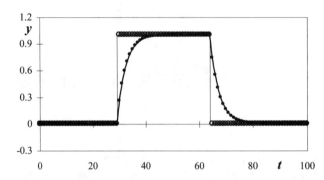

Fig. 6.1.1: The test function (open circles and, idealized, the thin line) and the same after filtering with a single time constant $k = 0.3$ (solid circles). The heavy line shows $1-e^{-k(t-\tau_1)}$ and $e^{-k(t-\tau_2)}$, where τ_1 and τ_2 are the times at which the signal jumps from 0 to 1 and from 1 to 0 respectively.

(10) Either copy A13:D137 to, say, G13 for a new signal, or just modify the signal in column B. Now you can give your imagination free reign; an example of such a signal and its filtered response is illustrated in Fig. 6.1.2.

(11) Figure 6.1.3 illustrates the response of such a filter to a sinusoidal signal. You will recognize the reduced amplitude as well as the phase shift of the filtered output, the short initial transient before a steady-state ac response is reached, and the transient when the signal is terminated abruptly. Play with it.

(12) Also try a test function with added Gaussian noise, as in Fig. 6.1.4. The filter greatly reduces the noise but also distorts the signal, the usual trade-off.

(13) Save the spreadsheet for subsequent use.

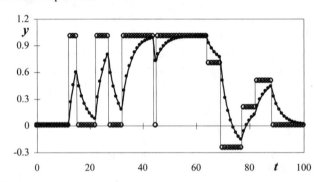

Fig. 6.1.2: A fantasy test function (open circles connected by a thin line) and the same after filtering with the same time constant $k = 0.3$ (solid circles connected by a heavier line).

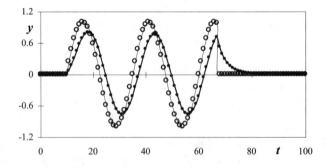

Fig. 6.1.3: A test function with a sinusoid (open circles connected by a thin line) and the same after filtering with the same time constant $k = 0.3$ (solid circles connected by a heavier line).

260

This simple spreadsheet program indeed mimics the effect of an RC filter. Regardless of the input signal to which it is applied, the RC filter is characterized by its rate constant $k = 1/RC$ or characteristic time constant RC. Its exponential response to a sudden input change of unit amplitude is called its *transfer function*. An interesting aspect of this simulation is that the filter function as it were looks backwards. The instruction under point (7) of exercise 6.1 multiplies the most recently observed signal value by $C$37 (which in this example has the value 1), the previously measured signal value by $C$36 (here 0.74), the point measured before that by $C$35 (only 0.55), and so on. In this manner the filter incorporates the past, but with factors that decrease as the information gets older, i.e., the past is included, but gradually forgotten. The smaller is k, the shorter is the memory, the faster the filter will respond to changes in the input signals, but (as trade-off) the less effective it will be in rejecting noise.

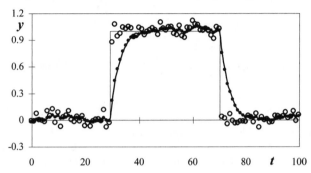

Fig. 6.1.4: A test function (thin line) with added noise (open circles), and the same after filtering with the same time constant $k = 0.3$ (solid circles connected by a heavier line).

This is no accident: an RC filter has a (short) memory, i.e., it stores the applied voltage as a charge, which then slowly leaks out. The asymmetry comes from the directionality (the 'arrow') of time: the past is knowable, whereas the future is not. Just ask your stockbroker: it is easy enough to spot, retrospectively, when the Dow Jones closing index last went through a maximum, but it is another matter entirely to predict correctly when next time it will crest. The filter therefore acts *asymmetrically*, in contrast to, e.g., the least squares smoothing method we encountered in section 3.14.

You can convolve the convolved data, and thereby achieve multiple filtering, just as you would with two successive, independent RC filters, as illustrated in Fig. 6.1.5, although it is usually more efficient to achieve the same in one single operation, by using a higher-order convolving filter.

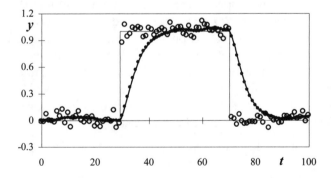

Fig. 6.1.5: The same test function (thin line) with added noise (open circles), filtered by convolution (see Fig. 6.1.4), and filtering that output again by convolution, in both cases with the same time constant $k = 0.3$ (solid circles connected by a heavier line).

If you want to use this method for symmetrical filtering, take the output of the filter (after it has been recorded in its entirety), copy it together with the associated time sequence using Edit ⇨ Paste Special ⇨

<u>V</u>alues, invert it with Sort Descending, and run it again through the convolution protocol. This will indeed yield a symmetrically filtered result, with twice the filtering action, see Fig. 6.1.6. Obviously, you can do this only *after* the output has been completed, at which point it has become a fixed sequence of numbers rather than a signal evolving in time.

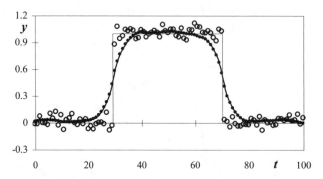

Fig. 6.1.6: The same test function (thin line) with added noise (open circles), after filtering, signal inversion, and filtering again with the same time constant $k = 0.3$ (solid circles connected by a heavier line). Signal inversion is possible only *after* the entire output of the first filter has been observed.

6.2 Convolution of large data sets

The above-described time-dependent filtering, in which we multiply a function term by term by the time-reverse of another function, is called convolution. When the data sets become large, the instructions required for direct spreadsheet convolution can become impractically large: just imagine typing in 100, 1000, or 10000 product terms. By now you will not be surprised that we can deal with this complication with a custom macro. The macro Convolve simply automates what we have done manually in section 6.1. A corresponding custom function is given in section 6.7.

Convolution is not only used for filters, but is also a very useful concept in describing how, e.g., an instrument can distort a phenomenon under observation. It is a mixed pleasure to listen to a superb musical performance on a tinny radio, because only distorted music reaches our ears, from which it may be difficult to reconstruct the original sound. When we use low-resolution equipment to observe a spectral feature, the output will reflect the original spectrum as well as the distorting effect of the instrument used. With a low-power microscope, we cannot expect to see fine details in the sample; those details exist, but they are lost to us in the limited resolution or chromatic aberration of our tool. In all the above examples we obtain a filtered, distorted signal; we get the image as if looking into a laughing mirror, as the Hubble telescope actually did before it got its eyeglasses. Convolution describes mathematically how the effect of the measurement instrument distorts the input signal to produce the observed output. When we use a filter we distort intentionally, typically in order to reduce noise, whereas in a measurement instrument we usually do not mean to distort, but the effect is nonetheless the same.

The macro Convolve operates exactly as exercise 6.1, i.e., it approximates the continuous integral

$$x(t) \otimes y(t) = \int_{-\infty}^{+\infty} x(\tau)\ y(t-\tau)\ d\tau \tag{6.2.1}$$

by its discrete equivalent

$$x(t) \otimes y(t) = \frac{1}{N} \sum_{\tau=1}^{N} x(\tau)\ y(t-\tau) \tag{6.2.2}$$

where x and y are both functions of t, while τ is a 'dummy' variable that does not figure in the final result. Convolution is a sufficiently common operation that it is denoted here by a special symbol, $\otimes$. (The asterisk * is often used for that purpose, but we will not do so here because * is easily confused with the multiplication symbol in computer code, including that of Excel and VBA.) The order of convolution makes no difference, i.e., convolution is commutative:

$$x(t) \otimes y(t) = y(t) \otimes x(t) \tag{6.2.3}$$

The macro requires three adjacent input columns, one each for time t, for $x(t)$, and for $y(t)$, and then produces the convolution $x(t) \otimes y(t)$ in the fourth column. The macro includes the inversion of $y(t)$ necessary to compute $y(\tau{-}t)$, so that both $x(t)$ and $y(t)$ should be listed as starting at $t = 0$ or 1, or at whatever starting number we want to assign. In fact, the macro does not use the time column, which is included here only for the sake of consistency with another macro, ConvolveFT, which we will encounter in section 6.4. If there are no time values, or even if that space is used for some other purpose, highlight it anyway; data or formulas in the first column will neither be used nor erased. The only requirements are that the time increments in the two data sets $x(t)$ and $y(t)$ are constant, and that the two signals $x(t)$ and $y(t)$ are defined at the same values of t.

Our first example will use the data already encountered in exercises 6.1.1 through 6.1.4.

Exercise 6.2.1:
(1) In a new spreadsheet, reserve the top 12 rows for graphs, and place column headings for time, input, filter, and output in, say, A15:D15.
(2) In cells A17:A216 deposit $t = 1$ (1) 200.
(3) In B17:B216 enter a simple test function such as used in exercise 6.1.1.
(4) In cell A13 write the label k=, and in cell B13 place a numerical value.
(5) In cell C17 place the instruction =exp(-$B$13*A17), and copy this instruction down to row 216.
(6) Highlight the area A17:C216, call Convolve, and plot your results.
(7) Plot the input signal B17:B216 and its convolution D17:D216 vs. A17:A216.

Figure 6.2.1 clearly shows the trade-off involved in filtering. We reduce the effects of high-frequency noise, but at the expense of a sluggish response to signal changes, because the filter also reduces the high-frequency components in the signal that describe its sudden jump. The distinction between 'signal' and 'noise' is usually a subjective one.

Exercise 6.2.1 (continued):
(8) Replace the input signal by a more fanciful one, perhaps resembling that in Fig. 6.1.2 or 6.1.3, highlight A17:C216, set the noise amplitude to zero, and call Convolve. You may have to reduce the filter time constant k in order to preserve some semblance of fidelity.
(9) Reset the noise amplitude, and again call the macro. Save the spreadsheet. Fig. 6.2.2 illustrates what you may obtain.

Again the trade-off is obvious: if k is too small, the signal is distorted beyond recognition; if k is chosen too large, the filter is inefficient in reducing noise. The best (pro-active rather than after-the-fact) solution is to reduce the noise at its source, and to shield all noise-sensitive parts of the signal path. Filtering is only the next-best option; in that case collect data as closely spaced as possible for maximum noise rejection at small k.

Exercise 6.2.2 illustrates using this macro for a transient such as might be encountered in the study of short-lived fluorescence. We will assume that a laser pulse with a reproducible and known intensity-time profile is used to excite molecules to excited states, from which they decay soon thereafter by fluorescence. For the time course of laser light emission we take a skewed Gaussian (a rather arbitrary function picked here merely because it starts rather quickly and decays slowly), and we describe the fluorescence decay by a first-order rate process with rate constant k. Whereas with an RC filter the distortion is usually intentional (in order to remove noise), here it is the undesirable consequence of the unavoidably finite rise and fall times of the laser pulse, and its nonzero width.

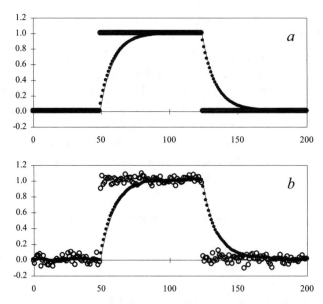

Fig. 6.2.1: The result of convolving a step function $x(t)$ with an exponential decay $y(t) = \exp[-kt]$ using the macro Convolve. The input function $x(t)$ is shown as open circles, and $x(t) \otimes \exp[-kt]$ as smaller solid points connected by line segments. In these examples $k = 0.1$. In panel (*b*) we use the same input as in panel (*a*) plus some Gaussian noise of standard deviation 0.04.

Exercise 6.2.2:

(1) In a new spreadsheet, reserve the top 12 rows for a graph, and place column headings for time, input, filter, and output in, say, A18:D18. Also place a value for the amplitude a of the exponential in cell B14, for its rate constant k in B15, and for its starting time t_0 in B16, with corresponding labels in column A. For curve *b* in Fig. 6.2.2 we have used $a = 1$, $k = 0.03$, and $t_0 = 30$.

(2) Start time at $t = 1$ in cell A20, then extend the column down to as far in the positive domain as desired, say, to $t = 300$ with increments Δt of 1.

(3) In cell B20 deposit the instruction `=IF(A20<$B$16,0,$B$14*EXP(-$B$15*(A20-$B$16)))`. Copy this instruction all the way down the column.

(4) In cell C17 deposit `=IF(1+(A20-$D$15)/$D$16>0,EXP(-1*(LN(1+ (A20-$D$15)/$D$16))^2),0)`, where D15, and D16 contain values for the filter parameters t_f and a_f of $y = \exp(-\{\ln[1+(t-t_f)/a_f]\}^2)$ for $1+(t-t_f)/a_f > 0$, and otherwise $y = 0$. In the example of Fig. 6.2.2 we have used $t_f = 10$ and $a_f = 7$.

(5) Call Convolve, then plot the functions in columns B, C, and D vs. time t in column A. Save your result, and compare it with Fig. 6.2.3.

Note that the macro simply uses the resulting numbers, and will work equally well if one uses an arbitrary shape for the laser pulse profile (such as one actually measured for a particular light source), and different fluorescent decay kinetics.

As our third example we will use the convolution macro to illustrate the effect of, say, limited optical resolution on spectral peaks, or of instrumental peak broadening on a chromatogram. For the sake of simplicity we will again assume simple forms, in this case Gaussians for both the undistorted peaks and for the broadening effect. The macro does not use the generating equations, only the resulting numbers, and arbitrary peak shapes and broadening functions will therefore work equally well.

Exercise 6.2.3:

(1) In yet another spreadsheet, again reserve the area A1:E16 for graphs, place the labels as1=, bs1=, cs1=, as2=, bs2=, cs2=, as3=, bs3=, cs3=, as4=, bs4=, cs4=, at=, bt=, ct= in cells F2:F16. Also place column headings for time, *s*, *t*, and *r* in, say, cells A20:D20.

264

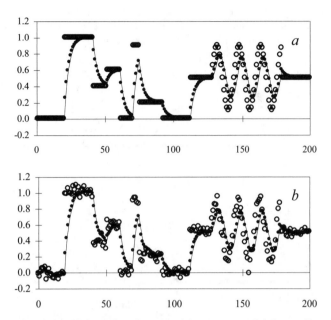

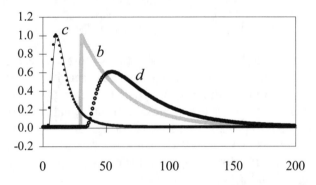

Fig. 6.2.2: Some results of convolving a function $x(t)$ with an exponential decay $y(t) = \exp[-kt]$ using the macro Convolve, with $k = 0.5$. In (a) the input function is a fanciful set of steps followed by a sinewave, and in (b) the same with added Gaussian noise with a standard deviation of 0.04. The input function $x(t)$ is shown as open circles, and $x(t) \otimes \exp[-kt]$ as smaller solid points connected by line segments.

Fig. 6.2.3: The exponential decay of simulated fluorescence, defined by a first-order rate process with amplitude $a = 1$, rate constant $k = 0.03$, and start time $t_0 = 30$, as convolved by an excitation light pulse with finite rise and decay times. Wide gray curve (labeled b): the theoretical, exponential decay for a delta-function as excitation source. Small solid circles connected by thin curve (labeled c): the assumed profile of the light pulse, with finite rise and fall times. Open circles (labeled d): the resulting, measurable fluorescence emission signal.

(2) Start time at $t = 1$ in cell A22, then with increments Δt of 1 extend the column as far down as desired, say, to A321 where $t = 300$.

(3) In column B generate a fantasy spectrum or chromatogram consisting of four Gaussian peaks, of different widths, and possibly overlapping or nearly so, using instructions such as, in cell B22, `=$G$2*EXP(-0.5*((A22-$G$4)/$G$3)^2)+ ... +$G$11*EXP(-0.5*((A22-$G$13)/$G$12)^2)`.

(4) Likewise, in column C, deposit the instruction for a single Gaussian representing the signal-distorting transfer function t with the parameters b_t and c_t, such as `=$G$14*EXP(-0.5*((A22-$G$16)/$G$15)^2)` in cell C22.

(5) Convolve the four-Gaussian signal s with the single-Gaussian function t, and use the area A1:F16 to plot the results, which might resemble Fig. 6.2.4. Save the spreadsheet. Unless you remove this feature from its code, the custom macro Convolve will ignore a_t and will, instead, normalize t to unit average value.

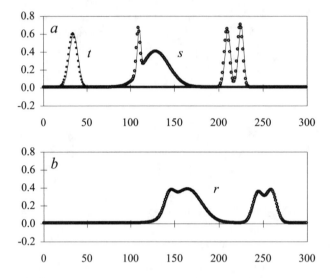

Fig. 6.2.4: A simulated spectrum s containing four Gaussians (connected open circles in panel a) calculated with the coefficients $a_{s1} = 0.5$, $b_{s1} = 2$, $c_{s1} = 110$, $a_{s2} = 0.4$, $b_{s2} = 15$, $c_{s2} = 130$, $a_{s3} = 0.65$, $b_{s3} = 3$, $c_{s3} = 210$, $a_{s4} = 0.7$, $b_{s4} = 3$, and $c_{s4} = 225$. The transfer function t (connected small solid circles in the same panel) with $a_t = 0.6$, $b_t = 5$, $c_t = 35$ is also displayed in panel a. The convolution r of s and t is shown in panel b, in which the peaks are shifted by the amount of c_t, as well as rounded.

We see that the convolved spectral peaks are broader (as is most noticeable with the narrower peaks) and less tall (because the convolution does not change their integrated areas), so that adjacent peaks tend to coalesce. The convolved spectrum is shifted with respect to the original spectrum by the amount of c_t. Therefore, make sure that there is enough space at the end of the signal to accommodate such a shift, otherwise just add zeros to the signal to provide that space. You can add any number of dummy data points: Convolve needs equidistant signals $x(t)$ and $y(t)$ (because these two functions will be sliding past each other), but requires neither symmetry, periodicity, nor a specific number of points. We will return to the last two examples in sections 6.7 and 6.8 respectively.

6.3 Unfiltering

Say that we have filtered a signal with an RC filter, and want to undo that operation. Just as we can exponentiate to counteract taking a (natural) logarithm, or integrate to undo differentiation, we can use the spreadsheet to *un*filter the data, as illustrated in exercise 6.3.1. The technical term for the undo operation of convolution is *deconvolution*. Beware: this term is sometimes misused to mean *decomposition* or *resolution*, i.e., the resolution of (often simply additive) constituent components, a much more trivial problem discussed in, e.g., section 4.6.

Exercise 6.3.1:

(1) Start a new spreadsheet, or add on to the spreadsheet of exercise 6.1.

(2) Make the following new columns (which, for ease of specifying the instructions, we will here assume to be columns H through L), leaving the top 12 rows for graphs, and with column headings for time, input, filter, output1, and output2.

(3) Also place the labels k= and norm= in cells H13 and J13 respectively, and repeat the earlier-used k-value, 0.3, in cell I13.

266

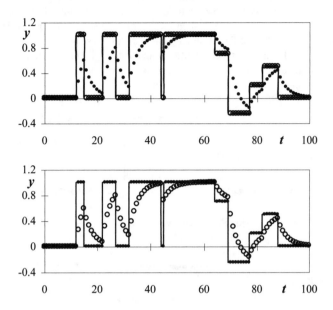

Fig. 6.3.1: Top: the original input signal, before filtering (open circles), and its filtered output (solid circles), as reproduced from Fig. 6.1.2. Bottom: using the filtered signal as input (open circles), the unfilter operation now recovers the original signal (solid circles).

(4) For the time column, copy the earlier values: $t = -20$ (1) 100. For input, copy the data from column D to column I with, e.g., =D17 in cell I17.

(5) In cell J17 place the instruction =EXP($I$13*H17), and copy this filter function down to row 37.

(6) In cell K13 enter =SUM(J17:J37).

(7) The expression for the deconvolution is, of course, slightly different from that for convolution. In cell K38 (to take a place equivalent to that of cell D37 in exercise 6.1.1) deposit the instruction =I37-(K36*$J$36+K35*$J$35+K34 *$J$34+K33*$J$33+K32*$J$32+K31*$J$31+K30*$J$30+K29*$J$29+ K28*$J$28+K27*$J$27+K26*$J$26+K25*$J$25+K24*$J$24+K23* $J$23+K22*$J$22+K21*$J$21+K20*$J$20+K19*$J$19+K18*$J$18+ K17*$J$17), and in cell L37 place =K37*$K$13. Copy these instructions all the way down to row 137.

(8) Plot L17:L137 vs. H17:H137. You have now unfiltered the original signal, as illustrated in Fig. 6.1.1.

(9) Check the residuals, the differences between corresponding values in columns K and B.

(10) Try the same spreadsheet for other input functions, by changing the data in column B to signals such as used in Figs. 6.1.2 and 6.1.3.

(11) If we use a different k-value in the unfiltering operation from the one used for filtering, we will not recover the original input signal. This is illustrated in Fig. 6.3.2 for the simple square pulse of Fig. 6.1.1. Try it for yourself.

Again we can use a custom macro, Deconvolve, to ease our work.

The few examples given so far suggest that we can always undo the effects of filtering or distortion, but that is, unfortunately, too good to be true. The following exercises illustrate some of the limits involved.

Exercise 6.3.2:

(1) Take the spreadsheet used in exercise 6.1, with a single step function as its signal in column B, and advance the function representing the RC filter in column C to start at $t = 10$ rather than at the very beginning of the data set, at $t = 1$, with the filter function set at 0 for $t < 10$.

267

(2) Set up columns F, G, and H to copy the data in columns A, D, and C respectively, so that convolution of the data in columns A through C can readily be followed by deconvolution of the data in columns F through H.

(3) Apply Convolve to the data in block A17:C217, then Deconvolve those in block F17:H217. You will find that the result of the deconvolution yields a wildly oscillating signal that bears little resemblance to the original.

(4) In order to see more clearly what happens, set the filter function for $t < 10$ to 1, and repeat the convolution and deconvolution. As you can see in Fig. 6.3.3, there is no problem here.

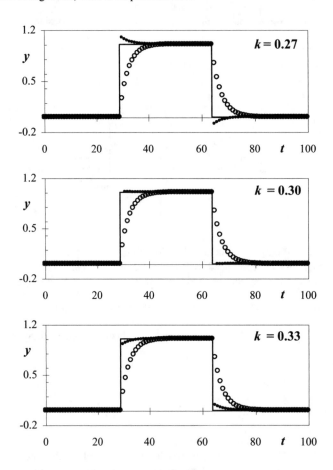

Fig. 6.3.2: Middle panel: when the filter rate constant in unfiltering is the same as that in filtering ($k = 0.30$ in this example), the original signal is recovered. Top and bottom: when a different k-value is used for filtering and unfiltering, distortion occurs, as shown here in the form of overshoot or undershoot.

(5) Now give the filter function a slightly positive slope over the first few points, e.g., by giving it the values 0.50 (0.05) 1.00 for $t = 1$ (1) 10. Figure 6.3.4 illustrates the result, which shows the onset of instability in the form of a damped oscillation. If we increase the initial slope, the problem worsens, and is fully out of control (i.e., the oscillation is no longer damped) with initial values for the filter function of, e.g., 0 (0.1) 1 for $t = 1$ (1) 10. As you already saw, it is even worse if one steps suddenly from 0 to 1 at $t = 10$.

Apparently the deconvolution works reliably only when the transfer function has nowhere a positive time derivative, a requirement that often cannot be met, as in Figs. 6.2.3 and 6.2.4. We therefore look for alternative methods to perform the deconvolution in those (many) cases in which direct deconvolution does not work.

268

6.4 Convolution by Fourier transformation

A different route to convolution and deconvolution can be based on Fourier transformation. One reason to consider such an alternative approach is algorithmic efficiency. For two 1000-point functions the direct method requires 1000^2 or 10^6 multiplications, whereas a Fourier transformation uses a number of operations of the order of $N \log_2 N$ rather than N^2. Even though convolution or deconvolution require three Fourier transformations plus a complex multiplication or division, this still works out as much faster for sufficiently large data sets.

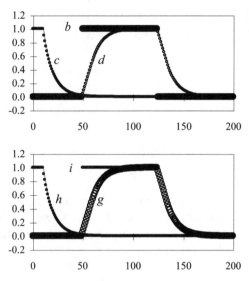

Fig. 6.3.3: Top panel: convolution of a step function (large circles) with an exponential filter function preceded by a constant level (connected small solid circles). Bottom panel: deconvolution of the same recovers the original step function (small circles) without problems. The labels refer to the spreadsheet columns used.

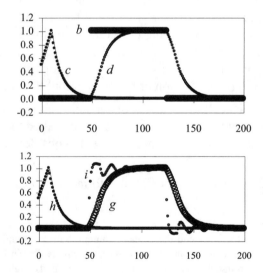

Fig. 6.3.4: Top panel: convolution of a step function (large circles) with an exponential filter function preceded by an initial rise (connected small solid circles). Bottom panel: deconvolution of the same recovers the original step function with a (damped) oscillation (small circles). The labels refer to the spreadsheet columns.

Parenthetically, when computers were slow, efficiency used to be an important problem. Now that the beast on your bench may work at or above 1 GHz, it may even get away with a rather inefficient method during the time it takes you to blink an eye. Computational efficiency still matters with large data sets, especially those in multidimensional arrays, which we will not consider here, as in general their handling should not be attempted on a spreadsheet. Because of their transparency, spreadsheets are great for learning and exploring the principles of the various methods, and for their applications to relatively small data sets, but they are often sub-optimal for collections of, say, more than a few thousand data points.

A second reason to consider Fourier transformation is that we already saw that direct deconvolution can lead to unstable results, and cannot be used for curves such as those of Figs. 6.2.3 and 6.2.4. Finally, as we will see in section 6.6, use of Fourier transformation can make sophisticated noise-rejection methods readily available.

A basic theorem states that the Fourier transform of the convolution of two continuous functions $x(t)$ and $y(t)$ is equal to the product of the Fourier transforms of those functions. In other words, when

$$z(t) = x(t) \otimes y(t) = \int_{-\infty}^{+\infty} x(\tau) \; y(t-\tau) \; d\tau \qquad (6.4.1)$$

where t is time, wavelength, or whatever the relevant parameter is, and τ is a 'dummy variable', then

$$Z(f) = X(f) \times Y(f) \qquad (6.4.2)$$

where $X(f)$, $Y(f)$, and $Z(f)$ are the Fourier transforms of $x(t)$, $y(t)$, and $z(t)$ respectively, and f is the reciprocal of t. Applied to instrumental distortion, we can symbolically express the observed result r in terms of the original input signal s and the *transfer function* t (here printed in bold to avoid confusion of, e.g., s with standard deviation s, and of t with time t) as

$$r = s \otimes t \qquad (6.4.3)$$

where r, s, and t are functions. Upon Fourier transformation this yields

$$R = S \times T \qquad (6.4.4)$$

so that we can compute r by Fourier transformation of s to S, and t to T, multiplication of S and T to form R, whereupon inverse Fourier transformation of R yields r. Apart from the fact that we are dealing here with functions rather than with single numbers, the procedure is analogous to computing $a = b^c$ by taking logarithms to obtain $\ln a = c \times \ln b$, performing the multiplication, and taking the antilog of $\ln a$ to find a. In both cases, a transformation (Fourier transformation or taking logarithms) allows us to reduce a more complicated mathematical operation (convolution or exponentiation) to a multiplication.

A note on nomenclature: it is difficult to find a set of symbols that is convenient across many different disciplines. For example, in electronics, the 'true' signal might be called the *i*nput signal i, and the filtered result the *o*utput o. In optics, the reverse might make sense: to consider the *o*bject o the true signal, the *i*mage i its distorted response.

In exercises 6.4.1 and 6.4.2 we will use Fourier transformation to calculate the convolution already encountered in exercise 6.2.3.

Exercise 6.4.1:

(1) Use the spreadsheet of exercise 6.2.2. Extend the times in column A to 255, similarly extend the computations in columns B and C, then recalculate the data in column D, all in order to facilitate Fourier transformation.

(2) In new columns copy the data from columns A (for time) and B (for input), highlight them plus a third blank column (for the complex input, to be left blank), and call the macro ForwardFT. Label the resulting columns (containing the Fourier-transformed input) freq, a, and b.

(3) In a separate cell compute the average of the filter data, for which you can use the convenient function =AVERAGE().

(4) Again copy the column for time (from column A), and next to it calculate the filter value (from column C) divided by its just-computed average. Highlight these two new columns, together with an adjacent blank column, and again call ForwardFT. Label the resulting columns (with the Fourier-transformed filter) freq, c, and d respectively.

(5) For the multiplication of the Fourier transforms use $(a+jb) \times (c+jd) = (ac-bd) + j(bc+ad)$. In yet another column copy the frequency (from one of the earlier columns labeled freq), and in the next columns calculate $(ac-bd)$ and $(bc+ad)$ respectively, using values from the columns labeled a, b, c, and d. This yields the complex multiplication.

(6) Highlight the just-made three columns, call InverseFT, and plot your result. It should be (within round-off errors) the same as obtained with Convolve, see curve d in Fig. 6.2.3.

The above illustrates the principle of the method, but uses quite some time, effort, and spreadsheet space. It is far simpler to use the custom macro ConvolveFT, which incorporates the forward and inverse Fourier transformations, scales the filter (by dividing it by its average value), and performs the complex multiplications. Moreover, by limiting the input to real functions, it has an even smaller spreadsheet 'footprint' than a single Fourier transformation macro. Below we will illustrate its use by applying it to the same problem.

Exercise 6.4.1 (continued):

(7) Select another three columns in which you copy the data from columns A (time), B (input), and C (filter).

(8) Highlight these three columns, call ConvolveFT, and bingo, you again find the convolved result.

Now that we have reduced the process to invoking a single macro, it is easy to verify that convolution is indeed commutative, see eq. (6.2.3):

Exercise 6.4.1 (continued):

(9) Move the output column to keep it for subsequent comparison. You can either cut and paste it into the adjacent column, or just insert a blank column between it and the copied filter function.

(10) Reverse the order of the columns in which you copied data from columns B (input) and C (filter).

(11) Highlight the three last columns, call ConvolveFT, and compare your latest result with the earlier one you just moved. There should be no significant differences, because convolution is indeed commutative.

Here is another application:

Exercise 6.4.2:

(1) Starting with cell A3 of column A in a new spreadsheet, enter 1 (1) 2048.

(2) In row M2:T2 enter the amplitudes 0.7, in row M3:T3 the standard deviations 100, 50, 30, 20, 10, 5, 3, 2, and 1, and in row M4:T4 the center values 500, 1050, 1370, 1590, 1740, 1840, 1910, 1970, and 2010.

(3) In cell B3 enter the instruction `=$M$2*EXP(-0.5*((A56-$M$4)/$M$3)^2)+`, copy the part beyond the equal sign, paste it back eight times in the instruction, and remove the final plus sign. Then change the M in `$M$3`, `$M$4`, and `$M$5` in the second exponential into an N to make `$N$3`, `$N$4`, and `$N$5`, in the third into an O to get `$O$3`, `$O$4`, and `$O$5`, etc.

(4) Click on the cell handle to copy this instruction all the way down to row 2048. Then plot B3:B2050 vs. A3:A2050. There is nothing special about this set, other than that it has nine essentially baseline-separated Gaussian peaks of varying widths. You can of course make your own signal instead, or use the data from Fig. 3.15.1, which contains four Lorentzians.

(5) In cell D1 place the value 0.1, and in cell C3 deposit the instruction `=EXP(-0.5*((A3)/$D$1)^2)+EXP(-0.5*((A3-2048)/$D$1)^2)`. Copy this instruction down to row 2048 as well. This is a *single* Gaussian peak centered at zero, and will represent our transfer function. Again, feel free to use another function instead.

(6) Highlight A3:C2050, and call the custom macro Convolve. Plot the result, which has appeared in D3:D2050, vs. A3:A2050. It should resemble Fig. 6.4.2a.

(7) Repeat this with different values in D1, such as 0.01, 0.001, and 0.0001, and plot the resulting curves, as in Figs. 6.4.2b,c,d.

(8) Save this spreadsheet for use in exercise 6.5.2.

Figure 6.4.2 illustrates how measurement instruments or other sources of broadening can distort a signal. Here we have assumed a Gaussian transfer function, but its precise form is less important than its characteristic width. We see that convolution can even wash out some of its qualitative features. In Fig. 6.4.2c the right-most peak has virtually disappeared, while Fig. 6.4.2d distorts all peaks and hides the narrower ones in a single broad shoulder.

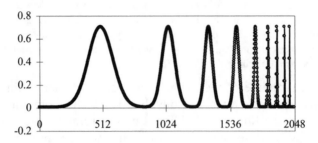

Fig. 6.4.1: The test function used in exercise 6.4.2. The open circles show the individual data points, the lines merely connect adjacent points.

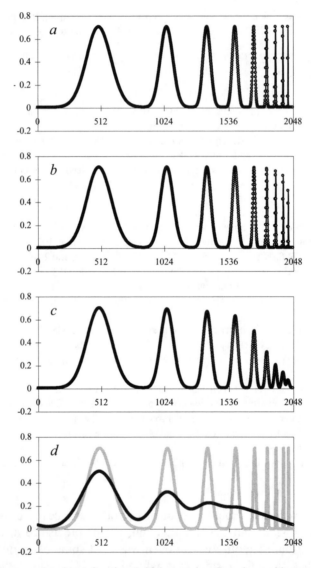

Fig. 6.4.2: The convoluted test function (which contains Gaussians with standard deviations ranging from 100 to 1) for (from *a* to *d*) increasingly broad transfer functions, with standard deviations of 0.1, 1, 10, and 100 respectively. The gray line in panel *d* repeats the test function.

272

Such broadening is not restricted to instruments. An atomic absorption line, e.g., has an inherent width governed by the Heisenberg uncertainty, because the product of the energy difference ΔE between the two states, and the sum of the reciprocals of their life times Δt, cannot be smaller than $h/2\pi$, where h is the Planck constant. This yields a Lorentzian line shape rather than the infinitely narrow line one might otherwise expect for a quantum transition. However, the thermal motion of gaseous atoms with respect to the 'laboratory frame' (containing the light source and the detector) causes line broadening, mathematically described as the convolution of the Lorentzian line with a Gaussian distribution due to diffusional motion (W. Voigt, *Ann. Phys.* 311 (1901) 459). High gas pressure may result in further, so-called collisional broadening.

The same applies to molecular spectra, which typically show rotational fine structure in the gas phase. In condensed phases such rotational fine structure is often blurred as the result of interactions with neighboring molecules. The effects of such interactions must, again, be described in terms of convolutions.

6.5 Deconvolution by Fourier transformation

While convolution is useful in understanding instrumental distortion and in instrument design, instrument *users* are often more interested in correcting for such distortion. They may want to compensate for a finite laser pulse width in order to determine the rate constant k of a fast fluorescence decay (i.e., recover curve b from the measured curve d in Fig. 6.2.3), or reconstruct an actual spectrum by correcting it for the distortion of the nonzero slit width of their instrument (as in going from curve r to curve s in Fig. 6.2.4). Assuming that the *transfer function t* is both reproducible and known, deconvolution *in principle* allows reconstruction of the original, distortion-free signal s from its corrupted response r.

Deconvolution based on Fourier transformation works as follows. Using an appropriate input signal, we first determine the transfer function t of the instrument. We then take the measured output of interest, r, which (assuming that the instrumental parameters have not changed) is given by $r = s \otimes t$, see (6.2.2), where s is the sought, undistorted signal. Now that we know both r and t, we want to find s. Fourier transformation of $r = s \otimes t$ yields $R = S \times T$, from which we obtain

$$S = R \diagup T \qquad\qquad (6.5.1)$$

or, in the time domain,

$$s = r \oslash t \qquad\qquad (6.5.2)$$

where $\oslash$ denotes deconvolution, the inverse operation of convolution $\otimes$. The symbol $\oslash$ suggests the corresponding Fourier-domain division ($\diagup$) just as $\otimes$ implies multiplication ($\times$) of the Fourier transforms. Consequently we transform r to R, and t to T, then calculate $S = R \diagup T$, and inverse transform the latter to find s. In exercises 6.5.1 and 6.5.2 we will illustrate this alternative method of deconvolution.

Finally we note that convolution, like multiplication, is always commutative: $a \times b = b \times a$ and $a \otimes b = b \otimes a$, but that in general deconvolution, like division, is not: $a \diagup b \neq b \diagup a$, and $a \oslash b \neq b \oslash a$.

Exercise 6.5.1:

(1) Modify, or copy and then modify, spreadsheet exercise 6.4.1 as follows.

(2) Instead of column B, as instructed under exercise 6.4.1 under point (2), copy the data in column D (for output), then proceed as before by highlighting them plus a third blank column, and by calling ForwardFT. Label the resulting columns (containing the Fourier-transformed output) freq, a, and b.

(3) Instead of multiplying the Fourier-transformed input and filter signal, we now divide the Fourier-transformed output and filter signal. Because they are both complex quantities, we have $(a+jb)/(c+jd) = (a+jb)(c-jd)/(c^2+d^2) = (ac+bd)/(c^2+d^2) + j(bc-ad)/(c^2+d^2)$.

(4) Therefore, in the columns where, according to the instructions in exercise 6.4.1 under point (5), you had earlier calculated $(ac-bd)$, now compute $(ac+bd)/(c^2+d^2)$. Likewise, in the next column, instead of $(bc+ad)$, now compute $(bc-ad)/(c^2+d^2)$.

(5) Proceed as before by highlighting these three columns (one for frequency, and two containing the real and imaginary parts of the quotient), call InverseFT, and compare your result with the original signal in column B.

(6) Instead of the instructions under point (7) of exercise 4.5.1 use copies of the data from columns A (time), D (output), and C (filter), i.e., replace the input from column B by the output from column D. Then highlight them, and call DeconvolveFT. (You will encounter two input boxes, one offering to apply an adjustable von Hann/Tuckey window and, if you decline that, a second to zero out high frequencies. Deny both by approving the default 0, i.e., by clicking on OK or pressing Enter.) DeconvolveFT condenses all this into a single macro operation.

Exercise 6.5.2:

(1) Use the spreadsheet of exercise 6.2.2. Extend the times in column A to 255, similarly extend the computations in columns B and C, then recalculate the data in column D, all in order to facilitate Fourier transformation.

(2) In new columns copy the data from columns A (for time) and D (for output), highlight them plus a third blank column, and call ForwardFT. Label the resulting columns (containing the Fourier-transformed output) freq, a, and b.

(3) Calculate the average of the filter function with =AVERAGE().

(4) Again copy the column for time (from column A), and next to it calculate the filter value (from column C) divided by the just-computed average.

(5) Highlight these two new columns, together with a blank column, and again call ForwardFT. Label the resulting columns (with the Fourier-transformed filter) freq, c, and d respectively.

(6) Now that you have Fourier-transformed both the distorted output signal and the filter, we need to divide the two. Since they are both complex quantities, we have $(a+jb)/(c+jd) = (a+jb)(c-jd)/(c^2+d^2) = (ac+bd)/(c^2+d^2) + j(bc-ad)/(c^2+d^2)$.

(7) In yet another column copy the frequency (from one of the columns labeled freq), in the next columns calculate the complex division $(ac+bd)/(c^2+d^2)$ and $(bc-ad)/(c^2+d^2)$ respectively, using values from the columns labeled a through d.

(8) All that still remains to be done is the inverse Fourier transformation. Highlight the just-made three columns, call InverseFT, and plot your result. You should recover the original exponential with very little distortion as the real result, together with a negligible imaginary result.

Exercise 6.5.3:

(1) We continue with the spreadsheet of exercise 6.4.2. In column E copy column A (i.e., in E3 place the instruction =A3 and copy this down to row 2050), and in columns F and G copy columns D and C respectively.

(2) Highlight E3:G2050, call the custom macro DeconvolveFT, and plot the result, i.e., H3:H2050 vs. either E3:E2050 or A3:A2050. Do this for the various transfer functions used in exercise 6.4. If there you obtained data resembling Fig. 6.4.2, you will now find results similar to those in Fig. 6.5.1.

Comparison of Fig. 6.5.1 with Figs. 6.4.1 and 6.4.2 shows that deconvolution has almost completely restored the original test function in panel *b*, and recovered sizeable parts of the narrower peaks in panel *c*. However, in panel *d* all peaks but the first remain strongly distorted. It looks as if deconvolution, even in the complete absence of noise, cannot recover the information blurred by the earlier convolution when the characteristic width (expressed, e.g., as its standard deviation) of the convolving and deconvolving function is larger by about an order of magnitude than that of the feature involved.

Admittedly, it is a tall order to want to recover peaks with a standard deviation of 1 when they were first convolved with a 100 times broader peak, as in the case of Fig. 6.5.1*d*. Still, since exercise 6.5.3 deals with noise-free, *synthetic* data, there must be a reason why recovery of the original signal is so poor. Exercise 6.5.4 indicates where the shoe pinches.

Exercise 6.5.4:

(1) It is easiest to add to the spreadsheet of exercise 6.4.2. Repeat columns for #, signal, and transfer function, and in them deposit instructions that copy the data in columns A through C, for a transfer function with a standard deviation of 100. The only difference is that, in the third column, instead of an instruction such as =B10 in the 10th row you now use =Int(16*B10)/16. This will make the transfer function exactly expressible in terms of binary numbers. (There is nothing special about the number 16. Other integer powers of 2 work equally well, as does the simple rectangular transfer function.)

(2) Call ConvolveFT, and plot your result. The curve you get is not very much different from what you found in Fig. 6.4.2*d*.

(3) Now use three more columns, one to copy time or #, the next to copy the result you just found, the third to copy the binarized transfer function.

(4) Call DeconvolveFT, and enter the result in the graph made under point (2). Now your result is quite different from that in Fig. 6.5.1*d*, compare Fig. 6.5.2. Apparently, the distortion is primarily associated with truncation errors in the transfer function *t*. Note that deconvolution does not commutate, but treats *r* and *t* differently.

Unfortunately we usually cannot exploit what we have just found in Fig. 6.5.2 because, unlike the situation in a synthetic example, in data analysis we seldom have control over the distorting process. (One can of course use it for cryptographic encoding and decoding. It might even be useful in designing instruments based on Fourier transformation, but only if its high sensitivity to noise in *r* could be remedied.)

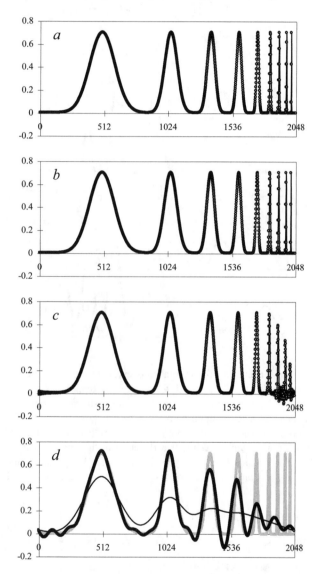

Fig. 6.5.1: The deconvolved test function for (from *a* to *d*) increasingly broad transfer functions, with standard deviations of (*a*) 0.1, (*b*) 1, (*c*) 10, and (*d*) 100. The thick gray line in panel *d* repeats the test function; the thin black line in *d* is a reminder of how convolution had distorted it.

For all practical purposes we therefore have to live with the rather unsatisfactory results of Fig. 6.5.1. These are summarized in Table 6.5.1, which lists the standard deviations s_s of the nine Gaussian peaks in Fig. 6.4.1, and the corresponding s_t values of the four Gaussians used to represent the transfer function in the convolutions and subsequent deconvolutions in panels *a* through *d* of Fig. 6.5.1. Practical signal re-

275

covery by Fourier transform deconvolution of noise-free signals is possible only for signals with characteristic widths not much smaller than that of the distorting transfer function t.

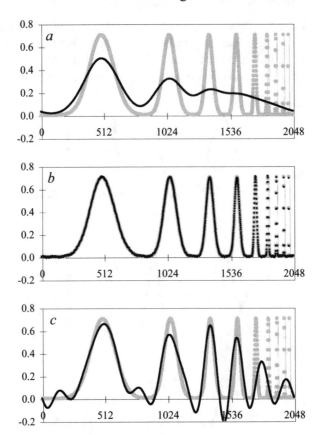

Fig. 6.5.2: Using a binarized transfer function allows total recovery, even when the transfer function has a standard deviation of 100. (*a*): The original function (gray), and its convolution (thick black curve) with a binarized transfer function (as shown here) is no different from that obtained with a non-binarized one, as shown in Fig. 6.4.2*d* for otherwise identical conditions. (*b*): Deconvolution with the same (binarized) transfer function (black points) recovers the original data (gray). (c) Normal convolution followed by deconvolution with the binarized transfer function (shown here as black points) yields results that (because of the mismatch in t) are slightly worse than those shown in Fig. 6.5.1*d*. (The original data are again shown in gray.) The same applies when binarization is used only in the convolution step, or when different binarizations are used. Clearly, identical binarization must be used for both convolution and deconvolution.

$s_s =$	100	50	30	20	10	5	3	2	1
(*a*): $s_t = 0.1$	●	●	●	●	●	●	●	●	●
(*b*): $s_t = 1$	●	●	●	●	●	●	●	●	⊙
(*c*): $s_t = 10$	●	●	●	●	⊙	●	●	●	●
(*d*): $s_t = 100$	⊙	●	●	●	●	○	○		

Table 6.5.1: A semi-graphical display of signal recovery after Fourier transform convolution and deconvolution, as a function of the standard deviations s_s of the Gaussian signal peaks and s_t of the equally Gaussian transfer function. Quality of recovery is indicated crudely in the style of Consumer Reports, with solid black circles indicating excellent recovery. Encircled solid circles ⊙ identify where $s_t = s_s$.

Now for the bad news. Convolution is an integration and, as such, attenuates noise: smoothing blurs many details. On the other hand its inverse operation, deconvolution, is akin to a differentiation, and tends to accentuate noise. We already saw the extreme sensitivity of the method to truncation errors in t, and below we will illustrate the effect of Gaussian noise added to r. Similar effects are observed by truncating or rounding the data for r to a limited number of digits, similar to what happens when analog signals are digitized. Truncation and rounding follow a triangular rather than a Gaussian distribution, with well-defined limits, but that detail is of minor importance here.

For noisy signals, deconvolution usually trades lower signal distortion for much enhanced noise. That may not be a problem if the enhanced noise can be removed subsequently, e.g., by fitting the data to a mathematical model expression, as was done in the paper by Hüfner & Wertheim in *Phys. Revs.* B11 (1975) 678 mentioned in section 6.6. Otherwise we may have to use filtering to reduce the noise, as illustrated in exercise 6.5.5.

Exercise 6.5.5:

(1) This will be a fairly wide spreadsheet, which (including a few empty 'spacer' columns) will take up more than a full alphabet. It is therefore best to start with a fresh sheet. In column A, under the heading #, deposit the numbers 0 (1) 2047.

(2) In column B, labeled s, generate the function s, or copy it from another worksheet. Reminder: to copy a value from, say, cell B2 of Sheet1 to cell C3 of Sheet2 in the same workbook, place in cell C3 of Sheet2 the instruction =Sheet1!B2. To copy from Book1 Sheet1 cell B2 to Book2 Sheet2 cell C3 use =′[Book1]Sheet1′!B2 in the receiving cell.

(3) In column C generate or copy a transfer function t.

(4) Highlight the data in these three columns, and call ConvolveFT. This will yield r in column D.

(5) In column F generate Gaussian (or other) noise, e.g., with <u>T</u>ools ⇒ <u>D</u>ata Analysis ⇒ Random Number Generation.

(6) In column H copy the numbers from column A. In column I copy r from column D, and add to it a ('noise amplitude') multiplier times noise from column F. Figure 6.5.3a illustrates what you would get if you used for input the same data as shown in Fig. 6.4.2c. plus noise with a standard deviation ('noise amplitude') of 0.1. We now have set up the problem.

(7) Highlight the data in columns H through J (the latter being empty) and call ForwardFT. This will deposit the corresponding frequencies in column K, and the real and imaginary components R' and R'' in columns L and M respectively.

(8) In column O calculate $\log M^2 = \log[(R')^2 + (R'')^2]$, and plot it versus frequency (in column K).

(9) Find approximate functions for the signal (in column P) and the noise (in column Q). For the data shown in Fig. 6.5.3b we have used (and shown) $\log S^2 = -2 - 125\,|f|$ and $\log N^2 = -4.6$. In column R then compute the Wiener filter as

$$10^{\log(S^2)}\big/\left(10^{\log(S^2)} + 10^{\log(N^2)}\right) = 10^{-2-125|f|}\big/\left(10^{-2-125|f|} + 10^{-4.6}\right).$$

(10) In column T copy the frequency from column K, in column U calculate the product of R' (from column L) and the Wiener filter (from column R), and in column V place the product of R'' (from column M) and the Wiener filter.

(11) Highlight the data in columns T through V, and call InverseFT. This will produce the numbers 0 through 2047 in column W, and the filtered real and imaginary components of r in columns X and Y respectively. The data in column X are shown in Fig. 6.5.3c; those in column Y reflect computational imperfections and should therefore be quite small.

(12) In column AA copy the numbers 0 (1) 2047, in column AB the data from column X, and in column AC the transfer function t from column C.

(13) Highlight the data in columns AA through AC, and call DeconvolveFT. Column AD will now contain the deconvolved data, see Fig. 6.5.3d.

The above procedure is rather laborious. Its tedium could be reduced somewhat by constructing a custom macro, which in this case would require two parts, one to generate the power spectrum, $\log[(R')^2 + (R'')^2]$, the second (after operator intervention to distinguish between signal and noise, and to approximate both components in terms of mathematical functions) to finish the process. We will leave this as an exercise to the interested reader.

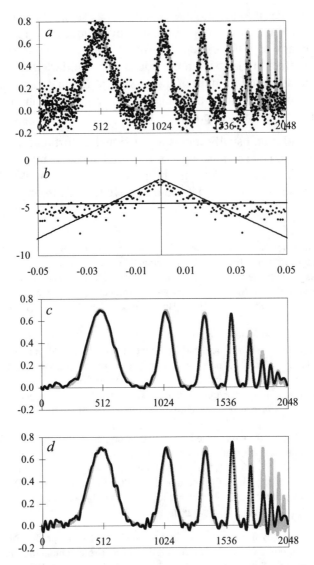

Fig. 6.5.3: Wiener filtering followed by deconvolution of a noisy signal. (*a*): The undistorted signal *s* (gray) and its convolution *r* with a Gaussian of standard deviation 10 (displayed in Fig. 6.4.2*c*), to which was added Gaussian noise, of zero mean and standard deviation 0.1 (black circles). (*b*): The central part of the power spectrum of the noisy *r*. This plot is used for the visual estimates of the parameters of the Wiener filter. (*c*): The resulting, smoothed *r* (black ccurve) with the corresponding noise-free curve (gray). (*d*): Upon deconvolving the smoothed data we obtain the final result (black curve), with (in gray) the corresponding noise-free curve.

What is worse than its tedium is that even the small amount of noise left after Wiener filtering interferes with the deconvolution which, after all this effort, often produces only a relatively minor correction for the original distortion.

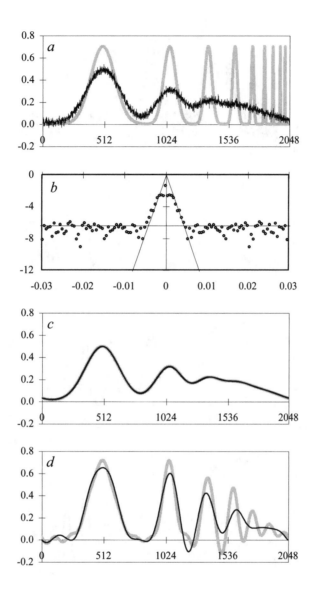

Fig. 6.5.4: Wiener filtering followed by deconvolution of a noisy signal. All data are as in Fig. 6.5.3, except that the original convoluting function had a standard deviation of 100 (see Fig. 6.4.2*d*), and the noise amplitude (the standard deviation of the added Gaussian noise) was only 0.02.

This is illustrated in Fig. 6.5.4, where we have used the same spreadsheet for the more strongly distorted case of Fig. 6.4.2*d*. Once the spreadsheet is set up and properly labeled (it helps to color code the data blocks to be highlighted for macro use), repeated operation is fairly easy, even though it still involves four macros (ConvolveFT, ForwardFT, InverseFT, and DeconvolveFT) and making the necessary adjustments in the parameter estimates S^2 and/or N^2 of the Wiener filter. Nonetheless, despite Wiener filtering, the method often tolerates very little noise, lest it yield wildly oscillating results.

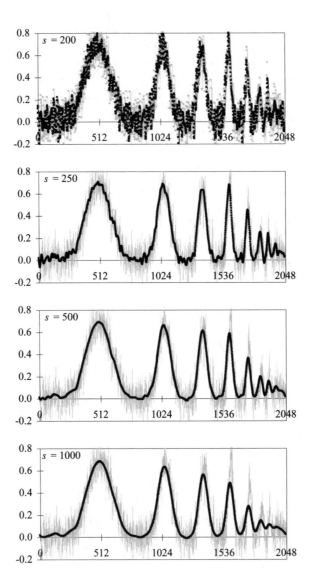

Fig. 6.5.5: The use of an adjustable von Hann filter for the deconvolution of the noisy trace illustrated in Fig. 6.5.3*a*. The input signal *r* is shown in gray, its devolution in black. The convolving and deconvolving *t* is a Gaussian curve of standard deviation 10; the signal has added Gaussian noise of standard deviation 0.1. The *s*-value used is noted in each panel.

When the effort involved in Wiener filtering is not warranted, some non-specific, 'general' filtering can be had with two filters included in the custom macro DeconvolveFT: an adjustable von Hann filter or, when this is rejected, a sharp frequency cut-off filter. The application of the von Hann filter is illustrated in exercise 6.5.6 and in Figs. 6.5.5 and 6.5.6. By increasing the value of the filter parameter *s* one can make the von Hann filter arbitrarily narrow, in which case it approaches a delta function. The deconvolution macro then merely reproduces its input. Similar results can be obtained with the sharper frequency cut-off filter, but its abruptness tends to enhance oscillations in the result.

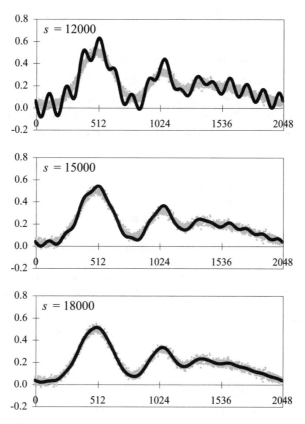

Fig. 6.5.6: The use of an adjustable von Hann filter for the deconvolution of the noisy trace illustrated in Fig. 6.5.4a. The input signal *r* is shown in gray, its devolution in black. The convolving and deconvolving *t* is a Gaussian of standard deviation 100; the signal has added Gaussian noise of standard deviation 0.02. The *s*-value used is noted in each panel. When *s* is too small, the result oscillates; when it is too large, there is no deconvolution.

Exercise 6.5.6:

(1) This will be a short continuation of exercise 6.5.5. In column AF copy the numbers from column A, in column AG copy the noisy test function *r*+n from column I, and in column AH copy the transfer function *t* from column C.

(2) Highlight the data in columns AF through AH, and call DeconvolveFT. Select an appropriate filter parameter *s*; some filter curves are displayed in Fig. 5.6.1. You will find your answer in column AH. Figure 6.5.6 shows that, when the noise is too large, this approach does not work, but merely causes the result to oscillate around the input curve.

6.6 *Iterative van Cittert deconvolution*

An alternative, relatively robust approach to deconvolution (which for single data sets is often easier to implement than Wiener filtering) can be based on the rather general principle of 'operating in reverse'. In exercise 4.21 we illustrated this for a *number*, by computing a cube root iteratively if knowing only how to calculate a cube. In the present case we try to find the unknown *function* that, when subjected to convolution, will yield the observed result. This approach was first applied to deconvolution by van Cittert, *Z. Phys.* 65 (1930) 547, 69 (1931) 298, and given a theoretical and instrumental basis by Burger & van Cittert, *Z. Phys.* 79 (1932) 722, 81 (1933) 428. After computers became readily available, van Cittert's method became much more practical. The idea is as follows. Say that we have a measured spectrum *r*, and the transfer function *t* with which is was convolved, and for which operation we want to correct *r*. In other words, we seek the undistorted spectrum $s = r \oslash t$ given the experimentally measured functions *r* and *t*. To this end we consider *r* the zeroth-order approximation s_0 to *s*, and convolve it with *t* to form $q_1 = s_0 \otimes t = r \otimes t$. This obviously goes the wrong way: q_1 is even more distorted than *r*. But we now assume that we can get a better approximation to s by adding to s_0 the difference between r and q_1, i.e., that $s_1 = s_0 + (r - q_1) = 2r - q_1$ will be a closer approximation to s than s_0.

Repeating this process, we compute $q_2 = s_1 \otimes t$, then add the difference $(r - q_2)$ to s_1 and obtain $s_2 = s_1 + (r - q_2) = 3r - q_1 - q_2$, etc. In general, after n such steps, we will have $s_n = (n+1) r - \sum_1^n q_i$. Burger & van Cittert already studied the convergence behavior of this method, but it is a fairly complicated matter, for which you may want to consult P. B. Crilly's chapter 5 in *Deconvolution of Images and Spectra*, P. A. Jansson ed., Acad. Press (1997) and the references therein for recent results. Exercise 6.6.1 illustrates this approach.

Exercise 6.6.1:

(1) In a new spreadsheet, enter in row 1 the following column headings: #, s, t, r, leave a column blank, then #, r, t, q1, blank column, #, s1, t, q2, blank, #, s2, t, q3, blank, etc.

(2) In the column under #, say A3:A18, deposit the number sequence 0 (1) 15.

(3) In cell B3 then use the instruction =0.9*EXP(-0.5*(A3-8)^2) to calculate a signal, for which we here use a simple Gaussian with amplitude 0.9, standard deviation 1, centered at 8. Copy this instruction down to row 18.

(4) Place =EXP(-0.25*(A3)^2)+EXP(-0.25*(16-A3)^2) in cell C3. This instruction again uses wrap-around to avoid a phase shift, by exploiting the fact that the Fourier transform assumes a cyclic repeat of the signal. (Incidentally, this only works for a *symmetrical* transfer function.) The amplitude of the transfer signal is immaterial, since ConvolveFT will normalize it anyway.

(5) Highlight A3:C18, and call ConvolveFT to compute r in column D.

(6) Copy #, r, and t into the next columns, e.g., with the instructions =A3, =D3, and =C3 in cells F3 through H3, to be copied down to row 18.

(7) Highlight F3:H18, call ConvolveFT, and thus calculate q_1 in column I.

(8) Copy # to column K, and t to M, and in L calculate s_1 as $s_1 = 2r - q_1$.

(9) Convolve s_1 with t to obtain q_2 in column N.

(10) Repeat the process: copy # and t into columns P and R, and in column Q calculate $s_2 = s_2 + r - q_2$. Then convolve to find q_3, and so on.

Fig. 6.6.1 illustrates that s_1 is indeed a better approximation to s than is r, s_2 is better than s_1, etc. For noise-free curves the method usually converges onto s, albeit slowly, even though convergence cannot be taken for granted for arbitrary transfer functions. The first few iterations are usually the most effective, and are easily performed on the spreadsheet. We illustrate this here with 28 synthetic Gaussian peaks that crudely mimic those of Fig. 9 in chapter 7 of P. B. Crilly, W. E. Blass & G. W. Halsey in *Deconvolution of Images and Spectra*, P. A. Jansson, ed., Academic Press (1997). In order to make the exercise more realistic, we will add some noise to r.

Exercise 6.6.2:

(1) In column A of a new spreadsheet place the numbers (0 (1) 511, and in column B generate a synthetic signal s using a number of Gaussian peaks of the form $a \exp[-b(x-c)^2]$. In the examples shown in Figs. 6.6.2 through 6.6.7 we have used $b = 0.1$ throughout (i.e., a standard deviation $s = 1/\sqrt{(2b)} = \sqrt{5} \approx 2.2$), and the parameters a and c as listed in Table 6.6.1.

(2) Column C for the transfer function t should again contain a simple Gaussian, split so that it has its maximum at the beginning of the data set, and its other half at the end of that set. In other words, for the 512-point data set used, the formula to be used is $\exp[-b_t t^2] + \exp[-b_t(t-512)^2]$ if t runs from 0 to 511. In our example we have used $b_t = 0.03125$, for a standard deviation of 4.

$a=$	0.5	0.5	0.6	0.2	0.25	0.15	0.6	0.6	0.25	0.15	0.5	0.6	0.4	0.2
$c=$	28	37	49	73	91	110	127	142	172	178	205	212	216	238

$a=$	0.2	0.25	0.2	0.7	0.6	0.57	0.3	0.03	0.6	0.4	0.35	0.6	0.6	0.07
$c=$	248	262	293	310	320	329	341	361	379	385	390	433	469	496

Table 6.6.1: The parameters used in exercise 6.6.2 for the synthetic 'spectrum'.

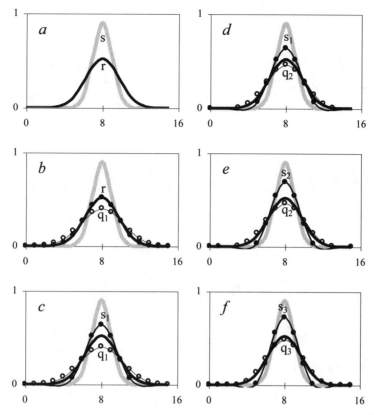

Fig. 6.6.1: The van Cittert *de*convolution method uses only *con*volutions to achieve its goal by working backwards, iteratively. (*a*): An assumed Gaussian signal *s* (gray) is convoluted by a Gaussian transfer function *t* (not shown here) to yield a measured result *r* (heavy black curve), which will be our starting function. (*b*): Convolution of *r* with *t* produces an even more broadened curve, q_1, shown as a thin line with open circles. (*c*): The difference between q_1 and *r* is then used to generate a better approximation s_1 of *s*, shown as a slightly thicker line with solid circles. The process is then repeated (*d*). Three cycles of this iterative procedure are shown, with panel (*e*) showing q_2 and s_2, and (*f*) illustrating q_3 and s_3. The latter is certainly much closer to *s* than *r* (shown as a thick black curve). For numerical details see exercise 6.6.1.

(3) Highlight the data in columns A:C, identify them (e.g., by giving them a light background color), and call ConvolveFT. This will place the function $r = s \otimes t$ in column D.

(4) In the next column, E, deposit Gaussian noise of zero mean and unit standard deviation.

(5) In column F repeat the order numbers from column A, in column G copy *r* plus a fraction of the noise from column E (in our example we have used 0.02) to make the noisy measured signal r_n, and in column H repeat *t*. The data for r_n in column G will be our points of departure.

(6) Highlight (and provide background color to) the data in columns F:H, and call ConvolveFT to compute $q_1 = r_n \otimes t$, which will appear in column I.

(7) In column J again copy the numbers from column A, in column K calculate $s_1 = 2r_n - q_1$, and in column L copy *t* from column C.

(8) Highlight (and color) the data in columns J:L, and call ConvolveFT to compute (in column M) the function $q_2 = s_1 \otimes t$.

(9) In column N copy the numbers from column A, in column O calculate $s_2 = s_1 + (r_n - q_2)$, and in column P copy *t* from column C.

(10) Repeat the instructions in (8) and (9) to calculate first $q_3 = s_2 \otimes t$, then $s_3 = s_2 + (r_n - q_3)$, etc.

(11) Plot your results. If you have used the numerical values listed, your results should resemble those in Figs. 6.6.2 and 6.6.3.

(12) Now if you want to modify the signal *s* and/or the transfer function *t*, just change them in column B and/or C, then highlight the color-coded areas one by one, going from left to right, and call ConvolveFT. In the same way you can change the noise level in column G and then call ConvolveFT starting with columns F:H.

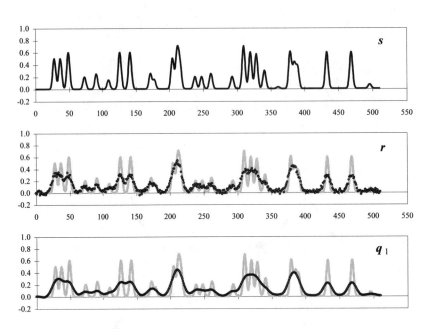

Fig. 6.6.2: Top panel: the mock undistorted 'spectrum' *s*, repeated in gray in the other panels. Middle panel: the convolution of *s* with a single Gaussian *t*, plus noise, simulating a measured spectrum. Bottom panel: q_1 as obtained by convolution of *r* with *t*.

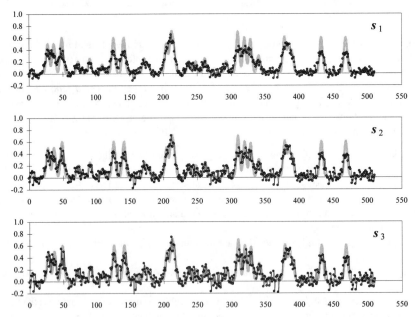

Fig. 6.6.3: Successive estimates of *s* by iterative deconvolution of the noisy simulated spectrum *r* shown in the middle panel of Fig. 6.6.2.

DeconvolveIt0

FilterLength 11

Figure 6.6.3 illustrates the usual problem with deconvolution: noise. While the signal 'grows into' the peaks with each successive iteration, the noise also grows, but faster. To understand why this happens, consider that $s_1 = r_n + (r_n - q_1)$, and that q_1 is much smoother than r_n, see Fig. 6.6.2. We now write $r_n = r_o + n$, where r_o represents *r* in the absence of noise, and *n* is the noise. Let the convolution reduce the noise *n* in r_n to αn in q_1, where $|\alpha| \ll 1$. Then $s1 = 2r_n - q_1 = (2r_o - q_1) + (2n - \alpha) n$, which has almost twice as

284

much noise as r since $|\alpha| \ll 1$. The same argument applies to subsequent iteration stages, so that the noise increases almost linearly with the number of iterations while s_i creeps up on s at the steadily decreasing rate of an asymptotic approach. But when the noise grows faster than the signal, the iteration cannot converge, and the process ultimately becomes oscillatory, obliterating the signal.

Exercise 6.6.2 (continued):

(13) In any iterative process we need to have a termination criterion, otherwise the process can go on indefinitely. Since our starting function is r_n, and the procedure is based on trying to match r_n with q_i, calculate the sum of squares of the residuals between the data in columns G and I, G and M, G and Q, etc., using the instruction =SUMXMY2 (*function1*, *function2*). These numbers duly decrease upon successive iterations. This suggests that you might be able to use this SSR to determine when to stop the iteration: whenever it becomes smaller than a given value, or starts to go up.

(14) But now try to use the same instruction to determine the sum of squares of the residuals between s (in column B) and successive versions of s_i (in columns K, O, etc.). Not realistic, because we normally have no access to s which, after all, is the function we *seek*. Still, in this simulation, it is instructive to take a look: in the presence of sufficient noise, as in our numerical example, this SSR *increases* with successive iterations. Therefore, using the sum of squares of the differences between r_n and q_i as suggested under point (13) can be misleading, yet in practice we have no other option.

A possible way to get around noise is to incorporate smoothing at every iteration step, as was done, e.g., by Herget et al., *J. Opt. Soc. Am.* 52 (1962) 1113. Now the spreadsheet becomes much more complicated, and we therefore use a custom macro to take care of the busywork. DeconvolveIt performs the convolutions interspersed with smoothing steps, using a moving least squares parabola of variable length to keep the noise in check. Since the data must be equidistant for the Fourier transform convolution, we can use the method of section 3.15.

Exercise 6.6.2 (continued):

(15) In the next three columns copy the data from columns A (the numbers representing the independent variable), G (for r_n) and C (for t), then highlight the data in these three new columns, and call DeconvolveIt0. Accept the default no-filter value 0, and let the macro run. You can follow its progress by observing its intermediate results, displayed in the left-hand corner of the bar below the spreadsheet. After your patience has grown thin, interrupt the program with the Escape key Esc, terminate it, and plot. You will find that the result oscillates wildly, and shows no inclination to converge.

(16) Again highlight the data in those three columns, and call DeconvolveIt0, but now use different lengths of the parabolic filter. If the noise level is not too high, you should be able to find a filter length that will generate a useful deconvolution, such as in the top panel of Fig. 6.6.4.

(17) For comparison, also try DeconvolveFT. Again, without filtering it will not converge (if you have noise comparable to that in Fig. 6.6.2r), but you should be able to find a workable result with the built-in, adjustable von Hann filter, see the bottom panel of Fig. 6.6.4.

Neither method would yield a convergent result without filtering. By using different filter parameters, both methods have some flexibility, and the nature of the filters is obviously quite different. Still, for comparable noise, the iterative method clearly outperforms direct deconvolution in this example.

Instead of relying on the smoothing filters that are built into these macros, one can use Wiener filtering followed by filter-free deconvolution. That gives a fairer comparison of the two methods, and is illustrated below and in Fig. 6.6.6. Again, the iterative method takes more time but comes out ahead of the direct one in terms of signal recovery.

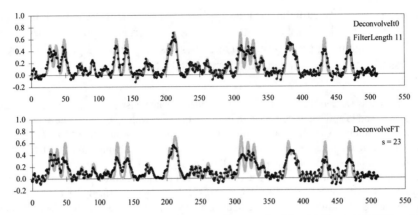

Fig. 6.6.4: Deconvolution of a noisy signal by the iterative macro DeconvolveIt0, which required 28 iterations (top panel) and, for comparison (bottom panel) the results of deconvolving with DeconvolveFT, using the adjustable von Hann filter with $s = 23$.

Exercise 6.6.2 (continued):

(18) In the next two columns again copy the numbers from column A and from column G (for r_n), and C (for t), then highlight the data in these two new columns plus the one to its right (which should be empty), and call ForwardFT. This will create three now columns, one for frequency, one for R', and one for R''.

(19) In the next column compute $\log M^2 = \log [(R')^2 + (R'')^2]$, and plot it versus frequency.

(20) Fit simple curves to $\log (S^2)$ and $\log (N^2)$, see Fig. 6.6.5, and in the next column compute the Wiener filter $10^{\log(S^2)}\big/(10^{\log(S^2)} + 10^{\log(N^2)})$ which, in our example, translates into $10^{-1.8-40|f|}\big/(10^{-1.8-40|f|} + 10^{-5.5})$.

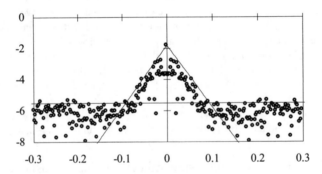

Fig. 6.6.5: The power spectrum of the noisy input data can be fitted to the simple, approximate expressions $\log(S^2) = -1.8 - 40|f|$ and $\log(N^2) = -5.5$, as shown.

(21) In the next column again copy the numbers from column A, and in the next two calculate the product of R' and R'' respectively with the data in the Wiener filter column.

(22) Call InverseFT. The second of these contains the filtered r, while the third contains only junk data that should all be zero. Replace the latter by copies of t, then highlight these three columns and call DeconvolveIt0. You may have to interrupt it fairly early; if you let it run, it can consume considerable time but most likely make a worse fit. Plot your result. In the example shown in Fig. 6.6.6, the iteration was cut short at 100.

(23) For comparison also run DeconvolveFT. The two results are compared in Fig. 6.6.6.

286

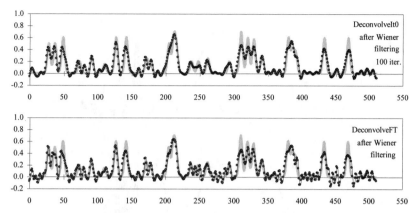

Fig. 6.6.6: The results of Wiener filtering followed by either iterative deconvolution (top panel) or straight Fourier transform deconvolution (bottom panel).

In this example, the iterative deconvolution again holds its own against direct deconvolution. We note that both methods produce negative values, mostly in regions where the signal is small. When these simulated data represent an actual optical spectrum, such negative values would be physically meaningless, and can of course be lopped off if that makes you feel better. DeconvolveIt1 removes the negative values during each iteration. The systematic bias introduced by doing so is believed to be small, because the correction occurs only in regions of weak signals. Results so obtained with DeconvolveIt1 are shown in Fig. 6.6.7.

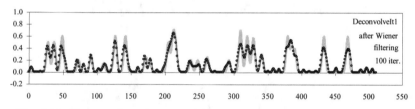

Fig. 6.6.7: The same data after Wiener filtering followed by use of DeconvolveIt1.

At this point it may be useful to look back, in order to compare Fig. 6.6.7 with Fig. 6.6.2*r* and the data of Table 6.6.1. Starting from the left, the two peaks at 28 and 37 are clearly resolved by deconvolution, and the peak at 49 is almost baseline-separated. On the other hand, deconvolution has introduced peaks centered at 5, 82, and 104 that do not occur in the original. Likewise, the two overlapping peaks at 172 and 178 are replaced by two that are more clearly resolved than the original ones, plus two satellite peaks, at 162 and 190. And so it goes for the rest of the spectrum: the shapes of existing peaks are often improved, but additional, fabricated peaks appear as well. It would seem that the Fourier transformation, by looking for sinusoidal components, is the primary source of these extra peaks, and that cutting off their negative portions makes them more convincingly look like peaks rather than processing noise.

One can combine a weighting function that discriminates against negative points with one that removes data above a given limit, say, 1. Such a modification was introduced by P. A. Jansson et al., *J. Opt. Soc. Am.* 58 (1968) 1665, 60 (1970) 184, and is implemented in DeconvolveIt2. If the latter macro is used, the data should be scaled to fit appropriately in the range from 0 to 1.

More efficient iterative deconvolution can often be achieved by introducing a relaxation factor. We will not do so here, as it would carry us too far from our simple goal of illustrating what deconvolution is and does. Instead, in section 6.7 we will offer an alternative approach that can give superior results in those cases to which it is applicable.

287

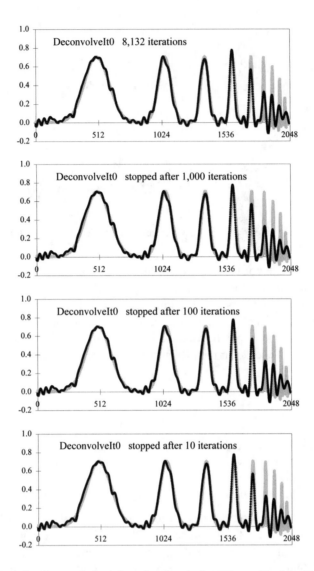

Fig. 6.6.8: Iterative deconvolution of a noisy signal after Wiener filtering, illustrating that the built-in termination criterion may be gross overkill. Then top panel ran for 8,132 iterations; shorter runs were obtained by changing the iteration limit in the DeconvolveIt macro.

The above involves a fairly typical, relatively easy deconvolution, because the original signal *s* did not contain any details that were lost completely in the original distortion. In this respect, iterative deconvolution has limitations similar to those of direct deconvolution, as illustrated in Fig. 6.6.8, where we use the noisy test data set illustrated in Fig. 6.5.3 after Wiener filtering, and merely replaced the final deconvolution step by DeconvolveIt0. The results are not significantly different from those of Fig. 6.5.3*d*.

We note that the iteration stopped after 8,132 steps, using as its termination criterion that SSR (for the difference between the input function *r* and that calculated during each iteration) decreases, but that there is relatively little gain (and much time to lose) in going beyond the first few iterations. It is amusing to look at those SSR values: SSR $= 4.8 \times 10^{-25}$ for 8,132 steps, 1.4×10^{-20} for 1,000 steps, 2.7×10^{-14} for 100 steps, and only 9.1×10^{-6} for 10 steps, yet the resulting deconvolutions are rather similar.

These examples suggest that the iterative method can yield marginally better results. Whether this holds true in general cannot be answered in the abstract, because it will depend on the nature of the signal,

288

on the kind of blurring for which correction is sought (such as amplifier distortion, optical aberration, camera motion, tip profile in scanning probe microscopy), and on the type of noise. The above comparisons all involved triply Gaussian data (based on Gaussian curves, with Gaussian blurring, plus Gaussian noise), and may therefore be most appropriate for classical (near-ultraviolet to infrared) optical spectroscopy and chromatography. Other methods may well yield other outcomes.

Sometimes the signal itself may suggest how best to approach it. If we see a spectrum that exhibits characteristic sinc-like sidelobes, we can estimate the width of the pulse that most likely caused it, and use that information for deconvolution. The same approach, in two dimensions, may be applicable to astronomical data that show the equivalent rings around inherently point-like object such as stars.

An early example of the application of the van Cittert approach was published by S. Hüfner & G. K. Wertheim in *Phys. Revs.* B11 (1975) 678. They deconvolved x-ray photo-emission spectra of a number of metals in order to correct for the broadening effect of the spectrometer. The resulting (considerably narrower and higher but also much noisier) curves were then fitted by nonlinear least squares to their theoretical line shapes.

6.7 *Iterative deconvolution using Solver*

The van Cittert deconvolution method is general but quite sensitive to noise. An alternative approach was introduced by Grinvald & Steinberg in Anal. Biochem. 59 (1974) 583. It uses reverse engineering based on an assumed analytical (and therefore noise-free) function for the undistorted model signal $s_m = f(a_i)$ in terms of one or more model parameters a_i. We convolve the model signal s_m based on guessed parameters a_i with the experimental transfer function t to obtain $r_m = s_m \otimes t$. We then use Solver to adjust the a_i by minimizing the sum of squares of the residuals between r_m and the experimental (or, in our example, simulated) r_{exp}. The requirement that s_m be describable as an explicit analytical function is somewhat restrictive but, when applicable, can greatly reduce noise.

Because macros do not self-update, Solver cannot respond automatically to the effect of parameter changes that involve macros. This means that, for a non-manual program, we can either rewrite Solver so that it can accommodate macros, or (much simpler) perform the convolution using a function rather than a macro. The latter approach is illustrated in exercise 6.7.1.

Exercise 6.7.1:

(1) Our example will be modeled after exercise 6.2.2 and fig. 6.2.3, i.e., based on a single exponential decay. In cells A1:D1 deposit the column labels #, s, t, and r for the rank number # (which can represent time, wavelength, etc), original (undistorted) signal *s*, filter or transfer function *t*, and result *r*.

(2) In A3 place the value –100, in A4 the instruction =A3+1, and copy this down to cell A303.

(3) In B103 insert the instruction =$D$97*EXP(-$D$98*A103) for the transfer function *t*, and copy this down to row 303. In cell D97 enter an amplitude value (such as 1) and in cell D98 a value for a rate constant (e.g., 0.03), with accompanying labels in column C.

(4) For the transfer function *t*, in cell C103 place the instruction =EXP(-1*(LN(1+(A103-$D$100)/$D$101))^2) and copy this down to row 303.

(5) Highlight A103:C303 and call the macro Convolve, which will write the convolution *r* in D103:D303.

(6) Deposit Gaussian ('normal') noise (with mean 0 and standard deviation 1) in N103:O303, and supply corresponding scale values, such as 0.01 in cell N100 and 0.02 in cell O100.

(7) In cell E103 place the instruction =C103+$N$100*N103 to simulate a noisy transfer function t_{exp}, in cell F103 use =D103+$O$100*O103 for a noisy response signal r_{exp}, and copy both instructions down to row 303. In row 1 place appropriate labels. You now have a set of simulated, noisy data to try the deconvolution. In a real application these simulated values should of course to be replaced by experimental data, as anticipated by their labels.

(8) In G103 place a model function, such as =$I$97*EXP(-$I$98*A103). Copy it down to row 303, and label it in G1 as s model. Place a guess value for the amplitude in I97, and an initial estimate for the rate constant in I98, with accompanying labels in column H. Do not place any numbers or text in G3:G102, but instead fill it with, e.g., yellow, to remind yourself to keep it clear.

(9) In cell H103 deposit the function `=Convol(G103:G202,$E$103: $E$202,100)` and copy it all the way to row 303. In cell H1 label the column as r model.

(10) Go to the VBA module and enter the following code for this function:

```
Function Convol(Array1, Array2, N)

Dim i As Integer
Dim Sum1 As Double, Sum2 As Double
Dim Array3 As Variant
ReDim Array3(1 To 2 * N)

Sum2 = 0
For i = 1 To N
  Sum2 = Sum2 + Array2(i)
Next i

For i = 1 To N
  Array3(i) = Array2(N + 1 - i)
Next i

Sum1 = 0
For i = 1 To N
  Sum1 = Sum1 + Array1(i - N + 1) * Array3(i)
Next i

Convol = Sum1 / Sum2

End Function
```

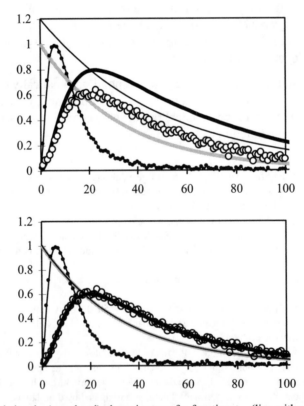

Fig. 6.7.1: The assumed signal s (gray band), the noisy transfer function t_{exp} (line with small solid points), the result r_{exp} obtained by convolving s with the (noise-free) transfer function and then adding noise (large open circles), the assumed model function s_m (line) and the resulting function r_m after convolving s_m with t_{exp} (heavy line). The top panel shows the situation just before calling Solver, the bottom panel that after Solver has been used.

290

(11) In cell I100 deposit the function `=SUMXMY2(F103:F303,H103:H303)` and place a corresponding label such as SSR= in H100.

(12) Call Solver, and Set Target Cell to I100, Equal to Min, By Changing Cells I97:I98. Then engage SolverAid to find the corresponding uncertainties.

(13) Compare your results with those in fig. 6.7.1 which shows them before and after using Solver.

This exercise demonstrates the principle of the method. We started with amplitude $a = 1$ and rate constant $k = 0.03$, used as initial guess values $a_m = 1.5$ and $k_m = 0.02$, and then found $a_m = 1.005 \pm 0.009$ and $k_m = 0.0300 \pm 0.0004$, with a standard deviation $s_y = 0.02_0$ of the fit in r.

In practice, try to keep the convolving custom function as simple as possible, and especially avoid IF statements which tend to slow it down. We have used a barebones custom function Convol() to keep it simple, even though it is wasteful of spreadsheet real estate.

When the data involve a shift in time, try to adjust its initial estimate by trial and error in the graph, using a critical region (such as where the response takes off) where it makes a significant difference, because the least squares criterion is often not very sensitive to horizontal shifts, but looks at vertical differences, and averages over the entire curve.

6.8 Deconvolution by parameterization

Many approaches to deconvolution are quite sensitive to noise, and may therefore require filtering, which (when not carefully compensated in the deconvolution routine) can again lead to distortion and loss of detail. The method described in section 6.7 avoids this problem by fitting the experimental data to a noise-free analytical function. Below we will carry this approach to its logical conclusion by using a noise-free convolution as well. Even though this approach has a somewhat limited applicability, it may still work when earlier-described methods fail.

To illustrate its basic idea (Am. J. Phys. 72 (2004) 644), we will here consider only a relatively simple case in which a measured $r$esult r of the convolution, say, a spectrum or a chromatogram, can be described as a sum of Gaussian curves, $r = \Sigma g_r$, while the $t$ransfer function t is given by a single Gaussian, $t = g_t$. We have already seen in chapter 4 how we can use Solver to fit complicated functions in terms of sums of Gaussians, and we will now apply this to deconvolution. Again we use bold lowercase symbols to indicate time-dependent functions rather than constants.

The approach we will take here substitutes deconvolving r with t by instead deconvolving Σg_r with g_t. Because g_r and g_t are fitted, noise-free analytical functions, this greatly reduces the effect of noise on the deconvolution. Noise only affects the result insofar as it limits the proper assignment of the Gaussians g_r and g_t. The actual calculation is straightforward, the most critical part of the procedure being the initial fitting of Gaussians to the experimental functions r and t.

We will first deconvolve two single N-point Gaussians, g_r and g_t that are both functions of a common parameter t which can represent elution time, wavelength, wavenumber, etc. We therefore start with the mathematical functions

$$g_r = a_r \exp\{-\tfrac{1}{2}\,[(t-c_r)/b_r]^2\} \tag{6.8.1}$$

and

$$g_t = a_t \exp\{-\tfrac{1}{2}\,[(t-c_t)/b_t]^2\} \tag{6.8.2}$$

which, upon analytical Fourier transformation, yield

$$G_r = [(2\pi)^{\frac{1}{2}}\,a_r\,b_r/N]\,\exp[-2\pi j f c_r]\,\exp[-2(\pi b_r f)^2] \tag{6.8.3}$$

$$= [(2\pi)^{\frac{1}{2}}\,a_r\,b_r/N]\,\exp[-2(\pi b_r f)^2]\,[\cos(2\pi f c_r) - j\sin(2\pi f c_r)]$$

and

$$G_t = [(2\pi)^{\frac{1}{2}}\,a_t\,b_t/N]\,\exp[-2\pi j f c_t]\,\exp[-2(\pi b_t f)^2]$$

$$= [(2\pi)^{\frac{1}{2}} a_t b_t / N] \exp[-2(\pi b_t f)^2] [\cos(2\pi f c_t) - j \sin(2\pi f c t_r)] \tag{6.8.4}$$

respectively, where we have used Euler's relation $e^{-jx} = \cos(x) - j\sin(x)$. From these we obtain by division

$$\boldsymbol{G_s} = \boldsymbol{G_r} / \boldsymbol{G_t} \tag{6.8.5}$$
$$= [a_r b_r / a_t b_t] \exp[-2\pi j f(c_r - c_t)] \exp[-2\pi^2 (b_r^2 - b_t^2) f^2]$$

so that the original, undistorted signal is given by

$$\boldsymbol{g_s} = \boldsymbol{g_r} \oslash \boldsymbol{g_t} = \frac{a_r b_r N}{a_t b_t \sqrt{2\pi(b_r^2 - b_t^2)}} \exp\frac{-(t - c_r + c_t)^2}{2(b_r^2 - b_t^2)^2} = a_s \exp\{-\tfrac{1}{2}[(t - c_s)/b_s]^2\} \tag{6.8.6}$$

where

$$a_s = \frac{a_r b_r N}{a_t b_t \sqrt{2\pi(b_r^2 - b_t^2)}} = \frac{a_r b_r N}{a_t b_t b_s \sqrt{2\pi}} \tag{6.8.7}$$

$$b_s = (b_r^2 - b_t^2)^{\frac{1}{2}} \tag{6.8.8}$$

and

$$c_s = c_r - c_t \tag{6.8.9}$$

In other words, once we have characterized the two Gaussian functionss $\boldsymbol{g_r}$ and $\boldsymbol{g_t}$ in terms of the constants a_r, b_r, c_r and a_t, b_t, and c_t respectively, we can simply *calculate* the deconvoluted Gaussian $\boldsymbol{g_s}$.

Note that the constants b in eqs. (6.8.1) and (6.8.2) have the dimensions and functions of standard deviations. Equation (6.8.8) shows that their squares, the corresponding variances, are additive in convolution, $b_r^2 = b_t^2 + b_s^2$, and subtractive in deconvolution, $b_s^2 = b_r^2 - b_t^2$. With Gaussians, it is therefore easy to predict how much convolution will broaden peaks, and how much deconvolution can possibly sharpen them.

Typically the experimental response r to be corrected by deconvolution is calibrated, in which case we will want to maintain that calibration by deconvolving with a function that has been scaled to have unit average. In the case of a Gaussian $\boldsymbol{g_t}$ that implies that we should use

$$a_t = \frac{N}{b_t \sqrt{2\pi}} \tag{6.8.10}$$

so that (6.8.7) reduces to

$$a_s = a_r b_r (b_r^2 - b_t^2)^{-\frac{1}{2}} = a_r b_r / b_s \tag{6.8.11}$$

Moreover, the value of c_t is usually arbitrary. If we simply set it to zero, (6.8.9) becomes

$$c_s = c_r \tag{6.8.12}$$

When r must be expressed as a *sum* of Gaussians, $r = \Sigma \boldsymbol{g_r}$, the same approach can be used, because then $\boldsymbol{R} = \Sigma \boldsymbol{G_r}$ and $\boldsymbol{T} = \boldsymbol{G_t}$ so that

$$\boldsymbol{S} = \frac{\boldsymbol{R}}{\boldsymbol{T}} = \frac{\sum\limits_{i=1}^{r} \boldsymbol{G_{ri}}}{\boldsymbol{G_t}} = \sum\limits_{i=1}^{r} \frac{\boldsymbol{G_{ri}}}{\boldsymbol{G_t}} = \sum\limits_{i=1}^{r} \boldsymbol{S_i} \tag{6.8.13}$$

Exercise 6.8.1 illustrates this procedure for the deconvolution of the data shown in Fig. 6.2.4.

Exercise 6.8.1:
   (1) Retrieve the spreadsheet used in exercise 6.2.3, or repeat that exercise.
   (2) In cells E20:H20 deposit column headings for t_{exp}, r_{exp}, t_{model}, r_{model}, and the recovered value s_{recov}, and in N20 and O20 place headings for noise n.
   (3) Generate Gaussian noise of zero mean and unit standard deviation in N22:O321.

292

(4) Place appropriate noise amplitudes for t and r in cells C19 and D19 respectively, in E22:E321 compute the function t with added noise with, e.g., the instruction =C22+$C$19*N22 in cell E22. Similarly compute a noisy version of r in column F, using noise from column O. Plot these noisy versions of t and s, as in Fig. 6.8.1c.

(5) In H2:H16 place the labels ar1=, br1=, cr1=, ar2=, br2=, cr2=, ar3=, br3=, cr3=, ar4=, br4=, cr4=, at=, bt=, and ct=. Alternatively you can copy them from F2:F16, then modify them.

(6) In cell G22 deposit =$I$14*EXP(-0.5*((A22-$I$16)/$I$15)^2), and copy this instruction down to row 321. Enter this curve in the just-made plot.

(7) Place numerical values in I14:I16 so that the resulting curve approximately fits curve t_{exp}. (You may first want to color the data in G2:G16 white, so that you will not be tempted to look at the data originally taken for the simulation of s. When you are done fitting the data, change their color back to black or whatever.)

(8) In cell F19 calculate SSR for t as =SUMXMY2(E22:E321,G22:G321).

(9) Call Solver, and let it minimize SSR in F19 by adjusting the guessed parameter values in I14:I16.

(10) Likewise, in cell H22 place the instruction =$I$2*EXP(-0.5*((A22-$I$4)/$I$3)^2)+ ... +$I$11*EXP(-0.5*((A22-$I$13)/$I$12)^2), copy this down to row 321, and enter this curve in the graph.

(11) Compute SSR for r as =SUMXMY2(F22:F321,H22:H321).

(12) Use the curve made under point (9) to guess numerical values for a_{r1} through c_{r4} in I2:I13 so that the resulting curve approximately fits the data r_{exp}.

(13) Call Solver to refine these values by minimizing SSR in cell H19. Do this adjustment groupwise: first let Solver adjust I2:I3, then call it again to adjust I5:I7, then I2:I7, then I8:I10, I11:I13, I8:I13, and finally I2:I13. The graph might now resemble Fig. 6.8.1d.

(14) In K2:K13 copy the labels as1=, bs1=, ... cs4= from F2:F13.

(15) In L4 calculate $c_{s1} = c_{r1} - c_t$, i.e., as =H3-$H$15.

(16) In L3 compute $b_{s1} = \sqrt{(b_{r1}^2 - b_t^2)}$, or =SQRT(H2^2-$H$14^2).

(17) In L2 calculate $a_{s1} = a_{r1} b_{r1} / b_{s1}$, with =H1*H2/J2.

(18) Copy the block L2:L4 to L5, L8, and L11.

(19) In cell H22 compute the reconstituted signal s_{recov} with the instruction =$L$2*EXP(-0.5*((A22-$L$4)/$L$3)^2)+ ... +$L$11*EXP(-0.5*((A22-$L$13)/$L$12)^2), and copy this down to row 321.

(20) Plot this curve, and compare it with Fig. 6.8.1f.

(21) In this graph also display the function s used as the starting point of this simulation from B22:B321, a repeat from Fig. 6.8.1a.

This method can indeed reconstitute most features of the original curve, at least in a favorable case such as shown Fig. 6.8.1f, where all peaks are Gaussian, and can be identified as such in r despite the noise.

Exercise 6.8.1 (continued):

(22) Call SolverAid, enter the Solver-determined parameters in I2:I13, the location of SSR for r (H19), and the column (H22:H321) in which r was calculated. Let SolverAid display the covariance matrix in N2:Y13. It will also deposit the standard deviations of the individual parameters in J2:J13.

(23) Once more call SolverAid, this time to find the uncertainty estimates for t. Therefore enter the location (I14:I16) of the Solver-determined parameters, the location (F19) of SSR for t, and that (G22:G321) of the column where t was computed. Place the covariance matrix in Z14:AB16, so that it shares its main diagonal with that in N2:Y13.

(24) Call Propagation, and give it I2:I16 as input parameters, N2:AB16 as covariance matrix, and L2 as function. It will then place the corresponding standard deviation in M2. Repeat this for the other 11 results in column L. Sorry, Propagation handles only one parameter at a time.

The data in Table 6.8.1 illustrate the results obtained, and allow one to consider them quantitatively, because the method can provide its own uncertainty estimates. These indicate the level of agreement between the parameters used to simulate s and those recovered after convolution, noise addition, and deconvolution. For all 12 coefficients of s_{recov} the agreement between the recovered value of s and that used in the simulation of Fig. 6.8.1a is within two standard deviations. Thus the original signal is retrieved within the uncertainty limits generated by the custom macros SolverAid and Propagation. The standard deviations depend, of course, on the amount of noise added.

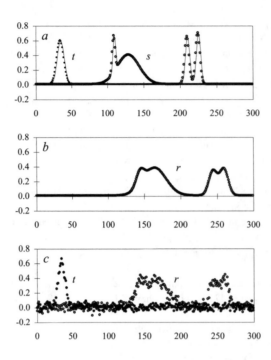

Fig. 6.8.1: Top and middle: replicas from Fig. 6.2.4, showing in panel *a* the original simulated spectrum *s* and the distorting transfer function *t*, and in panel *b* its convolution leading to the result *r*. Bottom panel, *c*: the same as in panel *b* after adding random noise.

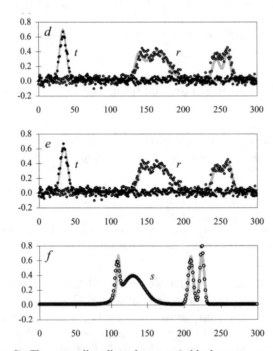

Fig. 6.8.1 (continued): The manually adjusted curves (with the parameters selected 'by eye') through the noisy data (gray curves in panel *d*), the same after Solver has refined the parameter estimates (panel *e*), and the resulting deconvoluted signal *s* (open circles in panel *f*). Panel *f* also displays, as a thick gray line, the original curve of the simulated function *s* repeated from panel *a*.

s_{taken}	$r_{guessed}$	r_{found}	$r_{st.dev.}$	s_{found}	$s_{st.dev.}$
$a_{s1}= 0.5$	$a_{r1}= 0.3$	0.23_1	0.03_0	$a_{s1}= 0.4_4$	0.1_4
$b_{s1}= 2$	$b_{r1}= 5$	5.6_9	0.7_5	$b_{s1}= 3._0$	$1._5$
$c_{s1}= 110$	$c_{r1}= 140$	144.3_0	0.4_9	$c_{s1}= 109.1_1$	0.5_1
$a_{s2}= 0.4$	$a_{r2}= 0.4$	0.36_4	0.01_0	$a_{s2}= 0.38_2$	0.01_1
$b_{s2}= 15$	$b_{r2}= 14$	15.9_5	0.9_6	$b_{s2}= 15._2$	$1._0$
$c_{s2}= 130$	$c_{r2}= 165$	$166._3$	$1._2$	$c_{s2}= 131._1$	$1._2$
$a_{s3}= 0.65$	$a_{r3}= 0.3$	0.34_5	0.01_7	$a_{s3}= 0.6_0$	0.1_3
$b_{s3}= 3$	$b_{r3}= 5$	5.9_5	0.6_0	$b_{s3}= 3._4$	$1._0$
$c_{s3}= 210$	$c_{r3}= 245$	245.3_6	0.7_1	$c_{s3}= 210.1_9$	0.7_2
$a_{s4}= 0.7$	$a_{r4}= 0.4$	0.37_7	0.01_9	$a_{s4}= 0.8_0$	0.2_6
$b_{s4}= 3$	$b_{r4}= 4$	5.5_0	0.5_0	$b_{s4}= 2._6$	$1._1$
$c_{s4}= 225$	$c_{r4}= 260$	260.7_5	0.6_1	$c_{s4}= 225.5_7$	0.6_2

t_{taken}	$t_{guessed}$	t_{found}	$t_{st.dev.}$
$a_t= 0.6$	0.7	0.61_5	0.01_3
$b_t= 5$	4.5	4.8_5	0.1_2
$c_t= 35$	34	35.1_8	0.1_2

Table 6.8.1: Some numerical results from exercise 6.8.1. The column labeled s_{taken} lists the values used for simulating the data in Fig. 6.8.1*a*. The columns $r_{guessed}$ and $t_{guessed}$ contain the initial guess values shown in Fig. 6.8.1*c.*, and the next two columns the values obtained by Solver for the parameters, and those obtained by SolverAid for their standard deviations. Finally, the column s_{found} displays the deconvolved signal *s* as computed from r_{found} and $t_{found,}$ and the column $s_{st.dev.}$ the corresponding uncertainty estimates. The added noise was Gaussian with zero mean and standard deviations of 0.04 and 0.03 for *r* and *t* respectively.

This method works, and does not lead to oscillatory instabilities. Its applicability depends, of course, on how well one can represent both the measured result **R** and the transfer function **T** in terms of model expressions with relatively simple Fourier transforms, so that the inverse Fourier transform of their quotient **R**/**T** can be expressed in analytical form. All baseline-separated peaks and peak aggregates can be treated individually. As a side benefit this method can furnish estimates of the standard deviations of the deconvolved signal *s*.

6.9 Time-frequency analysis

Fourier transformation presumes a steady state, because it considers the data set as one unit of an infinitely repeating sequence of identical units. Yet, there are many phenomena with frequency content that are not stationary, such as speech and music. In fact, music is an interesting example because its common form of notation, musical script, is really a graph of frequency (the pitch of the notes to be played) as a function of time, complete with grid lines for both time (vertical lines identifying the various measures) and frequency (the horizontal lines of the staff). It even has explicit time notation (for the lengths of notes and rests) and the corresponding scale factors (tempo indicators and/or metronome settings). Musical script is, of course, a set of instructions for the performer. We here address how, other than by ear, can we analyze and visualize sound (or any equivalent, non-auditory signal) as a function of time *and* frequency.

Time-frequency or Gabor transformation (D. Gabor, *J. Inst. Elect. Engin.* 93 (1946) 429) is an analysis in which a sliding time window moves stepwise along the data, dropping one or more points on one side, and gaining the same number of data points on the other. After each step, a Fourier transformation is applied. It is an inherently imprecise approach because the product of the resolutions in time and frequency is subject to the uncertainty relationship discussed in section 5.5. (That uncertainty is intrinsic to the problem of plotting frequency vs. time, and independent of the use of Fourier transformation or any other specific analysis method.) The uncertainty can be minimized with a Gaussian window function, which we therefore use. As a practical matter, we will exploit the fast Fourier transformation algorithm, and therefore require that the data be equidistant in time, as they usually are with sampled time-dependent signals.

The Gabor transform macro uses a Gaussian window function of N contiguous data points (with $N = 2^n$ where n is a positive integer) on a data set containing M data, where $M > N$. It starts with the first N data points in the set, multiplies these by the window function, and then performs a Fourier transformation on that product. It then moves the window function over by one point, and repeats this process $M–N+1$ times until it has reached the end of the data set. The results are returned to the spreadsheet as a function of time and frequency, and can then be plotted as, e.g., a 3-D plot of the absolute magnitude of the sound as a function of time and frequency. Such a plot is called a *sonogram*.

When the data set is so large that it would result in more than 250 columns (and therefore might exceed the 256-column width of the pre-2007 Excel spreadsheet), the macro will automatically move the window function each time by several data points, and the user can further restrict the size of the output file. If this presents a problem, modify the macro so that it stores rather than displays the data, or use rows instead of columns, since the spreadsheet contains many more rows than columns. In Excel 2007 and beyond, remove this condition from the code.

Exercise 6.9.1:

(1) Start a new spreadsheet. Leave the top 10 rows for graphs, and the next 4 rows for constants and column headings.

(2) Starting in cell A15 of column A deposit time t in constant increments Δt, such as $t = 0$ (1) 1000.

(3) In column B deposit as a trial function, such as with the instruction =(SIN($B$11*A15))/(EXP(-0.1*(A15-200))+EXP(0.003*(A15-200))) which has as frequency the value specified in B11 divided by 2π. Its amplitude, given by $1/\{\exp[-0.1(t–200)] + \exp[0.003(t–200)]\}$, quickly rises just before $t = 200$, and then slowly decays, somewhat like a note played on a piano.

(4) Plot the trial function; it should look like Fig. 6.9.1.

(5) Call the macro Gabor, and in its successive input boxes enter the time increments (here: 1), the location of the input data (here: B15:B1015), and the (optional) integer to restrict the number of samples to be analyzed (which you can leave at its default value of 5).

(6) The macro will now generate a data array, listing the frequency in its first column, and the rank number of the first data point used in each window in its top row. Inclusion of these parameters makes it easy to generate a labeled 3-D plot as well as a surface map.

(7) Make a 3-D plot of the result, and also a surface map with Mapper.

(8) Obviously, for such a simple trial function, you need not go through all this trouble. You may notice that the 3-D map for a sizable array is slow to rotate, and that its presence slows down the operation of the spreadsheet whenever it must be redrawn on the screen.

(9) Now add some harmonics, as in a chord. Extend the instruction in cells B15:B1015 to include three additional terms, identical to the first one except that their frequencies are specified by cells C11, D11, and E11 respectively.

(10) In C11 deposit the instruction =B11*2^(3/12), in D11 the instruction =C11*2^(4/12), and in E11 the instruction =D11*2^(5/12), for the harmonics of a major chord, such as C-E-G-C. On the Western, 'well-tempered' musical scale, all half-notes differ in frequency by a factor of 2^(1/12).

(11) The resulting signal is not so transparent any more, see Fig. 6.9.2.

(12) Now repeat the process of Gabor transformation and mapping. The map should now look similar to that of Fig. 6.9.3b.

(13) Now the surface map reveals very clearly the four different notes, starting at the same time but at different frequencies. The notes appear to start at about $t = 100$, whereas they really start only around $t = 200$. This time distortion results from the use of a Gaussian filter in the Gabor transformation macro.

(14) Modify the instruction in cells B15:B1015 to correspond with a broken chord, in which the various notes start one after the other, say, at $t = 200$, 300, 400, and 500 respectively. Fig. 6.9.4 illustrates such a signal, and Fig. 6.9.5 its Gabor transform.

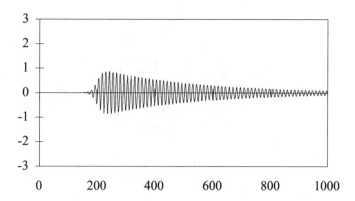

Fig. 6.9.1: The test function used, with the value 0.5 in cell B11.

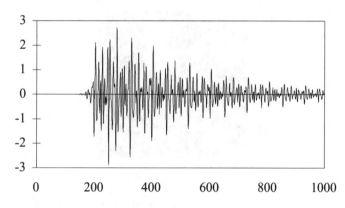

Fig. 6.9.2: The extended test function used, again with the value 0.5 in cell B11.

With such complicated signals we can readily appreciate the advantages of the Gabor transform and its representation as a 3-D graph or surface map. The different signal frequencies, and their time courses, are clearly displayed. This will become even more obvious when we consider more realistic musical signals, which may include short (staccato) and drawn-out (legato) notes, will have harmonics (characteristic for the musical instrument used), and may also exhibit gradually varying frequencies, as in a glissando.

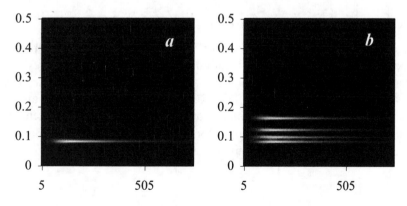

Fig. 6.9.3. Sonograms (i.e., surface maps of the Gabor transforms) of the functions shown in (*a*) Fig. 6.9.1 and (*b*) Fig. 6.9.2.

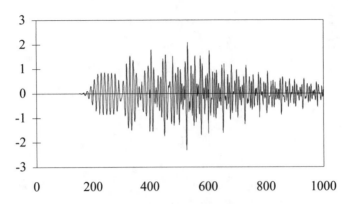

Fig. 6.9.4: The extended test function for a broken major chord.

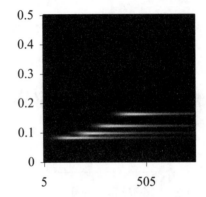

Fig. 6.9.5. The sonogram of the broken chord shown in Fig. 6.9.4.

The sonogram exhibits the three basic attributes of sound: time, frequency (pitch, tone-height), and amplitude (intensity, loudness, volume). In some respects it mimics musical notation, in that it uses the horizontal axis for time (indicating the duration of the various notes), while the vertical axis shows their pitch. In addition it displays their harmonics. In musical notation, amplitude (loudness) must be indicated separately, whereas the sonogram displays it as color or grayscale. We will analyze a real signal in the next section.

6.10 The echolocation pulse of a bat

Bats orient themselves at night by sending out short sound bursts of varying amplitude and frequency, and by analyzing the reflected sound. The echolocation pulses are short, so that they do not overlap with the reflected signals. A digitized echolocation pulse of a large brown bat (*Eptesicus fuscus*) can be down-loaded from http://www-dsp.rice.edu/ software/TFA/RGK/BAT/bat.html, and can also be obtained by e-mail from, e.g., richb@rice.edu. The recorded pulse, courtesy of Curtis Condon, Ken White, and Al Feng of the Beckman Center at the University of Illinois, contains 400 equidistant data points taken at 7 μs intervals, and therefore covers a total time of less than 3 ms duration.

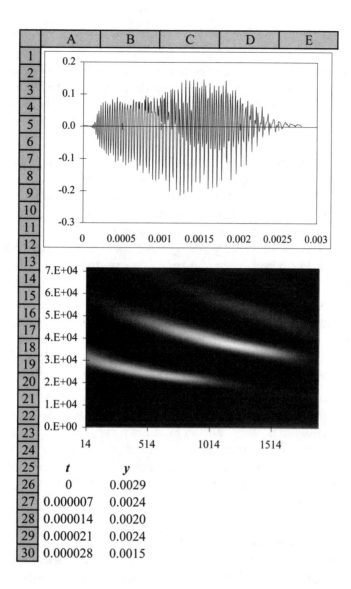

	A	B	C	D	E
25	*t*	*y*			
26	0	0.0029			
27	0.000007	0.0024			
28	0.000014	0.0020			
29	0.000021	0.0024			
30	0.000028	0.0015			

Fig. 6.10.1: The top of a spreadsheet for Gabor analysis of a bat chirp. Top graph: the echolocation signal as a function of time, in s. Bottom graph: the corresponding sonogram: frequency (in Hz) vs. time (in start-of-sequence number).

Exercise 6.10.1:

(1) Start a new spreadsheet, leaving the top rows for graphs. Import the bat data, and plot them.

(2) Apply the Gabor transform, and then map the results. The gray-scale of Fig. 6.10.1 illustrates what you might obtain. More subtle details can be discerned by using a full color palette, as with Mapper$n$ for $n > 0$.

(3) The back cover of this book contains the original graph as well as the resulting sonogram, in color. The latter is also used on the front cover, with the time axis reversed to run from right to left.

The signal in Fig. 6.10.1 starts out at about 30 kHz, descends to about 20 kHz, and after about 50 ms is joined by a second descending signal at its double frequency. The signal also contains weak higher harmonics at the triple and quadruple frequencies. The Gabor transform and its visualization make this much more transparent than the original data set.

The dominant sensory input of humans is visual. If we are trying to listen in on the meaning of whale songs, or on the communication between cawing crows, visualizing their sounds as Gabor plots may well help us to decode them.

6.11 Summary

This chapter illustrates two different applications of Fourier transformation: convolution and deconvolution, and time-frequency analysis. We have belabored deconvolution because it is the counterpart of least squares analysis. Where the latter tries to minimize the effects of *random* fluctuations, deconvolution addresses a particular (but equally ubiquitous) type of *systematic* distortion inherent in all physical measurements.

Because of the importance of deconvolution (even though it is often underemphasized in treatments of scientific data analysis) it has here been given rather extensive coverage, with several possible approaches. When direct or Fourier-transform deconvolution are not practicable, an iterative approach based on using convolution in reverse is often still possible, see section 6.6. In some favorable cases, an even more robust method can be based on combining nonlinear least squares with Fourier transformation, as described in sections 6.6 and 6.7. Incidentally, you may have noticed that least squares and Fourier transformation can often make a very powerful combination, as was already demonstrated in the analysis of the tides in section 5.10.

Some convolutions, such as those illustrated in section 6.1 and in Fig. 6.2.3, exhibit a clear sense of directionality, and consequently have an asymmetric action, while this is not the case in other examples, such as those in sections 6.4 through 6.8 and in Fig. 6.2.4. The distinction is due to the form of the transfer function used: asymmetrical transfer functions affect the signal asymmetrically, symmetrical transfer functions affect it symmetrically.

Analogous to cryptography, the transfer function is the key to the distortion, and to efforts to correct for it. Without knowledge of the transfer function, or of some calibration feature in the data set (cf. Fig. 6.3.2), deconvolution is usually not possible, and an essential part of knowing your instrument is knowing its transfer function. Moreover, deconvolution is an imperfect tool: whatever is lost to distortion to below the level of random noise is seldom retrievable. The prudent approach is, therefore, to design experiments with minimal distortion, and then to use deconvolution to reduce the effects of any residual distortion.

*****

Visual information is primarily steady state: lighting conditions usually change slowly, and most objects around us are stationary. Even moving objects can often be represented as a sequence of stationary states, as in a movie or on television. It is therefore not surprising that spectroscopy is predominantly a steady-state method, and that fast Fourier Transformation is its principal transformation tool.

On the other hand, sound is experienced primarily as a time-dependent phenomenon: we hear steps, voices, music, and tend to ignore constant background noises: the leaves rustling in the wind, the humming of fluorescent lamps, the sound of a refrigerator or of a fan moving air, the constant drone of car traffic near a highway. To analyze time-dependent phenomena we use time-frequency analysis, as described in sections 6.9 and 6.10. Note that a sonogram can be made continuously as the sound evolves, lagging only slightly because of the need to perform a single Fourier transformation.

6.12 For further reading

Many additional applications to electrical engineering and signal processing of the direct spreadsheet methods used in sections 6.1 and 6.3 are described by S. C. Bloch in his book *SSP, the Spreadsheet Signal Processor*, Prentice Hall (1992). The deconvolution of large data sets with the van Cittert algorithm is discussed in W. E. Blass and G. W. Halsey, *Deconvolution of Absorption Spectra*, Academic Press (1981), and in *Deconvolution of Images and Spectra*, edited by P. A. Jansson, Academic Press (1984, 1997).

Chapter 7

Numerical integration of ordinary differential equations

It is almost always easier to describe a complex physical system in terms of a set of differential equations than it is to solve them. Unfortunately, only relatively few of the differential equations encountered in science and technology have known solutions; many of these pertain to idealized geometries, such as that of the proverbial spherical cow. If airplane design had depended on closed-form solutions of aerodynamic equations, pigs might have evolved wings before humans would have flown in craft heavier than air.

If a closed-form solution does not exist, one can either simplify the problem while hoping to retain its most essential features, or use numerical integration. In principle, numerical integration can provide a solution to any desired accuracy for any properly specified set of differential equations. In practice, this is a large field of expertise, which often requires specialized hardware for complex problems such as the design of automobiles, camera lenses, or computer chips. However, for more mundane scientific tasks a spreadsheet may well fit the bill, which is why we will now illustrate how numerical integration can be performed in Excel. While a short chapter cannot begin to do justice to this topic, it may at least give you an idea of what is possible.

Ordinary differential equations only contain derivatives with respect to a single variable, such as time or distance, while partial differential equations have derivatives with respect to several such parameters, and are therefore more complicated. In this chapter we will illustrate the numerical integration of ordinary differential equations, with constant coefficients, that have initial or boundary conditions that are fully specified at one point in time or space. In that case, their solution can proceed in step-wise fashion from that starting moment or boundary. We will further restrict the discussion by illustrating only so-called one-point methods, and even there we will use only a few relatively simple ones.

We will use custom functions, written in VBA, the acronym for Visual BASIC for Applications. Readers unfamiliar with computer code may first want to read the introductory four sections of chapter 8 before delving into the present subject.

7.1 The explicit Euler method

When an ordinary differential equation is fully specified by initial conditions at one point in time or space, it is possible to start from that point, and to work systematically from there, repeatedly using the same *single step method*. For instance, when the differential equation is of first order, it describes the slope of the function $F(t)$, such as $dF(t)/dt$. Starting from the initial value F_0 at $t = t_0$ and its slope $(dF(t)/dt)_{t=t_0}$, we can compute $F(t_0+\Delta t)$ as long as the interval Δt is small enough so that we may consider the slope $dF(t)/dt$ as essentially constant over that interval. We then repeat this process by considering the value of $F(t_0+\Delta t)$ and the corresponding slope $(dF(t)/dt)_{t=t_0+\Delta t}$ to advance to $t = t_0 + 2\,\Delta t$, and so on. In its simplest form, the interval Δt is kept constant, but instead it might depend on some other criterion, such as the absolute magnitude of the slope at each point. On a spreadsheet, the time intervals are shown explicitly, and need not be constant throughout the calculation.

Below we will first consider two sequential first-order rate processes in series, such as occur in a two-step (mother/daughter) radioactive decay, or in two successive first-order chemical reactions. Since a closed-form solution is available, we can then determine the errors involved in the simulation by comparison with the exact solution. We will use that exact solution, plus Gaussian noise, to simulate an 'experimental' data set. We will then use Solver to adjust the parameters of the numerical integration to fit the experimental data, and we will compare the thus found rate parameters with their correct values.

In this chapter we primarily consider a particular type of errors, viz., the *algorithmic* deviations caused by replacing a differential equation by an approximation thereof. When these use many small steps, each causing a similar unidirectional error, their accumulation can lead to systematic bias, i.e., to major distortions. Other computational errors are usually less significant. Just for the record, among the errors not considered here are those caused by the finite representation of numbers in a computer, especially when taking differences between almost identical numbers.

Below we first describe the conceptually simplest method, published by Euler as early as 1768, while the next section will describe a very useful yet still rather simple modification. We will then consider how to use custom functions to make the calculation more efficient, and how to accommodate extreme parameter values. In sections 7.6 and 7.7 we will use the more sophisticated Runge-Kutta method, while sections 7.8 through 7.10 illustrate the application of these techniques to a system of equations that can lead to oscillatory behavior, and for which no analytical solutions is known. There are many other, worthwhile methods, but this chapter cannot replace entire tomes written on this topic, and will merely indicate how to use a few of the many useful algorithms.

Here, and in the next four sections, we will consider two sequential, irreversible, first-order reactions, schematically represented by

$$A \rightarrow B \rightarrow C \tag{7.1.1}$$

which we will assume to be described by the differential equations

$$\frac{da}{dt} = -k_1 a \tag{7.1.2}$$

$$\frac{db}{dt} = k_1 a - k_2 b \tag{7.1.3}$$

$$\frac{dc}{dt} = k_2 b \tag{7.1.4}$$

where the concentrations of species A, B, and C are denoted by a, b, and c respectively, and the rate constants by k_1 and k_2. We will simulate this reaction sequence for the initial conditions

$$a_{t=0} = a_0, \qquad b_{t=0} = 0, \qquad c_{t=0} = 0 \tag{7.1.5}$$

The simplest (and crudest) approach to simulating such a set of equations is merely to replace the *differential* quotients by the corresponding *difference* quotients,

$$\frac{\Delta a}{\Delta t} \approx \frac{da}{dt} = -k_1 a \tag{7.1.6}$$

$$\frac{\Delta b}{\Delta t} \approx \frac{db}{dt} = k_1 a - k_2 b \tag{7.1.7}$$

$$\frac{\Delta c}{\Delta t} \approx \frac{dc}{dt} = k_2 b \tag{7.1.8}$$

and to compute successive changes Δa, Δb, and Δc from the resulting, approximate relations. That is precisely what is done in the *explicit Euler method*. In the present example, we start from the initial conditions at time t, and then calculate the concentrations of a, b, and c at time $t + \Delta t$ as

302

$$\Delta a \approx -k_1\, a\, \Delta t \tag{7.1.9}$$

or

$$a_{t+\Delta t} = a_t + \Delta a \approx a_t - k_1\, a_t\, \Delta t = a_t\,(1 - k_1\, \Delta t) \tag{7.1.10}$$

and, likewise,

$$\Delta b \approx (k_1\, a - k_2 b)\ \Delta t \tag{7.1.11}$$

or

$$b_{t+\Delta t} = b_t + \Delta b \approx b_t + a_t\, k_1\ \Delta t - b_t\, k_2\ \Delta t$$

$$= a_t\, k_1\, \Delta t + b_t\,(1 - k_2\, \Delta t) \tag{7.1.12}$$

and

$$\Delta c \approx k_2\, b\ \Delta t \tag{7.1.13}$$

so that

$$c_{t+\Delta t} = c_t + \Delta c \approx c_t + b_t\, k_2\, \Delta t \tag{7.1.14}$$

by moving a distance Δt in the direction given by the slopes defined by the right-hand sides of (7.1.6) through (7.1.8) respectively. Once we have found the concentrations at $t + \Delta t$, we use that solution to compute the value at $t + 2\Delta t$, and so on, just the way we walk, one step at a time. Typically we start the process at $t = 0$, and (except in some *chaotic* systems) we will ultimately reach a time when, for all practical purposes, either equilibrium or a cyclically repeating state is obtained, at which point the calculation can be stopped. Note that we have arbitrarily called zero the starting time of the simulation (or of the corresponding experiment), just as we might do when resetting a timer or stopwatch.

Exercise 7.1.1:

(1) Start a new spreadsheet. At its top deposit labels and numerical values for the initial conditions $a_{t=0} = a_0$, $b_{t=0} = b_0$, and $c_{t=0} = c_0$, e.g., in cells A1:B3. Do the same for the rate constants k_1 and k_2, and for the interval Δt, in C1:D3. Below those, we will use column A for time, columns B through D for the exact solutions, and columns F through H for our simulation. Since we have the benefit of an exact solution, we will use columns I:K to display the differences between our simulated solution and the exact one.

(2) In column A start at $t = 0$, and then use constant increments Δt. In columns B through D compute a through c, using their exact solutions

$$a = a_0 e^{-k_1 t} \tag{7.1.15}$$

$$b = a_0 k_1 \left(e^{-k_2 t} - e^{-k_1 t}\right) / \left(k_1 - k_2\right) \tag{7.1.16}$$

$$c = (a_0 + b_0 + c_0) - (a + b) \tag{7.1.17}$$

so that the instructions in, e.g., cells B8 and B9 might read =$B$1 and =$B$1*EXP(-$D$1* $A8) respectively.

(3) In the row for $t = 0$, also deposit the initial values for a_0, b_0, and c_0 in columns F, G, and H respectively. In lower rows of those same columns, compute subsequent concentrations from their immediate predecessors using (7.1.10), (7.1.12) and (7.1.14) respectively.

(4) In column J show the differences between the simulated and exact results for a, and do the same in columns K and L for those in b and c. We use columns E and I merely as spacers.

(5) Plot your results. Your spreadsheet may now look like that in Figs. 7.1.1*a* and 7.1.1*b*, and the graphs like those in Figs. 7.1.2 and 7.1.3.

The comparison of the simulated and exact curves in Fig. 7.1.2 shows that the simulation indeed yields the correct over-all behavior, while focusing on their differences in Fig. 7.1.3 indicates that the agreement is only semi-quantitative. If maximum deviations of the order of a few percent are acceptable, stop right here; if not, read on.

In order to simulate a somewhat realistic data analysis, we create a make-believe data set from the exact theory with added Gaussian noise (to be replaced by experimental data if available), then use the numerical simulation to approximate the theory, and finally use Solver to adjust the latter to find the best-fitting concentration and rate parameters.

Exercise 7.1.1 (continued):

(6) Use Tools ⇨ Data Analysis ⇨ Random Number Generation to add three columns of Gaussian ('normal') noise of zero mean and unit amplitude in some out-of-sight columns, as in N8:P108.

(7) Insert four new columns: highlight the column labels E:H, right-click, and in the resulting menu click on Insert. In cell F8 place the instruction =B8+$G$1*N8, and copy this to the entire block F8:H108. Add the corresponding noise amplitude s_n in G1, with a label in F1.

(8) Temporarily set the value of s_n in G1 equal to zero. In block J1:K3 place another set of labels and numerical values for k_1, k_2, and a_0, and then make the necessary adjustments in the instructions in columns J through L so that these will now refer to the constants in K1:K3. Verify that this leaves the results in Fig. 7.1.1a unaffected. Then put a nonzero value of s_n (typically between 0.001 and 0.1) back in G1.

(9) Introduce the 'experimental' data of columns F:H into the concentration-time plot. Make the numbers in cells K1:K3 somewhat different from those in D1, D2, and B1. Now the plot will show show both the added noise and any misfit caused by changing the values in K1:K3.

(10) In order to provide Solver with criteria to gauge its progress towards a best-fitting solution, in cell N1 place the instruction =SUMXMY2(B8:DF108, F8:H108), then copy this instruction to cells O1 and P1.

	A	B	C	D	
1	a0 = 1		k1 = 1		
2	b0 = 0		k2 = 0.5		
3	c0 = 0		Δt = 0.1		
4					
5			*exact solution*		
6	*t*	*a*	*b*	*c*	
7					
8	0.0	1.000	0.000	0.000	
9	0.1	0.905	0.093	0.002	
10	0.2	0.819	0.172	0.009	
11	0.3	0.741	0.240	0.019	
12	0.4	0.670	0.297	0.033	
13	0.5	0.607	0.345	0.049	
14	0.6	0.549	0.384	0.067	
15	0.7	0.497	0.416	0.087	
16	0.8	0.449	0.442	0.109	
17	0.9	0.407	0.462	0.131	
18	1.0	0.368	0.477	0.155	
19	1.1	0.333	0.488	0.179	

Fig. 7.1.1a: The top left-hand corner of the spreadsheet of exercise 7.1.1.

(11) When we can monitor all three concentrations as a function of time *t*, a proper criterion for optimizing the adjustable parameters in K1:K3 with Solver might be the sum of the quantities computed in N1:P1. Therefore, calculate the sums of squares of all the residuals in O2 as =N1+O1+P1.

(12) Call Solver, and instruct it to minimize O2 while adjusting K1:K3. As your finishing touch, call SolverAid and find the associated uncertainties. Fig. 7.1.4 illustrates what you might get in the presence of a fair amount of noise.

(13) For smaller values of s_n the recovered parameters will be closer to those assumed in B1, D1, and D2, and the standard deviations will be smaller; for larger values of *na*, the opposite will be true.

(14) Save the spreadsheet for subsequent use in section 7.1.2.

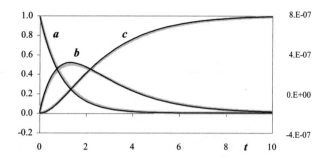

Fig. 7.1.2: The concentrations a, b, and c as a function of time t. Broad gray curves: exact solution; solid black curves: simulation.

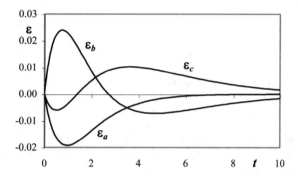

Fig. 7.1.3: The differences ε between the results from numerical integration and the exact solution, emphasized by using a greatly enlarged vertical scale.

	F	G	H	I	J	K	L	

explicit Euler integration				errors		
a	b	c		in a	in b	in c
1.0000	0.0000	0.000		0.0000	0.0000	0.0000
0.9000	0.1000	0.000		-0.0048	0.0072	-0.0024
0.8100	0.1850	0.005		-0.0087	0.0128	-0.0041
0.7290	0.2568	0.014		-0.0118	0.0170	-0.0052
0.6561	0.3168	0.027		-0.0142	0.0200	-0.0058
0.5905	0.3666	0.043		-0.0160	0.0220	-0.0060
0.5314	0.4073	0.061		-0.0174	0.0233	-0.0059
0.4783	0.4401	0.082		-0.0183	0.0239	-0.0056
0.4305	0.4659	0.104		-0.0189	0.0239	-0.0051
0.3874	0.4857	0.127		-0.0191	0.0235	-0.0044
0.3487	0.5001	0.151		-0.0192	0.0228	-0.0036
0.3138	0.5100	0.176		-0.0191	0.0218	-0.0028

Fig. 7.1.1b: Columns F through L of the spreadsheet of exercise 7.1.1.

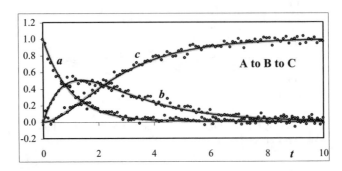

Fig. 7.1.4: Fitting simulated noisy data (open circles) to the model. The gray bands are the theoretical curves in the absence of noise; the found best-fitting curves are shown as thin black lines. Assumed data: $a_0 = 1$, $k_1 = 1$, $k_2 = 0.5$, $s_n = 0.03$.

(15) Using the explicit Euler method and Solver yields $a_0 = 0.9995$, $k_1 = 0.9411$, $k_2 = 0.5044$, while SolverAid yields the corresponding standard deviations $s_0 = 0.0111$, $s_1 = 0.1678$, $s_2 = 0.0665$, so that the results are best described as $a_0 = 0.99_9 \pm 0.01_1$, $k_1 = 0.9_4 \pm 0.1_7$, $k_2 = 0.50_4 \pm 0.06_7$, fairly close to the assumed values of $a_0 = 1$, $k_1 = 1$, and $k_2 = 0.5$.

(16) Keep in mind that the parameters you find will be correlated rather than independent, i.e., changes in one may affect the values of the others. If such parameters are to be used in subsequent calculations, the covariances between a_0, k_1, and k_2 should also be obtained from SolverAid, in the form of the corresponding covariance matrix.

(17) If you could only monitor the concentration b of species B as a function of time t, the proper criterion for optimizing Solver would instead be the sum of squares of residuals as calculated in O1. In that case you would obtain slightly different results; in the above example, you would find $a_0 = 0.97_3 \pm 0.07_0$, $k_1 = 0.9_8 \pm 0.1_0$, $k_2 = 0.49_7 \pm 0.04_2$. If you had only measurements on c, you would instead use the sum of the squares of the residuals in P1, and find $a_0 = 1.00_3 \pm 0.01_2$, $k_1 = 1.10 \pm 0.1_9$, $k_2 = 0.49_0 \pm 0.05_5$. A different simulation would also yield slightly different results, because (simulated or real) noise is never quite the same. Therefore, don't overspecify the found parameters: they are only estimates. Here they are given with one extra, subscripted guard digit that is *not* significant, but merely guards against systematic round-off errors in possible uses of these numbers in subsequent computations.

(18) Incidentally, measurements of a alone would not be as useful: since a does not depend on k_2, such measurements can only yield a_0 and k_1. If you tried, you would see that Solver in that case wouldn't change the value of k_2 from its initial guess, and that SolverAid would therefore, somewhat misleadingly, assign it a standard deviation of zero.

(19) Save the spreadsheet for later use.

7.2 The semi-implicit Euler method

The procedure illustrated above uses the *initial* concentrations to compute the behavior during the interval Δt. We do not know how those concentrations are going to change, but instead of assuming a to remain constant we will now approximate the change in a as linear over a sufficiently small interval Δt. This leads to the *semi-implicit Euler method*, in which we replace, say, the concentration a_n during the interval from t_n to t_{n+1} by its average value $(a_n+a_{n+1})/2 = a_n + (a_{n+1}-a_n)/2 = a_n + \Delta a/2$. Upon replacing the concentrations a, b, and c in (7.1.6) through (7.1.8) by their initial values plus half their anticipated changes we have

$$\frac{\Delta a}{\Delta t} \approx -k_1(a + \Delta a/2) \tag{7.2.1}$$

$$\frac{\Delta b}{\Delta t} \approx k_1(a + \Delta a/2) - k_2(b + \Delta b/2) \tag{7.2.2}$$

$$\frac{\Delta c}{\Delta t} \approx k_2(b + \Delta b/2) \tag{7.2.3}$$

from which we obtain

306

$$\Delta a \approx \frac{-a\,k_1\Delta t}{1+k_1\Delta t/2} \tag{7.2.4}$$

$$a_{t+\Delta t} = a_t + \Delta a \approx \frac{1-k_1\Delta t/2}{1+k_1\Delta t/2}\,a_t \tag{7.2.5}$$

$$\Delta b \approx \frac{a\,k_1\Delta t}{(1+k_1\Delta t/2)\,(1+k_2\Delta t/2)} - \frac{b\,k_2\Delta t}{(1+k_2\Delta t/2)} \tag{7.2.6}$$

$$b_{t+\Delta t} = b_t + \Delta b \approx \frac{a_t\,k_1\Delta t}{(1+k_1\Delta t/2)\,(1+k_2\Delta t/2)} + \frac{(1-k_2\Delta t/2)\,b_t}{(1+k_2\Delta t/2)} \tag{7.2.7}$$

We need not compute c, because it follows directly from the mass balance (7.1.17). Still, for the sake of completeness, we list it here as

$$\Delta c \approx (b+\Delta b/2)\,k_2\Delta t \tag{7.2.8}$$

$$c_{t+\Delta t} \approx c_t + (b_t + b_{t+\Delta t})\,k_2\Delta t/2 \tag{7.2.9}$$

We see that equations such as (7.2.1), (7.2.2), and (7.2.3) cannot be used directly, but must first be solved for the concentration changes Δa, Δb, and Δc. This accounts for the *implicit* in the semi-implicit Euler method. It is only *semi*-implicit because $(a_n+a_{n+1})/2 = a_n + \Delta a/2$ combines half of the known term a_n with half of the next unknown one, a_{n+1}. For linear systems, this is the best one can do and still retain an absolutely stable solution.

Exercise 7.2.1:

(1) Copy the spreadsheet of exercise 7.1 to a new page of the same workbook. In columns J and K of this copy, change the instructions to incorporate eq. (7.2.5) instead of (7.1.10), and (7.2.7) instead of (7.1.12). In column L you can either use (7.1.17) or (7.2.9).

(2) Click on the curves in your equivalent of Fig. 7.1.3 to the new page, then redirect their definitions in the formula box to the current worksheet. In doing so, be careful not to alter the general format of the argument: (,*sheetname*!*Xn:Xm*, *sheetname*!*Yn:Ym*,*p*), where *Xn:Xm* and *Yn:Ym* specify the ranges, and *p* defines the relative precedence of the curves, with the highest number being shown on top of the other curves. All you need to change in the argument is the *sheetname*, which you find on the tab at the bottom of the spreadsheet. Incidentally, the equivalent of Fig. 7.1.2 is immaterial, because any differences are too small to be visible on this scale.

(3) The improvement in Fig. 7.2.1 over the results shown in Fig. 7.1.4 is immediate and dramatic: for the same step size ($\Delta t = 0.1$) the errors are now more than an order of magnitude smaller.

(4) Repeat the analysis of the simulated data set with added Gaussian noise. For the same noisy data as used in Fig. 7.1.3 we now find $a_0 = 0.992_1 \pm 0.009_6$, $k_1 = 0.995_4 \pm 0.007_0$, $k_2 = 0.49_6 \pm 0.01_4$, a much better over-all fit to the assumed values of $a_0 = 1$, $k_1 = 1$, and $k_2 = 0.5$ than obtained earlier.

(5) As suggested by comparing Figs. 7.1.3 and 7.2.1, the improvement is more obvious for data that contain less noise. For example, for $\Delta t = 0.1$ and the same Gaussian noise but now with $s_n = 0.01$ the results of the explicit and semi-implicit Euler methods would be $a_0 = 0.998_3 \pm 0.003_8$, $k_1 = 0.94_4 \pm 0.05_8$, $k_2 = 0.50_3 \pm 0.02_3$ and $a_0 = 0.997_3 \pm 0.003_2$, $k_1 = 0.998_5 \pm 0.002_3$, $k_2 = 0.498_7 \pm 0.004_7$ respectively. Here the explicit method clearly shows its bias.

You may wonder what constitutes a *fully implicit* Euler method. Instead of the average value of the slope (as in the semi-implicit method), or its initial value (as in the explicit method), it uses the final value of the slope to evaluate the new value of $F(t)$. Since that is just as asymmetrical as using the initial value, the implicit Euler method has an inaccuracy proportional to Δt, i.e., comparable to that of the explicit Euler method, whereas the semi-implicit method has an inaccuracy $\propto (\Delta t)^2$.

In our example, the implicit Euler method would read

$$\frac{\Delta a}{\Delta t} \approx -k_1(a+\Delta a) \tag{7.2.10}$$

$$\frac{\Delta b}{\Delta t} \approx k_1(a+\Delta a) - k_2(b+\Delta b) \tag{7.2.11}$$

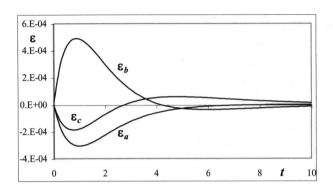

Fig. 7.2.1: The differences between the numerically integrated and exact solutions for the semi-implicit Euler method with $\Delta t = 0.1$.

from which we would obtain

$$\Delta a \approx \frac{-a\,k_1 \Delta t}{1 + k_1 \Delta t} \tag{7.2.12}$$

$$a_{t+\Delta t} = a_t + \Delta a \approx \frac{a_t}{1 + k_1 \Delta t} \tag{7.2.14}$$

$$\Delta b \approx \frac{a\,k_1 \Delta t}{(1 + k_1 \Delta t)\,(1 + k_2 \Delta t)} - \frac{b\,k_2 \Delta t}{(1 + k_2 \Delta t)} \tag{7.2.15}$$

$$b_{t+\Delta t} = b_t + \Delta b \approx \frac{a_t\,k_1 \Delta t}{(1 + k_1 \Delta t)\,(1 + k_2 \Delta t)} + \frac{b_t}{(1 + k_2 \Delta t)} = \frac{a_{t+\Delta t}\,k_1 \Delta t + b_t}{(1 + k_2 \Delta t)} \tag{7.2.16}$$

Upon comparing, e.g., (7.2.1) with (7.1.6) and (7.2.10), we verify that the semi-implicit method is indeed the average of the explicit and implicit Euler methods. It combines the absolute stability of the implicit method with an accuracy that is higher than that of either the explicit or implicit Euler method, and is therefore often the method of choice for solving simple problems involving ordinary differential equations.

7.3 Using custom functions

As indicated in the previous paragraph, the successful fitting of simulated, noisy data can be somewhat misleading, since a generous amount of noise may mask many inadequacies of the model. For fitting data with a high signal-to-noise ratio we may therefore need to improve the algorithm, as we will do in section 7.6. However, we can go a long way with the Euler methods by using the spreadsheet more intelligently.

Equations (7.1.6) through (7.1.8) clearly show that the simulation is based on replacing the differential quotients dy/dt by difference quotients $\Delta y/\Delta t$, a substitution that should become increasingly accurate as Δt becomes smaller. You can readily verify that the simulation errors shown in Figs. 7.1.3 and 7.2 indeed stem from the step size Δt. Upon reducing Δt by a factor of ten, the concentration differences Δc in Fig. 7.1.3 indeed also become smaller by an order of magnitude, and those in Fig. 7.2 by two orders of magnitude.

However, in order to cover the same total time (in the above example: from $t = 0$ to $t = 10$), we would have to lengthen the columns ten-fold, to 1000 rows. Further reductions in Δt would make the columns even longer. This will quickly lead to impracticably long columns. Moreover, it may be undesirable to lengthen the columns, e.g., because we may only have experimental data at given intervals Δt. Below we will indicate how we can improve the accuracy of our simulation *without* increasing the column length.

308

Exercise 7.3.1:

(1) Return to the spreadsheet of exercise 7.2.1, and set the values in K1:K3 back to the corresponding values in B1:B3.

(2) For the concentration a an elegant solution exists that does not require an increased column length. We saw in (7.2.5) that $a_{t+\Delta t} \approx a_t\,(1-k_1\Delta t/2)/(1+k_1\Delta t/2)$. Upon applying this n times with an n times smaller interval Δt we find $a_{t+n\Delta t} \approx a_t\,\{[1-k_1\Delta t/(2n)]\,/\,[1-k_1\Delta t/(2n)]\}^n$, so that we can replace the instruction in cell J9 for a by, say, `=J8*((1-$K$1*$D$3/20)/(1+$K$1*$D$3/ 20))^10` for $n = 10$. Copy this down through row 108. This will improve the precision of the simulated a-values another two orders of magnitude *without* lengthening the columns. Try it. Then change the value of n in these instructions from 10 to, say, 1000, and observe its effect.

Unfortunately, this trick does not work for the other concentrations, because (7.2.7) and (7.2.9) do not have such a simple recursivity. For those more general cases we will need to use some spreadsheet magic. Excel allows us to incorporate so-called *user-defined* or *custom* functions. These have much in common with small macros (to be discussed at length in chapter 8), except that they apply only to a *numerical value* in a *single* spreadsheet cell. On the other hand, custom functions update automatically, which in the present context is a significant advantage. Below we will use custom functions to compute the concentrations a, b, and c to higher accuracies by reducing the step size while keeping constant the number of spreadsheet cells used in the simulation. If writing computer code is new to you, you may first want to read sections 8.1 through 8.4 of the next chapter before continuing here.

Exercise 7.3.1 (continued):

(3) Return to the spreadsheet, and press Alt⌣F11 (on the Mac: Opt⌣F11). You will see a Microsoft Visual Basic screen appear, with its own menu bar. On *that* bar, select Insert ⇨ Module if the display does not show a white writing area to the right of the Project column; otherwise, if a page already exists, just move to the end of any text on it. Then enter (type, or copy from SampleMacros) the following instructions:

```
Function siEulerA(k1, oldT1, oldT2, n, oldA) As Double
'semi-implicit Euler method for A

Dim i As Integer
Dim A As Double, f As Double, step As Double

n = CInt(n)
A = oldA
step = (oldT2 - oldT1) / n
f = (1 - k1 * step / 2) / (1 + k1 * step / 2)

For i = 1 To n
  A = A * f
Next i
siEulerA = A

End Function
```

(4) A short explanation is in order. The top line specifies the name by which we can call this function, the parameters it will use (in exactly the same order as used here in the function *argument*, i.e., within the brackets following the function name), and (optionally) its precision, starting with an apostrophe. The next line contains a *comment* that will be ignored by the spreadsheet but reminds the user of the purpose of the function; the last line identifies its end.

(5) The next two lines of code (i.e., not counting empty lines inserted for better readability) define the types of constants used in the function; do *not* specify the dimensions of parameters (such as `k1`, `oldT1`, etc.) that are imported through the function argument. In general these lines are optional though very useful; they are mandatory if you use Option Explicit, an option that, when used, is listed at the very top of your module, and then applies to all procedures in that module.

(6) The fifth line (optional as well) makes sure that the method will work even if a non-integer value for n is used by mistake, by converting it to an integer n with the instruction `CInt` (for *c*onvert to *int*eger). This line will be executed from right to left, i.e., the computer takes the value of n, converts it to an integer (if it isn't already one), and then assigns that value to the variable to the left of the equal sign. We insert this line here merely to illustrate how you can make a function somewhat less error-prone by anticipating possible mistakes. This does not imply that the function is now immune to entry errors: using zero for n would certainly trip up the function when it tries to divide by 0 in the next line of code, and using a negative number, or a letter, would also give problems.

(8) Line 6 sets the concentration parameter A equal to the value of oldA imported through the function argument. The calculation starts in earnest on line 8 by defining the new step size, step. By letting oldT1 and oldT2 refer to relative addresses of cells containing *t* in successive rows of the spreadsheet, the time intervals in the spreadsheet need not be equidistant. Alternatively we can make the step size constant throughout the calculation by referring to absolute addresses for oldT1 and oldT2 respectively.

(9) Lines 9 through 11 contain the action part of the function, by *n* times repeating the computation of A for a time interval step that is *n* times smaller than the data spacing oldT2 − oldT1.

(10) Again, the equal sign here functions as an *assignment*. In other words, the line A = A * f should be read as if it were written as A ⇐ A * f, i.e., as "replace A by A * f."

(11) We calculate the value of f separately on line 8, rather than use, e.g., A= A*(1-k1*step/2)/(1+k1*step/2) directly in line 10, because line 8 is executed only once, whereas in line 10 the same calculation would be repeated *n* times. It is in such loops that we should be most careful to avoid busywork, because it can noticeably slow down the computation. Note that the line specifying f must follow the definition of step, because it uses its value which, otherwise, would not be defined.

(12) Finally, the output of the function is defined in its penultimate line. Incidentally, you will have noticed that a number of words you have entered (Function, As Double, Dim, As Integer, etc.) are displayed in blue after you have entered the line on which they appear. These are terms the VB Editor recognizes as instruction keywords, and seeing them in color therefore assures you that your instructions are being read.

(13) Now enter the corresponding instructions for siEulerB, or copy the instructions for siEulerA and then correct and amend that copy. For your convenience, the changes between the two sets of instructions are shown below in boldface.

```
Function siEulerB _
  (k1, k2, oldT1, oldT2, n, oldA, oldB) As Double
'semi-implicit Euler method for B

Dim A As Double, B As Double, step As Double
Dim f As Double, fA As Double, fB As Double
Dim i As Integer

n = CInt(n)
A = oldA
B = oldB
step = (oldT2 - oldT1) / n
f = (1 - k1 * step / 2) / (1 + k1 * step / 2)
fA = k1 * step / ((1 + k1 * step / 2) * (1 + k2 * step / 2))
fB = (1 - k2 * step / 2) / (1 + k2 * step / 2)
For i = 1 To n
  B = A * fA + B * fB
  A = A * f
Next i
siEulerB = B

End Function
```

(14) Note the use of a space followed by an underscore at the end of line 1, in order to indicate a *line continuation*. This allows us to break up a long instruction so that it will be visible on the monitor screen (or the printed page) while being interpreted by the computer as a single line. There can be no text on that line beyond the continuation sign.

(15) In order to use the functions you have just entered, exit the editor with Alt⌣F11 (Mac: Opt⌣F11), which toggles you back to the spreadsheet. On the spreadsheet, in cell F2 place the label n=, and in G2 its value, which should be a positive integer larger than 0.

(16) Replace the instruction in J9 by siEulerA($K$1,$A8,$A9,$G$2, J8), copy this instruction down to row 108. Likewise replace the instruction in K9 by siEulerB($K$1,$K$2,$A8,$A9,$G$2,J8,K8), and see what happens with the concentration differences in columns N through P.

(17) Convert the instructions in columns N through P to the corresponding logarithms, so that you need not change the scale of the graph every time you change the value of *n*.

(18) Run the spreadsheet with $\Delta t = 0.1$ and various values for *n*, such as 1, 10, and 100. With $n = 100$, the plot of the concentration errors should look like Fig. 7.3.1. By using one-hundred times smaller steps, the error in the semi-implicit Euler method has been reduced ten-thousand-fold.

(19) Try $\Delta t = 0.1$ with $n = 1000$. Depending on the speed of your computer, the computation may now take its sweet time (after all, in each of the 100 cells you make the For … Next loop do 1000 complete calculations), but you get rewarded with absolute errors that are all smaller than 5×10^{-10}! That will be good enough for almost any experiment.

(20) Reset the values in K1:K3 to new guess values, and rerun Solver and SolverAid. For almost any realistic noise the accuracy of your results will now be limited by that noise, rather than by inadequacies in the model. And that is precisely where you want to be: the computation should not add any inaccuracies to your experimental results.

(21) Go back to exercise 7.1.1 and write the corresponding functions `eEulerA` and `eEulerB` for the *explicit* case. Then try them out, see how they run. For the same $\Delta t = 0.1$, what value of n do you need in order to get the errors down to the same order of magnitude as those shown in Fig. 7.3.1?

(22) Save the spreadsheet for further use in section 7.6.

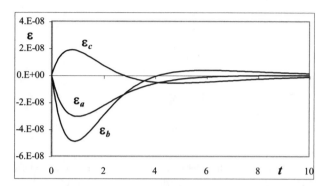

Fig. 7.3.1: The differences between the numerically integrated and exact solutions for the semi-implicit Euler method with $\Delta t = 0.1$ and $n = 100$ for an actual step size of 0.001.

7.4 The shelf life of medicinal solutions

The rate of decomposition of pharmaceutical solutions depends on the kinetics involved, which are characterized by reaction order, rate constant, and activation energy. This typically requires multiple rate measurements at different temperatures, which can then be combined to compute the activation energy. Industrially, this approach is often considered too time-consuming, especially since only a value for the shelf life is needed. A popular shortcut is therefore to use a single, *nonisothermal* data analysis, introduced to pharmacology by A. R. Rogers in *J. Pharm. Pharmacol.* 15 *Suppl.* (1963) 101T. Rogers used an inverse-logarithmic temperature profile that made the analysis mathematically tractable; others have used a reciprocal or linear temperature profile, and methods based on numerical differentiation or numerical integration have also been used. Here we will use a combination of numerical integration and nonlinear least squares fitting to illustrate its versatility as a generally applicable tool for any temperature profile.

As our specific example we will consider the alkaline degradation of riboflavin, also known as vitamin B2, as reported by B. W. Madsen, R. A. Anderson, D. Herbison-Evans and W. Sneddon in *J. Pharmac. Sci.* 63 (1974) 777. They listed experimental results for a 10^{-4} M solution of riboflavin in 0.1 M aqueous NaOH, on which they took temperature readings and reaction samples while the temperature was gradually raised. The samples were quenched in acetic acid to halt the reaction, and assayed spectrometrically. The reported temperature readings are shown in Fig. 7.4.1, and are listed in A16:B28 of Fig. 7.4.3). They can be represented by the quadratic relation $T - 273.15 = (20.9_2 \pm 0.2_7) + (0.445_6 \pm 0.009_8)\, t - (0.00050_3 \pm 0.00007_3)\, t^2$, where T is the absolute temperature in °K, and t is time in minutes.

We assume first-order kinetics, as common for decomposition reactions of a dilute (10^{-4} M) species in a large excess (0.1 M) of reactant. We will approximate the continuously increasing temperature t as a series of sufficiently short isothermal steps of length Δt, each at a slightly higher temperature ΔT than its predecessor. Using the semi-implicit Euler method we then have, see (7.1.2), (7.2.1) and (7.2.5),

$$c + \Delta c = \frac{1 - k\,\Delta t/2}{1 + k\,\Delta t/2}\, c \qquad (7.4.1)$$

where c is the riboflavin concentration at the start of an isothermal time interval Δt with rate constant k, and Δc is the (negative) riboflavin concentration change during that period Δt. For the dependence of the rate constant on temperature we will assume the Arrhenius equation

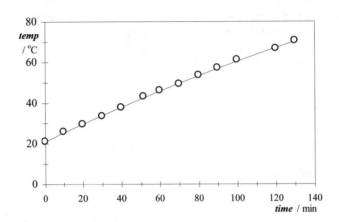

Fig. 7.4.1: The relationship between temperature and time reported by Madsen et al. (open circles) and a quadratic curve (drawn) fitting these data.

$$k = k' \exp\left[\frac{-E}{RT}\right] \tag{7.4.2}$$

where k' is a constant, and E is the activation energy of the reaction; the gas constant R has the value 1.9858775×10^{-3} kcal mol^{-1} K^{-1}. Madsen et al. used 20 °C = 293.15 °K as their reference temperature, and we will do likewise. Rewriting (7.4.2) for $k = k_{20}$ at $T = 293.15$ and combining this with (7.4.2) to eliminate k' yields

$$k = k_{20} \exp\left[\frac{E}{R}\left(\frac{1}{293.15} - \frac{1}{T}\right)\right] \tag{7.4.3}$$

Because Madsen et al. specified their times to the nearest 0.5 min, we write a custom function TStep to subdivide each time interval between successive data points into sub-intervals of 0.5, 0.05, or 0.005 min respectively, and use the earlier-established cubic relation between temperature and time to establish the corresponding temperatures during those sub-intervals. The rate constants at each of these sub-intervals then follow from (7.4.3), and the riboflavin concentrations c are computed from (7.4.1). TStep will then display that riboflavin concentration c at the end of each interval. Since the intervals between data points contain varying numbers of sub-intervals, a Do … Loop Until is used.

```
Function TStep (StepSize, Time1, Time2, c1, k20, E)

' StepSize = length of sub-intervals
' Time1 = time at start of interval
' Time2 = time at end of interval
' k20 = rate constant at 20 C
' E = activation energy, in kcal/mol
' R = 0.0019858775 is the gas constant, in kcal/(mol*K)
' c = concentration
' c1 = ealier-found concentration at start of interval
' c2 = computed concentration at end of interval

' NOTE: Before using this function, make sure that the
' correct equation is used for Temp as a function of Time,
' and that the reference temperature is correct as well

Dim c As Double, Temp As Double, Time As Double

c = c1
Time = Time1 + StepSize
```

312

```
Do
  Temp = 273.15 + 20.92789 + 0.4455754 * Time - 0.0005030758 * Time ^ 2
  k = k20 * Exp((E / 0.0019858775) * (1 / 293.15 - 1 / Temp))
  c = c * (1 - k * StepSize / 2) / (1 + k * StepSize / 2)
  Time = Time + StepSize
Loop Until Time > Time2 + 0.001
TStep = c

End Function
```

Figure 7.4.2 compares the observed dependence of the riboflavin concentration on time (open circles) with that using a rather crude guess value (gray line) and with the (visually indistinguishable) fits (thin black line) obtained with the three different step sizes. As Table 7.4.1 shows, the results obtained for the three step sizes are quite similar, and in this case are optimal for a step size of 0.05 min (3 sec). While TStep updates within the blink of an eye, repeating it inside the iterative Solver routine will quite noticeably slow Solver at the 0.005 min step size.

The entire spreadsheet, after use of Solver and SolverAid, is shown in Fig. 7.4.3. The strong collinearity between E and k_{20} (see cells D10 and E9) is not surprising for this type of exponential expressions, see section 4.21. The corresponding error surface is displayed in Fig. 7.4.4.

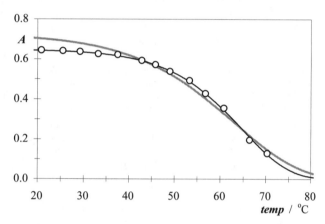

Fig. 7.4.2: The experimental data of Madsen et al. (open circles), a crude fit to them (broad gray line) with assumed values for c_{init}, E, and k_{init}, and the fit obtained by Solver (thin black line).

	guess value	step = 0.5 min	step = 0.05 min	step = 0.005 min	
A_{init}	0.6	$0.640_4 \pm 0.001_3$	$0.640_4 \pm 0.001_3$	$0.640_4 \pm 0.001_3$	
E	22	$20.3_1 \pm 0.2_3$	$20.2_9 \pm 0.2_3$	$20.2_8 \pm 0.2_3$	kcal mol^{-1}
k_{20}	0.00015	$0.00031_5 \pm 0.00001_3$	$0.00031_9 \pm 0.00001_3$	$0.00031_9 \pm 0.00001_3$	min^{-1}
SSR	0.02434765	0.00006423	0.00006422	0.00006422	
s_f		0.00253	0.00253	0.00253	

Table 7.4.1: The results obtained with different step sizes. In this case, a step size of 0.05 min suffices.

	A	B	C	D	E	F
1	**Analysis of data from B.W.Madsen et al.,** *J. Pharmac. Sci.* **63 (1974) 777-781.**					
2			A_{init} =	**0.640385207**	*0.001279146*	
3			E =	**20.28332305**	*0.225764006*	kcal mol^{-1}
4			k_{20} =	**0.000319187**	*1.33015E-05*	min^{-1}
5		*CM:*	*1.63621E-06*	*-0.000178882*	*1.14645E-08*	
6			*-0.000178882*	*0.050969387*	*-2.96704E-06*	
7			*1.14645E-08*	*-2.96704E-06*	*1.76929E-10*	
8		*CC:*	*1*	*-0.619428593*	*0.673809115*	
9			*-0.619428593*	*1*	*-0.988029796*	
10			*0.673809115*	*-0.988029796*	*1*	
11			*SSR* =	7.9969E-05	*0.002534388*	
12						
13	*t*	*T* -273.15	*T*	*k*	A_{exp}	A_{calc}
14	min	°C	°K	min^{-1}		
15						
16	0	21.0	294.15	3.593E-04	0.640	0.640
17	10	25.7	298.85	6.204E-04	0.637	0.637
18	20	29.4	302.55	9.423E-04	0.633	0.632
19	30	33.4	306.55	1.464E-03	0.622	0.625
20	40	37.7	310.85	2.321E-03	0.618	0.613
21	51.5	43.0	316.15	4.026E-03	0.589	0.591
22	60	46.0	319.15	5.454E-03	0.568	0.568
23	70	49.2	322.35	7.494E-03	0.534	0.532
24	80	53.5	326.65	1.137E-02	0.488	0.484
25	90	57.0	330.15	1.584E-02	0.423	0.423
26	100	61.0	334.15	2.294E-02	0.351	0.350
27	120	66.6	339.75	3.797E-02	0.191	0.191
28	130	70.5	343.65	5.341E-02	0.124	0.120
29	140					0.065
30	150					0.030
31	160	*cell: instruction:*			*copied to:*	0.011
32	170					0.003
33	180	D11 = SUMXMY2(F16:F28,E16:E28)				0.001
34	190	F16 = D2				0.000
35	200	F17 = TStep2(0.05,A16,A17,F16,$D$4,$D$3)			F18:F35	0.000

Fig 7.4.3: The spreadsheet after using Solver and SolverAid. The extension of *t* beyond 130 min and the corresponding extension of A_{calc} is so that Figs. 7.4.2 can show the entire theoretical curve; cells C13:D28 are not strictly needed either.

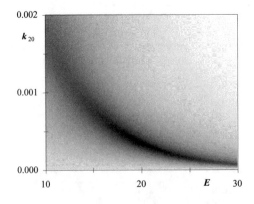

Fig. 7.4.4: The error surface of this problem

7.5 Extreme parameter values

The reaction scheme we have adopted here has two rate constants, k_1 and k_2. In our examples we have so far assumed that k_1 and k_2 are of a similar order of magnitude, but that is not necessarily the case. For purely mathematical solutions, such as (7.1.15) through (7.1.17), the particular values of the rate constants make no difference. (There is a trivial exception to this statement, because setting k_2 equal to k_1 makes (7.1.16) equal to 0/0. This complication can readily be avoided by making the difference between k_2 and k_1 negligibly small rather than zero.) By contrast, in a numerical simulation the specific values of the rate constants often do matter. For instance, when $k_2 \gg k_1$, the simulation may fail, because it is based on $k_1 \Delta t \ll 1$, whereas $k_2 \Delta t$ might then be much greater than 1. And when this is accommodated by taking more steps, the computation may become far too slow to be practicable. Below we consider what to do in such a situation.

We split the case into two parts. When k_2 is not much larger than k_1, we make sure that the step Δt size is appropriately decreased. However, with $k_2 \gg k_1$ this would lead to quite lengthy computations. On the other hand, in such an extreme case there is often a good approximation that can be used instead. Specifically, when the decay of B to C is very much faster than its generation from A, the concentration b will be small and, to a good approximation, will be given by the steady state approximation $db/dt \approx 0$, which upon substitution into (7.1.3) yields $b \approx k_1 a / k_2$. We can set the switch-over point such that the answers provided by the two methods coincide to within the desired accuracy. The following modified function will compute b for any value of k_2.

Exercise 7.5.1:

(1) Return to the spreadsheet of exercise 7.3.1, and test how far you can increase the value of k_2 (while keeping k_1 constant at, say, $k_1 = 1$) before the program starts to fail. Such failure is most readily seen in the plot of log ε vs. t, where ε is the inaccuracy obtained by comparison with the exact solution.

(2) Add the function iEulerBB listed below to the VBA module. The changes with respect to iEulerB are shown in bold.

```
Function siEulerBB _
  (k1, k2, oldT1, oldT2, n, crit, oldA, oldB) As Double
'semi-implicit Euler method for B, modified so that
'it will switch automatically to the steady state
'approximation when k2/k1 becomes larger than a
'given value, here called crit (for criterium).

Dim A As Double, B As Double, step As Double
Dim f As Double, fA As Double, fB As Double
Dim i As Long, m As Long

  n = CLng(n)
A = oldA
B = oldB
step = (oldT2 - oldT1) / n
f = (1 - k1 * step / 2) / (1 + k1 * step / 2)
If k2 / k1 > crit Then
  For i = 1 To n
    A = A * f
  Next i
  B = k1 * A / k2            ' The steady state approximation
End If
If (k2 / k1 > 1 And k2 / k1 <= crit) Then
  m = CLng(Sqr(k2 / k1))
  n = m * n
  step = step / m
  f = (1 - k1 * step / 2) / (1 + k1 * step / 2)
End If
  If k2 / k1 <= crit Then
  fA = k1 * step / ((1 + k1 * step / 2) * (1 + k2 * step / 2))
  fB = (1 - k2 * step / 2) / (1 + k2 * step / 2)
  For i = 1 To n
    B = A * fA + B * fB
```

```
      A = A * f
    Next i
  End If
  siEulerBB = B

  End Function
```

(3) The change from Integer to Long in the dimension statements reflects the fact that single precision integers can only count up to $2^{15}-1 = 32\,767$, which may not suffice for the product of n times *crit*.

(4) For extremely large k_2-values the function uses the steady-state approximation $b = k_1a/k_2$. Otherwise, the calculation is as before, except that the step size is enlarged for $k_2 > k_1$.

(5) The first If … Then statement singles out the case $k_2 / k_1 > crit$, calculates a in the usual way, then finds b with the steady state approximation. The second If … Then statement increases the value of n when $1 \le k_2 / k_1 \le crit$. The final If … Then condition contains code similar to that in siEulerB, except that the value of n will now depend on whether the second If … Then condition was met.

(6) Enter a label and value for *crit*. You might try an initial value for *crit* of 1000.

(7) Replace siEulerB by siEulerBB (including the added variable *crit* in its argument), and make sure that it yields the same results as before for values of k_2 not exceeding the product of k_1 and *crit*. Store a value for *crit* in G3. For ease of testing, again set the values in K1:K3 back to those in B1:D3.

(8) Now test whether the function yields satisfactory results for $k_2 > crit \times k_1$. This is most readily done by examining the plot of log ε vs. t just before and after k_2 crosses the value of $crit \times k_2$. You must of course change the values of k_2 in both D2 and K2.

(9) Implement and test an equivalent extension to include large k_2-values for the explicit Euler method, by creating the corresponding function eEulerBB.

(10) Save the spreadsheet.

When $k_2 \ll k_1$, for the same initial conditions (7.1.5), we essentially have two *decoupled* reactions: first A decays to B which, in turn, though at a much more leisurely pace, reacts to form C. Staying with constant time intervals Δt then becomes very inefficient, because the time scale of the simulation was chosen such that $k_1\Delta t \ll 1$, a time scale that is far more detailed than needed for the decay of B into C. Here, then, it is practical to change the data spacing after the concentration of A has decayed to near-zero. This is why it is convenient to let the function calculate the step size in every cell, depending on the local change in t between successive rows. It allows you to go slowly where needed, and fast where possible, just the way you would drive your car: slow near pedestrian crossings or in bad weather, fast on the open highway on a clear day with little traffic.

7.6   The explicit Runge-Kutta method

The combination of the semi-implicit Euler method with the increased efficiency (within a given column length) of custom functions can integrate virtually every ordinary differential equation to any desired accuracy. It will serve to solve almost any problem simple enough to be done on a spreadsheet, and almost always will produce model curves more than adequate for comparison with experimental data.

Still, while the Euler methods are *conceptually* simple, they are *computationally* relatively inefficient. In the present section we describe another approach that leads to algorithms that use the computer more efficiently, although they tend to take more time to implement. How to balance personal time versus computer time depends, of course, on the speed of your computer, on the anticipated amount of use of the computation, and on the value and availability of your time.

In the explicit Euler method, we solve equations of the type of (7.1.6) through (7.1.8) by making small steps from t to $t + \Delta t$ with the slopes specified by the differential equations at time t. In section 7.6.3 we saw that the semi-implicit Euler method averages over the interval Δt. The Runge-Kutta approach extends this approach to smaller intervals, thereby yielding a method that needs fewer steps for a given accuracy, reaches higher accuracies for the same number of steps, or some combination of these. Here we will illustrate the most popular, fourth-order explicit Runge-Kutta method. Even for a given order, there are several possible Runge-Kutta formalisms, but the resulting differences in performance are too inconsequential to concern us here.

316

When applied to a single ordinary first-order differential equation

$$\frac{dy}{dt} = F(y) \qquad (7.6.1)$$

such as encountered in (7.1.2), the explicit fourth-order Runge-Kutta method uses the relation

$$y_{n+1} = y_n + \left(K_1 + 2K_2 + 2K_3 + K_4\right)/6 \qquad (7.6.2)$$

where

$$K_1 = \Delta t\, F(y_n) \qquad (7.6.3)$$

$$K_2 = \Delta t\, F(y_n + K_1/2) \qquad (7.6.4)$$

$$K_3 = \Delta t\, F(y_n + K_2/2) \qquad (7.6.5)$$

$$K_4 = \Delta t\, F(y_n + K_3) \qquad (7.6.6)$$

Exercise 7.6.1:

(1) Extend the spreadsheet used in exercise 7.1 to accommodate additional columns: three for a through c, and three for the corresponding errors ε. Then Switch to the VB Editor module, and enter the following function:

```
Function e4RKA(k1, oldT1, oldT2, n, oldA) As Double
'explicit fourth-order Runge-Kutta method for A

Dim A As Double, step As Double
Dim KA1 As Double, KA2 As Double
Dim KA3 As Double, KA4 As Double
Dim i As Integer

n = CInt(n)
A = oldA
step = (oldT2 - oldT1) / n
For i = 1 To n
  KA1 = step * -k1 * A
  KA2 = step * -k1 * (A + KA1 / 2)
  KA3 = step * -k1 * (A + KA2 / 2)
  KA4 = step * -k1 * (A + KA3)
  A = A + (KA1 + 2 * KA2 + 2 * KA3 + KA4) / 6
Next i
e4RKA = A

End Function
```

(2) In the definition of KA1 you will recognize the *function* $F(y)$ of eq. (7.6.1) as `-k1*A`, while the *variable y* is there specified as A. Therefore, the expression $K_2 = \Delta t \times F(y_n + K_1/2)$ in (7.6.4) is coded in the function statement as `KA2=step*-k1*(A+KA1/2)`, i.e., with A replaced by `(A+KA1/2)`.

For b the situation is more complicated, because the expression for db/dt depends not only on b but also on a. For an ordinary first-order differential equation of the form

$$\frac{dy}{dt} = F(y, z) \qquad (7.6.7)$$

the corresponding relations for the explicit fourth-order Runge-Kutta method are

$$y_{n+1} = y_n + \frac{1}{6}\left(K_{y1} + 2K_{y2} + 2K_{y3} + K_{y4}\right) \qquad (7.6.8)$$

$$z_{n+1} = z_n + \frac{1}{6}\left(K_{z1} + 2K_{z2} + 2K_{z3} + K_{z4}\right) \qquad (7.6.9)$$

where

$$K_{y1} = \Delta t\, F(y_n,\ z_n) \qquad (7.6.10)$$

$$K_{y2} = \Delta t\, F(y_n + K_{y1}/2,\ z_n + K_{z1}/2) \qquad (7.6.11)$$

$$K_{y3} = \Delta t\, F(y_n + K_{y2}/2,\ z_n + K_{z2}/2) \qquad (7.6.12)$$

$$K_{y4} = \Delta t \, F(y_n + K_{y3}, \; z_n + K_{z3}) \tag{7.6.13}$$

$$K_{z1} = \Delta t \, G(y_n, \; z_n) \tag{7.6.14}$$

$$K_{z2} = \Delta t \, G(y_n + K_{y1}/2, \; z_n + K_{z1}/2) \tag{7.6.15}$$

$$K_{z3} = \Delta t \, G(y_n + K_{y2}/2, \; z_n + K_{z2}/2) \tag{7.6.16}$$

$$K_{z4} = \Delta t \, G(y_n + K_{y3}, \; z_n + K_{z3}) \tag{7.6.17}$$

which relations are used in the spreadsheet function e4RKB.

When the ordinary first-order differential equation has the form

$$\frac{dy}{dt} = F(t, y, z) \tag{7.6.18}$$

the corresponding relations for the explicit fourth-order Runge-Kutta method are

$$y_{n+1} = y_n + \left(K_{y1} + 2K_{y2} + 2K_{y3} + K_{y4}\right)/6 \tag{7.6.19}$$

$$z_{n+1} = z_n + \left(K_{z1} + 2K_{z2} + 2K_{z3} + K_{z4}\right)/6 \tag{7.6.20}$$

where

$$K_{y1} = \Delta t \, F(t_n, \; y_n, \; z_n) \tag{7.6.21}$$

$$K_{y2} = \Delta t \, F(t_n + \Delta t/2, \; y_n + K_{y1}/2, \; z_n + K_{z1}/2) \tag{7.6.22}$$

$$K_{y3} = \Delta t \, F(t_n + \Delta t/2, \; y_n + K_{y2}/2, \; z_n + K_{z2}/2) \tag{7.6.23}$$

$$K_{y4} = \Delta t \, F(t_n + \Delta t, \; y_n + K_{y3}, \; z_n + K_{z3}) \tag{7.6.24}$$

$$K_{z1} = \Delta t \, G(t_n, \; y_n, \; z_n) \tag{7.6.25}$$

$$K_{z2} = \Delta t \, G(t_n + \Delta t/2, \; y_n + K_{y1}/2, \; z_n + K_{z1}/2) \tag{7.6.26}$$

$$K_{z3} = \Delta t \, G(t_n + \Delta t/2, \; y_n + K_{y2}/2, \; z_n + K_{z2}/2) \tag{7.6.27}$$

$$K_{z4} = \Delta t \, G(t_n + \Delta t, \; y_n + K_{y3}, \; z_n + K_{z3}) \tag{7.6.28}$$

Exercise 7.6.1 (continued):

(3) Add the code for the function e4RKB; as before, regions different from e4RKA are shown in boldface.

```
Function e4RKB (k1, k2, oldT1, oldT2, n, oldA, oldB) As Double
'explicit fourth-order Runge-Kutta method for B

Dim A As Double, B As Double, step As Double
Dim KA1 As Double, KA2 As Double
Dim KA3 As Double, KA4 As Double
Dim KB1 As Double, KB2 As Double
Dim KB3 As Double, KB4 As Double
Dim i As Integer

n = CInt(n)
A = oldA
B = oldB
step = (oldT2 - oldT1) / n
For i = 1 To n
  KA1 = step * -k1 * A
  KA2 = step * -k1 * (A + KA1 / 2)
  KA3 = step * -k1 * (A + KA2 / 2)
  KA4 = step * -k1 * (A + KA3)
  KB1 = step * (k1 * A - k2 * B)
  KB2 = step * (k1 * (A + KA1 / 2) - k2 * (B + KB1 / 2))
  KB3 = step * (k1 * (A + KA2 / 2) - k2 * (B + KB2 / 2))
  KB4 = step * (k1 * (A + KA3) - k2 * (B + KB3))
  B = B + (KB1 + 2 * KB2 + 2 * KB3 + KB4) / 6
```

318

```
      A = A + (KA1 + 2 * KA2 + 2 * KA3 + KA4) / 6
Next i
e4RKB = B

End Function
```

(4) Return to the spreadsheet with Alt◡F11 (Mac: Opt◡F11).

(5) Refer to the numerical values of a_0, b_0, and c_0 in the top cells of the first three new columns.

(6) In the second row in the new column for a place the instruction =e4RKA(), where the addresses within the brackets refer to the parameters listed in the function argument.

(7) Similarly, in the cell to its immediate right, deposit the instruction =e4RKB() with the appropriate arguments. Copy both instructions down.

(8) In the third added column calculate c by difference, based on (7.1.17), as done earlier. And in the next three columns compute the algorithmic errors by comparing the results of the explicit fourth-order Runge-Kutta expressions for a, b, and c with their exact solutions.

(9) You should now find results similar to those shown in Fig. 7.6.1. The algorithmic errors are now already quite small for $n = 1$, i.e., for steps of Dt = 0.1, so that there is hardly a need for using multiple iterations per cell.

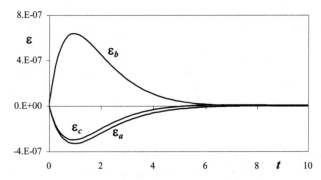

Fig. 7.6.1: The differences ε between the numerically integrated and exact solutions for the explicit fourth-order Runge-Kutta method with $\Delta t = 0.1$ and $n = 1$, i.e., for a step size of 0.1.

In this example, the much greater accuracy of the Runge-Kutta method makes it possible to use rather large steps and still have quite acceptable accuracy. Multiple steps per cell may still be needed to accommodate values of k_2 much larger than k_1, see section 7.5. Starting from the custom functions given here, the time and effort needed in order to apply the Runge-Kutta method to another set of differential equations is relatively small, since you only need to change the specific formulas in the definitions for the various K-values.

For example, we can increase the speed of TStep in section 7.4 by replacing the line

```
C = C * (1 - k * StepSize / 2) / (1 + k * StepSize / 2)
```

by

```
K1 = -StepSize * k * C
K2 = -StepSize * k * (C + K1 / 2)
K3 = -StepSize * k * (C + K2 / 2)
K4 = -StepSize * k * (C + K3)
C = C + (K1 + 2 * K2 + 2 * K3 + K4) / 6
```

because this modification makes TStep accurate to $(\Delta t)^4$.

The 4th order Runge-Kutta method does not provide error estimates, but these can be obtained efficiently by comparing the results of the fourth- and fifth-order approximations respectively, as described by J. R. Cash & A. H. Karp in *ACM Trans. Math. Software* 16 (1990) 201-222.

319

7.7 The XN 4th order Runge-Kutta function

XN contains several ODE-solving functions that are all listed in the Paste Function box once XN is installed. Here we will merely illustrate one of them, ODE_RK4, which makes it very simple to use the 4th order Runge-Kutta method. In exercise 7.7.1 we will use the simple differential expression $dy/dx = -2xy$, with the known solution $y = e^{-x^2}$, and in exercise 7.7.2 we will apply the same method to the sequential chemical reactions $A \rightarrow B \rightarrow C$, which also has known, algebraic solutions, see (7.1.15) though (7.1.17).

Exercise 7.7.1:

(1) On a new spreadsheet deposit the quasi-algebraic expression $y'=-2*x*y$ in cell C3, and in cell E3 put a value for the step size, say 0.1.

(2) In B4 place the label x, and in C4 the label y. These labels are needed so that the function can relate the variables in C3 with their numerical values, which must be listed immediately below their labels.

(3) In B5 write the initial value of x, and in C5 that of y. We will here use $x_0 = 0$ so that $y_0 = 1$.

(4) Highlight cells B6:C6, type in the function description, =ODE_RK4($C$3,B5:C5,$E$3), and deposit this instruction with Ctrl∪Shift∪Enter.

(5) Now comes a neat trick: again highlight B6:C6, grab its handle (at the lower-right corner of cell C6), pull it down to row 35, and release. You will now have the 4th-order Runge-Kutta approximation of the differential equation in cell C4, computed from $x = 0$ to $x = 3$ at intervals of 0.1.

(6) In cell D4 place a label for y_{ref}, and in D5 the instruction =EXP(-1*B5^2). Copy this instruction down to row 35.

(7) In cell E4 put a label for pE, in cell E6 the instruction ='IF(D6=E6," ! ",-LOG(ABS((D6-E6)/E6)), and pull this also down to row 35.

While the absolute error ε = C35–D35 at $x = 3$ is only about 10^{-6}, the value in C35 is still almost 1% off from its correct value of y_{ref} in D35. Can we do better with a smaller step size? Answer that question for yourself, using steps of 0.01 and 0.001 respectively. Reaching $x = 3$ from $x = 0$ with smaller steps implies longer columns, but the results (as summarized in the right bottom of Fig. 7.7.1) speak for themselves. As expected for a 4th order method, a tenfold reduction in step size leads to a decrease in the relative error of the order of 10^4. Again, we can avoid the longer columns with a function that, in turn, exercises the function ODE_RK4 with n times smaller increments, but displays its results only after n such steps.

For the sequence of chemical reactions $A \rightarrow B \rightarrow C$ with concentrations a, b, and c, we have the differential equations (7.1.2) through (7.1.4) with the initial conditions (7.1.5). Exercise 7.7.2 illustrates how we might approach this problem with the XN function ODE_RK4.

Exercise 7.7.2:

(1) On a new spreadsheet put symbols for elapsed time t, and for the concentrations a, b, and c in, say, B4:E4. Immediately below them place their initial conditions, for which we will here use those of section 7.1, i.e., $t_0 = 0$, $a_0 = 1$, $b_0 = 0$, and $c_0 = 0$.

(2) Above the labels for a, b, and c place the differential equations governing their behaviors, in quasi-algebraic form, i.e., $a' = -a$, $b' = a - b/2$, and $c' = b/2$, see (7.1.2) through (7.1.4) with $k_1 = 1$ and $k_2 = 0.5$.

(3) Place the value of the step size somewhere, say, 0.1 in cell E2.

(4) Highlight B6:E6, type the instruction =ODE_RK4($C$3:$E$3,B5:E5,$E$2)., and deposit it with the array instruction Ctrl∪Shift∪Enter.

(5) In B5 write the initial value of x, and in C5 that of y. We will here use $x_0 = 0$ so that $y_0 = 1$.

(6) Grab the handle of this array, and pull it down to, say, row 105.

(7) Highlight the block B5:E105, and plot it as an XY graph.

320

4th order Runge-Kutta ODE-solver:

ODE = y'=-2*x*y		step = 0.1		ODE = y'=-2*x*y		step = 0.01		ODE = y'=-2*x*y		step = 0.001	
x	y	y_ref	pE	x	y	y_ref	pE	x	y	y_ref	pE
0	1	1.000000		0	1	1.000000		0	1	1.000000	
0.1	0.990050	0.990050	9.38	0.01	0.999900	0.999900	!	0.001	0.999999	0.999999	!
0.2	0.960789	0.960789	8.39	0.02	0.999600	0.999600	!	0.002	0.999996	0.999996	!
0.3	0.913931	0.913931	7.91	0.03	0.999100	0.999100	!	0.003	0.999991	0.999991	!
0.4	0.852144	0.852144	7.71	0.04	0.998401	0.998401	!	0.004	0.999984	0.999984	!
0.5	0.778801	0.778801	8.49	0.05	0.997503	0.997503	15.18	0.005	0.999975	0.999975	!
0.6	0.697676	0.697676	7.06	0.06	0.996406	0.996406	14.95	0.006	0.999964	0.999964	!
0.7	0.612627	0.612626	6.45	0.07	0.995112	0.995112	14.75	0.007	0.999951	0.999951	!
0.8	0.527293	0.527292	6.02	0.08	0.993620	0.993620	14.57	0.008	0.999936	0.999936	!
0.9	0.444859	0.444858	5.66	0.09	0.991933	0.991933	14.42	0.009	0.999919	0.999919	!
1.0	0.367881	0.367879	5.35	0.10	0.990050	0.990050	14.29	0.010	0.999900	0.999900	!
1.1	0.298200	0.298197	5.08	0.11	0.987973	0.987973	14.18	0.011	0.999879	0.999879	!
1.2	0.236931	0.236928	4.84	0.12	0.985703	0.985703	14.09	0.012	0.999856	0.999856	!
1.3	0.184524	0.184520	4.62	0.13	0.983242	0.983242	14.00	0.013	0.999831	0.999831	!
1.4	0.140864	0.140858	4.41	0.14	0.980591	0.980591	13.92	0.014	0.999804	0.999804	!
1.5	0.105406	0.105399	4.22	0.15	0.977751	0.977751	13.87	0.015	0.999775	0.999775	!
1.6	0.077312	0.077305	4.04	0.16	0.974725	0.974725	13.82	0.016	0.999744	0.999744	!
1.7	0.055584	0.055576	3.88	0.17	0.971514	0.971514	13.78	0.017	0.999711	0.999711	!
1.8	0.039171	0.039164	3.72	0.18	0.968119	0.968119	13.76	0.018	0.999676	0.999676	!
1.9	0.027059	0.027052	3.57	0.19	0.964544	0.964544	13.77	0.019	0.999639	0.999639	!
2.0	0.018322	0.018316	3.43	0.20	0.960789	0.960789	13.80	0.020	0.999600	0.999600	!
2.1	0.012161	0.012155	3.29	0.21	0.956858	0.956858	13.87	0.021	0.999559	0.999559	!
2.2	0.007912	0.007907	3.17	0.22	0.952753	0.952753	14.06	0.022	0.999516	0.999516	!
2.3	0.005046	0.005042	3.04	0.23	0.948475	0.948475	14.76	0.023	0.999471	0.999471	!
2.4	0.003155	0.003151	2.93	0.24	0.944027	0.944027	14.08	0.024	0.999424	0.999424	!
2.5	0.001933	0.001930	2.81	0.25	0.939413	0.939413	13.66	0.025	0.999375	0.999375	!
2.6	0.001162	0.001159	2.70	0.26	0.934634	0.934634	13.40	0.026	0.999324	0.999324	!
2.7	0.000684	0.000682	2.60	0.27	0.929694	0.929694	13.20	0.027	0.999271	0.999271	!
2.8	0.000395	0.000394	2.50	0.28	0.924595	0.924595	13.03	0.028	0.999216	0.999216	!
2.9	0.000224	0.000223	2.40	0.29	0.919339	0.919339	12.89	0.029	0.999159	0.999159	!
3.0	0.000124	0.000123	2.30	0.30	0.913931	0.913931	12.76	0.030	0.999100	0.999100	!

row:	instruction:	pulled down to row:		h:	pE for x = 3:
B6:C6 =	ODE_RK4($C$3,B5:C5,$E$3)	35		0.1	2.30
F6:G6 =	ODE_RK4($G$3,F5:G5,$I$3)	305		0.01	6.47
J6:K6 =	ODE_RK4($K$3,J5:K5,$M$3)	3005		0.001	10.50
		copied to row:			
D5 =	EXP(-1*B5^2)	35			
E6 =	IF(C6=D6," ! ",-LOG(ABS((C6-D6)/D6)))	35			
H5 =	EXP(-1*F5^2)	305			
I6 =	IF(G6=H6," ! ",-LOG(ABS((G6-H6)/H6)))	305			
L5 =	EXP(-1*J5^2)	3005			
M6 =	IF(K6=L6," ! ",-LOG(ABS((K6-L6)/L6)))	3005			

Fig. 7.7.1: The top part of the spreadsheet of exercise 7.7.1 for the Runge-Kutta analysis of $dy/dx = -2xy$ using the XN function ODE_RK4.

(8) Note how quick and easy ODE_RK4 makes it to solve a set of coupled differential equations.

(9) Highlight B105:E105, grab its handle, and pull it all the way down to row 1005. For longer times t, the concentrations a and b become quite negligible vs. c., which means that the simulated reaction completely ran its course.

(10) Change the value of the step size in E2 to, say, 0.01. The graph will show the initial tenth of the reaction in ten times greater detail and with systematic errors reduced by about a factor of ten thousand. Changing the step size to 1 does just the opposite. Try it. Simulating such solutions to coupled ODE's can hardly be made any easier.

	A	B	C	D	E
1					
2		**A to B to C**		*step =*	**0.1**
3		*ODE =*	*a'=-a*	*b'=a-b/2*	*c'=b/2*
4		*t*	*a*	*b*	*c*
5	*InitVal =*	**0**	**1**	**0**	**0**
6		0.1	0.904838	0.092784	0.002379
7		0.2	0.818731	0.172213	0.009056
8		0.3	0.740818	0.239779	0.019402
9		0.4	0.67032	0.296821	0.032859
10		0.5	0.606531	0.34454	0.048929
11		0.6	0.548812	0.384013	0.067175
12		0.7	0.496586	0.416205	0.087209
13		0.8	0.449329	0.441982	0.108689
14		0.9	0.40657	0.462116	0.131314
15		1.0	0.36788	0.477302	0.154818
16		1.1	0.332871	0.488157	0.178972
17		1.2	0.301195	0.495234	0.203571
18		1.3	0.272532	0.499027	0.228441
19		1.4	0.246597	0.499976	0.253427
20		1.5	0.22313	0.498472	0.278397
21		1.6	0.201897	0.494864	0.303239
22		1.7	0.182684	0.489462	0.327854
23		1.8	0.165299	0.482541	0.35216
24		1.9	0.149569	0.474344	0.376087
25		2.0	0.135336	0.465088	0.399577

cells: instruction:
B6:E6 = ODE_RK4($C$3:$E$3,B5:E5,E

Fig. 7.7.2: The top of the spreadsheet simulating the chemical reaction A → B → C with the NX instruction ODE_RK4.

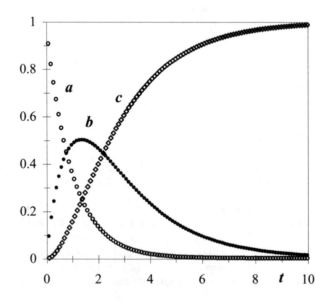

Fig. 7.7.3: The concentrations *a*, *b*, and *c* of the reacting chemical species A → B → C as a function of time *t*, as simulated with ODE_RK4.

322

7.8 The Lotka oscillator 1

We now apply the above methods to the Lotka model of two coupled autocatalytic reactions that, for certain combinations of concentrations and rate parameters, can give rise to steady-state oscillations. In a catalytic reaction, the catalyst speeds up (or retards) a reaction without being consumed itself. Formally, such a reaction can be depicted as $A \xrightarrow{C} B$ where C denotes the catalyst.

Of course, in order to affect the reaction rate, C cannot be a mere spectator, but must be involved in the reaction, e.g., as $A + C \to B + C$. The efficiency of many technologically important chemical processes, such as the production of gasoline or of nitrogen-based fertilizer, depend on catalytic processes. Similarly, many biochemical processes depend on nature's catalysts, the enzymes.

In an *auto*catalytic reaction, the reaction product itself serves as a catalyst. The simplest example of such a process is the reaction $A + B \to 2B$, which can be written alternatively as $A \xrightarrow{B} B$. One typically excludes from such chemical reaction schemes the (often catalytic) effects of macroscopic bodies, such as solid surfaces or water droplets.

There are many known examples of autocatalytic reactions, e.g., the Landolt clock reaction (Landolt, *Ber. Deut. Chem. Ges.* 19 (1886) 1317), or the MnO_2-catalyzed reduction of permanganate. The Lotka oscillator (A. J. Lotka, *J. Am. Chem. Soc.* 42 (1920) 1595; *Proc. Nat'l. Acad. Sci. USA* 6 (1920) 410) is based on the reaction scheme

$$A + B \xrightarrow{k_1} 2B \tag{7.8.1}$$

$$B + C \xrightarrow{k_2} 2C \tag{7.8.2}$$

$$C \xrightarrow{k_3} products \tag{7.8.3}$$

In order to obtain stationary oscillations, we will assume that the concentration a of A is kept constant, so that $da/dt = 0$, and that the concentrations of the reactants and products are homogeneous throughout the reaction vessel, e.g., by using a so-called continuously stirred reactor. The corresponding rate expressions for b and c then read

$$\frac{db}{dt} = k_1 a b - k_2 b c \tag{7.8.4}$$

$$\frac{dc}{dt} = k_2 b c - k_3 c \tag{7.8.5}$$

Below we will use the explicit Euler method, in section 7.9 we will solve the same problem with the semi-implicit Euler method, and in section 7.10 we will use the explicit fourth-order Runge-Kutta approach. For the explicit Euler method we approximate (7.8.4) and (7.8.5) as

$$\frac{\Delta b}{\Delta t} = k_1 a b - k_2 b c \tag{7.8.6}$$

$$\frac{\Delta c}{\Delta t} = k_2 b c - k_3 c \tag{7.8.7}$$

so that

$$b_n = b_{n-1} + \Delta b = b_{n-1} + (k_1 a b_{n-1} - k_2 b_{n-1} c_{n-1}) \Delta t \tag{7.8.8}$$

$$c_n = c_{n-1} + \Delta c = c_{n-1} + (k_2 b_{n-1} c_{n-1} - k_3 c_{n-1}) \Delta t \tag{7.8.9}$$

Exercise 7.8.1:

(1) Start a new spreadsheet. Leave space at its top for a row of figures. Below these place labels for a, k_1, k_2, k_3, and Δt, and their values, such as 1, 2, 2, 5, and 0.01.

(2) Name the cells containing these parameters a, k1k, k2k, k3k, and dt. Note that k1 cannot be used as a name because it is a valid cell address; kk1 etc. would be fine in pre-2007 Excel but are now inadvisable.

(3) Deposit column headings for time t and for the concentrations b and c.

(4) Fill the column for t with 0 (dt) 10.

(5) For $t = 0$ deposit the initial values $b = 1$ and $c = 2$.

(6) For $t = 0.01$ deposit the instructions =B21+(k1k*a*B21-k2k*B21* C21)*dt and =C21+(k2k*B21*C21-k3k*C21)*dt for b and c, assuming that B21 and C21 refer to b_0 and c_0 respectively.

(7) Copy these instructions all the way down to $t = 10$.

(8) Plot your results; they should look similar to those shown in Fig. 7.8.1.

Even though the value of Δt used, 0.01, is considerably smaller than $1/k$ for the largest k-value used ($1/k_3 = 0.2$), these results are clearly unsatisfactory, because they do not lead to the *steady-state* oscillations one should expect when the concentration a is kept constant. In a cyclic process, a small but systematic error can accumulate in successive cycles, thereby quickly leading to quite significant deviations. By reducing Δt we can verify that it was indeed too large, and thereby caused the run-away behavior shown in Fig. 7.8.1.

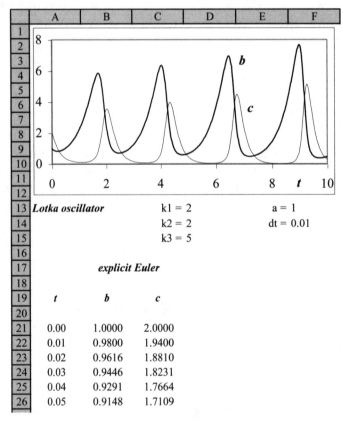

Fig. 7.8.1: The top of the spreadsheet for exercise 7.7.1.

Because the column is already fairly long, we use custom functions. Note that the concentrations b and c are mutually dependent, so that both must be computed inside the For … Next loop. And since this is an open system (in which we must continually supply A to keep its concentration a constant) there is no convenient mass balance equation to eliminate either b or c. The following custom functions will work.

324

Exercise 7.8.1 (continued):

(9) Replace the cell instructions for *b* and *c* by the custom functions shown below, and verify that they indeed work more efficiently.

```
Function eEb(a, oldb, oldc, k1k, k2k, k3k, dt, n) As Double

Dim b As Double, c As Double
Dim i As Integer

b = oldb
c = oldc
For i = 1 To n
  b = b + (k1k * a * b - k2k * b * c) * dt / n
  c = c + (k2k * b * c - k3k * c) * dt / n
Next i
eEb = b

End Function

Function eEc(a, oldb, oldc, k1k, k2k, k3k, dt, n) As Double

Dim b As Double, c As Double
Dim i As Integer

b = oldb
c = oldc
For i = 1 To n
  b = b + (k1k * a * b - k2k * b * c) * dt / n
  c = c + (k2k * b * c - k3k * c) * dt / n
Next i
eEc = c

End Function
```

For $n = 10$ this yields a stationary oscillation, see Fig. 7.8.2. How will you know whether this *n*-value is sufficient? Copy the numerical values (with Ctrl⌣c, Edit ⇨ Paste Special, Values) to another spot on the spreadsheet, then run the simulation with, say, $n = 20$, and compare the results. Keep increasing *n* by, say, factors of 2 until you are satisfied with the consistency of the result.

You can readily see whether you have reached a steady state from a phase diagram in which you plot *c* as a function of *b*, as illustrated in Fig. 7.8.3. In the steady state it shows a closed loop, a *limit cycle*.

Exercise 7.8.1 continued:

(10) Make a phase diagram by plotting *c* as a function of *b*. In such a diagram, the time *t* is an implicit parameter.

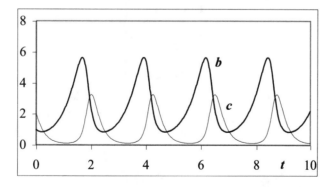

Fig. 7.8.2: The results for an explicit Euler simulation of the Lotka oscillator with $\Delta t = 0.01$ and $n = 10$ for effective time increments of 0.001. The resulting concentration oscillations are now strictly repetitive.

325

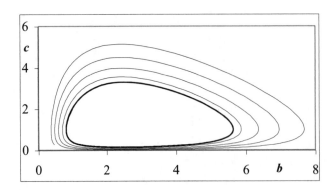

Fig. 7.8.3: The phase diagram, displaying c as a function of b. Thin line: results from explicit Euler method with $\Delta t = 0.01$, $n = 1$. Thick line: same with $\Delta t = 0.01$, $n = 10$ for an effective Δt of 0.001.

7.9 The Lotka oscillator 2

In a semi-implicit simulation we use

$$\frac{\Delta b}{\Delta t} = k_1 \, a \, (b + \Delta b/2) - k_2 \, (b + \Delta b/2)(c + \Delta c/2) \tag{7.9.1}$$

$$\frac{\Delta c}{\Delta t} = k_2 \, (b + \Delta b/2)(c + \Delta c/2) - k_3 \, (c + \Delta c/2) \tag{7.9.2}$$

Upon neglecting terms containing the product $\Delta b \, \Delta c$ this yields

$$\left(\frac{1}{\Delta t} - k_1 \, a/2 + k_2 c/2 \right) \Delta b + \left(k_2 \, b/2 \right) \Delta c = k_1 \, ab - k_2 \, bc \tag{7.9.3}$$

$$\left(-k_2 \, c/2 \right) \Delta b + \left(\frac{1}{\Delta t} - k_2 \, b/2 + k_3 /2 \right) \Delta c = k_2 \, bc - k_3 \, c \tag{7.9.4}$$

Thus we have two equations, (7.9.3) and (7.9.4), and two unknowns, Δb and Δc, which are most readily obtained by matrix algebra, using Cramer's rule, as

$$\Delta b = \frac{\begin{vmatrix} k_1 ab - k_2 bc & k_2 \, bc/2 \\ k_2 bc - k_3 c & 1/\Delta t - k_2 \, b/2 + k_3/2 \end{vmatrix}}{\begin{vmatrix} 1/\Delta t - k_1 \, a/2 + k_2 \, c/2 & k_2 \, b/2 \\ -k_2 \, c/2 & 1/\Delta t - k_2 \, b/2 + k_3/2 \end{vmatrix}}$$

$$= \frac{(k_1 ab - k_2 bc)(1/\Delta t - k_2 \, b/2 + k_3/2) - (k_2 \, b/2)(k_2 bc - k_3 c)}{(1/\Delta t - k_1 \, a/2 + k_2 \, c/2)(1/\Delta t - k_2 \, b/2 + k_3/2) - (k_2 \, b/2)(-k_2 \, c/2)} \tag{7.9.5}$$

and

$$\Delta c = \frac{\begin{vmatrix} 1/\Delta t - k_1 \, a/2 + k_2 \, c/2 & k_1 ab - k_2 bc \\ -k_2 \, c/2 & k_2 bc - k_3 c \end{vmatrix}}{\begin{vmatrix} 1/\Delta t - k_1 \, a/2 + k_2 \, c/2 & k_2 \, b/2 \\ -k_2 \, c/2 & 1/\Delta t - k_2 \, b/2 + k_3/2 \end{vmatrix}}$$

326

$$= \frac{(1/\Delta t - k_1\,a/2 + k_2\,c/2)\,(k_2 bc - k_3 c) - (k_1 ab - k_2 bc)\,(-k_2\,c/2)}{(1/\Delta t - k_1\,a/2 + k_2\,c/2)\,(1/\Delta t - k_2\,b/2 + k_3/2) - (k_2\,b/2)\,(-k_2\,c/2)} \qquad (7.9.6)$$

from which we can compute b_n as $b_{n-1} + \Delta b$ and c_n as $c_{n-1} + \Delta c$. Such results, for a column of 1001 rows, with $\Delta t = 0.01$, are visually indistinguishable from those obtained with the explicit method supplemented with functions to reduce their effective Δt to 0.001, shown in Fig. 7.9.2. If desired, we can further improve the numerical accuracy of these results with custom functions that subdivide the interval Δt into smaller steps.

Exercise 7.9.1:
(1) Implement the semi-implicit Euler method on your spreadsheet, using custom functions based on (7.9.5) and (7.9.6) for b and c respectively.

7.10 The Lotka oscillator 3

For applying the fourth-order Runge-Kutta method we combine (7.6.7) through (7.6.17) with (7.8.4) and (7.8.6), so that $F = k_1 ab - k_2 bc$, $G = k_2 bc - k_3 c$, and a is a constant. We therefore modify the custom function e4RKB of section 7.6 to

```
Function eRKb(a, kk1, kk2, kk3, oldb, oldc, dt, n) As Double

Dim b As Double, c As Double, step As Double
Dim KB1 As Double, KB2 As Double
Dim KB3 As Double, KB4 As Double
Dim KC1 As Double, KC2 As Double
Dim KC3 As Double, KC4 As Double
Dim i As Integer

step = dt / n
b = oldb
c = oldc
For i = 1 To n
  KB1 = step * (kk1 * a * b - kk2 * b * c)
  KB2 = step * (kk1 * a * (b + KB1 / 2) - kk2 * (b + KB1 / 2) * (c + KC1 / 2))
  KB3 = step * (kk1 * a * (b + KB2 / 2) - kk2 * (b + KB2 / 2) * (c + KC2 / 2))
  KB4 = step * (kk1 * a * (b + KB3) - kk2 * (b + KB3) * (c + KC3))
  KC1 = step * (kk2 * b * c - kk3 * c)
  KC2 = step * (kk2 * (b + KB1 / 2) * (c + KC1 / 2) - kk3 * (c + KC1 / 2))
  KC3 = step * (kk2 * (b + KB2 / 2) * (c + KC2 / 2) - kk3 * (c + KC2 / 2))
  KC4 = step * (kk2 * (b + KB3) * (c + KC3) - kk3 * (c + KC3))
  b = b + (KB1 + 2 * KB2 + 2 * KB3 + KB4) / 6
  c = c + (KC1 + 2 * KC2 + 2 * KC3 + KC4) / 6
Next i
eRKb = b

End Function
```

and

```
Function eRKc(a, kk1, kk2, kk3, oldb, oldc, dt, n) As Double

Dim b As Double, c As Double, step As Double
Dim KB1 As Double, KB2 As Double
Dim KB3 As Double, KB4 As Double
Dim KC1 As Double, KC2 As Double
Dim KC3 As Double, KC4 As Double
Dim i As Integer

step = dt / n
  b = oldb
c = oldc
For i = 1 To n
  KB1 = step * (kk1 * a * b - kk2 * b * c)
  KB2 = step * (kk1 * a * (b + KB1 / 2) - kk2 * (b + KB1 / 2) * (c + KC1 / 2))
  KB3 = step * (kk1 * a * (b + KB2 / 2) - kk2 * (b + KB2 / 2) * (c + KC2 / 2))
v
```

```
    KB4 = step * (kk1 * a * (b + KB3) - kk2 * (b + KB3) * (c + KC3))
    KC1 = step * (kk2 * b * c - kk3 * c)
    KC2 = step * (kk2 * (b + KB1 / 2) * (c + KC1 / 2) - kk3 * (c + KC1 / 2))
    KC3 = step * (kk2 * (b + KB2 / 2) * (c + KC2 / 2) - kk3 * (c + KC2 / 2))
    KC4 = step * (kk2 * (b + KB3) * (c + KC3) - kk3 * (c + KC3))
     b = b + (KB1 + 2 * KB2 + 2 * KB3 + KB4) / 6
   c = c + (KC1 + 2 * KC2 + 2 * KC3 + KC4) / 6
Next i
eRKc = c

End Function
```

Exercise 7.10.1:

(1) Implement the explicit fourth-order Runge-Kutta method on your spreadsheet, using the above custom functions.

It is the interplay between the two autocatalytic reactions that causes the oscillatory behavior. The conversion of A into B in reaction (7.8.1) is catalyzed by the reaction product B, while the conversion of B into C is catalyzed by C. When the concentration of C increases, it will speed up the decomposition of B, so that the corresponding concentration b will decrease. This is clearly visible in Fig. 7.8.2. However, the decrease in b will lead to a decrease in the rate of production both of B, through reaction (7.8.1), and of C, through reaction (7.8.2). Depending on the numerical values of the rate constants involved, b may recover while, initially, c remains low, in which case the process may become cyclic. In that case, the concentrations b and c will reach their maximum values at different times: while both are cyclic, they are out of phase with each other, see Fig. 7.8.2. Another way to display this behavior is to plot, e.g., c versus b, as in the phase diagram of Fig. 7.8.3, which shows a limit cycle. Figures 7.8.2 and 7.8.3 represent the same information in different formats, viz., in the time and frequency domains respectively. Such alternative representations are of course readily made on the spreadsheet, with its convenient, built-in graphing capabilities.

7.11 Stability

While the fourth-order Runge-Kutta method yields higher accuracy, the semi-implicit method is sometimes more stable. We will illustrate this by numerically integrating the differential equation

$$\frac{dy}{dx} = y^2 + 1 \tag{7.11.1}$$

with $y_{x=0} \equiv y_0 = 0$. For the semi-implicit Euler method we rewrite (7.11.1) as

$$\frac{\Delta y}{\Delta x} = (y + \Delta y / 2)^2 + 1 = y^2 + y\Delta y + (\Delta y)^2 / 4 + 1 \approx y^2 + y\Delta y + 1 \tag{7.11.2}$$

so that

$$\Delta y \approx \frac{y^2 + 1}{1 / \Delta x - y} \tag{7.11.3}$$

where we have again linearized y^2 by neglecting the term $(\Delta y)^2/4$.

Exercise 7.11.1:

(1) Start a new spreadsheet, with space for values of n at the top, and below this a column for x, and four columns for y. Fill the x-column with the numbers 0 (0.01) 3, and the top cells in the y-columns with zeroes for y_0.

(2) In the first y-column, implement the semi-implicit Euler method with the command (say in cell B6, assuming that the value of y_0 is placed in cell B5) =B5+(B5^2+1)/(1/(A6-A5)-B5).

(3) In the next y-column use a custom function to compute y with smaller time increments, such as

```
Function siEulerY(oldX1, oldX2, n, oldY) As Double
'semi-implicit Euler method for exercise 7.11

Dim Y As Double, step As Double
Dim i As Integer
```

```
n = CInt(n)
Y = oldY
step = (oldX2 - oldX1) / n
For i = 1 To n
  Y = Y + (Y * Y + 1) / ((1 / step) - Y)
Next i
siEulerY = Y

End Function
```

(4) Place a corresponding value of n in cell C1, and the instruction =siEulerY(A5,A6,$C$1,C5) in cell C7.

(5) In the next y-column compute y with the explicit fourth-order Runge-Kutta method, using a custom function such as

```
Function e4RKY(oldX1, oldX2, n, oldY)
'explicit fourth-order Runge-Kutta for exercise 7.11

Dim X As Double, Y As Double, step As Double
Dim k1 As Double, k2 As Double
Dim k3 As Double, k4 As Double
Dim i As Integer

X = oldX1
Y = oldY
n = CInt(n)
step = (oldX2 - oldX1) / n
For i = 1 To n
  k1 = step * (Y ^ 2 + 1)
  k2 = step * (((Y + k1 / 2) ^ 2) + 1)
  k3 = step * (((Y + k2 / 2) ^ 2) + 1)
  k4 = step * (((Y + k3) ^ 2) + 1)
  Y = Y + (k1 + 2 * k2 + 2 * k3 + k4) / 6
  X = X + step
Next i
e4RKY = Y

End Function
```

(6) Place the value $n = 1$ in cell D1, and in cell D6 the instruction =e4RKY(A5,A6,$D$1,D5).

(7) Use the same custom function in the last y-column, but this time with $n = 10$ (in cell E1).

(8) Plot the results for y as a function of x obtained with these two methods.

Figure 7.11.1 illustrates what you will find. The semi-implicit Euler method has no problem with the integration, either for a simple one-line instruction and $\Delta t = 0.01$, or with a custom function and an effective Δt of $0.01/1000 = 0.00001$. The Runge-Kutta method starts out fine, but stops at $x = 1.57$, regardless of whether we use $\Delta t = 0.01$ or multiple steps (as with $n = 10$).

By now you may have recognized the function we have just integrated: it is $y = \tan(x)$ which, as you can readily verify, is indeed the solution to (7.11.1) with $y_0 = 0$. The Runge-Kutta method apparently cannot get past the discontinuity in y at $x = \pi/2 \approx 1.5708$, while this same hurdle doesn't faze the semi-implicit Euler method. We merely illustrate this here for a particular differential equation, but it reflects a rather general property: implicit methods, and even semi-implicit ones, are more *stable* than explicit methods.

Having the exact solution allows us to compute and plot the errors. The results so obtained are shown in Figs. 7.11.2 and 7.11.3, and illustrate that the Runge-Kutta method has far smaller algorithmic errors when it works, but can also fail. When a custom function is used to reduce the effective step size, the semi-implicit Euler method can combine accuracy and reliability, as illustrated in Fig. 7.11.3.

It is sometimes suggested that the Runge-Kutta method is all you need for the numerical integration of ordinary differential equations with one-point boundary conditions. But in Fig. 7.11.2 the one-line semi-implicit Euler instruction eventually outperforms the Runge-Kutta method, and the use of smaller effective step sizes $\Delta t / n$ makes the corresponding inaccuracies quite acceptable, see Fig. 7.11.3. Because of its simpler coding and greater stability, the semi-implicit Euler method is often a better bet, except when you already *know* the function to be well behaved over the entire range of interest.

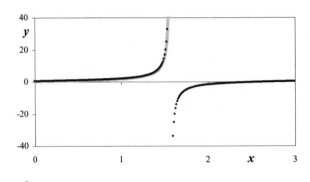

Fig. 7.11.1: The function *y* found by numerical integration of (7.11.1) with *y*0 = 0. Solid dots: results from the semi-implicit Euler method for $\Delta t = 0.01$. Broad gray band: results from the explicit fourth-order Runge-Kutta method for $\Delta t = 0.01$. Note that the latter fails for *x* > 1.57.

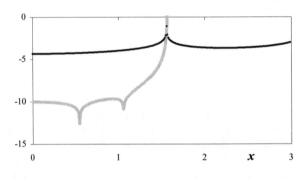

Fig. 7.11.2: The (logarithms of the absolute values of the) relative errors ε_r in the numerical simulation. Solid dots: results from the semi-implicit Euler method for $\Delta t = 0.01$. Broad gray bands results from the explicit fourth- order Runge-Kutta method for $\Delta t = 0.01$, which fails for *x* > $\pi/2$. The cusps in the latter curve correspond to sign changes in $\varepsilon_r(x)$.

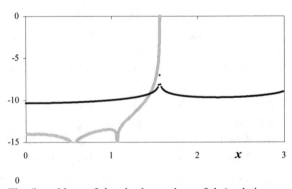

Fig. 7.11.3: The (logarithms of the absolute values of the) relative errors ε_r in the numerical simulation. Solid dots: results from the semi-implicit Euler method for Δt = 0.01 with *n* = 1000, yielding relative errors smaller than 10^{-7}. Broad gray band: results from the explicit fourth- order Runge-Kutta method for $\Delta t = 0.01$ with *n* = 10.

330

7.12 Chaos

Apart from problems caused by the method used for numerical integration, difficulties can be caused by the differential equation itself. This can occur, e.g., when the solution is highly dependent on the precise value of the initial condition. Since in science and technology (as distinct from mathematics) such an initial value is never known *exactly*, the solution can become uncertain. A prototypical example of this phenomenon is the weather forecast, which depends on equations that, when integrated over long periods to yield a prediction, turn out to depend critically on the precision of the (often imprecisely known) initial conditions. This is why the predictive power of the farmer's almanac is not much worse than the weatherman's long-term forecast.

A clear example, taken from section 9.1B of J. R. Rice, *Numerical Methods, Software, and Analysis*, McGraw-Hill (1983), is the differential equation

$$\frac{dy}{dx} = 5y - 6e^{-x} \qquad (7.12.1)$$

which has the general solution

$$y = e^{-x} + Ae^{5x} \qquad (7.12.2)$$

For the initial condition $y_{x=0} = 1$ we find $A = 0$, so that the solution is $y = e^{-x}$. For $y_0 = 1 \pm \varepsilon$, however, (7.12.2) yields $A = \pm\varepsilon$, with the solution $y = e^{-x} + \varepsilon e^{5x}$. As x increases, the term in e^{5x} will eventually dominate the solution no matter how small $|\varepsilon|$, as long as it is not *exactly* zero. This is illustrated in Fig. 7.12.1, and somewhat resembles a sharp needle balancing on its point, a situation that is unstable to any perturbation, no matter how small.

No numerical process handles data with complete accuracy. Consequently, pathological equations such as (7.12.1) will eventually give problems when integrated numerically with the simple methods described here. Figure 7.12.2 illustrates how the semi-implicit Euler and the explicit fourth-order Runge-Kutta methods fare with this equation.

Fig. 7.12.1: The solutions for $dy/dx = 5y - 6e^{-x}$ for various values of the initial condition $y_0 = 1 + \varepsilon$. Broad gray curve: $\varepsilon = 0$, where $y = e^{-x}$. Thin black curves above the line $y = e^{-x}$, from left to right, for

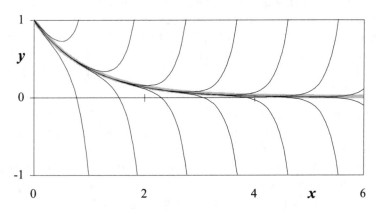

$\varepsilon = 10^{-2}$, 10^{-4}, 10^{-6}, 10^{-8}, 10^{-10}, 10^{-12}, and 10^{-14} respectively. Likewise, the thin black curves below the line $y = e^{-x}$, from left to right, for $\varepsilon = -10^{-2}$, -10^{-4}, -10^{-6}, -10^{-8}, -10^{-10}, -10^{-12}, and -10^{-14} respectively.

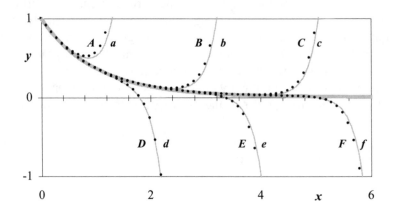

Fig. 7.12.2: Numerical integration of $dy/dx = 5y - 6e^{-x}$ with the semi-implicit Euler method (A through C) and the explicit fourth-order Runge-Kutta method (curves D through F) for $\Delta t = 0.1$. Curves B and C used custom functions with $n = 100$ and $n = 10^4$, effectively making Δt equal to 0.001 and 0.00001, while curves D through F used $n = 1$, $n = 10$, and $n = 100$ (or $\Delta t = 0.1$, 0.01, and 0.001) respectively. All these results are displayed as individual data points. For comparison, the curve $y = e^{-x} + \varepsilon\, e^{5x}$ for $\varepsilon = 0$ is shown as a thick gray line, with thin gray lines for $\varepsilon = 10^{-3}$ (a), 10^{-7} (b), 10^{-11} (c), -2×10^{-5} (d), -2×10^{-9} (e), and -2×10^{-13} (f).

7.13 Summary

In this chapter we have looked in some detail at a few simple methods for the numerical integration of ordinary differential equations with one-point boundary conditions. We have encountered three methods: the explicit and semi-implicit Euler methods, and the most popular of the explicit Runge-Kutta methods. The explicit Euler method is the simplest, both conceptually and in terms of its practical implementation, but it yields rather crude results. The explicit fourth-order Runge-Kutta method is much more efficient, and is readily implemented in Excel with custom functions. We have illustrated how to write such a function in section 7.6, and you can find more sophisticated versions in XN in the form of the function ODE_RK4 and the macro ODE Solver, see section 7.7. The ODE Solver macro implements the 4th order Runge-Kutta-Fehlberg method, which estimates the error at each step, and adjusts its step-size accordingly. For a stiff system of ordinary differential equations, try the XN implicit predictor/corrector function ODE_PC2I.

There are, of course, many other methods that are not even mentioned here. Many of them are described in standard textbooks on numerical integration of ordinary differential equations, and if desired can readily be implemented on a spreadsheet. The present chapter is merely meant to illustrate how to approach such problems. For more complicated systems or routine uses a spreadsheet may well be too slow and/or too limiting, in which case the user should explore the capabilities of more specialized software. But even then, the transparency and ease of visualizing intermediate results may well make the spreadsheet a useful first stage for exploring the underlying algorithms.

An additional advantage of the spreadsheet over dedicated software is that you already have it at your fingertips, and that you can have direct access to its code, and therefore complete control over its operation. A disadvantage is that you must know what you are doing, usually in more detail than necessary with prepackaged software, and that you may have to spend some time coding and trouble-shooting.

In order to demonstrate the properties of the few methods illustrated here we have first introduced them for differential equations with known solutions. Obviously, that is not where one would use numeri-

332

cal integration, and the example of the Lotka oscillator in sections 7.7 through 7.10 illustrates an application where no closed-form solution is available.

We have encountered some limitations of explicit methods, which may not be able to get past discontinuities, as in the example of section 7.11. Semi-implicit methods do better there, as they often do with so-called stiff systems of differential equations, which contain parameters of quite different orders of magnitude. Such stiff systems are often encountered in, e.g., chemical kinetics. For an extensive discussion of stiff problems, and ways to handle them, see C. M. Gear, *Numerical Initial-Value Problems in Ordinary Differential Equations*, Prentice-Hall (1971). G. Bader & P. Deuflhard describe an adaptation of the semi-implicit Euler method to stiff problems in *Numer. Math.* 41 (1983) 337, and J. R. Cash & A. H. Karp, *ACM Trans. Math. Software* 16 (1990) 201, describe a variable-order Runge-Kutta method that may, likewise, be suitable for handling stiff problems.

In section 7.12 we briefly encountered chaos, in which the differential equations are so sensitive to their boundary conditions that numerical integration becomes extremely difficult. Chaotic systems differ, at least in principle, from stochastics, where the phenomena are inherently subject to random effects, although the results may look quite similar. Fortunately, most differential equations of practical importance in the physical sciences are well behaved within the range of their practical applications.

Why is it that numerical methods can integrate differential equations that have no known algebraic solutions? A main reason is that the most general analytical methods, such as Laplace transformation, are effectively restricted to linear differential equations. This is not a requirement for numerical integration, which can either linearize the nonlinearities, as illustrated in sections 7.10 and 7.11, or can incorporate nonlinear methods such as Solver.

A well-known disadvantage of numerical integration is that it yields an answer valid only for the particular parameter values chosen. However, as illustrated in sections 7.1 and 7.4, this disadvantage vanishes when we use Solver to vary those parameters by optimizing the fit between the simulation and the experimental data. Because the simulation is virtually noise-free, this approach at the same time rejects random noise. Incidentally, the automatically self-updating *functions* we have used in this context are much easier to use in combination with Solver than *macros* would be.

7.14 *For further reading*

Virtually any college library will have books on numerical methods that provide different perspectives and more details than can possibly be provided here, in a single chapter. Numerical differentiation and integration will be discussed further in chapter 9. Many additional formulas for numerical integration are listed by P. J. Davis & I. Polonsky in chapter 25 of M. Abramowitz & I. Stegun, *Handbook of Mathematical Functions*, NBS (1964), Dover (1965), an extremely useful yet inexpensive book that should be on the desk of every scientist. The *Numerical Recipes* by Press et al., another highly recommended book, devotes three full chapters to the numerical integration of differential equations. For implicit Runge-Kutta methods see, e.g., M. K. Jain, *Numerical Solutions to Differential Equations*, Wiley (1979, 1984).

Chapter *8*

Write your own macros

In the preceding chapters we have seen that custom *procedures* make it possible to extend the already quite considerable range of capabilities of Excel, in order to suit your personal computing needs. Such procedures are of two types: *functions* and *subroutines*. Macros, the main topic of this chapter, are a special type of subroutines, directly callable from the spreadsheet, see section 1.9. This chapter will illustrate how to copy spreadsheet data into a macro, manipulate them, and return the result to the spreadsheet. Such input/output problems are often the most difficult aspects of custom macros. Functions have far fewer input and output options, but are also much easier to implement. In this chapter we will therefore highlight macros or, in general, subroutines, provide a few simple input and output procedures, consider some general aspects of VBA, and then illustrate their use in a number of case studies featuring sample macros. This material is augmented by a collection of MacroMorsels that highlight particular problems, and by the more extensive MacroBundle, which contains the custom macros described in this book, but doubles as a set of worked examples of custom applications. All of these can be found on my web site, http://www.bowdoin.edu/~rdelevie/ excellaneous.

All custom procedures will be written in VBA, short for Visual Basic for Applications. VBA contains a subset of Visual Basic, augmented with instructions specifically designed for interacting with its host application, in our case Excel. Visual Basic is a higher-level language developed (via Borland's Turbo Basic and Microsoft's Quick Basic) from the original Dartmouth BASIC (for Beginner's All-purpose Symbolic Instruction Code). On the way it has lost its original line numbers, and now is a quite competent mid-level computer language, resembling earlier versions of FORTRAN such as FORTRAN 77. VBA can be compiled, but as used here is interpreted line by line.

The computer codes of custom functions and custom macros reside in a *module*. In early versions of Excel, modules were like spreadsheets without row and column lines, but starting with Excel 97 the modules are hidden in a Visual Basic Editor, reachable with Alt‿F11 (Mac: Opt‿F11), or with <u>T</u>ools ⇨ <u>M</u>acro ⇨ <u>V</u>isual Basic Editor. In order to open a new module, use Alt‿F11 (Mac: Opt‿F11) to go to the VBEditor, followed by (on the Visual Basic Toolbar) <u>I</u>nsert ⇨ <u>M</u>odule. Thereafter, you can toggle back and forth between spreadsheet and module with Alt‿F11 (Mac: Opt‿F11) or, easier yet, use a split screen to place the module next to or below the spreadsheet, without overlap, so that you can switch between them merely by moving and clicking the mouse.

If `Option Explicit` appears at the top of your macro module, temporarily disable it by placing an apostrophe in front of it ('commenting it out'), at least until you have read most of this chapter. Then reactivate it, so that you can benefit from its typo-catching feature. In that case you must dimension every parameter used, at least *by name*, i.e., by statements such as `Dim A, B, C`, and preferably (since that makes the computer run somewhat more efficiently) by data type, see section 8.5, as `Dim A As Integer, B As Double, C As Variant`, etc. Dimension statements must occur *before* the dimensioned parameter is used; for substantial macros it is best to place all dimension statements at the top of the macro, arranged in some logical order, such as by data type, or alphabetically.

8.1 Reading the contents of a cell

We start by letting a macro read a number, then make it display that number to make sure it got it right. Open a spreadsheet, open a module (with Alt‿F11 or, on a Mac, Opt‿F11, then click <u>I</u>nsert on the VBEditor toolbar if no pre-existing module shows up), and at its top (clearly separate from any already existing code) type the following:

```
Sub Read()
'Read the cell value

CellValue = Selection.Value
MsgBox "The cell value is " & CellValue

End Sub
```

Notes:

(1) The first line defines the start of the macro and its name, here `Read`. The *empty* brackets following the name are necessary, and identify the subroutine as a *macro*. A function (which starts with `Function` rather than with `Sub`) also has brackets, but these are only empty for functions that do not need any input information, such as the function `Pi()`. The two differences between a macro and a (more general) subroutine are (a) that a subroutine has arguments within its brackets, and (b) is not directly callable from the spreadsheet, but only through a macro or function.

(2) The editor recognizes the term `Sub` (for *sub*routine) and shows it in blue, as a reserved word. (We assume here the default colors, which you can change to suit your own taste, like so much else in Excel.) Reserved words cannot be used as names of variables, but variations on them, such as sub1 or mySub, can be. Likewise, `Function` is a reserved word. While the editor recognizes case (which is useful for error-checking), it is not case-sensitive: you can type all instructions in lower case.

(3) The second line starts with an apostrophe, which defines it as a *comment* line. A comment is meant for the convenience of the user, and is ignored by the computer. The computer screen will show it in green, thereby identifying it as a comment, and letting the user know that the editor is working. Comments need not occupy an entire line: any text to the right of an apostrophe is considered a comment. Comments can be placed anywhere inside a macro, or even before or after them, except following a line continuation. We will mostly use comments (a) at the beginning of a procedure, to explain its function, requirements, nomenclature, etc., and (b) within a procedure, as a convenient label to identify a particular functional unit, serving the same function as a paragraph or section heading in regular text.

(4) The third line does all the work. Despite the (symmetrical) equal sign, the editor reads it as an *assignment*, to be interpreted *from right to left*, and to mean: take the value of the highlighted selection, and then assign it to the parameter named `cellValue`. Instead of `cellValue` you could have used any other parameter name, such as `Y` or `unknown` or `ThisIsIt`, but not a word the editor recognizes as an instruction, such as `value`. (Again, capitals or lower case makes no difference here. Except for literal quotes, VBA ignores the difference between capitals and lower case letters, but will make them uniform within a given procedure.) By adding the prefix `cell` we avoid this problem; any other prefix, suffix, or other name modification would also do the trick, such as `myValue`, `thisValue`, or, preferably, a more descriptive name. Parameter names cannot contain any empty spaces, but we can improve their readability by using capitals, as in `CellValue` or `ThisIsIt`, or by using underscores. In this book we use capitals rather than underscores, because they also serve to catch typos when you use Option Explicit.

(5) The fourth line is our check that the macro indeed reads the highlighted value. Upon execution of the macro a message box will appear in the spreadsheet, with the text `The cell value is` exactly as it appears within the quotation marks in the instruction, followed by its value as read. The empty space at the end of the quoted text string separates the text from the subsequent parameter value. The ampersand `&` both separates and ties together (concatenates) the two dissimilar parts of the line: the identifying text and the displayed contents. The text is helpful as a reminder of what is displayed, but is optional: `MsgBox CellValue` would also work.

(6) The last line specifies the end of the macro, and will be shown in blue. Recent versions of Excel write this line for you automatically as soon as you enter a line defining a macro name, so you may not even have to type it.

In order to run this macro, exit the VB Editor with Alt␣F11 (Mac: Opt␣F11), place a number somewhere on the spreadsheet, and enter it. Select Tools ⇨ Macro ⇨ Macros or Alt␣F8 and, in the macro listing, double-click on Read (or single-click on Read to select it, then click on Run). You should now see a message box that shows the value just entered in the spreadsheet. Click OK in the message box to make it disappear. Then change the number read by the macro, and check that the macro again reads it correctly. Also verify that it only reads the contents of the active cell, the one identified by a thick border.

You can use message boxes for feedback, i.e., to show that the macro has indeed registered the information. The VBA editor has a better option, which is less intrusive because it does not require you to acknowledge it every time, by pushing the OK button, before you can do anything else. Moreover, it allows you to stay in the VBEditor module, without the need to switch back and forth between it and the spreadsheet. That option is to use the Immediate Window, which you can open from within the VBEditor module with Ctrl␣g or with View ⇨ Immediate Window. To display messages in the Immediate Window, insert lines in your code that call the instruction `Debug.Print`, as in

```
Debug.Print "The cell value is " & cellValue
```

or, if you do not want the explanatory text, simply

```
Debug.Print cellValue
```

In the MacroMorsels accompanying this book we will often use the Immediate Window. From within the VBEditor you can also activate a macro, by placing the mouse pointer somewhere within the code of that macro, and pushing the functionkey F5.

Now go back to the VB Editor with Alt␣F11 (Mac: Opt␣F11), make the changes that are indicated below in bold, then run the macro again. The bold emphasis is only meant for you, to identify the changes.

```
Sub Read()
'Read & change the cell value

cellValue = Selection.Value
MsgBox "The cell value is " & cellValue
Debug.Print "The cell value is " & cellValue
cellValue = cellValue * 7
MsgBox "The cell value is " & cellValue
Debug.Print "The new cell value is " & cellValue
Selection.Value = cellValue

End Sub
```

Notes (continued):

(7) The editor does not recognize the difference between bold and ordinary characters, nor any other formatting details such as type font, font size, color, or italics, and you can therefore enter text containing them without problems, because the editor will just ignore such textual niceties. For that same reason, both the MacroMorsels and the MacroBundle can use color, bold and italic for emphasis and ease of reading.

(8) The sixth line is, again, an assignment, to be interpreted as: take the old value of `cellValue`, multiply it by 7, and make that the new value of `cellValue`. Again the equal sign acts like an arrow pointing from right to left, as in `cellValue` ⇐ `cellValue * 7`.

(9) The nineth line is also an assignment: it takes the new value of cellValue, and writes it in the highlighted cell (the `Selection`) of the spreadsheet. `Selection.Value = cellValue` is therefore a *writing* instruction, whereas `cellValue = Selection.Value`, in which the elements on either side of the assignment sign are interchanged, is a *reading* instruction. In both cases, the directionality of execution is from right to left.

(10) Place an apostrophe in front of the MsgBox instructions to mute them. From now on we will use no more message boxes in debugging, because having to acknowledge them in the spreadsheet is bothersome. They can still play a useful role in alerting the macro user of problems, and occasionally in providing spreadsheet output.

Try the macro, and verify that it indeed keeps multiplying the value in the highlighted cell by 7. Play with it by, e.g., changing the instruction in the fifth line to cellValue = -cellValue + 2, or whatever suits your fancy. Because it is usually undesirable to overwrite spreadsheet data, modify the macro as indicated below so that it will write its output one row *below* its input, then run this macro.

```
Sub Read()
'Read & change the cell value

cellValue = Selection.Value
'MsgBox "The cell value is " & cellValue
Debug.Print "The cell value is " & cellValue
cellValue = cellValue * 7
'MsgBox "The cell value is " & cellValue
Debug.Print "The new cell value is " & cellValue
Selection.Offset(1,0).Select
Selection.Value = cellValue

End Sub
```

Notes (continued):

(11) Verify that you can write the output *to the right of* the input cell with Offset(0,1) instead of Offset(1,0), and that you can place it anywhere else on the spreadsheet (as long as you stay within its borders) with Offset(r, c) where r and c are integers. A positive r moves the output down by r rows, a negative r moves it up. Likewise, a positive c moves it to the right by c columns while a negative c moves it to the left.

(12) You can now delete the line specifying the message boxes, and even the Debug.Print statements because, by displaying the answer, the spreadsheet shows that the macro works. Instead of deleting we so far used to *comment them out* by placing an apostrophe in front of these lines, so that the editor will ignore them. That may be useful during debugging, so that you can easily reactivate them in case you need to during troubleshooting. But don't forget to remove such auxiliary lines in the final, finished version of the macro: the finished painting should not show the underlying sketch.

(13) You may already have noticed that empty lines are ignored. They are used to make the code easier to read, just as paragraphs facilitate reading text. In long programs it is also good practice to use additional comment lines as paragraph headings, informing the user what that paragraph is supposed to accomplish.

There is more to a cell than the value it displays: there may be a formula (i.e., a mathematical instruction) that generates this value, and you may also want to read the cell address. In order to extract all these pieces of information from the spreadsheet, modify the macro as follows:

```
Sub Read()
'Read the cell address, formula, and value

cellAddress = Selection.Address
Debug.Print "The cell address is " & cellAddress
cellFormula = Selection.Formula
Debug.Print "The cell formula is " & cellFormula
cellValue = Selection.Value
Debug.Print "The cell value is " & cellValue
cellValue = cellValue * 7
Debug.Print "The new cell value is " & cellValue
Selection.Offset(1,0).Select
Selection.Value = cellValue

End Sub
```

Notes (continued):

(14) Again, Address and Formula are reserved terms recognized by the VB Editor, and therefore cannot be used without modification as parameter names. The variables called cellAddress, cellFormula, and cellValue are all extracted from a single spreadsheet cell, simply selected here as the highlighted Selection.

(15) By now you have written a completely functional macro, which (a) reads the contents of a cell, (b) manipulates it, and (c) provides one or more outputs to your specifications. Congratulations!

8.2 Reading & manipulating a cell block

Reading the contents of a highlighted cell block or *range* is as easy as reading that of a single cell, but using a message box to verify that the range was read correctly is more tedious. Open a spreadsheet, open a module, and type the following code:

```
Sub ReadRangeY()
aY = Selection.Address
Debug.Print "The range address is " & aY
vY = Selection.Value
Debug.Print "The value of cell (1,1) is " & vY(1,1)
Debug.Print "The value of cell (5,2) is " & vY(5,2)
fY = Selection.Formula
Debug.Print "The formula in cell (1,1) is " & fY(1,1)
Debug.Print "The formula in cell (5,2) is " & fY(5,2)
End Sub
```

Notes:

(1) The individual cells in a range are always specified as row first, then column, and the same applies to the arrays vY and fY. As a mnemonic, use the *RC* time of an electrical circuit: *R*(ow) followed by *C*(olumn). This conforms to the standard way indices are assigned in matrices, as in

$$\begin{vmatrix} a_{11} & a_{12} \\ a_{21} & a_{22} \end{vmatrix}$$

(2) The nomenclature used here, with a prefix specifying what kind of information is involved, makes it easy to replace Y by a more descriptive name. For the difference between a range and an array see section 8.6.

(3) The range has a single address, D1:E5, but it contains ten different cells, which each may contain a different value and formula. Now it is tedious to use message boxes to verify them all, and it is easier to use the Immediate Window with control loops to verify the code. We will describe control loops in more detail in section 8.8.

Test the above macro as follows. Return to the spreadsheet with Alt‿F11 (Mac: Opt‿F11), and deposit, say, 1, 2, 3, 4 and 5 respectively in cells A1:A5, and 6, 7, 8, 9, and 10 in B1:B5. In cell D1 deposit the instruction =sqrt(A1), copy this instruction to D1:E5, and (now that D1:E5 is already highlighted) call the macro.

Notes (continued):

(4) In Excel, the instruction for taking the square root of *x* is sqrt(*x*), but in VBA it is sqr(*x*). There are more such incongruencies between the two, because they started off independently, and were subsequently joined. We have listed several of these differences in section 1.14, and occasionally will alert you to them as we encounter them.

Now that we know how to read the data in a spreadsheet range, we will use a macro to modify them. Enter the macro shown below:

```
Sub Cube1()

For Each cell In Selection.Cells
  cell.Value = cell.Value ^ 3
Next cell

End Sub
```

Notes (continued):

(5) Here you encounter a For … Next loop, which performs an operation repeatedly until all the cells have been acted on. Note the indentation to make it easier for the user to identify the instructions inside the loop. The VBEditor will ignore such indentations.

(6) Cell is not a reserved word, but cells is. See what happens when you replace cell by cells in the above macro, or the other way around. Reserved terms are easily recognizable, because the editor colors them blue.

Also enter the following macro:

```
Sub Cube2()

Dim Array2 As Variant
Dim c As Integer, cMax As Integer
Dim r As Integer, rMax As Integer

Array2 = Selection.Value
cMax = Selection.Columns.Count
rMax = Selection.Rows.Count
For r = 1 To rMax
  For c = 1 To cMax
    Array2(r, c) = Array2(r, c) ^ 3
  Next c
Next r
Selection.Value = Array2

End Sub
```

Notes (continued):

(7) `Array` is also a reserved term, and cannot be used as a parameter name. Therefore use `Array2` or some other name, which can but need not contain the word Array, such as Arrhay, Hoorah, whatever suits your fancy.

(8) The crucial line here is `Array2 = Selection.Value`, which reads the values in the highlighted array.

(9) The dimensioning in the two lines following `Sub Cube2()` is not strictly necessary (as long as Option Explicit is not used), but it is good to start the habit of dimensioning early. Excel will determine the size of the array with the instruction `Array2 = Selection.Value`.

(10) Here we use two *nested* loops: for the first value of r the inner loop is executed until all values of c have been used, then the process is repeated for subsequent values of r.

(11) Alternatively you can let the VB Editor find the lower and upper bounds of the arrays automatically with `For r = LBound(Array2, 1) To UBound(Array2, 1)` and `For c = LBound(Array2, 2) To UBound(Array2, 2)`. The macro then simplifies to

```
Sub Cube3()

Dim Array2 As Variant
Dim c As Integer, r As Integer
Array2 = Selection.Value
For r = LBound(Array 2, 1) To UBound(Array 2, 1)
  For c = LBound(Array 2, 2) To UBound(Array 2, 2)
    Array2(r, c) = Array2(r, c) ^ 3
  Next c
Next r
Selection.Value = Array2

End Sub
```

Return to the spreadsheet. In cells A12 through A21 deposit the numbers 1 through 10, then copy A12:A21 to cells B12, D12, and G12. In cell E12 place the instruction =D12, and copy this instruction to E13:E21. Put the number 1 in cell H12, the instruction =H12+1 in H13, then copy this to H14:H21. Highlight A12:H21 and copy to A23 and to A34.

First test Cube2, then Cube3, and thereafter Cube1, as follows. Highlight A23:A32 and call Cube2, then do the same with D23:E32 and, finally, with G23:H32. Repeat this by applying Cube3 to A34:B43, D34:E43, and G34:H43, respectively. Finally, apply Cube1 to A12:B21, D12:E21, and G12:H21.

The results obtained for A23:B32, D23:E32, and G23:H32 should be identical, as will be those for A34:B43, D34:E43, and G34:H43. However, those for D12:E21 will be way off from what it was intended to do, and the macro will crash with G12:H21. (When an overflow error message appears, just press End.) What has happened here?

340

With Cube1, when the contents of cell D13 are cubed to the value $2^3 = 8$, the contents of cell E13 (which contains the instruction =D13) change from 2 to 8, and when this is then raised to the third power we get $8^3 = 512 = 2^9$ instead of 2^3. The same happens with E14:E21, i.e., we inadvertently therefore raise all numbers in E12:E21 to the ninth power!

And when H13 becomes 8, H14 becomes $8 + 1 = 9$, and is subsequently cubed to $9^3 = 729$. Then H15 is changed from 4 to $729 + 1 = 730$, and subsequently cubed to $730^3 = 389,017,000$, whereupon H16 is modified from 5 to 389,017,001, which is again cubed, and so on. By the time we reach cell H18, cubing its content will exceed the numerical capacity of the spreadsheet, which is about 10^{308}, and the program overflows!

The problem with Cube1 is that the numbers on which it operates are not fixed, but can change before the macro cubes them, leading to unintended results. Moreover, we have no control over the order in which Cube1 implements the instruction `cell.Value = cell.Value ^ 3`, which apparently is to take the cells in the top row first, from left to right, then those in the next row, and so on till it has covered all cells. And because the various cell values depend on other values in the array, and Cube1() updates the value of Array2 before it implements its next action of cubing a value, it runs into trouble.

Despite the appeal of the more compact code of Cube1, the code of Cube2 and Cube3 is much more reliable, because it first *internalizes* (and thereby fixes) all input values *before* it computes any results. Rather pedestrian code is sometimes preferable over its more 'clever' counterparts! In exercise 8.24.3 we will return to this example, and show you how to find out exactly what went wrong, and where. The type of code used in Cube1() is fine as long as the affected cells contain only fixed numbers but no equations or functions. In scientific data analysis, however, such code should be avoided like the plague!

8.3 Correcting run-time errors

The VBEditor may signal that you are using an incorrect instruction, but that only concerns syntax, because the code has not yet encountered any specific numbers. But when you try out a section of code, you may encounter a so-called *run-time error* that could not be flagged earlier because there was nothing wrong with the code per se. Say that you write a function in cell C2 that reads =LOG(B2). That is fine, as long as B2 contains a positive number, but log(–3) will not work, and log(a) may cause cell C2 to show an error message, #NUM! in the case of a negative input number, #VALUE! when you enter a letter.

Now consider performing the same operation in a macro. We will simulate this with a small macro that reads the contents of cell B2, calculates the answer (taking into account the different meanings of log in Excel and VBA, see section 1.14), and deposits it in cell C2.

```
Sub ReadAndComputeLog()
a = Selection.Value
b = Log(a) / Log(10)
Selection.Offset(0, 1).Select
Selection.Value = b
End Sub
```

Place the number 3 in cell B5, the number –3 in B6, and the letter a in B7. Now highlight cell B5, and call the macro, which is most readily done by having your pointer somewhere in the VBEditor code for ReadAndComputeLog, and merely pressing the F5 key. No problems, the value of log(3) = 0.477... will appear in cell C5, just as in cell C2.

But how does the macro handle the funny inputs? Highlight either B6 or B7, call the macro, and you will get a box warning you of "Run-time error '5': Invalid procedure call of argument". If you realize at this point what went wrong, you can press End, change the value in B6 or B7 to 0.3 or whatever you had intended to use, and call the macro again.

If you have no idea of what went wrong, instead press the Debug button, which will (usually) high-light the offending line of code, in this case `b = Log(a) / log(10)`. Now move your pointer over the letter a, and it will show you its value, as a = −3 in a little box. Also look at some other values: if you hover over the letter b you will see b = Empty, i.e., you are seeing exactly where the processor stopped, because it knew the value of *a* but could not take its logarithm to compute *b*. So now you know what went wrong, but if you try to go back to the spreadsheet, change the value in B6 to 0.3, and call the macro again, as you would with a function, it won't work, but will give you the message "Can't execute in break mode". (If, instead of F5, you had used the sequence Tools ⇨ Macro ⇨ Macros, you might even have noticed it, because the arrow to the left of Macros actually looks depressed!) Click OK, and fix the macro with Alt‿R‿R, which resets it. This is a general rule: once a macro has stopped at a particular line, you have to reset it before it (or any other macro) will work.

Since we all make mistakes, this is essential knowledge to have before you delve too deeply into more complicated macros, which invariably will need debugging. The take-home lesson: if a function or macro balks at an error message, click Debug to find the offending line, fix it if necessary, and then al-ways reset it, regardless of whether or not there was something wrong with it.

Note: this applies to all macros. In chapter 11 we will encounter XN macros; if they stop because of run-time errors, you need to localize and fix the offending instruction, and reset the macro as just ex-plained, and then *also* press Help ⇨ ReInit Mem Variables on the XN toolbar to re-initialize XN. In that case it is far better to intercept such errors, which you can do by error trapping, as explained in section 8.23.

8.4 *Computational accuracy*

In the module, make a copy of Cube2, then modify this copy as follows:

```
Sub Root3()
'Take the cube root of all array elements

Dim Array3 As Variant
Dim c As Integer, cMax As Integer
Dim r As Integer, rMax As Integer

Array3 = Selection.Value
cMax = Selection.Columns.Count
rMax = Selection.Rows.Count
For r = 1 To rMax
  For c = 1 To cMax
    Array3(r, c) = Array3(r, c) ^ (1 / 3)
  Next c
Next r
Selection.Value = Array3

End Sub
```

Return to the spreadsheet in order to test this macro. Make two test arrays containing some simple numbers, such as 1, 2, 3, 4, 5 in A1:A5, and 6, 7, 8, 9, 10 in B1:B5, then copy these data to A7:B11. In D4 enter the instruction =A1−A7, and copy this instruction to D4:E8. Call Cube3 and apply it, three times in succession, to the data in A1:B5. Then call Root3 and apply it, again three times, to the resulting data in that same block. You should of course end up with the original data. Is that what you see in D4:E8? What is going on now?

The answer to the above riddle is that Excel always, automatically, uses double precision, but VBA does *not* always do so, unless it is specifically told to. Therefore, force it to do so, as in

```
Sub Root3()
'Take the cube root of all array elements

Dim Array3 As Variant
```

342

```
Dim c As Integer, cMax As Integer
Dim r As Integer, rMax As Integer
Dim p As Double

p = 1 / 3
Array3 = Selection.Value
cMax = Selection.Columns.Count
rMax = Selection.Rows.Count
For r = 1 To rMax
  For c = 1 To cMax
    Array3(r, c) = Array3(r, c) ^ p
  Next c
Next r
Selection.Value = Array3

End Sub
```

Verify that you can now repeatedly cube a function, and subsequently undo it by taking the cube root, without accumulating unacceptably large errors.

8.5 Data types & dimensioning

VBA uses the least amount of memory, and speeds up the computation, when all variables are specified by data type before they are used. This practice is called dimensioning, of which we have already encountered several examples. Table 8.5.1 lists the most important data types used to classify data, including their numerical ranges, and their old suffix notations, which occasionally are still used (and grandfathered) in VBA. Numbers are divided into two categories, *integers* and *real numbers*. There are two additional categories, *complex* numbers (see appendices A5 and B7), and *decimal numbers* (see section 11.9.1). A complex number is either represented by a text string in a single cell, or by its separate real and imaginary component, i.e., by two real numbers, each occupying a single cell. Decimal numbers, a sub-category of Variant, use a text string representation.

Integers represented in 16 bits (a contraction of **bi**nary uni**ts**) are confusingly specified as Integer (with a numberlength of about 7 decimals) or Long (with 15-decimal numberlength). Long integers use 32 bits, and therefore consume more storage space in memory but lower the risk of numerical overflow. Integers are often used in loops as counters, specifying how often a particular procedure must be repeated, as described in section 8.8. If integers are used to increment data in an array, keep in mind that spreadsheet arrays can have dimensions exceeding the 32K limit of single-precision positive integers. (Here K is computer jargon for $2^{10} = 1,024$ rather than 10^3; likewise, M in computerese stands for $2^{20} = 1,048,576$ rather than 10^6, and G for $2^{30} = 1,073,741,824$ rather than 10^9.) Therefore, when there is a possibility that more than 32K rows and/or coluns may need to be addressed, use As Long in specifying your counters. Moreover, VBA arrays can have any size that the computer memory can hold, regardless of the dimensions of the spreadsheet. Therefore, when in doubt, play it safe and use As Long. With modern personal computers there is so much memory and speed that you can afford to be a little wasteful in order to avoid a possible program hiccup.

Real numbers are also subdivided into either Single or Double, depending on their memory requirements. Again, in scientific calculations, avoid using 'single precision' (32 bits) unless you know for sure that 'double precision' (64 bits) will not be needed: the memory savings and speed improvement are seldom worth the risk of much larger truncation errors. In fact, in chapter 11 we will describe the opposite approach, going to *longer* numerical representations in order to reduce such errors.

data type	old suffix	range
integer	%	$-32{,}768$ to $+32{,}767$
long	&	$-2{,}147{,}483{,}648$ to $+2{,}147{,}483{,}647$
single	!	-3.402823×10^{38} to $-1.401298 \times 10^{-45}$ and $+1.401298 \times 10^{-45}$ to $+3.402823 \times 10^{38}$
double	#	$-1.79769313486232 \times 10^{308}$ to $-4.94065645841247 \times 10^{-324}$ and $+4.94065645841247 \times 10^{-324}$ to $+1.79769313486232 \times 10^{308}$
variant		general default data type, required for arrays
decimal		$\pm 2^{96} \approx \pm 7.9 \times 10^{28}$
string	$	from zero to about 65,500 characters

Table 8.5.1: Some names and ranges of various specific data types of VBA. Other data types include date, time, Boolean, byte, currency, object, and range.

Variant is VBA's most general data type, and assumes that a number is real, and in double precision. Actually, the Variant type is much more general than that: it can also handle arrays, text strings, etc., and is the mandatory data type for arrays. However, because the Visual Basic editor does not know whether information specified As Variant is a number, a string, a date, an array, or whatever, the editor must reserve a large space in memory for that information, and these same uncertainties slow down the computer when handling that information. It is therefore best to specify numbers As Integer (if appropriate), As Long, As Single (if you must), or As Double, and only arrays (and decimal types) As Variant. Also note that the special add-in Xnumbers.dll described in chapter 11 requires the Variant type throughout. Variant is the default assignment, and therefore need not be specified.

An array, however, *must* be dimensioned (except inside XN). There are several ways to do this, some more useful than others. Excel allows dimensioning an array as, e.g., Dim myArray(3) but you will not find this approach used in this book, or in the MacroBundle, because it can be confusing. Such an instruction generates an array containing *four* items, numbered 0 through 3, except when Option Base 1 is specified for the entire module, in which case it specifies *three* items, numbered 1 through 3. Go figure! It is much safer always to specify both the lower and upper limits, as in Dim myArray(0 To 5) or Dim myArray(1 To 6, 1 To 1). Again, do *not* use Dim myArray(1 To 6, 1), because that may be interpreted as Dim myArray(1 To 6, 0 To 1).

Since an array is not tied to the spreadsheet, and therefore has no specific location, it also cannot be relocated, but it can be redimensioned with the instruction ReDim. Redimensioning an array is convenient because it can be done during program execution, after its size has been determined. In that case, it is first dimensioned by name only, and subsequently, at the right place in the program, redimensioned by size. Redimensioning can also be done with already filled arrays, but this will usually cause loss of its contents. To avoid this, it is usually better to create a new array, with a new name, and transfer information from the earlier array to the new one. The only exception: when redimensioning only involves an increase in the upper limit of its last-mentioned dimension, the original contents can be retained with the instruction ReDim Preserve.

Even when dimensioning is optional, it is highly recommended to at least dimension all variables *by name*, i.e., without specifying the data type, as in Dim a, b, c. The reason is that Option Explicit, when used, will then make sure that you cannot use any variable that has not been dimensioned, an approach that can weed out many typos. The trick is to dimension variables with names that include capitals, but to type them in the remaining code in lower case. The VBEditor will then capitalize them each time a line of code is entered, and its failure to do so provides a very helpful, visual spelling check on typos.

*****

VBA supports three different kinds of dimensioning: categoric, specific, and as a constant. The categoric dimensioning statements define all variables according to their first letter (regardless of whether these names start with lower case or capital letters), as in `DefInt`, `DefLng`, `DefSng`, `DefDbl`, `DefVar`, `DefObj`, etc. This is equivalent to the FORTRAN command Implicit. The following example defines all variables with names starting with I, J, or K categorically As Long:

```
DefLng = I-K
```

Specific dimensioning statements use the instruction `Dim`. Their specificity is such that they do not allow you to bundle dimension statements on a single line with a single declaration. Instead, each variable must be dimensioned individually with an As … specifier. For example,

```
Dim A As Double, B As Double
```

specifies both A and B as double-precision numbers, while

```
Dim A, B As Double
```

dimensions B as double-precision, but A by name only.

Individual variables with a name dimensioned with a generic (`Def`) statement can subsequently be re-assigned with a specific (`Dim`) statement.

The `Const` statement combines dimensioning and assigning a constant value to a variable. However, that constant value *cannot* be changed subsequently in the routine. It is therefore most useful for defining fixed parameters, such as the value of e, Bernoulli numbers, Planck's constant, the speed of light, Avogadro's number, the gas constant, etc.

8.6 Ranges & arrays

A typical stand-alone computer language uses *arrays*, i.e., collections of data ordered by indices, and VBA is no exception. Each element of an array is defined by its indices, which typically start counting from 1 or 0. Such array indices are purely a matter internal to the array, regardless of the origin of the information stored in it. Moreover, each array element contains only one item of information: a number, a text string, a date, etc. A VBA array must have at least two elements: `vA(1 To 1)` is not acceptable. Depending on its dimensionality, an array can use one or more indices to define its elements: `vA(1 To 7)`, `vB(1 To 7, 1 To 3)`, `vC(1 To 7, 1 To 3, 1 To 15)`, etc. Note that the number of array elements of multi-dimensional arrays can be quite large: as just defined, `vC` would have $7 \times 3 \times 15$ = 315 elements.

The integration of a computer language with a spreadsheet requires another structure, which is where *ranges* come in. VBA uses ranges to specify individual cells, cell blocks, or a collection of cells and/or cell blocks *on the spreadsheet*, including their locations and their contents. And those contents can have many aspects: each spreadsheet cell may not only specify, say, a formula, a resulting value, and an address, but also type font, color, and all kinds of other formatting properties.

A range contains its spreadsheet address(es), and therefore doesn't lose its connection with the spreadsheet. This allows the user to go back and forth between the spreadsheet and a VBA calculation. But because a range must hold so much information, much of it often peripheral to the computation, it is slow and tedious to use a range in complicated calculations. On the other hand, VBA arrays are strictly local to VBA, and are independent (and ignorant) of the location of the corresponding input information on the spreadsheet. In all but the simplest cases we will therefore read and write with ranges, then transfer the necessary information to arrays, and operate within VBA with those arrays. Finally, at the end of the calculation, we read the array(s) back into a range in order to make the result appear on the spreadsheet.

Other differences: a range can be defined by an explicit spreadsheet address or, as we have already seen, by the convenient `Selection`, in which case VBA associates the range address with that of the highlighted region. A range can refer to a single spreadsheet cell, as it did in the subroutines Read() of section 8.1. A range can be moved around on the spreadsheet with an instruction such as `rgName.Offset(3,-1).Select` which moves the range rgName 3 rows down and one column to the left. A range can also be resized with `rgName.Resize(5,4).Select`, in which its top left corner stays, but its number of rows and columns can either increase or decrease to 5 rows and 4 columns. Combining the offset and resize instructions allows complete freedom to move a range. No information is lost upon offsetting and/or resizing a range, see the MoveAndResizeARange MacroMorsel.

Because a range is tied to the spreadsheet, it is strictly one- or two-dimensional: one-dimensional for a single cell, row, or column, two-dimensional for any other collection of input cells. Excel does not support three- or higher-dimensional ranges.

An array can contain only one type of data, with a minimum of two elements. An array has an internal numbering system that starts with either index 1 or 0 (when Option Base 0 is used), and can have up to 60 dimensions. Because of the ambiguity of the base option used, it is best always to specify where you start and stop counting in an array.

For an array to be compatible with a range, that array must use two indices specifying (in this order) rows and columns. If the array contains only one row or one column, it must specify the other index as 1 in order to be compatible with a range.

As already mentioned, you can redimension an array, but all previous information in the array is lost, except when you enlarge the array with the combination `ReDim Preserve`, in which case you can add extra columns but no additional rows. This is because the array is actually stored as a linear sequence, first the first row, then the second, and so on. The data in the new columns can therefore simply be added at the end of this linear sequence.

In summary: ranges are tied to the Excel spreadsheet, while arrays exist only in either the spreadsheet, or VBA. For maximum efficiency, use a range to read information from the spreadsheet, extract the needed information into one or more specific arrays, use these arrays to manipulate the data in VBA, then write the results back into a range, and in that form return the results to the spreadsheet. In order to facilitate the translations from range to array and back, the array must be two-dimensional, even if it only represents data in a single row or column, in which case the unused dimension should be specified as 1 to 1. Conversion from spreadsheet array to VBA array via the corresponding range can often be achieved conveniently with an instruction such as `dataArray = Selection.Value` that extracts an array of values from `Selection`, the range highlighting the spreadsheet array. Conversely, writing the results back can often be done simply with `Selection.Value = dataArray`. We will revisit this matter in sections 8.9 and 8.10.

8.7 Conditional statements

Conditional statements make it possible for a program to make decisions. The spreadsheet contains an `If(condition,ifYes,ifNo)` function, which has the `Iff(condition,ifYes,ifNo)` as its precise VBA counterpart. Here `ifYes` is shorthand for some instruction to be executed if the condition is met or true, and `ifNo` represents what must be done if the condition is not met or is false.

The more flexible `If ... Then` statement also has a short one-line form, as in

```
If b ^ 2 - 4 * a * c < 0 Then MsgBox "The roots are imaginary"
```

When more than one consequence of the If decision must be spelled out, readability is enhanced by using the `If ... Then` block structure, in which case the end of the `If` statement must be specified, such as in

```
If b ^ 2 - 4 * a * c > 0 Then
  Root1 = (-b + Sqr(b ^ 2 - 4 * a * c)) / (2 * a)
  Root2 = (-b - Sqr(b ^ 2 - 4 * a * c)) / (2 * a)
End If
```

The latter format can be expanded to include multiple options, as in

```
Discr = b ^ 2 - 4 * a * c
If Discr > 0 Then
  RealRoot1 = (-b + Sqr(Discr)) / (2 * a)
  ImagRoot1 = 0
  RealRoot2 = (-b - Sqr(Discr)) / (2 * a)
  ImagRoot2 = 0
ElseIf Discr = 0 Then
  RealRoot1 = -b / (2 * a)
  ImagRoot1 = 0
  RealRoot2 = RealRoot1
  ImagRoot2 = 0
Else
  RealRoot1 = -b / (2 * a)
  ImagRoot1 = Sqr(-Discr) / (2 * a)
  RealRoot2 = RealRoot1
  ImagRoot2 = -ImagRoot1
End If
```

with as many commands `ElseIf` as necessary. The final, optional `Else` can take care of any unforeseen conditions. Note that `End If` has a space before the `If`, but that `ElseIf` doesn't, and that the VBEditor is not forgiving in this respect, as it is with `EndIf`. Indentation is used here to enhance readability. One can jump out of an `If ... Then` loop with an `If ... Then Exit If` or `If ... Then GoTo ...` and, of course, with a macro-terminating `End`. The macros in the MacroBundle contain many examples of `If ... Then` loops.

A largely equivalent, but sometimes more readable method uses the `Select Case` instruction. Especially for a large nmber of choices it can also be more efficient, because VBA will exit the method as soon as it finds a match. Therefore, put the possibilities in decreasing order of likelihood. You can (but need not) give the various cases names, or letters, etc. For the above example the syntax might be

```
Discr = b ^ 2 - 4 * a * c
Select Case Discr
Case Is > 0
  RealRoot1 = (-b + Sqr(Discr)) / (2 * a)
  ImagRoot1 = 0
  RealRoot2 = (-b - Sqr(Discr)) / (2 * a)
  ImagRoot2 = 0
Case 0
  RealRoot1 = -b / (2 * a)
  ImagRoot1 = 0
  RealRoot2 = RealRoot1
  ImagRoot2 = 0
Case Is < 0
  RealRoot1 = -b / (2 * a)
  ImagRoot1 = Sqr(-Discr) / (2 * a)
  RealRoot2 = RealRoot1
  ImagRoot2 = -ImagRoot1
End Select
```

8.8 Control loops

For repeat calculations, including iterations, VBA has several types of control loops. The `For ... Next` loop has a *fixed* number of repeats, whereas the number of repeat operations in a `Do ... Next` loop is *conditional*. In section 8.2 we already encountered a `For ... Next` loop in the macro Cube(), and two nested `For ... Next` loops in Cube2() and Cube3(). The counter is often an integer, and its default increment (or step size) +1, but neither of these are required: `For c = 0.7 to -1.301 Step -0.4` will assign the sequence $c = 0.7, 0.3, -0.1, -0.5, -0.9, -1.3$. Note that the limit -1.301 protects against a possible rounding error: because 0.4 has no exact binary representation, subtracting it five times from 0.7 might not be exactly -1.3. Such a precaution is, of course, needed only when nonintegers are used.

The `For Each ... Next` loop is similar to the `For ... Next` loop, and can be a convenient alternative involving an entire group of objects, such as all cells in an array, without the need to specify them more precisely. This convenience, however, has a price, because this instruction does not provide any control over the order in which it is executed, and therefore should only be used when the order of implementation is immaterial, see section 8.2.

The most useful Do loops are `Do While ... Loop`, `Do ... Loop While`, `Do Until ... Loop`, and `Do ... Loop Until`. They differ only in whether the condition is permissive (While) or prohibitive (Until), and in whether it is applied at the beginning or end of the loop. To exit a Do loop, use `If ... Then Exit Do` or `If ... Then GoTo`.

It is sometimes necessary to interrupt control loops, because we may have made a mistake and not provided a reachable exit point, in which case we might otherwise end up in an *infinite* loop. To end it, use the keyboard controls Esc or Ctrl⌣Break. But when there is any risk of creating an infinite loop, it is a good precaution to include an escape hatch into a Do loop, perhaps simply a loop counter that, when it exceeds a given value, exits the loop.

The GoTo statement requires a label on a single line, followed by a colon, as in `GoTo Output` followed at the appropriate place by the line `Output:`. In older code, the GoTo statement was often used as a main device for controlling the information flow in computer programs. This could lead to programs that were hard to follow and, therefore, difficult to maintain or modify, especially since the GoTo statements referred to line numbers rather than a name more easily associated with a new action. As a result, use of the GoTo statement now tends to be frowned upon. It is indeed good practice to avoid GoTo statements when possible, but we need not get too dogmatic about it, and should feel free to use them, sparingly, when it simplifies the code and does not lead to any confusion.

8.9 Data input

Managing the flow of information from the spreadsheet to VBA and back can give the novice VBA programmer many headaches, which is why we will consider it here in some detail. Fortunately, there are several alternative approaches to data input (which, in the present context, means from the spreadsheet into a VBA procedure), two of which we will describe here: input via highlighted cells, and through input boxes. There is yet a third approach, based on dialog boxes. These are more versatile and certainly more professional-looking. Constructing them, however, is also considerably more complex, and for that reason dialog boxes will neither be used nor be discussed here. For commercial software, however, dialog boxes are clearly the way to go, because they give the programmer maximal control over data input, and provide the user an overview of all available choices and options before calling the macro.

At the end of section 8.6 we already emphasized the different roles of ranges and arrays, but the main points bear repeating. The first of these is: *whenever we need to read information from the spreadsheet into a macro or subroutine, or back, we must use a range*. The most intuitive range commands, operating on highlighted cells or cell blocks, use `ActiveCell` for a single cell, or `Selection` for either a single cell or a collection of cells. Alternatively we can use an input box, which allows input by dragging &

348

dropping, and provides more flexibility and input control. *For further data processing in VBA it is usually much more efficient to extract the required information from the range into one or more parameters or, in the case of a block of cells, into one or more arrays.* In section 8.10 we will then consider the corresponding output, bringing the information from VBA macro or subroutine back to the spreadsheet, again via a range.

VBA code is written in the VBEditor module, and it is often convenient to test it from there, without having to toggle back and forth repeatedly between spreadsheet and module. After appropriately setting up the spreadsheet, and switching to the VBEditor, one can do this by writing intermediary and/or final results into the *Immediate Window*, which can be opened right below the module with Ctrl‿g or <u>V</u>iew ⇨ <u>I</u>mmediate Window, and closed with its top-right closing icon ×. Unlike a message box, which stops the program until it has been acknowledged by pushing its OK button, the Immediate Window merely shows whatever is written into it by the program. You can start a macro from within the editing mode by placing the pointer somewhere within the macro you want to call, and by then pressing the function key F5.

8.9.1 Inputting highlighted data

To use the following macros, the cell(s) must be activated (highlighted) *before* the macro is called. In case you do not need all three pieces of information (address, formula, value) shown below, just delete the superfluous one(s); all three are displayed here merely to show that the range contains different types of information about each cell. Check the answers in the Immediate Window and, if necessary, use its scroll bar to examine all its parts. Depending on your needs, you can also raise or lower the partition between the module and the Immediate Window.

We first consider reading a single cell, and thereafter a cell block. As a test, make a column containing, e.g., a number, a formula, a function, an empty cell, a date, a time, a dollar amount, a letter, a word. In the spreadsheet, place the pointer at the top cell of the column, switch to the VBEditor, place the pointer somewhere inside the ReadHighlightedCell code (to specify which procedure you want to run), and call it with F5. The macro will step down one row in the spreadsheet each time, making it easy for you to see what happens with each input cell.

```
Sub ReadHighlightedCell()

Dim aX, fX, vX

aX = ActiveCell.Address
fX = ActiveCell.Formula
vX = ActiveCell.Value

Debug.Print "Address: " & aX
Debug.Print "Formula: " & fX
Debug.Print "Value:   " & vX
Debug.Print ""
ActiveCell.Offset(1, 0).Select

End Sub
```

In the above example (and in many to follow) we only dimension by name. This gives us the advantage of error checking with Option Explicit, while avoiding problems with non-numeric input. Otherwise, text in the highlighted block would cause a run-time error when we try to assign a value to vX. Of course, the completely unstructured input by highlighting is extremely vulnerable to incorrect input, and you may want to incorporate guards against, say, textual input, but for now we merely want to show how easy it is to get information in, and we therefore let our guard down on purpose, if only temporarily.

Instead of `ActiveCell` we could have used `Selection`. Try it. For this example, we could even have used a function rather than a macro, since functions can also write to the Immediate Window, and nothing is written onto the spreadsheet. Just change the first word `Sub` in the top line of the macro to `Function`, make sure that its last line is changed accordingly, and rerun.

For a rectangular block of cells, a single column or a single row, but *not* for a single cell, we can use the following macro. Again, as its name implies, the cell block must be activated before the macro is called.

```
Sub ReadHighlightedCellBlock1()

Dim c As Long, cMax As Long
Dim r As Long, rMax As Long
Dim aA, fA, vA

cMax = Selection.Columns.Count
rMax = Selection.Rows.Count
If cMax = 1 And rMax = 1 Then
  MsgBox "The block must contain more than one cell"
  End
End If
ReDim fA(1 To rMax, 1 To cMax)
ReDim vA(1 To rMax, 1 To cMax)
aA = Selection.Address
fA = Selection.Formula
vA = Selection.Value

Debug.Print "Range Address: " & aA
For c = 1 To cMax
  For r = 1 To rMax
    Debug.Print "Formula(" & r & "," & c & "): " & fA(r, c)
    Debug.Print "Value(" & r & "," & c & "):   " & vA(r, c)
  Next r
Next c

End Sub
```

Again, we have only dimensioned aA, fA, and vA by name. aA could be dimensioned As String, but this causes problems in some Mac versions of Excel. Similarly, fA and vA could be dimensioned As Variant, but that is the default dimension anyway. For proper dimensioning of fA and vA, the order of the instructions is important: first count rows and columns, then redimension fA and vA accordingly, and finally read them.

Assigning arrays is quite simple, through instructions such as fA = Selection.Formula or vA = Selection.Value. However, in order to print them out in the Immediate Window, we need to enumerate their individual elements, as done in the two nested For … Next loops. And it is at this stage that a single-cell input, if not treated separately, would cause run-time errors while trying to assign an array formula and value. The range command Selection can handle both single and multiple inputs, but an array must contain more than one element. We can prevent this problem with the following macro, where we test the range and then select the appropriate data input pathway.

```
Sub ReadHighlightedCellBlock2()

Dim c As Long, cMax As Long
Dim r As Long, rMax As Long
Dim aA, fA, vA, fX, vX

cMax = Selection.Columns.Count
rMax = Selection.Rows.Count
aA = Selection.Address
Debug.Print "Range Address: " & aA

If cMax = 1 And rMax = 1 Then     ' for single cell input
  fX = Selection.Formula
  vX = Selection.Value
  Debug.Print "Formula: " & fX
  Debug.Print "Value:   " & vX
ElseIf cMax > 1 Or rMax > 1 Then  ' for multi-cell input
  ReDim fA(1 To rMax, 1 To cMax)
```

```
    ReDim vA(1 To rMax, 1 To cMax)
    fA = Selection.Formula
    vA = Selection.Value
    For c = 1 To cMax
      For r = 1 To rMax
        Debug.Print "Formula(" & r & "," & c & "): " & fA(r, c)
        Debug.Print "Value(" & r & "," & c & "):   " & vA(r, c)
      Next r
    Next c
  End If

End Sub
```

There is an interesting variant on the above, in which only a *single* cell of the cell block is highlighted, and instead of `Selection` one uses `ActiveCell.CurrentRegion`. The `CurrentRegion` encompasses all cells in direct contact with the `ActiveCell`. This approach is somewhat tricky because it only works when the cell block we want to identify is surrounded on all sides (including at its corners) by empty cells; otherwise the read block may be wider than intended. The advantage of this approach is that, for a very large cell block, one need not maneuver through that entire block to highlight it.

Here is a version that can accommodate both a single cell and a (properly isolated) cell block:

```
Sub ReadBlockOfHighlightedCell()

Dim c As Long, cMax As Long
Dim r As Long, rMax As Integer
Dim fX As String, vX As Double
Dim fA As Variant, vA As Variant

cMax = ActiveCell.CurrentRegion.Columns.Count
rMax = ActiveCell.CurrentRegion.Rows.Count
aA = ActiveCell.CurrentRegion.Address
Debug.Print "Address: " & aA

If cMax = 1 And rMax = 1 Then
  fX = ActiveCell.Formula
  vX = ActiveCell.Value
  Debug.Print "Formula: " & fX
  Debug.Print "Value:   " & vX
Else If cMax > 1 Or rMax > 1 Then
  ReDim fA(1 To rMax, 1 To cMax)
  ReDim vA(1 To rMax, 1 To cMax)
  fA = ActiveCell.CurrentRegion.Formula
  vA = ActiveCell.CurrentRegion.Value
  For c = 1 To cMax
    For r = 1 To rMax
      Debug.Print "Formula(" & r & "," & c & "): " & fA(r, c)
      Debug.Print "Value(" & r & "," & c & "):   " & vA(r, c)
    Next r
  Next c
End If

End Sub
```

Try it out on an isolated cell, on a clearly delimited cell block, on a rectangular block of cells with one adjacent cell that shares either an edge or a corner point, and on a diagonally connected string of non-empty cells, as in A1, B2, C3, D4, E5, D6.

The above methods only requires that you highlight a cell or cell block before the macro is called. That makes it quick, easy to program, and intuitive to use. However, it is error-prone, because it has no built-in protections against improper data input. If you use a macro only to analyze your own data, that risk is usually tolerably small, which is why this method is used in many of the macros of the Macro-Bundle.

8.9.2 Using input boxes

A more controllable (and therefore potentially safer) approach is to use an input box, into which a value is entered or a cell address is typed or dragged. The simplest of these uses the VBA instruction

```
a = Val(InputBox("a = ")
```

which displays an input box with the message a = in which you type the value of *a* and then hit OK or Enter. The name "*a*" is here used merely as a generic symbol for any name you want to use. Excel has a different, slightly more general input box, which can be accessed with the prefix Application. Here follow some examples. You will find several MacroMorsels that illustrate input boxes, and you can see their applications in the MacroBundle.

```
Sub InputBoxForCell()

Dim rgX As Range
Set rgX = Application.InputBox(Prompt:="InputCell: ", Type:=8)
rgX.Select
Debug.Print "Cell address: " & rgX.Address
Debug.Print "Cell formula: " & rgX.Formula
Debug.Print "Cell value:   " & rgX.Value
Debug.Print ""
ActiveCell.Offset(1, 0).Select

End Sub
```

Again, use a column of test data of various kinds; Debug.Print "" separates the output for the various input cells, while Offset(1, 0) lets you step through them with F5, one cell at a time, without leaving the VBEditor.

Input control is provided by the optional Type designations, listed in Table 8.9.1. When more than one type of input is acceptable, add the corresponding type numbers in the Type designation, e.g., Type:=17 allows input of either a single number or an array, since 17 = 1+16. When in doubt, make yourself a column of different data types, and use the Excel function =Type to display their type numbers. The number category includes times, dates, and monetary amounts. Logical (Boolean) values are true and false; error values are those listed in Table A.7, such as #N/A. Type:=32 apparently is not assigned.

Type number	Category
0	formula
1	number
2	text string
4	logical value
8	range
16	error value
64	array

Table 8.9.1: Type designations used in *Excel* input boxes.
Note that *VBA* input boxes do not allow type designations.

One can embellish input boxes, e.g., by displaying a title in the blue title bar above the message, and by specifying a default. The following example also includes extensive input checking, informs the user when the input is incorrect, yet is forgiving of such errors by allowing several repeat attempts. In this way, a trivial error with an input box way down a series of such input boxes will not force the user to start all over again.

```
Sub InputANumber()

Tries = 0
MaxTries = 5
Message = "Enter an integer" & Chr(13) & "between 1 and 100:"
```

352

```
Title = "Integer"
Default = "25"
Do
  myValue = InputBox(Message, Title, Default)
  Tries = Tries + 1
  If Tries > MaxTries Then End
  If myValue < 1 Then MsgBox _
    "The selected number is too small."
  If myValue > 100 Then MsgBox _
    "The selected number is larger than 100."
  If myValue - Int(myValue) <> 0 Then MsgBox _
    "The selected number is not an integer."
Loop Until (myValue >= 0 And myValue <= 100 _
  And myValue - Int(myValue) = 0)
MsgBox "You chose the number " & myValue

End Sub
```

Here is an example for use with a block of data, with a slight variation in the print-out in the Immediate Window, and an error intercept in case a single cell is used for input. Intercepting errors will be described in section 8.23.4.

```
Sub InputBoxForCellBlock()

Dim c As Long, cMax As Long, r As Long, rMax As Long
Dim rgA As Range, vA As Variant

Set rgA = Application.InputBox(Prompt:="InputArray: ", _
  Type:=8)
rgA.Select
cMax = rgA.Columns.Count
rMax = rgA.Rows.Count
ReDim vA(1 To rMax, 1 To cMax)
vA = Selection.Value

On Error Resume Next         ' for single-cell input

For c = 1 To cMax
  For r = 1 To rMax
    Debug.Print r, c, rgA.Formula(r, c), rgA.Value(r, c)
  Next r
Next c

End Sub
```

If the range address is fixed, no InputBox is needed, and the range can be set directly using that fixed address, as in `Set rgA = Range("B2:E5")`.

8.10 Data output

Even though data output, like data input, must involve a range, it is by far the simpler of the two. No output analog exists of highlighting a cell block when we start from VBA, but we can use an already existing highlighted cell or area (such as the one used for data input) on the spreadsheet as target area. There is an analog of an input box, viz. the message box, handy for troubleshooting but too limited for most purposes, because it disappears when acknowledged with OK. But neither one of these is needed, since we can simply load the information into a range, and then let the range send it back to the spreadsheet. In this section we will consider these options, starting with the message box.

8.10.1 Output through message boxes

Message boxes can carry a simple message, such as

```
MsgBox a
```
where *a* represents a value calculated by the macro, or
```
MsgBox "Well-done!"
```
or they can combine a message with specific information, as in
```
MsgBox "Excellent! The answer for pi is " & 3.14
```
or
```
MsgBox "The value of vA(" & i & ", " & j ") is " & vA(i, j))
```
where we switch back and forth between text and data. In the latter example, note the use of an ampersand & to concatenate the different parts, i.e., to *separate* the textual messages (within quotation marks) from the output values as well as to *link* them in one instruction. When a long text string is needed, the usual line break in the VBA code must be augmented by the use of closing and opening double quotes before and after the line break, plus an ampersand, as in
```
MsgBox "Excellent! The short answer " & _
   "to this long question is " & 3.14
```

Moreover, when the text gets too long for a single line in the message box, a carriage return can be included, such as
```
MsgBox "Excellent! The short answer " & Chr(13) & _
   "to this long question is " & 3.14
```

A list of often used text formatting characters and their abbreviations is given in Table 8.10.1.

formatting character		alternative abbreviation	meaning
Chr(9)	or	vbTab	tab
Chr(10)	or	vbLf	linefeed
Chr(11)	or	vbVerticalTab	tab
Chr(12)	or	vbFormFeed	page break
		vbCrLf	carriage return plus linefeed
Chr(13)	or	vbCr	carriage return
Chr(149)			bullet
Chr(150)			en dash (–)
Chr(151)			em dash (—)

Table 8.10.1: Some useful text formatting characters, their abbreviations, and meanings.

A message box can also return a simple message (but no numbers) to VBA, via its buttons. The standard message box only contains an OK button, but you can include several others, and also a few icons, as shown in Table 8.10.2.

When a button other than OK is used, the message box must subsequently be queried about it, as with `If vbYes Then …` You can also include a few warning icons (with their numerical values shown within brackets): CriticalMessage (16), Query (32), Warning (48), and Information (64). Add these numerical values to those listed in Table 8.10.2.

code	value	buttons
vbOKOnly	0	OK (default)
vbOKCancel	1	OK + Cancel
vbAbortRetryIgnore	2	Abort + Retry + Ignore
vbYesNoCancel	3	Yes + No + Cancel
vbYesNo	4	Yes + No
vbRetryCancel	5	Retry + Cancel

Table 8.10.2: The buttons available for use with a message box.

354

All of these aspects are included in the next code segment:

```
tAnswer = MsgBox ("Excellent! The short answer" & _
  Chr(13) & "to this long question was " & 3.14.", & _
  vbCr & "Do you want to continue?", 36, "Continue?")
If tAnswer = vbNo Then End
If tAnswer = vbYes Then MsgBox "The next question is …"
```

The message box is now treated as a parameter, i.e., used with brackets. Also note the numerical value used (36 = 32 + 4), the title `Continue?` in the title bar, and the subsequent testing of the answer given. Do not use a message box inside a loop while testing code: you will quickly tire of pushing OK's.

The major limitations of using a message box are (1) that it does not provide its output directly to the spreadsheet, so that numerical information must be hand-copied, and (2) that it stops all spreadsheet operations until the user has pushed a button.

8.10.2 Output to the spreadsheet

If the absolute range address for output is known, the range can be set directly using that address, as in `Set rgA = Range("B2:E5")` followed by, e.g., `rgA.Value = vA`, where `vA` is an array containing those values. If the range address is that of an earlier used input range, one can just call it by its name, which implies its range. For instance, when the range address corresponds to a highlighted cell or cell block, we can output a result with, e.g., `ActiveCell.Value = 654321` or `Selection.Value = vA` for a single cell. For multiple cells, we can either step through them cell by cell (as is done, e.g., in the labeling of the output for LS), or read an array into the range (as done in the next example with the array `t`), and then send it back as such with `rgA.Value = t`. We can also output to a different location by moving the range with `Offset` before calling it, as in

```
Selection.Offset(5, 7)
Selection.Value = vA
```

The following procedure uses the Excel function `TInv` to make a table of Student *t* values used in converting standard deviations into 'confidence' measures. This example requires you to highlight the spreadsheet cell you want to become the top left-hand corner cell of the array, before you call the macro.

```
Sub StudentT()

Dim c As Integer, cMax As Integer
Dim r As Integer, rMax As Integer
cMax = 4: rMax = 20
ReDim t(1 To rMax, 1 To cMax) As Double
Dim a(1 To 4) As Double, rgA As Range
alpha(1) = 0.03: alpha(2) = 0.01: alpha(3) = 0.003: alpha(4) = 0.001

' Compute the table of Student t values

For r = 1 To rMax
  For c = 1 To cMax
    t(r, c) = Application.TInv(alpha(c), r)
  Next c
Next r

' Write the array onto the spreadsheet

Set rgA = ActiveCell.Range(Cells(1, 1), Cells(rMax, cMax))
rgA.Value = t

End Sub
```

In this macro, `alpha(c)` specifies the probability, i.e., one minus the confidence interval, here computed for 3%, 1%, 0.3%, and 0.1%. The number of degrees of freedom, denoted by r, here ranges from 1 to 20. The SET instruction defines the range, in this case using the active cell to anchor the top left cell of the output data block, while the line `rgA . Value = t` transfers the information to the range, and therefore to the spreadsheet. Also note the condensed VBA writing, with several items combined on one line, separated by colons.

Letting the user select the anchoring cell minimizes the risk of overwriting valuable information. If this is insufficient, overwrite protection can be added. Other useful embellishments might be to check whether a cell has been activated (and, if not, remind the user to do so), to insert a row with labels specifying the probability or confidence of each column, and/or a column with the r-values indicating the number of degrees of freedom in each row. It is such extras, of which you can find several examples in the MacroBundle, that often make for a more finished product, but that also may expand the original code several-fold in both length and coding effort.

8.11 Timing

On contemporary computers, many simple macros will execute virtually instantaneously, but they may take much longer if you let them update the computer screen during computation. This is almost always unnecessary, and in Excel macros can be avoided with the line

```
Application.ScreenUpdating = False
```

to be placed *after* reading in the data (because it will prohibit drag & drop input) but *before* any major computations are performed. Screen Updating will be reset automatically to True at the end of macro execution, at which time the entire, final output will appear on the screen.

Some macros may take longer for other, more legitimate reasons, such as when they use Solver or other highly iterative routines, handle very large arrays, and/or involve extended precision. Here is how you can find out how much time they take, to the nearest microsecond.

Just as when you use a stopwatch, you must specify both when to start measuring, and when to stop. Start measuring somewhere inside your macro, say, just after the dimension statements, with the instruction

```
Time1 = Timer
```

and, at the end of your macro (or wherever else in the code you want to put it), place the instruction

```
Time2 = Timer
```

Now you can extract the time difference in seconds with

```
Dim Interval As Integer
Interval = Time2 - Time1
Debug.Print "The elapsed time is " & Interval
```

when you have activated the Immediate window, or on the spreadsheet with

```
MsgBox "The elapsed time is " & Interval
```

or in any other way that suits your fancy. You can insert as many time sampling statements as you wish.

The Time*r* function counts in seconds, and measures time starting from midnight. If you want to measure longer periods, or periods that might bracket midnight (at which moment the timer would be reset to zero), use the Time function instead, which measures time since January 1, 1900. In that case, the numbers in seconds may cause numerical overflow, and you would do well to organize the results in terms of hours, minutes, and seconds, as in

```
Time1 = Time
.....
Time2 = Time
```

356

```
. . . . .
DifH = Hour(Time2 - Time1)
DifM = Minute(Time2 - Time1)
DifS = Second(Time2 - Time1)
MsgBox "This part took " & DifH & " h," _
  & DifM & " min, and " & DifS & " s."
```

If you want to insert a time delay, perhaps to give viewers of a procedure time to read its legend or see its separate stages, you can also do that, with code such as

```
Time1 = Timer
Dim Interval As Single
Interval = 5.3
. . . . .
Do
Loop Until Timer > Time1 + Interval
```

where the value of Interval can either be fixed (as in the above example, to 5.3 seconds), or can have a value determined earlier in the macro.

If macro execution takes more than a few seconds, it may be helpful to the users (or at least give them something to look at, and thereby forget that they are twiddling their thumbs) to have a screen indication of where macro execution stands. The following code assumes that the program takes its sweet time because it has to plow through a set of k data points in a slow For i = 1 To k ... Next loop. Somewhere before the loop, dimension Perc and Percentage as double and integer respectively, and inside the loop place the instructions

```
Perc = 100 * i / k
Percentage = Int(Perc)
Application.StatusBar = "The calculation " & _
  "is " & Percentage & "% done."
```

to show its progress, as a percentage of the total job. In this case, don't forget to clear the status bar before you exit the program with

```
Application.StatusBar = False
```

Another way to keep the user informed, when there are several distinct, slow steps in the procedure, is to display in the status bar what part of a long program is running, such as with the message

```
Application.StatusBar = "Computing F-test values"
```

which can, of course, be combined with a percentage indicating the progress in that part. While the macro makes you wait, at least let the program report how far along it is, and give your eyes something to do.

Below are two simple macros that illustrate (1) the accelerating effect of inhibiting screen updating, and (2) the soothing effect of providing progress information in the status bar. For the first, highlight an empty cell, and make sure that the cell immediately below it is also empty. Then call the macro. The top cell writes intermediate answers; when it is done counting, the same counting is repeated (off-screen, and therefore much faster) for the bottom cell. There is no need to reset the screen inhibition to off, because that will happen automatically, just before the macro ends. Have the Immediate Window open, and compare the measured times.

```
Sub InhibitScreenUpdating()

Dim Time1, Time2, Time3, Time4
Dim i As Integer, j As Integer

Time1 = Timer
For i = 1 To 5000
  j = i
```

```
    Selection.Value = j
  Next i
  Time2 = Timer
  Debug.Print "ScreenUpdate On:   " & _
    Time2 - Time1 & " seconds"

  Selection.Offset(1, 0).Select
  Application.ScreenUpdating = False

  Time3 = Timer
  For i = 1 To 5000
    j = i
    Selection.Value = j
  Next i
  Time4 = Timer
  Debug.Print "ScreenUpdate Off: " _
    & Time4 - Time3 & " seconds"
  Selection.Offset(-1, 0).Select

End Sub
```

The following macro shows, in the status bar at the bottom of the screen, intermediate status information during a lengthy computation. In this example the procedure counts integers up to 40 million. You can of course change that number, and/or the intermediate values at which it updates the status bar.

```
Sub KeepUserInformed()

Dim i As Long, j As Double

Application.StatusBar = True            ' turn StatusBar on
Application.StatusBar = "The process is 0 % complete."

For i = 1 To 40000000
  j = i
  If Int(j / 2000000) = j / 2000000 Then _
    Application.StatusBar = "The process is " _
    & j / 400000 & " % complete."        'here: in 5% steps
Next i
MsgBox "You just counted to " & j

Application.StatusBar = False            'clean up

End Sub
```

It is amazing how much faster a macro seems to run when the user is kept informed of its progress.

8.12 Coloring

Custom functions provide no control over the color of the symbols displayed in a cell, or of its background, but custom macros or subroutines do. The Microsoft Office suite has two sets of color schemes.

8.12.1 The color palette

An array of 40 color samples is used by Excel in the Fill Color and Font Color icons on its Formatting toolbar, and is most useful for adding color emphasis or color coding to numbers and tables. Any color swatch in Fill Color and Font Color shows its name when a mouse pointer hovers over it, but in order to refer to this color in VBA you need its numerical Color Index, which the hovering mouse pointer does not provide. Figure 8.12.1 shows the correlation between sample position, name, and color index.

The numbering system seems to lack any recognizable organizing principle, and has 56 numbers for 40 different colors, with 10 Color Index duplications (25-31, 34, 54) and 6 extra, unnamed colors (17, 19, 21-24). You can use the 10 duplicate indices to define additional colors, reassign the unnamed colors, etc., but such redefinitions can only be transported to other computers when specified in terms of RGB colors, see below.

The lighter tints on the color palette are most helpful in marking particular areas of the spreadsheet, while the darker shades are best used to highlight characters and numbers, or to provide additional information on numerical output. The latter application is illustrated, e.g., in the least squares routines of the MacroBundle, where we print the standard deviation s_i in bold red whenever s_i is larger than the absolute value of the corresponding coefficient a_i, to alert the user that such a coefficient is without statistical significance. An easy way to find the color indices is with the following macro:

1 black	30 brown	52 olive green	51 dark green	49 dark teal	11, 25 dark blue	55 indigo	56 80% gray
9, 30 dark red	46 orange	12 dark yellow	10 green	14, 31 teal	5, 32 blue	47 blue- gray	16 50% gray
3 red	45 light orange	43 lime	50 sea green	42 aqua	41 light blue	13, 29 violet	48 40% gray
7, 26 pink	44 gold	6, 27 yellow	4 bright green	8, 28 turquoise	33 sky blue	18, 54 plum	15 25% gray
38 rose	40 tan	36 light yellow	35 light green	20, 34 light turquoise	37 pale blue	39 lavender	2 white

Fig. 8.12.1: The ColorIndex and corresponding name of the color palettes in Fill Color and Font Color.

```
Sub Color()
Dim colorValue As Integer
colorValue = Selection.Value
Selection.Interior.ColorIndex = colorValue
Selection.Offset(1, 0).Select
End Sub
```

On a spreadsheet, make two adjacent columns of the numbers 1 (1) 56. Highlight the top cell of the first column, containing the number 1. Switch back to the VBEditor, which you restrict in size to a fraction of the screen, placed in such a way that you can still see the two spreadsheet columns. Locate the pointer somewhere in the Color macro, and repeatedly push the F5 function key. Each time you depress F5 you will see the next cell change its background color. Change the fourth line in the Color macro to

```
Selection.Font.ColorIndex = colorValue.
```

and repeat the process with the second column.

You can easily modify the above macro so that it counts to 56 and displays two columns of colored cells and numbers with one single command, but even the simple, manual version shown here illustrates how you can manipulate both cell and font colors in a macro. For that, all you need to do is to choose a Selection, or an ActiveCell, and then to specify what you want, as in

```
ActiveCell.Interior.ColorIndex = 8
```

to color the whole cell turquoise, and/or

```
ActiveCell.Font.ColorIndex = 5
```

to make its text blue. For no color, use `ColorIndex = xlNone`.

8.12.2 The RGB code

VBA also has a second, more elaborate color scheme, called RGB, which lets you select mixtures of 255 intensities of each of the three additive primary colors, *r*ed, *g*reen, and *b*lue. The RGB scheme is used in figures and graphs with high color resolution, as in the custom macro Mapper of the MacroBundle, or where gradual color changes are needed.

If you try to use VBA to prescribe RGB colors with instructions such as `Selection.Font.Color = RBG(r,g,b)` or `ActiveCell.Interior.Color = RGB(r,g,b)`, where r, g, and b are integers between 0 and 255, the spreadsheet will select matching colors from its much more limited palette of 40. You can, however, redefine the palette colors in RGB terms. The workbook-wide instruction `ActiveWorkbook .Colors(3) = RGB (r,g,b)` will, e.g., change the definition of Color-Index 3 to the RGB color defined by r, g, and b.

A good way to get a feel for the RGB color scale is to go to Tools ⇨ Options, select the tab Color, click on one of the 40 colors of the fixed palette (the default is 1, for black), push the Modify button, then the Custom tab. Place the triangular pointer to the right of the color square in a middle position, and with the mouse pointer move the cross over the color square while watching the changing RGB coordinates. (You can actually use this to change any of the 40 fixed colors, as an alternative to the above method. But if you do it this way, that change would not easily be portable to another computer.) Unless you want to keep the change, go back to the Color tab, and use Reset to recover the original palette.

8.13 Using Excel functions in VBA

Excel has far more functions than VBA, and you can invoke many of these Excel functions by using the prefix `Application.`, as illustrated below. To see all the choices you have, type the full command, `Application.WorksheetFunction.`, and scroll through the list of available functions appearing as a small menu on the screen just below where you are typing. Then double-click to select the function you want to use. At the same time the example given here reminds you again of the nuisance that some functions have the same name in Excel and VBA but a different meaning, see section 1.14. Place a positive quantity in a spreadsheet cell, or highlight an existing one, and call the macro.

```
Sub UseExcelFunction()

Dim a As Double, b As Double, vX As Double

vX = Selection.Value
a = Application.Log(vX)  ' the Excel function log is the
                         ' 10-based, Briggsian form,
b = Log(vX)              ' while the VBA function log is the
                         ' e-based, natural logarithm, in
                         ' science typically denoted as ln
Debug.Print "Excel log(" & vX & ") = " & a & Chr(10) & _
  "  VBA log(" & vX & ") = " & b

End Sub
```

Incidentally, use Chr(10) for carriage return in the Immediate Window, because xlCR will not work there. As already mentioned, π is a special case, in that its value can be invoked with square brackets, as `[Pi()]`, so that you need not use the prefix Application.

Here is another example, this time of using an Excel array function. The macro reads a highlighted square array **A** of numbers from the spreadsheet, applies the Excel instruction MInverse to these numbers to compute and print the matrix inverse $\mathbf{A}^{-1}$, then multiplies these two to obtain their product $\mathbf{A}\,\mathbf{A}^{-1}$, which should be the unit matrix **I**. The original, square array needs to be activated (highlighted) before the macro is called. In this example, all action occurs on the spreadsheet, so call the macro from there.

```
Sub UseExcelArrayFunction()

Dim c As Long, cMax As Long, r As Long, rMax As Long
Dim vX As Variant, vY As Variant, vZ As Variant

' Check that the matrix is square

cMax = Selection.Columns.Count
rMax = Selection.Rows.Count
If cMax <> rMax Then
  MsgBox "Array must be square."
```

360

```
      End
   End If
   ' Read the array values in the highlighted range
   vX = Selection.Value
   ' Move the highlighted range
   Selection.Offset(rMax + 1, 0).Select
   ' Invert the matrix
   vY = Application.MInverse(vX)
   ' Write the inverse matrix back onto the spreadsheet
   Selection.Value = vY
   ' Once more move the highlighted range
   Selection.Offset(rMax + 1, 0).Select
   ' Multiply the matrices
   vZ = Application.MMult(vX, vY)
   ' Write the result back onto the spreadsheet.
   Selection.Value = vZ

End Sub
```

To start, fill a small array, such as the 3×3 array {1, 2, 3; 5, 6, 4; 7, 8, 11}, i.e., a block of cells with the numbers 1, 2, and 3 in its top row, below it 5, 6, and 4, etc. (This is also how Excel stores this array, as a linear number sequence.) Highlight that area, then call the macro. You will find that the unit matrix has ones on its main (top left to bottom right) diagonal, and zeros or close approximations thereof in all other, so-called off-diagonal places.

It is a good general precaution to test whether an Excel function acts the same when called by VBA as it does on the spreadsheet, because there may be subtle differences. For example, LinEst can use ranges for its *y*- and *x*-inputs, or data arrays, but `Application.Linest` doesn't appear to accept data arrays, only separate *y*- and *x*-inputs. In general you may have to write your own MacroMorsel to test whether a function you want to call from VBA will actually perform the required task.

8.14 Deconstructing an address

Sometimes it is necessary to parse a cell address. The address of cell C consists of four parts: a dollar sign $, a column name (up to three letters in Excel 2007), a second dollar sign, and a row number. The second dollar sign acts therefore as a convenient separator of the column name cC of cell C, and its row number rC.

Excel has a variety of functions to help parse a string of characters; of these, the most useful for our purposes are INSTR, LEFT, RIGHT, MID, and LEN. With INSTR one can find the position of a given character in a string, LEFT yields characters starting from the beginning of a string, RIGHT starts from the end of that string, and MID from a specified position somewhere inside the string; LEN gives its length.

To find the column name, find the location of the second dollar sign, then read the address string until there, and finally read the right-most part of it. To find the row number, return to the location of the second dollar sign, and read the string to the right of it. Highlight a spreadsheet cell, and call the macro. The column name and row number will be shown in the immediate window. Again, the strings are not dimensioned as string, because (at least in the past) this has given problems in some Mac versions of Excel.

```
Sub DeconstructACellAddress()

Dim aC, cC, rC, Pos$2, CLeft

aC = Selection.Address

Pos$2 = InStr(2, aC, "$")    ' yields position of 2nd $ in aC
CLeft = Left(aC, Pos$2 - 1)  ' yields string left of Pos$2
cC = Mid(CLeft, 2)           ' yields the column name
rC = Mid(aC, Pos$2 + 1)      ' yields the row number

Debug.Print "Address = " & aC
Debug.Print "Column Name = " & cC & ",  Row Number = " & rC

End Sub
```

We will now dissect the logic involved. `InStr(2, aC, "$")` looks at the second occurrence of the dollar sign in aC, and returns its numerical position, say 4 when aC = $AB$345, because it is the fourth character in that address. `Left(aC, C$ - 1)` then finds the string to the left of character 4, i.e., $AB. With `Mid(CLeft, 2)` we then take this string starting with its second character, hence AB; the instruction `Right(CLeft, 1)` would have achieved the same result. And with `Mid(aC, C$ + 1)` we find the characters starting with character 5, i.e., 123. Never mind that the second dollar sign is only one character, not two, as suggested by the difference between C$ - 1 and C$ + 1.

For the address of an array, i.e., a rectangular block of cells, a colon acts as the separator, and can therefore be used to isolate the *t*op *l*eft address Atl from the *b*ottom *r*ight address Abr. Those addresses can then be deconstructed separately as before. Here is an example. Alternatively, one could use the 1st, 2nd, 3rd, and 4th dollar signs.

```
Sub DeconstructAnArrayAddress()

Dim aA, aAbr, aAtl, cAbr, cAtl, rAbr, rAtl
Dim AColon, ADollar, A$

aA = Selection.Address

AColon = InStr(1, aA, ":")    ' yields the colon position
aAtl = Left(aA, AColon - 1)   ' yields top left address
aAbr = Mid(aA, Acolon + 1)    ' yields bottom right address

A$ = InStr(2, aAtl, "$")
ADollar = Left(aAtl, A$ - 1)
cAtl = Mid(ADollar, 2)
rAtl = Mid(aAtl, A$ + 1)

A$ = InStr(2, aAbr, "$")
ADollar = Left(aAbr, A$ - 1)
cAbr = Mid(ADollar, 2)
rAbr = Mid(aAbr, A$ + 1)

Debug.Print "ArrayAddress: " & aA
Debug.Print "TopLeft:     Cell Address = " & aAtl
Debug.Print "             Column Name  = " & cAtl
Debug.Print "             Row Number   = " & rAtl
Debug.Print "BottomRight: Cell Address = " & aAbr
Debug.Print "             Column Name  = " & cAbr
Debug.Print "             Row Number   = " & rAbr

End Sub
```

Text parsing tools allow you, e.g., to find the present address of a range, and with that knowledge construct a new address to which to move it. Section 8.15.2 will illustrate another use of text parsing.

8.15 Exploiting spreadsheet capabilities

Excel has a rich library of built-in functions and macros, but VBA does not. We may therefore want to use spreadsheet capabilities in VBA. Since Excel's *macros* are subroutines, this might seem a simple matter, as it indeed will be for your own, user-supplied macros. Unfortunately, the same does not apply to Excel's macros, because their code is not accessible to the user, and typically isn't even written in VBA. Only some special spreadsheet macros supplied by outside sources, such as Solver, provide the tools to call them from VBA, and the MacroBundle routines SolverScan (already encountered in section 4.17) and ColumnSolver (see section 4.18) illustrate their use.

Matters are more favorable for Excel's built-in *functions*, most of which are readily accessible in VBA with the prefix `Application.`, see section 8.13. Below we will describe two other approaches that are sometimes useful. One is to sneak into the spreadsheet and make it do our bidding, while the other (often orders of magnitude faster) approach is to reconstruct a spreadsheet expression in VBA.

8.15.1 Invasive sampling

It is sometimes convenient to change a parameter on the spreadsheet, and to exploit the consequences of that change. As our example, we will use this here to find the first derivative of a function $F(a)$ by changing a. The simplest approach is to read a range, change the contents of one of its cells, write that back onto the spreadsheet, and then read the resulting change(s) in other cells. In this manner we can, e.g., read values of a function $F(x)$ by changing x, without the need to code that function explicitly in the subroutine. Below we will illustrate this in order to compute the derivative of a function. Excel has two specific text functions that can be helpful in this respect: SUBSTITUTE and REPLACE.

The basis of numerical differentiation is that Excel can evaluate a function of one or more variables, and that, in order to find its (partial) derivative, we merely need to change one such variable by a known, relatively small amount Δa (i.e., a small *fraction* of the variable value a) and observe the resulting change ΔF in the function. After all, the derivative dF/da of a function F with respect to a (or, when F depends on more than one parameter, its partial derivative $\partial F/\partial a$) is defined as

$$\frac{dF}{da} = \lim_{\Delta a \to 0} \frac{F(a + \Delta a) - F(a)}{\Delta a} \tag{8.15.1}$$

which, for $\Delta a \ll a$, can be approximated by

$$\frac{dF}{da} \approx \frac{F(a + \Delta a) - F(a)}{\Delta a} \tag{8.15.2}$$

By letting the spreadsheet evaluate $F(a+\Delta a)$ and $F(a)$, we can find the value of dF/da of any function that Excel can compute. For a more detailed treatment see section 9.2.

In order to use (8.15.1) in a macro, place a in one spreadsheet cell, and in another cell deposit a formula for F that depends on a (and possibly on other factors, in which case we will compute the partial derivative). Note that we will only find the *numerical value* of the derivative of the function, *at its current value*, not a generally applicable formula.

For starters, just to illustrate how this macro works, try $a = 3$ with $F = 4 + 5\,a^2 = 49$, for which F_{deriv} should be $5 \times 2\,a = 30$, or with $F = 7 - 6\ln(a) = 0.408326268$, which should yield $F_{deriv} = -6/a = -2$. Then change the value of a and/or the formula for F to suit your own fancy.

```
Sub NumericalDifferentiation()

Dim A As Double, Amin As Double, Aplus As Double
Dim F As Double, Fmin As Double, Fplus As Double
Dim Fderiv As Double
Dim rgA As Range, rgF As Range
```

```
' Read the values of A and F

Set rgF = Application.InputBox(Prompt:= _
  "The function is located in ", Type:=8)
rgF.Select
F = rgF.Value

Set rgA = Application.InputBox(Prompt:= _
  "The variable a is located in ", Type:=8)
rgA.Select
A = rgA.Value

' Modify A to Aplus and read the corresponding Fplus

Aplus = A * (1 + 1 / 1048576)
Selection.Value = Aplus
rgF.Select
Fplus = rgF.Value

' Modify A to Aminus and read the corresponding Fminus

Aminus = A * (1 - 1 / 1048576)
rgA.Select
Selection.Value = Aminus
rgF.Select
Fminus = rgF.Value

' Clean up by restoring the initial value of A

rgA.Select
Selection.Value = A

' Compute and display the derivative

Fderiv = (Fplus - Fminus) / (A / 524288)
MsgBox "The first derivative of the function is " & Fderiv

End Sub
```

The above works when we change values, but is slightly more complicated when the cells to be invaded contain formulas but display their values, as in Figs. 2.14.1 and 2.14.2. To cover both values and formulas, we start the macro by copying their formulas, then temporarily replace these by their numerical values with an in-place Copy PasteSpecial as Values, operate on the resulting values, and finally restore the original formulas. This also works for numbers because asking the formula of a cell containing a number yields that number. For details, see how this approach is implemented in the custom macro Propagation. Since Solver only yields numbers, it is not necessary for SolverAid.

8.15.2 Reconstructing equations

Another way to exploit the spreadsheet is to read an expression from the sheet and to reproduce it in VBA. While it is usually simpler and faster to do this manually, there are occasions where that may be undesirable. In the following example we will illustrate how we can reconstruct in VBA a spreadsheet expression $F(x)$ as a function of a single spreadsheet parameter x. A specific example of such an approach is illustrated in the custom macro TrapezAuto that will be used in section 9.3.2 for trapezoidal integration.

We will start with two spreadsheet cells, the first one (say, cell B2) containing the *value* vX of x, the other (in this example: C2) holding the *formula* fF of the function $F(x)$. When we look at the form of an Excel function we notice that it does not contain the variable x explicitly, but instead refers to its location: the spreadsheet instruction =Sqrt(B2) does not mean to take the square root of some variable b_2, as it would be in an algebraic expression, but of the value found *at the location of* the cell at the address B2. Since VBA more closely follows the algebraic notation, a translation is required. An additional complication is that such an address, when extracted with, e.g., the VBA instruction Selection.Address, will yield its absolute form, i.e., $B$2. Fortunately, we already learned in section 8.14 how to strip those dollar signs away and recover B2.

VBA can easily read a formula from the spreadsheet with a command such as Selection.Formula. In our example, using this on cell C2 might yield, e.g., "=SQRT(B2)". Now we consider how to modify such a formula so that we can use it in VBA with numerical values x, rather than having to deposit such numerical values in cell B2 and read the resulting value in C2, as we did with invasive sampling. One obvious advantage over invasive sampling is that we then no longer need to go back and forth between Excel and VBA any time we change the input value, thereby making this method much faster. At this point we are not concerned with speed, but we will return to that aspect in section 9.3.2.

Leaving out dimensioning and other niceties for the sake of brevity, the following code will first reconstruct the cell address:

```
PosDollar1 = InStr(1, aX, "$")
PosDollar2 = InStr(2, aX, "$")
caX = Mid(aX, 2, PosDollar2 - PosDollar1 - 1)
raX = Mid(aX, PosDollar2 + 1, 8)
XX = caX & raX
LenXX = Len(XX)
```

Here the first two lines determine the positions of the first and second dollar sign in the address aX, with that knowledge caX then recovers the column letter(s) in the address of X, and raX its row number(s), XX reconstitutes the cell address, and LenXX determines its length, see the MacroMorsel ReconstructAnEquation. All this simply follows what we already encountered in section 8.14. We now add the following:

```
LenF = Len(fF)
PosXXinF = InStr(1, fF, XX)
LeftF = Left(fF, PosXXinF - 1)
RightF = Right(fF, LenF - PosXXinF - LenXX + 1)
vF = Application.Evaluate(LeftF & Str(X) & RightF)
```

where fF is the formula $F(x)$ as read from the spreadsheet. The second line locates the position of XX in the formula fF, LeftF and RightF then isolate the parts to its left and right respectively, and the bottom line computes the value vF of the reconstructed formula for any value of the variable X earlier specified by the VBA code. The reconstructed expression within the brackets following Evaluate must be handled with care: simply constructing that expression first for subsequent insertion into the evaluation formula can make Excel crash. Moreover, unless specifically protected, this method may fail due to possible differences between Excel and VBA instructions, see section 1.14. In this example, change SQRT into SQR.

If you have installed XN, section 8.16 describes yet another option, namely to use a formula evaluator, which is based on a math parser. This will allow you to write a mathematical expression in a function or macro statement as well as on the spreadsheet, and have the parser evaluate its value. The mathematical expression can be a function of multiple (up to 20 different) variables.

8.16 Using the XN equation parser

Invasive sampling works in general, because anything that can be computed on the spreadsheet can be read. But because it requires time-consuming switching between spreadsheet and VBA, using ranges loaded with excess information, it is often an impractical choice. A much faster, though somewhat less general approach illustrated in section 8.15.2 is analogous to what was described in section 8.14 as deconstructing an address, viz. deconstructing an equation, then reassembling it in VBA. This is precisely what the XN equation parser does: it relieves you of the need to enter this code yourself. The parser takes an equation written in quasi-algebraic, Excel-like notation and converts it into VBA code, so that the rest of the calculation can all be done in VBA.

Take, e.g., the integration of an algebraic function $F(x)$ in the range $a \le x \le b$. In chapter 9 we will use macros such as RombergAuto to exploit the spreadsheet formula in computing the integral, but it is much faster to code the function in VBA. However, it is more user-friendly, and the computation is equally fast, when we write that code as an Excel-style text string that can be converted into VBA code. This requires a parser, which evaluates the string and reformulates it in VBA, as in `=Integr("1.3*exp(-x^2 /6)*sin(pi/4)/Sqr(3/x)",0,13)`. In this example you can see the structure of the instruction: the formula $F(x)$ is entered in code between quotation marks, followed by the limits of integration, here 0 and 13. Below we list the rules used for writing code that the XN parser can interpret.

(1) Numbers can be integer, decimal, or in scientific (exponential) notation: 1, 2.34, –5.6, 7.8E–9.

(2) Complex numbers can be indicated as an ordered pair: (a,b), (1,-0.1), (-0.12345, 6.78E-19), or as a compound number: (a+bj), (1-0.1j), (-0.12345+6.78E-19j). For nested formulas, use a multiplier before the symbol j, as in ((2+3*4)+(5/6)*j. You can use either i or j.

(3) Angles must be specified as rad, deg, or grad, where rad(pi/2) = deg(90) = grad(100). Angles can also be written in degrees, minutes and seconds, as in 20d 34m 56s, always in the Sumerian sexagesimal (base 60) system with 60s = 1m and 60m = 1d.

(4) Variables can be any alphanumeric string that starts with a letter: a, x, Alpha, b1, time_2. Capitals are accepted but make no difference: alpha, Alpha and ALPHA are interpreted as the same quantity.

(5) The usual algebraic expressions are accepted, such as +, -, *, /, \, ^, | |, as well as the logical expressions <, >, =, <=, >=, <>, or, nor, nxor (for exclusive nor), not.

(6) The mathematical constants pi (= 3.1416..) and e (= 2.718..) are accepted.

(7) Most common mathematical functions are accepted, such as: exp, ln, log, sin, cos, atan, sqr, !. As in Excel, they must be followed by their argument, within parentheses. Separate multiple arguments by commas, as in max(a,b). The parser also accepts some multivariable arguments, as in DSNormal(x,m,s) or HypGeom(x,a,b,c) for a normal (Gaussian) distribution or a hypergeometric series respectively, and functions with a variable number of arguments (up to 20), as in mean(x1, x2, …).

(8) Implicit multiplication is (with some exceptions) not acceptable: xy is read as a separate symbol name, not as the product of x and y, which should be formulated as x*y. Similarly, write 2*a rather than 2a.

(9) The complete (and impressive) list of all operations and functions recognized by the parser of the current version of XN is given in Table 17.1. For more details, see the Help file under the "Math formula string" heading.

Function	Use	Function	Use
+	R C M	–	R C M
!	R C M	<	R C M
%	R C M	<= , =<	R C M
*	R C M	<>	R C M
/	R C M	=	R C M
\	R C M	>	R C M
^	R C M	||	R C M
abs(x)	R C M	DSBinom(k, n, p, [j])	R M
acos(x)	R C M	DSCauchy(x, m, s, n, [j])	R
acosh(x)	R C M	DSChi(x, r, [j])	R
acot(x)	R M	DSErlang(x, k, l, [j])	R
acoth(x)	R M	DSGamma(x, k, l, [j])	R
acsc(x)	R M	DSLevy(x, l, [j])	R

366

Function	*Use*	*Function*	*Use*
acsch(x)	R M	DSLogNormal(x, m, s, [j])	R M
AiryA(x)	R	DSLogistic(x, m, s, [j])	R M
AiryB(x)	R	DSMaxwell(x, a, [j])	R M
alog(z)	R C M	DSMises(x, k, [j])	R
and(a,b)	R C M	DSNormal(x, m, s, [j])	R M
arg(z)	C	DSPoisson(k, z, [j])	R
asec(x)	R M	DSRayleigh(x, s, [j])	R M
asech(x)	R M	DSRice(x, v, s, [j])	R
asin(x)	R C M	DSStudent(t, v, [j])	R
asinh(x)	R C M	DSWeibull(x, k, l, [j])	R M
atanh(x)	R C M	Ei(x)	R C
atn(x), atan(x)	R C M	Ein(x,n)	R
atan2(y,x)	R M	Elli1(f,k)	R
BesselI(x,n)	R	Elli2(f,k)	R
I0(x)	R	erf(x)	R C M
BesselJ(x,n)	R	erfc(x)	R C M
J0(x)	R	e#	R C M
BesselK(x,n)	R	eu#	R C M
K0(x)	R	exp(x)	R C M
BesselY(x,n)	R	exp(x)	R C M
Y0(x)	R	fact(x)	R C M
beta(x,y)	R C M	fix(x)	R C M
betaI(x,a,b)	R	FresnelC(x)	R
cbr(x)	R M	FresnelS(x)	R
Ci(x)	R	gamma(x)	R C M
clip(x,a,b)	R M	gammai(a,b)	R
comb(n,k)	R C M	gammaln(x)	R C
conj(x)	C	gcd(a,b)	R
cos(x)	R C M	grad(x)	R M
cosh(x)	R C M	hour(a)	R
cot(x)	R M	HypGeom(a,b,c,x)	R
coth(x)	R M	im(z)	C
csc(x)	R M	int(x)	R C M
csch(x)	R M	integral(f,z,a,b)	C
dateserial(a1,a2,a3)	R	inv(x)	R C M
day(a)	R	lcm(a,b)	R M
dec(x)	R M	ln(x)	R C M
deg(x)	R M	ln2#	R C M
digamma(x), psi(x)	R C	ln10#	R C M
DSBeta(x, a, b, [j])	R	log(x)	R C M
logn(a,b)	R M	rad(x)	R M
max(a,b,...)	R C M	rad5#	R C M
min(a,b,...)	R C M	re(z)	C
mcd(a,b,...)	R C M	rnd(x)	R C M
mcm(a,b,...)	R C M	root(x,n)	R C M
Mean(a,b,...)	R M	round(x,d)	R M

Function	Use	Function	Use
Meang(a,b,...)	R M	sec(x)	R M
Meanq(a,b,...)	R M	sech(x)	R M
minute(a)	R	second(a)	R
mod(a,b)	R C M	serie(....)	C
month(a)	R	sgn(x)	R C M
nand(a,b)	R M	Si(x)	R
neg(z)	R C M	sin(x)	R C M
nor(a,b)	R M	sinh(x)	R C M
not(a)	R C M	sq(x)	R C M
nxor(a,b)	R M	sqr(x), sqrt(x)	R C M
or(a,b)	R C M	Stdev(a,b,...)	R M
perm(a,b)	R M	Stdevp(a,b,...)	R M
pi	R C M	Step(x,a)	R M
pi2	R C M	sum(a1,a2,...)	R M
pi3	R C M	tan(x)	R C M
pi4	R C M	tanh(x)	R C M
pix2	R C M	timeserial(a1,a2,a3)	R
PolyCh(x,n)	R	Var(a,b,...)	R M
PolyHe(x,n)	R	Varp(a,b,...)	R M
PolyLa(x,n)	R	xor(a,b)	R C M
PolyLe(x,n)	R	year(a)	R
r2c(a,b)	C	zeta(x)	R C M

Table 8.16.1: The functions recognized by the MathParser. R = real, C = complex, M = multiprecision. Functions with M can be evaluated in double or multi-precision, those with only C can be used only with cplxEval, and those with only R with xEval or xEvall in standard precision (with DgtMax = 0).

You can use the parser in various ways, both as the explicit function Eval or implicitly, as in the above `=Integr("1.3*exp(-x^2/6)*sin(pi/4)/sqr(3/x)",0,13)`. You can also use it in writing your own custom functions. For extended precision, the functions xEval or xEvall are used instead. (The difference between xEval and xEvall is merely that xEvall first looks at the top of a column for its label, and is therefore somewhat slower.) The large range of functions and function names that the MathParser can handle can greatly simplify complicated calculations.

8.17 Attaching cell comments

When you see the result of a function, you can click on the cell that contains it, find its name, and (within its brackets) the cells that it used for its input. If the code of the function has been changed since it was used, the output will have changed accordingly. A macro is much sneakier: you find the result of its action, but you will not know what input information was used, or even which macro produced it. And even when that would be clear from the context, the macro may since have been updated, and you will not know which of its versions was used, or when. This, and the possibility of subsequent, undocumented changes in one or more of its input values (which will not be reflected in the macro output), are among the weak spots in trying to validate an Excel spreadsheet.

While this problem can be reduced by painstaking documentation, it helps to let the macro self-document its use, automatically. This can be built in with Cell Comments, which can identify all the needed information that would not be available otherwise, such as the name of the macro used, the date and time of use (which the computer can provide), the source(s) of its input, any options exercised or special conditions used, etc. Again, this will not prevent changes in the input parameters after the macro was last used, and the cell comments can easily be edited afterwards, but is still useful when the purpose is automatic documentation rather than fraud prevention.

Here is a simple example. Before calling the macro, highlight a cell. The specific information given will of course depend on the application.

```
Sub AttachCellComments()
ActiveCell.Select                       ' clear prior comments
ActiveCell.ClearComments
ActiveCell.AddComment
ActiveCell.Comment.Visible = False      ' if True, the comment will always be displayed
ActiveCell.Comment.Text Text:="Whatever text and/or" _
  & Chr(10) & "information you may wish" & Chr(10) & _
  "to put here, e.g.: " & Chr(10) & _
  "Date: " & Date & Chr(10) & "Time: " & Time
ActiveCell.Comment.Shape.Height = 100   ' default 56
ActiveCell.Comment.Shape.Width = 200    ' default 96
End Sub
```

Many custom macros in the MacroBundle use an output cell to show the macro name, and display the corresponding cell comments when the pointer hovers over that cell. (Permanently visible comments can block adjacent cells from view.) You can display a cell comment permanently by right-clicking on the cell, and then on Show Comment; you can undo this afterwards with Hide Comment.

8.18 Case study 1: the propagation of uncertainty

In this and the following few sections we will illustrate how to address some specific problems. We will focus primarily on the approach used, and on their first-order implementations, without too many bells and whistles. For several of these problems, more elaborate macros can be found in the MacroBundle, which otherwise might at first be somewhat overwhelming.

So-called 'error' propagation deals with the transmission of experimental uncertainty through a calculation. Say that we have a function $F(a)$ which is computed from a single parameter a. We then want to calculate the uncertainty $\pm\Delta F$ in F resulting from the (assumedly known) uncertainty $\pm\Delta a$ in the parameter a. For the usual assumption $\Delta a \ll a$ we have

$$\frac{\Delta F}{\Delta a} \approx \frac{dF}{da} \tag{8.18.1}$$

so that the magnitude of ΔF is given by

$$\Delta F \approx \left|\frac{dF}{dx}\right| \Delta x \tag{8.18.2}$$

or, in terms of (sample) standard deviations,

$$s_F = \left|\frac{dF}{da}\right| s_a \tag{8.18.3}$$

Spreadsheets cannot compute the *algebraic formula* for the derivative dF/da (as, e.g., Mathematica or Maple can), but they can find its *numerical value*, which is often all we need. As already explained in section 8.15, we do this by going back to the definition of the differential quotient as

$$\frac{dF}{da} \equiv \lim_{\Delta a \to 0} \frac{\Delta F}{\Delta a} = \lim_{\Delta a \to 0} \frac{F(a+\Delta a) - F(a)}{\Delta a} \tag{8.18.4}$$

Therefore we calculate dF/da by computing the function F twice, once with the original parameter a, and subsequently with that parameter slightly changed from a to $a + \Delta a$, using the Excel function Replace. We then divide their difference by the magnitude of that change, Δa. When Δa is sufficiently small (but not so small that Δa itself becomes imprecise), (8.18.4) will calculate the value of dF/da without requiring any *formal* differentiation. A value for $\Delta a/a$ of the order of 10^{-7} satisfies the requirements that $\Delta a \ll a$ while Δa is still much larger than the truncation errors of the program, which in Excel are of the order of 10^{-14}. We will write the macro in two parts: first the data input stage, then the actual calculation. If you prefer to push OK buttons, replace Debug.Print by MsgBox.

```
Sub PropagationDemo()

' Read the x-value

Dim XRange As Range
Set XRange = Application.InputBox _
  (Prompt:="The value of x is:", Type:=8)
XRange.Select
XValue = Selection.Value

' Read the corresponding standard deviation s

Set SValue = Application.InputBox _
  (Prompt:="The standard deviation s is:", Type:=8)

' Read the formula F and its value

Dim FRange As Range
Set FRange = Application.InputBox _
  ("The formula F is:", Type:=8)
FRange.Select
FFormula = Selection.Formula
FValue = Selection.Value

' Verify that x, s, and F are read correctly

Debug.Print "The value of x is " & XValue
Debug.Print "The standard deviation in x is " & SValue
Debug.Print "The formula has the value " & FValue
Debug.Print "The formula reads " & FFormula

End Sub
```

Test this section. When the input part of the program works correctly, comment out the verification section, and insert the following code on the lines just above End Sub:

```
' Change x

XRange.Select
NewXValue = XValue * 1.000001
Selection.Replace XValue, NewXValue
Debug.Print "The new value for x is " & NewXValue

' Read the resulting change in F

FRange.Select
NewFValue = Selection.Value
Debug.Print "The new value for F is " & NewFValue

' Compute the standard deviation SF in F

SFValue = Abs((NewFValue - FValue) _
  * SValue / (XValue * 0.000001))
MsgBox "The standard deviation in F is " & SFValue

' Reset x

XRange.Select
Selection.Replace NewXValue, XValue
```

370

Again, test the program, now with some numbers and equations for which you know how the uncertainty propagates, such as $F(x) = x^3$ or $\sqrt{x}$, for which $dF/dx = 3x^2$ or $1/(2\sqrt{x})$ respectively. The test will, of course, use numbers rather than abstract expressions for input, and likewise return numerical values rather than symbols for answer. For instance, place the number 7 in cell B2, and the expression =B2^3 in cell C2, so that it will show the number 343, i.e., 7^3. The PropagationDemo will then yield the answer 147, i.e., $3x^2$ for $x = 7$.

After testing has convinced you that everything works as intended, for positive and negative integers and fractions, delete all `Debug.Print` statements.

The macro Propagation in the MacroBundle uses the same logic. It can handle functions of multiple parameters, can use either standard deviations or the covariance matrix as input, and will write its results onto the spreadsheet unless that action would risk overwriting valuable data. Those 'extras' make the macro somewhat more complicated, and certainly much longer, but the principle of the method is the same. Still, it retains some semblance of readability by being broken up into small paragraphs, each with its own comment heading. Look it up to see whether you can now follow its logic.

8.19 Case study 2: Fourier transformation

The next example will illustrate a different approach to writing macros. We will address the spreadsheet differently, and take the core code from the literature. Left for us to write are then, mostly, error checking sections to prevent some common operator mistakes, lest we may be dismayed later to find ourselves in a trap of our own making.

Excel already provides a Fourier transformation routine, under Tools ⇨ Data Analysis ⇨ Fourier Analysis, so why re-invent the wheel? One reason is that, in this case, the wheel is not very serviceable: the output of the Excel Fourier transformation routine is coded as labels, from which the data need to be extracted with `=IMREAL()` and `=IMAGINARY()`. More importantly, with an open-access FT routine it is easier to write applications that use Fourier transformation, such as Gabor transformation or FT-based deconvolution, and we can then increase its accuracy by using extended numberlength, see chapter 11.

Fourier transformation is in principle a simple matter: once the input data have been provided, the computer needs no further information. Consequently no input boxes are needed, and the input process can be reduced to highlighting the data array and then calling the macro.

The so-called fast Fourier transformation is most efficient when applied to a number of data points that is an integer power of 2, and most software packages, including this one, are therefore restricted to 2^N data where N is a positive integer. (XN has several FT routines without this restriction.)

8.19.1 A starter macro

We start by putting together a rudimentary yet working Fourier transform macro by providing a simple input statement, a routine taken from the literature, and an output statement. Such a macro might just contain `dataArray = Selection.Value` as input statement, `Selection.Value = dataArray` as output instruction, and have the Fourier transform routine in the middle, together with whatever auxiliaries that routine requires.

There are many places in the literature where Fourier transform subroutines can be found. Here we use a particularly convenient source, the *Numerical Recipes* by W. H. Press, B. P. Flannery, S. A. Teukolsky and W. T. Vetterling, published in several versions (such as FORTRAN, Pascal, or C++) by Cambridge University Press. This book not only gives many useful routines, but also a very lucid explanation of their uses and limitations. Moreover, in an accompanying booklet complete with diskette, J. C. Sprott has provided these routines in BASIC, which you can use *as is* because it is fully compatible with VBA. Therefore, get hold of the diskette of Sprott's *Numerical Recipes: Routines and Examples in BASIC*, Cambridge University Press (1991), find yourself a diskette reader, and copy its contents onto your computer.

At the same time, if you want to use one or more of these routines, also get yourself a copy of the *Numerical Recipes* (preferably the FORTRAN 77 version that was the source for Sprott's BASIC programs) for useful (and sometimes essential) background information.

You will find that Press et al. describe a subroutine called FOUR1, which requires that the input data be arranged as alternating real and imaginary terms, and returns the answer in the same format. Since such a sequence is unsuitable for graphs, we will start with two input columns, one each for the real and imaginary signal components respectively. Likewise we will use two output columns Therefore we will need to rearrange the data from two columns to one, as input for the subroutine, and afterwards decode its single-column output into two columns in order to write the result on the spreadsheet. Open a new spreadsheet, and type:

```
Sub Fourier()

' Determine the array length

Dim r As Integer, rMax As Integer
rMax = Selection.Rows.Count

' Read the input

Dim dataArray As Variant
dataArray = Selection.Value

' Rearrange the input

ReDim Term(1 To 2 * rMax) As Double
For r = 1 To rMax
  Term(2 * r - 1) = dataArray(r, 1)
  Term(2 * r) = dataArray(r, 2)
Next r

' Call the subroutine

Dim iSign As Integer
iSign = 1
'Call Four1(Term, 2 * rMax, iSign)

' Rearrange the output

For r = 1 To rMax
  dataArray(r, 1) = Term(2 * r - 1)
  dataArray(r, 2) = Term(2 * r)
Next r

' Write the output data

Selection.Offset(0, 2).Select
Selection.Value = dataArray

End Sub
```

Notes:

(1) `Selection.Rows.Count` is a convenient instruction to find the length of the input columns.

(2) The macro reads the entire input array with the simple instruction `dataArray = Selection.Value`.

(3) The next few lines put the input data in the required format: Re_1, Im_1, Re_2, Im_2, etc., where Re_n and Im_n are the real and imaginary parts of the nth data point.

(4) An Array has two dimensions, one each for rows and columns. Therefore, `dataArray(r, 1)` refers to the cell at row number `r` and column 1 of the highlighted array.

(5) Specify any as yet undefined parameters that `Four1()` may need (here: `iSign`), and call the subroutine. By initially commenting out the subroutine call, as done here, this part can be checked out first, separately.

(6) You may have noticed that we here dimension the parameters as we go along. That is often convenient, especially with rather complex procedures, because on the way we may define several parameters that we end up not using. In that case it is most efficient to wait with collecting all dimension statements at the top of the routine until testing is complete, and dead-end sections have been removed.

372

(7) Unscramble the output by taking the alternating real and imaginary components from their single file, and putting them back into separate columns.

(8) Offset the highlighted array with `Selection.Offset(0, 2).Select` in order not to overwrite the input data, and return the result to the spreadsheet with `Selection.Value = dataArray`. We already encountered this type of code at the end of section 2.5.2.

(9) If you have followed the above, you will have dimensioned all variables. You need not do so (as long as you do not use Option Explicit), but in general it is a good practice. For one thing, it can make the computer run more efficiently. For another, it can alert you to some typos, because Option Explicit will catch most misspelled variable names.

(10) The typo alert works whenever you use variable names that contain at least one capital, provided that you type them everywhere in lower case, except in the dimension statement. The ever-alert VB Editor will then convert any lower case letters to the corresponding capitals in accordance with the dimension statement. When you see the computer-inserted capitals pop up on your screen you will know that the VB Editor has recognized the name. Most typos will be caught this way, unless your typo specifies another parameter name you have also dimensioned. Although it is good programming practice to use the dimension statement to specify the data type (e.g., `As Integer` or `As Variant`), you do *not* need do so to get this advantage. When in doubt about its proper data type, at least dimension the variable by name.

Now place the subroutine FOUR1 after the macro, or use its slightly modified form as shown below.

```
Sub Four1(Term, nn, iSign)
Dim tr As Double, ti As Double, theta As Double          ' note (1)
Dim wtemp As Double, wi As Double, wr As Double           ' note (1)
Dim i As Integer, istep As Integer, j As Integer
Dim m As Integer, mmax As Integer
j = 1
For i = 1 To nn Step 2
  If j > i Then
    tr = Term(j)
    ti = Term(j + 1)
    Term(j) = Term(i)
    Term(j + 1) = Term(i + 1)
    Term(i) = tr
    Term(i + 1) = ti
  End If
  m = Int(nn / 2)
  While m >= 2 And j > m
    j = j - m
    m = Int(m / 2)
  Wend
  j = j + m
Next i

mmax = 2
While nn > mmax
  istep = 2 * mmax
  theta = 2 * Application.Pi() / (-iSign * mmax)          ' notes (2) & (3)
  wpr = -2 * Sin(0.5 * theta) ^ 2
  wpi = Sin(theta)
  wr = 1
  wi = 0
  For m = 1 To mmax Step 2
    For i = m To nn Step istep
      j = i + mmax
      tr = wr * Term(j) - wi * Term(j + 1)
      ti = wr * Term(j + 1) + wi * Term(j)
      Term(j) = Term(i) - tr
      Term(j + 1) = Term(i + 1) - ti
```

```
      Term(i) = Term(i) + tr
      Term(i + 1) = Term(i + 1) + ti
    Next i
    wtemp = wr
    wr = wr * wpr - wi * wpi + wr
    wi = wi * wpr + wtemp * wpi + wi
  Next m
  mmax = istep
Wend

End Sub
```

Notes:

(1) The first modification here is the dimensioning, especially the use of double precision.

(2) Instead of spelling out the numerical value of π, we merely invoke the spreadsheet function `Pi()` by preceding it by `Application.`; in this particular case, placing `Pi()` between square brackets would also work.

(3) On that same line you may notice a sign change, because *Numerical Recipes* uses an engineering sign convention for Fourier transformation that is the opposite of the common scientific one used here, see section 5.11.

Remove the apostrophe in front of the `Call` statement, and test the entire macro. (The word `Call` in the line calling the subroutine is optional, but is highly recommended, because it makes it easier to see where the code switches to another module.) As test data you might first use $y_{Re} = \cos(\pi x/8)$ and $y_{Im} = 0$ for $x = 0$ (1) 15. Then try $y_{Re} = \sin(\pi x/8)$ and $y_{Im} = 0$ for the same x values. The cosine is symmetrical around $x = 0$, and therefore has a real Fourier transform, while the sine is/does not. Keep in mind that any numbers smaller than about 10^{-14} are likely to be zeros corrupted by computational (truncation and round-off) errors.

8.19.2 Comments & embellishments

a. Scaling: The Fourier transform of $y = \cos(\pi x/8)$ for $x = 0$ (1) 15 should yield two nonzero points, each of magnitude $0.5j$ (where $j = \sqrt{-1}$) at $f = +1/8$ and $-1/8$ respectively. You should find two nonzero points, in the second row and at the bottom of the first output column, but their magnitudes will be 8 instead of 0.5. However, if you had carefully read the section on FOUR1 in the *Numerical Recipes* you would have seen that you must still provide a normalizing factor, the reciprocal of the number of data points transformed. Here that number is 16, and $8/16 = 0.5$, so that this indeed explains the discrepancy. We should build this division into the macro.

b. Sign: The Fourier transform of $y = \sin(\pi x/8)$ for $x = 0$ (1) 15 should also be two points, of magnitude $-0.5j$ (where $j = \sqrt{-1}$) at $f = +1/8$, and of magnitude $+0.5j$ at $f = -1/8$. You obtained two nonzero points, in the second output column (which contains the imaginary parts of the output), viz. -8 in the second row, and $+8$ in the bottom row. Normalization through division by 16, and realizing that the second column represents the imaginary components, makes these $-0.5j$ and $+0.5j$ respectively. However, upon consulting a standard book on Fourier transformations, you will find that these signs are just the reverse from what they are supposed to be. Another look at the *Numerical Recipes* will show that it uses engineering definitions of the forward and inverse Fourier transforms, contrary to the usual mathematical convention. Consequently the problem is in the subroutine, and is easily fixed by placing a minus sign in front of the term `iSign` in the equation defining `theta`. This correction was already made in the modified version shown.

c. Driver macros: Now that we have calibrated the macro, it is time to consider some conveniences. We can use the very same macro for inverse transformation if we merely change the sign of `iSign`. That can of course be done with an input box, but it is easier to make two small macros, ForwardFT and InverseFT, that set `iSign` to +1 and -1 respectively, and let them call Fourier as a common subroutine that does all the hard work. Here are such drivers:

374

```
Sub ForwardFT()
Dim iSign As Integer
iSign = 1
Call Fourier(iSign)
End Sub

Sub InverseFT()
Dim iSign As Integer
iSign = -1
Call Fourier(iSign)
End Sub
```

Notes:

(1) Remember, a macro does not exchange information in its (therefore empty) argument (in the space between the brackets), but a subroutine does. In the above example, both driver macros tell the subroutine Fourier to use their particular value of iSign. And because the two driver macros are independent, iSign must be dimensioned in each of them.

(2) There is slightly more to combining forward and inverse transforms, because (in the common formalism we adopt here) the normalizing factor $1/N$ only applies to the forward transform. (An alternative convention, not followed here, uses identical normalizing factors $1/\sqrt{N}$ for both the forward and inverse transform.)

(3) The header of the main program must now be changed to `Sub Fourier(iSign)`.

d. Checking the input block dimensions: The fast Fourier transform subroutine requires that there are 2^N data points. It is convenient to check ahead of time whether the input range indeed contains such a number of data. We can also make sure that there are only two columns, and that there are at least two rows. The following code, to be placed immediately below the heading of Fourier(iSign), will accomplish all of these goals.

```
' Check the array width

Dim cMax As Integer
cMax = Selection.Columns.Count

If cMax <> 2 Then
  MsgBox "There must be 2 input columns."
  End
End If

' Check the array length

Dim rMax As Integer, Length As Integer
rMax = Selection.Rows.Count
If rMax < 2 Then
  MsgBox "There must be at least 2 rows."
  End
End If
Length = rMax
Do While Length > 1
  Length = Length / 2
Loop
If Length <> 1 Then
  MsgBox "The number of rows must be" _
    & Chr(13) & "an integral power of two."
  End
End If
```

Notes:

(1) `Selection.Columns.Count` finds the number of highlighted columns, which should be 2, one for the real component of the function to be transformed, the other for its imaginary component. Otherwise the macro alerts the user to the problem, and ends.

375

(2) Similarly, `Selection.Rows.Count` finds the number of rows of the highlighted array, rMax. This should be at least 2.

(3) The next check makes sure that rMax is an integer power of 2. This is accomplished here by using a second variable, `Length`, that we initially set equal to rMax. Then we divide `Length` repeatedly by 2, until it eventually becomes 1 or smaller than 1. If at that point there is a nonzero remainder, the number of rows was not an integer power of 2, and the input is rejected.

(4) We here divide `Length` rather than rMax in order to keep the latter intact for further use. Alternatively we could use rMax, and redetermine it the next time we need it. That approach was not used here as it might be confusing for someone trying to understand how the procedure works. Still, there are usually many possible ways to get the job done.

e. Checking for overwrite: It is convenient to place the output of the macro immediately to the right of the input data. We now make sure that this region does not contain valuable data that would be lost if overwritten, by letting the macro take a quick look at that area to make sure it can be used for output. Here is an example of code that will do this. It can be inserted just after the code discussed under (d), or before the data output.

```
' Make sure that the output will
' not overwrite valuable data
Dim outputArray As Variant, z As Double
Dim c As Integer, cMax As Integer
Dim r As Integer, rMax As Integer
Dim n As Integer
n = 0
Selection.Offset(0, 2).Select
OutputArray = Selection.Value
For r = 1 To rMax
  For c = 1 To cMax
    z = outputArray(r, c)
    If IsEmpty(z) Or z = 0 Then
      n = n
    Else
      n = n + 1
    End If
  Next c
Next r

If n > 0 Then
  answer = MsgBox("There are data in the" _
    & Chr(13) & "output space. Can they" _
    & Chr(13) & "be overwritten?", vbYesNo)
  If answer = vbNo Then
    Selection.Offset(0, -2).Select
    End
  End If
End If
```

Notes:

(1) `Selection.Offset(0, 2).Select` moves the highlighted area two cells to the right, to the place where the output will be deposited.

(2) The next line makes an output array of the same dimensions as the input array. It is used here only to see whatever is in the cells where the output should come.

(3) Now that we have read what is in the output space, the next lines check every cell in that area. Whenever a cell in this range is found not to be empty or zero, the variable n is incremented by one. Since n was initially set to zero, we see whether it is still zero at the end. If not, then the message box is activated, asking the user whether the data in the output array can be overwritten. If the answer is no, the highlighted area moves back, and the macro ends, to give the user time to move the endangered data out of harm's way.

(4) Since Fourier transformation is often applied to fairly large data files, no niceties such as an alternative output via message boxes is provided, since they would be awkward and time-consuming to use.

376

f. Converting time to frequency etc.: In the Fourier transformation

$$F(f) = \int_{-\infty}^{+\infty} f(t)\, e^{-2\pi j f t}\, dt$$

the product of the parameters f and t must be dimensionless, as it is in the usual pairs of time and frequency, or wavelength and wavenumber. Given t, we can let the computer calculate f, and vice versa. It is therefore convenient to extend the input block to include the independent variable x, to compute its inverse, and to provide that in a third output column.

h. Using a zero-centered scale: A related question is that of the scale to be used for the independent variable. Traditionally, t runs from 0 to t_{max}, while f starts at 0, runs till $f_{max}/2$, has a discontinuity, then continues to run from $-f_{max}/2$ to -0. We here adopt more rational scales that are continuous, and are centered around zero for both t and f. (The final version tolerates both types of input.)

g. Suppressing screen display: Often we will have graphs on the screen in order to visualize the functions. When a macro recalculates a data point, the entire screen will be updated. Usually this is precisely what we want. However, for a computation involving many points, as in a Fourier transformation of a large data set, it is convenient to suppress the screen updating until the entire output set has been computed, see section 8.11. This is accomplished with the instruction `Application. ScreenUpdating = False`, which can be placed just before the statement `Selection. Value = dataArray`. Screen updating should be suppressed only *after* all input and dialog boxes have been used, since it blocks entering ranges into input box windows by the highlight & click (drag & drop) method.

h. Modularizing: When you anticipate that a part of the code may also be useful in other macros, it may be convenient to compartmentalize that section of code as a separate subroutine, which can be called by different macros. In the present example, the actual fast Fourier transform algorithm can then be shared with, e.g., ConvolveFT. On the other hand, ConvolveFT could have used a more efficient fast Fourier transform algorithm that can simultaneously transform *two* real signals rather than one complex one. There is often such a trade-off between optimizing code for each specific application, or saving development time by using already existing code modules.

i. Dimensioning: By now you will be ready to dimension your parameters. The macro is getting too long to be typed without errors, and dimensioning has other benefits: the user can quickly see to what type each parameter belongs, and the computer can operate more efficiently. Here are some things to keep in mind.

In dimensioning several parameters you need not repeat the dimension statement `Dim` for parameters on one line, but you must repeat their type declarations (as in `Dim A As Double, B As Double, C As Double`) for each and every parameter, even when these statements are on the same line. You can consider this a nuisance of VBA, or the direct consequence of the fact that VBA allows you *not* to specify the data type in advance or, more precisely, to leave it open As Variant.

If you do not know their dimensions yet, dimension array variables As Variant or by name only, and then ReDimension them as soon as the macro knows the corresponding array size, and certainly before you put any date into it. Distinguish between arrays that start counting at 0 and those that start at 1. If you are unsure about the proper dimension type, just dimension it by name but leave the type unspecified. The program will run fine, though not quite with optimum efficiency. Fortunately, with today's processor speeds, it seldom makes a perceptible difference unless the macros are very computation-intensive.

All of the above embellishments have been incorporated in the Fourier transform macro which you already encountered in chapter 5, and which is fully documented in the MacroBundle. You will now appreciate the difference between a lean-and-mean macro and a mature but potbellied one. In the latter, more code is usually devoted to embellishments than to the primary function of the macro. One can only hope that the added effort pays off in terms of convenience of use and absence of frustrating program hang-ups.

8.20 Case study 3: specifying a graph

As our next example we will make a macro to generate a graph. Of course you can readily make a graph with the ChartWizard. But if you need to make many graphs for a report or a paper, and want them to be compatible in size and style, it may be convenient to have a standard format available. You can do this by creating a graph just the way you want it to look, and by then making that the default setting, as described in section 1.2.7.

Alternatively, just as an illustration of how much you can manipulate Excel, we will write a macro to specify a simple graph, so that the mouse can stay home for a while. (For another example see the custom macro Mapper.) For the sake of the argument, say that you want to plot the function $2.4\sqrt{x}$ for $x = 0$ (5) 100, where you have placed values for x in cells A7:A27, and computed the corresponding values for $y = 2.4\sqrt{x}$ in B7:B27. First reserve the location of the graph on the spreadsheet with

```
Sub MakeGraph()
' Create an embedded graph in the cell grid

Dim ch As ChartObject
Dim cw As Double, rh As Double
cw = Columns(1).Width
rh = Rows(1).Height
Set ch = ActiveSheet.ChartObjects. _
  Add(cw * 2, rh * 1, cw * 5, rh * 5)
End Sub
```

By setting `cw = Columns(1).Width` and `rh = Rows(1).Height` we make the graph fit the spreadsheet grid, providing a better visual fit of the graph in the spreadsheet, and facilitating copying it into a Word document. Otherwise we need to specify the placement and dimension of the graph in points, where 1 point = 1/72" ≈ 1/3 mm. See what happens when you change the parameter values to, e.g., Add(cw * 3, rh * 4, cw * 8, rh * 16).

Now define the data type, and the specific data to be plotted:

```
Sub MakeGraph()

' Create an embedded graph in the cell grid

Dim ch As ChartObject
Dim cw As Double, rh As Double

cw = Columns(1).Width
rh = Rows(1).Height
Set ch = ActiveSheet.ChartObjects. _
  Add(cw * 3, rh * 4, cw * 8, rh * 16)
' Select the graph type:
ch.Chart.ChartType = xlXYScatter
' Insert data series:
ch.Chart.SeriesCollection.Add Source:= ActiveSheet.Range("A7:B27")
End Sub
```

This short macro will give you a graph of the data in A7:B27, in the chosen place on the spreadsheet, with auto-scaled axes. If you want to specify your own axes, add instructions such as:

```
' Insert graph axes:
' (X = "Category", Y = "Value")

With ch.Chart.Axes(xlCategory)
   .MinimumScale = 0
   .MaximumScale = 100
   .MajorUnit = 20
End With
With ch.Chart.Axes(xlValue)
```

378

```
   .MinimumScale = 0
   .MaximumScale = 25
   .MajorUnit = 5
End With
```

Now that the basic choices have been made, the rest is fine-tuning and embellishment. Here are some options:

```
' Define the data range:

ch.Chart.SeriesCollection.Add _
   Source:=ActiveSheet.Range("A7:B27"), RowCol:=xlColumns, _
   SeriesLabels:=True, CategoryLabels:=True

' Define the axis labels:

With ch.Chart.Axes(xlCategory)
   .MinimumScale = 0
   .MaximumScale = 100
   .MajorUnit = 20
   .HasTitle = True
   With .AxisTitle
      .Caption = "time / s"
      .Font.Size = 12
   End With
End With
With ch.Chart.Axes(xlValue)
   .MinimumScale = 0
   .MaximumScale = 25
   .MajorUnit = 5
   .HasTitle = True
   With .AxisTitle
      .Caption = "signal / A"
      .Font.Size = 12
      .Orientation = xlUpward
   End With
End With

' If you don't want the legend box:

ch.Chart.Legend.Clear

' Specify a graph title

ch.Chart.HasTitle = True
With ch.Chart.ChartTitle
   .Caption = "Sample Chart #1"
   .Font.Name = "Times Roman"
   .Font.Size = 16
   .Font.FontStyle = "Italic"
   .Font.ColorIndex = 4
End With
```

The color scheme used is explained in section 8.12. Alternatively you could use the RGB system that lets you select any color combination using 256 shades of red, green and blue. For example, the most intense pure red would be coded as `.Color = RGB(255, 0, 0)`.

```
' Define the points and line in the graph

With ch.Chart.SeriesCollection(1)
   .MarkerBackgroundColorIndex = xlNone
   .MarkerForegroundColorIndex = 1
   .MarkerStyle = xlCircle
   .Smooth = True
   .MarkerSize = 7
```

```
  With .Border
    .ColorIndex = 7
    .Weight = xlHairline
    .LineStyle = xlContinuous
  End With
End With

' Do without gridlines:
ch.Chart.Axes(xlValue).HasMajorGridlines = False
ch.Chart.Axes(xlCategory).HasMajorGridlines = False

' Define the background color of the graph:
ch.Chart.ChartArea.Interior.ColorIndex = 2
ch.Chart.PlotArea.Interior.ColorIndex = xlNone

' Place tickmarks:
ch.Chart.Axes(xlValue).MajorTickMark = xlTickMarkCross
ch.Chart.Axes(xlValue).TickLabelPosition _
  = xlTickLabelPositionNextToAxis
' (and do similarly for xlCategory)

' Introduce a second data set:
ch.Chart.SeriesCollection.Add Range("C7:C27")

' Add a secondary vertical scale:
ch.Chart.SeriesCollection(2).AxisGroup = xlSecondary
With ch.Chart.Axes(xlValue, xlSecondary)
  .HasTitle = True
  .AxisTitle.Caption = "log conc"
End With
With ch.Chart.Axes(xlValue, xlSecondary).AxisTitle
  .Font.Size = 12
  .Orientation = xlUpward
  .Top = 60
End With

' Define markers for a second data set:
With ch.Chart.SeriesCollection(2)
  .MarkerBackgroundColorIndex = 8
  .MarkerForegroundColorIndex = 5
  .MarkerStyle = xlTriangle
  .Smooth = True
  .MarkerSize = 5
End With

' Add a textbox and specify its text
' (note that the numerical values are in points)
With ch.Chart.TextBoxes.Add(164, 116, 96, 50)
  .AutoSize = True
  .Text = "K1=3"
End With
With ch.Chart.TextBoxes
  With .Characters(Start:=1, Length:=4).Font
    .Name = "Times New Roman"
    .Size = 12
  End With
  .Characters(Start:=1, Length:=1).Font.FontStyle = "Italic"
  .Characters(Start:=2, Length:=1).Font.Subscript = True
End With
```

380

This is only a sampler of the many possibilities, but you get the idea. You can highlight specific points with different markers and/or colors, add error bars, whatever. Finally, once the macro makes the graph you want, suppress the screen updating during its execution (because it will speed it up and cleanly update the screen presentation) by placing the following lines at the beginning of the program:

```
'Suppress screen updating

Application.ScreenUpdating = False
```

8.21 Case study 4: raising the bar

Accompanying this book is the MacroBundle, a collection of custom macros that can be downloaded freely from the internet. This makes them widely accessible even to readers without access to this book. The web also makes it possible for me to correct and upgrade them when necessary, something that neither the printed page nor an enclosed compact disk would allow.

The present section is not about those macros, but about installing them on your machine in a way that makes them readily available. These installation procedures apply to all custom macros, not just those of the MacroBundle; once you understand how this is done, you can readily modify these macros to include (or only carry) your own creations. These procedures will work in Excel 97 and more recent versions, but not in Excel 5 or Excel 95. ⑦: As you will see when you look at the very end of InsertMB-Toolbar in the MacroBundle, it takes only a few minor modifications to make a toolbar for Excel 2007. However, you can only display it in the Developer ribbon. For often used macros, it may therefore be better to place them in the Quick Access Toolbar, see section 1.2.8.

When macros are used only occasionally, the standard facilities of Excel are optimal: the custom macros do not usurp monitor 'real estate' but are listed in the macro dialog box accessible with Tools ⇨ Macro ⇨ Macros or, more conveniently, with Alt‿F8. To operate them, merely double-click on their name, or single-click it followed by Run. If in doubt about their operation, instead single-click on a macro name and then click Edit, which will get you to the top of that macro's code in the VB Editor. The user instructions should be there, at the very top of that routine, and after reading it you can get back to the spreadsheet with Alt‿F11 (Mac: Opt‿F11) and then call the macro into action, or call it directly from the VBEditor with F5. If you need to use the macros frequently, it is more convenient to access them instead through a special toolbar. In the following example we will use the custom macros SolverAid and LS.

```
Sub InsertToolbarM()

Dim TBar As CommandBar
Dim Button1, Button2, Button20, Button21

' Delete a possible prior version of M to prevent conflicts

On Error Resume Next
CommandBars("M").Delete

' Create a commandbar

Set TBar = CommandBars.Add
With TBar
  .name = "M"
  .Position = msoBarTop
  .Visible = True
End With

' Create a control button for SolverAid

Set Button1 = CommandBars("M").Controls _
  .Add(Type:=msoControlButton)
With Button1
  .Caption = "SolverAid "
  .Style = msoButtonCaption
  .OnAction = "SolverAid"
End With
```

```
' Create a popup control for LS
Set Button2 = CommandBars("M").Controls __
  .Add(Type:=msoControlPopup)
With Button2
  .Caption = " LS "
  .TooltipText = "Highlight array" & Chr(13) & _
    "before pressing" & Chr(13) & "LS0 or LS1"
  .BeginGroup = True
End With

' Create submenus for LS0 and LS1 respectively
Set Button20 = Button2.Controls.Add(Type:=msoControlButton)
With Button20
  .Caption = "LS0"
  .Style = msoButtonCaption
  .OnAction = "LS0"
End With

Set Button21 = Button2.Controls.Add(Type:=msoControlButton)
With Button21
  .Caption = "LS1"
  .Style = msoButtonCaption
  .OnAction = "LS1"
End With

End Sub
```

Notes:

(1) In order to avoid inserting multiple copies, we start with deleting pre-existing versions of the toolbar. However, we would then get an error message when there is no toolbar yet, so we add the dodge `On Error Resume Next`, which bypasses any errors encountered by the delete instruction. However, this trick will not work if your spreadsheet is set to `Break on All Errors`. You can undo this in the VB Editor under <u>T</u>ools ⇨ <u>O</u>ptions, General tab, by setting the Error Trapping to `Break on Unhandled Errors` instead. Alternatively, you could insert the toolbar automatically when Excel is opened, and delete it just before closing Excel.

(2) For the macro SolverAid we use a control button, as we do for the macros LS0 and LS1. Clicking on a control button calls a macro, through its `OnAction` instruction. A popup control does not call a macro, but merely provides a further choice of popups and/or buttons. It is used here for LS, so that the user can select either LS0 or LS1. On the spreadsheet, a popup menu shows a right-pointing arrowhead.

(3) ToolTips will repeat the caption unless you specify them otherwise.

(4) The instruction `BeginGroup = True` inserts a vertical separator in the toolbar, useful for toolbars containing many items.

(5) When you are done experimenting with this macro, remove the inserted toolbar with

```
Sub RemoveToolbarM()
On Error Resume Next
CommandBars("M").Delete
End Sub
```

(6) Users of versions 2007 and 2010 should take a look at the end of their custom macro InsertMBToolbar of the MacroBundle to see how they can modify this type of code to work properly. There are two steps here, (a) making the macro recognize which version of Excel is used, and (b) making the appropriate changes.

8.22 Case study 5: modifying Mapper's BitMap

Mapper provides a convenient visualization of a monotonic function $z = F(x,y)$ of two variables, x and y, but there are many possible approaches as well as color schemes, and Exercise 8.22.1 will show you how to modify these. The examples will be for Mapper0, because we can show its gray-scale results here in print. The same principles apply to color images, some of which are illustrated on my Excellaneous website.

Exercise 8.22.1:

(1) On a new spreadsheet, place the number 0 in cell D20, the instruction =D20+1 in E20, and copy this to cell CZ20, so that you have a horizontal axis from 0 to 100.

(2) Likewise, in cell C21 put the number 100, with the instruction =C21−1 in cell C22, and copy this down to C121 to make your vertical scale.

(3) In cell D21 deposit the instruction =D$20+$C21, and copy this instruction to the entire block D4:CZ121. We will use this as our test pad.

(4) Highlight C20:CZ121, and call Mapper0, which will make a map like the one shown in Fig. 8.22.1*a*.

(5) Now go to the VBEditor (e.g., with Alt∪F11), find the code section for Mapper (near the end of the MacroBundle; it is easiest to step through the code using PageDown and PageUp, because then the name of the routine will show in the top-right window above the Module), find the subroutine BitMap0, highlight that bitmap, copy and paste it (e.g., with Ctrl∪c, Ctrl∪v, Ctrl∪v) so that you get two copies of it, one below the other, then rename one of them BitMap00. This is the spare copy of the original, which we will rename back to Bitmap0 once we are done with our experiment. Below we reproduce the code of BitMap0; the parts to be modified are bold-printed.

```
Private Sub BitMap0(hMax As Integer, wMax As Integer, pixelArray As Variant)

' Gray-scale, no color
Dim H As Integer, w As Integer, RedVal As Integer
Dim GreenVal As Integer, BlueVal As Integer
For H = hMax To 0 Step -1
  For w = 0 To wMax - 1
    RedVal = pixelArray(H, w)
    GreenVal = pixelArray(H, w)
    BlueVal = pixelArray(H, w)
    WriteAPixel RedVal Mod 256, GreenVal Mod 256, BlueVal Mod 256
  Next w
' Do not change the following, essential row padding
w = wMax * 3
  Do While (w Mod 4) <> 0
    WriteAByte 0
    w = w + 1
  Loop
Next H
End Sub
```

(6) In BitMap0, now make the following substitution (again shown in boldface), which replaces the direct proportionality of the earlier gray scale with three distinct *bands* covering specific intervals, converting Mapper into a Bander. The resulting map is shown in Fig. 8.22.1*b*, which now has boundaries similar to those of a contour diagram. These boundaries are crude, having their resolution determined by the size of the underlying array, but their computation requires no further processing and is therefore very quick. It can therefore serve as a quick-and-dirty substitute for a contour diagram.

```
Private Sub BitMap0(hMax As Integer, wMax As Integer, pixelArray As Variant)

' Gray-scale, no color
Dim H As Integer, w As Integer, RedVal As Integer
Dim GreenVal As Integer, BlueVal As Integer
For H = hMax To 0 Step -1
  For w = 0 To wMax - 1
    If pixelArray(H, w) < 85 Then
      RedVal = 85
      GreenVal = 85
      BlueVal = 85
    ElseIf pixelArray(H, w) < 170 Then
      RedVal = 170
      GreenVal = 170
      BlueVal = 170
    ElseIf pixelArray(H, w) >= 170 Then
      RedVal = 255
      GreenVal = 255
      BlueVal = 255
    End If
    WriteAPixel RedVal Mod 256, GreenVal Mod 256, BlueVal Mod 256
  Next w
' Do not change the following, essential row padding
w = wMax * 3
```

```
      Do While (w Mod 4) <> 0
        WriteAByte 0
        w = w + 1
      Loop
   Next H
End Sub
```

(7) Now that we have established the principle of plotting bands, here is a more flexible example of coding, for a flexible number of bands (here: 15). Incorporate this in your BitMap0, and verify that the resulting banded map is similar to Fig. 8.22.1c.

```
Private Sub BitMap0(hMax As Integer, wMax As Integer, pixelArray As Variant)

' Gray-scale, no color

Dim H As Integer, i As Integer, iMax As Integer, w As Integer
Dim RedVal As Integer, GreenVal As Integer, BlueVal As Integer

iMax = 15
For H = hMax To 0 Step -1
  For w = 0 To wMax - 1
    If pixelArray(H, w) < Int(255 / iMax) Then
      RedVal = 0
      GreenVal = 0
      BlueVal = 0
    End If
    For i = 1 To iMax - 1
      If pixelArray(H, w) > i * Int(255 / iMax) And _
        pixelArray(H, w) <= (i + 1) * Int(255 / iMax) Then
        RedVal = i * Int(255 / iMax)
        GreenVal = i * Int(255 / iMax)
        BlueVal = i * Int(255 / iMax)      End If
      End If
    Next I
    WriteAPixel RedVal Mod 256, GreenVal Mod 256, BlueVal Mod 256
  Next w

' Do not change the following, essential row padding

  w = wMax * 3
  Do While (w Mod 4) <> 0
    WriteAByte 0
    w = w + 1
  Loop
Next H

End Sub
```

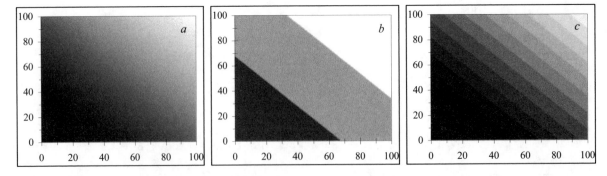

Fig. 8.22.1: Three maps of the same input data: *a*: with a gradual gray-scale, *b*: with three bands, and *c*: with a user-defined number of bands.

384

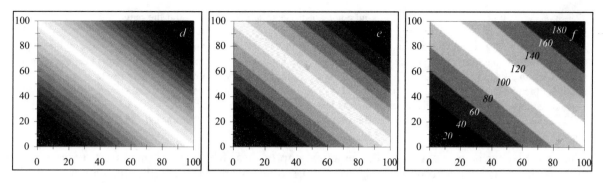

Fig. 8.22.1 cont'd: Three banded maps of the same input data, with emphasis on the central data values: *d*: with iMax = 15, *e*: with iMax = 8, and *f*: with iMax = 5. Panel *d* illustrates that too many bands will blur the effect, and approaches a gradual, non-banded display.

(8) Use the following code to emphasize the central portion of the graph, as was done, e.g., in Fig. 1.5.3. This leads to the banded map of Figs. 8.22.1*d* through 8.22.1*f* for various values of iMax.

```
Private Sub BitMap0(hMax As Integer, wMax As Integer, pixelArray As Variant)

' Gray-scale, no color

Dim H As Integer, i As Integer, iMax As Integer, w As Integer
Dim RedVal As Integer, GreenVal As Integer, BlueVal As Integer

iMax = 15
For H = hMax To 0 Step -1
  For w = 0 To wMax - 1
    If pixelArray(H, w) < Int(127 / iMax) Then
      RedVal = 0
      GreenVal = 0
      BlueVal = 0
    End If
    For i = 1 To iMax - 1
      If pixelArray(H, w) > i * Int(127 / iMax) And _
        pixelArray(H, w) <= (i + 1) * Int(127 / iMax) Then
        RedVal = i * Int(255 / iMax)
        GreenVal = i * Int(255 / iMax)
        BlueVal = i * Int(255 / iMax)
      End If
    Next i
    For i = iMax To 2 * iMax - 1
      If pixelArray(H, w) > i * Int(127 / iMax) And _
        pixelArray(H, w) <= (i + 1) * Int(127 / iMax) Then
        RedVal = (2 * iMax - i) * Int(255 / iMax)
        GreenVal = (2 * iMax - i) * Int(255 / iMax)
        BlueVal = (2 * iMax - i) * Int(255 / iMax)
      End If    Next I
    WriteAPixel RedVal Mod 256, GreenVal Mod 256, BlueVal Mod 256
  Next w

' Do not change the following, essential row padding
  w = wMax * 3
  Do While (w Mod 4) <> 0
    WriteAByte 0
    w = w + 1
  Loop
Next H

End Sub
```

(9) You can still use a "1" in the top left-hand corner of the highlighted array to limit the range of input values over which the bands apply.

(10) By carefully selecting your minimum and maximum limits as well as the value of iMax, you can control the range and values at the boundary lines. You can then identify these boundary lines with overlaying numbers on the banded map, by highlighting the plot area, typing the number in the formula window, and using the Enter key to deposit it in the middle of the plot area. Then highlight the deposited number and modify its appearance, and also change the size and position of the surrounding box, to yield a result such as shown in Fig. 8.22.1*f*. Try it!

(11) Finally, when you are done exploring such alternatives, interchange the labels BitMap0 and BitMap00 to return to the original Mapper.

The new Mapper is an elaboration of the above approaches, which you can consult to see what the code for such a finished macro might look like. Using color (or gray) bands rather than a gradual scale is helped by the optical illusion that enhances our perception of contrast between two adjacent areas of different uniform grayness or color.

The main point of this case study is to show how easily you can test a possible extension of existing, open-access code, such as in going from Fig. 8.22.1*a* to 8.22.1*b*, and how, through a series of small improvements, you can then get it to do what *you* want.

8.23 Tools for macro writing

8.23.1 Editing tools

Visual BASIC distinguishes between properties and methods. For every property there is a list of the specific methods you can invoke; likewise, methods only act on specific properties. The available options are not always obvious. Provided that you have activated the VBA help file, and in the VBEditor activated the Auto Quick Info option under the Editor tab of Tools ⇨ Options, you can get a drop-down listing of the options displayed on the VB Editor screen by typing a dot (period) behind a property or method, or an equal sign in an assignment, after waiting a short while. You can then choose from that list by double-clicking. This feature is especially useful when you need to check the order in which various arguments should be entered, and which ones should be left undefined but given explicit space, as in Mgs-Box("Message", ,"Label") when we do not want to modify the OK button. Annoyingly, recent versions of Excel no longer provide the VBA help files with the system disk, but require you to be hooked up to the internet. So much for Microsoft's real concern about the possible introduction of viruses and malicious macros through the internet.

The same list will appear when you select Edit ⇨ List Properties/ Methods or Ctrl⌣J.

In order to show the proper syntax for an instruction, use Edit ⇒ Quick Info or Ctrl⌣I. The proper arguments are displayed with Edit ⇨ Parameter Info or Ctrl⌣Shift⌣I.

A list of constants for a particular property is shown with Edit ⇨ List Constants or Ctrl⌣Shift⌣J.

In order to finish a common word, type Edit ⇨ Complete Word or Ctrl⌣space. If Excel knows more than one possible word ending, it will show a list from which you can choose.

The above options are available provided the corresponding settings have been enabled in the VBEditor. Here is a brief summary. You can change them in the VBEditor with Tools ⇨ Options. Under the Editor tab you find Auto Syntax Check, which when enabled provides a pop-up message box to flag syntax errors (which you may find overly intrusive); Require Variable Declaration, which automatically enters Option Explicit (highly recommended, but best temporarily turned off for novice VBA programmers); Auto List Members, which displays available members for each object; Auto Quick Info, which shows information regarding function arguments; Auto Data Tips, which reveals parameter values when the mouse pointer visits them; and Auto Indent, for automatically indenting using a selectable Tab Width.

8.23.2 *The Macro Recorder*

The Macro Recorder records keystroke sequences, so that repetitive operations can be automated. It records all keyboard and mouse actions in VBA notation, and can therefore be useful when you are writing a macro and have no idea how Excel codes a particular action. Macros can do many more things than you can do on the spreadsheet alone, but as long as what you need falls in the latter category, the Macro Recorder can show you a way to do it. While it may not be the optimal way, it will at least get you going, and you can always improve on it later.

In order to record, go to Tools ⇨ Macro ⇨ Record New Macro. This will produce a Record Macro dialog box, in which you can specify the name and a short description of the macro you are going to record, a shortcut key combination, and the file where to store it. All these are optional: the macro will be given a default name and stored in a module. Just click OK and start the Excel operations for which you want to know the VBA code. When you are done, press the Stop Recording button or select Tools ⇨ Macro ⇨ Stop Recording. Then select Tools ⇨ Macro ⇨ Macros, find the latest Macro*n* (they are numbered sequentially), and select Edit. You can now see how Excel codes these instructions.

Say that you don't know how to specify in VBA the color of text, even though you know how to do it in Excel, using the Font Color icon on your formula toolbar or drawing toolbar. The macro recorder lets Excel show you how to do it. On the spreadsheet, point to a cell, call the macro recorder (with Tools ⇨ Macro ⇨ Record New Macro), go to the Font Color icon, select your color, then stop the macro recorder. Now go to Tools ⇨ Macro ⇨ Macros, with a *single* click select the just-made macro, click on Edit, and voilà, you see how Excel does its own coding. You may find the instruction `Selection.Font.ColorIndex = 3`, which you can incorporate into your own macro. This instruction may be accompanied by other, peripheral information, such as the font used, its size, the absence of underlining, etc. Don't be discouraged by such informational overload, just disregard it: since the Macro Recorder did not know what specific information you were looking for, it often simply shows everything. Finally, check whether the solution suggested by the Macro Recorder indeed works in your code; it usually does, but every rule has its exceptions.

The above describes using the Macro Recorder to show you possible code. However, if you use the recorder for its more obvious purpose of facilitating repetitive operations, consider ahead of time whether the operation always occurs in the same location. If not, click on the Relative Reference button on the right-hand side of the Macro Recorder Stop Recording icon as soon as it appears, in order to enforce relative addressing rather than absolute, because the latter is the default.

8.23.3 *The Object Browser*

VBA is an object-oriented language, i.e., it is based on objects that each have their own properties, methods, and/or events. There are several ways to find out what options are associated with a given object. One is to type the name of that object in the VBEditor module, followed by a dot (period), and wait for the options to appear in a helpful drop-down menu, assuming that you have activated Show ToolTips in Tools ⇨ Options, General tab. A more systematic way is to consult the Object Browser, which lists these options, and even some hidden ones, often older ones that VBA still carries for the sake of backward compatibility.

You select the object browser from within the VBEditor with the function key F2, or with View ⇨ Object Browser. Its top window will show <All Libraries>; its subgroups (available when you click on <All Libraries>) include the Excel and VBA function libraries.

Below the top two rows of the Object Browser, is its Classes window, with a listing of classes, modules, etc. in all active libraries, as well as user-defined functions and subroutines. To restrict this long list, expand the <All Libraries> with its drop-down arrow and, e.g., select Excel. Right-click on Excel and select Group Members, which will organize the Members list (to the right of the Classes listing) into three separate categories: properties (with the icon of a hand pointing towards an envelope), then methods (a green sponge), then events.

Say that you want to make sure that a comment box is large enough to hold a certain text. How would you find the command to specify its size? You can click on a comment box on the spreadsheet, and then change its size, but if you do this while the Macro Recorder is on, and try to use its code, you are out of luck. So, instead, look up in the Object Browser under Excel, Classes: Comment, and you will find Shape as the most likely property. That will be your next keyword; look in Classes under Shape (either use the scrollbar, or click on a term in the Classes list, then type s to get you to Scenario, the first term starting with the letter s, then use the scrollbar to navigate to Shape), and observe that, in turn, it has the properties Height and Width. So here you have the commands to give your comment box the required size: Comment.Shape.Height and Comment. Shape.Width. Alternatively, instead of looking for the term Comment under Classes, you can type it into the empty window on the second line of the Object Browser, and then click the Search button (with the binoculars as its icon).

In this particular example, you might have found the answer faster by typing, in the VBEditor module, the code line Comment followed by a period, whereupon the drop-down menu would contain the option Shape, and typing that followed by a period would have given you the options Height and Width. In other words, the ToolTip menu can do the looking up for you!

When you look under WorksheetFunction you will find all Excel functions that you can incorporate in VBA code with the prefix `Application.WorksheetFunction.` or, for short, `Aplication.`, such as LinEst.

When you have checked atvbaen.xls in the References – VBAProject dialog box (in the VBEditor under Tools ⇨ References), you will find the instructions for, e.g., Random(NumberGenerator) and Regress(ion), and when you click on them, their input formats are shown, with brief descriptions of their functions. Likewise, when you have installed XN (see chapter 11) you will find the library XN.xla(m) displayed when you click on <All Libraries>, and if you select it, its Classes will include clsComplex and Xnumbers. Clicking on clsComplex will then show you the many Xnumber commands for working with complex numbers starting either with s (for standard, 15-decimal numberlength) or with x (for extended numberlength), while in the Xnumbers class you will find its many remaining extended numberlength instructions. Again, the ToolTip magic will also provide this information the moment you need it when writing code. But if you like to browse just to find out what is available, the Object Browser is a good place to go.

8.23.4 Error trapping

When you write code, you typically have a particular application in mind, and you will test the software to make sure that it indeed performs that task. But someone else using that code may not make the same assumptions, and therefore may, e.g., enter the wrong type of input information. Or the program may end up, for a particular combination of input data, trying to perform a non-allowed mathematical operation, such as taking the square root or the logarithm of a negative number. This would halt the program and display an error message. Then that user would have to go into the VBA code, try to make sense of the error message, and correct the problem. Error trapping tries to prevent such a scenario.

While some errors can be expected, there is no way to anticipate all eventualities, and it is therefore best to adopt the same attitude that, in Excel, lets you use a function such as =SQRT on a column that includes, e.g., a few cells containing negative numbers or text. In that case, rather than coming to a halt, Excel displays an appropriate (and often informative) error message in any cell that gives it trouble, and then goes on to the next cell. It does this with error trapping, i.e., by catching or intercepting errors before they can halt the program.

The simplest way to intercept errors in a VBA procedure is with `On Error Resume Next`, which simply ignores the offending line of code, and continues program execution with the next line. VBA recognizes specific errors, categorizes them with an error number, and can provide a corresponding text message. Although the error message is often rather cryptic, it can be helpful in finding out what went wrong, whereas the error number is more useful when you want to intercept or act on a specific error, such as division by zero. You can incorporate code to specify the error number, its text message, or both, as in the following fragment:

```
Function NatLog(a, b)
On Error Resume Next
NatLog = Log(a / b)
If Err.number <> 0 Then NatLog = "Err# " & _
  Err.number & ": " & Err.Description
End Function
```

Exercise 8.23.1:

(1) In a new spreadsheet, introduce the function NatLog into its VBA module, place labels for *a* and *b* in the spreadsheet cells A2 and A3. In cell B4 deposit the instruction =ln(B2/B3), and in cell B5 =NatLog(B2,B3). Reminder: the VBA instruction log computes the natural logarithm.

(2) Enter numbers in B2 and B3, and check your answers. When *a* and *b* have the same sign, and $b \neq 0$, both B4 and B5 should give equivalent results.

(3) When $b = 0$, cell B5 will display the error message 'Err# 11: Division by zero' because execution of the instructions on a given line progresses from right to left, so that the division is executed before taking the logarithm. B4 will show the equivalent warning #DIV/0!

(4) When *a* and *b* ($\neq 0$) have different signs, so that $a/b < 0$, you will obtain the much less specific 'Err# 5: Invalid procedure call or argument' in B5, and #NUM! in B4.

(5) And when you enter text in B2 and/or B3, such as the letter a in B2, you will get 'Err# 13: Type mismatch' in B5, and will find #VALUE! for the direct computation in B4.

(6) The absence of an error keeps Err.number at its default value 0; this is used in the If statement so that it does not interfere when no error is reported.

(7) Keep in mind that, in executing a macro, equivalent direct error messages such as displayed here in cell B4 will not be available.

You can do much more with error trapping than merely using it as a diagnostic tool. You can use `On Error GoTo ErrorHandler` (or any other line label), at the end of the procedure deposit the corresponding line label `ErrorHandler:`, and below it direct the program to a separate section of code and/or display a message specifying what to do. In that case, you may have to use `Exit Sub` or `Exit Function` to leave the procedure itself so that it not inadvertently reaches the ErrorHandler line label. A procedure can contain multiple error traps, each with its own error handler.

In general, prevention is better than cure, and one should use code to make sure, e.g., that a denominator is not zero before a division occurs. Likewise, check that a quantity is not negative before taking its square root, or that it is positive before computing its logarithm. Where appropriate, one can also test an argument with one or several of Excel's information functions, such as `IsBlank()`, `IsZero()`, `IsText()`, `IsNonText()`, `IsNumber()`, or `IsRef()`.

8.23.5 Error recovery

Even with the best of code, calling a macro will once in a while produce an error message. You can easily provoke such a situation with the macros in the MacroBundle, because they do not check, e.g., for textual input rather than numbers. In that case you might find a message box announcing an error, and giving you the option to End or Debug. (The Help option usually yields only generalities, and is seldom worthwhile.)

If you realize what went wrong, want to correct it, and then run the program again, select End, which cancels the macro call and gets you back to your starting point. If, on the other hand, you don't know what caused the error, click on Debug, which will show you the offending line, highlighted in the code window. At this point, do *not* make any corrections or reset the program. Instead, hover with the pointer over the various parameters until their values are revealed, one at a time, in a small Data Tip box, provided you have set the Tools ⇨ Auto Data Tip option.

Say that you center two adjacent columns, and in them enter the following y- and x-values: 5, 7, 6, 8 for y in the first column, and 8, 5, 2, and –1 for x in the second column. Highlight them, and call LS0. You will get the error message 'Run-time error 13: Type mismatch'. Select Debug; the highlighted line of VBA code will read XArray(i, j) = DataArray(i, j) inside a For-Next loop. Hover with the pointer over the i and see that it has the value 4; likewise, j has the value 2. Holding the pointer over the name DataArray will show DataArray(i, j) = "l". So the problem is in the fourth row (i = 4) of the second column (j = 2) of the input data, and it is a letter, as indicated by the quotation marks around the l. You must have typed a lower-case L instead of the number 1 (depending on the typeface used, and on whether or not the input data are centered, you might not notice any problem), and the VBEditor shows you the way out.

It is not always quite so simple. You may have dimensioned a parameter incorrectly, or an array may have outrun its assigned range, in which case the editor highlights the line where the procedure runs into trouble rather than, in this example, the offending dimension statement. Still, in all such cases, the ability to see the parameter values at the moment of program failure can be of great help to determine what went wrong. Only after you have understood the problem, and corrected it, relieve the error condition by pressing Alt‿R twice to reset the program.

A note of caution: when you deal with arrays, and check the array indices or any array element with these indices, keep in mind that Excel increments these indices by 1 before the For … Next loop terminates, and does not reset them. They may therefore show misleading values.

8.24 Code debugging

Writing functions and macros is not trivial, and the rules governing VBA are sufficiently impenetrable to keep it that way. Consequently you may spend at least as much time debugging your code as you spent writing it in the first place.

The VBEditor will often alert you that a line you just typed contains a *syntax* error. This is helpful because it localizes the problem. Using Option Explicit also operates at the single-line level, and can identify many typos, as long as (1) you dimension variable names so that they contain at least one capital, (2) you type your code only in lower-case (except for text within quotation marks, which is of no consequence to the VBEditor), and (3) you check whether the necessary caps appear magically as you press Enter at the end of each line.

Then there are the *runtime* errors, often caused by parameter values that make the program divide by zero, take the logarithm or the square root of a negative number, etc., errors of the type we encountered in section 8.23.3. These depend on the input parameters, and sometimes can only be caught by extensive testing over a wide range of input parameters.

Finally, there are the fool's errors, triggered by entering, say, text where numbers or ranges are expected, etc. These are perhaps the hardest errors to anticipate, because it is difficult to imagine what you (or some other user of your procedure) might try to put into an input box at some unguarded moment. Perhaps the best way to avoid this type of errant data entry is to use UserForms, which allow tight control over the allowed type(s) of input data. UserForms are described in many introductory books on the uses of VBA, such as John Walkenbach's *Excel 20xx Power Programming with VBA*, but are not discussed in this book in order to keep matters as simple as possible.

Instead, more emphasis has been given to the ideas behind the various methods, and to applying them appropriately, than to the prevention of fool's errors and the generation of 'industrial-strength' macros. It is one of the ironies of the spreadsheet that it has become the leading numerical analysis software in the world because of its flexibility, the very same property that makes it highly vulnerable to unintentional errors and, worse, outright fraud. We will (self-servingly) assume here that fraud is not quite so prevalent in scientific applications.

8.24.1 Simple debugging tools

Back to the main topic, finding what causes code to misbehave or fail. Excel contains many aids to debug VBA code. We already encountered the simplest of these whenever a test run fails, and displays a box with an (often helpful, but sometimes misleading) error message, read (and note down) that message, then click <u>D</u>ebug, and (before fixing anything) place the mouse pointer on a variable, parameter, or function at or close to where the VB Editor highlights the code. In recent versions of Excel this will create a yellow Data Tip message listing its value or property at the moment the procedure stopped. This will often allow you to identify what went wrong: perhaps an index fell outside its allotted range, a variable value was not specified properly, etc. In that case, make the correction, reset the procedure with Alt‿RR, and try again.

A second, simple method is to insert temporary Debug.Print or MsgBox instructions at crucial points in the code to see which hurdles are taken, and at the same time report crucial intermediate results. This can be helpful in programs that allow for various routes, because message boxes in paths not taken will not show. However, do not place message boxes *inside* loops, because this will generate as many boxes as there are repeats in the loop, and every one of them will have to be acknowledged manually with an OK. This does not apply to writing Debug.Print messages in the Immediate Window.

It is sometimes useful to test the beginning of a program by inserting a `Stop` instruction some distance down the code, and by then verifying that the program runs correctly till there. You can then move that stop instruction to a place further down the code, and repeat the process, until you find the region where it misbehaves. In this case there is, again, a better way of doing this, as described in section 8.24.3.

8.24.2 The Immediate Window

The Immediate Window was already used extensively, e.g., in section 8.14, and in the MacroMorsels. It is invoked *from within the VBEditor* with Ctrl‿G or with <u>D</u>ebug ⇨ Immediate Window, and is closed with the closing icon × at its top-right corner. After opening it, you can move it around if you prefer it in another screen location. Its simplest function is to display values specified with the line Debug.Print followed by an optional label (between quotation marks) and the item to be shown, as in

```
Debug.Print A
Debug.Print A, B          ' yields tab-delimited output
Debug.Print "A = " & A & ",   B = " & B ' same with labels
```

We already encountered examples of such output in earlier sections of this chapter, as well as in many MacroMorsels. You can print entire arrays, complete with column headings, and insert empty lines with the line `Debug.Print ""`. The major advantages of using the Immediate Window over message boxes is that they need not be acknowledged individually (by clicking OK every time), and that the results they display remain visible. But it is still temporary, limited storage, because it can hold only about 200 lines, and its contents are not retained when the file is saved.

The Immediate Window can also be used proactively, when you develop a code fragment and want to test it. Whenever you want to use a function but are not sure of its proper format or its behavior, write a separate, three-line macro, such as

```
Sub Test()
     ' on this line place the instruction to be tested
End Sub
```

You can then test it while remaining inside the VBEditor, simply by placing the pointer somewhere within that testing subroutine and clicking the function key F5. Include `Debug.Print` statements if you want to make it self-documenting.

If you use Option Explicit, do include the dimension statement(s), and be aware that errors frequently occur because the dimension specified is incompatible with the instruction used.

8.24.3 *The Debugging toolbar*

From within the VB Editor, call the Debugging toolbar with <u>V</u>iew ⇨ <u>T</u>oolbars, then check-mark Debug. This toolbar has icons for Design Mode, Run Sub/UserForm, Break, Reset, Toggle Breakpoint, Step Into, Step Over, Step Out, Locals Window, Immediate Window, and Watch Window. Here we will concentrate on Break and the three Step instructions.

Breakpoints are the equivalent of Stop instructions in the VBA code, but they are less intrusive. You place them *outside* of the code, in the light-gray margin area just to its left, by holding the pointer in that area at the level of the line just before which you want execution to stop, and by clicking once. A brown dot and brown highlighting of the corresponding line of code shows where you placed a breakpoint, but these will not be saved, so you need not remove them when you are done testing. At any rate, removing them is easy enough: just click on the brown dot again. Clicking on the Break/Continue toggle of the Debugging toolbar similarly sets and removes the break, and combines it with F5, so that it also runs the routine each time.

Write the following sample macro in the VBEditor:

```
Sub TestImmediateWindow()
Dim A As Double
Dim B As Double
A = Selection.Value
Debug.Print A
For i = 1 To 5
  B = Log(A - i)
  Debug.Print B
Next i
End Sub
```

Place the number 4 somewhere on the spreadsheet, and leave it highlighted. Return to the VBEditor, open the Immediate Window, then place your pointer inside the macro, and press F5. You will see an error message: "Invalid procedure call or argument". Press <u>D</u>ebug, and see the highlighted, offending line: `B = Log(A - i)`. Letting the pointer hover over the value of A yields $A = 4$; likewise, i reads 4, so that $A - i = 0$. Taking the (natural) logarithm of 0 is clearly the problem. The three times the loop went through were indeed for $A - i = 4 - 1 = 3$, $4 - 2 = 2$, and $4 - 3 = 1$.

If you are still uncertain, or simply curious, press Alt‿RR to reset (so that the highlighting disappears) while remaining in the VBEditor, and repeatedly tap F8, or the Step Into icon on the Debugging toolbar. Notice that you skip the dimension statements (empty and comment lines are also passed over), that the number 4 is written in the Immediate Window when you execute the line `A = Selection.Value`, and that you then step through the For...Next loop several times, computing $\ln(3) \approx 1.0986$, $\ln(2) \approx 0.6931$, $\ln(1) = 0$, before you run into trouble trying to compute $\ln(-1)$, where -1 is indeed an invalid argument.

In a long program you can insert multiple breakpoints, then with F5 step from start to the first break, then on to the second, etc., all simply with repeated taps on the function key F5, to localize where the problem occurs. Again, upon saving the routine, none of these breaks will be retained. You will get maximum benefit from such tests when you place `Debug.Print` statements in strategic places, and observe

392

the corresponding behavior in the Immediate Window. If the routine affects the spreadsheet, use small windows so that you can simultaneously observe what happens on the sheet. Or, if you know where you want to go, place the pointer in that line of code, and use Ctrl⌣F8 to execute until there.

In order to examine a small section of a long stretch of code line by line, again use strategically placed Debug.Print statements, put a single breakpoint where you want to start examining your code, and click F5 to execute the routine till that breakpoint. From then on use F8 (or the Step Into icon) and observe in the Immediate Window what happens as you advance through the code, one line at a time. A yellow line pointer and yellow code highlighting indicates the next line to be executed.

When your code contains subroutine calls, Step Into will go there. If you want to avoid that (e.g., because that subroutine has already been tested) use Shift⌣F8 or Step Over, which behaves just as Step Into except that it executes any subroutine call it encounters and then goes back to single-step mode. When you are done stepping, use Ctrl⌣Shift⌣F8 or Step Out to complete the routine. Table 8.24.1 summarizes these commands, plus some others you may find useful.

General commands:

Alt⌣F11	toggle between the spreadsheet and the VBEditor
Ctrl⌣G	display the Immediate Window
F2	display the Object Browser

Commands for controlling break points:

F5	execute the routine till the next break point
F9	toggle to set or remove a break point
Ctrl⌣F9	set next break point at pointer location
Ctrl⌣Shift⌣F9	clear all break points
Ctrl⌣F8	execute until the line with the pointer

Commands for stepping through codes:

F8	step into: execute next line
Shift⌣F8	step over: execute the next line and its calls
Ctrl⌣Shift⌣F8	step out: execute till end

Table 8.24.1: A few useful debugging commands to be used inside the VBEditor.

8.24.4 Other windows

Here we briefly mention several other useful debugging windows. You can follow a specific variable or parameter, from anywhere within the VBEditor, by right-clicking and selecting Add Watch. In the resulting Add Watch dialog box specify the expression you want to watch, say B in the example of section 8.24.3, and click OK. This will open the Watch Window. Now you can follow just B as you step through the routine; the Watch Window does away with the need to insert any Debug.Print statements, as long as you have an idea which parameter may cause the problem. You can follow multiple variables by adding as many watches as you like; each will get its own line in the Watch Window, and will update as you step through the program.

There is also a Quick Watch Window, obtained by highlighting a variable, expression, etc., and pressing Shift⌣F9. It will display essentially the same information as obtained by a ToolTip by hovering over it with the mouse pointer, but may sometimes yield information where the ToolTip won't.

Then there is the Locals Window, available with View ⇨ Locals Window, which is similar to the Watch Window but automatically follows all declared names and variables in your procedure. However, complex procedures will give you an overload of information, in too large a window to keep track of anything in particular. Expanding the first item listed in the Locals Window (by clicking on the boxed plus sign in front of it) will display all variables and constants used in that procedure.

A special button in the Locals Window (with the icon ... , directly under the close button ×) gets you to the Call Stack (also directly accessible with Ctrl⌣L) which, provided you are in break mode, shows the prior path of the procedure. You can use this Call Stack to walk your procedure backwards.

For a lucid description of the many code debugging methods available in Excel and VBA, see chapter 16 of *Professional Excel Development* by S. Bullen, R. Bovey & J. Green, Addison-Wesley (2005).

*****

In this section you encountered a number of debugging tools: printing out intermediate results with Debug.Print or MsgBox statements, inserting stops and breakpoints, stepping though ther code line-by-line, and using Watches or Locals. With all these tools at your disposal, it is really hard *not* to find the problem that made you need to use debugging tools in the first place.

8.24.5 Some practical examples

Some complex skills, such as swimming, dancing, bicycling, skiing, and driving a car, are learned faster and better by doing rather than by just reading and/or hearing about them. The same applies to debugging computer code. We will therefore illustrate debugging by following a few short pieces of code in order to understand what they do. When you write such code, and it does not behave as intended, this is how you find out what actually happens, from which you can usually deduce what needs to be fixed.

Since many problems in writing Excel macros occur at the interface between the spreadsheet and the VBA code, our examples will emphasize that aspect, by following what the code does, and how it is linked to the spreadsheet. Because our non-compiled VBA code is always executed one line at a time, we will likewise follow the implementation of macros line by line.

In section 8.2 we used a seemingly inoccuous macro, Cube1(), and ran into trouble. Here we will illustrate how you can step through the code to find out exactly what went wrong.

Exercise 8.24.1:

(1) On a new spreadsheet, reproduce the sequence 1 (1) 10 in cells A12:A21, either by entering their individual values or by entering 1 in A12, 2 in A13, highlighting both, and pulling the handle down to A21. Both methods deposit numbers, no equations.

(2) Copy A12:A21 to B12, D12, and G12.

(3) Place the number 1 in cells E12 and H12, the instruction =D13 in E13, and the instruction =H12+1 in H13. Copy these instructions down to row 21 by clicking on their handles. You have now reproduced the three samples used in section 8.2.

(4) Highlight A12:B21, then use Tools ⇨ Macro ⇨ Macros, highlight Cube1, and click on Edit.

(5) In the VBEditor module of Cube1() place a breakpoint in front of the line For Each Cell in Selection. Cells. Make sure that your monitor screen displays both your spreadsheet and the macro code, without overlap, so that you can follow both side-by-side.

(6) With the cursor pointing somewhere inside the code of Cube1(), call the macro, e.g., with the function key F5. Then step through the code with the function key F8. After each keystroke, observe what happens on the spreadsheet.

(7) After a few keystrokes you will see the value in A13 change from 2 to 8, then that in B13. Subsequently, A14 will switch value to 27, then B14, etc., until all values in A12:B21 have been cubed. This is what Cube1() is supposed to do.

(8) Highlight D12:E21, and again step through Cube1() with F5 followed by multiple keystrokes F8. After tapping F8 six times, the number $8 = 2^3$ will appear in *both* A13 and B13, and two keystrokes later the value in E13 will be cubed to 512 or 2^9. Two more keystrokes of F8 will yield $3^3 = 27$ in both D14 and E14, and two more keystrokes will change the value in E14 to $19683 = 3^9$. Continue this; when the macro is done, D12:D21 will contain the cubes of its original numbers, but E12:E21 the ninth powers. This was clearly caused by the instruction =D13 in E13, etc., which copies the cube of the original number first, and then again cubes that value.

(9) Now repeat this trouble-shooting exercise with G12:H21. Highlight it, go to its VBA code, place your pointer within that code, start macro execution with F5, and past the breakpoint step through it with F8, while you observe what happens on the spreadsheet.

(10) After six keystrokes on F8, G13 will change from 2 to 8. Two keystrokes later, H13 will also show 8. So far, so good. But look at H14: it will now hold 8 + 1 = 9, H15 will display 9 + 1 = 10, etc., all because of the instructions placed in H13:H21.

(11) Two keystrokes later, G14 reads $3^3 = 27$, as intended. But after two more keystrokes you will have H14 = $(8+1)^3$ = 429 and H15:H21 are again modified. Then G15 is cubed from 4 to $4^3 = 64$, and H15 from $(8+1)^3+1$ to its cube, etc.

(12) The game is up at H19, when it reads 8.4948E+231, because cubing it would yield 6.13E+695, which causes the spreadsheet to overflow, since its double-precision numbers cannot exceed 2E+308.

The next two examples will use the sample macro NumericalDifferentiation which uses invasive sampling to calculate the derivative of a function $F(a)$ for a given value of a. As explained in section 8.15.1, this macro first reads a and $F(a)$, then modifies the value of a to $a+\Delta a$, and reads the corresponding value of $F(a+\Delta a)$. It then changes $a+\Delta a$ into $a-\Delta a$, and reads the corresponding value of $F(a-\Delta a)$. Finally the macro computes the derivative as $[F(a+\Delta a) - F(a-\Delta a)] / (2\Delta a)$, restores the original value of a, and displays the value of the derivative. This method is used in a somewhat more elaborate way in the custom macro Deriv of the MacroBundle.

Exercise 8.24.2:

(1) Copy the macro NumericalDifferentiation from the SampleMacros; this will store it in the Clipboard.

(2) Start a new spreadsheet, place a numerical value 3 (or any other value you want to use) for the variable a in, say, cell A5, and the function =SQRT(A5) using it (or, again, another function of your choice) in, e.g., B5. In order to see rather small changes, display both with 7 or more decimal places. Use the middle icon in the top right-hand corner of the spreadsheet to reduce its size to less than half the width of the monitor screen, and move it to the left side of that screen.

(3) Open the VBEditor module with Alt‿F11, and paste the macro from the Clipboard in the module.

(4) Reduce the size of the module and move it to the right of the spreadsheet, without overlapping with it. You can then switch from one to the other by moving and clicking the pointer, while simultaneously seeing the spreadsheet and the VBA code. This is a good way to debug code that switches between these two.

(5) In the module, go to the line Aplus = ... , and enter a breakpoint by clicking once inside the light-gray vertical strip to its left. This will create a large brown dot in this strip, and will highlight the line in the same brown color.

(6) Place the pointer anywhere inside the macro code, and use the function key F5 to call the macro.

(7) In the first input box place or drag the address B5 of the function, and OK it. In the second input box put the location of the variable a, in our example A5. Once this is entered, the macro code will stop at the breakpoint, which will now be highlighted in yellow.

(8) Hovering with the pointer over the symbol A in the highlighted line will verify that the code has indeed read a from the spreadsheet. Likewise you can hover over the opening bracket of (1+1/1048576) and see its value displayed as 1.00000095367432. But because code execution stopped at the breakpoint, i.e., before the corresponding line is executed, Aplus is still shown as 0.

(9) From here on, proceed one line at a time by pressing the function key F8 rather than F5. After the first use of F8 the highlight moves down one line, but nothing else seems to have changed. However, move your pointer over Aplus, and you will find that it has now assumed the new value specified in the instruction at the breakpoint, 3.0000029, even though the spreadsheet still shows the earlier value, 3.

(10) The next F8 brings the new value of a to the spreadsheet cell A5. Cell B5 immediately adjusts to the new value of a, but this is not yet read by the VBA code, because moving your pointer over Fplus shows it with a value of zero.

(11) Press F8, and the spreadsheet highlight will move from cell A5 to cell B5. Press F8 once more, and Fplus will have read its new value.

(12) The next step executes the calculation of Aminus, to 2.9999972, then it takes three more steps to transfer this to cell A5 on the spreadsheet, and two more to read thie resulting Fminus into the VBA code.

(13) The next steps move the spreadsheet highlight back to A5, and then re-insert the original value, 3, with cell B5 following suit. But Fderiv is still 0, even though you can already see all its ingredients with the ToolTip: Fplus = 1.73205163, Fminus = 1.73204998, A = 3, and even (by pointing towards the leading brackets) (Fplus-Fminus) = 1.651812E-6 and (A/524288) = 5.722046E-6.

(14) Another F8, and Fderiv will show 0.288675, but the message box bearing that news will only come to the spreadsheet when you press F8 again.

(15) Press OK, then press F8 one more time to end the subroutine and thereby cancel the debugging session.

You just saw how, by stepping through a crucial part of the code, you can verify every step, look at all its intermediate values, see all its details. If there is a problem, you should be able to pinpoint it now. With this tool, the macro cannot keep its secrets from you.

Exercise 8.24.3:

(1) Now we will make it even easier, by bringing in the Watch and Locals Windows.

(2) In the VBEditor module, click on <u>V</u>iew ⇨ Watc<u>h</u> Window. Grab the Watch Window by its blue TitleBar, move it over an unused part of the spreadsheet, and make it as wide as possible.

(3) Move your pointer inside the Watch Window, right-click, click on <u>A</u>dd Watch, and in the resulting Add Watch dialog box type the Expression: Aplus, followed by OK. The Context will be the NumericalDifferentiation Procedure, the Watch Type a Watch Expression.

(4) Do the same for Aminus, Fplus, Fminus, and Fderiv. They will each be shown with a line, in alphabetical order.

(5) Now click <u>V</u>iew ⇨ Loca<u>ls</u> Window, and place it below the Watch Window, without touching it. In the Locals Window the VBEditor will enter all items, so you can just sit back and watch it.

(6) Place your pointer in the NumericalDifferentiation code, and press F5. Answer the input boxes as before, specifying where the function and its variable are located. As in exercise 8.24.1 you will now progress to the breakpoint at `Aplus = ...` . The Locals Window will show the values of A and F; all other values will be either 0 or Empty.

(7) Step through the remaining code with F8, and you will see the various values appear, first Aplus, then Fplus, Aminus, Fminus, and Fderiv, each at the line of code that defines it.

(8) Press OK when you see the message box.

(9) Pressing F8 once more will end the show, and will empty the Watch and Locals Windows in anticipation of the next show.

The Locals Window holds much more information than just the values of the variables, especially on the module and on the ranges involved, rgA and rgF. Such additional information is accessible by clicking on the square box with a plus sign in front of these items; in our example they are rather immaterial. At any rate, you get the idea: the VB-Editor is well-stocked with tools to help you to follow the flow of the code, and to display what happens when. The rest is up to you.

8.24.6 Calling your macro

Finally a practical hint. While writing and debugging a new macro, you will need to exercise that macro often to check the proper functioning of what you have written so far. The simplest method is to run the routine from the VBEditor with the function key F5, provided the pointer is located somewhere within its code (so that the VBEditor 'knows' which routine you want to be exercised). If you want to see the spreadsheet and the VBEditor module simultaneously, so that you can see how they interact, reduce both in size, place them side by side, without overlap, so that you can go from one to the other while both stay in view.

Alternatively, if you just want to see the response on the spreadsheet, it may be helpful to assign a short-cut keycode to your macro, make a specific button to activate a macro from the spreadsheet, or include the budding macro in the MacroBundle toolbar. Here is how you can do any of these.

To assign a *shortcut key-code* to a macro, use Alt‿F8 or <u>T</u>ools ⇨ <u>M</u>acro ⇨ <u>M</u>acros and, in the Macro dialog box, single-click on the macro name. Click on <u>O</u>ptions, and assign a lower-case letter or capital as Shortcut <u>k</u>ey. Exit with OK and <u>R</u>un. Thereafter, the macro is callable with Ctrl‿n or Ctrl‿N where n or N is the shortcut key, which must be one letter. (This is one of the few cases where Excel *is* case-sensitive.) Make sure not to redefine common keystroke combinations you may want to keep, such as Ctrl‿c. (But you *can* assign Ctrl‿Shift‿c, i.e., Ctrl‿C, to another macro.) Use the same procedure to reassign a shortcut key. By erasing the shortcut key, Excel will revert to its default assignment if there is one, but your macro will still be callable from the Macro dialog box with <u>T</u>ools ⇨ <u>M</u>acro ⇨ <u>M</u>acros or its shortcut, Ctrl‿F8.

For a *spreadsheet button* to call your macro, on the spreadsheet click on <u>V</u>iew ⇨ <u>T</u>oolbars ⇨ Forms, which will display a Forms mini-toolbar with a set of tool icons. Click on the button icon, which has the shape of a raised rectangle; when you then move the pointer away, the button icon shows that it is activated. Move the pointer (which now shows as a thin plus sign) to where you want the button, depress the left-hand mouse key, and draw a rectangle in the shape of the desired button. (If you want it to fit the spreadsheet grid, outline the button area while depressing the Alt key, as you would do when outlining a chart area.) Release the mouse key, and the Assign Macro dialog box will appear. Click on the macro name, and from then on the button will call it. If you have not yet saved the macro, you can do the assignment later, by right-clicking on the button (to get its properties) and selecting Assi<u>g</u>n Macro. The same properties will allow you to change its label (with Edit Te<u>x</u>t), its appearance (with Format C<u>o</u>ntrol), etc. Note: in earlier incarnations of Excel the button icon was part of the Drawing toolbar.

You can also include your macro in a toolbar, such as that for the MacroBundle. In the latter case, edit the InsertMBToolbar macro, pick a toolbar item that has only one topic, such as Propagation, copy it to the end of the macro, and modify its text to fit your new macro. If, e.g., your new macro is called Hullabalou, and your MBToolbar contains 17 numbered buttons (excluding sub-categories such as 160, 161, etc.), then the added paragraph in InsertMBToolbar might read something like

```
' Create Button18 for Hullabalou

Set Button18 = CommandBars("MacroBundle").Controls _
  .Add(Type:=msoControlButton)
With Button18
  .Caption = "Hullabalou"
  .Style = msoButtonCaption
  .OnAction = "Hullabalou"
End With
```

with

```
Dim Button18 As CommandBarButton
```

added to the very first paragraph of InsertMBToolbar.

8.25 Summary

This chapter has focused on the actual writing of macros. It is one of the best-kept secrets of Excel that you are not restricted to the functionalities provided by Microsoft, but can make Excel do your own bidding. Most owners of Excel do not realize that they have a tiger in their tank, a powerful programming language that can readily be learned simply by following, borrowing, modifying, and trying out examples such as those provided here, in the MacroMorsels and MacroBundle, and by having a few good books on VBA programming handy to consult in case you run into trouble.

The functions, macros, and subroutines used in the present book were mostly written by the author, and therefore have a particular style and format. They are somewhat old-fashioned, in that they are modularized only where that has a clear advantage, e.g., when two or more macros can exploit the same subroutine. Still, in many cases they are rather repetitive. You may therefore want to write your own macros in a more modern, modular fashion, which leads to more compact but harder-to-follow code. At any rate, don't worry, and use them as you might the Macro Recorder: they will get you going, and after you have written several macros yourself, you will find your own style and format, which is how it should be.

With today's computer speed and abundant working memory, writing numerically efficient code is no longer as important as it was, e.g., when I bought my first laboratory computer in 1974, a PDP-11 that occupied the space of a clothes cabinet, and boasted all of 32 KB of memory (of which I could only use 28 KB, because the top 4 KB was reserved for accessories such as the paper tape punch and reader). Then, efficiently written code could save substantial amounts of execution time and overlay effort. Now, personal computers are likely to have gigabytes rather than kilobytes of memory, and the time needed for elementary computer steps is measured in nanoseconds rather than microseconds. Consequently, many computer tasks described in this book can be performed within the blink of an eye, and the most critical aspect of macros is that they work correctly, i.e., give reliable answers. With Excel and VBA, that is eminently feasible even when, as scientists or engineers, our main focus lies elsewhere. Therefore we can usually leave it to the computer professionals to fret over code efficiency and, yes, elegance.

This is not to suggest that the macros in the MacroBundle are only useful as a set of examples, good for cutting and pasting as you assemble your own functions and macros. They can indeed serve that purpose, and you are welcome to use them that way, but they also provide a set of convenient tools that make some common scientific data analysis methods more readily accessible. In terms of general availability, ease of learning, and ease of use, spreadsheets are without peer, and the computational aids you can now make yourself, together with the many extra functions and macros described in this book, will make your spreadsheet into an even more powerful tool.

And as you continue to read this book, you will find that Excel will get even better: the added matrix facilities of Matrix.xla, and the extended precision of XN.xla(m), can make the spreadsheet into a true computational powerhouse, while retaining all the conveniences of the spreadsheet.

One aspect we have not included here is the use of *compiled* code, because this book addresses an audience of scientists and engineers rather than of computer specialists. Compiled code would get us too far afield, and also far beyond the competence of your author. However, it can execute much faster than interpreted code; moreover, there are many free sources of well-vetted open-access FORTRAN and C/C++ codes available, most of them generated under U.S. Government auspices, that can be converted into Excel-usable DLL's and XLL's. Those readers interested in using these vast stores of sophisticated programs and incorporating them into Excel should consult specialized books such as R. Bovey, D. Wallentin, S. Bullen, & J. Green, *Professional Excel Development* (2nd ed., Addison-Wesley 2009).

8.26 For further reading

There are many books that can help you find your way in VBA for Excel. An excellent, highly readable and quite comprehensive general guide is John Walkenbach, *Microsoft Excel 20xx Power Programming with VBA*, IDG Books or Wiley, where 20xx denotes its approximate publication year, with (so far) xx = 00, 02, 03, 07, and 10. Another good source of ideas and help is *Mastering VBA6* by Guy Hart-Davis, Sybex (1999). For earlier versions of Excel you may need an older book, such as John Webb, *Using Excel Visual Basic*, Que, 2nd ed. (1996). For Excel 2007 and 2010, Bill Jelen's *Using Microsoft Office Excel 2007* and its 2010 edition with Tracy Syrstad (Que) and John Walkenbach's *Microsoft Office Excel 2007* and *Excel 2010* (Wiley) are both good general books, and more are likely to appear soon.

For the scientific part of macro writing an excellent source is *Numerical Recipes, The Art of Scientific Computing* by W. H. Press, B. P. Flannery, S. A. Teukolsky & W. T. Vetterling, Cambridge Univ. Press, which comes in several flavors: Fortran, Pascal, C and C++, as well as an update for parallel computing with Fortran 90. The original version, for Fortran 77, now in its second edition (1992), comes closest to Basic as used in VBA, and should be read for its very clear explanations. It is also freely available on the web, at http://apps.nrbook.com/fortran/index.html. A complete set of the software routines accompanying the first (1986) edition was machine-translated into Basic, and is directly usable in Excel. It can be found on the 3.5" diskette that accompanies J. C. Sprott, *Numerical recipes, Routines and Examples in Basic*, Cambridge Univ. Press 1991, if you still have access to a computer that can read such diskettes.

For algorithms as well as numerical tables of mathematical functions, use the *Handbook of Mathematical Functions* edited by M. Abramowitz and I. Stegun, and/or *An Atlas of Fuctions* by K. Oldham, J. Myland and J. Spanier, The second edition of the latter book has a very useful CD, Equator, with software that can generate numerical values of all the functions listed. (The Equator CD is also available separately.) The recently updated version of the *NIST Handbook of Mathematical Functions*, edited by F. W. J. Olver et al., is more up-to-date than Abramowitz & Stegun, but is also much less accessible to non-mathematicians. It has many recent references, but lacks many of the explicit formulas, and all of the numerical tables, that made A&S so useful. It can only be hoped that updated numerical tables will eventually appear in the web-based NIST Digital Library of Mathematical Functions.

Chapter *9*

Some mathematical operations

This chapter surveys some common mathematical operations often encountered in scientific data analysis, and their numerical implementations on the spreadsheet. The discussion will be rather general, but the exercises illustrating them will, of course, be Excel-specific. Given the limited space for theory in this book of practical examples, only a few options are presented, and even for those few, many details (and certainly all theorems, proofs, lemmas and corollaries) are left out. The main topics discussed in this chapter are differentiation, integration, and interpolation, which each merit entire tomes dedicated to those subjects. Here we only provide a small selection from this material, especially as it pertains to problems addressed in the preceding chapters of this book.

In considering these methods, and especially in choosing between their various options, we will need a measure of the errors involved, and this will be our first order of business, in section 9.1. Then follow sections on differentiation, integration, interpolation, and complex numbers. Differentiation and interpolation will lead to the next chapter, which deals with matrix operations. Finally, in chapter 11, we will consider methods to make Excel's mathematical operations more accurate.

9.1 A measure of error, pE

So far we have dealt mostly with experimental uncertainty and the resulting *imprecision*. However, in this and the following chapters we will often encounter well-defined mathematical functions $f(x)$, which are not subject to the inherent vagaries of experimental variability (i.e., they are *precise*) but which, for a variety of reasons, can still be *inaccurate*.

Before delving into a detailed discussion of likely sources of numerical inaccuracy, which we will postpone until chapter 11, we must first define a useful criterion for the reliability of computed results or, if you will, a measure of their 'number of significant figures'. Several such criteria have been proposed, all relying on reference functions f_{ref} that are supposed to be above reproach, so that we can find the absolute error, $E_{abs} = f - f_{ref}$, the relative error, $E_{rel} = (f - f_{ref})/f_{ref}$ or, more usefully, the absolute values of these, $|E_{abs}| = |f - f_{ref}|$ and $|E_{rel}| = |(f - f_{ref})/f_{ref}|$ respectively.

Usually, the relative error is the more useful quantity, because Excel displays and stores its results as up to 15 decimals, regardless of the number of leading or trailing zeros. Unfortunately, the relative error $|E_{rel}|$ cannot be computed when $f_{ref} = 0$. Here we will therefore use a combined criterion, based on either $|E_{rel}|$ or $|E_{abs}|$, viz.,

$$pE = -\log |f| \qquad \text{if } f \neq 0, \ f_{ref} = 0$$

$$pE = -\log \left| \frac{f - f_{ref}}{f_{ref}} \right| \qquad \text{if } f \neq f_{ref}, \ f_{ref} \neq 0 \qquad (9.1.1)$$

$$pE = pE_{max} \qquad \text{if } f = f_{ref}$$

where p denotes the negative ten-based logarithm, as in pH. This definition specifies the magnitude (i.e., the absolute value) of the error in a way that approximates the number of unaffected, significant decimals. Furthermore we will use

$$pE_{min} = 0 \qquad\qquad pE_{max} = 14 \qquad\qquad (9.1.2)$$

where a rather conservative definition for pE_{max} is used because reference data are often rounded from results with higher numerical accuracy, and the rules used for such rounding are not always evident, see section 9.6.4. It can make a difference of ±1 in the least significant digit whether one consistently rounds up (i.e., from 3.5 to 4 and from –3.5 to –3) or down, rounds away from zero (i.e., from 3.5 to 4 and from –3.5 to –4) or towards it, or uses some other rounding scheme, such as bankers' rounding (to the nearest even digit, i.e., round 2.5 down to 2, but round 3.5 up to 4) to avoid systematic bias in the above methods. When the last digit is uncertain to ±1, a 15-digit number starting with 1.001 will have a corresponding relative uncertainty of about 10^{-14}, whereas a 15-digit number starting with 0.999 with the same uncertainty of ±1 in its last digit will have a resulting relative uncertainty of 10^{-15}. Given that a common rounding error of ±1 in the least significant digit can lead to a pE-value between 14 and 15, we will consider pE = 14 to be as good as can be expected, and usually truncate the pE scale accordingly in displaying pE-values. Excel will still display a 15th digit, which may be considered a guard digit. The only time we will use the full pE_{max} = 15 is when calibrating algorithms with NIST StRD tests or with equivalent results obtained with extended-precision XN. (The NIST data were obviously obtained with MPFun, the model for XN.)

A pE-value of 14 indicates that the first 13 decimals displayed will be reliable, and the 14th will be correct to within ±1; a pE of 6.4 that the first six decimals can be trusted; and a pE of 0 that none of them can be. In Excel, with its present limit of 15 decimals, little useful information is gained by extending the pE scale below 0 or beyond 14. This range, incidentally, is like that of the pH, which chemists have used since 1909.

We note that pE depends on the error of the function f for a particular set of input parameters. Therefore, the pE of a function of n parameters will itself be a function of those n parameters. Especially for functions of a single parameter, pE is often best displayed graphically, as illustrated in sections 9.2, 11.6 and 11.7. When a single, fixed number characterizing the accuracy of a function or macro over its entire range is required, the most conservative measure would be to list its lowest value, pE_{min}. For many practical applications, however, such a number might scare users away from perfectly acceptable behavior in a more limited range of input parameters. A graphical display of pE as a function of x will then be more informative than a single number, as it allows users to draw their own conclusions.

The concept of pE used here is closely related to that of *LRE* (Logarithm of the Relative Error) introduced by B. D. McCullough in *Am. Statist.* 52 (1998) 358. The shorter expression pE explicitly denotes the *negative* ten-based logarithm of (the magnitude of) the *relative or absolute* error.

Other criteria are sometimes useful, such as the performance measure $P(x)$ used by Cook, Cox, Dainton & Harris in their *NPL Report CISE*27/ 99, downloadable from http://www.npl.co.uk/ssfm/ download/ documents/cise27_99.pdf, which highlights how many more significant decimals are lost by a particular function than would be lost by an optimally stable algorithm performing the same task. Such a criterion can be very helpful to designers of algorithms, but has little relevance for most end users, who will often not know (or may not even have access to) information on such an optimal algorithm. The latter is, anyway, a moving target.

The definition (9.1.1) depends on the availability of a reliable set of reference algorithms. Here we will use cases with known derivatives, and in chapter 11 we will use as reference those otherwise well-tested algorithms that, through the use of extended numberlengths, can move their unavoidable truncation errors to digits sufficiently far down to become insignificant. The higher accuracy functions described in sections 11.6 and 11.7 were indeed checked by comparison with their extended numberlength versions, as well as with standard tables. The latter are limited to specific input values, but a set of high-quality comparison values for a large number of scientific functions, for any input value, is available in Jan Myland's Equator software.

Please keep in mind that even a function $f(x)$ of a single variable x will typically cover an infinite number of values, so that testing it for all possible values x would still take an infinite time, an uninviting proposition. Instead, we will sample the function over its applicable range, and will thereby run the risk of

400

missing some peculiar behaviors restricted to small patches in parameter space. This cannot be helped, other than by being vigilant about sampling with higher resolution in suspect areas, such as those near discontinuities and singularities.

Another benefit of a graphical display of pE is that it can highlight major discontinuities, and thereby may identify regions in parameter space where the function as provided might, e.g., cause problems when differentiated numerically. In Excel functions, such discontinuities are sometimes artifacts caused by piecemeal approximations, see Fig. 11.7.1.

*****

As calculators and computers replaced longhand calculations, the concept of *significant digits* (decimals, numbers, or figures) was introduced as a didactic device to indicate the inherent limitations of numerical answers. That measure, however, cannot withstand close scrutiny, and tends to disappear later in the curriculum, to be replaced by more specific estimates, such as standard deviations or confidence limits. Indeed, standard statistical textbooks and NIST standards don't even mention it.

In binary counting, each digit is either right or wrong, and is therefore, unambiguously, significant or not. But in decimal counting this is not the case: 8.3, when known to ± 0.4, is underspecified with one digit, and overspecified with two. This illustrates the problem with significant decimals: it implies an *integer* for answer. But once we realize this implied constraint, and drop it, the solution is obvious: the number of significant digits is then simply pE, which in this example is –log(0.4/8.3) = 1.3 or, if you wish, 1.32, indeed *between* 1 and 2. (It is seldom useful to specify pE to more than one or two decimal places.) This simple generalization of the concept of significant digits can thus rescue its scientific significance.

9.2 Differentiating theoretical expressions

9.2.1 An intuitive approach

The spreadsheet cannot use symbolic algebra to find derivatives of a given theoretical (i.e., mathematically explicit, and noise-free) function. The user can, of course, supply explicit expressions for the derivatives of the models used, and many software packages indeed require that, or provide it as an option. We can do the same in Excel, either by incorporating such explicit expressions for the derivative in the functions or subroutines using it, or by placing them in separate functions to which the subroutines refer. Here we will consider what we can do in the absence of such explicit expressions for the derivative, i.e., when the spreadsheet is tasked with generating those derivatives itself, on the basis of the available numerical information. With smooth theoretical expressions, i.e., with noise-free functions that are finite, continuous, and have a sufficient number of continuous derivatives, our primary concern will be numerical accuracy.

Perhaps the most intuitive way to differentiate a smooth function numerically is based directly on the definition

$$\frac{d\,f(x)}{dx} = \lim_{\delta \to 0} \frac{f(x+\delta) - f(x)}{\delta} \tag{9.2.1}$$

which leads to the numerical approximation

$$\frac{d\,f(x)}{dx} \approx f_+^{\mathrm{I}}(x) = \frac{f(x+\delta) - f(x)}{\delta} \qquad \text{for } \delta \ll x \tag{9.2.2}$$

where we use the Roman numeral superscript I to denote the first derivative. By replacing δ by $-\delta$ we likewise have

$$\frac{d\,f(x)}{dx} \approx f_-^{\mathrm{I}}(x) = \frac{f(x) - f(x-\delta)}{\delta} \qquad \text{for } \delta \ll x \tag{9.2.3}$$

which will be identical to (9.2.2) in the limit of $\delta \to 0$ unless $f(x)$ has a discontinuity or a discontinuous first derivative at x. By averaging (9.2.2) and (9.2.3) we obtain $f_\pm^{\mathrm{I}}(x) = [\,f_+^{\mathrm{I}}(x) + f_-^{\mathrm{I}}(x)\,]\,/\,2$ or

$$\frac{d\,f(x)}{dx} \approx f_\pm^I(x) = \frac{f(x+\delta) - f(x-\delta)}{2\delta} \qquad \text{for } \delta \ll x \qquad (9.2.4)$$

Equations (9.2.2), (9.2.3), and (9.2.4) are called forward, backward, and central differences respectively, as indicated by the subscripts $+$, $-$, and $\pm$ on f^I. The term *differencing* is used to indicate the discrete nature of this approximation to differentiation, and x and δ are used in a generic sense, and can of course be replaced by t and τ, or by whatever other symbols are convenient for a variable and an associated small deviation in that variable. All three expressions for the first derivative f^I are exact for any value of δ as long as $f(x)$ is a linear function of x, i.e., they all yield $f^I = a_1$ for $f(x) = a_0 + a_1 x$, while (9.2.4) also generates the exact result $f^I = a_1 + 2a_2 x$ for the quadratic function $f(x) = a_0 + a_1 x + a_2 x^2$.

We can derive similar expressions for the second derivative by using forward, central, or backward differencing on forward, central, or backward differencing respectively, nine possible combinations that yield five distinct answers. But this approach gives no indication of how to choose between them. Yet when we try them out, they yield different numerical results. And it gets progressively worse for higher derivatives.

9.2.2 Including truncation errors

A Taylor expansion specifies the errors involved, as in

$$f(x \pm \delta) = f(x)\big|_{x=0} \pm \frac{\delta}{1!}\frac{df(x)}{dx}\bigg|_{x=0} + \frac{\delta^2}{2!}\frac{d^2 f(x)}{dx^2}\bigg|_{x=0} \pm \frac{\delta^3}{3!}\frac{d^3 f(x)}{dx^3}\bigg|_{x=0}$$
$$+ \frac{\delta^4}{4!}\frac{d^4 f(x)}{dx^4}\bigg|_{x=0} \pm \frac{\delta^5}{5!}\frac{d^5 f(x)}{dx^5}\bigg|_{x=0} + \frac{\delta^6}{6!}\frac{d^6 f(x)}{dx^6}\bigg|_{x=0} \pm \ldots \qquad (9.2.5)$$

and therefore provides a more useful starting point. For the sake of notational compactness we will here write derivatives with Newton-like notation (but again with Roman superscripts rather than dots or apostrophes), use the abbreviation $f_{\pm i}$ for the function f at $x = x \pm i\delta$, i.e., $f_{\pm i} = f(x \pm i\delta)$, and write the derivatives of f at $\delta = 0$ as $f_0^I = df(x)/dx|_{x=x_0}$, $f_0^{II} = d^2 f(x)/dx^2|_{x=x_0}$, $f_0^{III} = d^3 f(x)/dx^3|_{x=x_0}$, etc., so that (9.2.5) can be condensed to

$$f_{\pm 1} = f_0 \pm \frac{f_0^I \delta}{1!} + \frac{f_0^{II}\delta^2}{2!} \pm \frac{f_0^{III}\delta^3}{3!} + \frac{f_0^{IV}\delta^4}{4!} \pm \frac{f_0^V \delta^5}{5!} + \frac{f_0^{VI}\delta^6}{6!} \pm \ldots \qquad (9.2.6)$$

$$f_0^I = \frac{f_1 - f_0}{\delta} - \frac{f_0^{II}\delta}{2!} - \frac{f_0^{III}\delta^2}{3!} - \frac{f_0^{IV}\delta^3}{4!} - \frac{f_0^V\delta^4}{5!} - \frac{f_0^{VI}\delta^5}{6!} - \ldots \qquad (9.2.7)$$

$$f_0^I = \frac{f_0 - f_{-1}}{\delta} + \frac{f_0^{II}\delta}{2!} - \frac{f_0^{III}\delta^2}{3!} + \frac{f_0^{IV}\delta^3}{4!} - \frac{f_0^V\delta^4}{5!} + \frac{f_0^{VI}\delta^5}{6!} - \ldots \qquad (9.2.8)$$

while averaging (9.2.7) and (9.2.8) yields

$$f_0^I = \frac{f_1 - f_{-1}}{2\delta} - \frac{f_0^{III}\delta^2}{3!} - \frac{f_0^V\delta^4}{5!} - \frac{f_0^{VII}\delta^6}{7!} - \frac{f_0^{IX}\delta^8}{9!} - \frac{f_0^{XI}\delta^{10}}{11!} - \ldots \qquad (9.2.9)$$

These expressions therefore lead to the same differencing formulas as (9.2.2) through (9.2.4), but with specific expressions for the errors of truncating the Taylor series, and therefore can be made to be exact to within any specified numbers of digits by taking into account a sufficient number of these error terms.

We can now see why central differencing provides a better approximation than either forward or backward differencing, because the leading error term in (9.2.9) is the third derivative, f_0^{III}, whereas the leading error term in (9.2.7) and (9.2.8) is f_0^{II}. This also explains why (9.2.4) is indeed exact for a quadratic function of x, whereas (9.2.2) and (9.2.3) are not.

Expressions that include explicit error terms are needed because we cannot handle $\delta \to 0$ as the limit in a numerical computation in the same way in which it is used in mathematics. We face an interesting conundrum: when δ is finite, what value should it be assigned? When too small a value for δ is used, we

402

run the risk of *numerical imprecision*, since the differences between $f_1 = f(x+\delta)$, $f_0 = f(x)$, and $f_{-1} = f(x-\delta)$ in the numerators of (9.2.7) through (9.2.9) may be too small with respect to x to remain significant. (Cancellation errors will be discussed in more detail in section 11.3.) On the other hand, when we choose too large a value for δ, we may have a problem of *algorithmic inaccuracy* when truncating a Taylor series, because the deleted higher-order derivatives in the corresponding Taylor expansion may no longer be negligible.

This problem can only be resolved through a compromise, by selecting δ so as to minimize the combined effects of the estimated inaccuracy and imprecision. For first-order differencing formulas, this typically results in setting the relative step size δ/x equal to about $\varepsilon^{1/(J+1)}$ for forward or backward differencing, and to $\varepsilon^{1/(J+2)}$ for central differencing, where ε is the relative numerical resolution (in Excel, ε is of the order of magnitude of 10^{-16}) and J denotes the order of the derivative: J = 1 for f^{I}, J = 2 for f^{II}, etc., see J. R. Rice, *Numerical Methods, Software, and Analysis*, McGraw-Hill (1983) pp. 185-186. Some resulting values for δ/x, and the estimated relative uncertainties $E_{rel} \approx \varepsilon^{1/(J+1)}$ and $\varepsilon^{2/(J+2)}$ for first and second derivatives respectively are listed in Tables 9.2.1 and 9.2.2 for single, double, and quadruple precision, i.e., for numberlengths of approximately 8, 16, and 32 decimals respectively. The larger numberlength is included because many cpu's produced since 2003 already have that capability, typically denoted as "x64", and it is only a matter of time until Microsoft will decide (or be forced by its competitors) to incorporate 64-bit data manipulation in Excel. In sections 9.2.8 through 9.2.10 we will refine these estimates.

numberlength as "precision"	ε	forward or backward differencing with (9.2.7) or (9.2.8)		central differencing using (9.2.9)	
		δ/x	E_{rel}	δ/x	E_{rel}
single	10^{-8}	10^{-4}	10^{-4}	2×10^{-3}	5×10^{-6}
double	10^{-16}	10^{-8}	10^{-8}	5×10^{-6}	2×10^{-11}
quadruple	10^{-32}	10^{-16}	10^{-16}	2×10^{-11}	5×10^{-22}

Table 9.2.1: Typical order-of-magnitude values for δ/x and the resulting relative uncertainties E_{rel} for computing the first derivative f^{I} with the simplest expressions for first-order single, double, and quadruple "precision". Forward or backward differencing makes about half of the available decimals non-significant (i.e., $-\log E_{rel} \approx -\frac{1}{2}\log \varepsilon$), and central differencing about one-third of them ($-\log E_{rel} \approx -\frac{2}{3}\log \varepsilon$).

numberlength as "precision"	ε	forward or backward differencing		central differencing	
		δ/x	E_{rel}	δ/x	E_{rel}
single	10^{-8}	2×10^{-3}	2×10^{-3}	10^{-2}	10^{-4}
double	10^{-16}	5×10^{-6}	5×10^{-6}	10^{-4}	10^{-8}
quadruple	10^{-32}	2×10^{-11}	2×10^{-11}	10^{-8}	10^{-16}

Table 9.2.2: Typical order-of-magnitude values for δ/x and the resulting relative uncertainties E_{rel}, for computing the second derivative f^{II} with the simplest expressions for first-order single, double, and quadruple "precision". Forward or backward differencing makes roughly two-thirds of the available decimals non-significant (i.e., $-\log E_{rel} \approx -\frac{1}{3}\log \varepsilon$), and central differencing about one-half of them ($-\log E_{rel} \approx -\frac{1}{2}\log \varepsilon$).

Because the relative errors E_{rel} resulting from central differencing are consistently smaller than those from forward and backward differencing, central differencing is the preferred choice among these three methods, except at the extremes of a data range, where we may have no choice if the range of available data is limited by one or two discontinuities or, worse, singularities. We almost always can (and then should) select the range to have no such discontinuities and singularities *inside* it.

For closed-form analytical functions, forward or backward differencing should only be used at or very close to discontinuities. At $x = 0$, e.g., we can use central differencing for $y = e^{-x}$, while $y = e^{|x|}$ requires one-sided differencing. Extrapolation may be needed for singularities, or at the very limit of the definition of a function, such as for $\log(x)$ at $x = 0$.

In order to keep matters simple, we will here focus primarily on central differencing, although we will indicate in section 9.2.6 how the present approach can also be applied to asymmetric expressions.

9.2.3 Multi-point central differencing

While central differencing is preferable to one-sided (forward or backward) differencing, at its very best it still loses about a third of the available decimals to non-significancy, i.e., at least five decimal places in standard Excel. However, given a noise-free function, numerical differentiation need not be so grossly inferior to algebraic differentiation. At the cost of somewhat more complicated, multi-point expressions, we can derive differencing formulas that lose fewer significant digits. This will be illustrated first for central differencing of the first derivative. The same approach can be applied to derivatives of any (positive integer) order, and in section 9.2.7 will be illustrated for the second derivative.

We start by rewriting (9.2.9) as

$$f_1 - f_{-1} = \frac{2f_0^{I}\delta}{1!} + \frac{2f_0^{III}\delta^3}{3!} + \frac{2f_0^{V}\delta^5}{5!} + \frac{2f_0^{VII}\delta^7}{7!}$$
$$+ \frac{2f_0^{IX}\delta^9}{9!} + \frac{2f_0^{XI}\delta^{11}}{11!} + \frac{2f_0^{XIII}\delta^{13}}{13!} + \frac{2f_0^{XV}\delta^{15}}{15!} + \dots \quad (9.2.10)$$

Upon doubling the value of δ, so that $f_1 = f(x+\delta)$ becomes $f(x+2\delta) = f_2$ etc., we find

$$f_2 - f_{-2} = \frac{4f_0^{I}\delta}{1!} + \frac{16f_0^{III}\delta^3}{3!} + \frac{64f_0^{V}\delta^5}{5!} + \frac{256f_0^{VII}\delta^7}{7!}$$
$$+ \frac{1024f_0^{IX}\delta^9}{9!} + \frac{4096f_0^{XI}\delta^{11}}{11!} + \frac{16384f_0^{XIII}\delta^{13}}{13!} + \dots \quad (9.2.11)$$

We now remove the term in f_0^{III} by subtracting $2^3 = 8$ times (9.2.10) from (9.2.11), which after some reshuffling yields

$$f_0^{I} = \frac{f_{-2} - 8f_{-1} + 8f_1 - f_2}{12\delta} + \frac{4f_0^{V}\delta^4}{5!} + \frac{20f_0^{VII}\delta^6}{7!}$$
$$+ \frac{84f_0^{IX}\delta^8}{9!} + \frac{340f_0^{XI}\delta^{10}}{11!} + \frac{1364f_0^{XIII}\delta^{12}}{13!} + \dots \quad (9.2.12)$$

which, lacking a term in f_0^{III}, yields a smaller relative uncertainty E_{rel} in the first derivative for the same value of δ.

Next we can eliminate the term in f_0^{V}, by again doubling δ in (9.2.11) and then subtracting $2^5 = 32$ times (9.2.12) from it. In the same way we can successively eliminate as many of the remaining higher-order error terms in f_0^{VII}, f_0^{IX}, f_0^{XI}, etc. as we wish, and thereby find increasingly accurate expressions. Some resulting expressions are listed in Table 9.2.3.

Alternatively, we can use extended numberlength (to be discussed in chapter 11) to eliminate rounding errors affecting small δ-values, and then select δ small enough to make the remaining, leading relative error term due to truncation of the Taylor series smaller than 10^{-16}. But even with extended (but still finite) precision, the same principles apply.

j	formula for f_0^{I}	error estimate
3	$(-f_{-1}+f_1)/(2\delta)$	$-f_0^{III}\delta^2/3! - f_0^{V}\delta^4/5! - f_0^{VII}\delta^6/7! - f_0^{IX}\delta^8/9! - \dots$
5	$(f_{-2}-8f_{-1}+8f_1-f_2)/(12\delta)$	$4f_0^{V}\delta^4/5! + 20f_0^{VII}\delta^6/7! + 84f_0^{IX}\delta^8/9! + \dots$
9	$(-f_{-4}+40f_{-2}-256f_{-1}+256f_1-40f_2+f_4)/(360\delta)$	$-64f_0^{VII}\delta^6/7! - 1344f_0^{IX}\delta^8/9! - \dots$
17	$(f_{-8}-168f_{-4}+5376f_{-2}-32768f_{-1}+32768f_1-5376f_2+168f_4-f_8)/(45360\delta)$	$4096f_0^{IX}\delta^8/9! + \dots$

Table 9.2.3: Central differencing formulas for the first derivative f_0^{I}, with its leading error term(s). The number j reflects the range used in terms of δ, e.g., $j = 3$ for f_i with $i = -1, 0, 1$, and 17 for $i = -8, -7, -6, \dots, -1, 0, 1, \dots, 7, 8$. A Roman numeral for n is used as superscript to indicate the nth derivative. See also Table 9.2.4 for different results.

Exercise 9.2.1 illustrates the use of some of these expressions for the smooth function $f_0 = \sin(x)$, for which the derivatives are $f_0^{I} = \cos(x)$, $f_0^{II} = -\sin(x)$, $f_0^{III} = -\cos(x)$, $f_0^{IV} = \sin(x)$, $f_0^{V} = \cos(x)$, $f_0^{VII} = -\cos(x)$, $f_0^{IX} = \cos(x)$, etc., evaluated here at and around $x = \pi/3$. We select that particular value because its first derivative, $\cos(\pi/3)$, is an easily recognized 0.5000, but you can of course pick a different function and/or value.

Exercise 9.2.1:

(1) In a new spreadsheet, deposit the label d = , highlight the d, then select the Symbol font to get δ = . Below this, place column headings for i, x, f_0, and $f_0{}^I{}_{calc}$.

(2) Next to the label for δ, place the value 0.1. In the column for i, insert the numbers –8 (1) +8. In the column for x, calculate its value as $\pi/3+i\delta$. In the columns for f_0 and $f_0{}^I{}_{ref}$ compute the values for $\sin(x)$ and $\cos(x)$ respectively.

(3) Extend the column headings to include $f_0{}^I$, $-\Delta$, and a label for the leading error term. Precede the label $-\Delta$ by an apostrophe, i.e., enter it as '$-\Delta$.

(4) For $i = -7$ through +7, compute $f_0{}^I$ with (9.2.4), in the next column calculate minus the difference $-\Delta = f_0{}^I{}_{ref} - f_0{}^I$, and in the rightmost column display the value of the leading error term in (9.2.9), $-f_0{}^{III}\delta^2/3! = +f_0{}^I\delta^2/6$ where $f_0{}^{III} = -f_0{}^I$ for $f = \sin(x)$. For ease of comparison we show *minus* Δ because the error made is opposite to the correction made by the higher-order terms in the Taylor series.

(5) Repeat the extension described under point (4) twice more, once for the formula for $j = 5$ in Table 9.2.3, then for its formula for $j = 9$.

(6) Finally, copy the block of calculations you have just made, and in this copy change the value of δ to 0.001. The complete spreadsheet may now look similar to that in Fig. 9.2.1.

The data in the top 22 rows of Fig. 9.2.1 illustrate that, for this trial function and this range of its variable, the first-order approach (9.2.9) with δ = 0.1 yields results that are accurate to within ±0.2% or pE ≈ 2.7, see column F, while those in column L are five orders of magnitude better, with pE ≈ 7.8.

Comparison of the data for δ = 0.1 in columns F and G with those in I and J, or in L and M, indicates that the attendant errors are predicted quite well by the leading terms in the Taylor expansions. In the bottom half of Fig. 9.2.1 we see that a 100-fold reduction in δ further increases the accuracy, but only up to the point where other (random, and therefore non-algorithmic) errors become dominant, as in L33:L41. Still, all errors in I31:I43 and in L33:L41 have relative errors smaller than ±2×10^{-13}, within two orders of magnitude of the analytical expression in column D.

9.2.4 A more powerful formalism

We can find a more powerful (and also more spreadsheet-friendly) way to generate these and related results as follows. We write

$$f_{-1} = f_0 - \frac{f_0{}^I\delta}{1!} + \frac{f_0{}^{II}\delta^2}{2!} - \frac{f_0{}^{III}\delta^3}{3!} + \frac{f_0{}^{IV}\delta^4}{4!} - \frac{f_0{}^V\delta^5}{5!} + \ldots \tag{9.2.13}$$

$$f_0 = f_0 \tag{9.2.14}$$

$$f_1 = f_0 + \frac{f_0{}^I\delta}{1!} + \frac{f_0{}^{II}\delta^2}{2!} + \frac{f_0{}^{III}\delta^3}{3!} + \frac{f_0{}^{IV}\delta^4}{4!} + \frac{f_0{}^V\delta^5}{5!} + \ldots \tag{9.2.15}$$

where the expressions (9.2.13) and (9.2.15) are merely the two specific forms of the Taylor expansion (9.2.6), while (9.2.14) is self-evident. We now consider the composite function

$$F = a_{-1}f_{-1} + a_0 f_0 + a_1 f_1 \tag{9.2.16}$$

$$= (a_{-1}+a_0+a_1) f_0 + (-a_{-1}+a_1) f_0{}^I\delta/1! + (a_{-1}+a_1) f_0{}^{II}\delta^2/2! + \ldots$$

and choose its coefficients a_{-1}, a_0, and a_1 such that the multipliers of f_0, $f_0{}^I\delta/1!$, and $f_0{}^{II}\delta^2/2!$ in F become 0, 1, and 0 respectively. By collecting terms of F in f_0, $f_0{}^I\delta/1!$, and $f_0{}^{II}\delta^2/2!$, which in (9.2.13) through (9.2.15) are found in vertical columns, we find the simultaneous equations

$$a_{-1} + a_0 + a_1 = 0 \tag{9.2.17}$$

$$-a_{-1} \qquad\quad a_1 = 1 \tag{9.2.18}$$

$$a_{-1} \qquad\quad\;\, a_1 = 0 \tag{9.2.19}$$

	A	B	C	D	E	F	G	H	I	J	K	L	M
1	$\delta = 0.1$												
2							leading			leading			leading
3	i	x	f_0	$f_{0\,ref}^{\rm I}$	$f_0^{\rm I}$	$-\Delta$	error	$f_0^{\rm I}$	$-\Delta$	error	$f_0^{\rm I}$	$-\Delta$	error
4			=sin(x)	=cos(x)	$j=3$		term	$j=5$		term	$j=9$		term
5													
6	-8	0.2472	0.2447	0.9696									
7	-7	0.3472	0.3403	0.9403	0.9388	0.0016	0.0016						
8	-6	0.4472	0.4324	0.9017	0.9002	0.0015	0.0015	0.9017	3.0E-06	3.0E-06			
9	-5	0.5472	0.5203	0.8540	0.8526	0.0014	0.0014	0.8540	2.8E-06	2.8E-06			
10	-4	0.6472	0.6030	0.7978	0.7964	0.0013	0.0013	0.7978	2.7E-06	2.7E-06	0.7978	1.0E-08	1.0E-08
11	-3	0.7472	0.6796	0.7336	0.7324	0.0012	0.0012	0.7336	2.4E-06	2.4E-06	0.7336	9.3E-09	9.3E-09
12	-2	0.8472	0.7494	0.6621	0.6610	0.0011	0.0011	0.6621	2.2E-06	2.2E-06	0.6621	8.4E-09	8.4E-09
13	-1	0.9472	0.8118	0.5840	0.5830	0.0010	0.0010	0.5840	1.9E-06	1.9E-06	0.5840	7.4E-09	7.4E-09
14	0	1.0472	0.8660	**0.5000**	**0.4992**	0.0008	0.0008	**0.5000**	1.7E-06	1.7E-06	**0.5000**	6.3E-09	6.3E-09
15	1	1.1472	0.9116	0.4110	0.4104	0.0007	0.0007	0.4110	1.4E-06	1.4E-06	0.4110	5.2E-09	5.2E-09
16	2	1.2472	0.9481	0.3180	0.3175	0.0005	0.0005	0.3180	1.1E-06	1.1E-06	0.3180	4.0E-09	4.0E-09
17	3	1.3472	0.9751	0.2217	0.2214	0.0004	0.0004	0.2217	7.4E-07	7.4E-07	0.2217	2.8E-09	2.8E-09
18	4	1.4472	0.9924	0.1233	0.1231	0.0002	0.0002	0.1233	4.1E-07	4.1E-07	0.1233	1.6E-09	1.6E-09
19	5	1.5472	0.9997	0.0236	0.0236	0.0000	0.0000	0.0236	7.9E-08	7.9E-08			
20	6	1.6472	0.9971	-0.0763	-0.0762	-0.0001	-0.0001	-0.0763	-2.5E-07	-2.5E-07			
21	7	1.7472	0.9845	-0.1755	-0.1752	-0.0003	-0.0003						
22	8	1.8472	0.9620	-0.2729									
23													
24	$\delta = 0.001$												
25							leading			leading			leading
26	i	x	f_0	$f_{0\,ref}^{\rm I}$	$f_0^{\rm I}$	$-\Delta$	error	$f_0^{\rm I}$	$-\Delta$	error	$f_0^{\rm I}$	$-\Delta$	error
27			=sin(x)	=cos(x)	$j=3$		term	$j=5$		term	$j=9$		term
28													
29	-8	1.0392	0.8620	0.5069									
30	-7	1.0402	0.8625	0.5060	0.5060	8.4E-08	8.4E-08						
31	-6	1.0412	0.8630	0.5052	0.5052	8.4E-08	8.4E-08	0.5052	7.9E-14	1.7E-14			
32	-5	1.0422	0.8635	0.5043	0.5043	8.4E-08	8.4E-08	0.5043	3.7E-14	1.7E-14			
33	-4	1.0432	0.8640	0.5035	0.5035	8.4E-08	8.4E-08	0.5035	-1.6E-14	1.7E-14	0.5035	-1.8E-15	6.4E-21
34	-3	1.0442	0.8645	0.5026	0.5026	8.4E-08	8.4E-08	0.5026	6.1E-14	1.7E-14	0.5026	7.2E-14	6.4E-21
35	-2	1.0452	0.8650	0.5017	0.5017	8.4E-08	8.4E-08	0.5017	2.6E-14	1.7E-14	0.5017	5.4E-14	6.4E-21
36	-1	1.0462	0.8655	0.5009	0.5009	8.3E-08	8.3E-08	0.5009	-7.8E-15	1.7E-14	0.5009	-3.5E-14	6.4E-21
37	0	1.0472	0.8660	**0.5000**	**0.5000**	8.3E-08	8.3E-08	**0.5000**	1.5E-13	1.7E-14	**0.5000**	4.8E-14	6.3E-21
38	1	1.0482	0.8665	0.4991	0.4991	8.3E-08	8.3E-08	0.4991	-1.2E-14	1.7E-14	0.4991	9.4E-16	6.3E-21
39	2	1.0492	0.8670	0.4983	0.4983	8.3E-08	8.3E-08	0.4983	3.7E-14	1.7E-14	0.4983	1.6E-14	6.3E-21
40	3	1.0502	0.8675	0.4974	0.4974	8.3E-08	8.3E-08	0.4974	4.1E-14	1.7E-14	0.4974	1.3E-14	6.3E-21
41	4	1.0512	0.8680	0.4965	0.4965	8.3E-08	8.3E-08	0.4965	4.7E-14	1.7E-14	0.4965	4.7E-14	6.3E-21
42	5	1.0522	0.8685	0.4957	0.4957	8.3E-08	8.3E-08	0.4957	-5.4E-15	1.7E-14			
43	6	1.0532	0.8690	0.4948	0.4948	8.2E-08	8.2E-08	0.4948	-2.8E-14	1.6E-14			
44	7	1.0542	0.8695	0.4939	0.4939	8.2E-08	8.2E-08						
45	8	1.0552	0.8700	0.4931									

Fig. 9.2.1: A spreadsheet illustrating central differencing of the smooth function $f = \sin(x)$, using the first three expressions for f^1 in Table 9.2.3, and two different step sizes, viz. $\delta = 0.1$ and $\delta = 0.001$. The results for $x = \pi/3$ are highlighted in boldface.

Solving such simultaneous linear equations, especially when there are many of them, is most conveniently done with matrix algebra, see section 1.11.2. Chapter 10 will have much more on matrix methods, but here we only need the two Excel array functions MMULT and MINVERSE.

In matrix notation we write (9.2.17) through (9.2.19) as the product of a matrix containing the coefficients of a_{-1}, a_0, and a_1, and a vector containing the coefficients a_{-1}, a_0, and a_1 themselves, as equal to the vector representing the right-hand sides of (9.2.17) through (9.2.19), i.e., as

$$\begin{vmatrix} 1 & 1 & 1 \\ -1 & 0 & 1 \\ 1 & 0 & 1 \end{vmatrix} \begin{vmatrix} a_{-1} \\ a_0 \\ a_1 \end{vmatrix} = \begin{vmatrix} 0 \\ 1 \\ 0 \end{vmatrix} \tag{9.2.20}$$

with the solution

$$\begin{vmatrix} a_{-1} \\ a_0 \\ a_1 \end{vmatrix} = \begin{vmatrix} 1 & 1 & 1 \\ -1 & 0 & 1 \\ 1 & 0 & 1 \end{vmatrix}^{-1} \begin{vmatrix} 0 \\ 1 \\ 0 \end{vmatrix} = \begin{vmatrix} -0.5 \\ 0 \\ 0.5 \end{vmatrix} = \begin{vmatrix} -1 \\ 0 \\ 1 \end{vmatrix} / 2 \tag{9.2.21}$$

so that $a_{-1} = -\frac{1}{2}$, $a_0 = 0$, and $a_1 = \frac{1}{2}$. Consequently

$$F = a_{-1} f_{-1} + a_0 f_0 + a_1 f_1 = -\tfrac{1}{2} f_{-1} + \tfrac{1}{2} f_1$$
$$= f_0^{\mathrm{I}} \delta/1! + f_0^{\mathrm{III}} \delta^3/3! + f_0^{\mathrm{V}} \delta^5/5! + f_0^{\mathrm{VI}} \delta^7/7! + f_0^{\mathrm{IX}} \delta^9/9! + \dots \tag{9.2.22}$$

and

$$f_0^{\mathrm{I}} = \frac{-f_{-1} + f_1}{2\delta} - \frac{f_0^{\mathrm{III}} \delta^2}{3!} - \frac{f_0^{\mathrm{V}} \delta^4}{5!} - \frac{f_0^{\mathrm{VII}} \delta^6}{7!} - \dots \tag{9.2.9}$$

As our second example we rederive the five-point expression (9.2.12). We substitute 2δ for δ in (9.2.6), and then combine this with (9.2.13) through (9.2.15) to

$$f_{-2} = f_0 - 2\frac{f_0^{\mathrm{I}}\delta}{1!} + 4\frac{f_0^{\mathrm{II}}\delta^2}{2!} - 8\frac{f_0^{\mathrm{III}}\delta^3}{3!} + 16\frac{f_0^{\mathrm{IV}}\delta^4}{4!} - 32\frac{f_0^{\mathrm{V}}\delta^5}{5!} + \dots \tag{9.2.23}$$

$$f_{-1} = f_0 - \frac{f_0^{\mathrm{I}}\delta}{1!} + \frac{f_0^{\mathrm{II}}\delta^2}{2!} - \frac{f_0^{\mathrm{III}}\delta^3}{3!} + \frac{f_0^{\mathrm{IV}}\delta^4}{4!} - \frac{f_0^{\mathrm{V}}\delta^5}{5!} + \dots \tag{9.2.13}$$

$$f_0 = f_0 \tag{9.2.14}$$

$$f_1 = f_0 + \frac{f_0^{\mathrm{I}}\delta}{1!} + \frac{f_0^{\mathrm{II}}\delta^2}{2!} + \frac{f_0^{\mathrm{III}}\delta^3}{3!} + \frac{f_0^{\mathrm{IV}}\delta^4}{4!} + \frac{f_0^{\mathrm{V}}\delta^5}{5!} + \dots \tag{9.2.15}$$

$$f_2 = f_0 + 2\frac{f_0^{\mathrm{I}}\delta}{1!} + 4\frac{f_0^{\mathrm{II}}\delta^2}{2!} + 8\frac{f_0^{\mathrm{III}}\delta^3}{3!} + 16\frac{f_0^{\mathrm{IV}}\delta^4}{4!} + 32\frac{f_0^{\mathrm{V}}\delta^5}{5!} + \dots \tag{9.2.24}$$

This time consider the composite function

$$F = a_{-2} f_{-2} + a_{-1} f_{-1} + a_0 f_0 + a_1 f_1 + a_2 f_2 \tag{9.2.25}$$

and choose its coefficients a_{-2}, a_{-1}, a_0, a_1, and a_2 to make the multipliers of f_0, $f_0^{\mathrm{I}}\delta/1!$, $f_0^{\mathrm{II}}\delta^2/2!$, $f_0^{\mathrm{III}}\delta^3/3!$, and $f_0^{\mathrm{IV}}\delta^4/4!$ in F equal to 0, 1, 0, 0, and 0 respectively. Collecting terms in each derivative then leads to the five simultaneous equations

$$a_{-2} + a_{-1} + a_0 + a_1 + a_2 = 0 \tag{9.2.26}$$
$$-2a_{-2} - a_{-1} + a_1 + 2a_2 = 1 \tag{9.2.27}$$
$$4a_{-2} + a_{-1} + a_1 + 4a_2 = 0 \tag{9.2.28}$$
$$-8a_{-2} - a_{-1} + a_1 + 8a_2 = 0 \tag{9.2.29}$$
$$16a_{-2} + a_{-1} + a_1 + 16a_2 = 0 \tag{9.2.30}$$

which can be written in matrix form as

$$\begin{vmatrix} 1 & 1 & 1 & 1 & 1 \\ -2 & -1 & 0 & 1 & 2 \\ 4 & 1 & 0 & 1 & 4 \\ -8 & -1 & 0 & 1 & 8 \\ 16 & 1 & 0 & 1 & 16 \end{vmatrix} \begin{vmatrix} a_{-2} \\ a_{-1} \\ a_0 \\ a_1 \\ a_2 \end{vmatrix} = \begin{vmatrix} 0 \\ 1 \\ 0 \\ 0 \\ 0 \end{vmatrix} \qquad (9.2.31)$$

with the solution

$$\begin{vmatrix} a_{-2} \\ a_{-1} \\ a_0 \\ a_1 \\ a_2 \end{vmatrix} = \begin{vmatrix} 1 & 1 & 1 & 1 & 1 \\ -2 & -1 & 0 & 1 & 2 \\ 4 & 1 & 0 & 1 & 4 \\ -8 & -1 & 0 & 1 & 8 \\ 16 & 1 & 0 & 1 & 16 \end{vmatrix}^{-1} \begin{vmatrix} 0 \\ 1 \\ 0 \\ 0 \\ 0 \end{vmatrix} = \begin{vmatrix} 1/12 \\ -2/3 \\ 0 \\ 2/3 \\ -1/12 \end{vmatrix} = \begin{vmatrix} 1 \\ -8 \\ 0 \\ 8 \\ -1 \end{vmatrix} /12 \qquad (9.2.32)$$

so that $a_{-2} = 1/12$, $a_{-1} = -8/12$, $a_0 = 0$, $a_1 = 8/12$, and $a_2 = -1/12$, and

$$f_0^I = \frac{f_{-2} - 8f_{-1} + 8f_1 - f_{-2}}{12\delta} + \frac{4f^V \delta^4}{5!} + \frac{20f^{VII} \delta^6}{7!} + \dots \qquad (9.2.12)$$

9.2.5 Putting the model on the spreadsheet

It would appear to be a lot of trouble if the benefit of the above matrix formalism would merely be to recreate (9.2.9) or (9.2.12), but here is its pay-off: the same method works with the same effort for a larger number j of samples, for higher-order derivatives, and for asymmetric expressions such as we already encountered with forward and backward differencing. And it is readily implemented on a spreadsheet. The following exercise illustrates this for a larger sampling base.

Exercise 9.2.2:

(1) In a new spreadsheet, place the label j in cell A1, and the numbers 0 (1) 13 in cells A3:A16. In cell C3 place the label f_0, in cell C4 the label $f_0^I \delta/1!$, in cell C5 the label $f_0^{II} \delta^2/2!$, and so on down until $f_0^{XIII} \delta^{13}/13!$ And in cells E3:E16 deposit the number 0, then go back to cell E4 and change its content into a 1.

(2) In cells G1:Q1 put the labels for T_{-5}, T_{-4}, T_{-3}, T_{-2}, T_{-1}, T_0, T_1, T_2, T_3, T_4, and T_5 respectively. Then fill G3:Q3 with ones.

(3) In G4:Q4 place the numbers –5 (1) 5. In G5 compute the square of –5 with the instruction =G$4^$A5, then copy this instruction to G5:Q16. This completes the needed data array.

(4) Now take a look at the array you just made. The data block K3:M5 contains the 3×3 matrix you encountered in (9.2.20), the block J3:N7 the 5×5 matrix in (9.2.31). All other matrices and vectors you will need in this and the next sections are also contained within G3:Q16 or its obvious extensions beyond $T_{\pm5}$ and $j = 13$. Figure 9.2.2 shows part of the spreadsheet created so far.

(5) In S1 place the label j =, and in T1 the value 3.

(6) Highlight S3:S5, enter the array formula =MMULT(MINVERSE(K3:M5),E3:E5), and enter this instruction with Ctrl∪Shift∪Enter. This will compute the vector containing the coefficients a_{-1}, a_0, and a_{-1} in (9.2.21). Change the format to fractions with Format ⇨ Cells ⇨ Number ⇨ Fraction ⇨ Up to one digit.

(7) In order to convert these coefficients into integers, find their smallest common divider, in this case 2, and place it in cell T2.

(8) In T3 deposit =S3*T$2, copy this down to T4:T5, and you will have the coefficients –1, 0, 1 divided by 2 as shown on the right-most side of (9.2.21).

(9) To find the coefficients of the error terms, in cell U3 enter the instruction =-MMULT(K3:M3,S$3:S$5), and copy this down to U16. You can correlate the coefficient in, say, cell U8 with the formula given in column C in that same row, in this example $f_0^V \delta^5/5!$.

	j	C	F	T_{-5}	T_{-4}	T_{-3}	T_{-2}	T_{-1}	T_0	T_1	T_2	T_3	T_4
3	0	f_0	0	1	1	1	1	1	1	1	1	1	1
4	1	$f_0^{\,I}\,\delta/1!$	1	-5	-4	-3	-2	-1	0	1	2	3	4
5	2	$f_0^{\,II}\,\delta^2/2!$	0	25	16	9	4	1	0	1	4	9	16
6	3	$f_0^{\,III}\,\delta^3/3!$	0	-125	-64	-27	-8	-1	0	1	8	27	64
7	4	$f_0^{\,IV}\,\delta^4/4!$	0	625	256	81	16	1	0	1	16	81	256
8	5	$f_0^{\,V}\,\delta^5/5!$	0	-3125	-1024	-243	-32	-1	0	1	32	243	1024
9	6	$f_0^{\,VI}\,\delta^6/6!$	0	15625	4096	729	64	1	0	1	64	729	4096
10	7	$f_0^{\,VII}\,\delta^7/7!$	0	-78125	-16384	-2187	-128	-1	0	1	128	2187	16384
11	8	$f_0^{\,VIII}\,\delta^8/8!$	0	390625	65536	6561	256	1	0	1	256	6561	65536
12	9	$f_0^{\,IX}\,\delta^9/9!$	0	-1953125	-262144	-19683	-512	-1	0	1	512	19683	262144
13	10	$f_0^{\,X}\,\delta^{10}/10!$	0	9765625	1048576	59049	1024	1	0	1	1024	59049	1048576
14	11	$f_0^{\,XI}\,\delta11/11!$	0	-48828125	-4194304	-177147	-2048	-1	0	1	2048	177147	4194304
15	12	$f_0^{\,XII}\,\delta^{12}/12!$	0	244140625	16777216	531441	4096	1	0	1	4096	531441	16777216
16	13	$f_0^{\,XIII}\,\delta^{13}/13!$	0	-1220703125	-67108864	-1594323	-8192	-1	0	1	8192	1594323	67108864

Fig. 9.2.2: The left-hand part of the spreadsheet after step 5.

(10) Repeat the same process for $j = 5$, where V3:V7 (now formatted for up to two digits) should contain the instruction =MMULT(MINVERSE(J3:N7), E3:E7), the common denominator in W2 should be 12, copy T3 to W3 (where it will read =V3*W\$2) and copy this to W4:W7. Finally, cell X3 should contain the instruction =-MMULT(J3:N3, V\$3:V\$7), copied down to X16. This solves our second example.

(11) The spreadsheet is large enough to find the next results in this series. In Y3:Y9 the coefficients a_{-3} through a_3 for the central difference expression for $j = 7$ using =MMULT(MINVERSE(I3:O9),E3:E9), and find the corresponding error term in AA3 with =-MMULT(I3:O3,Y\$3:Y\$9).

(12) To test yourself, find the corresponding answers for $j = 9$ and $j = 11$, and verify your answers by comparison with those in Table 9.2.4. In the latter case, the fraction format of up to three digits is insufficient, and you will have to find the common denominator yourself.

(13) If you want to use larger j-values, extend the width of array G3:Q16 by inserting one or more columns to the left of column R for new columns with headings such as T_6, T_7, etc., and also inserting columns to the left of column E for columns with the headings T_{-6}, T_{-7}, etc. For more error terms, insert rows below row 16 and then extend the array downwards.

In section 9.2.3 we used a different approach, repeatedly doubling δ, which led to expressions covering larger sampling intervals for larger j-values, see Table 9.2.3. This yields expressions that each time double their 'footprint', i.e., in the range of x-values sampled, even though the actual number of samples taken increases much slower, in arithmetic rather than geometric progression. By contrast, the *compact* approach used here has a minimal footprint for the number of coefficients involved. Comparison of

$$(-f_{-4}+40f_{-2}-256f_{-1}+256f_1-40f_2+f_4)\,/\,(360\,\delta) \qquad -64f_0^{\,VII}\,\delta^6/7!-\cdots$$

of Table 9.2.3 for $j = 9$ with the corresponding compact expression from Table 9.2.4 for the same order of the error term but smaller j-value

$$(-f_{-3}+9f_{-2}-45f_{-1}+45f_1-9f_2+f_3)\,/\,(60\,\delta) \qquad -36f_0^{\,VII}\,\delta^6/7!-\cdots$$

or for the same value of $j = 9$,

$$(3f_{-4}-32f_{-3}+168f_{-2}-672f_{-1}+672f_1-168f_2+32f_3-3f_4)/(840\,\delta) \qquad +576f_0^{\,IX}\,\delta^8/9!+\ldots$$

suggests that the compact expressions also have smaller errors and/or footprints, advantages that become more important as the expressions become longer.

409

To illustrate cancellation noise we will first consider the arguments of the functions $-f_{-1}$ and f_1 in the simplest equation for central differencing, (9.2.4) or (9.2.9), where cancellation noise results from taking the relatively small difference between f_{-1} and f_1.

Lopping off all bits in the mantissa beyond the effectively available 53 results in relative errors that are randomly distributed between 0 and ε. These errors can be described as ε times a *uniform distribution* $U(0, 1)$, with a lower limit a of 0 and an upper limit b of 1 or, equivalently, as a bias of $\varepsilon/2$ plus a uniform distribution $\varepsilon\, U(-\frac{1}{2}, \frac{1}{2})$. A uniform distribution $U(a, b)$ has a mean value of $(a+b)/2$ and a variance of $(b-a)^2/12$, so that the mean $\varepsilon/2$ of $\varepsilon\, U(0, 1)$ replaces the just-mentioned bias plus the zero mean of $\varepsilon\, U(-\frac{1}{2}, \frac{1}{2})$. Both $\varepsilon\, U(0, 1)$ and $\varepsilon\, U(-\frac{1}{2}, \frac{1}{2})$ have a variance of $1/12$ and, therefore, a standard deviation of $1/\sqrt{12} \approx 0.2887$.

The numerical computation of a difference such as $f_1 - f_{-1}$ in the numerator of (9.2.4) or (9.2.9) involves three distinct stages: we first generate the arguments $x+\delta$ of f_1 and $x-\delta$ of f_{-1}, then compute their formulas, f_1 and f_{-1}, and finally find their difference, $f_1 - f_{-1}$. In the first stage we replace x by $x_0 (1+\varepsilon/2 \pm \varepsilon/\sqrt{12})$, and therefore compute the functions $f_1 = f(x+\delta)$ and $f_{-1} = f(x-\delta)$ as

$$f_1 = f(x_0 + \varepsilon x_0/2 \pm \varepsilon x_0/\sqrt{12} + \delta) \approx f_0 + (\varepsilon x_0/2 \pm \varepsilon x_0/\sqrt{12} + \delta) f_0^{\mathrm{I}} \qquad (9.2.44)$$

and

$$f_{-1} = f(x_0 + \varepsilon x_0/2 \pm \varepsilon x_0/\sqrt{12} - \delta) \approx f_0 + (\varepsilon x_0/2 \pm \varepsilon x_0/\sqrt{12} - \delta) f_0^{\mathrm{I}} \qquad (9.2.45)$$

where we approximate the function by the first two terms of its Taylor series, see (9.2.5).

Before they can be subtracted, these functions must be computed and then temporarily held or stored, at which point they will again be truncated. Inclusion of the corresponding errors will then lead to

$$f_1 \approx (1+\varepsilon/2 \pm \varepsilon/\sqrt{12}) f_0 + (\varepsilon x_0/2 \pm \varepsilon x_0/\sqrt{12} + \delta)(1+\varepsilon/2 \pm \varepsilon/\sqrt{12}) f_0^{\mathrm{I}}$$
$$\approx (1+\varepsilon/2 \pm \varepsilon/\sqrt{12}) f_0 + (\varepsilon x_0/2 \pm \varepsilon x_0/\sqrt{12} + \delta) f_0^{\mathrm{I}} \qquad (9.2.46)$$

and a corresponding expression for f_{-1}. Taking their difference yields

$$f_{0\,calc}^{\mathrm{I}} = (f_1 - f_{-1})/2\delta \approx f_0^{\mathrm{I}} \pm \varepsilon f_0/2\delta\sqrt{6} \pm \varepsilon x_0 f_0^{\mathrm{I}}/2\delta\sqrt{6} \approx f_0^{\mathrm{I}} \pm (\varepsilon/\delta\sqrt{24})(f_0 + x_0 f_0^{\mathrm{I}}) \qquad (9.2.47)$$

where the bias terms cancel each other, and the two noise terms come from computing x and $f(x)$ respectively, and are combined by adding their variances, i.e., as the square root of the sum of the squares of their standard deviations, in this case $\sqrt{(1/12+1/12)} = \sqrt{(1/6)} = 1/\sqrt{6}$.

For $j = 5$, see (9.2.12), we likewise find

$$f_{0,calc}^{\mathrm{I}} = f_0^{\mathrm{I}} \pm \frac{(\varepsilon/\sqrt{12})\sqrt{1^2+8^2+8^2+1^2}\,(f_0 + x_0 f_0^{\mathrm{I}})}{12\delta}$$

$$\approx f_0^{\mathrm{I}} \pm 0.27428\,\varepsilon\,\frac{(f_0 + x_0 f_0^{\mathrm{I}})}{\delta} \qquad (9.2.48)$$

and, in general, $f_{0\,calc}^{\mathrm{I}} = f_0^{\mathrm{I}} \pm c_j (f_0 + x_0 f_0^{\mathrm{I}})/\delta$. Dependent on the nature of the function f_0 and on the magnitude of x_0, one of the two error terms in $(f_0 + x_0 f_0^{\mathrm{I}})$ may be dominant.

It may be useful to consider the *magnitude* (i.e., absolute value) of the *relative* errors. For a value a, with an error Δ, the relative error is Δ/a, and its absolute value is $|\Delta/a|$, which can therefore be formulated for the expressions in Table 9.2.4 as

$$E_{canc} = \frac{c_j}{\delta}\left|\frac{f_0 + x_0 f_0^{\mathrm{I}}}{f_0^{\mathrm{I}}}\right| \qquad (9.2.49)$$

Some values of c_j are listed in Table 9.2.6, as calculated from the integers that multiply the terms $f_{\pm i}$ in the equations of Table 9.2.4. Table 9.2.6 also contains some related coefficients.

j	b_j	c_j	d_j	$\varepsilon^{1/j}$
3	1.666667×10^{-1}	2.266233×10^{-17}	4.081395×10^{-6}	4.8062174×10^{-6}
5	3.333333×10^{-2}	3.045159×10^{-17}	7.442764×10^{-4}	6.4429097×10^{-4}
7	7.142857×10^{-3}	3.467493×10^{-17}	6.982307×10^{-3}	5.2574226×10^{-3}
9	1.587502×10^{-3}	3.741589×10^{-17}	2.429285×10^{-2}	1.6875933×10^{-2}
11	3.607504×10^{-4}	3.937709×10^{-17}	5.379360×10^{-2}	3.5447266×10^{-2}
13	8.325008×10^{-5}	4.086932×10^{-17}	9.335571×10^{-2}	5.9254845×10^{-2}
15	1.942502×10^{-5}	4.205382×10^{-17}	1.399440×10^{-1}	8.6369555×10^{-2}

Table 9.2.6: Approximate numerical values of the coefficients b_j, c_j, and d_j, in equations (9.2.49), (9.2.50), and (9.2.54) for the compact central differencing expressions of the first derivative f_0^{I} listed in Table 9.2.4 for $\varepsilon = 1/(2^{53}-1) \approx 1.110223\times10^{-16}$. The last column lists the values of $\varepsilon^{1/j}$.

In numerical differentiation by compact central differencing, we have control over only one parameter, the step size δ. How do we choose it so that our answer has the best possible accuracy? We will here focus on the first derivative, using the expressions listed in Table 9.2.4. Our answers will therefore contain both the cancellation noise of (9.2.49) and the systematic errors that can be summarized from section 9.2.5 as

$$E_{syst} = b_j\, \delta^{j-1} \left| f_0^{\mathrm{J}} / f_0^{\mathrm{I}} \right| \tag{9.2.50}$$

where b_j is the absolute value of the coefficient of the term $f_0^{\mathrm{J}} \delta^{j-1}$ on the right-hand side of Table 9.2.4 for a given value of j; $b_3 = 1/3!$, $b_5 = 4/5!$, $b_7 = 36/7!$, etc. In total we then have

$$E_{total} = E_{syst} + E_{canc} = b_j\, \delta^{j-1} \left| \frac{f_0^{\mathrm{J}}}{f_0^{\mathrm{I}}} \right| + \frac{c_j}{\delta} \left| \frac{f_0 + x_0 f_0^{\mathrm{I}}}{f_0^{\mathrm{I}}} \right| \tag{9.2.51}$$

where we again use the absolute values to ensure that the logarithms and/or roots can always be computed, regardless of the signs of f_0, f_0^{I}, and f_0^{J}. After all, we are only interested in minimizing the absolute magnitude of the total error, which at the optimal value δ_{opt} of δ follows from (9.2.51) as

$$\frac{d\,E_{total}}{d\,\delta} = (j-1)b_j\, \delta_{opt}^{j-2} \left| \frac{f_0^{\mathrm{J}}}{f_0^{\mathrm{I}}} \right| - \frac{c_j}{\delta_{opt}^2} \left| \frac{f_0 + x_0 f_0^{\mathrm{I}}}{f_0^{\mathrm{I}}} \right| = 0 \tag{9.2.52}$$

so that

$$\delta_{opt} = \left(\frac{c_j}{(j-1)b_j} \right)^{1/j} \left| \frac{f_0 + x_0 f_0^{\mathrm{I}}}{f_0^{\mathrm{J}}} \right|^{1/j} = d_j \left| \frac{f_0 + x_0 f_0^{\mathrm{I}}}{f_0^{\mathrm{J}}} \right|^{1/j} \tag{9.2.53}$$

with

$$d_j = \left(\frac{c_j}{(j-1)b_j} \right)^{1/j} \tag{9.2.54}$$

for which Table 9.2.6 includes some values.

Figure 9.2.6 illustrates the above relations with the function $f(x) = x^{20}$ for $x_0 = 1.234$, by varying the magnitude of δ over eight decades, from $\delta = 10^{-3}$ to $\delta = 10^{-11}$. In Fig. 9.2.7 we display equivalent results for two different values of x_0, one negative and one positive, as well as of different magnitudes, and in Fig. 9.2.8 for two larger values of j.

In Fig. 9.2.6 the asymptotes are well represented by the lines predicted by (9.2.49) and (9.2.50), while the maximum in pE is indeed found near the value δ_{opt} given by (9.2.53) as indicated by an arrow.

418

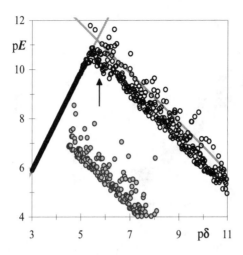

Fig. 9.2.6: Plot of pE vs. pδ for $f(x) = x^{20}$, and its numerical analysis for $j = 3$ with $x_0 = 1.234$ (open black circles). The gray straight line with slope -1 through the data is computed with (9.2.49), and the gray line with slope $+2$ with (9.2.50). The vertical arrow drawn at pδ = pδ_{opt} is calculated with (9.2.53). The gray-filled circles near the center-bottom represent uniform noise $U(-\frac{1}{2}, \frac{1}{2})$ added to a baseline with slope -1.

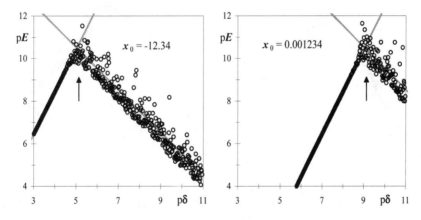

Fig. 9.2.7: Plot of pE vs. pδ for $f(x) = x^{20}$, and its numerical analysis for $j = 3$ with $x_0 = -12.34$ (left panel) and 0.001234 (right panel). The gray straight lines with slope -1 are based on (9.2.49), those with slope $+2$ on (9.2.50), and the vertical arrows are drawn for pδ_{opt} as found from (9.2.53).

Different behavior can be expected depending on whether f_0 is larger or smaller than $x_0 f_0^{I}$. We can see this with the exponential function $f(x) = e^x$, where $f_0^{I} = f_0$, where merely changing x_0 from $x_0 \gg 1$ to $x_0 \ll 1$ can serve as our test. We illustrate in Figs. 9.2.9 and 9.2.10 that this model prediction indeed holds. For $x_0 \gg 1$, the location of the right-hand asymptote and the value of pδ_{opt} change with x_0 as $-(1/j) \log(x_0)$, whereas both are essentially constant for $x_0 \ll 1$, confirming the presence of two different stages where cancellation errors can occur in central differencing, each with its own response.

419

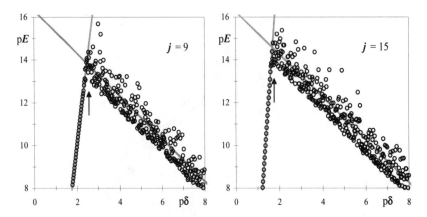

Fig. 9.2.8: Plot of pE vs. pδ for $f(x) = x^{20}$ with $x_0 = 1.234$, for $j = 9$ (left panel) and 15 (right panel). The gray straight lines with slope −1 are based on (9.2.49), those with slope +2 on (9.2.50), and the vertical arrows are drawn for pδ_{opt} as found from (9.2.53). Note that the pE and pδ scales are both shifted with respect to those in Figs. 9.2.6 and 9.2.7.

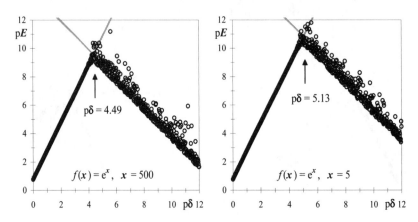

Fig. 9.2.9: Plot of pE vs. pδ for $f(x) = e^x$, and its numerical analysis for $j = 3$ with $x_0 = 500$ (left panel) and 5 (right panel). The gray straight lines are the model asymptotes, the vertical arrow is positioned at pδ_{opt}.

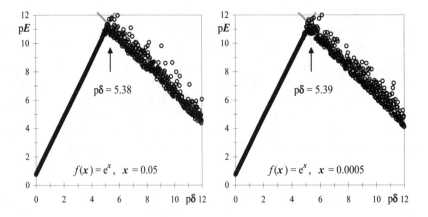

Fig. 9.2.10: Plot of pE vs. pδ for $f(x) = e^x$, and its numerical analysis for $j = 3$ with $x_0 = 0.05$ (left panel) and 0.0005 (right panel). The gray straight lines are the model asymptotes, the vertical arrow is positioned at pδ_{opt}.

420

9.2.10 Implementation

How can we use the above to compute the first derivative when, according to (9.2.53), the crucial parameter, the step size δ_{opt}, not only requires the function f_0, but also its sought first derivative f_0^I, and even the higher derivative f_0^J? We solve this riddle by realizing that we can use *approximate* values for f_0^I and f_0^J, based on a first estimate, such as $\delta \approx |x| \, \varepsilon^{1/j}$, and follow where that leads us. This yields the following iterative algorithm:

(1) read the number j of equidistant samples (an odd integer), the function $f(x)$, and the particular value $x = x_0$ for which the derivative is sought;

(2) use $\delta \approx |x_0| \, \varepsilon^{1/j}$ to estimate the step spacing, where $\varepsilon = 2^{-52}$ for Excel's double precision;

(3) sample the function in j equidistant steps from $x = x_0 - (j+1)\,\delta/2$ to $x_0 + (j+1)\,\delta/2$;

(4) use these samples to estimate both f_0^I and f_0^J;

(5) now estimate δ_{opt} with (9.2.53); and finally

(6) use this estimate for δ_{opt} to compute an improved value for f_0^I.

In a single iteration, this algorithm produces quite satisfactory results when tested with simple functions for which the first derivative f_0^I is known, as in Fig. 9.2.11, where we find $pE \geq 9.5$ for $j = 3$, $pE \geq 11$ for $j = 5$, $pE \geq 12$ for $j = 7$, and $pE \approx 13$ for $j = 9$. While there is no guarantee that such good values will be observed with other functions or x-values, these are certainly encouraging results. This approach is implemented in the macro Deriv1 of the MacroBundle, and is more fully described in *J. Chem. Sci* 121 (2009) 935-950, see http://www.ias.ac.in/chemsci/Pdf-Sep2009/671.pdf. No significant further improvement is obtained with further iterations.

As can be seen in Figs. 9.2.7 through 9.2.11, random noise limits a more accurate single determination, but averaging over a small range of neighboring δ-values might yield a more precise result. However, a tenfold increase in noise reduction would require 100 repeats. It is therefore much easier to use XN's extended precision to obtain similar or better answers.

Since we here consider accuracies beyond the first six or seven digits, Fig. 9.2.11 does not display the values of the derivatives themselves, but instead their pE-values, i.e., their number of significant figures, using as reference their algebraic first derivatives as evaluated on Excel. In a few cases we had to deviate from this: for the error function $erf(x)$ we instead used the function $cErf(x)$ of section 11.8, but let Excel evaluate its analytical derivative, $(2/\sqrt{\pi}) \exp(-x^2)$ for computing pE. For the Bessel functions, which in Excel appear to use single-precision algorithms, we used the corresponding double-precision functions from XN.xla for both the function $f(x_0)$ to be differentiated and as reference values $f^I(x_0)_{ref}$ for determining pE. Comparison of Excel's $J_0(x)$, $J_1(x)$, $Y_0(x)$, and $Y_1(x)$ with their numerical values as listed in, e.g., the *Handbook of Mathematical Functions*, M. Abramowitz & I. A. Stegun, eds., Dover (1968) pp. 390-391, confirms the low accuracy of Excel's Bessel functions, which were part of the Data Analysis Toolkit that was fully integrated into Excel 07. It is beyond my comprehension why Microsoft in 2007, when they could (and should) have exploited the *quadruple* precision option made possible by the wide availability of x64 cpu's, decided to incorporate their old *single*-precision algorithms instead.

We see that the approximation $\delta \approx x_0 \, \varepsilon^{1/j}$ is equivalent to approximating d_j by $\varepsilon^{1/j}$, and $x_0 f_0^I / f_0^J$ by x_0. This is appropriate for $|f_0| \ll |x_0 f_0^I|$, while the alternative $\delta \approx \varepsilon^{1/j}$ is more appropriate when $|f_0| \gg |x_0 f_0^I|$. At a practical level, in a double-precision environment, one should preferably use $j = 5$, 7, or 9 (for the most accurate results) when the sampling range or footprint $\pm (j-1)\,\delta/2$ is not important, and $j = 3$ when it is, choices that Deriv1 leaves to the user. In double precision, there appears to be no good reason to use j-values higher than 9.

Differentiation obviously requires special care when the function to be differentiated has discontinuities and/or singularities. Discontinuities occur in nature with, e.g., phase transitions. We can also encounter them with functions, especially with those computed using piecemeal approximations, as illustrated in Fig. 11.7.1. In the case of discontinuities, the function value changes suddenly, and so may its derivative, and it is therefore crucial that all data used in computing the derivative are taken on the same side of that discontinuity.

x_0	$f(x)$	$f^1(x)$	pE at j = 3	5	7	9	11	13	15
1.234	$4\text{-}3x+2x^2\text{-}x^3$ = 1.46443110	$-3+4x-3x^2$ = -2.63226800	10.62	14.16	13.82	14.36	14.52	15.77	15.47
1.234	x^{20} = 67.0352439	$20x^{19}$ = 1086.47073	10.00	11.89	12.65	13.83	13.70	15.20	14.73
1.234	x^{-20} = 0.01491753	$-20x^{-21}$ = -0.24177514	9.87	11.69	12.62	13.05	13.31	13.74	13.65
1.234	$x^{1/20}$ = 1.01056850	$0.05x^{-19/20}$ = 0.04094686	10.47	12.20	13.06	13.85	12.84	13.07	14.31
1.234	$x^{-1/20}$ = 0.98954202	$-0.05x^{-21/20}$ = -0.04009490	10.35	11.40	12.59	13.10	12.95	13.60	13.28
1.234	$\ln(x)$ = 0.21026093	$1/x$ = 0.81037277	11.70	13.69	13.98	13.72	14.86	14.12	15.86
1.234	$\exp(x)$ = 3.43494186	$\exp(x)$ = 3.43494186	10.78	12.99	14.01	14.93	14.71	14.47	15.04
1.234	$\sin(x)$ = 0.94381821	$\cos(x)$ = 0.33046511	10.97	12.93	13.96	14.08	15.77	14.50	15.77
1.234	$\sinh(x)$ = 1.57190806	$\cosh(x)$ = 1.86303380	11.13	13.01	15.02	14.29	14.53	14.56	14.88
0.567	$\arcsin(x)$ = 0.60285925	$1/\sqrt{(1-x^2)}$ = 1.21400801	11.52	12.73	14.01	14.23	14.59		
1.234	$\text{arsinh}(x)$ = 1.03755875	$1/\sqrt{(1+x^2)}$ = 0.62959660	10.86	12.98	13.45	14.01	15.45	14.50	14.16
1.234	$\tan(x)$ = 2.85602984	$1+\tan^2(x)$ = 9.15690644	10.38	13.51	12.78	13.79	13.33	14.37	13.61
1.234	$\tanh(x)$ = 0.84373566	$1-\tanh^2(x)$ = 0.28811013	10.69	12.36	13.18	13.32	14.04	14.14	13.81
1.234	$\arctan(x)$ = 0.88976245	$1/(1-x^2)$ = 0.39639188	11.47	13.05	13.45	13.77	14.95	14.90	14.51
0.567	$\text{artanh}(x)$ = 0.64309026	$1/(1+x^2)$ = 1.47381546	11.76	12.89	13.02	13.89	14.00	14.02	
1.234	$\text{erf}(x)$ = 0.91903942	$(2/\sqrt{\pi})\exp(-x^2)$ = 0.24611072	10.25	12.10	12.62	13.36	13.07	13.52	13.78
1.234	$I_0(x)$ = 1.41848958	$I_1(x)$ = 0.742135021	11.39	12.58	13.20	13.85	15.13	14.38	14.32
1.234	$J_0(x)$ = 0.65404541	$-J_1(x)$ = -0.50677701	10.70	13.22	14.01	14.05	14.10	14.62	14.38
1.234	$K_0(x)$ = 0.30411714	$-K_1(x)$ = -0.41218265	10.45	12.75	12.86	13.60	14.83	14.29	14.33
1.234	$Y_0(x)$ = 0.24877388	$-Y_1(x)$ = 0.596023514	10.91	12.53	13.62	14.58	15.73	14.30	14.33

Fig. 9.2.11: The accuracy of the first derivative $f_0{}^1{}_{calc}$ obtained with Deriv1 for various values of j, for a number of simple functions $f(x)$ at $x = x_0$ for which the first derivative f_0^1 is known. Because the values of $f_0{}^1{}_{calc}$ differ only in their less significant digits, we only show their pE-values.

Exercise 9.2.5:

(1) To illustrate the use of Deriv1, on a new spreadsheet place labels for x, $f(x)$, $f'(x)$, and $f''(x)$ in cells B2:B5. Next to these, place a value for x in C2, and in C3, next to the label $f(x)$, deposit an explicit, *quasi-algebraic* function $f(x)$, i.e., written in the Excel-like parser formalism described in the Math Formula String section of the help file, and as text, i.e., *not* preceded by an equal sign, see Fig. 9.2.12. In this example, a truly algebraic expression would read x^2 instead of x^2. You can precede the formula by a (non-showing) apostrophe. (Such an apostrophe is not needed here, since Excel interprets this as text, but is a still good general practice, because it would be required if the expression were to start with, e.g., a minus sign.) Verify that C4 indeed yields the first derivative $f'(x) = [(x^2+1)-2x(x+3)]/(x^2+1)^2$ of the function $f(x) = (x+3)/(x^2+1)$ in cell C3 for the x-value in C2.

(2) In cell C4, next to the label for $f'(x)$, insert the instruction `=Diff1(C2,C3)`, which will yield $f'(x)$, the first derivative of the mathematical expression for $f(x)$ in C3 for the x-value in C2.

In such cases we may have to use the asymmetric expressions for lateral differencing. The approach is the same as for central differencing, but the pE-values will be somewhat lower. Incidentally, please keep in mind that a function at its discontinuity has two values, and is often represented on a spreadsheet by their average, but such an average value should *not* be used in asymmetric differencing.

Singularities are rather rare in nature, but are quite common in math. Consequently, our necessarily simplified models of natural phenomena may well include such singularities.

The approach used in this section is quite general, but has here been limited to equidistant data, because these yield simpler solutions. When f is a function of multiple variables, as in $f(x, y, z, ...)$, the above method yields estimates of the *partial* derivative, $\partial f / \partial x$.

$$*****$$

In this section we have seen how, starting from the Taylor expansion, and with a little matrix algebra, we can find useful approximations to compute derivatives. At this point you may well ask why, in this book about scientific data analysis, so much space is devoted to differentiating *theoretical* expressions. One reason is to illustrate that mathematical conditions such as $\lim \delta \to 0$ do not translate as such into computer routines, because additional error sources can get involved, as cancellation errors do with differentiation. Another is the interesting interplay of systematic and random-like errors, i.e., of aspects resembling inaccuracy and imprecision. Moreover, we see that problems that are relatively straightforward in formal mathematics may sometimes be complicated numerically, while integration illustrates the opposite, see section 9.4.

But the most compelling reason for our emphasis on differentiation is that it is involved in virtually all optimization methods. Moreover, while most mathematical functions can be differentiated formally, in practice this can be quite cumbersome, and often requires the numerical evaluation of special functions anyway. Consequently, in a spreadsheet environment, a numerical differentiation is almost always more convenient. On the other hand, non-optimal numerical differentiation can limit the ultimate reliability of an algorithm. For instance, Excel's Solver only offers its users the choice between the simplest forms of forward and central differencing, i.e., between (9.2.2) and (9.2.4). Not surprisingly, when tested with demanding NIST reference data sets such as MGH10 or Bennett5, it only gets the first two decimals consistently right! As a result of such experiences, it is often stated that optimization methods need analytical derivatives because they are the only ones that have the required high accuracy. With the approach outlined here, and implemented in Deriv1, that argument is no longer so compelling.

9.2.11 The XN differentiation add-ins

In section 1.2.5 we described how you can download the XN.xla or XN.xlam file, which enables you to make calculations with more than double precision, as will be explained in chapter 11. However, as a byproduct of that effort, a number of functions were also introduced in their double-precision form, thereby greatly expanding the Excel instruction set. The XN instructions useful for double-precision differentiation are listed in Table 9.2.12, and their use is explained in exercise 9.2.1 and in the XN Help file. Note that these are functions, which therefore update automatically when their inputs are changed.

Diff1	First derivative of $f(x)$ in formula format
Diff2	Second derivative of $f(x)$ in formula format
Grad	Vector of first derivatives of a multivariate function
Hessian	Hessian matrix of multivariate function
Jacobian	Jacobian matrix of a vector function
DPoly	First derivative of polynomial at x_0

Table 9.2.12: The double-precision differentiation functions in XN. The top two operate on univariate functions $f(x)$, the next yields a vector of partial derivatives of a multivariate function such as $f(x,y,z,t)$, then follow two functions to generate matrices for the partial derivatives of vector inputs, while the last function operates on polynomials such as $P = a_0 + a_1 x + a_2 x^2 + a_3 x^3 + a_4 x^4$ of integral positive powers of x. They all take the quasi-algebraic parser formulas as input.

Exercise 9.2.6:

(1) On a new spreadsheet, place labels for $x, f(x), f'(x)$, and $f''(x)$ in cells B2:B5. Next to these, place a value for x in C2, and in C3, next to the label $f(x)$, deposit an explicit, *quasi-algebraic* function $f(x)$, i.e., written in the Excel-like parser formalism described in the Math Formula String section of the help file, and as text, i.e., *not* preceded by an equal sign, see Fig. 9.2.12. In this example, a truly algebraic expression would read x^2 instead of x^2. You can precede the formula by an (non-showing) apostrophe. (Such an apostrophe is not needed here, since Excel interprets this as text, but is a still good general practice, because it would be required if the expression were to start with, e.g., a minus sign.)

(2) Verify that C4 indeed yields the first derivative $f'(x) = [(x^2+1)-2x(x+3)]/(x^2+1)^2$ of the function $f(x) = (x+3)/(x^2+1)$ in cell C3 for the x-value in C2.

(3) In cell C4, next to the label for $f'(x)$, insert the instruction =Diff1(C2,C3), which will yield $f'(x)$, the first derivative of the mathematical expression for $f(x)$ in C3 for the x-value in C2.

(4) In cell C5 place the instruction =Diff2(C2,C3) next to the label for the second derivative $f''(x)$ of the function.

(5) The above instructions will yield the first and second derivatives of the function, for the x-value specified, as computed with *central* differencing for $j = 5$. For forward or backward differencing use Diff1(C2,C3,1) or Diff1(C2,C3,-1) respectively, as illustrated in cells F3 and F5; the indicator 0 for central differencing in F4 is optional, see C4. Having access to forward, central, and backward differencing can also be convenient for checking whether the function is differentiable at that particular x-value.

(6) In cells C8:C10 place values for three variables x, y, and z, with associated labels in B8:B10. In C11 then place (again in this quasi-algebraic formalism) an equation for a function $f(x,y,z)$. You can then find the three partial derivatives of that function with respect to the three variables in, e.g., E8:E10 with the array instruction =grad(C8:C10,C11). Reminder: first highlight the block E8:E10, then type the above instruction, and finally use Ctrl‿Shift‿Enter. This yields the gradient vector of the function.

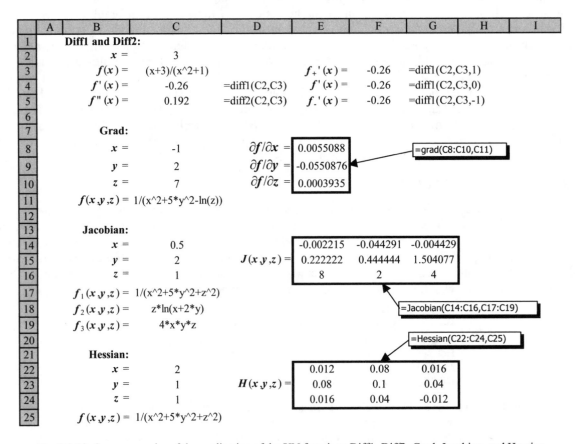

Fig. 9.2.12: Some examples of the application of the XN functions Diff1, Diff2, Grad, Jacobian, and Hessian.

(7) The Jacobian matrix yields, e.g., the partial derivatives $\partial f_1(x,y,z)/\partial x$ through $\partial f_3(x,y,z)/\partial z$ of a multivariate function $f(x,y,z)$. Enter three numbers in C14:C16 to represent x, y, and z, and provide quasi-algebraic formulas for three multivariate functions $f_1(x,y,z)$ through $f_3(x,y,z)$ in C17:C19. In E14:G17 (or anywhere else on the spreadsheet) then use the array instruction =Jacobian(C14:C16, C17:C19) to compute and display that matrix.

(8) The first row of terms in the Jacobian, E14:G14, shows the partial derivatives of the function $1/(x^2+5y^2+z^2)$ in C17 versus x, y, and z respectively. You can easily check that these results are indeed correct by calculating $-2x/(x^2+5y^2+z^2)^2$, $-10y/(x^2+5y^2+z^2)^2$, and $-2z/(x^2+5y^2+z^2)^2$ somewhere else on the spreadsheet for the values given in C14:C16 for x, y, and z. Likewise E15:G15, the second row of the Jacobian, contains the numerical values for $\partial f_2/\partial x = z/(x+2y)$, $\partial f_2/\partial y =$

424

$2z/(x+2y)$, and $\partial f_2/\partial x = \ln(x+2y)$ of the function $f_2 = z \ln(x+2y)$ in C18, and row E16:G16 has the partial derivatives $4yz$, $4xz$, and $4xy$ of $f_3 = 4xyz$. Try it out, and you'll see that it certainly is far easier to have a single command for such a tedious computation.

(9) The Hessian matrix yields the second partial derivatives of a multivariate function $f(x,y,z)$, including their mixed derivatives such as $\partial^2 f(x,y,z)/\partial x\,\partial y$. To see how it works, in cells C22:C24 deposit some values for x, y, and z, in C25 place a quasi-algebraic formula for $f(x,y,z)$, and in, e.g., E22:G24 use the array function =Hessian(C22:C24,C25).

(10) All of these are illustrated in ig. 9.2.12. Note that the XN functions Grad, Jacobian, and Hessian are restricted to four variables, x, y, z, and t, in this implied order when operating on multivariate functions. In general, consult the Help file for specific information and constraints.

9.3 Differentiating experimental data

Reducing the influence of experimental noise is often a major preoccupation in differentiating experimental data. We can, at least conceptually, assume that experimental data consist of a *signal* plus *offset* and *noise*, where offset is a constant error, while both signal and noise are time-dependent. On relatively short time scales, low-frequency noise (as may be caused by, e.g., instrumental warm-up and daily or seasonal temperature cycles) may be experienced as long-term drift, which can still be described in terms of its major frequency components.

Here we briefly consider both signal and noise in their Fourier-analyzed form as a set of sines and cosines with arbitrary angular frequencies ω and phase shifts φ. As can be seen from (9.3.1), such a formal analysis shows that differentiating a signal plus noise and offset yields a result that is immune to offset, but is sensitive to noise, the more so the higher its frequency:

$$\frac{d}{dt}\left\{f(t) + noise(t) + offset\right\} =$$

$$\frac{d}{dt}\left\{\begin{array}{l}\sum_i A_i \sin(\omega_i t + \varphi_i) + \sum_i B_i \cos(\omega_i t + \varphi_i) + \\ \sum_j a_j \sin(\omega_j t + \varphi_j) + \sum_j b_j \cos(\omega_j t + \varphi_j) + C\end{array}\right\} =$$

$$\sum_i \omega_i A_i \cos(\omega_i t + \varphi_i) - \sum_i \omega_i B_i \sin(\omega_i t + \varphi_i) +$$

$$\sum_j \omega_j a_j \cos(\omega_j t + \varphi_j) - \sum_j \omega_j b_j \sin(\omega_j t + \varphi_j) \tag{9.3.1}$$

where we have assigned the Fourier coefficients A_i and B_i to the signal $f(t)$, while the noise is described with the coefficients a_i and b_i respectively. (Before the days of instrumental Fourier transformation, most experimental data were obtained sequentially, and noise could therefore be considered a function of time t. The reasoning used here does not change when one replaces t by, e.g., x, but we will stay with time t here because it has a well-recognized inverse, the angular frequency ω.)

Differentiation of the constant C (representing the signal average plus any offset) yields zero, so that an offset in the data does not affect the derivative. On the other hand, the multiplying factors ω_i and ω_j in the bottom lines of (9.3.1) show that differentiation enhances each frequency component in direct proportion to its frequency. Therefore, noise components at frequencies higher than those in the signal will also be enhanced more than the signal, thereby reducing the signal-to-noise ratio. This enhanced sensitivity to high-frequency noise is one reason why direct differentiation of experimental data is often inadvisable.

A second reason is that experimental data may not be spaced closely enough. When the data intervals δ are large, the resulting error terms (from truncating the Taylor expansion) will also be large, except when sufficiently high-order approximations such as those listed in Table 9.2.3 are used.

One therefore usually performs "differentiation" by fitting the data to a noise-free model, which can then be differentiated symbolically. We have already encountered an example of such an approach in section 3.16, where we applied least squares to fit a moving polynomial to the data, and then used the parameters of that (noise-free) polynomial to compute the local values of the derivative.

Moreover, in section 5.7 we combined noise filtering with Fourier transformation to find the first derivative of a curve. Both of these methods happened to use equidistant data, but that is not a requirement: one can, e.g., use Solver to fit a (smooth) model to arbitrarily spaced, noisy data, and then compute the derivatives of that model at any point.

Computing the derivative at the center of five equidistant data can be done, e.g., with the results obtained in Table 9.2.4, or with the least squares formulas used in the macro ELS. These are, in fact, equivalent: the result listed in Table 9.2.4 for $j = 5$ is precisely what is found for the convoluting integers for the first derivative in a linear least squares fitting of five equidistant data points to a quartic equation, that for $j = 7$ is identical with the result for the convoluting integers for the same $j = 7$ for the first derivative for a sextic equation, etc. Higher-order derivatives require using a larger, higher-order moving polynomial.

Note the trade-offs: by making the moving polynomial longer and of higher order, one reduces noise but enhances model distortion, since a larger part of the data set is forced to fit within the straightjacket of the higher polynomial used. On the other hand, while using a shorter, lower-order polynomial can reduce such distortion, it will also tend to filter noise less efficiently: you either get bitten by the dog, or scratched by the cat.

What applies to the first derivative holds even more for the second or higher derivatives: their calculation becomes more sensitive to noise the higher the derivative, especially insofar as the noise frequencies lie above those of the signal. For that reason, high-order derivatives are seldom computed directly from experimental data, except when the latter have a sufficiently high signal-to-noise ratio.

Preventing (or at least reducing) noise at its source is, of course, preferable to having to clean up the signal afterwards, because data smoothing invariably introduces distortion. Such distortion can be reduced by using the theoretically most appropriate model. For example, when trying to determine the location of a mass-spectrometric peak (i.e., the mass-over-charge ratio of its maximum), from which one may be able to identify the chemical formula of that ion, one might want to fit the data near the peak maximum to a Gaussian curve rather than to a parabola.

Because integration tends to reduce rather than amplify the effects of high-frequency noise, one may instead prefer the alternative, of integrating the model expression (which, for a smooth model function, can often be done with high accuracy) and then comparing this directly with the experimental data.

9.4 Integrating theoretical expressions

Integration is the method used to find areas in two dimensions, or volumes in three or more dimensions. One of the early examples of integration is the determination of the area $A = \pi r^2$ enclosed by a circle of radius r, for which Archimedes, more than 22 centuries ago, found the (for that time amazingly close) limits $3^{10}/_{71} < \pi < 3^{10}/_{70}$ by using inscribed and circumscribed polygons. This famous example also illustrates a common aspect of integration: even when one integrates a known analytical function, and can find a symbolic mathematical expression for the result, as in $A = \pi r^2$, this frequently still requires a numerical evaluation. For π, such a numerical evaluation can now generate the essentially unlimited accuracy of millions of decimals, but in general we may sometimes have to settle for far less accurate answers than the more than 99.95% relative accuracy achieved by Archimedes.

Below we will describe some aspects of the numerical, two-dimensional integration of one-parameter model functions, while section 9.5 will briefly consider the integration of experimental data. The numerical integration of simple differential equations was discussed in chapter 7.

9.4.1 Trapezoidal integration

For a function that is smooth (i.e., finite, continuous, and with a sufficient number of continuous derivatives) and can be integrated throughout the integration range considered, the trapezoidal model is the simplest way to integrate a set of sequential data points. It describes the integral of the function $f(x)$ between the finite limits $x = a$ and $x = b$ in terms of sufficiently thin, vertical slices of width δ. The area of

426

each slice is computed as a rectangular trapezoid (i.e., with two adjacent right angles) formed by the horizontal base of width δ, the vertical distances $f(x)$ and $f(x+\delta)$, and the straight line connecting the points x, $f(x)$ and $x+\delta$, $f(x+\delta)$, i.e., as

$$\int_{x_0}^{x_0+\delta} f(x)\,dx \approx \frac{f(x_0) + f(x_0+\delta)}{2}\delta \tag{9.4.1}$$

whereupon the area estimates for all such slices between $x = a$ and $x = b$ are added to calculate the desired integral. The segments need not have uniform widths δ, and it may be advisable to use narrower segments in regions where $f(x)$ exhibits strong curvature.

For $n+1$ *equidistant* data, i.e., with n segments of uniform width $\delta = (b-a)/n$, and denoting $f(x)_{x=x_0}$ by f_0, and $f(x)_{x=x_0+i\delta}$ by f_i (where $i = 1, 2, 3, \ldots, n$), we have

$$\int_{x_0}^{x_0+n\delta} f(x)\,dx \approx \left(\frac{f_0+f_1}{2} + \frac{f_1+f_2}{2} + \frac{f_2+f_3}{2} + \ldots + \frac{f_{n-1}+f_n}{2}\right)\delta$$

$$= \left(\frac{f_0}{2} + f_1 + f_2 + f_3 + \ldots + f_{n-1} + \frac{f_n}{2}\right)\delta \tag{9.4.2}$$

which treats the function $f(x)$ as a piece-wise linear one.

From here on we will assume that the function $f(x)$ can be integrated and is smooth over the entire integration range considered. Under these conditions, both Euler and Maclaurin found that the resulting error in (9.4.2) can be expressed in terms of the derivatives at the edges of that range, i.e., at x and $x+\delta$ in (9.4.1) and, by extension, at x_0 and x_n respectively in (9.4.2), as

$$\int_{x_0}^{x_0+n\delta} f(x)\,dx = \left(\frac{f_0}{2} + f_1 + f_2 + f_3 + \ldots + f_{n-1} + \frac{f_n}{2}\right)\delta$$

$$- \frac{\delta^2}{12}(f_n^{\mathrm{I}} - f_0^{\mathrm{I}}) + \frac{\delta^4}{720}(f_n^{\mathrm{III}} - f_0^{\mathrm{III}}) - \frac{\delta^6}{30240}(f_n^{\mathrm{V}} - f_0^{\mathrm{V}}) + \ldots \tag{9.4.3}$$

where f_i^{I} denotes $(df(x)/dx)_{x=x_i}$, the first derivative of $f(x)$ at $x = x_i$, f_i^{III} denotes the third derivative at $x = x_i$, etc. Because the error in (9.4.2) is, to a first approximation, proportional to δ^2, one gains precision by decreasing the size of δ, as illustrated in exercises 9.4.1 and 9.4.2.

Exercise 9.4.1:

(1) As a first example, integrate $f(x) = \exp[-x^2]$ from $x = -1$ to $x = +1$.

(2) In cells B3:C3 of a new spreadsheet, place column headings for x and $\exp[-x^2]$ respectively. In cells B5:B9 enter the x-values -1 ($\frac{1}{2}$) $+1$, and in C5:C9 calculate the corresponding values of $\exp[-x_2]$, e.g., as =EXP(-1*B5^2) or =EXP(-(B5^2)) in cell C5. (Remember: =EXP(-B5^2) would lose its minus sign because Excel computes it as =EXP((-B5)^2)).

(3) In cell D5 compute the integral I as $[(f_0+f_4)/2 + (f_1+f_2+f_3)]\,\delta$ where $\delta = \frac{1}{2}$ with, e.g., the instruction ((C5+C9)/2+SUM(C6:C8))*(B6-B5).

(4) In cells B11:B19 place the x-values -1 ($\frac{1}{4}$) $+1$, in column C compute the corresponding values for $\exp[-x^2]$, and in cell D11 find the integral I, which is now given by $I = [(f_0+f_8)/2 + (f_1+f_2+f_3+f_4+f_5+f_6+f_7)]\,\delta$ with $\delta = \frac{1}{4}$, computed with, e.g., ((C11+C19)/2+SUM(C12:C18))*(B12-B11).

(5) In cells B21:B37 place -1 ($\frac{1}{8}$) $+1$, again compute the corresponding values for $\exp[-x^2]$ in column C, and in cell D21 calculate the integral I as $[(f_0+f_{16})/2+(f_1+f_2+f_3+\ldots+f_{14}+f_{15})]\,\delta$ with $\delta = \frac{1}{8}$.

(6) Continue this process, by halving δ each time, with a corresponding increase in the number of data points used. The results you should find for I are 1.46274, 1.48597, 1.49173, 1.49317, 1.49353, 1.49362, etc., indeed gradually approaching the correct value of 1.49364_8.

(1) As our second example, integrate the same function $f(x) = \exp[-x^2]$ from $x = -\infty$ to $x = +\infty$. This integral has the known value of $\sqrt{\pi}$. Since $\exp[-x^2]$ is symmetrical around $x = 0$, it suffices to integrate from $x = 0$ to $x = +\infty$, which yields $\frac{1}{2}\sqrt{\pi}$.

(2) In cells F3:G3 of the same spreadsheet, again place column headings for x and $\exp[-x^2]$, in cells F5:F9 enter the x-values 0 (2) 8, and in G5:G9 calculate the corresponding values of $\exp[-x^2]$. Infinity is not a number on the keyboard, but $\exp[-8^2] \approx 1.6 \times 10^{-28}$ is small enough for $x = 8$ to stand in for $x = \infty$.

(3) In cell H5 compute the integral, as before, and in cell H6 divide that answer by its exact value, $\frac{1}{2}\sqrt{\pi}$.

(4) In cells F11:H19 repeat this integration for $x = 0$ (0.5) 4 as $I = [(f_0+f_8)/2 + (f_{0.5}+f_1+f_{1.5}+\ldots+f_7+f_{7.5})]\,\delta$ with $\delta = 1$, then in F21:H37 do the same for $x = 0$ ($\frac{1}{2}$) 8, and in F39:H71. for $x = 0$ ($\frac{1}{4}$) 8.

(5) The results found for I show no further improvement between the last three integrations. Indeed, the values found for I are 1.036632, 0.886319, 0.886227, 0.886227, and those for $2I/\sqrt{\pi}$ will be 1.1697, 1.0001034, 1.00000000000000, and 1.00000000000000 respectively. You have reached the end of the line in just three steps! Save the spreadsheet for exercise 9.4.3.

Both exercises illustrate that the accuracy of the trapezoidal integration increases by reducing the step size δ. In general, such improvement takes many steps, see exercise 9.4.1. Then why did the integration in exercise 9.4.2 converge so much faster, even with larger steps δ?

For the answer we look at the error terms in (9.4.3). By selecting the integration range in exercise 9.4.2 such that both f_0^I (at $x = 0$) and f_n^I (at $x = 8$) were essentially zero, convergence actually went at least as δ^4 rather than δ^2, thereby considerably speeding up the process. It also follows from (9.4.3) that trapezoidal integration will yield excellent results when integrating a smooth, *periodic* function over one or more entire periods, as long as the differences $f_n^I - f_0^I$, $f_n^{III} - f_0^{III}$, etc., are zero.

9.4.2 Automating trapezoidal integration

Numerical integration by equidistant trapezoidal integration between fixed limits is automated in the custom macros TrapezAuto and Trapez-Specify of the MacroBundle. Both macros use three spreadsheet rows for input, one for its lower limit, one for its upper limit, and one for computing the integral. (Additional rows are allowed, but are ignored in the calculation.) The macro starts at $k = 1$ with using just three ($= 2^k + 1$) points. For $k = 2$ it adds two points to halve the widths of the trapezoids (for a total of $2^k + 1 = 5$ points), then (for $k = 2$) it adds four ($= 2^2$) more points in the next refinement, eight ($= 2^3$) in the next, and so on. In this way the macro need not recompute points already calculated before. Since all function values other than those at its lower and upper limits (f_0 and f_n in (9.4.2) respectively) are weighted equally, their values need not be retained: they are merely added to the earlier sum, and only this sum is kept.

The macro lets the user specify a desired *number of significant figures*. This quantity is often defined as an integer, in which case it is too crude to be of much quantitative use. However, in section 9.1 we redefined it as a continuous value, no longer restricted to integers. The quantity specified there as pE measures the negative 10-based logarithm (the p as in **pH**) of the (relative or absolute) Error, i.e., the difference between a result and its correct answer. When we numerically integrate an equation we will usually not know its 'true' value, otherwise we would not bother with a numerical integration. The quantity pD used in the Trapez and Romberg custom macros therefore measures the negative 10-based logarithm of the Difference between successive approximations. This provides an internal, relative measure of convergence pD, analogous to (but somewhat more conservative than) pE. The macro will keep refining its answer, by halving the width δ of the integration interval, until pD surpasses the specified value.

As a safety precaution against endless computing, in case the termination criterion cannot be reached, a given maximum number of iteration cycles must also be specified. The latter constraint can easily be replaced by a maximum execution time, because the total time elapsed since the start of the calculation is also monitored by the macro. (How many iteration cycles are needed for an answer with a given number of significant digits, or how much time, strongly depends on the particular integral, as we just saw in exercises 9.4.1 and 9.4.2.) The user is informed, through a cell comment, when the macro does not reach its assigned criterion within its specified constraint.

TrapezAuto and TrapezSpecify call the same subroutine, Integrate, which is written for general-purpose use and, as all open-source code in the MacroBundle, can readily be modified to suit your needs. For routine applications you might, e.g., comment out the input boxes specifying the number of significant figures D and the maximum number of iterations kMax because, with fixed values of D and kMax, it would be even easier to use these macros. You might also want to restrict the output to just the final result. Now that you know this horse, take it by its reigns.

The difference between TrapezAuto and TrapezSpecify lies in the way in which the macro finds the expression to be integrated. In TrapezAuto the macro uses the reconstruction method described in section 8.14.2, whereas TrapezSpecify requires the user to specify in advance, in the function Equation(x), the mathematical expression to be integrated. The latter greatly shortens execution times, in slowly converging cases often by one to two orders of magnitude. However, when you forget to update the equation you might integrate the wrong expression. Below we illustrate the speed and convenience of the custom macro Trapez.

	A	B
1	Integrate a function: $y = \exp[-(x^2)]$	
2		
3	x	$F(x)$
4		
5	0	1
6	1	0.367879441
7	8	1.60381E-28
8		
9	*integral*	*time/s*
10		
11	2.000000450140700	0
12	1.036631502847820	0
13	0.886318602413326	0
14	0.886226925452758	0
15	0.886226925452758	0

Fig. 9.4.2: The slightly annotated output obtained upon highlighting the input data block A5:B7 and calling TrapezAuto to find the integral with six or more significant decimals in no more than 15 iterations. A comment in cell A11 contains documentation of the macro used, its input block and settings, as well as the date and time of use; its text is displayed when the pointer hovers over it. The time displays the cumulative integration interval, in seconds.

Exercise 9.4.3:

(1) Integrate $f(x) = \exp[-x^2]$ from $x = 0$ to $x = +8$ using TrapezAuto. In a block three rows high and two columns wide, say A5:B7, place the x-values in the first column (A5:A7), with the lower integration limit (0) in the first row (i.e., in cell A5), the upper limit (8) in the third row (A7), and an intermediate x-value (e.g., 1) in the middle row (A6).

(2) In the top right cell of that block (B5) place an instruction embodying the equation to be integrated, in this case = EXP(-1*A5^2) or =EXP(-(A5^2)), then copy this instruction down to B6 and B7. Note that TrapezAuto can handle expressions that contain up to six different places where the variable x (here: A5) is mentioned, and can be extended to accommodate more.

(3) Highlight the block (A5:B7), and call the macro TrapezAuto. When the two input boxes ask you to specify the number of significant digits (up to 14), and the maximum number of iterations (up to 30), either enter your choices, or simply push OK or Enter; in the latter case the macro will use the default values shown.

(4) In this case, three iterations suffice to find the answer, with at least 14 significant decimals, within the blink of an eye. As can be seen in Fig. 9.4.2, the macro exactly reproduces the intermediate and final values for the integral from exercise 9.4.2.

Exercise 9.4.4:

(1) For the problem of exercise 9.4.1 we keep the function in B5:B7, and merely change the initial and final values to -1 in A5, and +1 in A7. (The value in A6 is immaterial, as long as it does not lead to an error message.) Again highlight the input data block A5:B7, and call TrapezAuto. Specify 10 significant digits, within up to 25 iterations. The macro may take a few seconds to achieve a result to 10 significant digits.

(2) Now repeat this numerical integration with TrapezSpecify, which will speed it up considerably. Again highlight the input data block (A5:B7), call the Macro dialog box (with Alt⌣F8), but now click only *once* on the name TrapezSpecify, and then on <u>E</u>dit. This will bring you to the VBEditor at the beginning of TrapezSpecify. Go up a few lines to Function Equation(*x*), and there specify your function as `Equation = Exp(-1 * x ^2)`.

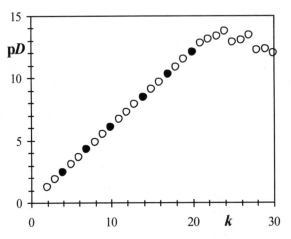

Fig. 9.4.3: The relative measure pD used to gauge the degree to which the results remain the same in two successive iterations of exercise 9.4.4, as a function of the number *k* of iterations used so far. Solid points show *k*-values that yield 2, 4, 6, 8, 10, and 12 such decimals; pE ≥ 14 is out of reach. This graph was made after commenting out the termination criterion that guards against non-convergence.

(3) Either move down a few lines until your pointer is within TrapezSpecify, and then click the function key F5, or exit the VBEditor and call TrapezSpecify. Again select six significant digits; the macro should produce its answer almost immediately (in about 0.2 s on my 3 GHz Pentium-4 pc).

(4) Call TrapezSpecify again, this time for eight significant digits. If you get an alert that the numerical integration did not reach its goal; solve this by rerunning TrapezSpecify with eight significant digits and within, say, at most 20 iterations.

(5) Repeat for 12 significant decimals, then for 13. At this accuracy you will need to set the maximum number of iterations high, say at 25. And you may just have to wait a few seconds, but you will get your answers.

(6) Can you get 14 significant digits? Set the number of iterations to 26 and try it. Better yet, if you have enough time (over lunchbreak, during some other time-out, or preferably overnight), set kMax to its highest value, 30, and try it again.

(7) Your patience will be rewarded with a surprise: the answer turns out to be out of reach, not because you did not give the computer enough time or a sufficient number of iterations, but because the integration no longer converges onto the correct answer, see Fig. 9.4.3. (You can compute the pD values shown in that graph by depositing the instruction =– LOG(ABS((B12-B11)/B11)) in cell C12, and copying it down. For *k* deposit 1, 2, etc. in D11, D12, and so on down.) Or look at the numerical values produced for the integral, which seem to approach a value close to 1.49364826562481 in cell A34, for *k* = 24, and then start to drift away from convergence. Incidentally, the correct answer is 1.49364826562485.

What happens here is simply a case of too many data points, each good to about 2×10^{-16}, that must all be added to compute the integral. For *k* = 24 we have $2^{2(k-1)} + 1 = 2^{46} + 1 = 70,368,744,177,665$ data points, for *k* = 30 we use $2^{58} + 1 = 288,230,376,151,712,001$. With such huge numbers of data, their accumulated round-off errors finally get in our way.

Here, then, you encounter a limit of what trapezoidal integration can do. In many cases, a relatively low accuracy of, say, six to eight significant digits is good enough, and when you need more, Trapez usually lets you make a convenient trade-off between the number of significant digits and the time needed to reach that accuracy, and alerts you when it cannot reach that goal. But even when you are willing to spend an inordinate amount of time, Trapez cannot find the integral of $y = \exp[-x^2]$ between 0 and 1 to 14 significant digits. And while this is not quite a trivial integration, it is certainly not the most challenging integration problem you are likely to encounter in practice.

430

In the trade-off between accuracy and efficiency, only the latter is under our control. We therefore look for more efficient ways to perform this integration. One obvious way is to consider the implementation of the present algorithm to see if we can speed it up. We already did this, by moving from invasive sampling (section 8.14.1) to reconstructing equations (8.14.2) so that we need not switch multiple times between spreadsheet and macro code for each data point, and finally to incorporating the expression specifically in VBA code, either directly or, as done here, in a separate function. That gained us between one and two orders of magnitude in speed, without any loss in accuracy. But still we hit a limit, this one set by accumulated round-off error. Time is not the culprit in Fig. 9.4.2, and neither is the limit $k \leq 30$.

Because we have most likely exhausted the possibilities for finding a significantly better *implementation*, we will look for a more efficient *algorithm* in the next section.

9.4.3 Romberg trapezoidal integration

Comparison of the results in exercises 9.4.1 and 9.4.2 illustrated that reducing the leading error term in (9.4.3) could be much more effective than reducing the step size δ, especially since we have just seen that further decreasing δ can extract a price in accuracy. Here, then, is a general approach that, systematically and in order of relative importance, removes one error term after another, and thereby yields a very efficient yet still equidistant trapezoidal integration routine. We will first illustrate its principle with a fixed number $n+1 = 17$ of equidistant data points, so that the distance δ between them is $(x_n - x_0)/16$.

The error terms in (9.4.3) depend only on the derivatives at the extremes of the integration range, at $x = x_n$ and $x = x_0$, and on the step size δ. We therefore apply (9.4.3) twice: first for step size δ, then for step size 2δ. In the latter case we use only nine data points (i.e., eight double-width intervals instead of 16 single-width ones) for the same integration range. For step size δ we have

$$I_{16}^{(1)} = \left(f_0 + 2f_1 + 2f_2 + ... + 2f_{15} + f_{16}\right)\delta/2 + A\delta^2 + B\delta^4 + C\delta^6 + D\delta^8 + ... \tag{9.4.4}$$

where we have abbreviated this first approximation of the integral with 16 intervals as $I_{16}^{(1)}$, and the δ-independent parts of the error terms as $A = -(f_{16}^I - f_0^I)/12$, $B = +(f_{16}^{III} - f_0^{III})/720$, $C = -(f_{16}^V - f_0^V)/30240$, etc.

For step size 2δ we have, likewise,

$$I_8^{(1)} = \left(f_0 + 2f_2 + 2f_4 + ... + 2f_{14} + f_{16}\right)\delta + A(2\delta)^2 + B(2\delta)^4 + C(2\delta)^6 + D(2\delta)^8 + ...$$
$$= \left(f_0 + 2f_2 + 2f_4 + ... + 2f_{14} + f_{16}\right)\delta + 4A\delta^2 + 16B\delta^4 + 64C\delta^6 + 252D\delta^8 + ... \tag{9.4.5}$$

Consequently we can eliminate the leading error term in A by subtracting (9.4.5) from four times (9.4.4), resulting in thrice the sought integral. We therefore find an improved formula for the integral as

$$I_{16}^{(2)} = \left(4I_{16}^{(1)} - I_8^{(1)}\right)/3 = (f_0 + 4f_1 + 2f_2 + 4f_3 + 2f_4 + 4f_5 + 2f_6 + 4f_7 + 2f_8 + 4f_9 + 2f_{10} + 4f_{11} + 2f_{12}$$
$$+ 4f_{13} + 2f_{14} + 4f_{15} + f_{16})\,\delta/3\ -12\,B\,\delta^4 - 60\,C\,\delta^6 - 252\,D\,\delta^8 - ... \tag{9.4.6}$$

This result, with its alternating inner terms (but usually without its Euler-Maclaurin error estimates) is often called Simpson's formula, even though it was described more than a century earlier by Cavalieri and, subsequently, by Gregory and by Cotes, two contemporaries of Newton. In fact, Simpson's rule follows directly from the "barrel problem" solved by Kepler in 1612, long before the invention of calculus.

Of course we need not stop with (9.4.6), because we can repeat the process and eliminate the B-term to find the Boolean formula

$$I_{16}^{(3)} = \left(16I_{16}^{(2)} - I_8^{(2)}\right)/15 = 16 \times (f_0 + 4f_1 + 2f_2 + 4f_3 + 2f_4 + 4f_5 + 2f_6 + 4f_7 + 2f_8 + 4f_9 + 2f_{10} + 4f_{11} + 2f_{12}$$
$$+ 4f_{13} + 2f_{14} + 4f_{15} + f_{16})\,\delta/45 - 16 \times (12B\delta^4 + 60C\delta^6 + 252D\delta^8 + ...)/15$$
$$- 2 \times (f_0 + 4f_2 + 2f_4 + 4f_6 + 2f_8 + 4f_{10} + 2f_{12} + 4f_{14} + f_{16})\,\delta/45$$
$$+ (12B \times 16\delta^4 + 60C \times 64\delta^6 + 252D \times 256\delta^8 + ...)/15$$

$$= (14f_0+64f_1+24f_2+64f_3+28f_4+64f_5+24f_6+64f_7+28f_8+64f_9+24f_{10}+64f_{11}+28f_{12}$$
$$+46f_{13}+24f_{14}+64f_{15}+14f_{16}) \; \delta/45 +192\,C\delta^6 + 4032D\delta^8 +... \tag{9.4.7}$$

The next stage eliminates the C-term, and results in

$$I_{16}^{(4)} = \left(64I_{16}^{(3)} - I_8^{(3)}\right)\!\big/63= (868f_0+4096f_1+1408f_2+4096f_3+1744f_4+4096f_5$$
$$+1408f_6+4096f_7+1736f_8+4096f_9+1408f_{10}+4096f_{11}+1744f_{12}+4096f_{13}$$
$$+1408f_{14}+4096f_{15}+868f_{16}) \; \delta/2835 - 967680D\delta^8 -... \tag{9.4.8}$$

By using 32, 64, 128 etc. rather than 16 intervals δ, this approach can be refined further, leading to the coefficients of y listed in Table 9.4.1. Figure 9.4.4 displays these sequences of Romberg coefficients, after scaling by their common denominators. Clearly, the higher-order Romberg coefficients are relatively minor variations on the $(1, 4, 2, 4, ... , 4, 2, 4, 1) / 3$ scheme of (9.4.6), while improving the accuracy of the integration.

The most efficient approach, at each successive step, is to eliminate the leading error term by doubling the number n of segments used, i.e., by halving δ. This algorithm starts with $n = 2$, i.e., with just two segments of width $\delta = f_n-f_0$, and consequently with only $n+1$ or three data points, f_0 through f_2. At each iteration stage, the macro doubles n and halves δ. While the coefficients listed in Table 9.4.1 can be used as such, one more often only follows the logic that led to them, in terms of the successive integrals $I_n^{(k)}$, which can be written in a very compact code.

Romberg integration is usually the best available general-purpose algorithm for the integration of equidistant data points with model functions that are integratable and smooth (i.e., continuous, with continuous derivatives, and without singularities) over their entire integration range, including their edges. Trapezoidal integration is only more efficient when the derivatives of the function at both integration limits are either zero (as in exercise 9.4.1) or equal (as in integrating a repetitive function over exactly one or more repeat cycles).

Romberg integration is automated in the custom macro Romberg which, like Trapez, comes in two flavors: RombergAuto and RombergSpecify. In fact, the Romberg approach involves such a small modification of the Trapez macro that they are both implemented by the subroutine Integrate.

Exercise 9.4.5:

(1) We will once more visit the problem of the exercises 9.4.2 through 9.4.4, namely the integration of $\exp[-x^2]$ between $x = -1$ and $x = +1$.

(2) Somewhere on a spreadsheet place an appropriate input data block for this problem, two columns wide and at least three rows high, and highlight it.

(3) Call RombergAuto, and specify 14 significant digits in no more than 30 iterations. The answer will appear almost instantaneously, using only nine iterations.

(4) Make sure that the function Equation(x) carries the correct expression. Again highlight the input data block, and call RombergSpecify. You get the same answer, but now even faster, although the difference between a blink of an eye, and a tenth of one, will hardly matter.

(5) Verify that Romberg integration of this function between zero and infinity (in practice, the range from 0 to 8 will do) likewise yields a fast response with either RombergAuto or RombergSpecify.

The fast convergence of Romberg integration, to a higher accuracy than could be obtained with Trapez, says it all: when given a choice such as you now have with the availability of these two custom macros, Romberg integration is almost always superior to trapezoidal integration, both in terms of accuracy and speed. The only time that trapezoidal integration holds an advantage is when the function has equal derivatives at its integration limits.

The Romberg method is clearly an equidistant trapezoidal method with successively refined weights. Why does it often work where the trapezoidal method fails? Because, by using non-uniform weights, it manages to reduce a number of error sources, and therefore converges at a lower number of iterations, which don't require such a huge number of data points and therefore cause smaller round-off errors.

Eventually, when an integral is sufficiently difficult, we will again run into the same problem but, in practice, Romberg integration makes a large number of integration problems amenable to numerical solution that is accurate (to within 14 significant decimals, which is about all one can expect in software that follows the IEEE 754 protocol, see section 9.1), and usually is fast. Moreover, if ever needed, you can modify an open-source macro such as Romberg to obtain still higher accuracy by using XN.

n	scheme	coefficients						denominator
2	a *(b)* a	$a=1$	$b=2$					2
2^2	$a\,b\,$ *(c* $b)\,a$	$a=1$	$b=4$	$c=2$				3
2^3	$a\,b\,c\,b\,$ *(d* $b\,c\,b)\,a$	$a=14$	$b=64$	$c=24$	$d=28$			45
2^4	$a\,b\,c\,b\,d\,b\,c\,b\,$ *(e* $b\,c\,b\,d\,b\,c\,b)\,a$							
		$a=868$	$b=4096$	$c=1408$	$d=1744$	$e=1736$		2835
2^5	$a\,b\,c\,b\,d\,b\,c\,b\,e\,b\,c\,b\,d\,b\,c\,b\,$ *(f* $b\,c\,b\,d\,b\,c\,b\,e\,b\,c\,b\,d\,b\,c\,b)\,a$							
		$a=220472$	$b=1048576$	$c=352256$	$d=443648$	$e=440928$	$f=440944$	722925
2^6	$a\,b\,c\,b\,d\,b\,c\,b\,e\,b\,c\,b\,d\,b\,c\,b\,f\,b\,c\,b\,d\,b\,c\,b\,e\,b\,c\,b\,d\,b\,c\,b$							
	(g $b\,c\,b\,d\,b\,c\,b\,e\,b\,c\,b\,d\,b\,c\,b\,f\,b\,c\,b\,d\,b\,c\,b\,e\,b\,c\,b\,d\,b\,c\,b)\,a$							
		$a=225322384$	$b=1073741824$	$c=358612992$	$d=453591040$			
		$e=450622976$	$f=450644800$	$g=450644768$				739552275
2^7	$a\,b\,c\,b\,d\,b\,c\,b\,e\,b\,c\,b\,d\,b\,c\,b\,f\,b\,c\,b\,d\,b\,c\,b\,e\,b\,c\,b\,d\,b\,c\,b$							
	$g\,b\,c\,b\,d\,b\,c\,b\,e\,b\,c\,b\,d\,b\,c\,b\,f\,b\,c\,b\,d\,b\,c\,b\,e\,b\,c\,b\,d\,b\,c\,b)$							
	(h $b\,c\,b\,d\,b\,c\,b\,e\,b\,c\,b\,d\,b\,c\,b\,f\,b\,c\,b\,d\,b\,c\,b\,e\,b\,c\,b\,d\,b\,c\,b$							
	$g\,b\,c\,b\,d\,b\,c\,b\,e\,b\,c\,b\,d\,b\,c\,b\,f\,b\,c\,b\,d\,b\,c\,b\,e\,b\,c\,b\,d\,b\,c\,b)\,a$							
		$a=922469840096$	$b=4398046511104$	$c=1466731331584$	$d=1857191673856$			
		$e=1844844527616$	$f=1844939854848$	$g=1844939680128$	$h=1844939680192$			3028466566125

Table 9.4.1: The coefficients of the Romberg trapezoid scheme for its first seven iterations. Each subsequent iteration doubles n and uses one additional coefficient, which is highlighted in boldface. Brackets indicate potential repeat units.

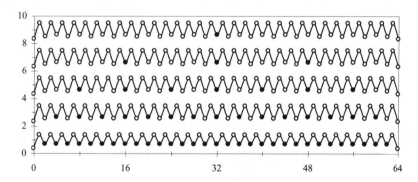

Fig. 9.4.4: The sequence of Romberg coefficients for (from bottom to top) $n = 4$, 8, 16, 32, and 64, after division by the corresponding denominator, for a data set of 65 points. For the sake of clarity, successive curves are each shifted upwards by 2. The filled circles correspond to the boldface letters in Table 9.4.1. The next-higher-order Romberg sequence, for $n = 2^7$, would require at least 129 data points.

When, at a particular x-value, a function cannot be evaluated because it is *indeterminate*, such as 0/0 or ∞/∞, the spreadsheet can often provide an easy numerical way to find its limiting behavior. In computing, e.g., the value of $f = (x^3-8)/(x-2)$ at $x = 2$, one obtains the error message #DIV/0! But calculating and plotting f as a function of x *around* $x = 2$ (at, say, $x = 1.999$, 1.999999, $2-10^{-9}$, $2-10^{-12}$, $2+10^{-12}$, $2+10^{-9}$, 2.000001, and 2.001) strongly suggests that $f = 12$ at $x = 2$, the same result that one would obtain by using the rule of de l'Hôpital. Similarly, for $f = \sin(x)/x$ at $x = 0$ we find $f = 1$, for $f = [\cos(2x)/(x-\pi/4)]^2$ at $x = \pi/4$ we get 4, etc.

433

When you encounter such indeterminate points at the edge of the integration range, simply replace them by their correct limiting value, and proceed with Romberg. If they happen to lie inside the integration range, divide the range into subranges such that all indeterminate points are at their edges, integrate the individual subranges, and add their integrals.

Exercise 9.4.6:

(1) We once more integrate $\exp[-x^2]$ for $0 \le x \le 8$. Make a column with the values 0, 1, and 8, and next to it calculate the corresponding values of $\exp[-x^2]$. Highlight the array, and see that, when demanding 15-decimal accuracy, Romberg-Auto yields the result $\frac{1}{2}\sqrt{\pi} = 0.886226925452758$.

(2) Likewise, with x-values of -1, 0, and 1, RombergAuto indeed delivers the correct answer, 1.49364826562485.

While most functions that a scientist or engineer would need to integrate numerically are rather well behaved, that need not always be the case. Even a simple function such as $f(x) = 1/x$ approaches $\pm\infty$ when x approaches 0, and will give difficulties at this *singularity*. In such a case, again split the integration range into subranges so that all singularities occur only at their edges, and then use either Romberg midpoint integration (see the next section) or, when there is no need to use equidistant data, Romberg-Kahan integration (outlined in section 9.4.5), or Gauss-Legendre integration (not discussed here at all, to keep this chapter from growing into an entire book).

9.4.4 Romberg midpoint integration

Occasionally one may need to integrate so-called *improper* integrals that cannot be integrated using the trapezoidal rule, e.g., when one or both of the integration limits has integrable singularities. In such cases it is sometimes possible to modify the Romberg trapezoid method to account for additional error terms introduced by singularities, or to avoid problems by clever parameter substitution, but for users without the specialized knowledge or patience to sort this out in each individual case, it may be simpler to use a general method that avoids evaluating the function at such points altogether. Midpoint integration can sometimes provide such an alternative. Figure 9.4.5 illustrates the difference between trapezoidal and midpoint integration; in the latter case, we approximate the integral from x_0 to $x_0+\delta$ with a rectangle of width δ and height $y_{x=x_0+\delta/2}$, i.e., as

$$\int_{x_0}^{x_0+\delta} f(x)\,dx \approx f(x_0 + \delta/2)\times\delta \quad \text{instead of as} \quad \approx \left[f(x_0) + f(x_0 + \delta)\right]\times\delta/2 \tag{9.4.9}$$

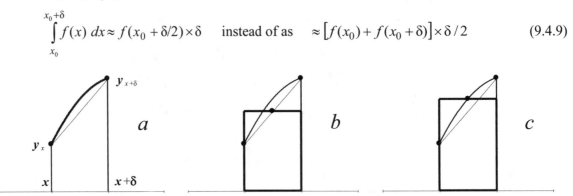

Fig. 9.4.5. *a*: The function $y(x)$ (heavy curve) and its linear approximation (thin line between y_x and $y_{x+\delta}$). *b*: The corresponding area as approximated by the trapezoidal method, where the rectangle has the height $(y_x+y_{x+\delta})/2$. *c*: The corresponding area as approximated by the midpoint method, with a rectangle height of $y_{x+\delta/2}$.

In the limit of infinitely narrow widths δ, the curvature of the function $y(x)$ will become negligible, so that the two approaches will yield the same results. While the midpoint method is somewhat less efficient when combined with Romberg's approach, it has the advantage that no function evaluations are required at x and $x+\delta$, but only at $x+\delta/2$, slightly removed from the edge. Again, the segments need not have equal widths δ, but we will adopt that restriction in order to use the Romberg method. For the integration inter-

434

val from $x = x_0$ to $x = x_n$ we now divide that interval into n equal intervals of width $\delta = (x_n - x_0)/n$, and include the corresponding Euler-Maclaurin error estimates in

$$\int_{x_0}^{x_n} f(x)\, dx = \left(f_{1/2} + f_{3/2} + f_{5/2} + f_{7/2} + \ldots + f_{n-3/2} + f_{n-1/2}\right)\delta$$

$$+ \frac{\delta^2}{24}(f_n^{\mathrm{I}} - f_0^{\mathrm{I}}) - \frac{7\delta^4}{5760}(f_n^{\mathrm{III}} - f_0^{\mathrm{III}}) + \frac{31\delta^6}{967680}(f_n^{\mathrm{V}} - f_0^{\mathrm{V}}) - \ldots$$

(9.4.10)

where the signs of the Euler-Maclaurin correction terms are the opposites of those in (9.4.3), because the trapezoidal model either underestimates the actual area when the midpoint method overestimates it, as illustrated in Fig. 9.4.5, or vice versa.

Applying the same formula to segments that are thrice as wide yields

$$\int_{x_0}^{x_n} f(x)\, dx = \left(f_{3/2} + f_{9/2} + f_{15/2} + \ldots + f_{n-9/2} + f_{n-3/2}\right)3\delta$$

$$+ \frac{9\delta^2}{24}(f_n^{\mathrm{I}} - f_0^{\mathrm{I}}) - \frac{567\delta^4}{5760}(f_n^{\mathrm{III}} - f_0^{\mathrm{III}}) + \frac{22599\delta^6}{967680}(f_n^{\mathrm{V}} - f_0^{\mathrm{V}}) - \ldots$$

(9.4.11)

As in the case of (9.4.3), we can again eliminate the leading error terms, one by one. Say that we start with $n = 3^2 = 9$ equal segments, then we can use

$$I_9^{(2)} = \left(9I_9^{(1)} - I_3^{(1)}\right)/8 = (9f_{1/2} + 9f_{3/2} + 9f_{5/2} + 9f_{7/2} + 9f_{9/2} + 9f_{11/2} + 9f_{13/2}$$

$$+ 9f_{15/2} + 9f_{17/2} - 3f_{3/2} - 3f_{9/2} - 3f_{15/2})\delta/8$$

$$- \frac{7\times(9-81)\delta^4}{5760}(f_n^{\mathrm{III}} - f_0^{\mathrm{III}}) + \frac{31\times(9-729)\delta^6}{967680}(f_n^{\mathrm{V}} - f_0^{\mathrm{V}}) - \ldots$$

$$= (9f_{1/2} + 6f_{3/2} + 9f_{5/2} + 9f_{7/2} + 6f_{9/2} + 9f_{11/2} + 9f_{13/2} + 6f_{15/2} + 9f_{17/2})\delta/8$$

$$+ \frac{7\delta^4}{80}(f_n^{\mathrm{III}} - f_0^{\mathrm{III}}) - \frac{31\delta^6}{1344}(f_n^{\mathrm{V}} - f_0^{\mathrm{V}}) + \ldots$$

(9.4.12)

and so on, see Table 9.4.2 and Fig. 9.4.3.

n	scheme	coefficients				denominator
3	*a b a*	$a = 9$	$b = 6$			8
3^2	*a b a a c a a b a*	$a = 729$	$b = 459$	$c = 468$		640
3^3	*a b a a c a a b a a b a a d a a b a a b a a c a a b a*					
		$a = 531441$	$b = 332424$	$c = 339795$	$d = 339768$	465920
3^4	*a b a a c a a b a a b a a d a a b a a b a a c a a b a a b a a c a a b a a b a a* **e**					
	a a b a a b a a c a a b a a b a a c a a b a a b a a d a a b a a b a a c a a b a					
	$a = 3486784401$	$b = 2179439541$	$c = 2228397723$	$d = 2228198463$	$e = 2228198544$	3056435200

Table 9.4.2: The coefficients of the Romberg midpoint scheme for its first four iterations. Each subsequent iteration triples n and uses one additional coefficient, here highlighted in boldface.

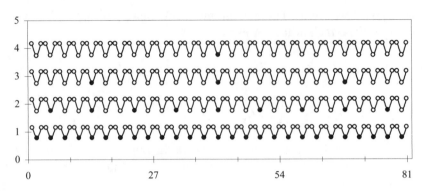

Fig. 9.4.6: The sequence of Romberg midpoint coefficients for (from bottom to top) $n = 3$, 9, 27, and 81, after division by the corresponding denominator, for a data set of 81 points. For the sake of clarity, successive curves are each shifted upwards by 1. The filled circles correspond to the boldface letters in Table 9.4.2. The next-higher-order Romberg midpoint sequence, for $n = 3^5$, would require at least 729 data points.

In Fig. 9.4.6 we plot the sequence of Romberg midpoint coefficients of Table 9.4.2 in the order specified, each divided by their denominator. These coefficients are seen to stay close to the trend of (9.4.12), with $9/8 = 1.125$ and $6/8 = 0.75$, just as those plotted in Fig. 9.4.5 resemble (9.4.6).

While the midpoint method makes it at least possible to integrate functions that include singularities (assuming of course that these functions have integrals), its results are often still rather unsatisfactory. You can improve on it by splitting the problem up into two or more integrals, using smaller steps δ close to the singularity in order to improve the accuracy of the result. If that still yields unsatisfactory results, you may have to resort to determining, theoretically, whether the function can be integrated and, if so, how it approaches the singularity. Then use that information to integrate the function symbolically in the vicinity of that singularity.

In section 9.4.1 we derived Simpson's formula (9.4.6) in terms of the Romberg approach, but the same result can also be understood as a combination of trapezoidal and midpoint rules, combined in such a way that the overestimate of one compensates for the underestimate of the other. For, say, five data points y_0 through y_4 with uniform x-spacing δ we can find the integral from the trapezoidal rule (9.3.4) as

$$I_t = (f_0 + 2f_1 + 2f_2 + 2f_3 + f_4)\delta/2 - \delta^2(f_n^{\mathrm{I}} - f_0^{\mathrm{I}})/12 + \delta^2(f_n^{\mathrm{III}} - f_0^{\mathrm{III}})/720 - \ldots \tag{9.4.13}$$

or from the midpoint rule (9.4.10) as

$$I_m = (f_1 + f_3)2\delta + 4\delta^2(f_n^{\mathrm{I}} - f_0^{\mathrm{I}})/24 - 7 \times 16\delta^4(f_n^{\mathrm{I}} - f_0^{\mathrm{I}})/5760 + \ldots \tag{9.4.14}$$

so that $I = (2I_t + I_m)/3$ yields

$$I = (f_0 + 4f_1 + 2f_2 + 4f_3 + f_4)\delta/3 - 128\delta^4(f_n^{\mathrm{III}} - f_0^{\mathrm{III}})/720 + \ldots \tag{9.4.15}$$

which is precisely (9.4.6).

9.4.5 Implementations

The MacroBundle contains two integration macros: Romberg (for general use) and Trapez (for periodic functions), both in two flavors: "Auto" or "Specify". Of these you would normally use the automatic version, which uses invasive sampling, unless the data set is so long that it takes an inordinate execution time; its faster alternative requires that you specify the equation to be integrated in VBA code. In addition, the XN collection has two functions for integrating a function f specified in quasi-algebraic form on the spreadsheet, viz. Integr(f,a,b) and cplx_Integr(f,a,b), the latter for integrating a complex function $f(z)$. Moreover, the XN collection contains a number of other functions and macros that can integrate specified functions, as listed in Table 9.4.3.

Integr(f,a,b)	Romberg integration of the real function $f(x)$ for $a \le x \le b$; a and/or b can be inf.
Integr_2D(f,a,b,c,d)	Double Romberg integration of the real function $f(x,y)$ for $a \le x \le b$ and $c \le y \le d$.
Cplx_Integr(f,a,b)	Romberg integration of the complex function $f(z)$ for $a \le z \le b$.
Integr_DE(f,a,b)	Integration of a real function $f(x)$ by double exponential transformation.
Integr_NC(f,a,b,n)	Newton-Cotes integration of degree n of a real function $f(x)$ for $a \le x \le b$.
Integr_fsin(f,a,b,k)	Filon integration of the oscillating function $f(t)\sin(kt)$ for $a \le x \le b$.
Integr_fcos(f,a,b,k)	Filon integration of the oscillating function $f(t)\cos(kt)$ for $a \le x \le b$.

Table 9.4.3: The integration functions in XN for algebraic functions. Moreover, in the XN toolbar under Macros $\Rightarrow$ Integral, you will also find a macro for integrating a real function $f(x)$ between $-\infty$ and $+\infty$. For integrating experimental data see section 9.5.

Exercise 9.4.6:

(1) The Romberg macro in the Macrobundle was designed primarily to illustrate how Romberg integration works; they can readily be simplified to show only their final resultsvRoundR(. But this is not necessary, because the XN function Integr already serves that function, as illustrated here.

(2) In a spreadsheet place the following labels in a contiguous row, let's say in cells B2:B4: F(x). a, and b. Directly below these, in C2:C4, place the expression exp(-1*x^2) and the numbers 0 and 8 respectively. In C5 now enter the instruction =Integr(C2,C3,C4). The answer, 0.886226925452758, is equal to the value of the integral from 0 to $+\infty$, $\frac{1}{2}\sqrt{\pi}$.

(3) You will get the same result when incorporating the equation for $F(x)$ directly, within quotation marks, into the function argument as =Integr("exp(-1*x^2)",C3,C4), or even by using no labels and other cells but simply, anywhere on the spreadsheet, depositing the instruction =Integr("exp(-1*x^2)",0,8).

(4) Similarly, the instruction =Integr ("exp(-1*x^2)",-1,1) will net you 1.49364826562485.

9.4.6 Romberg-Kahan integration

With an elegantly simple transformation, W. M. Kahan showed how one can avoid the effects of singularities at the integration limits on trapezoidal Romberg integration, so that their presence doesn't require a separate, midpoint-based approach. Consider the identity

$$\int_a^b f(x)\,dx = \int_{-1}^{1} f(y)\,dy \tag{9.4.16}$$

where the left-hand side of the expression represents the integral of the specific function $f(x)$ we want to integrate between the arbitrary limits $x = a$ and $x = b$, and where y is as yet undetermined. Defining y through the cubic relation

$$x = \frac{(b-a)(3y-y^3)}{4} + \frac{b+a}{2} \tag{9.4.17}$$

so that

$$x = a \text{ for } y = -1, \qquad x = b \text{ for } y = +1 \tag{9.4.18}$$

and

$$dx = \frac{(b-a)(3-3y^2)}{4}\,dy \tag{9.4.19}$$

then leads to

$$\int_a^b f(x)\,dx = \frac{3(b-a)}{4}\int_{-1}^{1}(1-y^2)f\left\{\frac{(b-a)(3y-y^3)}{4} + \frac{b+a}{2}\right\}dy \tag{9.4.20}$$

which indeed has the form of (9.4.16).

The main advantage of using (9.4.20) for Romberg integration is that the term $(1-y^2)$ forces the values at the limits of the integration range (i.e., at $x = a$ and $x = b$) to zero, so that possible singularities at those edges become unimportant. This approach also avoids potential aliasing problems of the trapezoidal Romberg method with periodic (e.g., trigonometric) functions, because y is clearly a nonlinear function of x.

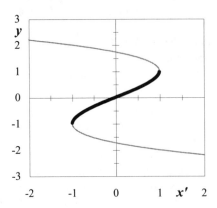

Fig. 9.4.8: The quantity y as a function of $x' = (3y-y^3)/2$. For $x' = -1$, $y = -1$; for $x' = +1$, $y = +1$. Since $x = \frac{1}{2}\{(b-a)\,x' + (b+a)\}$, we have $y = -1$ for $x = a$, and $y = +1$ for $x = b$. The thick black curve lies within the integration limits.

The above mapping of x onto y is unambiguous, as is readily seen by computing $x' = (3y-y^3)/2$ as a function of y, and by then plotting y vs. x' or x, see Fig. 9.4.8. Within the corresponding integration intervals $a \leq x \leq b$ and $-1 \leq y \leq +1$, y is a monotonic function of x, so that the mapping is indeed one-on-one. An obvious (though somewhat slower) variant of Romberg-Kahan integration might use the function $y = \mathrm{cosec}(x)$ or $x' = \sin(y)$ instead.

9.4.7 Multivariable integration

Here we merely sketch the simple case of doubly integrating a function $z = f(x,y)$ over a rectangular domain, in order to determine the enclosed volume $\iint z \, dx \, dy$. Just as, numerically, symbolic integration of $f(x)$ is replaced by summation, the numerical double integration of a function z of both x and y requires a double summation. While this can be treated formally, it is perhaps best illustrated here with a few simple examples. Applying (9.4.6) for just two equidistant steps (of sizes δ_x and δ_y respectively) in two dimensions, yields

$$I = \{f(x_0,y_0) + f(x_2,y_0) + f(x_0,y_2) + f(x_2,y_2)$$
$$+ 4[f(x_0,y_1) + f(x_2,y_1) + f(x_1,y_0) + f(x_1,y_2)] + 16\,f(x_1,y_1)\}\,\delta_x\delta_y/9 \qquad (9.4.21)$$

With m and n such steps in the x- and y-direction respectively, one can conveniently display the corresponding coefficients of $f(x_i,y_j)$ as a grid overlaying the block of spreadsheet cells, as in

$$
\begin{array}{ccccccccc}
1 & 4 & 2 & 4 & 2 & 4 & \cdots & 4 & 1 \\
4 & 16 & 8 & 16 & 8 & 16 & \cdots & 16 & 4 \\
2 & 8 & 4 & 8 & 4 & 8 & \cdots & 8 & 2 \\
4 & 16 & 8 & 16 & 8 & 16 & \cdots & 16 & 4 \\
\vdots & \vdots & \vdots & \vdots & \vdots & \vdots & \ddots & \vdots & \vdots \\
4 & 16 & 8 & 16 & 8 & 16 & \cdots & 16 & 4 \\
1 & 4 & 2 & 4 & 2 & 4 & \cdots & 4 & 1 \\
\end{array}
\qquad (9.4.22)
$$

438

where we can replace the 1,4,2,4, … ,4,2,4,1 sequences of (9.4.6) in either or both directions by other sequences, such as those listed in Table 9.4.1, if *m* and/or *n* are sufficiently large. In (9.4.22) we have left out their common factor, $\delta_x\delta_y/9$.

For an array of 7×9 cells one could, likewise, use two different Romberg sequences, such as shown in (9.4.23), with the common multiplier $\delta_x\delta_y/135$. These coefficients are readily obtained as the vector product of the Romberg sequences 1, 4, 2, 4, 2, 4, 1 and 14, 64, 24, 64, 28, 64, 24, 64, 14 respectively, see exercise 10.1.4. For more on multiple integration see, e.g., A. H. Stroud, *Approximate Calculation of Multiple Integrals*, Prentice Hall (1971).

$$
\begin{array}{ccccccccc}
14 & 64 & 24 & 64 & 28 & 64 & 24 & 64 & 14 \\
56 & 256 & 96 & 256 & 112 & 256 & 96 & 256 & 56 \\
28 & 128 & 48 & 128 & 56 & 128 & 48 & 128 & 28 \\
56 & 256 & 96 & 256 & 112 & 256 & 96 & 256 & 56 \\
28 & 128 & 48 & 128 & 56 & 128 & 48 & 128 & 28 \\
56 & 256 & 96 & 256 & 112 & 256 & 96 & 256 & 56 \\
14 & 64 & 24 & 64 & 28 & 64 & 24 & 64 & 14
\end{array}
\qquad (9.4.23)
$$

XN has a convenient function, IntegrData_2D, for double Romberg integration. Check it out.

9.5 Integrating experimental data

For integration we again consider the Fourier-analyzed components of signal, noise, and offset:

$$
\int \{f(t) + noise(t) + \mathit{offset}\}\,dt
$$

$$
= \int \{\sum_i A_i \sin(\omega_i t + \varphi_i) + \sum_i B_i \cos(\omega_i t + \varphi_i)\}\,dt
$$

$$
+ \int \{\sum_j a_j \sin(\omega_j t + \varphi_j) + \sum_j b_j \cos(\omega_j t + \varphi_j)\}\,dt + \int C\,dt
$$

$$
= -\sum_i \frac{A_i}{\omega_i}\cos(\omega_i t + \varphi_i) + \sum_i \frac{B_i}{\omega_i}\sin(\omega_i t + \varphi_i)
$$

$$
- \sum_j \frac{a_j}{\omega_j}\cos(\omega_j t + \varphi_j) + \sum_j \frac{b_j}{\omega_j}\sin(\omega_j t + \varphi_j) + Ct
\qquad (9.5.1)
$$

By dividing each contribution by its own angular frequency ω, integration is seen to attenuate both signal and noise, the more so the higher the frequency. Thus, noise at frequencies much higher than those of the signal does not strongly affect the integral. On the other hand, integration is very sensitive to offset and to low-frequency noise or drift. Proper zeroing and thermal equilibration of all equipment used in the measurement is therefore necessary whenever data integration is anticipated.

Again, direct integration of experimental data may not always be desirable, e.g., when one needs to determine the areas of individual, partially overlapping peaks in, e.g., a chromatogram or a spectrum. In that case it may be preferable to fit the peaks to some applicable theoretical function, such as a Lorentzian, Gaussian, or Voigt curve, and to determine their areas from the resulting curve-fitting parameters.

A nonzero baseline (or, more often, base curve) is not a problem, as long as it can be determined by itself, and is reproducible, requirements that apply both to direct integration of the experimental data, and to indirect integration by curve fitting.

In the direct integration of experimental data, one must be aware of the constraint that the data available for the integration are fixed, and you therefore cannot go back (as is possible with a model function) to obtain additional data points where needed. For the integration of experimental data, it is therefore essential to consider the requirements of integration in the experimental design, i.e., *before* the data are collected. This is no different from, e.g., using Fourier transformation, where the most efficient analysis routines require that the data points are equidistant, and their number is 2^n where n is a positive integer.

Likewise, use of trapezoidal Romberg integration is most efficient for equidistant data sets numbering either $2^n + 1$ or $3 \times 2^{n-1} + 1$ data points, in which case one can use the custom macro RombergFixed. One can readily modify this macro for use of Romberg midpoint integration, which would accommodate sets of 3^n equidistant data points.

The standard approach to integrating experimental data that do not contain singularities is the trapezoidal method, see sections 9.4.1 and 9.4.2. It allows any number of segments, of arbitrary widths. If neither of the limits of the integration range coincides with the data points, one may instead have to use the midpoint method or variants thereof, see section 9.4.3, to match the integration range.

For an odd number of equidistant data, Simpson's rule, with its alternating coefficients 4 and 2 in the interior of the integration range, as in (9.4.7), is usually more accurate than (9.4.3), except for periodic functions sampled over precisely one repeat period, or an integer multiple thereof. When the number of equidistant segments is an integer power of 2, say 2^k (i.e., the corresponding number of data points 2^k+1), the Romberg trapezoidal method can be exploited to maximum benefit. After relatively few iterations, the Romberg coefficients become so large that they can no longer be represented in Excel without truncation. When highly accurate Romberg integration is desired, e.g., when the spacing between successive experimental measurements is rather large, high-order Romberg integration may therefore have to use the extended numberlength described in chapter 11, even though the precision of the experimental data themselves might not indicate such a need.

As we have seen in section 9.4, singularities can complicate integration. Fortunately, experimental data exist in a context, and there is usually a theoretical model predicting how the measured phenomenon approaches the singularity. In that case, in the region close to the singularity, a theoretical model should be used to fit the approach to that singularity, followed by symbolic integration of the model equation.

The most important point to remember here is that more accurate integrals may be had with a little bit of forethought, by making sure that, for any integrals of consequence, the integration interval is such that the leading error terms in (9.4.3) or (9.4.10) are negligible, see exercise 9.4.2. If that cannot be done, optimize the number of data points for subsequent integration. For Romberg trapezoidal integration, the number of data points should be odd, and optimally 2^k+1, i.e., 5 to get Simpson's rule, 9 for Boole's formula, 17 for (9.4.8), etc. For Romberg midpoint integration, the number of data points should be an integer power of 3. The results in the top-right corner of Fig. 9.2.1 suggest that, even with a rather large data spacing, a high-order Romberg integration may yield a reasonably accurate result.

But, again, you need not reinvent the wheel, because XN already has convenient functions for integrating experimental data, IntegrData for $y = f(x)$, IntegrData2D for $f(x,y)$, and IntegrDataC for Newton-Cotes integration of a data vector (x_i, y_i).

9.6 Interpolating, smoothing & rounding

If we know which function $f(x)$ describes a set of data (x_i, y_i), interpolation is not needed, because we can just *evaluate* the function at any required x-value. And even if we do not have access to an explicit function $f(x)$, as in section 1.10, we can use Solver to generate the required answers, see section 4.18. The latter, incidentally, is in principle a better way to interpolate the titration data in section 1.10, because it can be based on the theoretical titration model rather than on fitting an arbitrary polynomial, but this might not have been understandable at the introductory stage of this book. At any rate, when the data spacing is sufficiently small, differences between the various interpolation methods tend to become unimportant.

When we consider the interpolation of data of which we know nothing other than their coordinates (x_i, y_i), we clearly have a mission impossible, because what isn't there, simply isn't there, and we cannot just make it up. There is no way to fill in the blanks between individual data points without some kind of assumed model. Consequently, interpolation always involves an implied model, including the assumption that the data are samples of an underlying, continuous function.

In the preceding chapters we have already devoted considerable space to fitting models to experimental data. Polynomial models are usually adjusted to data by using least squares, while other models may be more easily fitted with nonlinear least squares methods, such as Solver, or with Fourier transformation in cases where they can be expressed in terms of sines and cosines. However, modeling the entire function in order to interpolate it is often undesirable, and the preferable approach usually is to perform the interpolation locally, based on a relatively small number of data points adjacent to the desired x-value.

We will illustrate interpolation with a simple data set consisting of eight equidistant data points (x_i, y_i), viz., (−4,0), (−3,0), (−2,0), (−1,0), (0,0), (1,1), (2,1), and (3,1), as shown in Fig. 9.6.1. This data set, with its apparent discontinuity, is chosen to illustrate some of the uncertainties and trade-offs involved. If one merely wanted to highlight the power of interpolation, a smooth signal such as a power law or a sine wave would do, and all of the methods described below would perform equally well.

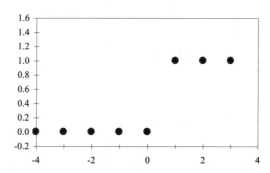

Fig. 9.6.1: A made-up data set to illustrate the pitfalls of interpolation.

When these data represent, say, the readings in eight adjacent channels of a radioactivity counter, then this is all there is, and interpolation is neither needed nor warranted. But when they represent samples of a step function in current, voltage, temperature, pressure, or in some other continuous parameter as a function of time (in which case you might want to use the symbol t instead of x), we can interpolate the points for $-4 \le x \le 0$ and $1 \le x \le 3$, but we will have no way to ascertain from these data at what x-value between $x = 0$ and $x = 1$ the transition occurred, whether it was steep or gradual, with or without overshoot, etc. Obviously, interpolation (without added information on the underlying phenomenon) cannot provide what was not observed.

Figures 9.6.2 and 9.6.3 show fits of all eight data points to a seventh-order polynomial, as well as one based on the fast Fourier transform. We see in Fig. 9.6.2 that a high-order polynomial fit can generate large fluctuations between the data points, and even more dubious behavior when *extrapolated* outside the data range. In the latter respect, interpolation based on Fourier transformation is somewhat more constraining by the implied assumption that the data set is periodic.

Exercise 9.6.1:
(1) In a spreadsheet, make two columns, one for x with the values −4 (1) 3, the other for y with the values 0, 0, 0, 0, 0, 1, 1, 1. Below we will refer to these as xarray and yarray respectively.
(2) Make a third, much longer column for x, with the values −4 (1/16) 3.

(3) In an adjacent column, compute a seventh-order interpolating polynomial through the eight original data points with the instruction =LAGRANGE (*xarray, yarray,x*,7), where *x* refers to the corresponding *x*-values in the long *x*-column. The references to xarray and yarray should be absolute, with dollar signs for both letters and numbers. Make sure that the custom function Lagrange (see section 1.12) is available; if not, fetch it from the MacroBundle.

(4) At this point you may want to review the material in section 5.8 on Fourier transform interpolation, in order to understand what comes next.

(5) If the columns for xarray and yarray are adjacent, in the correct order (yarray to the right of xarray), and with free space in the four columns to the right of yarray, highlight xarray, yarray, and one adjacent empty column, then call the custom macro ForwardFT. Otherwise, copy xarray and yarray to an appropriate place on the spreadsheet and do the same.

(6) Copy the two columns made under (2) and (3). Replace the contents of the latter, copied column by zeros.

(7) Copy the block of three short columns generated in the Fourier transformation step (4) to the long columns you just made, at the corresponding *x*-values. This will place the Fourier-transformed data in the very middle of a much larger data set, ready for inverse transformation.

(8) Highlight these two long data sets, plus the empty row to its right, and use InverseFT to generate the interpolated data set.

(9) Use the in-phase response for your interpolation; you should find a result like that illustrated in Fig. 9.6.3. Keep the spreadsheet for use in exercise 9.6.2.

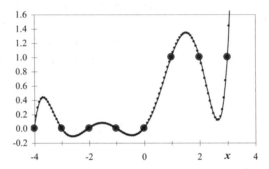

Fig. 9.6.2: The seventh-order polynomial $y = a_0 + a_1x + a_2x^2 + \ldots + a_7x^7$, exactly fitted through the eight points with the custom function Lagrange. Note the wild oscillations of this function near the ends of the range.

While the interpolations shown in Figs. 9.6.2. and 9.6.3 are both smooth, i.e., continuously differentiable everywhere, and pass exactly through all eight points, they will yield quite different interpolated values, because interpolation based merely on the data (without additional information on the nature of the underlying functionality) *is not uniquely defined*. In fact, there are infinitely many functions that can pass through these eight points in their given order, but differ in how they go from one point to the next.

Below we will briefly describe two common interpolation methods that only utilize local information. While these are, likewise, guesswork, at least they tend to restrain the otherwise sometimes unexpectedly large fluctuations of the interpolated curve between its fixed points, as in Fig. 9.6.2, or to avoid the periodicity implied in Fig. 9.6.3 that forces the values and slopes at $x = -4$ and $x = +4$ to be equal.

Both methods to be discussed below will be based on a cubic polynomial, and will therefore tend to represent the transition between points (0,0) and (1,1) with an S-shaped curve. Please keep in mind that this may or may not be any more realistic than a unit step somewhere between $x = 0$ and $x = 1$, or a simple straight line connecting points (0,0) and (1,1). Without additional information on where these data come from and what they represent, *we simply don't know* how to go from point (0,0) to point (1,1).

In Lagrange interpolation, a low-order polynomial of order *n* is fitted exactly to *n*+1 consecutive data points. The resulting coefficients are then used to find interpolates within that small range. This is an efficient way to find one or more interpolates in a narrow region of the data set. If additional interpolates outside this region are needed, the fitting polynomial moves on, by dropping one or more data points on one side while adding the same number of data points on the other, and this process is repeated until all re-

442

quired interpolates are found. In Excel, Lagrange interpolation is readily accomplished with a simple function, as was illustrated in section 1.10.

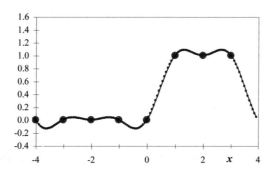

Fig. 9.6.3: Interpolation by Fourier transformation also yields a smooth function which, however, assumes a periodically repeating pattern.

Both methods to be discussed below will be based on a cubic polynomial, and will therefore tend to represent the transition between points (0,0) and (1,1) with an S-shaped curve. Please keep in mind that this may or may not be any more realistic than a unit step somewhere between $x = 0$ and $x = 1$, or a simple straight line connecting points (0,0) and (1,1). Without additional information on where these data come from and what they represent, *we simply don't know* how to go from point (0,0) to point (1,1).

In Lagrange interpolation, a low-order polynomial of order n is fitted exactly to $n+1$ consecutive data points. The resulting coefficients are then used to find interpolates within that small range. This is an efficient way to find one or more interpolates in a narrow region of the data set. If additional interpolates outside this region are needed, the fitting polynomial moves on, by dropping one or more data points on one side while adding the same number of data points on the other, and this process is repeated until all required interpolates are found. In Excel, Lagrange interpolation is readily accomplished with a simple function, as was illustrated in section 1.10.

We will restrict the discussion to a cubic, $y = a_0 + a_1x + a_2x^2 + a_3x^3$ as a common interpolating function. Its four coefficients require four independent pieces of information. In Lagrange interpolation, these are provided by the coordinates of four consecutive data points.

9.6.1 Lagrange interpolation

The polynomial $f = a_0 + a_1x + a_2x^2 + a_3x^3 + \ldots + a_nx^n$ has $n+1$ coefficients a_i, and is therefore fully defined by $n+1$ data points. The resulting polynomial is given by the Lagrange formula (1.10.2), which we rewrite here in condensed form as

$$f = \sum_{i=0}^{n} L_i(x) \, y_i \tag{9.6.1}$$

where

$$L_i(x) = \frac{(x-x_0)(x-x_1)\cdots(x-x_{i-1})\,(x-x_{i+1})\cdots(x-x_{n-1})(x-x_n)}{(x_i-x_0)(x_i-x_1)\cdots(x_i-x_{i-1})\,(x_i-x_{i+1})\cdots(x_i-x_{n-1})(x_i-x_n)}$$

$$= \frac{\prod_{j\neq i}(x-x_j)}{\prod_{j\neq i}(x_i-x_j)} \tag{9.6.2}$$

The specific points used to define the interpolation function y are called the *nodes*; in (9.6.2) the nodes are points (x_0,y_0) through (x_n,y_n).

443

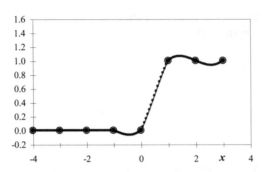

Fig. 9.6.4: Lagrange interpolation of the same data set. Note that the interpolated segment between $x = -2$ and $x = -1$ is flat because it uses the data from $x = -3$ through $x = 0$. On the other hand, the segment between $x = 2$ and $x = 3$ is based on the data from $x = 0$ through $x = 3$, because there is no information available at $x = 4$.

The Lagrange coefficient $L_j(x)$ is 1 for $x = x_j$, and 0 for $x = x_{i \neq j}$, so that (9.6.1) indeed passes through all nodes (x_i, y_i). In between those nodes, (9.6.1) is a continuous function that provides an exact interpolation, insofar as the function is indeed described correctly by a power series of order n. When the function is represented only approximately by such a power series in x, Lagrange interpolation may still be useful as an approximation. The order n should be chosen low enough to ensure a smooth interpolating polynomial without large oscillations. When an entire data set must be interpolated, Lagrange interpolation is often best applied as a moving fit using a small subset of nodes, as with the custom macro ELS.

Exercise 9.6.2:

(1) In the spreadsheet of exercise 9.6.1, once more copy or make two columns, the first containing the x-values -4 (1/16) 3. At the top of the second column, deposit the instruction =LAGRANGE (*xarray, yarray,x*,7), but now make xarray and yarray refer only to their top four rows, corresponding with the x-values -4 through -1. Copy this instruction all the way down.

(2) Go to $x = -2$, and in the corresponding y-column increment the row numbers of the references to xarray and yarray by one each, so that they refer to the data points at $x = -3, -2, -1$, and 0. Copy this instruction down.

(3) Go to $x = -1$, and again increment the references to xarray and yarray by one, to make them refer to $x = -2, -1, 0$, and 1. Again copy this instruction down.

(4) Similarly repeat at $x = 0$ by incrementing the references to xarray and yarray by one, to make them refer to $x = -1$, 0, 1, and 2, and by copying this instruction down.

(5) Finally, at $x = 1$, once more increment the references to xarray and yarray by one, so that they now refer to $x = 0$, 1, 2, and 3, and copy this instruction down.

(6) Plot the resulting Lagrange interpolation, and compare with Fig. 9.6.4.

Piece-wise Lagrange interpolation can exhibit sudden changes in slope at its nodes, as is clearly visible at $x = -1$ in Fig. 9.6.4.

9.6.2 Interpolating with a cubic spline

Here is another interpolation method. A cubic has four adjustable coefficients, a_0 through a_3, which in a cubic spline are used to make the fitting function pass through two adjacent nodes (x_i, y_i) and (x_{i+1}, y_{i+1}), and to make its first and second derivatives at these two nodes continuous with those of the adjacent segments. On first count that might seem impossible: to pass through two points, *and* to specify both the first and the second derivatives in those two points, would seem to require six constants, not four. But rather than fix those first and second derivatives at specific values, we will make them continuous at the nodes by insisting that they are the same when approached from either side. By doing so, such boundary conditions serve simultaneously for two adjacent intervals, and therefore count only as half a condition per interval. This does not work at the extremes of the data range, where we therefore must introduce additional boundary conditions.

444

Here we briefly outline this approach in mathematical terms; its actual implementation will be given in section 10.4. In order to avoid double indices, we will here write a cubic in x as $y = a + bx + cx^2 + dx^3$.

Imagine a set of $n+1$ contiguous data points or nodes, covering n adjacent intervals. In every one of these intervals, identified by the index i (where $0 \leq i < n$), we assume that the interpolated function is

$$f_i = a_i + b_i(x-x_i) + c_i(x-x_i)^2 + d_i(x-x_i)^3 \qquad x_i \leq x \leq x_{i+1} \qquad (9.6.3)$$

which automatically passes through the point (x_i, y_i), where $x-x_i = 0$, i.e.,

$$a_i = y_i \qquad\qquad 0 \leq i \leq n \qquad (9.6.4)$$

Moreover, the constraint that the function must go through the next point, (x_{i+1}, y_{i+1}) is expressed by the condition

$$a_i + b_i(x_{i+1}-x_i) + c_i(x_{i+1}-x_i)^2 + d_i(x_{i+1}-x_i)^3 = a_{i+1} \qquad 1 \leq i \leq n-1 \qquad (9.6.5)$$

Again denoting the first and second derivative of f_i as f_i^{I} and f_i^{II} respectively, we have

$$f_i^{\mathrm{I}} = b_i + 2c_i(x-x_i) + 3d_i(x-x_i)^2 \qquad (9.6.6)$$

$$f_i^{\mathrm{II}} = 2c_i + 6d_i(x-x_i) \qquad (9.6.7)$$

and equality of the first and second derivatives at nodes i and $i+1$ requires that

$$b_i + 2c_i(x_{i+1}-x_i) + 3d_i(x_{i+1}-x_i)^2 = b_{i+1} \qquad 1 \leq i \leq n-1 \qquad (9.6.8)$$

$$2c_i + 6d_i(x_{i+1}-x_i) = 2c_{i+1} \qquad 1 \leq i \leq n-1 \qquad (9.6.9)$$

For the entire set of n intervals we have n equations of type (9.6.4) and (9.6.5), and $n-1$ relations (9.6.8) and (9.6.9), for a total of $4n-2$ equations, i.e., the system is mathematically underdetermined. Still missing is information on the unknown derivatives at the very edges of the data set, i.e., at x_0 and x_n. Although other, equally plausible assumptions can be used, we will here simply assume them to extrapolate linearly, so that their second derivatives at x_0 and x_n can be set equal to zero, i.e.,

$$2c_0 = 0 \qquad (9.6.10)$$

$$2c_n = 0 \qquad (9.6.11)$$

We now have $4n$ equations in $4n$ unknowns, and we can therefore, in principle, solve these expressions, find all the coefficients a_i, b_i, c_i, and d_i, and calculate any value of f_i for $0 \leq i \leq n+1$. In practice, solving $4n$ equations in $4n$ unknowns would be a tedious task to do by hand, except when n is trivially small, but here matrix algebra comes to the rescue, and we will illustrate how to solve such a system of coupled mathematical equations in section 10.4.

XN has a very convenient cubic spline function, CSpline_Coeff, which yields the parameters of fitting an ordinary cubic spline through any set of data. From these, we can reconstruct the entire cubic spline function at any desired point within the range of the experimental data, as illustrated in exercise 9.6.3 or, faster, use the interpolating function Cspline_Interp.

Cspline_Coeff takes as its input a contiguous set of x-values and the corresponding *nodes* y through which the cubic spline should pass. The output is then in the form of a table of coefficients a_3, a_2, a_1, and a_0 for the expression $y = a_0 + a_1(x - x_n) + a_2(x - x_n)^2 + a_3(x - x_n)^3$ where x_n is the x-value of the node starting the interval for which the values of a_0 through a_3 apply. In Fig.9.6.5, e.g., B3 is the x_n-value for the a's in G3:J3, and C3 will be equal to J3. The superfluous bottom row of G3:J10 contains only zeroes.

Exercise 9.6.3:

(1) In B3:B10 on a fresh spreadsheet deposit the x-values -4 (1) 3 and, in C3:C10, the corresponding function values y as used in Fig. 9.6.1.

(2) Leaving some room for labels, highlight next to these a block of the same length as the data set (or, at no loss of information, one row shorter), and four columns wide, say G3:J10. Type the instruction CSpline_Coeff(B3:B10,C3:C10) where the arguments are the columns of x- and y-values, and deposit this with Ctrl$\cup$Shift$\cup$Enter. This command will generate all cubic spline coefficients involved.

(3) Above the four columns pl;ace the names of the coefficients a_i involved, in the order indicated in Fig. 9.6.6. Also label the top row as 1st spline, then click on that label to generate the lower labels.

(4) Now we will use the information in G3:J9 to interpolate this cubic spline. In L3:L38 place the sequence –4 (0.2) +3, then leave cell L39 empty, and place –4 (1) +3 in L40:L47.

(5) In M3, M8, M13, M18, and M23 deposit the value 0, and in M28, M33, and M38 the value 1. Copy C3:C10 to M40:M47.

(6) Highlight L3:M47 and plot them as an XY graph, using large markers for the data points and a broad gray band plotted with the "S̲moothed line" option in the Format Data Series dialog box.

(7) For the interpolation we could use just one column. However, in order to emphasize its construction from separate segments, we will here use two adjacent columns for the cubic spline interpolation. In N3 deposit the instruction =$J$3+$I$3*(L3+4)+$H$3*(L3+4)^2+$G$3*(L3+4)^3, and copy it down to row 8. In O8 place the command =$J$4+$I$4*(L8+3)+$H$4*(L8+3)^2+$G$4*(L8+3)^3. and copy it to cell O13. Back to N13, where you place =$J$5+$I$5*(L13+2)+$H$5*(L13+2)^2+$G$5*(L13+2)^3 and copy it to N18, etc., until you have reached row 38. Note that these instructions use the formalism $y = a_0 + a_1(x-x_s) + a_2(x-x_s)^2 + a_3(x-x_s)^3$. where x_s is the x-value at the anchoring point of that particular section, N3 for the first, O8 for the next, etc.

(8) Add N3:N38 and O3:O38 to the graph, using small dots and a thin connecting smooth line. This should complete your version of Fig. 9.6.5.

(9) To verify that the above indeed yields interpolated data for any x-value within its range, change an x-value in the range of greatest change, say the x-value of 0.4 in cell L25, to say 0.56, and see that the corresponding y-value in N25 indeed tracks the thin black curve.

An example of using a cubic spline can be found in BitMap1, the color scheme for Mapper1 of the MacroBundle, which uses a smoothly varying RGB color scheme. In that case, problems with overshoot were avoided by keeping the lowest and highest assumed values of the nodes away from the upper and lower limits of the color arrays, at 255 and 0 respectively.

Both Lagrange and cubic spline interpolation can use non-equidistant data. In both cases, a cubic may be fitted, but there is a significant difference: Lagrange interpolation is then based on four contiguous x,y-values, whereas a cubic spline is based on just two such x,y-values, but is linked to the adjacent cubics in terms of continuous first and second derivatives at those nodes. The differences between Figs. 9.6.4 and 9.6.5 are most pronounced for the segments $-2 < x < -1$ and $2 < x < 3$.

Lagrange interpolation is most efficient where only one or a few interpolations are needed, while the cubic spline is more efficient for interpolating large data sets in a single operation. Moreover, because its slope remains continuous at the nodes, a cubic spline produces a visually more pleasing interpolate than a Lagrange interpolation. That is all one can ask for, since it is unknown which of these interpolations is "better", i.e., more accurate.

Most interpolation methods will do fine with smooth data sets. It is when there are discontinuities that differences between the various approaches become readily visible, which is why these were chosen here to make the point. The methods considered so far exhibit oscillations with our test data set, both before and after the transition in f from 0 to 1 between $x = 0$ and $x = 1$; of course, the available data provide no justification for either a sudden or a gradual transition, nor for the presence or absence of oscillations. It is possible to reduce the adjacent oscillations by using so-called taut or tensioned splines, as described, e.g., in chapter 16 of C. de Boor, *A Practical Guide to Splines*, Springer 1978.

As illustrated by the broad gray curve shown in Fig. 9.6.5, Excel appears to use such less oscillatory splines to connect the dots when plotting a function with the "S̲moothed line" option of the Format Data Series dialog box, a feature that works only for uninterrupted data sets. The corresponding fitting parameters are not available to the user, who therefore can only use them for visual presentation, but not for numerical interpolation, which in many cases is a wise constraint. In computer games, cubic splines are often used to make continuous motions of moving objects seem natural and fluid, without the need to specify all coordinates for every frame.

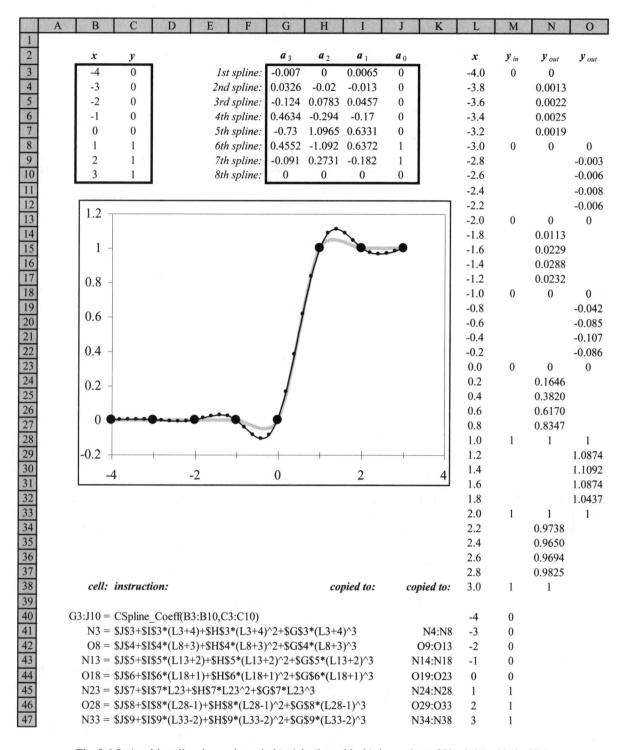

Fig. 9.6.5: A cubic spline drawn through the eight (large black) data points of Fig. 9.6.1 with the XN instruction =CSpline_Coeff, and interpolated data (small black points connected by a thin line) computed from the fitting coefficients at a ten times smaller *x*-spacing. Also shown, as a broad gray line, is Excel's "Smoothed line" interpolation, which in this example effectively restricts the oscillations to the adjacent data intervals, at the expense of slight discontinuities in slope at those data points.

The above will work provided that the user has XN activated. In order to make Mapper available without that restriction, the actual code uses explicit cubic equations based on three-digit versions of the fitting parameters.

9.6.3 Interpolation using continued fractions

Another method is to use a continued fraction, which is of the type

$$ y = a_0 + \cfrac{x - x_1}{a_1 + \cfrac{x - x_2}{a_2 + \cfrac{x - x_3}{a_3 + \cfrac{x - x_4}{a_4}}}} = a_0 + \frac{x - x_1}{a_1 +} \frac{x - x_2}{a_2 +} \frac{x - x_3}{a_3 +} \frac{x - x_4}{a_4} \tag{9.6.12} $$

where the right-most form is a common typographical simplification. We can fit this equation exactly to the four data points x_1 through x_4 with the coefficients a_0 through a_4, and can then use these coefficients to interpolate the function for intermediate x-values. Here we will not explain the method in detail, but merely demonstrate how to apply it.

Exercise 9.6.4:
(1) On a new spreadsheet, place the labels x, interp, $f(x)$, and coeff in B2:E2.
(2) In B4:B11 deposit the numbers –4, –3, –2, –1, 0, 1, 2, and 3, in D4:D11 the corresponding values 0, 0, 0, 0, 0, 1, 1, and 1, and in B14:B84 place the numbers –4 (0.1) 3. Plot D4:D84 vs. B4:B84, as before.

(3) Now highlight E4:E11, type the instruction =Fract_Interp_Coef(B4:B11,E4:E11), and enter this array instruction with Ctrl␣Shift␣Enter. These are the coefficients to fit the data in D4:D11.
(4) Highlight D18:D138, type =Fract_Interp (B14:B84, B4:B16,G4:G16), and again enter it as an array instruction.
(5) Plot the interpolated data points as small markers, without a connecting line.

The fit (or, rather, lack thereof) is shown in Fig. 9.6.6. The small points are clearly useless for interpolation, as they seem to have no relation to the large ones that specify the problem posed. Then why demonstrate this method? Because there is a simple reason why there are so many different interpolation methods: none will be good for all problems. To demonstrate this, consider the following problem, which would lead to a comparable failure if used with the methods we looked at before.

Exercise 9.6.5:
(1) On a new spreadsheet, place the labels x, tan(x), interp, pE, tan(x), and coeff in B2:G2.
(2) In B4:B16 deposit the numbers 0 (0.5) 6, in B18 place a 0, in B19 the instruction =B18+0.05, and copy this down to row 138, so that it will contain the ten times expanded set 0 (0.05) 6.
(3) In F4 deposit the instruction =TAN(B4), and copy this down to row 16.
(4) In C18 place the equivalent =TAN(B18), and copy it down to row 138 by double-clicking on its handle.
(5) Plot F4:F138 vs. B4:B138, and show the data as large open circles, without a connecting line. These are the data between which you want to interpolate.
(6) Highlight C4:C138, import it into the graph, and display it as a line. This is what you hope the interpolation will approximate.
(7) Now highlight G4:G16, type the instruction =FractInterpCoef(B4:B16,F4:F16), and enter this array instruction with Ctrl␣Shift␣Enter. This will determine and show the coefficients needed to fit the data in F4:F16.
(8) Highlight D18:D138, type =FractInterp(B18:B38,B4:B16,G4:G16), and again enter it as an array instruction.
(9) Plot the interpolated data points as small markers, without a connecting line. Figure 9.6.7 shows the resulting graph. The interpolated points fall on the theoretical line, and inside the circles representing the original data points. Judged purely visually, the interpolation works.

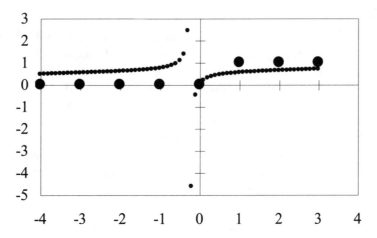

Fig. 9.6.6: The continued fraction interpolation of the data of Fig. 9.6.1.

(10) Because we here used a simple mathematical formula as the source of our test data set, we also can get a more quantitative idea of the quality of this interpolation. In E18 compute pE with the MacroMorsel function pE, or with the equivalent XN instruction =LRE(C18,D18), and copy this down to row 138.

In this case, the interpolation is quite good (at least pE > 4) considering that the discontinuities make this is quite a nasty function to interpolate, especially since the input data set did not reveal the locations of the discontinuities. Of course, this was an ideal case, without noise, but so was our earlier test data set.

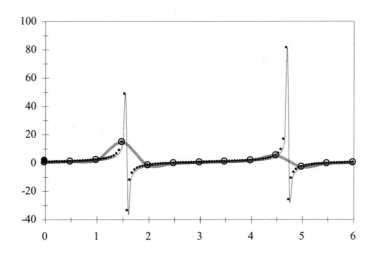

Fig. 9.6.7: The continued fraction interpolation (small solid points) of a sparse subset (large open circles) of $f(x) = \tan(x)$ (thin drawn line, which of course should be discontinuous at $x = \pi/2$ and $3\pi/2$). The broad gray curve shows how Excel's cubic spline would interpolate the input points.

Most interpolation methods will do fine with smooth data sets. It is when there are discontinuities that differences between the various approaches become readily visible, which is why these were chosen here to make the point. Unfortunately, there exists no universal interpolation routine to fit all problems.

9.6.4 Interpolating noisy data

Fitting (9.6.1) and (9.6.2) to a set of $n+1$ data automatically yields an nth order polynomial exactly fitting through those $n+1$ points. That may be fine for a smooth model function. However, for the interpolation of noisy *experimental* data, one specifically does *not* want that function to pass through all measurement points, because interpolation in such a curve would merely accentuate the noise. In that case, nodes (i.e., particular points in the data set through which the model function must pass) are *not* used. Instead, one typically first *fits* the data to a smooth model function, and *interpolates* in the latter. Often, a low-power polynomial can be fitted to (a small section of) the data with linear least squares (by using an excess of data rather than the $n+1$ required for an exact fit to an nth power polynomial), whereupon the resulting coefficients can be used to compute the desired interpolates. In other cases, some other function may be more appropriate, in which case Solver can often be used to adjust an appropriate model function to the data.

Automated scientific instruments often produce equidistant data, i.e., with constant x-spacing δ. In that case, least squares fitting to a power series in x can be done efficiently using Gram polynomials, as explained in section 3.11, and as implemented in the custom macro ELS. When the number of equidistant data points is an integer power of 2, fast Fourier transformation may also be considered, as described in section 5.8.

Here is a simple explanation of the approach used in the macro ELS of the MacroBundle. One can fit a parabola $f = a_0 + a_1 x + a_2 x^2$ to pass exactly through three data points. If one uses more than three input data, e.g., 5, 7, or 29, one cannot expect an exact fit, because the problem is over-determined, but now least squares can be used. For an odd number (here: five) of properly centered, equidistant data, symmetry makes many of the least squares sums zero, and the coefficients are readily determined in terms of five f-values f_{-2}, f_{-1}, f_0, f_1, and f_2 as $a_0 = (-3f_{-2}+12f_{-1}+17f_0+12f_1-3f_2)/35$, $a_1 = (-2f_{-2}-f_{-1}+f_1+2f_2)/10\,\delta$, and $a_2 = (2f_{-2}-f_{-1}-2f_0-f_1+2f_2)/14\,\delta^2$. From these results one can calculate the smoothed value of f_0 (for the middle point, at $x_0 = 0$) as a_0, which is therefore a simple weighted sum of the five experimental f-values. The weighting factors are readily computed in ELS from Gram polynomials.

9.6.5 Smoothing, rounding & truncating

Smoothing can be considered a special case of fitting experimental data to find an underlying, assumedly continuous curve. ELS can fit a low-order moving polynomial to a set of noisy data, and then replace those data by the corresponding value of the least-squares fitted polynomial. By reducing the noise, this may make the data look better than they really are. Often, such smoothing is merely an exercise in cosmetics, in which case the temptation should be resisted. When displaying smoothed experimental data, at least use a continuous curve, and in the same graph also display the original, unsmoothed data as individual points.

There are some situations where smoothing may be necessary, as when one must find a derivative of noisy experimental data. Still, it is useful to keep in mind that any type of smoothing introduces some distortion as the price for noise reduction.

Rounding is smoothing to a specified number of decimal places. Beware: once a number is rounded, its original value is lost. For simple display purposes use cell formatting instead, because that does not affect the underlying number, but only how it is displayed on the spreadsheet.

The term rounding is often used without a clearly specified meaning. Microsoft, by its own account (kb 196652), states that its Round() function is not implemented in a consistent fashion among different Microsoft products. Typically, rounding rounds to the nearest integer, but that criterion is ambiguous when the last digit is a 5. Moreover, a number that should end in a 5 may be represented in a binary computer as a slightly larger or smaller number.

number	Excel RoundUp	Excel Round	VBA Round	Excel RoundDown
-0.11	-0.2	-0.1	-0.1	-0.1
-0.10	-0.1	-0.1	-0.1	-0.1
-0.09	-0.1	-0.1	-0.1	0
-0.08	-0.1	-0.1	-0.1	0
-0.07	-0.1	-0.1	-0.1	0
-0.06	-0.1	-0.1	-0.1	0
-0.05	-0.1	*-0.1*	*-0*	0
-0.04	-0.1	*0*	*-0*	0
-0.03	-0.1	*0*	*-0*	0
-0.02	-0.1	*0*	*-0*	0
-0.01	-0.1	*0*	*-0*	0
0.00	0	0	0	0
0.01	0.1	0	0	0
0.02	0.1	0	0	0
0.03	0.1	0	0	0
0.04	0.1	0	0	0
0.05	0.1	**0.1**	**0**	0
0.06	0.1	0.1	0.1	0
0.07	0.1	0.1	0.1	0
0.08	0.1	0.1	0.1	0
0.09	0.1	0.1	0.1	0
0.10	0.1	0.1	0.1	0.1
0.11	0.2	0.1	0.1	0.1

Fig. 9.6.8: Comparison of various Excel and VBA rounding functions. Absolute value differences between Round in Excel and VBA are boldfaced, sign differences italicized. Background shading is used to emphasize the absolute values obtained.

Rounding 'up' or 'down' can also be ambiguous, at least for negative numbers: do we mean up or down for the number, or only for its absolute value? In view of these uncertainties we adopted a criterion of 14 rather than 15 decimals in the definition of pE in section 9.1.

Excel's rounding functions all result in *biased* smoothing. You would expect this for RoundUp, RoundDown, and Trunc, because they clearly say so, upfront, but you might not do so for Round. Here is the score.

Despite its name, the Excel function RoundUp(x, n) rounds *away from zero*, i.e., it indeed rounds up for $x > 0$, but it rounds down for $x < 0$: ROUNDUP(0.025,2) = 0.03 and RoundUp(-0.025,2) = –0.03. Likewise, Excel's RoundDown(x, n) has a misleading name: it rounds *towards zero*, i.e., it rounds down for $x > 0$, and up for $x < 0$: RoundDown (0.025,2) = 0.02 and RoundDown(-0.025,2) = –0.02. In both cases, the operation is equivalent to rounding the absolute magnitude of the number, either up in RoundUp or down in RoundDown, and adding the sign back afterwards (except when the result is zero).

Trunc(x, n) is properly named: it merely truncates a number to n remaining decimal places. Consequently, Trunc(0.035,2) = 0.03 and Trunc(-0.035,2) = –0.03. But truncation yields a result that is strongly biased towards zero: Trunc(0.039,2) = Trunc(0.031,2) = 0.03, and Trunc(-0.039,2) = Trunc(-0.031,2) = –0.03.

The *Excel* function Round(x, n) rounds towards the nearest integer, *except* for a trailing 5 (not followed by any non-zero digits), which is always rounded *away from* zero. For a large set of positive numbers, this introduces a 5% upward bias in the last digit, because on average 1 in 10 trailing digits is a 5, and unbiased rounding should round down about half of them. The only unbiased rounding available in Excel is through the *VBA* instruction Round, which can be invoked on the spreadsheet through a function or subroutine, e.g., with the custom function cRound:

```
Function cRound(x, n)
cRound = Round(x, n)
End Function
```

Only the VBA function Round uses unbiased (statistician's, or banker's) rounding, i.e., it rounds to the nearest integer, except to the nearest even integer for a trailing 5 not followed by nonzero digits, in which case "nearest integer" is otherwise ambiguous. This is the only rounding functions that yield reproducible, unbiased results, and are therefore the only rounding functions that should be used in scientific data analysis. Figure 9.6.9 illustrates the results obtained with these instructions for the sequence $x = -0.11$ (0.01) 0.11 and $n = 1$. Note: XN's double-precision vRound also uses unbiased rounding, and can be used in Excel (provided that XN has been loaded), and XN's extended precision vRoundR provides for relative rounding, i.e., to a given total number of significant digits.

number	VBA Fix	Excel Trunc	VBA CInt, CLng	Excel Int
-1.1	-1	-1	-1	-2
-1.0	-1	-1	-1	-1
-0.9	-0	0	-1	-1
-0.8	-0	0	-1	-1
-0.7	-0	0	-1	-1
-0.6	-0	0	-1	-1
-0.5	-0	0	0	-1
-0.4	-0	0	0	-1
-0.3	-0	0	0	-1
-0.2	-0	0	0	-1
-0.1	-0	0	0	-1
0.0	0	0	0	0
0.1	0	0	0	0
0.2	0	0	0	0
0.3	0	0	0	0
0.4	0	0	0	0
0.5	0	0	0	0
0.6	0	0	1	0
0.7	0	0	1	0
0.8	0	0	1	0
0.9	0	0	1	0
1.0	1	1	1	1
1.1	1	1	1	1

Fig. 9.6.9: Comparison of various Excel and VBA truncating functions. Background shading is again used to emphasize the absolute values obtained.

When you verify the results shown in Fig. 9.6.8, you may notice a quirk: a minus sign in front of a zero may not always show (but is correctly carried internally) depending on how you format the cells. The General format displays the sign of zero properly. The same applies to the results in Fig. 9.6.9.

Truncation is rounding to zero digits past the decimal point, and again can be achieved with several instructions. The various options are illustrated in Fig. 9.6.9. Note that VBA Fix retains the sign of x when it truncates to zero, whereas Excel's Trunc does not. This can be consequential, e.g., if you later test whether a result is positive or not. Table 9.6.1 summarizes the results for both rounding and truncation.

452

Excel function	action
Round(x,n)	rounds towards the nearest integer; 5 rounded away from zero
vRound(x,n)	rounds towards the nearest integer; 5 rounded to nearest even integer (requires XN)
RoundUp(x,n)	rounds towards the next integer away from zero
RoundDown(x,n)	rounds towards the next integer towards zero
Int(x)	truncates
Trunc(x)	truncates towards zero, loses sign when result is zero

VBA function	action
Round(x,n)	rounds towards the nearest integer; 5 rounded to nearest even integer
Fix(x)	truncates x for positive x; truncates $(x-1)$ for negative non-integer .
Cint, CLng	truncates to the nearest integer; .5 rounded to nearest even integer

Table 9.6.1: A comparison of rounding and related double-precision functions in Excel and VBA.

Unfortunately, both Excel and VBA lack a function for rounding to a *relative* precision, such as to 7 or 12 significant figures s, regardless of the position of the decimal point. XN provides such relative rounding with the functions vRoundR(x,s) and xRoundR(x,s), where vRoundR provides banker's rounding, just as vRound(x,n) does, and is therefore preferable.

9.7 *Working with complex numbers*

Complex numbers contain a real and an imaginary component, and are typically represented as $a + jb$, where $j = \sqrt{(-1)}$ is the imaginary unit. Mathematicians typically use i instead of j for this *i*maginary number, but in the physical sciences the symbol i is often used to represent the *i*ntensity of, e.g., light or electrical current. Here we will use the j-notation; Excel accepts either i (its default) or j, but not their capitalized forms, I or J.

There are two approaches to represent a complex quantity on the spreadsheet. One is to use one cell for its real part, and an adjacent cell (typically its right-hand neighbor) for its imaginary component, just as one would with a two-dimensional vector. (In the so-called number plane, complex numbers are indeed treated as 2-D vectors.) This requires that one perform all calculations using the special mathematical rules for working with complex quantities, and keeps track of their separate, real and imaginary components.

The alternative is to contract $a + jb$ into a single cell. Because a single spreadsheet cell can hold only one number, the complex numbers are then kept as *text strings*, and their mathematical operations require special commands to code, manipulate, and decode these strings. Excel allows both approaches, but its built-in functions only support complex numbers encoded as text strings. Below we will encounter add-in functions that support both formats.

The rules governing their most basic mathematical operations are

$$(a + jb) \pm (c + jd) = (a \pm c) + j(b \pm d) \tag{9.7.1}$$

$$(a + jb) \times (c + jd) = (ac - bd) + j(bc + ad) \tag{9.7.2}$$

$$(a + jb) \, / \, (c + jd) = \frac{(a + jb)\,(c - jd)}{(c + jd)\,(c - jd)} = \frac{(ac + bd) + j(bc - ad)}{c^2 + d^2} \tag{9.7.3}$$

These rules apply regardless of the type of display used. For relatively simple operations, the use of two adjacent cells (often in columns labeled Re for the real component, and Im for the imaginary component) is perhaps the simpler, although it may take up more spreadsheet space. We already used this approach with Fourier transformation in chapter 5. The space saving of the more compact text string format is often illusory anyway, because much wider columns may have to be used to display the real and imaginary components in the exponent.

This is because the text string format does not allow the user to limit the number of digits displayed, and therefore usually requires more space except when the results are integers. When cells B2 and C2 contain the instruction =COMPLEX(1,2) and =IMSQRT(B2) respectively, cell B2 will display 1+2j, while C2 will show 1.27201964951407+0.786151377757423j, in its complete and unabridged 15-digit glory, in which case you may only see the start, middle, or end of $\sqrt{(1+2j)}$, depending on the column width and cell alignment (left-, center-, or right-aligned) used, unless adjacent cells are empty and can be used for text overflow.

Excel provides three types of special commands for use with complex numbers encoded as text strings. One instruction, =COMPLEX(*a*,*b*), converts two input numbers, *a* and *b*, or the numbers stored in two corresponding cell addresses, such as C4,C5, into the requisite text string. Commands with names starting with the letters IM perform operations between such text-encoded complex quantities. Commands in the third set, again starting with IM, decode them, by converting the text-encoded quantities into numbers in single cells. This last category contains four members: =IMREAL and =IMAGINARY can be used to recover *a* and *b* respectively, while =IMABS and =IMARGUMENT produce the corresponding vector length $\sqrt{(a^2+b^2)}$ and vector angle arctan(*b*/*a*). All these commands are listed in appendix A.5. In pre-2007 versions of Excel, they can only be used after the Data Analysis Toolpak has been loaded, once.

In order to use *j* instead of *i* as the imaginary unit, you must specify this, e.g., with =COMPLEX(*a*,*b*, "j") instead of =COMPLEX(*a*,*b*). In any case, stick with one formalism, based on either *i* or *j*, because upon mixing them you will get no answer beyond the error message #VALUE! Usually, this will be a moot point, because we will use the side-by-side notation for individual complex numbers, and the side-by-side blocks of real and imaginary components for complex matrices.

You can now perform mathematical operations on these text-encoded complex numbers. Say that you have stored the two complex quantities 2+3j and 4+5j in cells C5 and C6 respectively, and want to compute the sum of their squares. You can do this with a sequence of individual instructions or, much more efficiently, with the composite instruction =IMSUM(IMPOWER(C5,2),IMPOWER(C6,2)). Note: with text-encoded complex quantities, you cannot use signs such as +, −, *, /, or ^ as shorthand operational instructions, but you must use their explicit, named complex functions, in this case IMSUM instead of +, and POWER instead of ^. We will encounter the same approach with XN.xla(m) in chapter 11

The XN collection of higher-precision add-in functions for Excel also includes a large number of double-precision functions (without the prefix x for extended numberlength) for operations on or with complex numbers, as listed in. Table 9.7.1. All complex XN instructions have corresponding double-precision versions. Moreover, XN contains a number of functions that have no Excel counterparts, even in double precision, such as those in Table 9.7.2.

Excel codes its complex numbers as a string in one cell, and you can use the XN functions in the same way. Alternatively you can use two (horizontally or vertically) adjacent cells for the real and imaginary parts of a complex number. Exercise 9.7.1 and Fig. 9.7.1 illustrate how this works.

Exercise 9.7.1:

(1) Deposit the numbers 2, -5, 4, and 3.7 in cells B2, C2, E2, and F2 respectively. These are your complex input numbers, representing 2–5j and 4+3.7j. Now highlight the cell block H2:I2, type =cplxAdd(B2:C2,E2:F2) and deposit this instruction with Ctrl⌣Shift⌣Enter. If you just depress the Enter key you will get the correct answer, but in the form of a string such as shown in H7.

(2) Place the same (or other) input numbers in vertical combinations, as illustrated in rows 4 and 5 of Fig. 9.7.1. Now highlight, e.g., I4:I5, type the instruction =cplxAdd(C4:C5,F4:F5) and again use Ctrl⌣Shift⌣Enter.

(3) In I7 deposit the Excel instruction =COMPLEX(H2,I2,"j"), which will yield the Excel string format of the complex sum in one cell.

(4) Now that you have XN active, you can take a sneak preview at how Excel stores integers and decimal fractions, using the extended-precision *c*onversion to *str*ing format =xCStr instruction of XN. In C8 you see that integers represented in binary are recovered intact, as integers (and XN deletes insignificant trailing zeroes), whereas in C9 the recovery of −1.3 stored in binary is shown to be correct to only about 17 significant decimals, because most decimal fractions do not have exact binary representations. But for double-precision that suffices, because Excel will round it back to −1.3.

454

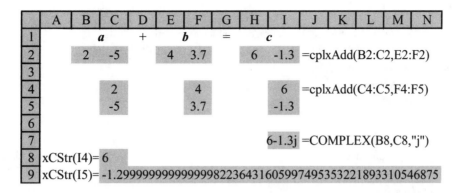

Fig. 9.7.1: Adding two complex numbers using double-precision XN instructions. Source and target cells are shown with gray backgrounds. The contents of cells are readable only because the text can overflow in adjacent, empty cells. Combining horizontally linked and vertically linked cell pairs automatically reverts to the Excel string notation. Cell I7 is right-aligned, and cell G8 center-aligned.

A sampler of some other complex operations can be found in Fig. 9.7.2. For further details on their operation, click on the extensive Help file downloaded with XN.

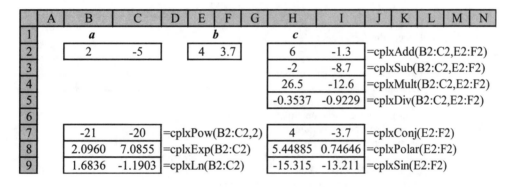

Fig. 9.7.2: Examples of applying XN functions for complex numbers.

Fourier transformation in general involves complex quantities, even when applied to real data. Excel's Fourier transformation macro (Tools ⇨ Data Analysis ⇨ Fourier Analysis) encodes its output as text strings, which can be decoded with =IMREAL and =IMAGINARY. On the other hand, the custom macros ForwardFT and InverseFT of the MacroBundle use two separate columns for the real and imaginary components of the data input and output, without encoding. Use whichever suits your fancy. In comparing them, keep in mind that even standard mathematics isn't always quite standardized yet. Excel's Fourier transform routine uses the *engineering* sign convention of, e.g., the *Numerical Recipes*, whereas the custom macros of chapter 5 follow the *mathematical* sign convention found in most books on Fourier transformation. If you change the sign convention used in the custom macro, please alert others (and even yourself, for future use) of this modification, e.g., within the comment label of the macro.

Basic operations on one complex number

cplxAbs	Absolute value	$|z| = \sqrt{(z_1^2 + z_2^2)}$
cplxConj	Complex conjugate	$a - j\,b$
cplxInv	Inversion	$1/z$
cplxNeg	Negation	$-z$
cplxPolar	Converts from rectangular to polar coordinates	
cplxRect	Converts from polar to rectangular coordinates	

cplxRoot	Taking the nth root	$z^{1/n} = \|z\|^{1/n} \{\cos[(\theta+2\pi k)/n] + j\sin[(\theta+2\pi k)/n]\}$, $k = 0, 1, \ldots, n-1$
cplxSerie	Returns a series for a function of complex argument	
cplxEval	Evaluation of mathematical expression in terms of complex numbers	

Basic operations on two complex numbers

cplxAdd	Addition	
cplxSub	Subtraction	
cplxMult	Multiplication	
cplxDiv	Division	
cplxPow	Raising to the nth power	$z^n = \|z\|^n [\cos(n\theta) + j\sin(n\theta)]$
cplxExp	Exponentiation	$e^z = e^a \cos(b) + j\,e^a \sin(b)$
cplxLn	Taking the natural logarithm	$\ln(z) = \ln\sqrt{(a^2+b^2)} + j\arctan(a/b)$

Trigonometric and related functions

cplxSin	Sine
cplx Cos	Cosine
cplxTan	Tangent
cplxSinH	Hyperbolic sine
cplxCosH	Hyperbolic cosine
cplxTanH	Hyperbolic tangent
cplxASin	Arcsine
cplxACos	Arccosine
cplxATan	Arctangent
cplxASinH	Hyperbolic Arcsine
cplxACosH	Hyperbolic Arccosine
cplxATanH	Hyperbolic Arctangent

Otherfunctions

cplxEi	Exponential integral of a complex argument
cplxEquation2	Solution of quadratic equation $az^2 + bz + c = 0$ where z is a complex number
cplxErf	Error function of a complex argument
cplxErfC	Error function complement of a complex argument
cplxFact	Factorial of a complex number
cplxGamma	Gamma function of a complex argument
cplxGammaLn	Natural logarithm of gamma function of a complex argument
cplxDiGamma	Digamma function of a complex argument
cplxZeta	Riemann zeta function of a complex argument
cplxIntegr	Romberg integration of a function of a complex argument

Table 9.7.1: The XN double-precision functions for working with complex numbers $z = a + jb$. For their extended-precision equivalents see chapter 11.

There are also some XN functions for which no separate double-precision equivalents are available as of this writing. These can of course be used with the instruction xCDbl, which converts the output back to double precision. In section 10.17 we will illustrate the use of partitioned matrices by writing a custom function for the pseudo-inverse of a complex rectangular matrix. However, if you are merely interested in computing the pseudo-inverse of a complex matrix, it is far simpler just to use the XN instruction =xCDbl(xMPseudoInvC(M)). In fact, XN contains a whole series of functions for or based on the singular value decomposition (SVD) of complex matrices, as listed in Table 9.7.2.

xMCondC	condition number κ of a complex matrix
xMpCondC	$p\kappa = -\log \kappa$ of a complex matrix
xMPseudoInvC	complex SVD-based pseudo-inverse, $\mathbf{V}\,\Sigma^{-1}\,\mathbf{U}^{\text{H}}$
xRegrLC	complex SVD-based linear least squares
xSVDUC	complex SVD matrix $\mathbf{U}$
xSVDDC	complex SVD matrix Σ
xSVDVC	complex SVD matrix $\mathbf{V}$

Table 9.7.2: The SVD-based XN functions for working with complex matrices.

9.8 Summary

In this chapter we have taken a selective look at some of the mathematics underlying a few standard numerical methods used in scientific data analysis. In our extensive discussion of numerical differentiation, we illustrated developing a fairly general mathematical model, then simplifying it and applying this to the spreadsheet and as a custom macro. In contrast to the material in chapter 8, our focus here was on the theoretical background of the method used rather than its actual coding. It is gratifying to see that a careful consideration of the dominant types of error, and of the necessary compromise between accuracy and precision, can actually lead us to a powerful novel algorithm.

We then focused on integration, basing our approach on the Euler-Maclaurin formulas that, again, specify the systematic errors, and their interplay with the more random cancellation errors. This lead us to formulas that can yield highly accurate results with relatively little extra computing effort. The differentiation and integration formulas considered here assume that the functions are smooth, i.e., without discontinuities and/or singularities, and we have restricted the discussion mainly to methods that are applicable to the broad class of equidistant data sets, as are often obtained from scientific instruments.

Experimental data are just numbers, which mean little if anything without their context, which is necessary for their interpretation. A quantitative interpretation typically yields a model function, which is to be fitted to the data. In that sense, all scientific data analysis is primarily an exercise in fitting some theoretically more or less justifiable model to the experimental data. This was clearly on display in section 9.6 on interpolation, a technique that is sometimes useful to fill in gaps between sampled data.

When one is merely given a set of data, such as those in Fig. 9.6.1, without any additional information about their origin and context, one would neither know whether interpolation is appropriate nor, if it is, how to implement it properly. Conversely, a given data set might be treated quite differently in different contexts. On the other hand, when we know that a given data set represents, e.g., an underlying smooth function, as in the calibration curve plotting the response of a well-designed instrument as a function of a stimulus, both interpolation based on an appropriate model function and its counterpart, inverse interpolation (see section 2.14), are perfectly legitimate, well-defined operations. In such cases, using nonlinear least squares is often the easiest approach.

The sections on differentiation and integration obviously require some background in calculus. Their primary aim is to showcase some of the more general numerical methods, such as central differencing and Romberg integration, and to illustrate their ease of use with a few examples within the general context of this book. Custom macros are provided to facilitate applying these methods to actual problems.

In the next chapter we will expand the set of spreadsheet tools available to include matrix operations, and we will also encounter new tools for working with complex numbers.

9.9 For further reading

There are many excellent books on differentiation, integration, and interpolation. As always, *Numerical Recipes* is a good place to start, because of its clear, conceptual explanations, and the books of F. S. Acton, *Numerical Methods that Work*, Math. Assoc. Am. (1990) and *Real Computing Made Real* (Princeton Univ. Press (1996) are full of good advise. Many useful expressions for all three techniques are listed by P. J. Davis & I. Polonsky in chapter 25 of M. Abramowitz & I. Stegun, *Handbook of Mathematical Functions*, NBS (1964), Dover (1965). A wealth of information on numerical integration can be found in P. J. Davis & P. Rabinowitz, *Methods of Numerical Integration*, 2nd ed., Academic Press (1984). Other helpful texts for writing the present chapter were *Numerical Mathematics* by G. Hämmerlin & K.-H. Hoffmann, Springer (1990) and W. Gautschi, *Numerical Analysis*, Birkhäuser (1997).

Chapter *10*

Matrix operations

The general layout of a spreadsheet, as a rectangular array of cells that can each hold either a number or an instruction, would seem to make it an ideal vehicle for both teaching and applying matrix algebra. Unfortunately, this has not been the case, possibly because matrix algebra is often considered too abstract and/or too difficult, but also because Excel provides only a minimal set of matrix operations. Yet the pervasiveness of matrix algebra in modern science is undeniable, and the recent expansion of the Excel grid, especially its widening from 256 to 16,384 columns, has made its use for matrix algebra even more appealing.

Obviously, there is neither space for a full-fledged review of linear algebra here, nor a need, since there are many fine books on that topic in virtually every college library. However, our focus clearly differs from that of standard college textbooks, which tend to deal with the mathematical structure of matrices, and/or with the coding of the corresponding algorithms. Our emphasis will be on numerical accuracy and ease of use, on the assumption that most Excel users of linear algebra will have applications in mind, usually with relatively small matrices, and will know when to migrate to more specialized programs when their matrices become too big. In other words, we will downplay the time difference between a tenth of an eye blink and half of one. (The reader should be forewarned that, in the next chapter, we may sometimes accept longer and sometimes quite noticeable execution times in exchange for higher accuracy.) We will, likewise, stress the use of the matrix inverse (of square matrices) and pseudo-inverse (of rectangular matrices) as convenient approaches, despite their numerical inefficiency. After all, this book is intended for scientists and engineers rather than for mathematicians and software developers. If your matrices are so large that they noticeably slow down Excel, consider more appropriate, specialized software.

In view of the heavy emphasis in this book on least squares analysis, we will stress this topic also in our survey of matrix methods. Appendices C.2 through C.10 contain many additional functions that are not explored here in any detail, just as appendix A.4 shows many engineering functions by name only. Their names will not scare you if you don't recognize them, but if you do, you will know how to use them. They are listed to indicate how much is available in Matrix.xla, i.e., to whet your appetite.

10.1 Some general features

10.1.1 Addressing a matrix

As with all its mathematical operations, Excel has two ways to deal with matrix algebra: in plain view on the spreadsheet, or invisibly in background. Both methods have their advantages. Here we will consider the direct spreadsheet manipulation of two-dimensional matrices, assisted by the use of functions. Similar tools available for use in macros and subroutines at higher precision will be described in chapter 11. And unlike the few Excel matrix functions, which are not available in VBA, the matrix functions of Matrix.xla and XN.xla(m) can be used both on the spreadsheet and in custom functions and subroutines once these add-ins are installed in both Excel and, for the latter, also in the VBEditor.

A matrix is most readily seen as a rectangular array of numbers in a single plane. (One can extend this concept, and fill the matrix instead with formulas rather than numbers.) In order to distinguish such a block of data from a single constant or function, matrices are usually represented in print with boldfaced capitals, such as **M**. The *size* of a matrix is specified by the number m of its rows, and the number n of its columns, numbers that, always in this order, are often used as subscripts, as in $\mathbf{M}_{r \times c}$ or **M** ($r \times c$). A square matrix has equal numbers of rows and columns ($r = c$), while a row vector occupies only one row ($r = 1$), as in $\mathbf{v}_{1 \times c}$, and a column vector such as $\mathbf{v}_{r \times 1}$ uses only one column ($c = 1$) but r rows. Vectors are one-dimensional matrices, i.e., they consist of only one column or one row, and are typically shown in bold lower case. They are treated in Excel as (one-dimensional) matrices. Transposition can convert a column vector into the corresponding row vector, and vice versa. Individual matrix *elements* are often denoted by a_{ij} or m_{ij}, where $1 \le i \le r$ and $1 \le j \le c$. Note that we distinguish here between matrix *size* and *dimension*, where the dimension will be restricted here to 0 (for scalars), 1 (for vectors), or 2 (for square and rectangular matrices). The planar spreadsheet is rather inconvenient for matrices of higher dimensionality, and the software described here isn't suitable for it either. On the other hand, arrays in Excel can have dimensions from 1 (*but* not 0) up to 60.

In order to handle matrices as single units, all matrix operations on the Excel spreadsheet require that the area to be occupied by any matrix instruction be specified as such, by first highlighting that area before the matrix instruction is typed, and then, upon entry of the matrix instruction, by using the special keystroke combination Ctrl◡Shift◡Enter (or by Command◡Return on a Mac). The resulting instruction will then show in the formula box with curly brackets, indicating that it is a matrix instruction. (However, do *not* type an instruction using curly brackets and expect it to be treated as a matrix; it will not.) The output area, where the result of the matrix operation is to be deposited, should therefore have the correct size. If the designated area is too small, any output that does not fit in it will be lost; if it is too large, the unused cells will be filled with the error message #N/A. Only with macros, such as with <u>E</u>dit ⇨ Paste <u>Sp</u>ecial ⇨ Transpo<u>s</u>e, does Excel allow the user to specify only the left-top cell of the output. There is one general exception to the above rule: when the instruction generates an answer that fits inside a *single* cell, as in =MDETERM, one can use Enter instead of Ctrl◡Shift◡Enter.

Because the *output* of a matrix instruction is considered as a single unit, you cannot erase, cut, or modify a single element of its multi-celled output. (But you can *read* the contents of any individual cell in that output in any other cell outside the array, e.g., with =C19 when C19 is an element of the matrix B18:D23, and *copy* its value to another spreadsheet cell.) However, a matrix instruction does not affect its *input*, i.e., when you generate an array of numbers, and perform a matrix operation on that array, you can still modify any aspect of that input and, as with any other Excel function, and see how the output automatically updates its response. And if the operation is impossible, such as when you instruct Excel to generate the inverse of a singular matrix, it will instead show the error message #NUM! in every designated output cell, but will not hang up on you, and will allow you to change the input.

Exercise 10.1.1:

(1) In a spreadsheet, enter a rectangular array of numbers, such as 1 in cell A1, 2 in A2, 3 in B1, and 4 in B3.

(2) Just to practice entering a matrix instruction, highlight another 2×2 area, such as D1:E2, type =MINVERSE(A1:B2), with two left-hand fingers press down the Control and Shift keys, and *only then* with a right-hand finger press Enter. You should see the result in D1:E2: –2 in D1, 1 in D2, 1.5 in E1, and –0.5 in E2. Note: as you type this instruction, the text will appear in cell D1 as well as in the formula box. Only after you have used Ctrl◡Shift◡Enter will the instruction in the formula box acquire its curvy brackets, { and }. Instead of typing the array address A1:B2 you can highlight that area with your mouse. In either case, don't forget to end the instruction with its closing bracket,).

(3) Change the value in cell B2 to 5, and observe that the output in D1:E2 automatically updates its answer. Change the value in B2 to 6, and see what happens now. (With these input numbers, this particular matrix instruction has no answer, just as the logarithm or the square root of a negative number would not yield an answer.) Go back to the value 5 in B2, or deposit a number other than 6, and see the output again show a result.

(4) In cell G1 place the instruction =D1. Copy this instruction to G1:H2 to make a replica of D1:E2.

(5) Cut and paste the instruction in G1 to another cell.

(6) Try to copy or delete the value in D1. Sorry, this cannot be done, but you can copy or delete the entire array D1:B2. If you want to access a single cell in the array, use the method shown under (4) and (5).

(7) Repeat instruction (2) while highlighting too small or too large an area for the result, and see what you get.

The individual numbers (or instructions) inside the matrix are its matrix elements, such as $m_{3,2}$, where the first index always denotes the row number, and the second index the column number. Row and column indices count from the left-top matrix element, and in general do not coincide with the spreadsheet cell coordinates. In Excel, which doesn't use subscripts, $m_{3,2}$ is written as M(3,2), again with the indices r and c in their obligatory order.

10.1.2 Transposition, addition & subtraction

The simplest matrix operations are transposition, addition, and subtraction. The *transpose* of a matrix **M** is symbolically denoted as $\mathbf{M}^T$. In matrix terms, transposition merely exchanges row and column indices: $m^T_{i,j} = m_{j,i}$. Transposition is also commonly used in business, in order to exchange the rows and columns of a table, and Excel therefore has a macro that doesn't even identify it as a matrix operation, using the keystroke combination Edit ⇨ Paste Special ⇨ Transpose. But if you want the transposition to self-update, use the equivalent function, =TRANSPOSE.

In this chapter we will encounter complex as well as real matrices. The generalization of transposition to complex matrices is the *conjugate transpose*, **M***, in which each element is the conjugate complex $a - bj$ from the corresponding element $a + bj$ in **M**. The conjugate transpose **M*** is also called the *adjoint* or *Hermitian conjugate* of **M**.

Addition and subtraction are very much like the addition and subtraction of single numbers, except that they perform the addition or subtraction in one single operation, and require that the two matrices involved have the same sizes. The addition or subtraction of two matrices **A** and **B** to yield the sum or difference matrix **C** can therefore be written as

$$\mathbf{A} = \begin{bmatrix} a_{1,1} & a_{1,2} & \dots & a_{1,c} \\ a_{2,1} & a_{2,2} & \dots & a_{2,c} \\ a_{3,1} & a_{3,2} & \dots & a_{3,c} \\ \dots & \dots & \dots & \dots \\ a_{r,1} & a_{r,2} & \dots & a_{r,c} \end{bmatrix}, \qquad \mathbf{B} = \begin{bmatrix} b_{1,1} & b_{1,2} & \dots & b_{1,c} \\ b_{2,1} & b_{2,2} & \dots & b_{2,c} \\ b_{3,1} & b_{3,2} & \dots & b_{3,c} \\ \dots & \dots & \dots & \dots \\ b_{r,1} & b_{r,2} & \dots & b_{r,c} \end{bmatrix},$$

$$\mathbf{C} = \begin{bmatrix} a_{1,1} \pm b_{1,1} & a_{1,2} \pm b_{1,2} & \dots & a_{1,c} \pm b_{1,c} \\ a_{2,1} \pm b_{2,1} & a_{2,2} \pm b_{2,2} & \dots & a_{2,c} \pm b_{2,c} \\ a_{3,1} \pm b_{3,1} & a_{3,2} \pm b_{3,2} & \dots & a_{3,c} \pm b_{3,c} \\ \dots & \dots & \dots & \dots \\ a_{r,1} \pm b_{r,1} & a_{r,2} \pm b_{r,2} & \dots & a_{r,c} \pm b_{r,c} \end{bmatrix} \qquad (10.1.1)$$

Matrix addition and subtraction simply represents addition and subtraction of the corresponding matrix elements, i.e., for each element i,j we have $c_{i,j} = a_{i,j} \pm b_{i,j}$. These operations are only defined when the two matrices **A** and **B** have identical sizes. **C** will then have the same size as **A** and **B**. The operation is commutative, i.e., $\mathbf{A} \pm \mathbf{B} = \mathbf{B} \pm \mathbf{A}$, as well as associative, i.e., $(\mathbf{A} \pm \mathbf{B}) \pm \mathbf{C} = \mathbf{A} \pm (\mathbf{B} \pm \mathbf{C})$. As illustrated in exercise 10.1.1, in Excel matrices can be added or subtracted directly, without the need for special functions, as long as one properly uses the Ctrl⌣Shift⌣Enter sequence.

Exercise 10.1.2:

(1) In a spreadsheet, enter a rectangular array of numbers, such as 1 in cell A1, 2 in A2, 3 in A3, 4 in B1, 5 in B2, and 6 in B3.

(2) Enter a second array of the same size, i.e., with the same number of rows, and the same number of columns. You might, e.g., enter 8 in D2, 7 in D3, 6 in D4, 0 in E2, –1 in E3, and –2 in E4.

(3) Highlight a rectangular area of the same size to receive the result, such as C6:D8. Then type `=A1:B3+D2:E4` and deposit this instruction with Ctrl␣Shift␣Enter. With the numbers given above, you should find an array with three nines in its first column, and three fours in its second column.

(4) Now try it with subtraction as well as addition, and with more than two input arrays, as in $\mathbf{A} + \mathbf{B} - \mathbf{C}$.

(5) When you use arrays of different sizes to form, say, the matrix sum $\mathbf{C} = \mathbf{A} + \mathbf{B}$, the above method will only compute that sum for the array parts of A, B, and C with a common size, which is called their *intersection*. All other elements in the resulting array will contain the #N/A error message.

(6) So-called scalar multiplication works in a similar way. In the above example you might highlight an array of the same size as A1:B3, say G1:H3, then type the instruction `=3*A1:B3`, and enter it with Ctrl␣Shift␣Enter. This will multiply all elements of the array by 3. Again, one can combine addition, subtraction, and scalar multiplication in a single instruction, as in `=3*A1:B3-D2:E4` as long as all matrices involved have the same sizes.

10.1.3 Multiplication & inversion

We consider two types of multiplication. The first of these, *scalar* multiplication, is rather trivial: the product of a single number (or *scalar*) s and a matrix $\mathbf{M}$ or vector $\mathbf{v}$ is defined as a matrix or vector in which each element of is multiplied by s, as in

$$s\,\mathbf{M} = s \begin{bmatrix} m_{1,1} & m_{1,2} & \dots & m_{1,c} \\ m_{2,1} & m_{2,2} & \dots & m_{2,c} \\ m_{3,1} & m_{3,2} & \dots & m_{3,c} \\ \dots & \dots & \dots & \dots \\ m_{r,1} & m_{r,2} & \dots & m_{r,c} \end{bmatrix} = \begin{bmatrix} sm_{1,1} & sm_{1,2} & \dots & sm_{1,c} \\ sm_{2,1} & sm_{2,2} & \dots & sm_{2,c} \\ sm_{3,1} & sm_{3,2} & \dots & sm_{3,c} \\ \dots & \dots & \dots & \dots \\ sm_{r,1} & sm_{r,2} & \dots & sm_{r,c} \end{bmatrix} \tag{10.1.2}$$

and, e.g.,

$$s\,\mathbf{v} = s \begin{bmatrix} v_1 & v_2 & \dots & v_c \end{bmatrix} = \begin{bmatrix} sv_1 & sv_2 & \dots & sv_c \end{bmatrix} \tag{10.1.3}$$

Since the products of the individual matrix elements sm_{ij} or sv_i are commutative, i.e., $sm_{i,j} = m_{i,j}s$ and $sv_i = v_i s$, the same must apply to their scalar products, i.e.,

$$s\,\mathbf{M} = \mathbf{M}\,s \quad \text{and} \quad s\,\mathbf{v} = \mathbf{v}\,s \tag{10.1.4}$$

The second type, *matrix* multiplication, involves the sums of products of matrix elements. First a restriction: in order to compute the matrix product $\mathbf{C} = \mathbf{A}\,\mathbf{B}$, the number of *columns* of matrix $\mathbf{A}$ must be equal to the number of *rows* of matrix $\mathbf{B}$. The reason for this requirement will become obvious once we see how matrix multiplication is defined. Multiplication of a matrix $\mathbf{A}$ of size $r_A \times c_A$ and a matrix $\mathbf{B}$ of size $r_B \times c_B$ requires that $c_A = r_B$, and then yields a product matrix $\mathbf{C}$ with the size $r_A \times c_B$ and with the elements

$$c_{i,j} = a_{i,1}b_{1,j} + a_{i,2}b_{2,j} + \dots + a_{i,c_A}b_{r_B,j} = \sum_{k=1}^{n} a_{i,k}b_{k,j} \tag{10.1.5}$$

where the two matrices $\mathbf{A}$ and $\mathbf{B}$, *considered in this order*, must have the same *inner* indices, $c_A = r_B$. The matrices $\mathbf{A}$ and $\mathbf{B}$ need not have the same size, merely the same inner indices, and the size of the product matrix $\mathbf{C}$ is defined by their *outer* indices, $r_A \times c_B$. Excel has the function `=MMULT` to implement matrix multiplication.

What constitute inner and outer indices in a matrix product depends, of course, on how that product is written, i.e., the inner indices of the product $\mathbf{A}\,\mathbf{B}$ are the outer indices of the product $\mathbf{B}\,\mathbf{A}$, and vice versa. In general, matrix multiplication is therefore *not commutative*, i.e., $\mathbf{A}\,\mathbf{B} \neq \mathbf{B}\,\mathbf{A}$. This even applies to square matrices, and right-multiplying and left-multiplying are separate operations: right-multiplying $\mathbf{A}$ by $\mathbf{B}$ yields $\mathbf{A}\,\mathbf{B}$, left-multiplying $\mathbf{A}$ by $\mathbf{B}$ produces $\mathbf{B}\,\mathbf{A}$. In matrix algebra, the *order* of the symbols in an equation is important.

Exercise 10.1.3:

(1) On a spreadsheet, enter the number sequence 1, 2, 3 in cells B10:B12, and the sequence 4, 5, 6 in C10:C12. This will constitute matrix **A**.

(2) In E10:G11 place some other numbers, to define the matrix **B**.

(3) What will be the size of the matrix product **A B**? The product of a 3×2 and a 2×3 matrix should have the size 3×3. Therefore, highlight an appropriate area, such as I10:K12, and there deposit the result of the matrix multiplication **A B**, using the instruction =MMULT(B10:C12,E10:G11).

(4) Determine the correct area for computing the matrix product **B A**, then find it with the instruction MMULT. Note that this answer is, in general, completely different from that found for the matrix product **A B**.

The rules for multiplying vectors are the same as those for matrices. Here is an example of multiplying a vertical vector $\mathbf{v}_{h \times 1}$ and a horizontal vector $\mathbf{v}_{1 \times k}$.

Exercise 10.1.4:

(1) On a spreadsheet, enter the number sequence 1, 4, 2, 4, 2, 4, 1 in cells B4:B10, and the sequence 14, 64, 24, 64, 28, 64, 24, 64, 14 in D2:L2. These two will be our starting vectors.

(2) Now make their vector product as follows. Highlight the area D4:L10, type =MMULT(B4:B10,D2:L2), and enter this with Ctrl⌣Shift⌣Enter. This works because the numbers in B4:B10 form a 7×1 matrix (i.e., a vertical vector) and those in D2:L2 a 1×9 matrix (a horizontal vector), so that the result is a 7×9 matrix.

(3) Simply because of their sizes, the above is the only way one can multiply these two matrices. They only have one common size (the size 1), which therefore must form the inner indices in the product $\mathbf{A}_{h \times i} \, \mathbf{B}_{j \times k} = \mathbf{C}_{h \times k}$.

(4) Try to invert the order of multiplication, by instead giving the instruction =MMULT(D2:L2,B4:B10). What do you get?

Unit matrices are a particular type of matrices that play a special role in matrix algebra. They have zeroes everywhere, except on their main diagonal (containing the elements with equal indices, a_{ii}), where the elements are all ones. Unit matrices are typically denoted by **I**, as in

$$\mathbf{I} = \begin{bmatrix} 1 & 0 & 0 & \dots & 0 \\ 0 & 1 & 0 & \dots & 0 \\ 0 & 0 & 1 & \dots & 0 \\ \dots & \dots & \dots & \dots & \dots \\ 0 & 0 & 0 & \dots & 1 \end{bmatrix} \tag{10.1.6}$$

with a size *m*×*m* that is typically assumed to fit the occasion.

For every *square* matrix **A** there may exist one other square matrix **B** such that **A B** = **I**. Matrix division as such does not exist, but matrix *inversion*, its rough equivalent, is defined in such a way that **B** is the inverse of **A** when **A B** = **I**, analogous to the algebraic definition $b = 1/a$ when $ab = 1$. In fact, even the notation shows this analogy: just as one can write $b = 1/a = a^{-1}$, it is common to indicate a matrix inverse with the superscript –1, i.e.,

$$\mathbf{A} \, \mathbf{A}^{-1} = \mathbf{I} \tag{10.1.7}$$

Note that, when $\mathbf{A}^{-1}$ exists, one also has

$$\mathbf{A}^{-1} \, \mathbf{A} = \mathbf{I} \tag{10.1.8}$$

Finding $\mathbf{A}^{-1}$ for a given matrix **A** is not trivial, and will be described in section 10.3, but for now it suffices that Excel provides the function MINVERSE for that purpose. Note that multiplying a square matrix by the unit matrix is without consequence:

$$\mathbf{A} \, \mathbf{I} = \mathbf{I} \, \mathbf{A} = \mathbf{A} \tag{10.1.9}$$

10.2 Solving simultaneous equations

Assume that we have n mutually independent equations in n unknowns, and that these equations are linear in the n unknowns, as in

$$
\begin{aligned}
a_{11} x_1 + a_{12} x_2 + \ldots + a_{1n} x_n &= b_1 \\
a_{21} x_1 + a_{22} x_2 + \ldots + a_{2n} x_n &= b_2 \\
a_{31} x_1 + a_{32} x_2 + \ldots + a_{3n} x_n &= b_3 \\
&\ldots \\
a_{n1} x_1 + a_{n2} x_2 + \ldots + a_{nn} x_n &= b_n
\end{aligned}
\tag{10.2.1}
$$

where the unknown coefficients may multiply highly nonlinear functions x_i, such as roots, logarithms, power laws, exponentials, etc. We formulate (10.2.1) in terms of matrix algebra as

$$
\mathbf{A}\,\mathbf{x} = \mathbf{b} \tag{10.2.2}
$$

where

$$
\mathbf{A} = \begin{bmatrix} a_{11} & a_{12} & \ldots & a_{1n} \\ a_{21} & a_{22} & \ldots & a_{2n} \\ \ldots & \ldots & \ldots & \ldots \\ a_{n1} & a_{n2} & \ldots & a_{nn} \end{bmatrix}, \qquad \mathbf{x} = \begin{bmatrix} x_1 \\ x_2 \\ \ldots \\ x_n \end{bmatrix}, \qquad \mathbf{b} = \begin{bmatrix} b_1 \\ b_2 \\ \ldots \\ b_n \end{bmatrix} \tag{10.2.3}
$$

It is easily verified that the matrix product $\mathbf{A}\,\mathbf{x}$ indeed regenerates the set of equations on the left-hand side of (10.2.1), while $\mathbf{b}$ represents its right-hand side. The formal solution of (10.2.1) can then be found by left-multiplying both sides of (10.2.2) by $\mathbf{A}^{-1}$ to yield

$$
\mathbf{A}^{-1}\,\mathbf{A}\,\mathbf{x} = \mathbf{A}^{-1}\,\mathbf{b} \tag{10.2.4}
$$

where $\mathbf{A}^{-1}\,\mathbf{A}\,\mathbf{x} = \mathbf{I}\,\mathbf{x} = \mathbf{x}$, so that this leads directly to the sought answer,

$$
\mathbf{x} = \mathbf{A}^{-1}\,\mathbf{b} \tag{10.2.5}
$$

This is, therefore, a *general* procedure to solve n independent, simultaneous, linear equations in as many unknowns. When the n simultaneous equations are not linearly independent, i.e., when at least one of them can be written as a weighted sum of some or all of the others, no unique solution can be found. In terms of matrix algebra, $\mathbf{A}$ is then called *singular*, and $\mathbf{A}^{-1}$ does not exist.

Interestingly, both matrix multiplication and matrix inversion are computer-intensive operations, and are therefore often avoided in specialized applications, especially when large matrices are involved. Approaches to solve for $\mathbf{x}$ in (10.2.5) without having to compute $\mathbf{A}^{-1}$ are called decompositions, factorizations, or eliminations. But don't worry: we will not get into the nitty-gritty of writing code to implement these approaches, a task we will relegate to the spreadsheet, and we will consider them only to learn the terminology, and to get a feel for the problems involved.

10.2.1 The diagonal matrix

There are a few special cases in which a set of simultaneous equations such as (10.2.1) can be solved directly, without matrix inversion. Here we will consider three of them. The first, rather trivial case is when all terms a_{ij} in (10.2.1) are zero except when $i = j$, so that the equations are not coupled at all, and have the mutually independent solutions $x_1 = b_1/a_{11}$, $x_2 = b_2/a_{22}$, $x_3 = b_3/a_{33}$, $\ldots$, $x_n = b_n/a_{nn}$. As an illustration, here is its formal matrix description. We have

$$
\begin{aligned}
a_{11}\,x_1 \quad\quad\quad\quad\quad\quad &= b_1 \\
a_{22}\,x_2 \quad\quad\quad\quad\quad &= b_2 \\
a_{33}\,x_2 \quad\quad\quad &= b_3 \\
\cdots \\
a_{nn}\,x_n &= b_n
\end{aligned}
\tag{10.2.6}
$$

so that **A** is now a *diagonal* matrix,

$$
\mathbf{A} =
\begin{bmatrix}
a_{11} & 0 & \dots & 0 \\
0 & a_{22} & \dots & 0 \\
\dots & \dots & \dots & \dots \\
0 & 0 & \dots & a_{nn}
\end{bmatrix}
\tag{10.2.7}
$$

which, provided that no a_{ii} is zero, has the inverse

$$
\mathbf{A}^{-1} =
\begin{bmatrix}
1/a_{11} & 0 & \dots & 0 \\
0 & 1/a_{22} & \dots & 0 \\
\dots & \dots & \dots & \dots \\
0 & 0 & \dots & 1/a_{nn}
\end{bmatrix}
\tag{10.2.8}
$$

as can be verified by computing the matrix product $\mathbf{A}\,\mathbf{A}^{-1}$ and verifying that it leads to the unit matrix, see (10.1.7). Consequently, (10.2.5) indeed yields the solutions $x_1 = b_1/a_{11}$, $x_2 = b_2/a_{22}$, $x_3 = b_3/a_{33}$, ... , $x_n = b_n/a_{nn}$, as you would expect from (10.2.6).

Make sure to exclude equations with zero terms a_{ii} because, obviously, no answer can be found for these as $x_i = b_i/a_{ii}$ cannot be calculated when $a_{ii} = 0$. A diagonal matrix is often denoted as **D**.

10.2.2 The lower triangular matrix

A more significant special case is that in which the simultaneous equations can all be written in terms of a *lower triangular* matrix, i.e.,

$$
\mathbf{A} =
\begin{bmatrix}
a_{11} & 0 & \dots & 0 \\
a_{21} & a_{22} & \dots & 0 \\
\dots & \dots & \dots & \dots \\
a_{n1} & a_{n2} & \dots & a_{nn}
\end{bmatrix}
\tag{10.2.9}
$$

corresponding to the set of equations

$$
\begin{aligned}
a_{11}\,x_1 \quad\quad\quad\quad\quad\quad &= b_1 \\
a_{21}\,x_1 + a_{22}\,x_2 \quad\quad\quad &= b_2 \\
a_{31}\,x_1 + a_{32}\,x_2 + a_{33}\,x_3 &= b_3 \\
\cdots \\
a_{n1}\,x_1 + a_{n2}\,x_2 + a_{n3}\,x_3 + \dots + a_{nn}\,x_n &= b_n
\end{aligned}
\tag{10.2.10}
$$

which can be solved by successive (so-called *forward*) substitution. We have $x_1 = b_1/a_{11}$, which upon substitution into the next equation yields $x_2 = (b_2 - a_{21}x_1)\,/\,a_{22} = (b_2 - a_{21}b_1/a_{11})\,/\,a_{22}$ and, in general,

$$
x_j = \left(b_j - \sum_{k=1}^{j-1} a_{jk} x_k \right) \Big/ a_{jj}
\tag{10.2.11}
$$

as long as no diagonal term a_{jj} is zero. A lower triangular matrix is often written as **L**.

10.2.3 The upper triangular matrix

Likewise, the set of equations

$$
\begin{aligned}
a_{11}x_1 + a_{12}x_2 + a_{13}x_3 + \dots + a_{1n}x_n &= b_1 \\
a_{22}x_2 + a_{23}x_3 + \dots + a_{2n}x_n &= b_2 \\
a_{33}x_3 + \dots + a_{3n}x_n &= b_3 \\
\dots \\
a_{nn}x_n &= b_n
\end{aligned}
\tag{10.2.12}
$$

leads to the *upper diagonal* matrix

$$
\mathbf{A} = \begin{bmatrix}
a_{11} & a_{12} & \dots & a_{1n} \\
0 & a_{22} & \dots & a_{2n} \\
\dots & \dots & \dots & \dots \\
0 & 0 & \dots & a_{nn}
\end{bmatrix}
\tag{10.2.13}
$$

which upon *backward* substitution yields the solutions

$$
x_j = \left(b_j - \sum_{k=j+1}^{n} a_{jk}x_k \right) \Big/ a_{jj}
\tag{10.2.14}
$$

again provided that all a_{jj} are non-zero. A common symbol for an upper triangular matrix is $\mathbf{U}$.

Note that the above approaches can be used to avoid matrix inversion, because they require relatively few multiplications and additions, and are therefore rather efficient. For relatively small matrices, such efficiency considerations are usually secondary, especially for problems that are suitable for solution on a spreadsheet, where user-friendliness is, typically, a more important consideration. They are essential, however, for solving problems involving hundreds or thousands of simultaneous equations, as in simulations of airplane aerodynamics or of enzyme-substrate docking.

10.3 Matrix elimination

10.3.1 Gaussian elimination

We now consider the set of simultaneous equations (10.2.1) in some more detail. Obviously, the order in which the equations appear in (10.2.1) is arbitrary, i.e., their solution is not changed by interchanging their relative positions. Likewise, neither multiplying one of these equations by a non-zero scalar, nor replacing an equation by itself plus a constant times a second equation, will affect their solutions. Below we will use these manipulations to bring the equations in upper triangular form, and then to solve them.

Such a procedure for solving a system of simultaneous equations is called *matrix elimination*. It is readily illustrated with a specific numerical example, such as with the following three simultaneous equations

$$
\begin{aligned}
3x_1 + 2x_2 + 2x_3 &= 5 \\
6x_1 + x_2 + 2x_3 &= 7 \\
x_1 + x_2 + x_3 &= 3
\end{aligned}
\tag{10.3.1}
$$

We designate the top left-most coefficient, 3, as our *pivot*, i.e., as the coefficient to make all coefficients directly below it zero. (We can always do this as long as the coefficient taken as pivot is not zero. There are better ways to choose a pivot rather than just its position, because the ordering of the equations, as well as the ordering of the terms inside them, is arbitrary. Such details, while important in practice, will not concern us here.) In order to make the coefficient of x_1 in the second row of (10.3.1) equal to zero we subtract two times the top line from that second line. Likewise we multiply the third equation by 3, and then subtract the top equation from it. The result then reads

$$\begin{array}{rcl} 3x_1 + 2x_2 + 2x_3 &=& 5 \\ 0 - 3x_2 - 2x_3 &=& -3 \qquad \text{row2} - 2 \times \text{row1 of } (10.3.1) \\ 0 + x_2 + x_3 &=& 4 \qquad 3 \times \text{row3} - \text{row1 of } (10.3.1) \end{array} \qquad (10.3.2)$$

Now we select the second coefficient on the second row, -3, as our pivot, and use it to make the coefficient of x_2 on the bottom line vanish, by taking three times the bottom equation plus the middle equation:

$$\begin{array}{rcl} 3x_1 + 2x_2 + 2x_3 &=& 5 \\ 0 - 3x_2 - 2x_3 &=& -3 \\ 0 + 0 + x_3 &=& 9 \qquad 3 \times \text{row3} + \text{row2 of } (10.3.2) \end{array} \qquad (10.3.3)$$

We have now brought the left-hand side of (10.3.3) in the upper triangular form, as in (10.2.12), and we can therefore find the solutions directly by backward substitution from (10.2.14) as $x_3 = 9$, $x_2 = (-3 + 2 \times 9)/(-3) = -5$, and $x_1 = [5 - 2 \times (-5) - 2 \times 9]/3 = -1$. Verify that these are indeed correct solutions by back-substitution into (10.3.1).

Exercise 10.3.1:

(1) On a spreadsheet, enter the matrix **A** and the vector **b** expressing (10.3.1), by placing 3, 6, and 1 in B2 through B4, the numbers 2, 1, and 1 in C2:C4, then 2, 2, and 1 in D2:D4, and finally 5, 7, and 3 in F2:F4.

(2) Highlight a 3×3 area such as B6:D8, and compute $\mathbf{A}^{-1}$ with the instruction =MINVERSE(B2:D4) followed by Ctrl⌣Shift⌣Enter.

(3) Highlight a 3×1 area such as F6:F8, and compute $\mathbf{x} = \mathbf{A}^{-1}\mathbf{b}$ with the instruction =MMULT(B6:D8,F2:F4) followed by Ctrl⌣Shift⌣Enter.

(4) You have just solved the three simultaneous equations (10.3.1), and found $x_1 = -1$, $x_2 = -5$, and $x_3 = 9$. You could also have solved these by hand, but in matrix form this approach is readily automated and made suitable for computer solution, so that it works the same for, say, seven simultaneous equations in seven unknowns, or seven thousand simultaneous equations in seven thousand unknowns.

Note that the above *Gauss elimination* scheme does not utilize any special information about the coefficients involved, other than that no zero can serve as a pivot. For the sake of simplicity we have here demonstrated the method with integer coefficients, but real numbers can be used just as well.

Because the above operations involve not just the coefficients a_{ij} on the left-hand side of the equations, but also their right-hand counterparts b_i, they are often handled in *augmented* matrices that contain both a_{ij} and b_i, with a vertical line to indicate the locations of the equal signs in the original equations. In this formalism, (10.3.1) would be written as

$$\left[\begin{array}{ccc|c} 3 & 2 & 2 & 5 \\ 6 & 1 & 2 & 7 \\ 1 & 1 & 1 & 3 \end{array} \right] \qquad (10.3.4)$$

while (10.3.3) would read

$$\left[\begin{array}{ccc|c} 3 & 2 & 2 & 5 \\ 0 & -3 & -2 & -3 \\ 0 & 0 & 1 & 9 \end{array} \right] \qquad (10.3.5)$$

10.3.2 Gauss-Jordan elimination

An extension of the above approach is to make all off-diagonal terms zero, rather than just those below the main diagonal. This *Gauss-Jordan elimination* procedure directly generates a diagonal matrix of the coefficients a_{ij}, and thereby avoids the need for subsequent substitutions. Here is how one can do this, starting with (10.3.3) or the equivalent (10.3.5).

Leave the bottom row as is, but take the middle equation in (10.3.3) and add twice the bottom equation to it, to yield

$$
\begin{aligned}
3x_1 + 2x_2 + 2x_3 &= 5 \\
0 - 3x_2 + 0 &= 15 \qquad \text{row2} + 2 \times \text{row3 of (10.3.3)} \\
0 + 0 + x_3 &= 9
\end{aligned}
\tag{10.3.6}
$$

Then take the top row, add two-thirds times the middle row, and subtract twice the bottom row. This results in $3x_1 + 0x_2 + 0x_3 = -3$, so that the set of three equations is reduced to

$$
\begin{aligned}
3x_1 + 0 + 0 &= -3 \qquad \text{row1} + (2/3) \times \text{row2} - 2 \times \text{row3 of (10.3.6)} \\
0 - 3x_2 + 0 &= 15 \\
0 + 0 + x_3 &= 9
\end{aligned}
\tag{10.3.7}
$$

or, in augmented matrix form,

$$
\left[\begin{array}{ccc|c}
3 & 0 & 0 & -3 \\
0 & -3 & 0 & 15 \\
0 & 0 & 1 & 9
\end{array}\right]
\tag{10.3.8}
$$

The final x-values can be read directly from both formats as $x_1 = -3/3 = -1$, $x_2 = -15/(-3) = 5$, and $x_3 = 9$. Better yet, the first row can be divided by 3, and the second by -3, in which case the left-hand part of the augmented matrix has the form of a unit matrix, while its right-most column will contain the values for x_1, x_2, and x_3,

$$
\left[\begin{array}{ccc|c}
1 & 0 & 0 & -1 \\
0 & 1 & 0 & -5 \\
0 & 0 & 1 & 9
\end{array}\right]
\tag{10.3.9}
$$

Consequently, by following the forward substitutions of Gaussian elimination by backward substitutions, the left-hand side of the augmented matrix can be converted into a unit matrix, while its right-hand side contains the sought answers.

10.3.3 Matrix inversion by Gauss-Jordan elimination

In section 10.1.3 we merely assumed that a square matrix $\mathbf{A}$ might have an inverse, $\mathbf{A}^{-1}$, but did not indicate how it might be found. The Gauss-Jordan scheme now allows us to specify a method to obtain that inverse as follows. When we form an augmented matrix $[\mathbf{A} \mid \mathbf{I}]$ and apply the Gauss-Jordan elimination to it, retracing the same operations that led us from (10.3.1) via (10.3.2), (10.3.3), and (10.3.7) to (10.3.8), we obtain

$$
\left[\begin{array}{ccc|ccc}
3 & 2 & 2 & 1 & 0 & 0 \\
6 & 1 & 2 & 0 & 1 & 0 \\
1 & 1 & 1 & 0 & 0 & 1
\end{array}\right]
\tag{10.3.10}
$$

$$
\left[\begin{array}{ccc|ccc}
3 & 2 & 2 & 1 & 0 & 0 \\
0 & -3 & -2 & -2 & 1 & 0 \\
0 & 1 & 1 & -1 & 0 & 3
\end{array}\right]
\tag{10.3.11}
$$

$$\begin{bmatrix} 3 & 2 & 2 & 1 & 0 & 0 \\ 0 & -3 & -2 & -2 & 1 & 0 \\ 0 & 0 & 1 & -5 & 1 & 9 \end{bmatrix} \tag{10.3.12}$$

$$\begin{bmatrix} 3 & 0 & 0 & 3 & 0 & -6 \\ 0 & -3 & 0 & -12 & 3 & 18 \\ 0 & 0 & 1 & -5 & 1 & 9 \end{bmatrix} \tag{10.3.13}$$

$$\begin{bmatrix} 1 & 0 & 0 & 1 & 0 & -2 \\ 0 & 1 & 0 & 4 & -1 & -6 \\ 0 & 0 & 1 & -5 & 1 & 9 \end{bmatrix} \tag{10.3.14}$$

By matrix multiplying the left-hand 3×3 *submatrix* in (10.3.10), i.e., **A**, with the right-hand 3×3 submatrix in (10.3.14), we find that their matrix product is the unit matrix **I**. Consequently, the right-hand submatrix in (10.3.14) must be the inverse of **A**, i.e., it must be $\mathbf{A}^{-1}$. This turns out to be true in general. In other words, the Gauss-Jordan elimination applied to the augmented matrix $[\mathbf{A} | \mathbf{I}]$ yields the augmented matrix $[\mathbf{I} | \mathbf{A}^{-1}]$.

Obviously, it would be rather tedious to compute $\mathbf{A}^{-1}$ in this way by hand, but tediousness is no problem for a computer. And the number of mathematical operations (additions and subtractions, multiplications and divisions) used in the Gauss-Jordan inversion of an $n \times n$ matrix actually turns out to be similar to that involved in multiplying two $n \times n$ matrices. To see the Gauss-Jordan elimination in action, use GJStep.

10.4 The cubic spline

Now that we have seen how matrices can be used to solve a set of simultaneous equations, we will illustrate their use by formally solving- the $4n$ simultaneous equations that arose in trying to fit a cubic spline through $n+1$ data points in section 9.6.2. Although this restriction is not necessary, we will here simplify the problem by applying it to $n+1$ *equidistant* points, i.e., we will assume that $x_{i+1} - x_i = \delta$ for $0 \leq i < n$. Moreover, we will introduce the parameter g_i to denote the *value* of the second derivative of the *function f_i* at $x = x_i$, in which case (9.6.7) yields

$$g_i = (f_i'')_{x=x_i} = 2c_i + 6d_i(x-x_i)|_{x=x_i} = 2c_i \tag{10.4.1}$$

or

$$c_i = g_i/2 \qquad\qquad 1 \leq i \leq n-1 \tag{10.4.2}$$

so that we can reformulate (9.6.9) as

$$g_i + 6d_i\,\delta = g_{i+1} \tag{10.4.3}$$

or

$$d_i = (g_{i+1} - g_i)/(6\delta) \qquad\qquad 1 \leq i \leq n-1 \tag{10.4.4}$$

while the combination of (9.6.4), i.e.,

$$a_i = y_i \qquad\qquad 1 \leq i \leq n \tag{10.4.5}$$

with (9.6.5) yields

$$y_i + b_i\,\delta + c_i\,\delta^2 + d_i\,\delta^3 = y_{i+1} \qquad\qquad 1 \leq i \leq n-1 \tag{10.4.6}$$

or, upon substitution of (10.4.1) and (10.4.2) plus some reshuffling,

$$b_i = (y_{i+1} - y_i)/\delta - (2g_i + g_{i+1})\,\delta/6 \qquad\qquad 1 \leq i \leq n-1 \tag{10.4.7}$$

We rewrite (9.6.8) as $b_i + 2c_i\delta + 3d_i\delta^2 = b_{i+1}$ and, after substitution of (10.4.2), (10.4.4), and (10.4.7), as

$$(y_{i+1}-y_i)/\delta - (2g_i+g_{i+1})\delta/6 + g_i\delta + (g_{i+1}-g_i)\delta/2 = (y_{i+2}-y_{i+1})/\delta - (2g_{i+1}+g_{i+2})\delta/6 \quad (10.4.8)$$

from which we obtain, upon collecting terms,

$$g_i + 4g_{i+1} + g_{i+2} = (y_i - 2y_{i+1} + y_{i+2})6/\delta^2 \qquad 1 \le i \le n-1 \quad (10.4.9)$$

Combining (10.4.2) with (9.6.10) and (9.6.11) yields the boundary conditions $g_0 = g_n = 0$, so that we need not calculate these terms. We now reformulate (10.4.9) in matrix terms as

$$\mathbf{A\,G} = (6/\delta^2)\,\mathbf{Y} \qquad \text{or} \qquad \mathbf{G} = \mathbf{A}^{-1}\,\mathbf{A\,G} = (6/\delta^2)\,\mathbf{A}^{-1}\,\mathbf{Y} \quad (10.4.10)$$

where

$$\mathbf{A} = \begin{bmatrix} 4 & 1 & 0 & \cdots & 0 & 0 & 0 \\ 1 & 4 & 1 & \cdots & 0 & 0 & 0 \\ 0 & 1 & 4 & \cdots & 0 & 0 & 0 \\ \cdots & \cdots & \cdots & \cdots & \cdots & \cdots & \cdots \\ 0 & 0 & 0 & \cdots & 4 & 1 & 0 \\ 0 & 0 & 0 & \cdots & 1 & 4 & 1 \\ 0 & 0 & 0 & \cdots & 0 & 1 & 4 \end{bmatrix}, \quad \mathbf{G} = \begin{bmatrix} g_1 \\ g_2 \\ g_3 \\ \cdots \\ g_{n-3} \\ g_{n-2} \\ g_{n-1} \end{bmatrix}, \quad \mathbf{Y} = \begin{bmatrix} y_0 - 2y_1 + y_2 \\ y_1 - 2y_2 + y_3 \\ y_2 - 2y_3 + y_4 \\ \cdots \\ y_{n-4} - 2y_{n-3} + y_{n-2} \\ y_{n-3} - 2y_{n-2} + y_{n-1} \\ y_{n-2} - 2y_{n-1} + y_n \end{bmatrix} \quad (10.4.11)$$

Note that $\mathbf{A}$ is a *tridiagonal* matrix, with zeros everywhere beyond the main diagonal and its adjacent subdiagonals. This reflects the local nature of the spline, with parameters that interact only with their immediate neighbors. Consequently, all terms a_{ij} involving non-nearest-neighbor interactions (i.e., for $|i-j| > 1$) are zero.

While we are on the topic of nomenclature: $\mathbf{A}$ is also *symmetrical*, $m_{ij} = m_{ji}$, i.e., its diagonal is a mirror plane, so that $\mathbf{A}^T = \mathbf{A}$. Moreover, $\mathbf{A}$ is a *Toeplitz* matrix, i.e., each diagonal or subdiagonal has identical elements. Tridiagonal Toeplitz matrices occur quite often in scientific applications, which is convenient because they have eigenvalues that can be calculated directly.

Once the vector $\mathbf{G}$ is computed from (10.4.9) as $\mathbf{G} = (6/\delta^2)\,\mathbf{A}^{-1}\,\mathbf{Y}$, the terms a_i, b_i, c_i, and d_i are readily found from (10.4.5), (10.4.7), (10.4.2), and (10.4.4) respectively. Below we illustrate this procedure for fitting a cubic spline to the made-up set of eight data in section 9.6.

Exercise 10.4.1:

(1) On a spreadsheet, such as that shown in Fig. 10.4.1, enter the 6×6 matrix $\mathbf{A}$ of (10.4.11) in, e.g., A2:F7.

(2) Highlight a block of the same size, such as A10:F15, and use the instruction =MINVERSE(A2:F7) followed by Ctrl⌣Shift⌣Enter to compute its inverse.

(3) Note that the inverse of a tridiagonal $n \times n$ matrix is neither tridiagonal nor necessarily has any zeroes, but that it has kept the mirror symmetries of $\mathbf{A}$, both along its main diagonal (so that $a_{i,j} = a_{j,i}$) and along its second diagonal (hence $a_{i,j} = a_{n-j,n-i}$).

(4) Copy the values of y somewhere, say in A19:A26, and compute the corresponding values of $\mathbf{Y}$ as given in (10.4.11) in, e.g., C20:C25.

(5) Highlight an appropriate area, such as E20:E25, and use it to compute $\mathbf{G}$ (note that $\delta = 1$) as $6\,\mathbf{A}^{-1}\,\mathbf{Y}$ with =6*MMULT(A10:F15,C20:C25). Add zero values at the top and bottom, to reflect the chosen boundary conditions (9.6.10) and (9.6.11).

(6) Now compute the parameter values for the cubics in the various internodal sections, using (10.4.5), (10.4.7), (10.4.2), and (10.4.4) respectively.

(7) Plot these as a function of x with 15 interpolated points in each segment. Such a plot should resemble Fig. 9.6.5.

	A	B	C	D	E	F
1	A =					
2	4	1	0	0	0	0
3	1	4	1	0	0	0
4	0	1	4	1	0	0
5	0	0	1	4	1	0
6	0	0	0	1	4	1
7	0	0	0	0	1	4
8						
9	A-1 =					
10	0.267949	-0.071797	0.019237	-0.005153	0.001374	-0.000344
11	-0.071797	0.287187	-0.076950	0.020611	-0.005496	0.001374
12	0.019237	-0.076950	0.288561	-0.077293	0.020611	-0.005153
13	-0.005153	0.020611	-0.077293	0.288561	-0.076950	0.019237
14	0.001374	-0.005496	0.020611	-0.076950	0.287187	-0.071797
15	-0.000344	0.001374	-0.005153	0.019237	-0.071797	0.267949
16						
17	y		Y		G	
18						
19	0				0	
20	0		0		-0.039162	
21	0		0		0.156647	
22	0		0		-0.587427	
23	0		1		2.193061	
24	1		-1		-2.184816	
25	1		0		0.546204	
26	1				0	
27						
28	a	b	c	d		
29						
30	0	0.006527	0	-0.006527		
31	0	-0.013054	-0.019581	0.032635		
32	0	0.045689	0.078324	-0.124012		
33	0	-0.169701	-0.293714	0.463415		
34	0	0.633116	1.09653	-0.729646		
35	1	0.637238	-1.092408	0.45517		
36	1	-0.182068	0.273102	-0.091034		
37	1	-1	0	0		

Fig. 10.4.1: A spreadsheet for the calculation of a cubic spline through the eight data, as shown in Fig. 9.6.1. For details see Exercise 10.4.1. These results can be compared with those in block G3:J10 of Fig. 9.6.5.

10.5 The traditional linear least squares formalism

With least squares we encounter a different problem. In that case the number of data points used exceeds the number of adjustable parameters. In such an *overdetermined* system, with more equations than unknowns, the matrix **A** has more rows than columns, i.e., **A** is no longer square, the inverse **A**$^{-1}$ does not exist, and the above method cannot be used. At any rate, in this case one emphatically does *not* look for an exact function to fit through the data but, rather, to an equation that minimizes the sum of the squares of the residuals. Here is how to do this for, say, fitting N data pairs x_i, y_i to a straight line $y = a_0 + a_1 x$.

For such a straight line, the residuals are $y_i - a_0 - a_1 x_i$, and the sum of the squares of these residuals is $\sum_{i=1}^{N} (y_i - a_0 - a_1 x_i)^2$, which we minimize by setting to zero its partial derivatives with respect to a_0 and a_1 respectively, i.e.,

$$\frac{\partial \sum_{i-1}^{N}(y_i - a_0 - a_1 x_i)^2}{\partial a_0} = \sum_{i=1}^{N}\frac{\partial (y_i - a_0 - a_1 x_i)^2}{\partial a_0} = -2\sum_{i=1}^{N}(y_i - a_0 - a_1 x_i)$$

$$= -2\sum_{i-1}^{N} y_i + 2a_0 \sum_{i-1}^{N}1 + 2a_1 \sum_{i-1}^{N} x_i = 0 \qquad (10.5.1)$$

and

$$\frac{\partial \sum_{i-1}^{N}(y_i - a_0 - a_1 x_i)^2}{\partial a_1} = \sum_{i=1}^{N}\frac{\partial (y_i - a_0 - a_1 x_i)^2}{\partial a_1} = -2\sum_{i=1}^{N} x_i(y_i - a_0 - a_1 x_i)$$

$$= -2\sum_{i-1}^{N} x_i y_i + 2a_0 \sum_{i-1}^{N} x_i + 2a_1 \sum_{i-1}^{N} x_i^2 = 0 \qquad (10.5.2)$$

where we have exchanged the order of differentiation and summation, as is permissible since the set of N data is finite. Consequently we have

$$a_0 \sum_{i-1}^{N}1 + a_1 \sum_{i-1}^{N} x_i = \sum_{i-1}^{N} y_i \qquad (10.5.3)$$

$$a_0 \sum_{i-1}^{N} x_i + a_1 \sum_{i-1}^{N} x_i^2 = \sum_{i-1}^{N} x_i y_i \qquad (10.5.4)$$

which are the two simultaneous equations in the two unknowns, a_0 and a_1, that we want to solve. To formulate this problem in terms of matrix algebra we now define

$$\mathbf{X} = \begin{bmatrix} 1 & x_1 \\ 1 & x_2 \\ \cdots & \cdots \\ 1 & x_N \end{bmatrix}, \qquad \mathbf{y} = \begin{bmatrix} y_1 \\ y_2 \\ \cdots \\ y_N \end{bmatrix}, \qquad \mathbf{a} = \begin{bmatrix} a_0 \\ a_1 \end{bmatrix} \qquad (10.5.5)$$

and form the products

$$\mathbf{X}^{\mathrm{T}}\mathbf{X} = \begin{bmatrix} 1 & 1 & \cdots & 1 \\ x_1 & x_2 & \cdots & x_N \end{bmatrix} \begin{bmatrix} 1 & x_1 \\ 1 & x_2 \\ \cdots & \cdots \\ 1 & x_N \end{bmatrix} = \begin{bmatrix} \sum_{i=1}^{N}1 & \sum_{i=1}^{N} x_i \\ \sum_{i=1}^{N} x_i & \sum_{i=1}^{N} x_i^2 \end{bmatrix} \qquad (10.5.6)$$

and

$$\mathbf{X}^{\mathrm{T}}\mathbf{y} = \begin{bmatrix} 1 & 1 & \cdots & 1 \\ x_1 & x_2 & \cdots & x_N \end{bmatrix} \begin{bmatrix} y_1 \\ y_2 \\ \cdots \\ y_N \end{bmatrix} = \begin{bmatrix} \sum_{i=1}^{N} y_i \\ \sum_{i=1}^{N} x_i y_i \end{bmatrix} \qquad (10.5.7)$$

In view of (10.5.6) and (10.5.7), we can now write (10.5.3) and (10.5.4) in matrix form as

$$(\mathbf{X}^{\mathrm{T}}\mathbf{X})\,\mathbf{a} = \mathbf{X}^{\mathrm{T}}\mathbf{y} \qquad (10.5.8)$$

so that

$$\mathbf{a} = (\mathbf{X}^{\mathrm{T}}\mathbf{X})^{-1}(\mathbf{X}^{\mathrm{T}}\mathbf{X})\,\mathbf{a} = (\mathbf{X}^{\mathrm{T}}\mathbf{X})^{-1}\mathbf{X}^{\mathrm{T}}\mathbf{y} = \mathbf{X}^{+}\mathbf{y} \qquad (10.5.9)$$

where $X^+ = (X^T X)^{-1} X^T$ is called the *pseudo-inverse* of X. Consequently, the least squares problem of finding the solution to $X a = y$ is formally given by $a = X^+ y$. It allows us to find a, and in this case therefore its elements a_0 and a_1, from the known matrix X and vector y.

Note that this approach is easily extended to fitting a polynomial to data, by adding expressions such as (10.5.1) and (10.5.2) for the additional adjustable parameters a_2, a_3, etc. This adds individual elements to the matrix X and the vector a in (10.5.5), but does not change the general form of the solution (10.5.9). Likewise, by merely deleting from X in (10.5.5) its left-most column of ones, we can extend the formalism of (10.5.9) to those cases where the fitted model function should pass through the origin, as with the proportionality $y = a_1 x$, the quadratic through the origin, $y = a_1 x + a_2 x^2$, or the multivariate function $y = a_1 x + a_2 x_2 + a_3 x_3 + a_4 x_4$ we encountered in section 3.15.

Exercise 10.5.1:

(1) Here is an illustration of the application of (10.5.9), using a simple data set.

(2) In cells A2 and D2 deposit labels for y and x, and next to these, say in B2:B6 and E2:E6, enter a data set such as 5, 8, 11, 14, 17 for y, and 1, 2, 3, 4, and 5 for x.

(3) In cell G2 deposit a label for X, in H2:H6 place ones, and in I2:I6 copy the x-values from E2:E6 by placing the instruction =E2 in cell I2, and copying it down.

(4) A short explanation of the source of those ones in H2:H6. If we were to fit data to an equation of the type $y = ax$, the first column wouldn't be needed. But here we fit to $y = a_0 + a_1 x = a_0 x^0 + a_1 x^1$, where $x^0 = 1$ for every x.

(5) In cell A8 deposit a label for X^T, then highlight B8:F9, type the instruction =TRANSPOSE(H2:I6), and enter it with Ctrl⌣Shift⌣Enter. Do *not* use the sequence Edit ⇨ Paste Special ⇨ Transpose, even though it generates the transpose: that sequence calls a macro, and therefore doesn't self-update, as functions do.

(6) In cell A11 deposit a label for $X^T X$, highlight B11:C12, type the instruction =MMULT(B8:F9,H2:I6), and again enter it with Ctrl⌣Shift⌣Enter.

(7) Likewise, place a label for $(X^T X)^{-1}$ in E11, highlight the target area F11:G12, and compute it with the matrix instruction =MINVERSE(B11:C12).

(8) In cell A14 deposit a label for X^+ (or for $(X^T X)^{-1} X^T$), highlight B14:F15, and use the matrix instruction =MMULT(F11:G12,B8:F9).

(9) Finally, place a label for a in H14, and in I14:I15 compute the matrix product $X^+ y$ with =MMULT(B14:F15,C2:B6).

(10) Figure 10.5.1 illustrates such a spreadsheet. Blocks can be identified with fill colors and/or borders. You can make superscripts using Format ⇨ Cells ⇨ Effects: Superscript, OK. While the same result can be obtained much more conveniently with the function LinEst, or with either of the macros Regression and LS1, Fig. 10.5.1 shows the actual computational steps taken in those routines.

	A	B	C	D	E	F	G	H	I
1									
2	y	5		x	1		X	1	1
3		8			2			1	2
4		11			3			1	3
5		14			4			1	4
6		17			5			1	5
7									
8	X^T	1	1	1	1	1			
9		1	2	3	4	5			
10									
11	$X^T X$	5	15		$(X^T X)^{-1}$	1.1	-0.3		
12		15	55			-0.3	0.1		
13									
14	X^+	0.8	0.5	0.2	-0.1	-0.4		a	2
15		-0.2	-0.1	0	0.1	0.2			3

Fig. 10.5.1: A spreadsheet illustration of the application of (10.5.9).

(11) Because all of the above operations are functions, the entire calculation is self-updating, i.e., you can change the y input data in B2:B6 and/or the x input data in I2:I6, and see the resulting response, as long as your changes stay within the 5×1 sizes of **y** and **x**, i.e., within the heavy frames around B2:B6 and E2:E6. Try it.

(12) Notice that, with array functions, the array size becomes fixed as soon as it is defined, and cannot be changed afterwards. In that respect, macros are more flexible. On the other hand, macros will not automatically self-update.

(13) Save this spreadsheet for future use.

10.6 Multivariate centering

We will now use the above spreadsheet to explore the effect of a large offset in x. Such an offset can occur, e.g., when we can only measure y over a relatively small range of x-values, relatively far away from zero, as in chemical kinetics when we can only change the temperature over, say, a $10°C$ interval near room temperature to stay within a particular mesophase, and then plot the measured parameter y, or a quantity derived thereof, as a function of absolute temperature $T = t + 273.16$. The next exercise shows what can happen in the presence of a sufficiently large offset in x, while exercises 10.6.2 and 10.7.2 will illustrate remedies.

Exercise 10.6.1:

(1) Recall the spreadsheet of exercise 10.5.1.

(2) In cell H8 place a label for x_{av}, and in cell I8 enter the value 0.

(3) In cells F2:F6 place the values 1, 2, 3, 4, 5, and 6. (Do *not* copy them from either E2:E6 or I2:I6.) Then, in cell E2, place the instruction =F2+$I$8, and copy this instruction down to E6.

(4) In cell I10 place the number 2, and in cell I11 the number 3. In cell B2 now deposit the instruction =$I$10+$I$11*E2, and copy this down to B6.

(5) So far, none of the earlier numbers in your spreadsheet will have changed. But you can now very easily add an offset to the x-values, and immediately see whether they result in a change in **a** in I14:I15. If everything is OK, there should be no change, because we now compute y in B2:B6 as $y = 2 + 3x$ using the numbers 2 and 3 stored in cells I10 and I11 respectively.

	A	B	C	D	E	F	G	H	I
1									
2	y	3000005.00		x	1000001.00	**1**	X	1	1000001.00
3		3000008.00			1000002.00	**2**		1	1000002.00
4		3000011.00			1000003.00	**3**		1	1000003.00
5		3000014.00			1000004.00	**4**		1	1000004.00
6		3000017.00			1000005.00	**5**		1	1000005.00
7									
8	X^T	1	1	1	1	1		*x offset =*	**1.00E+06**
9		1000001.00	1000002.00	1000003.00	1000004.00	1000005.00			
10									**2**
11	$X^T X$	5	5000015		$(X^T X)^{-1}$	99994882215	-99994.58		**3**
12		5000015	5.00003E+12			-99994.58223	0.0999943		
13									
14	X^+	199989.3645	99994.78221	0.199981689	-99994.38225	-199988.9645		a	-55.34960938
15		-0.199988564	-0.099994282	0	0.099994282	0.199988565			2.999915779

Fig. 10.6.1: The effect of a large offset x_{av} on the coefficients a_0 and a_1 in **a**.
The cells shaded in gray show the additions to the spreadsheet since Fig. 10.5.1.

(6) Now change the offset in cell I8 to 10, 100, 1000, etc., until you see a change in I14:I15. That will most likely occur around $x_{av} = 10^3$, but only becomes crippling around $x_{av} = 10^6$, see Fig. 10.6.1, and will become even more serious as you keep increasing x_{av}. (You can code, e.g., 10^6 as either 1E6 or as =10^6; in the latter case, the equal sign is required, because Excel interprets raising to a power as part of an equation.)

(7) Again save the spreadsheet: there is still more to come.

474

What happens here is that the matrix operations are overwhelmed by the few large numbers, such as 5×10^{12} in $\mathbf{X}^T \mathbf{X}$, that dwarf some of the other terms, and lead to a distorted result, initially mostly affecting the value of a_0. If you format $\mathbf{y}$ (i.e., B2:B6) and $\mathbf{x}$ (E2:E6) to show their data in scientific notation with 14 decimal places, and widen columns B and E accordingly, you will see that the numerical values of x and y are not distorted, so that the matrix operations must indeed be the culprits.

Even though this problem of possible distortion occurs rather rarely (and might not be too serious in the above example of a 10°C range with an offset of less than 300°C), it is relatively easy to guard against; this therefore has become standard practice. This is done by *centering*, see section 2.10, and here is how it works.

From the experimental data we first determine the averages x_{av} and y_{av}. We can then write

$$y = y_{av} + y' = a_0 + a_1 x = a_0 + a_1 x_{av} + a_1 x' \tag{10.6.1}$$

so that

$$y_{av} = a_0 + a_1 x_{av} \qquad \text{and} \qquad y' = a_1 x' \tag{10.6.2}$$

Consequently we can avoid the sensitivity of matrix manipulations to a large offset by first computing the average values x_{av} and y_{av}, subtracting these from x and y to yield $x' = x - x_{av}$ and $y' = y - y_{av}$ respectively, and by then using least squares to fit $y' = a_1 x'$, where both x' and y' no longer contain those very large numbers. This will yield a_1, which upon substitution into $y_{av} = a_0 + a_1 x_{av}$ gives us the intercept $a_0 = y_{av} - a_1 x_{av}$.

Exercise 10.6.2:

(1) Recall the spreadsheet of exercise 10.6.1.

(2) Click on the rownumber 7 at the left edge of the spreadsheet, right-click, and use the resulting pop-up menu to Insert a new row.

(3) In (the new) cell E7 compute x_{av} with =AVERAGE(E2:E6). Add a label.

(4) Replace the existing instruction in cell I2 by =E2-$E$7, and copy this down to cell I6.

(5) In cell C2 deposit the instruction =$I$11+$I$12*E2, and copy this down to C6.

(6) In cell C7 compute y_{av} with =AVERAGE(C2:C6), and label it.

(7) Replace the instruction in cell B2 by =C2-$C$7, and copy this down to B6.

(8) Finally, in cell I14, compute a_0 as =C7-I16*E7.

(9) Now you are ready to play again, because $\mathbf{x}$ in I2:I6 contains $x' = x - x_{av}$, B2:B6 contains $y' = y - y_{av}$, and a_0 is calculated as $y_{av} - a_1 x_{av}$ in cell I14. Ignore the zero in cell I15, because the least squares fit to $y' = a_1 x'$, see (10.6.2), only computes a_1. For the answer, therefore, look in I14 for a_0, and in I16 for a_1.

(10) Increase the value of the offset x_{av} in I9. You can now go considerably higher than in Fig. 10.6.1 before you will encounter distortion in the a-values. In fact, as you can see in Fig. 10.6.2, even with $x_{av} = 10^{14}$ the distortion is now still less than 4% in a_0, certainly quite moderate by comparison with Fig. 10.6.1.

If nothing else, the above illustrates how helpful it can be to use functions to gain insight into what happens within an algorithm such as that for least squares. We can test a system under rather extreme conditions, and see whether it either holds out or gives in. And, in case it buckles, we can test possible remedies before implementing them in, say, a macro.

Incidentally, the above approach is readily extended to the general case

$$y = y_{av} + y' = a_0 + a_1 x_1 + a_2 x_2 + \dots + a_n x_n \tag{10.6.3}$$

with

$$x_1' = x_1 - x_{1,av}, \qquad x_2' = x_2 - x_{2,av}, \qquad \dots \qquad x_n' = x_n - x_{n,av} \tag{10.6.4}$$

so that

$$y_{av} = a_0 + a_1 x_{1,av} + a_2 x_{2,av} + \dots + a_n x_{n,av} \tag{10.6.5}$$

$$y' = \qquad a_1 x_1' + a_2 x_2' + \dots + a_n x_n' \tag{10.6.6}$$

	A	B	C	D	E	F	G	H	I
1									
2	y	-6.00	3.000000E+14	x	1.000000E+14	1	X	1	-2.00
3		-3.00	3.000000E+14		1.000000E+14	2		1	-1.00
4		0.00	3.000000E+14		1.000000E+14	3		1	0.00
5		3.00	3.000000E+14		1.000000E+14	4		1	1.00
6		6.00	3.000000E+14		1.000000E+14	5		1	2.00
7		$y\,av =$	3.000000E+14	$x\,av =$	1.000000E+14				
8									
9	$\mathbf{X}^T$	1	1	1	1	1		$x\,offset =$	1.00E+14
10		-2.00	-1.00	0.00	1.00	2.00			
11									2
12	$\mathbf{X}^T\mathbf{X}$	5	0		$(\mathbf{X}^T\mathbf{X})^{-1}$	0.2	0		3
13		0	10			0	0.1		
14								$a\,0 =$	1.9375
15	$\mathbf{X}^+$	0.2	0.2	0.2	0.2	0.2		$\mathbf{a}$	0
16		-0.2	-0.1	0	0.1	0.2			3

Fig. 10.6.2: After centering both x and y, the spreadsheet is much more immune to an offset in x, as inserted here in cell I9.

By solving (10.6.6) with least squares we find the coefficients $a_1, a_2, \ldots, a_n$, while a_0 is subsequently computed from (10.6.5) as

$$a_0 = y_{av} - a_1 x_{1,av} - a_2 x_{2,av} - \ldots - a_n x_{n,av} \qquad (10.6.7)$$

which only involves the intercept a_0, because the coefficients $a_{i\neq0}$ are the partial slopes $\partial y/\partial x_i$, and are therefore unaffected by subtracting the constants $x_{i,av}$ from the various x_i.

For a multivariate problem, the above is standard procedure, a natural extension of section 2.10, and the best one can do. We will call it *multivariate* centering to distinguish it from the more specific centering discussed in the next section.

10.7 Polynomial centering

A different centering approach should be taken when fitting an integer power series in x, such that $x_1 = x^1, x_2 = x^2, \ldots, x_m = x^m$. The reason is that x^n (where n is an integer larger than 1) is a nonlinear function of x, i.e., the average value $(x^n)_{av}$ of x^n in general differs from the nth power of x_{av}, $(x_{av})^n$ and, more significantly, $(x-x_{av})^n$ can differ greatly from $x^n-(x_{av})^n$, as illustrated in exercise 10.7.1.

Exercise 10.7.1:
  (1) On a spreadsheet place the numbers 101, 102, 103, 104, and 105 in a column.
  (2) Two rows below these numbers, use the function AVERAGE to calculate x_{av}, which should be 103.
  (3) Next to the values of x, now compute the corresponding values for $(x-x_{av})^3$. You should find –8, –1, 0, 1, and 8.
  (4) Two rows below the value of x_{av}, calculate the corresponding values for x^3. Then find their average, $(x^3)_{av}$, and finally the values of $x^3-(x^3)_{av}$. These latter values are much bigger, ranging from –63044 to 64280 rather than from –8 to +8.

This effect, already quite substantial with $n = 3$, will be even more pronounced when higher than cubic powers of x are used. Clearly, if one wants to keep the values of the higher-order terms small in the presence of a substantial relative offset, $(x-x_{av})^i$ should be used instead of $x^i - (x^i)_{av}$. But, in that case, the corrections are somewhat more complicated, as indicated below.

	A	B	C	D	E
1	Comparison of different ways to center a polynomial in x :				
2	$(x - x_{av})^3$ versus $x^3 - (x_{av})^3$				
3					
4		x	x^3	$(x - x_{av})^3$	$x^3 - (x_{av})^3$
5					
6		101	1030301	-8	-63044
7		102	1061208	-1	-32137
8		103	1092727	0	-618
9		104	1124864	1	31519
10		105	1157625	8	64280
11					
12	$x\,av =$	103	1093345		
13					
14	cell:	instruction:			copied to:
15		B12 = AVERAGE(B6:B10)			
16		C6 = B6^3			C7:C10
17		C12 = AVERAGE(C6:C10)			
18		D6 = (B6-B$12)^3			D7:D10
19		E6 = B6^3-B$12^3			E7:E10

Fig. 10.7.1: For $n > 1$, centering a polynomial in x as $(x–x_{av})^n$ can be much more effective than as $x^n–x_{av}{}^n$

Say that we want to fit the function

$$y = a_0 + a_1 x + a_2 x^2 + a_3 x^3 + a_4 x^4 \tag{10.7.1}$$

to a set of data. However, in order to keep higher-order terms from growing too fast in the presence of an offset in x, we use $y - y_{av} = a_0' + a_1'(x - x_{av}) + a_2'(x - x_{av})^2 + a_3'(x - x_{av})^3 + a_4'(x - x_{av})^4$ instead, so that

$$\begin{aligned} y - y_{av} = {}& a_0' + a_1'x - a_1'x_{av} + a_2'x^2 - 2a_2'x\,x_{av} + a_2'(x_{av})^2 \\ & + a_3'x^3 - 3a_3'x^2 x_{av} + 3a_3'x(x_{av})^2 - a_3'(x_{av})^3 \\ & + a_4'x^4 - 4a_4'x^3 x_{av} + 6a_4'x^2(x_{av})^2 - 4a_4'x(x_{av})^3 + a_4'(x_{av})^4 \end{aligned} \tag{10.7.2}$$

where we can use the Pascal triangle to find the coefficients of the mixed terms, such as $4x^3 x_{av}$, $6x^2(x_{av})^2$, and $4x(x_{av})^3$ in $(x - x_{av})^4$. When we equate terms of equal power in x, and work backwards from the highest-order term x^n, for which $a_n' = a_n$, we can reconstruct the relations between the sought coefficients a_i and the coefficients a_i' obtained from the least squares fitting. In the present example, with $n = 4$, we have

$$a_4 = a_4' \tag{10.7.3}$$

$$a_3 = a_3' - 4a_4' x_{av} = a_3' - x_{av}(4a_4') \tag{10.7.4}$$

$$a_2 = a_2' - 3a_3' x_{av} + 6a_4'(x_{av})^2 = a_2' - x_{av}(3a_3' - x_{av}(6a_4')) \tag{10.7.5}$$

$$a_1 = a_1' - 2a_2'x_{av} + 3a_3'(x_{av})^2 - 4a_4'(x_{av})^3$$
$$\quad = a_1' - x_{av}(2a_2' - x_{av}(3a_3' - x_{av}(4a_4'))) \tag{10.7.6}$$

$$a_0 = y_{av} + a_0' - a_1'x_{av} + a_2'(x_{av})^2 - a_3'(x_{av})^3 + a_4'(x_{av})^4$$
$$\quad = y_{av} + a_0' - x_{av}(a_1' - x_{av}(a_2' - x_{av}(a_3' - x_{av}(a_4')))) \tag{10.7.7}$$

where the right-most expressions in (10.7.5) through (10.7.7) are efforts to keep intermediate numbers as small as possible in case x_{av} is large. Exercise 10.7.2 tests this approach by using functions rather than macros, because functions respond immediately to varying input parameters.

	A	B	C	D	E	F	G	H
1	offset =	100	coeff:	5.42E+08	-6.7E+06	57559.79	-563.761	3.695596
2								
3	x	x+offset	y	x^0	x^1	x^2	x^3	x^4
4								
5	1	101	2.05E+08	1	101	10201	1030301	1.04E+08
6	2	102	2.13E+08	1	102	10404	1061208	1.08E+08
7	3	103	2.22E+08	1	103	10609	1092727	1.13E+08
8	4	104	2.31E+08	1	104	10816	1124864	1.17E+08
9	5	105	2.4E+08	1	105	11025	1157625	1.22E+08
10	6	106	2.49E+08	1	106	11236	1191016	1.26E+08
11	7	107	2.59E+08	1	107	11449	1225043	1.31E+08
12								
13	cell:	instruction:						copied to:
14								
15		B5 = A5+$B$1						B6:B11
16		C5 = 6-5*E5+4*F5-3*G5+2*H5						C6:C11
17		E5 = B5						E6:E11
18		F5 = B5^2						F6:F11
19		G5 = B5^3						G6:G11
20		H5 = B5^4						H6:H11
21	D1:H1 = TRANSPOSE(MMULT(MMULT(MINVERSE(MMULT(							
22		TRANSPOSE(D5:H11),D5:H11)),TRANSPOSE(D5:H11)),C5:C11))						

Fig. 10.7.2: The spreadsheet of exercise 10.7.2.

	A	B	C	D	E	F	G	H	I
1	offset =	100			-5.15E+05	8.90E+06	1.29E+05	8.29E+02	2.00E+00
2				coeff:	6.00E+00	-5.0000	4.0000	-3.000	2.0000
3	x	x+offset	y	y-y_{av}	$(x$-$x_{av})^0$	$(x$-$x_{av})^1$	$(x$-$x_{av})^2$	$(x$-$x_{av})^3$	$(x$-$x_{av})^4$
4									
5	1	101	205070204	-26085162	1	-3	9	-27	81
6	2	102	213343920	-17811446	1	-2	4	-8	16
7	3	103	221865508	-9289858	1	-1	1	-1	1
8	4	104	230639870	-515496	1	0	0	0	0
9	5	105	239671956	8516590	1	1	1	1	1
10	6	106	248966764	17811398	1	2	4	8	16
11	7	107	258529340	27373974	1	3	9	27	81
12									
13	average =	104	231155366						
14									
15	cell:	instruction:							
16									
17		B5 = A5+$B$1						copied to:	B6:B11
18		C5 = 6-5*E5+4*F5-3*G5+2*H5							C6:C11
19		D5 = C5-C$13							D6:D11
20		F5 = B5-B$13							F6:F11
21		G5 = F5^2							G6:G11
22		H5 = F5^3							H6:H11
23		I5 = F5^4							I6:I11
24	D1:H1 = TRANSPOSE(MMULT(MMULT(MINVERSE(MMULT(								
25		TRANSPOSE(E5:I11),E5:I11)),TRANSPOSE(E5:I11)),D5:D11))							
26		I2 = I1							
27		H2 = H1-B13*(4*I1)							
28		G2 = G1_B13*(3*H1-B13*(6*I1))							
29		F2 = F1-B13*(2*G1-B13*(3*H1-B13*(4*I1)))							
30		E2 = C13+E1-B13*(F1-B13*(G1-B13*(H1-B13*(I1))))							

Fig. 10.7.3: The spreadsheet of exercise 10.7.3.

Exercise 10.7.2:

(1) On a spreadsheet place the *x*-values 1 (1) 7. (As before, we will suggest a particular location, here A5:A11. We specify cell positions only for convenience: any other cell coordinates will work as long as the functional, but not necessarily spatial, relationships between the cells are the same.)

478

(2) In B1 place an offset (0 for the time being), and in B5:B11 compute x + offset.

(3) Leave a column free for y, and in D5 place a 1 (for x^0), in E5 copy B5, in F5 compute the square of B5, in G5 its cube, and in H5 its fourth power. Copy these all the way down to row 11. Block D5:H11 will constitute the matrix $\mathbf{X}$.

(4) In D5:D11 place an expression for y as a quartic function of x, preferably with easily recognized coefficients (for ease of checking) such as $= 6 - 5x + 4x^2 - 3x^3 + 2x^4$. In D13 compute y_{av}. In terms of linear algebra, D5:D11 is the vector $\mathbf{y}$.

(5) Just for the heck of it, we will use a so-called mega-formula in D1:H1. When typing it in, pay close attention to the closing brackets, which are sometimes bundled. What will be coded here is the matrix expression $[(\mathbf{X}^T\mathbf{X})^{-1}\mathbf{X}^T\mathbf{y}]^T$, where $\mathbf{X}^+ = (\mathbf{X}^T\mathbf{X})^{-1}\mathbf{X}^T$, and where the over-all transpose of $\mathbf{X}^+\mathbf{y}$ merely places the coefficients in a row rather than a column.

(6) So here goes: highlight D1:H1, type the megaformula, and then use Ctrl⌣Shift⌣Enter to deposit it. If you get it right on the first try, you are entitled to sit back with a smug, self-congratulatory grin. The megaformula is

	A	B	C	D	E	F	G	H
1	offset =	100	coeff:	2.4E+06	-30708.122	170.4105	-4.119902	2.0022486
2								
3		x	x+offset	y	$x^\wedge 0$	$x^\wedge 1$	$x^\wedge 2$	$x^\wedge 3$	$x^\wedge 4$
4								
5	1	101	205070204	1	101	10201	1030301	104060401
6	2	102	213343920	1	102	10404	1061208	108243216
7	3	103	221865508	1	103	10609	1092727	112550881
8	4	104	230639870	1	104	10816	1124864	116985856
9	5	105	239671956	1	105	11025	1157625	121550625
10	6	106	248966764	1	106	11236	1191016	126247696
11	7	107	258529340	1	107	11449	1225043	131079601
12								
13	average =	104	231155366		104	10820	1126112	117245468
14								
15			$y - y_{av}$		$x - x_{av}$	$x^2 - x_{av}^2$	$x^3 - x_{av}^3$	$x^4 - x_{av}^4$
16								
17			-26085162		-3	-619	-95811	-13185067
18			-17811446		-2	-416	-64904	-9002252
19			-9289858		-1	-211	-33385	-4694587
20			-515496		0	-4	-1248	-259612
21			8516590		1	205	31513	4305157
22			17811398		2	416	64904	9002228
23			27373974		3	629	98931	13834133
24								
25	cell:		instruction:					copied to:
26								
27		B5 = A5+$B$1						B6:B11
28		C5 = 6-5*E5+4*F5-3*G5+2*H5						C6:C11
29		E5 = B5						E6:E11
30		F5 = B5^2						F6:F11
31		G5 = B5^3						G6:G11
32		H5 = B5^4						H6:H11
33		B13 = AVERAGE(B5:B11)						
34		C13 = AVERAGE(C5:C11)						
35		E13 = AVERAGE(E5:E11)						
36		F13 = AVERAGE(F5:F11)						
37		G13 = AVERAGE(G5:G11)						
38		H13 = AVERAGE(H5:H11)						
39		C17 = C5-C$13						C18:C23
40		E17 = E5-E$13						E18:E23
41		F17 = F5-F$13						F18:F23
42		G17 = G5-G$13						G18:G23
43		H17 = H5-H$13						H18:H23
44	E1:H1 = TRANSPOSE(MMULT(MMULT(MINVERSE(MMULT(							
45	TRANSPOSE(E17:H23),E17:H23)),TRANSPOSE(E17:H23)),C17:C23))							
46	D1 = C13-E1*E13-F1*F13-G1*G13-H1*H13							

Fig. 10.7.4: The spreadsheet of exercise 10.7.4. The final coefficients a_i now appear in cells E2:I2.

(6) So here goes: highlight D1:H1, type the megaformula, and then use Ctrl‿Shift‿Enter to deposit it. If you get it right on the first try, you are entitled to sit back with a smug, self-congratulatory grin. The megaformula is =TRANSPOSE(MMULT(MMULT(MINVERSE(MMULT(TRANSPOSE(D5:H11),D5:H11)),TRANSPOSE(D5:H11)),C5:C11)). If you want it in slightly more readable form, you can name D5:H11 as, e.g., MX, and name C5:C11 as, say, vy, and then use =TRANSPOSE(MMULT(MMULT(MINVERSE(MMULT(TRANSPOSE(MX),MX)),TRANSPOSE(MX)),vy)). You will find the expected answer: a_0 through a_4 are 6, −5, 4, −3, and 2 respectively.

(7) Now change the offset in B1 from 0 to, say, 1, 2, 5, 10, 20, 50, 100, etc., and notice what happens in D1:H1. The effect is shown in Fig. 10.7.2 for an offset of 100. This result is not unexpected, because no centering was used.

(8) Save your spreadsheet for subsequent use.

Exercise 10.7.3:

(1) Modify the spreadsheet of exercise 10.7.2 to use average values of y, x, x^2, x^3, and x^4, as described in (10.6.1) through (10.6.7). As you can see in Fig. 10.7.3, this requires a rather elaborate extension of the spreadsheet: adding a row for calculating the averages, adding columns for computing the centered values of y, x, x^2, x^3, and x^4, and an extra cell (D2 in Fig. 10.7.2) for implementing (10.6.7). Because (10.6.6) contains no term a_0, $\mathbf{X}$ now refers to E17:H23, and yields its answer in E1:H1. The value for a_0 in cell D1 is calculated from (10.6.7). The final result is marginally better than without centering at an offset of 10, but is still quite inadequate at an offset of 100. In this case the improvement due to centering is not nearly as dramatic as in Fig. 10.7.2 because we have now greatly aggravated the problem by including higher-order terms in x.

Exercise 10.7.4:

(1) Modify the spreadsheet of exercise 10.7.2 to make it compatible with (10.7.3) through (10.7.7), and see whether this improves matters. Your final spreadsheet might now be similar to Fig. 10.7.4.

In this example, the answer clearly is: yes, power-law centering does the job, whereas multivariate centering does not. Of course, the above approach has its limits: it can be overwhelmed by too large an offset, as is easily verified by substituting an offset of 1000 in the example. Still, power-law centering can sometimes make the difference between an otherwise intractable problem and a quite adequate solution, as illustrated below.

10.8 A tough test case

The NIST Statistical Reference Dataset contains a notoriously difficult test case, Filip.dat, accessible at http://www.itl.nist.gov/div898/strd/lls/data/LINKS/DATA/Filip.dat. This file contains 82 x,y data pairs, to be fitted to a tenth-order polynomial in x. Go to the web site, highlight and copy the page, save it in Notepad, then import the Notepad file into Excel. LS1 fails completely when applied to Filip.dat. The same applies to pre-2003 versions of LinEst and Regression, although their more recent implementations yield results that agree with those given by NIST to about eight decimal places.

One of the obvious difficulties with Filip.dat is that it specifies x to 10 decimal places, and involves powers of x up to x^{10}. Between 81 and 100 decimals would be needed to represent x^{10} without distortion; with only 15 decimals available, even x^2 cannot be represented correctly. We therefore investigate how LS1 fares with power-law centering along the lines indicated in (10.7.3) through (10.7.7). First we indicate how to generalize the approach, so that it can be applied to any n^{th} order polynomial in x. To that end, we write the first ten terms of the Pascal triangle as half of a rectangle, as in Fig. 10.8.1.

Exercise 10.8.1:

(1) In this exercise we will construct a Pascal triangle by simple addition. We will merely generate and use its first eleven lines, sufficient for a tenth-order polynomial, although the method is applicable to any positive integer. Of course, we could express its individual members in terms of binomials, but here our emphasis will be on simplicity rather than mathematical elegance.

(2) Place the number 1 in cells A1:K1 and A2:A11.

(3) In cell B2 place the instruction =B1+A2.

(4) Copy that instruction to C2:J2, then to B3:I3, B4:H4, B5:G5, B6:F6, etc., all the way till B10.

(5) This completes the first ten members of the triangle. Your result should resemble Fig. 10.8.1. It is usually displayed as an equilateral triangle, but the way we compute it here, as the top left half of a square, is easier in the spreadsheet and, incidentally, agrees with how Pascal showed it in his 1654 *Traité du triangle arithmétique* (see, e.g., A. W. F. Edwards, *Pascal's Arithmetic Triangle*, 2nd ed., Johns Hopkins Univ. Press, 2002).

(6) Upon comparing the coefficients in (10.7.3) through (10.7.7) with the numbers in this triangle you may notice that the numbers 1, 1, 1, 1, 1 multiplying a_0', a_1', a_2', a_3', and a_4' in (10.7.7) occur in A1:E1, the sequence 1, 2, 3, and 4 in (10.7.6) in A2:D2, the coefficients 1, 3, 6 in (10.7.5) in A3:C3, the terms 1 and 4 in (10.7.4) in A4:B4, and the number 1 multiplying a_4' in (10.7.3) in A5.

(7) For proper centering of the power series $y = a_0 + a_0 x + a_0 x^2 + \ldots + a_0 x^{10}$ we must use the coefficients in rows 1, 2, 3, 4, 5, etc. of Fig. 10.8.1. In terminology that dates back to the Pythagoreans, these rows contain collections of the various *figurate* numbers. It is these figurate numbers that occur in power-law centering.

	A	B	C	D	E	F	G	H	I	J	K
1	1	1	1	1	1	1	1	1	1	1	1
2	1	2	3	4	5	6	7	8	9	10	
3	1	3	6	10	15	21	28	36	45		
4	1	4	10	20	35	56	84	120			
5	1	5	15	35	70	126	210				
6	1	6	21	56	126	252					
7	1	7	28	84	210						
8	1	8	36	120							
9	1	9	45								
10	1	10									
11	1										

Fig. 10.8.1: The first ten terms of the Pascal triangle

Exercise 10.8.2:

(1) Copy the data of Filip.dat, and make a second, centered copy of this data set by replacing all y by $y–y_{av}$, all x by $x–x_{av}$, and all higher powers of x by the corresponding powers of $x–x_{av}$.

(2) Apply LS1 to this centered data set.

(3) Correct the resulting coefficients a_0' through a_{10}' as indicated above. In other words, $a_{10} = a_{10}'$ according to row 11 in Fig. 10.8.1; $a_9 = a_9'–x_{av}(10a_{10}')$ using the numbers 1 and 10 in row 10; $a_8 = a_8'–x_{av}(9a_9'–x_{av}(45a_{10}'))$ using the sequence 1, 9, and 45 in row 9; $a_7 = a_7'–x_{av}(8a_8'–x_{av}(36a_9'–x_{av}(120a_{10}')))$, etc.

(4) In the line for a_0, don't forget to include the term y_{av}; it therefore should read $a_0 = y_{av}+a_0'–x_{av}(a_1'–x_{av}(a_2'–x_{av}(a_3'– \ldots –x_{av}a_{10}')))))))))$.

(5) Compare your results for a_0 through a_{10} with the reference answers given by NIST (where they are called B0 through B10). Whereas the data without proper centering didn't have a single correct digit, your answers now agree with those of NIST to at least 10 decimal places!

This is a very encouraging result, and confirms that inadequate computational numberlength is indeed a significant cause of the difficulties posed by Filip.dat. However, it doesn't address another problem that is cleverly hidden in that same test set. In practice, the "independent" parameters in the **X** matrix are not always quite independent. If two or more of these "independent" parameters have a total linear dependency, the matrix will be singular, and therefore cannot be inverted. (Remember that *non*linear interdependency, such as in a power law, doesn't count in this respect, see section 2.9.) But the more common (and more pernicious) situation is of parameters that exhibit a *partial* linear correlation, in which case inversion of **X** can yield incorrect answers. This problem can be minimized by using a method for solving least squares problems (to be described in section 10.14) quite different from the "classical" approached described in section 10.5. However, before we can discuss this and other useful aspects of linear algebra, we must first discuss eigenvalues and singular values, and correspondingly extend the functionality of Excel.

481

10.9 Additional matrix instructions: Matrix.xla

Microsoft provides only a handful of tools for dealing with matrices in Excel, see appendix A.6. Of the five instructions listed there, TRANSPOSE is not even a matrix function, because it handles text as well as numbers. Fortunately, Leonardo Volpi has added a large collection of VBA functions and macros to facilitate matrix operations. These can be downloaded from his web site, http://digilander.libero.it/foxes/SoftwareDownload.htm, and by Volpi's kind permission can also be found on (and downloaded from) my "excellaneous" web site, http://www.bowdoin.edu/~rdelevie/excellaneous, where you will find versions of Matrix.xla (or Matrix.xlam for Excel 2007 and beyond) as updated, adapted and expanded by John Beyers. They are great, freely available, open-access tools for spreadsheet computations as well as for learning about matrices, and are listed alphabetically in Table 10.9.1. A more detailed, categorized overview can be found in appendix B, and an extensive on-line help file with many worked-out examples is included in the download.

As you will see when perusing this added functionality, there is much more here than we can properly discuss in the present context; in fact, it contains most of the tools for an introductory course in linear algebra. In the following sections we will merely provide a few applications that mostly stay within the much narrower framework of scientific data analysis to illustrate how to use them, but feel free to experiment with the other facilities.

Matrix.xla(m) is primarily a set of *functions*, listed in appendices C.1 through C.9, but it also contains a small collection of *macros*, including a very flexible set of matrix generators, see appendix C.10. For didactic purposes, functions are often more useful because they can be more transparent in their composite operations; moreover, they respond immediately and automatically to input changes. On the other hand, macros are often more convenient for more complicated problems, are more readily packaged for routine applications, and can perform tasks beyond the power of functions. It is great to have both options available. Section 1.2.6 contains instructions on how to install Matrix.xla(m) if you have not already done so.

After you have installed Matrix and BigMatrix, they are immediately available for use. Click on the function icon f_x, select the Function category Matrix, then click on the desired Function name. If it doesn't show, look in the category All for function names. Use the scroll bar to its right in order to find the function. For the help file (an online version of the Reference Guide for Matrix.xla) click on its icon (showing a book cover) after you have successfully installed it. ⓪⑦-①⓪: Click on Office ⇨ Excel Options ⇨ Add-Ins, at the bottom of that dialog box click on Go… and in the resulting Add-Ins dialog box click on Browse. In the next box manipulate the Look in: to find the location of Matrix.xla, and click on it. Make sure that the Files of type shows AllAddIns(*.xlam, *.xla, *.xll) and, in the window just above that, type the file name Matrix (without its extension). Repeat for BigMatrix, then click OK.

The following information was abstracted from the December 2006 version of the *Tutorial of Numerical Analysis for Matrix.xla*, and the associated *Reference Guide for Matrix.xla*. These documents (or those that came with your version) should be consulted for further details. Very brief descriptions are also provided in the Paste Function dialog box; you get these by clicking on the f_x icon, provided that your cursor points to an unused, blank cell. (If pointed to a function instruction, you get its specific help window. If you use this convenient window for matrix instructions, do *not* press OK after you have filled all its windows but, instead, use the block-entry instruction Ctrl∪Shift∪Enter.)

Except where indicated otherwise, all instructions listed here require the user to highlight the target area first, before calling the function, and to enter the instruction with Ctrl∪Shift∪Enter. When you are uncertain of the correct size (block size) of the result of a matrix instruction, first try it out using an ample test target area in an unused part of the spreadsheet. Superfluous cells will exhibit the error message #N/A, except when one or both of the sizes is 1, in which case the same result will be repeated in that size. Note the correct block size, erase the entire test block (you cannot alter only a part of it), and redo now that you know its proper block format.

For the sake of notational compactness, we will here denote a square *diagonal* matrix by $\mathbf{D}$ with elements d_{ii}, a square *tridiagonal* matrix by $\mathbf{T}$ with elements t_{ij} where $|j - i| \le 1$, most other *square* matrices by $\mathbf{S}$, *rectangular* matrices by $\mathbf{R}$, and all matrix elements by m_{ij}. A *vector* will be shown as $\mathbf{v}$, with elements v_i, and a *scalar* as s. Particular values are denoted by x when real, and by z when complex. In Appendix B all optional parameters are shown in straight brackets, [ ]. All matrices, vectors, and scalars are assumed to be real, except when specified otherwise. All matrices are restricted to two dimensions; for manipulating matrices of higher dimensions, the spreadsheet will seldom be a suitable computational environment anyway.

With some functions, the user is given the option *Integer* of applying integer arithmetic. When a matrix only contains integer elements, selecting integer arithmetic may avoid most round-off problems. On the other hand, the range of integer arithmetic is more limited, so that overflow errors may result if the matrix is large and/or contains large numbers.

Another common option is *Tiny*, which defines the absolute value of quantities that can be regarded as most likely resulting from round-off errors, and are therefore set to zero. When not activated, many routines will use its default value, Tiny $= \varepsilon \approx 10^{-15}$.

The various instructions listed in appendix B are grouped by functionality, a necessarily somewhat arbitrary arrangement. We therefore show here, in Table 10.9.1, an alphabetical listing of the all functions available in the latest version of Matrix.xla(m) as of July 2011, with a one-line function description, so that the reader can get a rough idea of the richness of this instruction set.

function	brief description
GJStep	Step-by-step tracing of Gauss-Jordan algorithm
MAbs	norm (square root of sum of squares of elements) of vector $\mathbf{v}$ or matrix $\mathbf{R}$
MAbsC	norm of complex vector $\mathbf{v}$ or matrix $\mathbf{C}$
MAdd	add two matrices: $\mathbf{R}_1 + \mathbf{R}_2$
MAddC	add two complex matrices: $\mathbf{C}_1 + \mathbf{C}_2$
MAdm	Create an admittance matrix from a branch matrix
MBAB	similarity transformation $\mathbf{S}_1^{-1} \mathbf{S}_2 \mathbf{S}_1$
MBlock	transform reducible sparse $\mathbf{S}$ into block-partitioned form
MBlockPerm	permute matrix for MBlock
MChar	compute characteristic matrix of $\mathbf{S}$ at x
MCharC	compute characteristic matrix of $\mathbf{C}$ at z
MCharPoly	compute characteristic polynomial of $\mathbf{S}$
MCharPolyC	compute characteristic polynomial of $\mathbf{C}$
MCholesky	Cholesky decomposition of square matrix $\mathbf{S}$
MCmp	companion matrix of monic polynomial
MCond	condition number κ of $\mathbf{R}$
MCorr	correlation matrix
MCovar	covariance matrix
MCplx	combine two real matrices into one complex matrix
MDet	determinant of $\mathbf{S}$
MDet3	determinant of $\mathbf{T}$ in $n \times 3$ format
MDetC	determinant of a complex square matrix
MDetPar	determinant of $\mathbf{S}$ containing symbolic parameter k
MDiag	convert vector $\mathbf{v}$ into diagonal matrix $\mathbf{D}$
MDiagExtr	extract the diagonal of $\mathbf{D}$
MEigenSortJacobi	sort eigenvectors of $\mathbf{S}$ by absolute value of eigenvalues
MEigenValJacobi	Jacobi sequence of orthogonality transforms
MEigenValMax	find dominant eigenvalue of $\mathbf{S}$, i.e., eigenvalue with largest absolute value
MEigenValPow	eigenvalues of $\mathbf{S}$ by power method

MEigenValQL	eigenvalues of $\mathbf{T}$ by QL algorithm
MEigenValQR	eigenvalues of $\mathbf{S}$ by QR decomposition
MEigenValQRC	eigenvalues of $\mathbf{C}$ by QR decomposition
MEigenValTTpz	eigenvalues of tridiagonal Toeplitz matrix
MEigenVec	eigenvectors of $\mathbf{S}$ for given eigenvalues
MEigenVecC	eigenvectors of $\mathbf{C}$ for given eigenvalues
MEigenVecInv	eigenvectors of eigenvalue by inverse iteration
MEigenVecInvC	complex eigenvectors of eigenvalue by inverse iteration
MEigenVecJacobi	orthogonal similarity transform of symmetric matrix $\mathbf{S}$
MEigenVecMax	eigenvector for dominant eigenvalue
MEigenVecPow	eigenvector of $\mathbf{S}$ by power method
MEigenVecT	eigenvectors for given eigenvalues of $\mathbf{T}$
MExp	matrix exponential, $e^{\mathbf{S}}$
MExpErr	error term in $e^{\mathbf{S}}$
MExtract	extract submatrix of $\mathbf{R}$
MHessenberg	convert $\mathbf{S}$ into Hessenberg form
MHilbert	create Hilbert matrix
MHilbertInv	create inverse Hilbert matrix
MHouseholder	create Householder matrix
MIde	generate an identity matrix
MInv	invert $\mathbf{S}$
MInvC	invert a complex square matrix
MLeontInv	invert the Leontief matrix
MLU	LU decomposition
MMopUp	eliminate round-off errors in $\mathbf{R}$
MMult	Excel's matrix multiplication, $\mathbf{R}_1\,\mathbf{R}_2$
MMult3	multiply $\mathbf{T}$ and $\mathbf{R}$
MMultC	Multiply two complex matrices: $\mathbf{C}_1\,\mathbf{C}_2$
MMultS	multiply a matrix and a scalar
MMultSC	multiply a complex matrix and a scalar
MMultTpz	multiply a Toeplitz matrix and a vector
MNorm	find matrix or vector norm
MNormalize	normalize $\mathbf{R}$
MNormalizeC	normalize $\mathbf{C}$
MOrthoGS	modified Gram-Schmidt orthogonalization
MpCond	$-\log_{10}$ of the condition number κ
MPerm	generate permutation matrix from permutation vector
MPow	integer power of square matrix: $\mathbf{S}^n$
MPowC	integer power of a complex square matrix
MProd	product of two or more matrices: $\mathbf{R}_1\,\mathbf{R}_2\,\mathbf{R}_3\,...$
MPseudoInv	SVD pseudo-inverse of $\mathbf{R}$
MPseudoInvC	SVD pseudo-inverse of complex rectangular matrix $\mathbf{C}$
MQH	decomposition of $\mathbf{S}$ with vector $\mathbf{v}$
MQR	QR decomposition
MQRIter	eigenvalues of $\mathbf{S}$ by iterative QR diagonalization
MRank	rank of $\mathbf{R}$
MRnd	generate a random matrix $\mathbf{R}$
MRndEig	generate a random matrix with given eigenvalues
MRndEigSym	generate a symmetrical matrix with given eigenvalues
MRndRank	generate a random matrix of given rank or determinant
MRndSym	generate a symmetrical matrix of given rank or determinant
MRot	orthogonal rotation matrix
MRotJacobi	Jacobi orthogonal rotation of symmetrical matrix $\mathbf{S}$
MSub	subtract two matrices, $\mathbf{R}_1-\mathbf{R}_2$
MSubC	subtract two complex matrices: $\mathbf{C}_1 - \mathbf{C}_2$

MT	transpose, $\mathbf{R}^T$
MTartaglia	create Tartaglia (Pascal) matrix
MTC	transpose a complex matrix: $\mathbf{C}^T$
MTH	conjugate (Hermitian) transpose of a complex matrix: $\mathbf{C}*$
MTrace	trace of $\mathbf{S}$
MVandermonde	create Vandermonde matrix
PathFloyd	Floyd sequential algorithm for shortest-path pairs
PathMin	vectors of shortest-path pairs between given sites
PolyRoots	find roots of a polynomial
PolyRootsQR	find roots of a polynomial using QR algorithm
PolyRootsQRC	find roots of a complex vector using QR algorithm
ProdScal	scalar product of two vectors, $\mathbf{v}_1 \bullet \mathbf{v}_2$
ProdScalC	scalar product of complex vectors
ProdVect	vector product of two vectors, $\mathbf{v}_1 \bullet \mathbf{v}_2$
RegrCir	least squares fit to a circle
RegrL	linear least squares fit based on singular value decomposition
RegrP	RegrL for a polynomial fit
Simplex	simplex optimization
SVDD	yields diagonal matrix Σ of singular values
SVDU	yields $\mathbf{U}$ of singular value decomposition
SVDV	yields $\mathbf{V}$ of singular value decomposition
SysLin	Gauss-Jordan linear system solver
SysLin3	tridiagonal linear system solver
SysLinC	Gauss-Jordan linear solver of complex system
SysLinIterG	iterative Gauss-Seidel linear system solver
SysLinIterJ	iterative Jacobi linear system solver
SysLinSing	singular linear system solver
SysLinT	triangular linear system solver
SysLinTpz	solve Toeplitz system by Levinson's method
TraLin	linear transformation
VarimaxIndex	varimax index for given factor loading matrix
VarimaxRot	orthogonal rotation of factor loading matrix
VectAngle	angle between two vectors

Table 10.9.1: List of functions in Matrix.xla version 2.3. For a more detailed description see appendix B and, especially, Volpi's Reference Guide for Matrix.xla and his Tutorial on Numerical Analysis with Matrix.xla.

10.10 Matrix inversion, once more

Matrix inversion provides an elegant, formal way to solve many problems. However, not all square matrices can be inverted; those that cannot be inverted are called *singular*. Mathematically, there is a sharp distinction between singular and nonsingular matrices: a singular matrix has a determinant equal to zero, whereas a non-singular matrix doesn't. Excel has the corresponding instruction MDETERM. But such a seemingly well-defined difference can become rather fuzzy when matrices are evaluated on a computer with floating-point math, which cannot represent most numbers exactly. How should we interpret a finding that the determinant of a square matrix is about 10^{-17}, or 10^{-40}? Those values are not per se small for Excel, which can represent numbers smaller than 10^{-300}. But how do we know whether 10^{-17} or 10^{-40} is significantly different from 0, or is just a zero disguised by round-off errors?

In least squares analysis, only the matrix $\mathbf{X}$ is inverted, or a function thereof, such as $\mathbf{X}^T \mathbf{X}$ in (10.5.6), where $\mathbf{X}$ is usually assumed to be noise-free. Uncertainties in inverting such a matrix then have nothing to do with experimental noise, which would only appear in $\mathbf{y}$, but must be the result of algorithmic inaccuracy and/or numerical imprecision in the matrix algebra used.

As our illustration of the problem, we will use an example taken from Meyer's *Matrix Analysis and Applied Linear Algebra*, SIAM (2000) pp. 33 and 128. Consider the two simultaneous equations

$$835 \, x_1 + 667 \, x_2 = 168 \tag{10.10.1}$$

$$333 \, x_1 + 266 \, x_2 = 67$$

which have the solution

$$x_1 = 1; \qquad x_2 = -1 \tag{10.10.2}$$

as you can readily verify by substituting these values for x_1 and x_2 back into (10.10.1).

Now let there be a small amount of noise in the constant on the right-hand side of the first expression in (10.10.1), changing its value from 168 to, say, 167. The solution then becomes

$$x_1 = 267; \qquad x_2 = -334 \tag{10.10.3}$$

Likewise, replacing 67 in the second expression of (10.10.1) by 66 will modify the answer to

$$x_1 = -666; \qquad x_2 = 834 \tag{10.10.4}$$

while changing 168 to 169 and, simultaneously, 67 to 66, yields

$$x_1 = -932; \qquad x_2 = 1167 \tag{10.10.5}$$

When we write (10.10.1) in matrix form as

$$\mathbf{A} \, \mathbf{x} = \mathbf{b} \tag{10.10.6}$$

with

$$\mathbf{A} = \begin{bmatrix} 835 & 667 \\ 333 & 266 \end{bmatrix}, \qquad \mathbf{x} = \begin{bmatrix} x_1 \\ x_2 \end{bmatrix}, \qquad \mathbf{b} = \begin{bmatrix} 168 \\ 67 \end{bmatrix} \tag{10.10.7}$$

we see that (10.10.1) through (10.10.5) show quite different answers for the coefficients x_1 and x_2 of $\mathbf{x}$ as the result of rather minor changes in b_1 and/or b_2.

Exercise 10.10.1:

(1) In rows 3 and 4 of a new spreadsheet, enter the numerical values of $\mathbf{A}$ of (10.10.6) in columns B and C, and the corresponding values of $\mathbf{b}$ in column E. Use row 2 for appropriate labels.

(2) Verify that (10.10.2) is, indeed, the solution of (10.10.1), by computing $\mathbf{x}$ in G3:G4 with the matrix instruction =MMULT(MINVERSE(B3:C4),E3:E4) because $\mathbf{x} = \mathbf{A}^{-1} \mathbf{A} \mathbf{x} = \mathbf{A}^{-1} \mathbf{b}$.

(3) In cell B6 place the instruction =$B$3, put =$B$4 in B7, =$C$3 in C3, =$C$4 in C7, =$E$4 in E7, but =$E$3−1 in E6. Then copy G3:G4 to G6. You should now find the result of (10.10.3).

(4) Copy B6:G7 to B8, then replace the minus sign in E8 by a plus sign. This will yield x_1 = -265 and x_2 = +332, the same distance 266 away from x_1 = 1and -333 x_2 = -1 but in the opposite direction. These are large effects in $\mathbf{x}$ for small changes in $\mathbf{b}$, but they are symmetrical.

(5) To clearly offset B8:G9 from B6:G7, you might want to put some light background color in B8:C9, E8:E9, and G8:G9, and/or put frames around the areas containing the matrix $\mathbf{A}$ and the vectors $\mathbf{b}$ and $\mathbf{x}$.

(6) Copy B6:G9 to B10, and then change the terms 1 in B10 and B12 to 10. The result is again a linear response to the change, now by ten times larger amounts. The spreadsheet you have made so far should resemble that in Fig. 10.10.1.

(7) When you get tired of this game, change the approach to use this spreadsheet more efficiently, as follows.

(8) Go to Tools ⇨ Data Analysis, select Random Number Generation, then set Distribution: Normal, Mean = 0, Standard Deviation =: 1, click on the round "radio button" to the left of Output Range:, then click on the associated window, enter I6:K105, and click OK. This will fill I6:K105 with random Gaussian numbers, our usual approximation of random noise.

(9) In cell I3 place a label for a noise amplitude, and in J3 a value, such as 1E-7.

(10) Modify the instruction in E6 to =$E$3*(1+$J$3*K6), and that in E7 likewise to =$E$4*(1+$J$3*K7).

(11) Copy B6:G7 to B8, repair any cell coloring and framing, then copy B6:G9 to B10, B14, B18, B22, ... B102.

A	B	C	D	E	F	G
1						
2		A		b		x
3	835	667		168		1
4	333	266		67		-1
5						
6	835	667		167		267
7	333	266		67		-334
8	835	667		169		-265
9	333	266		67		332
10	835	667		158		2661
11	333	266		67		-3331
12	835	667		178		-2659
13	333	266		67		3329

Fig. 10.10.1: A spreadsheet illustrating various solutions $\mathbf{x} = \mathbf{A}^{-1}\mathbf{b}$ obtained with a near-singular matrix $\mathbf{A}$ by varying b_1.

(12) In order to plot the results, in M4 place labels for x_1, and in N4 for x_2, then place the instruction =G6 in M6, and =G7 in N6. Highlight M6:N:7, and copy it to M8, then copy M6:N9 to M10, and so on, to fill the entire column M6:N133. Delete M106:N133.

(13) It is useful to place the instruction =MAX(M6:M105) in cell M2, and then copy it to cell N2, where it will read =MAX(N6:N105). Similarly, place the instruction =MIN(M6:M105) in cell M3, then copy it to cell O3. This will help you see what axis scales are needed to show all data.

(14) Highlight M6:N105 and plot x_2 vs. x_1. Because you cannot exactly reproduce random noise, you will get some other data than shown here, but their general behavior will be the same.

(15) Repeat with other values for the relative noise amplitude. Two such examples are shown in Fig. 10.10.2.

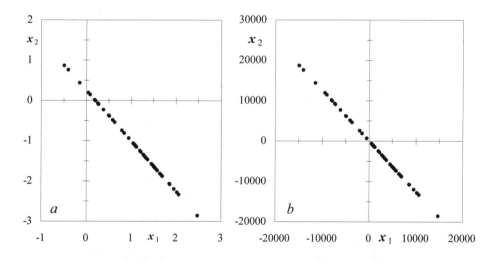

Fig. 10.10.2: Results obtained with the same spreadsheet after modification to compute and display the effect of noise in $\mathbf{b}$ on the computation. Relative noise amplitude in panel a: 1E–5, in panel b: 1E–1.

The data shown in Fig. 10.10.2 illustrate that the input noise added to $\mathbf{b}$ results in output noise in $\mathbf{x}$ that is directly proportional to its amplitude, i.e., the response of the matrix operation is linear. That is also to be expected: the inversion of $\mathbf{A}$ is unaffected by the noise in $\mathbf{x}$, while the multiplication of $\mathbf{A}^{-1}$ and $\mathbf{x}$ is a strictly linear operation.

Incidentally, the points in the two plots lie on a straight line through $x_1 = 1$, $x_2 = -1$, with slope -1.251877, a number that is the average of the slopes mentioned later in this section, and their distribution along that line is indeed Gaussian. Each point on that line in panel *b* is exactly 10000 times more widely spaced on the line through $(1, -1)$ than it is in panel *a*, just as the relative noise amplitude is also 10000 times larger.

Now we ask a different question: what will happen when we add such noise to the elements of **A**? Exercise 10.10.2 considers that issue, using the very same spreadsheet you have just made.

Exercise 10.10.2:

(1) Copy the spreadsheet of Exercise 10.10.1 into a new sheet. Then make the following changes.

(2) Replace the instruction in B6 by =$B$3*(1+$J$3*I6), that in B7 by =$B$4*(1+$J$3*I7), and likewise place =$C$3*(1+$J$3*J6) in C6, and =$C$4*(1+$J$3*J7) in C7. Moreover, to simplify matters, set E6 back to =$E$3, and E7 to =$E$4.

(3) Verify that, for a relative noise amplitude of 0, you get everywhere the same answers, identical to those in G3:G4. If not, check your equations.

(4) Now try various sets of random numbers at a given relative noise amplitude, and then experiment with different relative noise amplitudes. You will, again, find different answers than shown in Fig. 10.10.3, because your specific noise values will differ, but you will also get the general point: the effect of noise is now highly *nonlinear*. And the results look decidedly non-Gaussian.

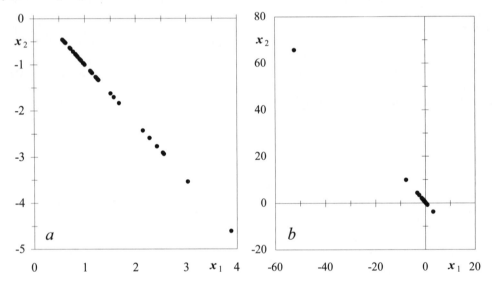

Fig. 10.10.2: The same spreadsheet after modification to compute and display the effect of noise in **A** on the computation. Same set of noise data, but with different relative amplitudes: 1E–6 in panel *a*, 1E–5 in panel *b*.

What causes this great sensitivity of **x** to relatively small fluctuations in **A**? To find the answer, it is helpful to step away from the algebra, and to look instead at a physical interpretation of expressions such as (10.10.1), which we can consider as representing two straight lines, say,

$$x_2 = \frac{168}{667} - \frac{835}{667}x_1 \qquad \text{or, in general,} \qquad x_2 = \frac{b_1}{a_{12}} - \frac{a_{11}}{a_{12}}x_1 \qquad (10.10.8)$$

and

$$x_2 = \frac{67}{266} - \frac{333}{266}x_1 \qquad \text{or} \qquad x_2 = \frac{b_2}{a_{22}} - \frac{a_{21}}{a_{22}}x_1 \qquad (10.10.9)$$

where the solution of these simultaneous equations defines the values of x_1 and x_2 at their intersection.

Look at the slopes of these lines, a_{11}/a_{12} and a_{21}/a_{22}. Their numerical values are $835/667 \approx \mathbf{1.2518}74$ and $333/266 \approx \mathbf{1.2518}80$ respectively, where we have used bold-facing to emphasize their common digits. These lines therefore have *near-identical slopes*. Consequently, the place where these two lines intersect is extremely sensitive to small changes in their intercepts, and therefore to changes in the coefficients b_i, but the real culprits are their almost identical slopes, a_{11}/a_{12} and a_{21}/a_{22} respectively, which these intercepts b_i do not affect, see (10.10.8) and (10.10.9). The basic problem, therefore, lies in the matrix **A** rather than in the vector **b**, as exercises 10.10.1 and 10.10.2 confirmed.

If the slopes a_{11}/a_{12} and a_{21}/a_{22} were identical, the matrix **A** would be singular, and we would not find any answer, because parallel lines have no (finite) intersection, but only intersect at "infinity". In our case, **A** is merely *very close* to singular. In the next section we will therefore consider how we can characterize matrices in terms of their near-singularity or *conditioning*. With a matrix that is almost singular, it is merely a matter of chance how added noise may occasionally bring it very close to that abyss of singularity. In fact, it is not a single singularity, but an infinite collection of them, because for every ratio a_{11}/a_{12} there will be a corresponding ratio a_{21}/a_{22} that will make the second line parallel to the first, and therefore create a singularity! And the closer one gets to a singularity, the more even very small fluctuations tend to become magnified to noticeable levels. Such a highly *nonlinear* effect in general will *not* yield a Gaussian output for a Gaussian input.

A prominent feature of Fig. 10.10.2b is what one might consider an outlier. (If you didn't find any, return to <u>T</u>ools ⇨ <u>D</u>ata Analysis ⇨ Random Number Generation, and click OK; this will update the computations with a new set of Gaussian numbers, and also update the graph. You will soon, usually within a few tries, find some seemingly extreme points.) Of course, these simulations merely illustrate that, upon inverting a near-singular matrix, Gaussian noise *affecting the matrix elements* does not produce an outcome with a Gaussian distribution. If you were to make that latter (faulty) assumption, you might be tempted to reject the outliers because, were they Gaussian, they would be highly unlikely events indeed. But in this case there is no good reason for doing so, other than that such a point might not fit your (incorrect) expectation of a linear operation, with a consequently Gaussian output.

The above, geometric argument is convenient for 2×2 matrices. For larger matrices it is more difficult to visualize matters, although it can still be done for 3×3 matrices. There, the general intersection between two planar surfaces is a line, and this line in general intersects with the third plane at a point. The three space coordinates of that common point are the elements x_1 through x_3 of the solution, **x**. When at least two of these planes have a similar *tilt* (as, for lack of a better term, I will call the three-dimensional equivalent of the slope of a line), their intersection will again be very sensitive to small parameter changes; when those two tilts are identical, the planes are parallel and don't intersect, and the corresponding matrix is singular. Again, there will be more than one combination of parameter values where this can occur. For larger matrices, things are harder to imagine, but you get the idea of what makes some matrices inherently difficult to work with.

10.11 Eigenvalues and eigenvectors

A singular matrix occurs when the simultaneous equations to be solved are fully linearly dependent. We have seen in, e.g., sections 2.9, 8.14, and 10.10, that such dependency is not a black-and-white proposition, but instead can exhibit shades of gray. Near-singular matrices are often called *ill-conditioned*, and their numerical inversion may cause problems due to the finite numberlength used in the computations. One possible remedy would be to use a longer numberlength, an option we will indeed entertain in chapter 11. Another will be described in section 10.13. But first we will consider an important aspect of square matrices that we have not discussed so far, namely its eigenvalues and eigenvectors.

In section 10.10 we considered two simultaneous equations, and formulated them in matrix format as

$$\mathbf{A}\,\mathbf{x} = \mathbf{b} \tag{10.10.6}$$

where **x** and **b** were vectors, and **A** denoted a square matrix. We can interpret such a formalism as follows: the product of **A** with the vector **x** is another vector, **b**, of the same size as **x**. In the example of section 10.10 the vectors were of size 2×1 and can therefore be visualized easily in a graph as arrows pointing from the origin to points defined by the two coordinates x_1 and x_2 of **x**, or b_1 and b_2 of **b**. Forming the matrix product **A** **x** can then be seen as **A** transforming vector **x** into a new vector **b** of the same size but, in general, with a different direction and/or magnitude. And even where we cannot easily visualize vectors in four or more dimensions, this conceptual interpretation of the action of **A** as operating on **x** in (10.10.6) is readily generalized to more simultaneous equations in more unknowns.

We will from now on use different symbols in order to make some useful distinctions. We will denote *s*quare matrices by **S**, and *r*ectangular ones by **R**. In this section we will deal only with square matrices, and ask whether there are any special *n*×1 vectors **x** which, after such action by an *n*×*n* matrix **S**, yield a new *n*×1 vector **q** that points in the very same (*n*-dimensional) direction as **x**, and therefore is only changed in length. In that case we should be able to write

$$\mathbf{S}\,\mathbf{q} = \lambda\,\mathbf{q} \qquad (10.11.1)$$

where λ is a *scalar*, i.e., a simple (real or complex) numerical multiplier. It turns out that nonsingular (i.e., invertible) square matrices **S** indeed have *n* such special scalars, which are called their *eigenvalues* λ, with *n* corresponding *eigenvectors* **q**. The German term *eigen* indicates that these characteristic properties as it were *belong to* **S**, and the term has stuck in English.

Eigenvalue problems are quite common in matrix algebra, and typically occur not so much when we consider simultaneous *algebraic* equations, as we have mostly done so far, but with simultaneous *differential* equations. A famous eigenvalue problem is the Schrödinger wave equation

$$\mathbf{H}\,\mathbf{\psi} = E\,\mathbf{\psi} \qquad (10.11.2)$$

shown here in its simplest (time-independent) form, which relates the Hamiltonian operator (a differential equation in matrix form) **H** of a quantum-mechanical system and its wavefunctions (eigenvectors) **ψ** to its scalar eigenvalues, the energies E. The field of resulting *quantum mechanics* is heavily dependent on matrix algebra. Quantum mechanics is the basis of modern atomic-scale physics and chemistry, relativity theory applies mostly to very large-scale phenomena, and Newtonian physics to most everything in-between. Matrix algebra plays a huge role in Newtonian mechanics, and its importance in quantum mechanics and relativity is even larger.

For a 2×2 matrix, the eigenvalues can be found by solving a quadratic *characteristic polynomial*. If its roots are complex, these eigenvalues are each other's complex conjugates. For a 3×3 matrix, the eigenvalues are given by a cubic equation, i.e., the characteristic polynomial is of 3rd order, etc. Unfortunately, equations of fifth or higher order have no known exact solutions, and must therefore be found iteratively. General-purpose software for finding eigenvalues and eigenvectors therefore uses an iterative approach that approximates the eigenvalues and eigenvectors to within a desired accuracy.

Only square, nonsingular matrices have eigenfunctions. In general, a nonsingular *n*×*n* matrix will have *n* eigenvalues, which need not all be different. When two or more eigenvalues are identical, they are called *degenerate*.

Matrix.xla(m) has several functions for finding eigenvalues and eigenvectors, most with names starting with MEigen, as listed in Table 10.9.1. They differ in capability, complexity, and execution speed, and which one is best will depend on the particular matrix to which it is applied. For the small matrices we will use in our exercises, you will not notice any such differences. Some examples are illustrated in exercise 10.11.1.

Exercise 10.11.1:

(1) On a clean spreadsheet, place the real, symmetric matrix **S** shown in B3:C4, as in Fig. 10.11.1. A real (rather than complex) square matrix has only real matrix elements m_{ij}, and its symmetry (along its main diagonal) requires that it be square with $m_{ij} = m_{ji}$. Any real symmetric matrix, or any complex square matrix with complex elements m that are its own conjugate transpose (so that the matrix elements m_{ij} are the complex conjugates of the elements m_{ji}), is called *Hermitian*, and has real eigenvalues. Hermitian matrices are fairly common, as they automatically arise when we form the product of a matrix with its transpose (or, in the case of a complex matrix, with its conjugate transpose, which we will denote as $\mathbf{S}^H$ with the superscript H of Hermitian in order to distinguish it from the normal transpose $\mathbf{S}^T$). Matrix.xla has the instruction =MTC() for a complex transpose, and =MTH() for a Hermitian or complex conjugate transpose.

(2) Highlight E3:E4, type the instruction =MEigenValQR(B3:C4), and enter it with Ctrl‿Shift‿Enter. You will indeed get two real eigenvalues, but they need not be positive integers as in this example.

(3) Use several other instructions instead, such as MEigenValQL which is meant for tridiagonal matrices (which any 2×2 matrix automatically is) or the general MEigenValPow. They should all yield the same two eigenvalues, although not necessarily in the same order, as you can see in Fig. 10.11.1.

(4) For each eigenvalue λ there should be one associated eigenvector **q**. In C7 place the instruction =E3, and find the corresponding eigenvector in E7:E8, e.g., with the instruction =MEigenVec(B3:C4,C7).

(5) In H7:H8 compute the product of S and $\mathbf{q}_1$, and in J7:J8 calculate λ_1 times $\mathbf{q}_1$. Check that the two answers (in Fig. 10.11.1 connected by double-headed arrow) are identical, i.e., verify that (10.11.1) indeed applies in this example.

(6) Highlight B6:J8, and copy it to B10, then change the instruction in C11 to =E4, and adjust the references to **S** in E11:E12 and H11:H12 to B3:C4. You should again find an eigenvector that satisfies (10.11.1). Also adjust the labels.

(7) With the instruction =MEigenVec(B3:C4,E3:E4) in, e.g., F15:G16 you can simultaneously display both eigenvectors. Your spreadsheet should now resemble that of Fig. 10.11.1.

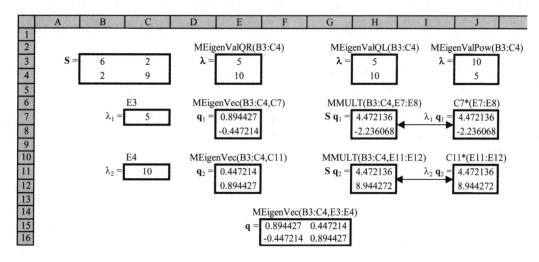

Fig. 10.11.1: An annotated spreadsheet of Exercise 10.11.1 for the eigenvalues and eigenvectors of a real Hermitian matrix.

So far we have glossed over two points. The first is that the eigen*values* are uniquely defined, but the corresponding eigen*vectors* are not, in the sense that multiplication of the vector **q** by any scalar affects the left- and right-hand sides of (10.11.1) in the same way, and therefore keeps that equation intact no matter what multiplier we use. It is therefore customary to normalize the eigenvectors by dividing them by their Euclidian vector length (or Frobenius norm) $\|\mathbf{q}\|$ which is the positive square root of the sum of squares of the individual vector elements. You can readily verify on the spreadsheet that, e.g., $0.894427^2 + (-0.447214)^2 = 1$ in E7:E8. In that way, the eigenvectors are standardized, except for their signs. Matrix.xla(m) has the convenient functions MNorm to compute the matrix or vector norm, and MNormalize and MNormalizeC to perform that normalization for you.

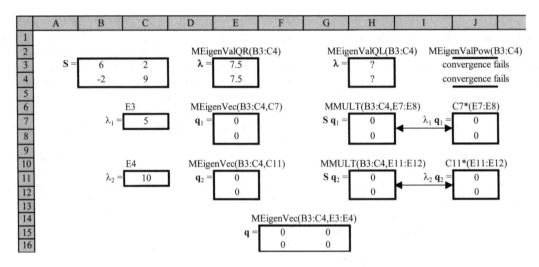

Fig. 10.11.2: A mere change from 2 to –2 in cell B4 yields an output full of warning signs, such as question marks in H3:H4, error messages in J3:J4, and zeroes in many derived results. Clearly, the software commands used are inadequate for a complex output.

The second point is that the eigenvalues and/or eigenvectors of a square matrix with real elements can be complex, just as the roots of a quadratic equation with real coefficients can be. We did not have to worry about that in exercise 10.11.1 because we used a Hermitian matrix **S**. But as Fig. 10.11.2 illustrates, as soon as we deviate from a Hermitian matrix, we run the risk of a nonsensical answer when we don't anticipate a complex result.

In general, therefore, we need instructions that can handle complex eigenanalysis, such as MEigen-ValQRC and MEigenVecC. In this book we will use the default (split) complex format, which assigns separate blocks to the real and imaginary components of **S** and **q** as illustrated in Fig. 10.11.2. For added clarity we have used a thin separator between the real and imaginary components. Alternatively you can use two different, light background colors, or two different shades of gray. Exercise 10.11.2 will use the equivalent spreadsheet for general, complex numbers

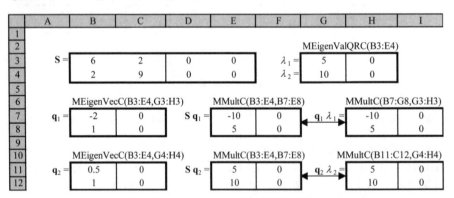

Fig. 10.11.3: A general spreadsheet for finding the eigenfunctions of a nonsingular 2×2 matrix, allowing for complex input and output which, in this case, is actually not needed since **S** is real and Hermitian.

Note that we consider S in B3:E4 as a square 2×2 matrix, even though its notation takes twice as much spreadsheet space because we *display* their real and imaginary components in separate cells. Likewise, λ in G3:H3 is a 1×1 scalar, whether or not it has a non-zero imaginary component and takes up one or two cells.

Exercise 10.11.2:

(1) Open a new spreadsheet, and model it after Fig. 10.11.3, i.e., with the same Hermitian matrix **S** as used there. You need not specify the zeroes in D3:E4; leaving those cells unspecified will be interpreted as zeroes.

(2) As you will see, the results are the same as those obtained in Fig. 10.11.1, except that MEigenVecC can only deal with one eigenvalue at a time, and therefore cannot generate **(3)** in a single instruction, as in F15:G16 of Fig. 10.11.1.

(3) Note that λ_1 is now no longer a scalar but a vector, so that vector dimensionality requires that $\lambda_1\,\mathbf{q}_1$ actually be computed as $\mathbf{q}_1\,\lambda_1.$, because λ_1 is displayed as a 1×2 vector, and the sought product should be 2×1.

(4) Change the 2 in cell B4 into –2. It will show you why Fig. 10.11.2 did not work, because both the eigenvalues and eigenvectors are now complex.

(5) Note that the output of MEigenVecC is not normalized, because no single element in a normalized vector can ever be outside the range from –1 to +1, whereas there are many numbers exceeding that range in B7:C8 and B11:C12. To normalize the eigenvectors you can use the instruction MNormalizeC, as long as you use the block containing both its real and imaginary components as its argument.

(6) Here is the result for a complex Hermitian matrix **S**, in which case the top and bottom triangle of the imaginary part must have opposite signs. Its diagonal can only contain zeroes, the only value that is equal to its own negative.

(7) We see that this complex Hermitian input indeed has real eigenvalues, but its eigenvectors are complex.

(8) Finally, Fig. 10.11.6 shows the results for a general nonsingular square matrix. Play with it by varying the values of **S**.

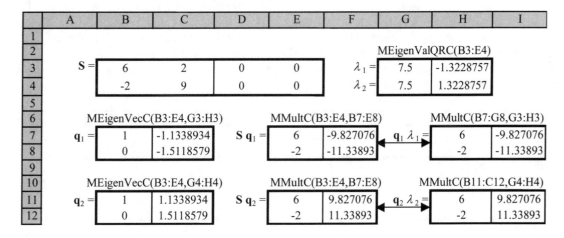

Fig. 10.11.4: The correct result for the problem shown in Fig. 10.11.2.

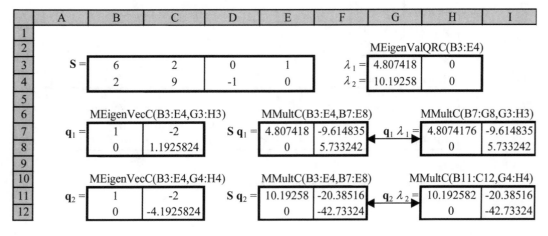

Fig. 10.11.5: A complex Hermitian matrix has real eigenvalues but complex eigenvectors.

493

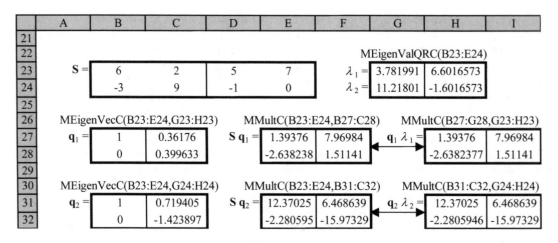

Fig. 10.11.6: An annotated spreadsheet of Exercise 10.11.2 for the eigenfunction analysis of a general complex matrix.

So far we have used the instruction MEigenVecC which handles one eigenvector at a time. Often it is more efficient to use MEigenVecInvC to make one complex matrix; its underlying routine is also more robust, and it yields normalized eigenvectors where, for complex vectors, normalization of course includes both the real and imaginary components. The self-annotated Fig. 10.11.7 therefore shows how such an analysis is most efficiently achieved, using a minimum of instructions and spreadsheet real estate. Eigenfunction analysis can hardly be simpler.

	A	B	C	D	E	F	G	H	I
1									
2									
3	S =	4	2	4	5	3	-4	5	7
4		1	2	1	2	2	0	13	-1
5		-2	4	-2	2	4	2	2	6
6		3	-3	3	1	-3	-3	11	-3
7									
8			MEigenvalQRC(B3:I6)						
9	$\lambda_1 =$	-4.742506	-10.70001						
10	$\lambda_2 =$	0	1						
11	$\lambda_3 =$	4.836931	2.04102						
12	$\lambda_4 =$	4.905575	9.658987						
13									
14			MEigenVecInvC(B3:I6,B9:C12)						
15	Q =	-0.102320	0.707107	0.730422	-0.438015	-0.178527	0	0	-0.200275
16		-0.138442	0	-0.499653	0.001996	0.493799	-0.707107	-0.011032	-0.696918
17		-0.183668	0	-0.139464	-0.009612	-0.408504	0	0.113374	-0.510347
18		0.067940	0	-0.042364	0.118771	0.699593	0	-0.427328	-0.087645

Fig. 10.11.7: An annotated spreadsheet for the eigenfunction analysis of a general complex matrix.

494

10.12 Eigenvalue decomposition

Now that we now know how to find the eigenvalues λ and eigenvectors $\mathbf{q}$ of $\mathbf{S}$, we can ask whether we can travel this route in reverse, and compute $\mathbf{S}$ from its eigenvalues and eigenvalues. The answer is yes, and is in fact simple to derive as well as to implement. In general, an $m \times m$ matrix will have m eigenvalues λ (which, just like the roots of a higher-order polynomial, need not all be distinct), and each eigenvalue λ_i will have an associated eigenvector $\mathbf{q}_i$. Place the eigenvalues λ_i on the diagonal of a diagonal matrix $\mathbf{\Lambda}$, so that all off-diagonal elements are zero. Then arrange all eigenvectors $\mathbf{q}_i$ in a matrix $\mathbf{Q}$, by placing them one next to the other in the same order as that of the corresponding eigenvalues λ_i in $\mathbf{\Lambda}$, i.e., in our chosen format for complex notation, grouping the real components first and then, separately, the imaginary ones. We then have $\mathbf{S\,q} = \mathbf{q}\,\lambda$. (Mathematically, it doesn't matter whether we write $\lambda\,\mathbf{q}$ or $\mathbf{q}\,\lambda$, because both merely mean that each element of $\mathbf{q}$ is multiplied by the scalar λ. But on the spreadsheet we treat vectors as either column or row vectors, and if we elect to write $\mathbf{q}$ as a column vector, as in Fig. 10.12.1, we obviously must use $\mathbf{q}_{r \times 1}$ times $\lambda_{1 \times 1}$ in order to make their inner indices equal, as necessary for matrix multiplication, see section 10.1.3.) Application of the rules of matrix multiplication will then quickly convince you that we can condense the n equations $\mathbf{S\,q} = \mathbf{q}\,\lambda$ and into the single matrix equation

$$\mathbf{S\,Q} = \mathbf{Q}\,\mathbf{\Lambda} \tag{10.12.1}$$

so that we can reconstruct $\mathbf{S}$ simply as

$$\mathbf{S} = \mathbf{S\,Q\,Q}^{-1} = \mathbf{Q}\,\mathbf{\Lambda}\,\mathbf{Q}^{-1} \tag{10.12.2}$$

as will be illustrated in the next two exercises. Alternatively, we can consider (10.12.2) as a way to decompose any nonsingular square matrix $\mathbf{S}$ into the product of three separate matrices of the same size $m \times m$ as $\mathbf{S}$. The middle matrix of this trio, $\mathbf{\Lambda}$, is diagonal and contains only the eigenvalues of $\mathbf{S}$, while its two neighbors derive from the corresponding eigenvectors. We will illustrate these relationships in exercise 10.12.1 for a square matrix (which need not be Hermitian) with real eigenfunctions, and in exercise 10.12.2 for a general square matrix.

Exercise 10.12.1:

(1) On a new spreadsheet enter a square matrix $\mathbf{S}$ such as shown in B3:D5 of Fig. 10.12.1, which was carefully selected to have only real eigenvalues and eigenvectors to keep the spreadsheet simple.

(2) Verify that it has only real eigenvalues by filling the block E3:G5 with zeroes, and in block I3:J5 use `=MEigenValQRC(B3:G5)` to find the corresponding eigenvalues. With both $\mathbf{S}$ and the λ's real, the $\mathbf{q}$'s must also be real, but you need not take my word for it: test it yourself. As you can see from Fig. 10.12.1, this is indeed the case.

	A	B	C	D	E	F	G	H	I	J
1										
2									MEigenValQRC(B3:G5)	
3	$\mathbf{S} =$	-1	6	7	0	0	0		-7.834209	0
4		2	2	8	0	0	0		-3.924174	0
5		5	4	-3	0	0	0		9.758383	0
6										
7	MEigenVecC(B3:G5,I3:J3)			MEigenVecC(B3:G5,I4:J4)				MEigenVecC(B3:G5,I5:J5)		
8	-0.377465	0		1.226825	0			1.431538	0	
9	-0.736721	0		-1.764575	0			1.400173	0	
10	1.000000	0		1.000000	0			1.000000	0	

Fig. 10.12.1: Verifying that the square matrix $\mathbf{S}$ has real eigenvalues and real eigenfunctions.

(3) On a new spreadsheet, copy the real part of $\mathbf{S}$ in B2:D4, find its eigenvalues in F3:F5, and all eigenvectors in H3:J5.

(4) In B8:D10 enter the eigenvalues on its main diagonal, and place zeroes in all off-diagonal positions. (In this case you cannot leave them blank.) This will generate $\mathbf{\Lambda}$.

(5) In B13:B16 calculate the matrix product **S Q**. In G8:G10 compute $\mathbf{q}_1 \, \lambda_1$, in I8:I10 the product of Q and the first column in L, and compare these two with each other as well as with the first column in **S Q**. All should be the same. Do the same for the second and third eigenvalues and their eigenvectors, and compare with the second and third column of **S Q**.

(6) Finally, in B18:D20, construct $\mathbf{Q} \, \boldsymbol{\Lambda} \, \mathbf{Q}^{-1}$ and verify that it indeed regenerates **S**. In Fig. 10.12.2 this is done with one compound instruction (to keep the picture compact) but you may prefer to do this in several simpler steps, e.g., by first computing $\mathbf{Q} \, \boldsymbol{\Lambda}$ and $\mathbf{Q}^{-1}$ separately.

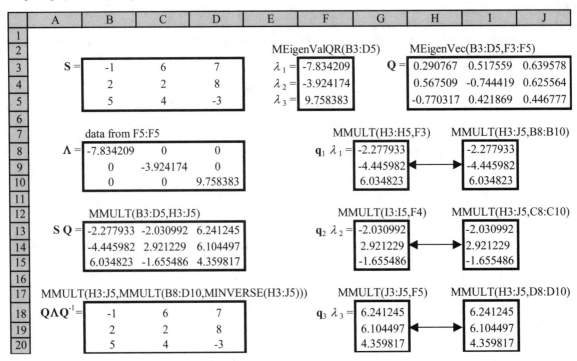

Fig. 10.12.2: Illustrating (10.12.1) and (10.12.2), the reconstruction of a square matrix **S** from its eigenvalues λ_i and its eigenvectors $\mathbf{q}_i$, for the special case where **S**, **Λ**, and **Q** are all real.

In the above example we made sure that **S** only had real eigenvalues and real eigenvectors, but in general that will not be the case. Just play with the numbers in Fig. 10.12.1 and you will realize that this is the exception rather than the rule. Merely changing the sign of one of its elements generates a complex response for 7 of the 9 numbers in B2:D4. Here we will just change the 8 in D3 to –8, while keeping E2:G4 empty (or filled with zeroes). Of course, when **S** itself already contains imaginary components, some or all of the eigenvalues and/or eigenvectors must be complex.

Exercise 10.12.2:

(1) On a new spreadsheet enter a square matrix **S** such as shown in B3:D5 of Fig. 10.12.3.

(2) In I3:J5 use =MEigenValQRC(B3:G5) to find the corresponding eigenvalues.

(3) For each of the eigenvalues λ_i find the corresponding eigenvector $\mathbf{q}_i$ in C8:D10, F8:G10, and I8:J10.

(4) Construct the matrix **Λ** from two adjacent zero matrices, one using the real components I3:I5 of **λ**, and the other its imaginary components from J3:J5.

(5) Likewise, in B13:G15, stitch together the matrix Q from its individual pieces in rows 8:10.

(6) Compute the matrix product **Q Λ** in E23:J25, and the inverse **$\mathbf{Q}^{-1}$** of **Q** in B28:G30.

(7) Finally calculate **Q Λ $\mathbf{Q}^{-1}$** in E33:J35, which should reconstruct **S** from its eigenvalues and eigenvectors. Your spreadsheet should now resemble Fig. 10.12.3.

	B	C	D	E	F	G	H	I	J
								MEigenValQRC(B3:G5)	
S =	-1	6	7	0	0	0	**λ** =	-8.139768	0
	2	2	-8	0	0	0		3.069884	-4.533442
	5	4	-3	0	0	0		3.069884	4.533442

	(MEigenVecC(B3:G5,I3:J3))			MEigenVecC(B3:G5,I4:J4)			MEigenVecC(B3:G5,I5:J5)	
$\mathbf{q}_1$ =	-1.969985	0	$\mathbf{q}_2$ =	0.033746	1.293202	$\mathbf{q}_3$ =	0.033746	-1.293202
	1.177539	0		1	-0.221110		1	0.221110
	1	0		0	0.919551		0	-0.919551

from I3:J5

	B	C	D	E	F	G
Λ =	-8.139768	0	0	0	0	0
	0	3.069884	0	0	-4.533442	0
	0	0	3.069884	0	0	4.533442

A8:A10	E8:E10	I8:I10	B8:B10	F8:F10	J8:J10
Q = -1.969985	0.033746	0.033746	0	1.293202	-1.293202
1.177539	1	1	0	-0.221110	0.221110
1	0	0	0	0.9195511	-0.919551

MMultC(B18:G20,B13:G15)

Q Λ =	16.035217	5.966254	5.966254	0	3.816993	-3.816993
	-9.584892	2.067493	2.067493	0	-5.212225	5.212225
	-8.139768	4.168732	4.168732	0	2.822915	-2.822915

MInvC(B18:G20)

$\mathbf{Q}^{-1}$ =	-0.292041	0.009855	0.413079	-1.08E-17	-2.71E-17	8.67E-18
	0.207056	0.493013	-0.172644	-0.158795	0.005359	-0.319135
	0.207056	0.493013	-0.172644	0.158795	-0.005359	0.319135

MMultC(E23:J25,B28:G30)

$\mathbf{Q \Lambda Q}^{-1}$ =	-1	6	7	0	0	0
	2	2	-8	0	0	0
	5	4	-3	0	0	0

Fig. 10.12.3: Illustrating (10.12.1) and (10.12.2), the reconstruction of a square matrix **S** from its eigenvalues λ_i and its eigenvectors $\mathbf{q}_i$ for the general case where **S**, **Λ**, and **Q** are all potentially complex quantities.

Now play with this spreadsheet, by changing the values in B3:D5, and by inserting non-zero numbers into E2:G4, and see what happens. If your spreadsheet is built correctly, it will automatically reproduce its input **S** in its output $\mathbf{Q \Lambda Q}^{-1}$. That, of course, is the point of this exercise.

A final note: the eigenvectors in rows 8:10 are not normalized. However, do *not* try to normalize them, as the above check will not work. Normalization seems not to work properly with some of the complex number operations of Matrix.xla.

497

10.13 Singular value decomposition

A singular matrix occurs when the simultaneous equations to be solved are not linearly independent. We have seen in sections 2.9, 8.14 and 10.10 that such independency is not an all-or-none proposition, but instead can exhibit some uncertainty, because round-off errors can make a singular matrix appear to be nonsingular. Near-singular matrices are often called *ill-conditioned*, and their numerical inversion may cause problems due to the finite numberlength used in floating-point calculations.

One possible remedy would be to use a longer numberlength, an option we will consider in chapter 11. There is, however, a powerful matrix method that can reduce some of the problems involving ill-conditioned matrices, even while remaining in the usual "double precision" mode. We will briefly describe this method, called *singular value decomposition* (SVD), which is based on the decomposition of any *r*ectangular matrix **R** into three matrices, just as eigenvalue decomposition does for square matrices. This method constitutes a useful generalization of eigenvalue decomposition, because it applies to all rectangular matrices, including those that are square, and even to those that are both square and singular.

In the compact notation used by Matrix.xla(m) as well as the Numerical Recipes, singular value decomposition of a rectangular real matrix **R** of size $m \times n$ where $m \geq n$ yields

$$\mathbf{R} = \mathbf{U} \, \mathbf{\Sigma} \, \mathbf{V}^\mathrm{T} \tag{10.13.1}$$

where **U** is an $m \times n$ orthogonal matrix (*not* an upper triangular one, as traditionally indicated by the same symbol), and **Σ** and **V** are square matrices of size $n \times n$. We may compare (10.13.1) with the somewhat simpler (10.12.2) for a square matrix. The corresponding pseudo-inverse $\mathbf{R}^+$ of **R** is

$$\mathbf{R}^+ = (\mathbf{U} \, \mathbf{\Sigma} \, \mathbf{V}^\mathrm{T})^{-1} = \mathbf{V} \, \mathbf{\Sigma}^{-1} \, \mathbf{U}^\mathrm{T} \tag{10.13.2}$$

because

$$\mathbf{R}^+ \mathbf{R} = \mathbf{V} \, \mathbf{\Sigma}^{-1} \, \mathbf{U}^\mathrm{T} \, \mathbf{U} \, \mathbf{\Sigma} \, \mathbf{V}^\mathrm{T} = \mathbf{V} \, \mathbf{\Sigma}^{-1} \, (\mathbf{U}^\mathrm{T} \, \mathbf{U}) \, \mathbf{\Sigma} \, \mathbf{V}^\mathrm{T} = \mathbf{V} \, (\mathbf{\Sigma}^{-1} \, \mathbf{\Sigma}) \, \mathbf{V}^\mathrm{T} = \mathbf{V} \, \mathbf{V}^\mathrm{T} = \mathbf{I} \tag{10.13.3}$$

where we have used the properties that **U** and $\mathbf{U}^\mathrm{T}$ as well as **V** and $\mathbf{V}^\mathrm{T}$ are orthogonal, i.e., $\mathbf{U}^\mathrm{T} \, \mathbf{U} = \mathbf{V} \, \mathbf{V}^\mathrm{T} = \mathbf{I}$. (In general, however, $\mathbf{U} \, \mathbf{U}^\mathrm{T} \neq \mathbf{I}$. and $\mathbf{U}^\mathrm{T} \, \mathbf{U} \neq \mathbf{I}$.) Because **Σ** is diagonal, with diagonal elements σ_i and off-diagonal zeroes, its inverse $\mathbf{\Sigma}^{-1}$ is found directly by replacing all non-zero terms σ_i by $1/\sigma_i$.

Several special properties of singular value decomposition are:

(1) Singular value decomposition is possible for both square and rectangular matrices, and for both singular and non-singular matrices.

(2) The diagonal elements σ_i of **Σ** are called the *singular values* of **R**. These singular values are all non-negative, and are usually presented in order of decreasing magnitude: $\sigma_1 \geq \sigma_2 \geq \sigma_3 \geq \ldots \geq \sigma_r \geq 0$, where the index r denotes the *rank* of **R**, i.e., the number of columns in **R** that are not completely linearly dependent on one or more of the other columns.

(3) For a Hermitian matrix (i.e., either a symmetrical real square matrix for which $\mathbf{R} = \mathbf{R}^\mathrm{T}$, or a complex square matrix for which $\mathbf{R} = \mathbf{R}^\mathrm{H}$, its conjugate, Hermitian transpose) the singular values are the square roots of the absolute values of its eigenvalues, i.e., $\sigma_i^2 = |\lambda|$.

(4) The ratio of the largest to smallest singular value yields the *condition number* $\kappa = \sigma_1 / \sigma_r \geq 1$. Singular value decomposition therefore provides a direct way to characterize a matrix in terms of its robustness against the effects of numerical errors. If the matrix **R** is singular, κ should go to infinity, but since the spreadsheet cannot represent infinity, κ either becomes a very large number or shows a divide-by-zero error message. If **R** is near-singular, the condition number κ is very much larger than 1. In all such cases, the quantity $p\kappa$ (pronounced as "pee-kappa") $= -\log(\kappa)$ provides an estimate (in terms of decimal places) of the maximum loss of precision in inverting a matrix, in terms of number of decimals. The corresponding decimal places are not lost, but their significance usually is. In exercise 10.10.1 we already encountered an example of an ill-conditioned matrix which, as you will see shortly, has a $p\kappa$ of about –6, i.e., its last six decimals become statistically insignificant, because inverting that matrix can amplify the noise-to-signal ratio by a factor of the order of κ or, in the above example, about a million-fold.

498

Exercise 10.13.1 illustrates the following basic properties of singular value decomposition:

(1) *Any* rectangular matrix $\mathbf{R}$ can be written as $\mathbf{U}\,\boldsymbol{\Sigma}\,\mathbf{V}^{\mathrm{T}}$.

(2) The singular values on the diagonal of $\boldsymbol{\Sigma}$ are the positive square roots of the non-zero eigenvalues of $\mathbf{R}^{\mathrm{T}}\mathbf{R}$ or $\mathbf{R}\,\mathbf{R}^{\mathrm{T}}$.

(3) The columns of $\mathbf{U}$ are the eigenvectors of $\mathbf{R}\,\mathbf{R}^{\mathrm{T}}$.

(4) The columns of $\mathbf{V}$ are the eigenvectors of $\mathbf{R}^{\mathrm{T}}\mathbf{R}$.

These properties establish SVD as the most useful generalization to rectangular matrices of the eigen-analysis of square matrices. This is why singular value decomposition plays such a central role in applied matrix algebra.

Exercise 10.13.1:

(1) On a new spreadsheet place a small non-singular, non-square matrix $\mathbf{R}$ in B3:C5

(2) In E3:G4 place its transpose, $\mathbf{R}^{\mathrm{T}}$.

(3) In B8:C10, F8:G9, and I9:J10 compute the SVD matrices $\mathbf{U}$, $\boldsymbol{\Sigma}$, and $\mathbf{V}$ respectively. Note that Matrix.xla uses the symbol $\mathbf{D}$ for the *d*iagonal matrix we here call $\boldsymbol{\Sigma}$ containing the *s*ingular values σ_i in order to distinguish it from the diagonal matrix $\boldsymbol{\Lambda}$ containing the eigenfunctions λ_i.

(4) In J3 use =MpCond(B3:C5) to find pκ, the negative logarithm of the condition number κ, and in J6 verify that κ is the ratio of the largest to smallest singular value.

(5) In B13:D15 calculate the matrix product $\mathbf{R}\,\mathbf{R}^{\mathrm{T}}$, which you can readily verify is a symmetrical square matrix.

(6) In F13:F15 find the three eigenvalues of the square matrix $\mathbf{R}\,\mathbf{R}^{\mathrm{T}}$. You need not consider complex eigenvalues, because $\mathbf{R}\,\mathbf{R}^{\mathrm{T}}$ is a symmetrical square matrix, and is therefore Hermitian.

(7) In B18:C19 calculate the matrix product $\mathbf{R}^{\mathrm{T}}\mathbf{R}$, in E18:E19 its eigenvalues, and in G18:G19 their square root. (Here the eigenvalues are all positive. If not, compute the square roots of their absolute values.) Verify that the eigenvalues (in F14:F15 and E18:E19 respectively) and F14:F15 are the same.

(8) Verify that the *non-zero* eigenvalues of $\mathbf{R}\,\mathbf{R}^{\mathrm{T}}$ and $\mathbf{R}^{\mathrm{T}}\mathbf{R}$ in F14:F15 and E18:E19 respectively are the same, as they should be. This therefore also applies to their square roots. Verify that the latter are indeed the same as the significant values on the main diagonal of $\boldsymbol{\Sigma}$ in F8:G9. This illustrates point (2) just above this exercise.

(9) In I13:J15 compute the eigenvectors of $\mathbf{R}\,\mathbf{R}^{\mathrm{T}}$, again using only the *non-zero* eigenvalues in F14:F15, and compare these eigenvectors with the columns of $\mathbf{U}$ in B8:C10. This illustrates point (3) given above his exercise. The signs of entire columns may differ, because normalized vectors still have an inherent sign ambiguity.

(10) Likewise, in I18:J19 find the eigenvectors of $\mathbf{R}^{\mathrm{T}}\mathbf{R}$, which should be the same (but for their signs) as those in I9:J10 for $\mathbf{V}$, and thereby illustrate point (4).

(11) In B22:C24 calculate the product $\mathbf{U}\,\boldsymbol{\Sigma}$, and in F22:G24 $\mathbf{U}\,\boldsymbol{\Sigma}\,\mathbf{V}^{\mathrm{T}}$. This should reconstitute $\mathbf{R}$, as it indeed does, see point (1) above.

Note the ease of getting these results on the spreadsheet. Moreover, once you have made the spreadsheet, you can change one or more elements of $\mathbf{R}$ and immediately see how such changes affect the answers. You need to make a new spreadsheet only when the size of $\mathbf{R}$ changes.

Use the just-made spreadsheet to see what happens in Fig. 10.13.1 when you make the two columns in $\mathbf{R}$ linearly dependent, e.g., by putting 3, 5, 7 in C3:C5 so that the second column is twice the first + 1 (which in matrix parlance does *not* count as "fully linearly dependent" because of the additive constant 1) or 3, 6, and 9 (which does count as such because the second column is now a multiple of the first). In the latter case, there is only one nonzero singular value in $\boldsymbol{\Sigma}$, and only one nonzero eigenfunction in F15 or E19, and the condition number exceeds 16, yet $\mathbf{R}$ is still properly reproduced in F22:G24 by $\mathbf{U}\,\boldsymbol{\Sigma}\,\mathbf{V}^{\mathrm{T}}$.

The compact notation omits singular values that are zero, and the corresponding rows and columns in $\boldsymbol{\Sigma}$, $\mathbf{U}$ and $\mathbf{V}$. Figure 10.13.2 shows what the corresponding "full" SVD would look like. It makes both $\mathbf{U}$ and $\mathbf{V}$ square, while $\boldsymbol{\Sigma}$ assumes the size of $\mathbf{R}$. (We will use $\mathbf{U}^{\wedge}$ and $\boldsymbol{\Sigma}^{\wedge}$ to distinguish them from their compact values $\mathbf{U}$ and $\boldsymbol{\Sigma}$.) When R is $m{\times}n$, $\mathbf{U}^{\wedge}$ will have the size $m{\times}m$, and $\boldsymbol{\Sigma}^{\wedge}$ $m{\times}n$. For a typical least squares problem, where there are often many more data (m) than variables (n–1), the difference in space requirements can be significant, while the final results are identical. Both $\mathbf{U}^{\mathrm{T}}\,\mathbf{U} = \mathbf{I}$ and $(\mathbf{U}^{\wedge})^{\mathrm{T}}\,\mathbf{U}^{\wedge} = \mathbf{I}$ apply, but in general $\mathbf{U}\,\mathbf{U}^{\mathrm{T}} \neq \mathbf{I}$ and $\mathbf{U}^{\wedge}\,(\mathbf{U}^{\wedge})^{\mathrm{T}} \neq \mathbf{I}$.

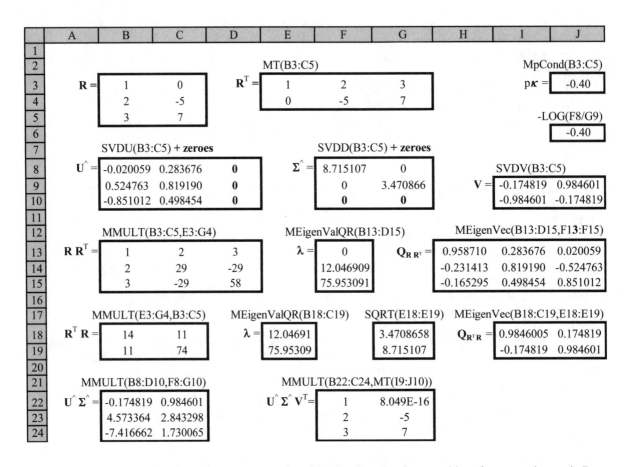

Fig. 10.13.1: A spreadsheet illustrating some properties of the singular value decomposition of a rectangular matrix **R**.

The above rules establishing the relation between the SVD of rectangular matrices (including square and/or singular ones) and the eigenanalysis of non-singular square matrices are readily generalized to complex matrices by replacing the transpose $\mathbf{R}^T$ by the conjugate (Hermitian) transpose $\mathbf{R}^H$. In this more general form, applicable to both real and complex matrices, these rules therefore are:

(1) Any rectangular matrix $\mathbf{R}$ can be written as $\mathbf{U}\,\boldsymbol{\Sigma}\,\mathbf{V}^T$.
(2) The singular values on the diagonal of $\boldsymbol{\Sigma}$ are the positive square roots of the non-zero eigenvalues of $\mathbf{R}^H\mathbf{R}$ or $\mathbf{R}\,\mathbf{R}^H$.
(3) The columns of $\mathbf{U}$ are the eigenvectors of $\mathbf{R}^H\mathbf{R}$.
(4) The columns of $\mathbf{V}$ are the eigenvectors of $\mathbf{R}\,\mathbf{R}^H$.

Here is a simple demonstration of rule (2) in the above list. We start from a real rectangular matrix $\mathbf{R}$, and form the square product $\mathbf{R}^T\mathbf{R}$, which is Hermitian. We now apply singular value decomposition to $\mathbf{R}^T$ and $\mathbf{R}$, and combine these to

$$\mathbf{R}^T\mathbf{R} = (\mathbf{U}\,\boldsymbol{\Sigma}\,\mathbf{V}^T)^T\,(\mathbf{U}\,\boldsymbol{\Sigma}\,\mathbf{V}^T) = (\mathbf{V}\,\boldsymbol{\Sigma}^T\,\mathbf{U}^T)\,(\mathbf{U}\,\boldsymbol{\Sigma}\,\mathbf{V}^T)$$

$$= \mathbf{V}\,\boldsymbol{\Sigma}^T\,(\mathbf{U}^T\mathbf{U})\,\boldsymbol{\Sigma}\,\mathbf{V}^T = \mathbf{V}\,\boldsymbol{\Sigma}^T\boldsymbol{\Sigma}\,\mathbf{V}^T = \mathbf{V}\,\boldsymbol{\Sigma}^2\,\mathbf{V}^T \qquad (10.13.3)$$

where we have used the rule of matrix transposition that $(\mathbf{A}\,\mathbf{B})^T = \mathbf{B}^T\mathbf{A}^T$ and hence $(\mathbf{A}\,\mathbf{B}\,\mathbf{C})^T = \mathbf{C}^T\,\mathbf{B}^T\,\mathbf{A}^T$, together with the facts that $\mathbf{U}^T\mathbf{U} = \mathbf{I}$ because the columns of $\mathbf{U}$ contain orthogonal eigenvectors, and that $\boldsymbol{\Sigma}$ is diagonal, so that $\boldsymbol{\Sigma}^T = \boldsymbol{\Sigma}$ and $\boldsymbol{\Sigma}^T\boldsymbol{\Sigma} = \boldsymbol{\Sigma}^2$. An equivalent derivation applies to complex matrices, with the superscript T (for transposition) replaced by H (for Hermitean transposition).

500

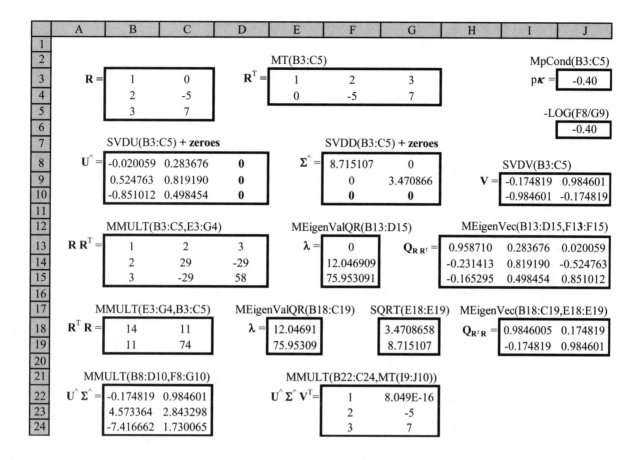

Fig. 10.13.2: The corresponding spreadsheet using the full format of the singular value decomposition. The added zeroes are printed in bold numbers.

Comparing (10.13.3) with the eigenvalue decomposition of the square matrix $\mathbf{R}^T \mathbf{R}$, see (10.12.1), yields

$$\mathbf{V} \, \mathbf{\Sigma}^2 \, \mathbf{V}^T = \mathbf{Q}_{\mathbf{R}\mathbf{R}^T} \, \mathbf{\Lambda} \, (\mathbf{Q}_{\mathbf{R}\mathbf{R}^T})^{-1} \tag{10.13.4}$$

from which we see that $\mathbf{\Sigma}$ is indeed the square root of $\mathbf{\Lambda}$ and, because both $\mathbf{\Sigma}$ and $\mathbf{\Lambda}$ are diagonal, the individual singular values σ_i are the square roots of the eigenvalues λ_i. Moreover, $\mathbf{V}$ is the matrix containing the eigenvectors of $\mathbf{R}\,\mathbf{R}^T$, and $\mathbf{V}^T$ is its inverse. In general, for a complex rectangular matrix $\mathbf{R}$, replace the real transpose by its conjugate counterpart.

10.14 SVD and linear least squares

The benefit of using singular value decomposition for least squares analysis is that it is much less sensitive to ill-conditioning than the traditional approach of section 10.5. Below we will first illustrate the use of singular value decomposition in solving least squares problems.

Exercise 10.14.1:

(1) We now use the same data set as in exercise 10.5.1, i.e., with the x,y coordinates (1,5), (2,8), (3,11), (4,14), and (5,17). These data fit the line $y = 2 + 3x$ exactly, and are so close to the origin that there is no need for centering.

(2) Take a new spreadsheet, and enter the values 5, 8, 11, 14, and 17 of the input data vector **y** in cells B2:B6, and the associated x-values in D2:D6.

(3) In F2:G6 place the matrix **Q**, with its first column of $x^0 = 1$ (in all five cells F2:F6), and with the *x*-values 1, 2, 3, 4, and 5 as its second column, G2:G6. (If we were forcing the line to pass through the origin, the first column of matrix **Q**, F2:F6, would contain zeros rather than ones.)

(4) In B9:C13 compute **U** with the instruction =SVDU(F2:G6). Note that **U** must have the same size as **X**, in this case 5×2.

(5) In E9:F10 deposit the instruction for **Σ**, =SVDD(F2:G6), and in H9:E10 likewise compute **V**.

(6) In F13:G14 calculate the product $\mathbf{V}\,\boldsymbol{\Sigma}^{-1}$.

(7) In B16:F17 compute the SVD pseudo-inverse $\mathbf{X}^+ = \mathbf{V}\,\boldsymbol{\Sigma}^{-1}\,\mathbf{U}^T$ as the product of $\mathbf{V}\,\boldsymbol{\Sigma}^{-1}\,\mathbf{U}^T$.

(8) Finally, in I16:I17, find **a** as the product $\mathbf{X}^+\,\mathbf{b}$. Your spreadsheet should now resemble Fig. 10.14.1. The results for $\mathbf{X}^+$ and **a** are, of course, the same as those for $\mathbf{X}^+$ and **a** in Fig. 10.5.1, although the steps leading from **X** to $\mathbf{X}^+$ are quite different. Figure 10.14.1.shows what, with some annotation, you might see on your monitor screen.

	A	B	C	D	E	F	G	H	I
1									
2		y =	5		x =	1	**X** =	1	1
3			8			2		1	2
4			11			3		1	3
5			14			4		1	4
6			17			5		1	5
7									
8		SVDU(F2:G6)			SVDD(F2:G6)			SVDU(F2:G6)	
9		**U** =	0.160007	-0.757890	**Σ** =	7.691213	0	**V** =	0.266934	-0.963715
10			0.285308	-0.467546		0	0.91937		0.963715	0.266934
11			0.410609	-0.177202					
12			0.535909	0.113142		MMULT(H9:I10,MInv(E9:F10))			
13			0.661210	0.403486		$\mathbf{V}\,\boldsymbol{\Sigma}^{-1}$ =	0.034706	-1.048234	
14							0.125301	0.290344	
15		MMULT(F13:G14,MT(B9:C13))						MMULT(B16:F17,B2:B6)	
16		$\mathbf{X}^+$ =	0.8	0.5	0.2	-0.1	-0.4	**a** =	2
17			-0.2	-0.1	2.78E-17	0.1	0.2		3

Fig. 10.14.1: A spreadsheet illustrating the individual steps in the solution of a least squares problem using singular value decomposition.

The above exercise illustrates the principle of SVD-based least squares, but for a problem that doesn't really need it. In exercise 10.14.2 we show another example, written with more compact instructions.

Exercise 10.14.2:

(1) Open a new spreadsheet, which we will use for this and the next three exercises. In order to keep the instructions compact, we will again specify locations of the various spreadsheet elements, so that they will also correspond to those in the accompanying figures, and will therefore be easy to compare. Feel free, however, to use your own layout, rather than one driven by the author's need to make compact figures. The same applies to matrix operations you may want to combine in a single instruction, and to labeling used to keep the spreadsheet readable. The best way to get acquainted with matrix operations is to play around with them, and to see what works for you.

(2) In cells all cells in B3:B9 deposit the values 1, in C3:C9 the *x*-values 1 (1) 7, and in D3:D9 compute the corresponding values for x^2. These are the elements of matrix **X** in B3:D9.

(3) In F3:H9 compute **U** with the matrix instruction =SVDU(B3:D9).

(4) In B15:D17 calculate **Σ** with =SVDD(B3:D9), and in B20:D22 find **V** with =SVDV(B3:D9).

(5) In F14:H20 recover the matrix **X** as $\mathbf{U}\,\boldsymbol{\Sigma}\,\mathbf{V}^T$ through =MProd(F3:H9,B15:D17,MT(B20:D22)). Verify that you indeed have reconstructed the original matrix **X**. Using MProd yields more compact and better readable code than twice MMULT.

(6) If you want to make the spreadsheet even smaller, you could of course skip displaying **U**, **S**, and **V** entirely, and merely use the megaformula =MProd(SVDU(B3:D9),SVDD(B3:D9),MT(SVDV(B3:D9))), or write a function that will do this automatically for you.

502

(7) In cell F23 calculate pκ as the negative ten-based logarithm of the ratio of the larger to the smaller of the singular values in Σ, and in H23 compute the same pκ as =MCond(B3:D9).

(8) In J3:J9 compute $\mathbf{y}$ as $y_i = 4 + 3x_i + 2x_i^2$ using the values of x_i and x_i^2 in B2:D8. If you want to play with fitting a line through the origin, code it in J3 as =4*B3+3*C3+2*D3, and copy this down to J9.

(9) Just for kicks (because it is not really recommended to use such long, hard-to-read instructions) in J12:J14 compute the least-squares solution of the problem $\mathbf{X}\,\mathbf{a} = \mathbf{y}$. Notice that you can do this indeed with one line of code, without any other input information than X in B3:D9 and y in J3:J9.

(10) For comparison, in J17:J20 compute a with the traditional formula (10.5.9) as $(\mathbf{X}^T\,\mathbf{X})^{-1}\,\mathbf{X}^T\,\mathbf{y}$. You could use the formula =MProd(MInv(MMULT(MT(B3:D9),(B3:D9))),MT(B3:D9),J3:J9); the answers in J13:J15 and J17:J20 should of course be the same. Your annotated spreadsheet may now resemble Fig. 10.14.2. Save it for the next exercise.

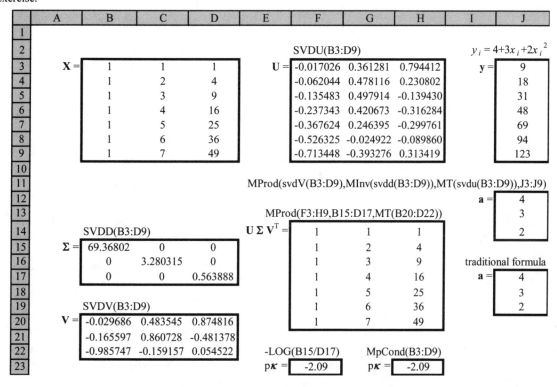

Fig. 10.14.2: A spreadsheet illustrating the individual steps in the solution of a least squares problem using both singular value decomposition and the traditional approach.

The matrices $\mathbf{X}$ in exercises 10.14.1 and 10.14.2 are perfectly well behaved, which is also reflected in their pκ values: you should be able to get answers correct to 13 or 14 decimals respectively. Now we are going to tinker with $\mathbf{X}$, in order to make it increasingly ill-conditioned, and observe what happens. One way to do that is to make the third column in $\mathbf{X}$, representing the x^2-values, approach the value $x+1$, in which case this column no longer contains linearly independent parameters, because the third column is then the algebraic sum of the corresponding values in the first two columns.

Exercise 10.14.3:

(1) Leave cell D3 alone, and change the instruction in cell D4 to =B4+C4. Notice that not much changes with pκ in H23, and nothing with the coefficients in J12:J14 and J17:J20.

(2) Copy the instruction from D3 to D4:D8. Still not much change, because y_1, the lone holdout in cell D2, does not fit the expression $x+1$, and the pκ in cell H23 certainly does not indicate a very ill-conditioned, near-singular matrix. Of course, things would change if we were to insert a 2 in cell D3.

503

(3) Change the value in D3 from 1 to 1.9, and notice any changes. Then add another nine to make it 1.99, see what happens, add another to yield 1.999, etc.

(4) You should observe that $p\kappa$ in F23 and H23 decrease by about 1 each time the difference between y_1 and 2 is reduced by an order of magnitude by adding another nine.

(5) Table 10.14.1 lists what happens with the retrieved least squares coefficients in J17:J19 with the traditional approach, and in J12:J14 with SVD.

y_1	$p\kappa$	singular value decomposition			standard matrix inversion		
		a_0	a_1	a_2	a_0	a_1	a_2
1	−1.6	4	3	2	4	3	2
1.9	−2.6	4	3	2	4	3	2
1.99	−3.6	4	3	2	4	3	2
1.999	−4.6	4	3	2	4	3	2
1.999 9	−5.6	4	3	2	3.99998	2.99997	2.00001
1.999 99	−6.6	4	3	2	3.99548	2.99619	2.00390
1.999 999	−7.6	4	3	2	3.68331	2.44161	2.24540
1.999 999 9	−8.6	4	3	2	7.66292	10.02230	3.11833
1.999 999 99	−9.6	4	3	2	6.10507	8.33944	−0.60507
1.999 999 999	−10.6	3.99999	2.99999	2.00001	6.54691	3.93753	−1.45316
1.999 999 999 9	−11.6	3.99997	3.00002	2	5.64844	8.51563	0.65625
1.999 999 999 99	−12.6	4.00024	3	1.99976	−7.62500	8.87500	7.18750
1.999 999 999 999	−13.6	4.00195	3.00391	2.00195	3.14063	1.17188	3.67187
1.999 999 999 999 9	−14.6	4.07813	3.10938	1.90625	1.43750	5.35937	2.30469
1.999 999 999 999 99	−15.6	4.50000	3.25000	1.5	9.02344	10.21094	−2.45688
2	−16.6	12	5	−3	#NUM!	#NUM!	#NUM!

Table 10.14.1: The results obtained, to within ±0.00001, with the spreadsheets built in exercises 10.11.3 through 10.11.5 when y_i for $i = 2$ through 7 (in D3:D8) is redefined as $y_i = 1+x_i$, while the value of y_1 (in D2) gradually approaches the value 2 that would make **X** singular. The penultimate value for y_1 contains 15 decimals, i.e., 14 behind the decimal point; Excel truncates after 15 decimals and therefore either ignores the last-added 9 or reads 1. followed by more than 14 nines as 2. Values for a_0 through a_2 that end in .00000 are shown as integers.

Table 10.14.1 illustrates that singular value decomposition is much more immune to ill-conditioning than the traditional matrix inversion approach, and this observation is generally valid. With y_1 in cell D3 equal to 1.999 999 99, $p\kappa = -9.6$, and the least squares coefficients a_0 through a_2 with the traditional method are all far off, while those found with SVD are still good to six significant figures. Even when y_1 differs from 2 by only 1×10^{-12}, the values obtained for a_0 through a_2 are still within 0.2% of their correct values, whereas the standard method already exhibits errors of that order of magnitude when the deviation of the value in cell D3 from 2 is five orders of magnitude larger! Moreover, as long as y_1 differs from 2 by only 1×10^{-14}, the smallest possible difference the spreadsheet can display, the coefficients in a remain of the correct order of magnitude, whereas those in the last three columns of Table 10.14.1 start to fluctuate wildly already when $p\kappa \approx -8$. Section 10.15 will reinforce this message with a further analysis of the NIST reference data set Filip.dat. Note that **y** contains no experimental noise in this exercise, so that we only probe the numerical sensitivity to ill-conditioning of the algorithm used.

The approach sketched here is mathematically sound, but computationally dangerous, because a near-singular matrix **R** will have a large spread of singular values σ_i. In that case the smaller singular values σ_i in **Σ**, which percentage-wise are most strongly affected by round-off errors and data uncertainty, will become the dominant terms $1/\sigma_i$ in **Σ**$^{-1}$. That is a prescription for obtaining nonsense, and computationally stable algorithms for **R**$^+$ therefore avoid formally inverting **Σ** by replacing all its singular values σ_i by their inverses, $1/\sigma_i$.

10.15 A second look at Filip.dat

In section 10.8 we addressed one of the problems posed by Filip.dat, namely its use of high powers (up to x^{10}) of high-precision numbers (specified up to 10 decimals), and we minimized this problem by using polynomial centering. That correction got us from zero to ten significant digits in the coefficients a_i. We already indicated that this problem with computing high-order powers of x is not the only difficulty posed by this test data set and, specifically, that the matrix **X** of Filip.dat is also ill-conditioned. We now have the means to test and remedy this. In exercise 10.15.1 we therefore consider the matrix formed by the columns for $x^0, x^1, x^2, x^3, \ldots, x^{10}$, both before and after polynomial centering.

Exercise 10.15.1:

(1) On a new spreadsheet, copy the original Filip.dat test data set, i.e., the column for y in, e.g., B4:B85, and that for x in, e.g., E4:E85.

(2) Generate the **X** matrix by filling D4:D85 with ones, and calculate $x^2, x^3, \ldots, x^{10}$ in the corresponding rows of columns F through N.

(3) Take an empty 11×11 area, such as D87:N97, and in it compute the singular values with the instruction =SVDD(D4:N85).

(4) Compute the condition κ of **X** as the ratio of the largest and smallest singular value, and also pκ. For the latter you should find the value –14.8, indicating that you cannot use standard numberlength software to invert this matrix. Compare this with what you get with the functions MCond and MpCond..

(5) In P4:P85 repeat the ones from D4:D85. And in E1 compute x_{av} as =Average(E4:E85).

(6) In Q4:Q85 calculate $x – x_{av}$, and in columns R through Z the corresponding powers $(x–x_{av})^2, (x–x_{av})^3, \ldots, (x–x_{av})^{10}$.

(7) In P87:Z97 compute the singular values of the polynomially centered matrix in P4:Z85.

(8) Find the corresponding values of κ and pκ. The latter is –5.1, indicating that matrix inversion will now yield about $15 – 5 = 10$ decimal places. This indeed fits with what you found in section 10.7: in cases like these, polynomial centering can sometimes dramatically reduce the ill-conditioning of a matrix.

(9) Copy the instruction from E1 to F1:N1 in order to compute $(x^2)_{av}, (x^3)_{av}, \ldots, (x^{10})_{av}$.

(10) In AB4:AB85 deposit ones, and in AC4:AL85 compute $x–x_{av}, x^2–(x^2)_{av}, x^3–(x^3)_{av}, \ldots, x^{10}–(x^{10})_{av}$, to generate the equivalent matrix with multivariate centering of each column.

(11) Calculate the corresponding values of κ and pκ. You will obtain p$\kappa = –14.0$, indicating that the standard, multivariate centering approach is barely better than no centering at all (p$\kappa = –14.8$, see under point (4) above) and therefore is not very useful in this case.

The next step is to use single value decomposition instead of the approach of section 8.11. We can use either the individual functions SVDU, SVDD, and SVDV, see section 10.13, or use RegrL or RegrP. If you have Excel 2003 or a more recent version, simply call the function LinEst or the macro Regression, since these are now based on an orthogonal QR matrix decomposition method that has many of the advantages of singular value decomposition.

Exercise 10.15.2:

(1) On another spreadsheet, again copy the original Filip.dat test data set, i.e., the columns for y and x, e.g., in B4:B85 and C4:C85 respectively.

(2) Also copy the reference coefficients a_0 through a_{10}, which NIST denotes as B0 through B10.

(3) In D4:M85 calculate the corresponding values for $x^2, x^3, \ldots, x^{10}$.

(4) If you have Excel2003 or a later version, call either LinEst (see section 2.3) or Regression (section 2.4); otherwise call RegrL or RegrP.

(5) Compare the coefficients found with those listed, e.g., by computing their relative error, $E = (a_{i,found} – a_{i,ref})/a_{i,ref}$ or, better yet, its negative 10-based logarithm. With the Excel instructions, you will find values for $pE = –\log E$ of about 7.7.

(6) Now do the same with a set of the corresponding polynomially centered data. This time the pE values are around 13.7, which means that the relative error in the coefficients a_i is of the order of $10^{-13.7}$, about as good as one can wish.

Thus we see that the combination of polynomial centering and singular value decomposition can nicely overcome the two major hurdles posed by Filip.dat.

Matrix.xla(m) has two convenient SVD-based functions for least squares analysis: RegrL for the usual linear least squares analysis, and RegrP for fitting to a polynomial. The latter does not include polynomial centering, but merely removes the need to compute the higher polynomial powers explicitly on the spreadsheet. When applied to Filip.dat, both yield results comparable to those obtained with Excel's 2003 version of LinEst, i.e., a pE of both the coefficients a_i and of their corresponding standard deviations s_i of at least 7. Matrix.xla(m) also has the instruction MPseudoInv for the general SVD pseudo-inverse $\mathbf{V}\,\mathbf{\Sigma}^{-1}\,\mathbf{U}^{T}$ of the $\mathbf{X}$-matrix which, for a large matrix $\mathbf{X}$, is about three times as fast as combining SVDS, SVDD, and SVDU, because MPseudoInv performs the time-consuming singular value decomposition only once.

10.16 Partitioned real-matrix operations for complex matrices

In using the split notation of complex matrices, we actually exploit *partitioned* matrices, in this case by separating the real and the imaginary components of their complex elements. Calculations using the resulting submatrices are sometimes handy, as we will illustrate here.

We first consider the simple addition of two complex numbers, $(a + j\,b)$ and $(c + j\,d)$, for which

$$(a + j\,b) + (c + j\,d) = (a + c) + j\,(b + d) \tag{10.16.1}$$

When we write $(a + j\,b)$ and $(c + j\,d)$ as square real matrices of the form $\begin{bmatrix} a & -b \\ b & a \end{bmatrix}$ and $\begin{bmatrix} c & -d \\ d & c \end{bmatrix}$ we find

that matrix addition yields the corresponding sum, $\begin{bmatrix} \mathbf{a+c} & -(b+d) \\ \mathbf{b+d} & a+c \end{bmatrix}$, where the real and imaginary

components of the sum (10.16.1) can also be found in its top-left and bottom-left elements, here emphasized in bold. Moreover, this correspondence applies just as well to complex matrices as to single complex numbers, as can be seen in exercise 10.16.1 and the corresponding Fig. 10.16.1.

Exercise 10.16.1:

(1) On a new spreadsheet, deposit a small rectangular complex matrix $\mathbf{R}_1$ in split format, such as the 3×2 matrix in B3:E5. We use double the spreadsheet space because this notation uses separate cells for the real and imaginary components. Do the same for a second rectangular complex matrix $\mathbf{R}_2$ of the same size in G3:J5, so that they can be added.

(2) You can perform the addition in two ways: either element-by-element, where you use in cell M3 the instruction =B3+G3, and then copy this instruction to M3:P5, or (simpler) with the block instruction =(B3:E5)+(G3:J5) in block M3:P5.

(3) Now form the matrices $\mathbf{R}_1'$ and $\mathbf{R}_1'$ by copying B3:C5 to both B8:C10 and D11:E13, copying D3:E8 to B11:C13, and –(D3:E8) to D8:E10. Do the same with $\mathbf{R}_2'$.

(4) Add $\mathbf{R}_1'$ and $\mathbf{R}_2'$ in M8:P13 and verify that, indeed, M8:N10 and O11:P13 are identical to N3:N5 and, likewise, M11:N13 and –(O8:P10) to O3:P5.

The same holds for matrix multiplication. We have

$$(a + j\,b)\,(c + j\,d) = (a\,c - b\,d) + j\,(a\,d + b\,c) \tag{10.16.2}$$

while applying the rules of matrix multiplication leads to

$$\begin{bmatrix} a & -b \\ b & a \end{bmatrix} + \begin{bmatrix} c & -d \\ d & c \end{bmatrix} = \begin{bmatrix} \mathbf{ac-bd} & -ad-bc \\ \mathbf{bc+ad} & -bd+ac \end{bmatrix} \tag{10.16.3}$$

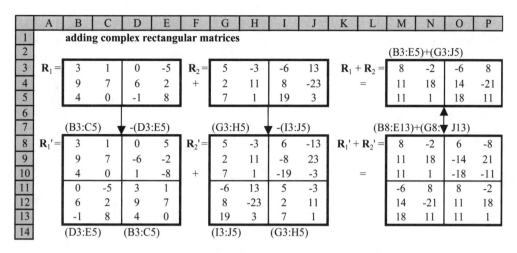

Fig. 10.16.1: A way to add complex matrices by using real matrices.

where the right-hand matrix again contains the real and imaginary components of the product (10.16.2) in its top-left and bottom-left elements. This can be generalized from complex numbers to complex matrices, as illustrated in exercise 10.16.2.

Exercise 10.16.2:

(1) On a new spreadsheet, deposit two small rectangular complex matrices, R_1 and R_2, both in split format. Note that two matrices of size $m \times n$ and $p \times q$ can only be multiplied when $n = p$. For the sake of keeping the figure small enough to be readable, we here use $n = p = 2$ and $m = q = 3$, but at the end of this exercise please verify that you will get the same general result when $m \neq q$.

(2) Now perform the addition in two ways: first by complex matrix multiplication (with MMultC, as shown in the top rows of Fig. 10.16.2) and then using MMULT for real matrices in the bottom rows. Again you will find that the above trick works.

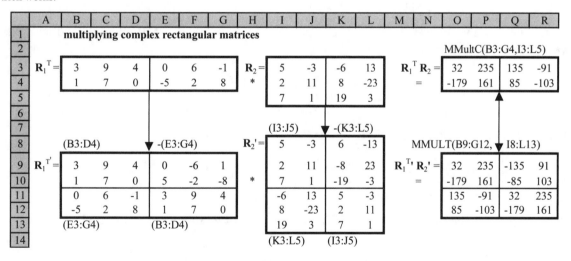

Fig. 10.16.2: Multiplying complex matrices directly or through the use of real ones.

Now we make a large jump, and try to use the above approach to find the pseudo-inverse of a rectangular complex matrix. In other words, we treat partitioned matrices just as we would individual matrix elements. First let us verify that, in this case, such an approach is indeed valid.

In order to keep them straight we will, whenever needed, indicate matrix dimensions directly as subscripts on the boldfaced capitals used to denote the matrices. Note that all matrices written in split format are twice as wide as their actual form when their elements are considered as single (though complex) quantities.

In split format we write the real and imaginary components of a complex matrix $\mathbf{R}$ as separate rectangular submatrices $\mathbf{A}$ and $\mathbf{B}$, so that

$$\mathbf{R}_{m\times 2n} = \mathbf{A}_{m\times n} + j\,\mathbf{B}_{m\times n} \tag{10.16.4}$$

where $j = \sqrt{-1}$. We want to find its pseudo-inverse $\mathbf{R}^+{}_{n\times 2m}$, i.e., the matrix that obeys the relation $\mathbf{R}^+\,\mathbf{R} = \mathbf{I}$ or, in split format,

$$\left[\mathbf{P}_{n\times m} + j\,\mathbf{Q}_{n\times m}\right]_{n\times 2m}\left[\mathbf{A}_{m\times n} + j\,\mathbf{B}_{m\times n}\right]_{n\times 2m} = \left[\mathbf{I}_{n\times n} + j\,\mathbf{O}_{n\times n}\right]_{n\times 2n} \tag{10.16.5}$$

By treating this as the product of two complex scalars, say $(p + j\,q)$ times $(a + j\,b)$, we would obtain $(p\,a - q\,b) - j\,(p\,b + q\,a)$, and we can therefore write (10.16.5) as

$$\left(\mathbf{P}_{n\times m}\,\mathbf{A}_{m\times n} - \mathbf{Q}_{n\times m}\,\mathbf{B}_{m\times n}\right) - j\left(\mathbf{P}_{n\times m}\,\mathbf{B}_{m\times n} + \mathbf{Q}_{n\times m}\,\mathbf{A}_{m\times n}\right) = \mathbf{I}_{n\times n} + j\,\mathbf{O}_{n\times n} \tag{10.16.6}$$

so that

$$\mathbf{P}_{n\times m}\,\mathbf{A}_{m\times n} - \mathbf{Q}_{n\times m}\,\mathbf{B}_{m\times n} = \mathbf{I}_{n\times n} \tag{10.16.7}$$

and

$$\mathbf{P}_{n\times m}\,\mathbf{B}_{m\times n} + \mathbf{Q}_{n\times m}\,\mathbf{A}_{m\times n} = \mathbf{O}_{n\times n} \tag{10.16.8}$$

Now assume that we can associate with our complex matrix $\mathbf{R}_{m\times 2n}$ a real matrix $\mathbf{R}'_{2m\times 2n}$ of the form

$$\mathbf{R}'_{2m\times 2n} = \begin{bmatrix} \mathbf{A}_{m\times n} & -\mathbf{B}_{m\times n} \\ \mathbf{B}_{m\times n} & \mathbf{A}_{m\times n} \end{bmatrix}_{2m\times 2n} \tag{10.16.9}$$

for which we can find the pseudo-inverse $\mathbf{R}'^+$ with the Matrix instruction MPseudoInv, and let the latter be written in the corresponding submatrices as

$$\mathbf{R}'^+{}_{2n\times 2m} = \begin{bmatrix} \mathbf{C}_{n\times m} & -\mathbf{D}_{n\times m} \\ \mathbf{D}_{n\times m} & \mathbf{C}_{n\times m} \end{bmatrix}_{2n\times 2m} \tag{10.16.10}$$

so that, by definition, we have $\mathbf{R}'^+{}_{2n\times 2m}\,\mathbf{R}'_{2m\times 2n} = \mathbf{I}'_{2n\times 2n}$ or, in split format,

$$\begin{bmatrix} \mathbf{C}_{n\times m} & -\mathbf{D}_{n\times m} \\ \mathbf{D}_{n\times m} & \mathbf{C}_{n\times m} \end{bmatrix}_{2n\times 2m} \cdot \begin{bmatrix} \mathbf{A}_{m\times n} & -\mathbf{B}_{m\times n} \\ \mathbf{B}_{m\times n} & \mathbf{A}_{m\times n} \end{bmatrix}_{2m\times 2n} = \begin{bmatrix} \mathbf{I}_{n\times n} & \mathbf{O}_{n\times n} \\ \mathbf{O}_{n\times n} & \mathbf{I}_{n\times n} \end{bmatrix}_{2n\times 2n} \tag{10.16.11}$$

We now perform the multiplication in (10.16.11) in terms of its submatrices, and find

$$\mathbf{C}_{n\times m}\,\mathbf{A}_{m\times n} - \mathbf{D}_{n\times m}\,\mathbf{B}_{m\times n} = \mathbf{I}_{n\times n} \tag{10.16.12}$$

$$-\mathbf{C}_{n\times m}\,\mathbf{B}_{m\times n} - \mathbf{D}_{n\times m}\,\mathbf{A}_{m\times n} = \mathbf{O}_{n\times n} \quad \text{or} \quad \mathbf{D}_{n\times m}\,\mathbf{A}_{m\times n} = -\,\mathbf{C}_{n\times m}\,\mathbf{B}_{m\times n} \tag{10.16.13}$$

$$-\mathbf{D}_{n\times m}\,\mathbf{B}_{m\times n} + \mathbf{C}_{n\times m}\,\mathbf{A}_{m\times n} = \mathbf{I}_{n\times n} \tag{10.16.14}$$

$$\mathbf{D}_{n\times m}\,\mathbf{A}_{m\times n} + \mathbf{C}_{n\times m}\,\mathbf{B}_{m\times n} = \mathbf{O}_{n\times n} \quad \text{or} \quad \mathbf{D}_{n\times m}\,\mathbf{A}_{m\times n} = -\,\mathbf{C}_{n\times m}\,\mathbf{B}_{m\times n} \tag{10.16.15}$$

where (10.16.14) duplicates (10.16.12), and (10.16.15) is equivalent to (10.16.13).

Now please note that (10.14.7) would be equal to (10.14.12) if **P** were equal to **C**, and that the same would apply to (10.14.8) and (10.14.13) if **Q** were to equal **B**. Because a matrix can have only one unique pseudo-inverse, these similarities can be no accident, but must be equalities, i.e., we have

$$\mathbf{P} = \mathbf{C} \qquad\qquad (10.16.16)$$

$$\mathbf{Q} = \mathbf{D} \qquad\qquad (10.16.17)$$

That means that we can indeed compute the *complex* pseudo-inverse using the instruction for its *real* counterpart! Exercise 10.16.3 illustrates this for a square 2×2 matrix **S**, and exercise 10.16.4 for a rectangular 3×2 matrix **R**.

Exercise 10.16.3:

(1) On a new spreadsheet, deposit the real elements of a 2-by-2 square matrix **A** in B3:C4, and the corresponding imaginary elements of **B** in D3:E4. This will yield a complex square matrix **S**, although in split spreadsheet notation it will occupy two adjacent squares, one for **A**, and one for **B**.

(2) In B7:C8, and also in D15:E16, place the array instruction =(B3:C4), ending the instruction with a block enter. This will put two copies of the submatrix **A** into **S**'. Then use =(D3:E4) in B9:C10 to copy **B** there, and likewise in D7:E8 deposit –**B** with =-(D3:E4).

(3) In B13:E16 deposit the instruction =MPseudoInv(B7:E10) for **S**'⁺, the pseudo-inverse of **S**'. And in order to check it, in G13:J16 compute the product **S**'⁺ **S**', which should yield a unitary matrix **I**.

(4) Now comes the trick: we had found earlier that the real part of **S**⁺ could be found as the top left block of **S**'⁺, and the imaginary part as the block just below it. Use this information to construct **S**⁺ in, e.g., B19:E20.

(5) The final test is to see whether the product **S**⁺ **S** indeed yields the complex unitary matrix. Note that, for this, you should deal with the matrices **S**⁺ and **S** as complex numbers, i.e., you should use complex matrix multiplication instruction =MMultC(B19:E20,B3:E4), as also indicated in Fig. 10.14.3. The answer illustrates that this approach indeed works.

(6) Play with different numbers in **S**, and see what happens further down the computation. Of course, blocks G13:J16 and G19:J20 should not show any significant changes.

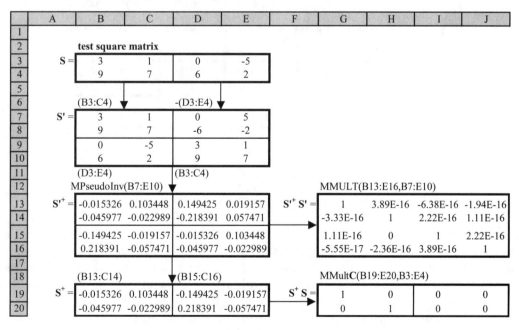

Fig. 10.16.3: The completed, annotated and self-documented spreadsheet of exercise 10.14.3.

Exercise 10.16.4:

(1) On a second spreadsheet, repeat the same sequence of operations on a rectangular matrix **R**, such as in C3:F5. The spreadsheet is fully self-documented, and follows the same logic as its left neighbor (except that the check on the product $\mathbf{R'^+ R'}$ is left out to save figure space), so you will need no further handholding. Figure 10.16.4 shows an example.

(2) Verify that you indeed find a unitary matrix in C26:D27, regardless of what values you enter in C3:F5. (The spreadsheet will not let you modify individual elements in intermediate results, because a matrix is considered as a single, indivisible unit, but the input block is just a set of individual data.) And even though C26:F27 is not strictly needed, it nicely illustrates that the method works properly.

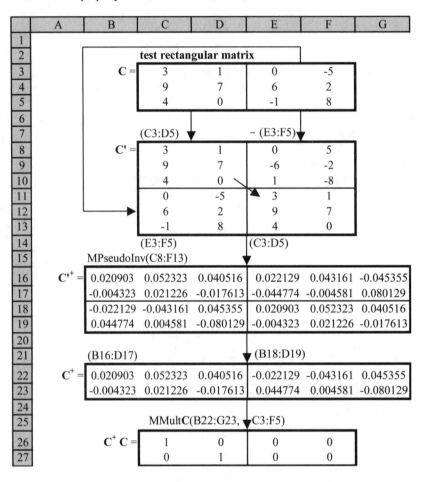

Fig. 10.16.4: The spreadsheet of exercise 10.14.4 illustrates how to compute the pseudo-inverse of a *complex* rectangular matrix by using instructions for *real* rectangular matrices.

The same also approach works for solving *n* simultaneous equations in *n* complex unknowns, i.e., for the complex analog of **A x** = **b** in (10.2.2), as illustrated in Fig. 10.16.5, where the top rows show the direct route with the Matrix.xla(m) instruction MMultC, and the bottom rows the detour via real matrix algebra. However, this trick doesn't always work, and it fails, e.g., with the components of SVD. You should therefore always verify mathematically, along the lines indicated above, whether this is a permissible approach. Fortunately, with the many complex matrix functions now available in both Matrix.xla(m) and XN.xla(m), this will often be unnecessary.

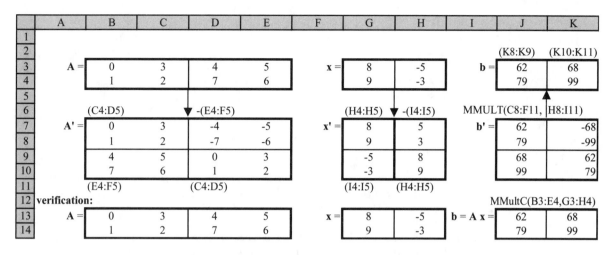

Fig. 10.16.5: Solving 2 simultaneous equations in two complex unknowns using the operations for real matrices. Rows 2:10 illustrate this method, while rows 12:14 show the much simpler use of the instruction MMultC.

10.17 Writing matrix functions

The computation of the pseudo-inverse of a rectangular complex matrix using the instruction MPseudoInv for real rectangular matrices provides a good example of how to write a function (or macro) using the instructions from Matrix.xla(m). As explained in the preceding section, starting from **R** we can construct a real image **R′**, take its pseudo-inverse **R′⁺**, and convert this back to the sought pseudoinverse **R⁺**. In writing a custom routine to do this, a major hurdle is that these four matrices all have different sizes: in split notation, when **R** occupies r rows and $2c$ columns, **R′** will be twice as tall, i.e., $2r$ rows and $2c$ columns, **R′⁺** will have their size inverted, and the final answer, **R⁺**, will use r rows and $2c$ columns. Because this is a common problem in writing matrix code, we will here look at it in some detail. The simplest approach is to settle first on a suitable unit to measure matrices in terms of their spreadsheet row and column counts, which now clearly depends on the chosen display format. In exercise 10.17.1 we will use the just-indicated approach, and use the sizes of the *input* matrix as our basis.

Exercise 10.17.1:

(1) As our first step we write a function in a VBEditor module (accessible with Alt‿F11) to convert the complex matrix **R** to its real image **R′**. For convenience of coding, we will call these matrices M and N respectively. The argument M should not be dimensioned, because the function statement already reads it, but N must be dimensioned, for which you must first dimension N in general As Variant, read the size (rows × columns) of the highlighted target area where N will be deposited, and then use ReDim to specify its actual size.

(2) A double For … Next loop can then compute the values of the individual elements N(i,j). This loop is best written and tested first with just its top line, N(i, j) = M(i, j), to make sure the rest of the function works. Then add one line at a time until you have it working properly for all four submatrices in **R′**. Here is an example of such code.

```
Function F1(M)
' M = {P, Q} where P and Q contain the components of the real
'   and imaginary parts of the complex matrix M in split format
' N = {P, -Q; Q, P} is the real square image of M
Dim i As Long, j As Long, cMax As Long, rMax As Long
Dim N As Variant
rMax = UBound(M, 1)
cMax = UBound(M, 2) / 2
ReDim N(1 To 2 * rMax, 1 To 2 * cMax) As Double
```

511

```
For i = 1 To rMax
  For j = 1 To cMax
    N(i, j) = M(i, j)
    N(i, cMax + j) = -M(i, cMax + j)
    N(rMax + i, j) = M(i, cMax + j)
    N(rMax + i, cMax + j) = M(i, j)
  Next j
Next i
F1 = N                                                                    '
End Function                                                              '
```

(3) For matrices it is not necessary to call the selected area to get their sizes, and much faster to avoid such a VBA-to-spreadsheet-to-VBE transfer with LBound and UBound statements, where L and U denote Lower and Upper respectively, and the second argument specifies rows (as 1) or columns (as 2), see the MacroMorsels DetermineMatrixSize and List-MatrixElements.

(4) To try it out, make a copy of, say, block C3:F5 of Fig. 10.14.4 on a new spreadsheet. Then highlight C8:F13 and enter the block instruction =F1(C4:F6). The code shown will then compute and write **R'** in C8:F13.

(5) In the next stage compute the pseudo-inverse of N. This is done in function MPsInvC2, where you must be careful to maintain the earlier-chosen row and column counting method, so that this piece of code, as well as the next, can then be merged with MPsInvC1 into the final function MPsInvC or whatever you want to call it. Specifically, the row count is now twice cMax, and the column count is equal to 2 times rMax, where rMax and cMax are the sizes of C3:D5. Then test F2 below the test area for F1, and make sure it works properly. Here is the code:

```
Function F2(N)                                                           ''
' NPI = pseudo-inverse of N                                              ''
Dim i As Long, j As Long, cMax As Long, rMax As Long                     ''
Dim NPI As Variant
cMax = UBound(M, 2) / 2                                                   ''
rMax = UBound(M, 1) / 2                                                   ''
ReDim NPI(1 To 2 * cMax, 1 To 2 * rMax) As Double
NPI = MPseudoInv(N)
F2 = NPI                                                                  ''
End Function                                                             ''
```

(6) Now you take the pseudo-inverse of the real image and convert it to the pseudo-inverse of the original, complex matrix. Try it out and make it work properly; you have the answer in B22:G23 of Fig. 10.14.4. Here is a sample code:

```
Function F3(NPI)                                                         ''
' MPI = pseudo-inverse of M, as calculated                              ''
'    from the pseudo-inverse NPI of the real                            ''
'    square image N of the complex matrix M                             ''
Dim i As Long, j As Long, cMax As Long, rMax As Long                     ''
Dim MPI As Variant
cMax = UBound(M, 1)   '''Selection.Rows.Count                            '''
rMax = UBound(M, 2)   '''Selection.Columns.Count / 2                     '''
ReDim MPI(1 To cMax, 1 To 2 * rMax) As Double
For i = 1 To cMax
  For j = 1 To rMax
    MPI(i, j) = NPI(i, j)
    MPI(i, rMax + j) = -NPI(i, rMax + j)
  Next j
Next i
F3 = MPI
End Function
```

(7) Finally put it all together in one function, here called MPsInvC, by eliminating the lines indicated above with two apostrophes. Moreover, replace the two lines adorned by single apostrophes by those that have three of them, because the

512

dimension statements of MPsInvC3 must now be used, as these fit with the size of the pseudo-inverse of the complex matrix. The final code, with a brief description of its function, now might look like this:

```
Function MPsInvC(M)
' Computes the pseudo-inverse of the complex matrix M in split format
' M = {P,Q} where P and Q are the real and imaginary
'   parts of the complex matrix M in split format
' N = {P,-Q;Q,P} is the real square image of M
' NPI = pseudo-inverse of N
' MPI = pseudo-inverse of M
Dim i As Long, j As Long
Dim cMax As Long, rMax As Long
Dim N As Variant, NPI As Variant, MPI As Variant

cMax = UBound(M, 2) / 2
rMax = UBound(M, 1)
ReDim N(1 To 2 * rMax, 1 To 2 * cMax) As Double
For i = 1 To rMax
  For j = 1 To cMax
    N(i, j) = M(i, j)
    N(i, cMax + j) = -M(i, cMax + j)
    N(rMax + i, j) = M(i, cMax + j)
    N(rMax + i, cMax + j) = M(i, j)
  Next j
Next i

NPI = MPsInv(N)

ReDim MPI(1 To cMax, 1 To 2 * rMax) As Double
For i = 1 To cMax
  For j = 1 To rMax
    MPIC(i, j) = NPI(i, j)
    MPIC(i, rMax + j) = -NPI(i, rMax + j)
  Next j
Next i
MPsInvC = MPIC
End Function
```

(8) The result is mercifully short, but might be rather difficult for a novice to put together. It often simplifies the task to split the task into several individual pieces, as illustrated here, so that each piece can be tested individually. You can then combine them afterwards.

(9) To test the function, add one more test stage, e.g., in I12:L13, where you calculate MMULT(H8:M9,I3:L5) to obtain a unitary matrix in I12:J13 and a zero matrix in K12:L13 if your answer in H8:M9 is indeed the pseudo-inverse.

(10) Play with the numbers in I3:L5 to convince yourself that you don't get the correct test result in I12:L13 by accident. Then, elsewhere on the spreadsheet, perform a similar test with a complex matrix M of a different size. The function should accommodate any sizes, as long as you use the split format.

You can embellish this result in various ways, e.g., by allowing it to use the various complex notation formats of Matrix.xla(m), of which we have here used only the default mode. But that will quickly make the code much more complex, with relatively little gain, which is why it is not done here. Moreover, it is not really necessary, for two reasons: (1) John Beyers has kindly included a version of MPseudoInvC equivalent to the above, compatible with all three complex notation formats in Matrix.xla(m), so that you need not go though this exercise anymore. (2) Moreover, he has also incorporated a set of SVD-related functions in the latest version of XN.xla(m) which (as all XN functions) can be used effectively as double-precision functions when preceded by the instruction xCDbl, as in =xCDbl(xMPseudoInvC(R)) where R denotes the location of the complex rectangular matrix. These were listed in Table 9.7.2, and of course will work only when you have also installed XN.

10.18 Tools for testing matrix operations

How, in general, do we test matrix operations? Below we list a few test matrices with special features that make them very convenient for this purpose. This section is based on Volpi's web memo *Matrices for testing algorithms* that you can find (among many other interesting memos) in http://digilander.libero.it/ /foxes/Documents.htm. Below we will briefly describe, in this order, three matrix types useful for testing inversion, and one that can test solvers of systems of simultaneous linear equations. Good final tests for statistical applications of matrix algebra are, of course, the NIST Statistical Reference Datasets.

10.18.1 The Tartaglia matrix

A Tartaglia matrix, a square matrix also known as Pascal's matrix (in fact, the Pascal triangle of Fig. 10.8.1 is the left top half of a Tartaglia matrix), has as its top left element the value 1:

$$a(1, 1) = 1 \tag{10.18.1}$$

The value of any other element is given by the element directly above it plus that directly to its left:

$$a(i, j) = a(i-1, j) + a(i, j-1) \quad \text{for} \quad i + j > 1 \tag{10.18.2}$$

Consequently, the elements in the first (top) row and in the first (left-most) column all have the value 1, and all elements of a Tartaglia matrix are integers. The latter property turns out to apply also to its inverse, which makes small round-off errors in matrix inversion easy to spot. This is especially so because Tartaglia matrices are quite ill-conditioned, the more so the larger their size.

Exercise 10.18.1:

(1) In the first book of a new spreadsheet, construct a 6×6 Tartaglia matrix S_T as follows. Click on the empty light-gray left-top corner cell (at the intersection of the letter row and the number column) to highlight the entire sheet, center it, and select Format ⇨ Cells ⇨ Number ⇨ General ⇨ OK to make sure that you will see what is described below.

(2) Highlight B2:G7, enter the instruction =MTartaglia(6), and block-enter it with Ctrl⌣Shift⌣Enter. Done! Or place the instruction =A2+B1 in cell B2. Then copy this instruction to cells B2:G7. You will find a field full of zeros. Did you make a mistake? No, just overwrite cell B2 by entering the value 1. Alternatively, you could have entered a 1 in each cell of B2:G2 and B3:B7, placed the instruction =A3+B2 in cell B3, and copied this to B3:G7, or used one of many other, equivalent ways to create S_T.

(3) Highlight B10:G15, and use =MINVERSE(B2:G7) to generate its inverse. You will see only integers, because the numerical results are *nearly* integer. To illustrate that, deposit the instruction =B9-ROUND(B9,0) in cell B18, and copy this to B18:G23. This method obviously works only when the deviations are small enough, which they clearly are here. A more efficient way would be to use the single block instruction = (B10:G15)-ROUND((B10:G15),0); try it.

(4) In B26:G31 enter the instruction =MInv(B2:G7), and in B34:G39 find their (nonexisting) deviations from zero.

(5) In cell G41 calculate the pk of S_T, the negative 10-based logarithm of its condition number, with the instruction =MpCond(B2:G9). Your spreadsheet should resemble Fig. 10.18.1.

(6) Is the Matrix.xla function MInv so cleaner than its Excel equivalent, MINVERSE? Not really, because MInv treats matrices containing only integers differently. You can easily verify this by copying A9:G41 toH9, placing the instruction =1.23*B2 in cell I2, and copying it to I2:N7.

(6) On a second spreadsheet, use the equivalent instructions to see what results you get with a 12×12 Tartaglia matrix. We will not show it here, because it is too large, and the lay-out and instructions are all equivalent, but you should see that the errors obtained with MINVERSE are now much larger, with some absolute errors coming close to 1 or, on a relative scale, close to 1E-6. The value of pκ is now -11.9. Again, MInv does well because it rounds all results to integer values!

(7) On sheet 3 push your luck by repeating the same process for an 18×18 Tartaglia matrix, with p$\kappa = -19.0$, where MINVERSE is powerless. This is why MInv was modified: to accommodate otherwise difficult all-integer matrices.

514

	A	B	C	D	E	F	G
1		MTartaglia(6)					
2	S =	1	1	1	1	1	1
3		1	2	3	4	5	6
4		1	3	6	10	15	21
5		1	4	10	20	35	56
6		1	5	15	35	70	126
7		1	6	21	56	126	252
8							
9		MINVERSE(B2:G7)					
10	S^{-1} =	6	-15	20	-15	6	-1
11		-15	55	-85	69	-29	5
12		20	-85	146	-127	56	-10
13		-15	69	-127	117	-54	10
14		6	-29	56	-54	26	-5
15		-1	5	-10	10	-5	1
16							
17		(B10:G15)-ROUND((B10:G15),0)					
18	inversion	-1.51879E-13	9.23706E-13	-1.36069E-12	1.85807E-12	-8.17124E-13	1.54099E-13
19	errors:	8.29559E-13	-4.4551E-12	8.37019E-12	-9.09495E-12	4.41247E-12	-8.64198E-13
20		-1.73017E-12	8.85336E-12	-1.76499E-11	1.79199E-11	-8.92442E-12	1.76748E-12
21		1.73905E-12	-8.7681E-12	1.75078E-11	-1.75362E-11	8.73968E-12	-1.73372E-12
22		-8.51763E-13	4.27036E-12	-8.5052E-12	8.48388E-12	-4.22062E-12	8.36664E-13
23		1.64868E-13	-8.2423E-13	1.6378E-12	-1.6307E-12	8.10019E-13	-1.60316E-13
24							
25		MInv(B2:G7)					
26	S^{-1} =	6	-15	20	-15	6	-1
27		-15	55	-85	69	-29	5
28		20	-85	146	-127	56	-10
29		-15	69	-127	117	-54	10
30		6	-29	56	-54	26	-5
31		-1	5	-10	10	-5	1
32							
33		(B26:G31)-ROUND((B26:G31),0)					
34	inversion	0	0	0	0	0	0
35	errors:	0	0	0	0	0	0
36		0	0	0	0	0	0
37		0	0	0	0	0	0
38		0	0	0	0	0	0
39		0	0	0	0	0	0
40							
41					MpCond(B2:G7) =	-5.04	

Fig. 10.18.1: A 6×6 Tartaglia matrix used to test two matrix inversion routines, Excel's MINVERSE and MInv from Matrix.xla(m).

10.18.2 The Hilbert matrix

A Hilbert matrix is a square matrix with the generating function

$$a(i,j) = 1/(i+j-1) \qquad (10.18.3)$$

with the useful property that all elements of its inverse are integers that can be expressed in terms of binomial coefficients. Its first (top left) element is usually taken as 1. Even at a fairly low order it is quite ill-conditioned, which again makes it a good matrix to gauge how well an inversion routine handles such a matrix. In this case, such a test also reflects the round-off errors in representing the fractions $1/(i+j-1)$ in binary.

Exercise 10.18.2:

(1) Prepare block B2:G7 on a new spreadsheet with Format ⇨ Cells ⇨ Number ⇨ Fraction ⇨ Up to two digits, then enter the numbers shown in Fig. 10.18.2 to form a 6×6 Hilbert matrix.

(2) Compute its inverse in B10:G15. In Fig. 10.18.2 you can already see some small deviations from integer numbers in that result.

(3) In B18:G23 compute the product of the Hilbert matrix and its inverse, which should yield a unitary matrix. It will show errors of the order of 1E-10.

(4) The same happens when you look at the relative errors in the inverse, by comparing each term with itself when rounded to zero digits past the decimal point, as illustrated in B26:G31.

(5) These results, with relative errors of the order of 1E-10, roughly agree with the pκ shown in cell G8, which predicts a maximum loss in significance of seven decimals.

	A	B	C	D	E	F	G
1							
2	S$_H$ =	1	1/2	1/3	1/4	1/5	1/6
3		1/2	1/3	1/4	1/5	1/6	1/7
4		1/3	1/4	1/5	1/6	1/7	1/8
5		1/4	1/5	1/6	1/7	1/8	1/9
6		1/5	1/6	1/7	1/8	1/9	1/10
7		1/6	1/7	1/8	1/9	1/10	1/11
8						MpCond(B2:G7) =	-7.17
9		MINVERSE(B2:G7)					
10	S$_H^{-1}$ =	36	-630	3360	-7560.000001	7560.000001	-2772
11		-630	14700	-88200.00001	211680	-220500	83160.00001
12		3360	-88200.00001	564480.0001	-1411200	1512000	-582120.0001
13		-7560.000001	211680	-1411200	3628800	-3969000	1552320
14		7560.000001	-220500	1512000	-3969000	4410000	-1746360
15		-2772	83160.00001	-582120.0001	1552320	-1746360	698544.0001
16							
17		MMULT(B2:G7,B10:G15)					
18	S$_H$ S$_H^{-1}$ =	1	0	0	2.91038E-11	0	0
19		1.13687E-13	1	2.91038E-11	1.45519E-10	5.82077E-11	0
20		5.68434E-14	0	1	8.73115E-11	-2.91038E-11	0
21		0	-1.81899E-12	2.18279E-11	1	2.91038E-11	1.45519E-11
22		0	-1.81899E-12	2.91038E-11	0	1	-1.45519E-11
23		0	0	2.18279E-11	2.91038E-11	0	1
24							
25		(B10-ROUND(B10,0))/B10 etc.					
26	relative	3.36924E-11	5.78092E-11	7.54707E-11	8.904E-11	9.9569E-11	1.0811E-10
27	errors in	5.69656E-11	7.31968E-11	8.49018E-11	9.37549E-11	1.00663E-10	1.06213E-10
28	S$_H^{-1}$:	7.37332E-11	8.41373E-11	9.14494E-11	9.69031E-11	1.01132E-10	1.04511E-10
29		8.63503E-11	9.23215E-11	9.62995E-11	9.9185E-11	1.01386E-10	1.03125E-10
30		9.61791E-11	9.86762E-11	1.00046E-10	1.00925E-10	1.01543E-10	1.02002E-10
31		1.04049E-10	1.03754E-10	1.0303E-10	1.02301E-10	1.01649E-10	1.01082E-10

Fig. 10.18.2: A 6×6 Hilbert matrix together with its inverse.

In this case, singular value decomposition yields only marginally smaller errors. A 6×6, 8×8, 10×10 and 12×12 Hilbert matrix yields pκ-values of −7.2, −10.2, −13.2 and −16.2 respectively, making inversion increasingly difficult. In those cases where pκ is −16 or smaller, no known double-precision matrix inversion method will work well, and extended precision is necessary. We will return to this problem in section 11.12.5.

516

10.18.3 A special sparse matrix

Sparse matrices are usually much less problematic to invert, because a substantial fraction of their elements are zero-valued. The following group of sparse, square matrices has zeros everywhere except in its first row, first column, and main diagonal. At its top row and as its first column it has the elements

$$a(1,j) = -1/(j-1) \qquad \text{for } j = 2, 3, \dots, n \tag{10.18.4}$$

$$a(i,1) = -1/(i-1) \qquad \text{for } i = 2, 3, \dots, n \tag{10.18.5}$$

while the elements on the main diagonal are

$$a(i,i) = 1/(i-1) \qquad \text{for } i = 2, 3, \dots, n \tag{10.18.6}$$

Finally, its first element $a(1,1)$ is determined as

$$a(1,1) = 1 + \sum_{i=2}^{n} a(i,i) \tag{10.18.7}$$

This matrix $\mathbf{S}$ has a very simple inverse $\mathbf{S}^{-1}$, with unit elements everywhere except on its the main diagonal, which reads $1, 2, 3, \dots, n$, and with a determinant $(n-1)!$.

You can readily verify that such sparse matrices give no problems to either MINVERSE or MInv, not surprising since they have quite small condition numbers that increase little with increasing size n: $p\kappa = -1.5$ for $n = 6$, $p\kappa = -1.9$ for $n = 12$, and $p\kappa = -2.1$ for $n = 18$.

10.18.4 A VanderMonde matrix

We now consider an example of a matrix that makes it easy to test solutions of systems of simultaneous linear equations. It is a class of square matrices with ones in its top row,

$$a(1,j) = 1 \qquad \text{for } j = 1, 2, \dots, n \tag{10.18.8}$$

and in its remaining elements the terms

$$a(i,j) = (k+j-1)^{i-1} \qquad \text{for } i, j = 1, 2, \dots, n \tag{10.18.9}$$

where k is an integer. We use this matrix $\mathbf{A}$ in combination with the vector $\mathbf{b}$ with elements

$$b(i) = \sum_{j=1}^{n} a(i,j) \tag{10.18.10}$$

This system of linear equations $\mathbf{A}\,\mathbf{x} = \mathbf{b}$ has the very simple solution $\mathbf{x} = [1, 1, \dots, 1]^{\mathrm{T}}$. Such a system can be solved directly by a command such as SysLin, or as $\mathbf{x} = \mathbf{A}^{-1}\,\mathbf{b}$. We can make our test more demanding by increasing the order n of the matrix, or the value of the integer k.

Exercise 10.18.2:

(1) On the first book of a new spreadsheet, enter $k=$ in cell A1, and the value 0 in cell B1. In cells A3:A8 place the row indices 1 through 6, and likewise deposit the column indices 1 through 6 in C1:H1.

(2) Construct a 6×6 VanderMonde matrix as follows. In each cell of C3:H3 deposit the number 1, see (10.18.8). In cell C4 place the instruction =($B$1+C$1-1)^($A3), and copy this to C4:H8. This is your 6×6 VanderMonde matrix for $k = 0$.

(3) In cell G2 put the label $p\kappa=$, and in cell H2 place the instruction =MpCond(C3:H8).

(4) In J3 use =SUM(C3:H3), then copy this instruction down to J4:J8. This calculates $\mathbf{b}$ according to (10.16.10).

(5) In L3:L8 compute x with the matrix instruction =SysLin(C3:H8,J3:J8).

(6) Now we use alternate ways to get the same answer. First, in C10:H15, compute $\mathbf{A}^{-1}$ with =MINVERSE(C3:H8). Then, in L10:L15, use =MMULT(C10:H15,J3:J8) to compute **x**.

(7) Likewise, in C17:H22 compute $\mathbf{A}^{-1}$ with =MInv(C3:H8), and in L17:L22 the corresponding value of $\mathbf{A}^{-1}\,\mathbf{b}$.

(8) Finally, in N3:N8, N10:N15, and N17:N22 find b_i-1. You will find zero values for SysLin, and values smaller than 10^{-11} for the other two approaches. Fig. 10.18.3 shows what you should have by now.

(9) Now increase the value of k in cell B1 and see what happens. The numerical values in C3:H8 and J3:J8 increase, as does the value of pκ in H2. The errors in **x** shown in N10:N15 and N17:N22 increase, but those in N3:N8 stay zero. Even at $k = 50$, with p$\kappa = -17.1$, SysLin yields zero errors in **x**, the combination of MInverse and MMult gives results good to at least five decimals, while MInv plus MMult produces wild results. In this case, both MINVERSE and MInv are trumped by SysLin.

	A	B	C	D	E	F	G	H
1	$k = 0$		*1*	*2*	*3*	*4*	*5*	*6*
2			**A:**				pκ =	-4.76109
3	*1*		1	1	1	1	1	1
4	*2*		0	1	2	3	4	5
5	*3*		0	1	4	9	16	25
6	*4*		0	1	8	27	64	125
7	*5*		0	1	16	81	256	625
8	*6*		0	1	32	243	1024	3125
9			**A** $^{-1}$ =MINVERSE(C3:H8)					
10			1	-2.28333	1.875	-0.70833	0.125	-0.00833
11			0	5	-6.41667	2.958333	-0.58333	0.041667
12			0	-5	8.916667	-4.91667	1.083333	-0.08333
13			0	3.333333	-6.5	4.083333	-1	0.083333
14			0	-1.25	2.541667	-1.70833	0.458333	-0.04167
15			0	0.2	-0.41667	0.291667	-0.08333	0.008333
16			**A** $^{-1}$ =MInv(C3:H8)					
17			1	-2.28333	1.875	-0.70833	0.125	-0.00833
18			0	5	-6.41667	2.958333	-0.58333	0.041667
19			0	-5	8.916667	-4.91667	1.083333	-0.08333
20			0	3.333333	-6.5	4.083333	-1	0.083333
21			0	-1.25	2.541667	-1.70833	0.458333	-0.04167
22			0	0.2	-0.41667	0.291667	-0.08333	0.008333

Fig. 10.18.3*a*: The left-hand side of the spreadsheet for exercise 10.18.4, with some added labels.

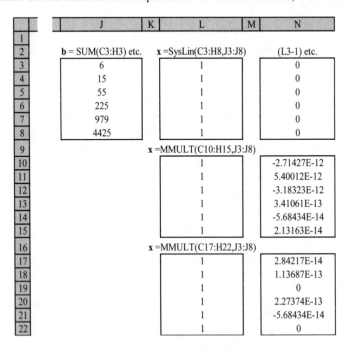

	J	K	L	M	N
1					
2	**b** = SUM(C3:H3) etc.		**x** =SysLin(C3:H8,J3:J8)		(L3-1) etc.
3	6		1		0
4	15		1		0
5	55		1		0
6	225		1		0
7	979		1		0
8	4425		1		0
9			**x** =MMULT(C10:H15,J3:J8)		
10			1		-2.71427E-12
11			1		5.40012E-12
12			1		-3.18323E-12
13			1		3.41061E-13
14			1		-5.68434E-14
15			1		2.13163E-14
16			**x** =MMULT(C17:H22,J3:J8)		
17			1		2.84217E-14
18			1		1.13687E-13
19			1		0
20			1		2.27374E-13
21			1		-5.68434E-14
22			1		0

Fig. 10.18.3*b*: The right-hand side of the spreadsheet for exercise 10.18.4, with some added labels.

518

(10) Which method is 'best' clearly depends on the problem posed, which is why it is useful to have several alternative approaches available. But it also implies that testing an algorithm with a model system can give results that are model-dependent, and therefore may not be applicable to your particular problem. Consequently, the best strategy is to *always test the validity of your actual result*. Here, where the question is which vector **x** satisfies **A x** = **b**, given values for **A** and **b**, test your result for **x** by afterwards computing the quantity **A x** − **b** with the value of **x** obtained. This is the ultimate test of a linear system solver. Implement it in column P, e.g., with the instruction =MMULT(C3:H8,L3:L8)-J3:J8 in P3:P8, and equivalent expressions for P10:P15 and P17:P22. See for yourself what you get for, e.g., $n = 6$ and $k = 50$.

(11) Finally, increase the size of the matrix **A** to, say, 12×12, and gradually increase the k-values. Because you only use functions, the spreadsheet provides a quick response. Amazingly, SysLin delivers error-free results for the 12×12 matrix up to $k = 16$, at which point **A** has a pκ of −22.3, while **A x** − **b** for both MINVERSE and MInv includes a term of the order of 10^{+12}, not quite equal to zero! Again, save your spreadsheet for another round.

10.19 *Removing less significant eigenvalues or singular values*

Data filtering or smoothing is removing as much noise as possible within acceptable levels of resulting signal distortion, regardless of how we define the terms "noise" and "signal". In least squares analysis, we minimize the sum of squares of the deviations, typically in one variable but in principle in more, assuming a Gaussian noise distribution, in which small fluctuations are more likely than large ones. We will then approach the correct average better the larger the data set and the more closely the noise can be approximated as Gaussian. In Fourier transform filtering, we assume that the noise is at a significantly higher frequency than the signal, and we achieve better noise rejection the larger the ratio of noise to signal frequencies. With different implied criteria for signal/noise enhancement we must expect different results for different methods.

In working with matrices we encounter yet another option to define "signal" and "noise". Eigenvalues or singular values that should be zero sometimes show as small numbers, typically of the order of magnitude of the computer round-off error ε, and we will feel justified to ignore such numbers by setting them equal to zero. But what if those numbers are small but not quite as small as to be unambiguously assignable to numerical computation errors? Can we remove smaller eigenvalues or singular values to emphasize the main features of a phenomenon, and at what cost? What is the signal distortion that will be incurred when we do so?

While the latter questions may not always be easy to answer, many applications have appeared in the past few decades that use this approach, and these have found uses in many areas of science, especially in the "softer" sciences such as psychology and economics, but also in chemistry, where they are often considered part of *chemometrics*. This is a large and active area of current research that cannot be treated here, and we will therefore merely highlight some of the main ideas and mechanics involved.

Eigenvalue or singular value filtering are relatively straightforward when we select (by whatever criterion) a cut-off in the (absolute value of the) eigenvalues, or in the (always positive) singular values, below which they are replaced by zeroes, and then proceed to analyze the so filtered data. This approach is therefore analogous to Fourier transform filtering with a sharp cut-off window, but the resulting signal distortion is of course different, because it is done in the eigenvalue/singular value domain rather than in the frequency domain. It can often lead to useful results, but without clear guidelines it is prone to misuse. Fortunately, we can reconstitute the corresponding, filtered data and compare them with the original input, which will give us an idea of the severity of the distortion versus the magnitude of the (estimated or experimentally determined) noise. Below we will briefly illustrate this approach.

The procedure is as follows. We take a square matrix **S** that has a large spread of eigenvalues or, more generally, a rectangular matrix **R** with a wide distribution of singular values, replace the smallest eigenvalue(s) or singular value(s) by zeroes, then use the so-modified matrices Σ' or Λ' together with the originally associated vectors to compute the correspondingly modified input matrices **S'** or **R'**. When the resulting changes are smaller than the measured or estimated experimental noise, this approach would seem justifiable, although we really compare apples and pears by comparing a systematic bias (due to removing eigenvalues or singular values) with (often predominantly random) experimental errors. Less stringent criteria may well be appropriate, depending on our purpose: we may only want to extract some general information from a data set, such as the main factors driving a particular effect, or determine to what sub-category of a data set a particular data point belongs. Here we will not go into such details.

In exercise 10.19.1 we will consider a small rectangular matrix such as **R** in (10.19.1) which you will recognize is singular, because its third column is twice the second minus the first or, in terms of rows, the third is twice the second minus the first, etc., viz.

$$\mathbf{R} = \begin{bmatrix} -2 & -1 & 0 \\ 1 & 2 & 3 \\ 4 & 5 & 6 \\ 7 & 8 & 9 \end{bmatrix} \tag{10.19.1}$$

Exercise 10.19.1:

(1) In a new spreadsheet enter the matrix R in B2:D5.

(2) In B8:D11 use SVDU to compute the vectors **U**, in F3:H5 find the singular values with SVDD, and in F8:H10 calculate **V** with SVDV. Figure 10.19.1 indicates the specific instructions used.

(3) The smallest singular value, in cell H5, should of course be zero for a singular matrix, and is clearly the result of numerical errors in the algorithms used. Therefore, in cell B14 place the instruction =F3, in C15 put =G4, and place zeroes in C14, D14, B15, D15, B16, C16, and D16. This matrix B14:D16 is the corrected value Σ' of Σ. (Strictly speaking, we should remove the effect of the smallest singular value by inversion of Σ while setting $1/\sigma_{min}$ equal to zero. This avoids overflow or, at minimum, a very large value for $1/\sigma_{min}$, just what we do *not* want.)

(4) In F13:H16 verify that $\mathbf{R}' = \mathbf{U} \, \Sigma' \, \mathbf{V}^T$.

(5) Without having to expand the column widths you can check in J6:L9 that the differences between **R'** and **R** are indeed of the order of the common round-off errors, i.e., negligibly small compared to those in **R**. You can also compute p_κ of R in cell K3, showing that **R** is indeed very ill-conditioned.

(6) Now copy A1:L16 to A18, and make a minor change in one of the values in B19:D22. Also adjust the descriptions of the specific matrix instructions. Then, separately, copy I16:L20 to I33. In Fig. 10.19.1 the value in C22 is altered, but you can instead use any other element(s) of R, just as you could have started with any other set of numbers in B2:D5 that would give you a singular matrix. But let's stick with a specific example.

(7) When the value 8 in C22 is changed to, say, 8.000001 or 7.999999, and we monitor it and the difference matrix in F30:H33 to five decimals beyond the decimal point, no change will be on display. When you remove one zero from 8.000001 to make it 8.00001, it will show in both B19:D22 and in F30:H33, without any visible changes in the other matrix elements, i.e., **R'** appears to be tracking **R** correctly. When you look at the differences in J34:L37 you will recognize that this is because these differences are still too small to show.

(8) But when you delete one more zero from C22 by giving it the value 8.0001, the other values in **R** will start showing the distortion introduced by deleting the smallest singular value (shown in cell H22), which is now eleven orders of magnitude larger than its counterpart in cell H5 for a truly singular matrix **R**.

(9) In J30:L33 use the instruction =MProd(B25:D28,F20:H22,MT(F25:H27)) to compute **R** as $\mathbf{U} \, \Sigma \, \mathbf{V}^T$, which reproduces the individual elements of **R** in B19:D22 to within 1E-14, but that deletion of the smallest singular value causes errors of the order of 1E-5 in **R'**, i.e., the distortion in **R'** is almost twice as large as one would (mistakenly) expect on the basis of p_κ. Also note the relative changes in the remaining singular values in Σ'. This stage of the exercise is illustrated in Fig. 10.19.1.

(10) Removing more zeroes, or otherwise moving the matrix **R** in B19:D22 further away from ill-conditioning, leads to larger distortion with respect to the original data, e.g., a 1% change in cell C22, from 8 to 8.08, will cause similar relative errors in all elements of F30:H33. This distortion is distributed among all elements of **R'**. Play with this and the other elements of **R** in B19:D22 to get a feel for how such errors propagate.

It was shown by C. Eckart & G. Young (*Psychometrika* 1 (1936) 211) that the above is indeed the optimal method (in a least squares sense) to approximate a given matrix by another one of lower rank. And our numerical examples suggest that the resulting distortion is spread rather widely amongst the matrix elements.

As already indicated, whether such distortion is acceptable or not depends on the purpose behind the calculation. When quantitative conclusions must be drawn, a reasonable criterion might be whether or not such distortion exceeds the experimental uncertainty in the data, and you now know how to estimate such distortion. When a more qualitative conclusion is needed, a more lenient criterion might be appropriate.

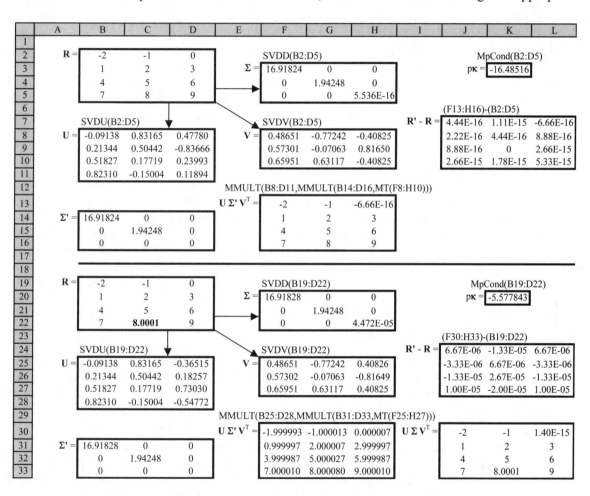

Fig. 10.19.1: The annotated spreadsheet of exercise 10.19.1.

We end this section by mentioning a few of the many applications of singular value decomposition, merely to illustrate how many such applications it has found, in a wide array of fields, especially after convenient computer algorithms for numerical SVD were developed by E. Kogbetliantz (Quart. Appl. Math 13 (1955) 123), M. R. Hestenes (*SIAM J.* 6 (1958) 51) and, especially, by G. H. Golub et al. (*SIAM J. Num. Anal.* 2 (1965) 205, *SIAM J. ACM.* 12 (1969) 564, *Numerische Math.* 14 (1970) 403).

At a purely mathematical level, SVD is

(1) the most useful generalization to rectangular matrices of the eigenvalue decomposition of square matrices;

(2) a practical approach to determine the *rank* of a matrix, i.e., its number of independent singular values (where singular values σ of the order of or less than ε times the largest singular value are usually not counted in numerical analysis) and associated singular vectors;

(3) a means to measure the conditioning of a matrix, the condition number κ; and

(4) a way to estimate, through its $p\kappa$, up to how many decimals may lose significance upon inverting that matrix.

So far we have emphasized the relative immunity of singular value decomposition to ill-conditioning in connection with least squares analysis. In statistics, SVD is used primarily to find lower-rank approximations of matrices. Examples are principal component analysis, partial least squares, canonical correlation analysis, reduced rank regression, and many related and/or derivative methods. In signal analysis, SVD is used for pattern recognition; in language analysis for latent semantic indexing, in weather forecasting for estimating the relative importance of small perturbations for developing weather patterns, in the analysis of photographs for correcting perspective distortion. Some applications in physics and chemistry are, e.g., the Schmidt decomposition to determine whether two quantum states are entangled, and the Kabsch/Procrustes analysis to compute the optimal rotations (again in a least squares sense) of matching two sets of data points that, e.g., may represent the locations of atomic nuclei in a molecule or of amino acid residues in a protein. In short, the applications of SVD are numerous and diverse, and will become even more so as general familiarity with the method grows.

10.20 Summary

In principle, a spreadsheet is a near-ideal platform for one- and two-dimensional matrix operations, and the increase in spreadsheet area in Excel 2007, especially its widening from 256 to 16K columns, promises to make it even more suitable for this purpose, although many operations on large matrices will be too slow on the spreadsheet except for occasional use. Unfortunately, Microsoft provides only a meager set of matrix operations, which it has not updated since its market introduction in 1985, now more than a quarter of a century ago. The resulting void was filled admirably by Volpi's wide selection of additional matrix functions and macros. Readers with a need for matrix operations will find many more examples in the associated, quite extensive yet down-to-earth documentation accompanying these downloads: the *Tutorial of Numerical Analysis for Matrix.xla*, and the *Reference Guide for Matrix.xla*. We have especially emphasized least squares applications, as well as those involving eigenfunctions and their generalization in terms of singular value decomposition. The exercises in the latter areas can also provide practice in handling complex numbers, vectors, and matrices on the spreadsheet. Linear algebra is used increasingly in solving all kinds of practical problems, and Volpi's add-ins are bound to facilitate a greater use of Excel in science, engineering, and statistics. The advantages of the spreadsheet in its widespread distribution, direct visual display, and ease of learning, must of course be balanced against the higher computational speed and larger choice of functions of dedicated programs such as Matlab.

Matrix operations are the heart and soul of *linear* algebra. But this term should not be taken to imply that all matrix operations are linear. Matrix inversion, e.g., is nonlinear in the same sense that the value of the algebraic inverse $1/x$ is not directly proportional to the value of the number x. Moreover, as we saw in section 10.10, mutual dependencies between variables (as expressed in their covariances v_{ij} and associated linear correlation coefficients r_{ij}, or in the ill-conditioning of one or more matrices) can lead to wild fluctuations and to seeming "outliers", as the result of the rather minuscule "noise" from computer round-off errors in floating-point arithmetic. In that sense they are somewhat similar to natural phenomena, such as the movements of tectonic plates, which are usually smooth but now and then lead to violent "catastrophes" such as earthquakes, tsunamis, and volcanic eruptions, events that we know from past experience to occur occasionally, but for which the statistics are too sporadic to allow for predictions with much accuracy in either space or time.

There are of course many systems that have multiple, mutually more or less strongly dependent variables: the movement of tectonic plates is an example from nature, but the economy is clearly a man-made one. Models for such systems are invariably based on past experience, and since catastrophes occur only occasionally and follow poorly understood statistics, they are hard to model and consequently are often left out. One should therefore be highly skeptical of systems of equations representing moderately understood phenomena, and the more so the more complicated these phenomena are, regardless of the sophistication of the matrix algebra used. If you consider the disappointing retrospective power of chemical analysis of single chemical species under carefully controlled conditions, as illustrated in section 4.26, what might a similar, critical test of the predictive power of large-scale economics look like?

It is tempting to put the above observations in a more general context. Much of our economy nowadays relies on econometric models, and we have recently learned, at a great cost to society, what can happen when those models are inadequate. As Gerd Gigerenzer, author of "Calculated Risk", likes to say, such models typically do well at representing the past (with which they have been calibrated), but have problems predicting the future, because they do not incorporate unforeseen events.

Some of the financial catastrophes have been defended as unforeseeable, "ten sigma" outliers, but that is the typical language of combining *mutually independent* Gaussian distributions. Econometric models will often be based on many simultaneous, empirical equations, and will use these to generate a prediction. But even assuming that the input data are accurate (which empirical data seldom are), that the models are also correct (how can we know?), and that they were indeed valid "predictors" of the past at the time they were made, over time laws will be amended, rule enforcement may become lax, circumstances change, and so will the coefficients in those equations. Insofar as such changes affect the coefficients of near-singular matrices, they will occasionally lead to otherwise quite unexpected results. Earthquakes do happen, as do tsunamis and volcanic eruptions. And so do stock market crashes and other man-made disasters. The problem doesn't seem to lie so much in assuming a particular distribution of unavoidable fluctuations, as suggested by N. N. Talib in his *"Black Swan"* (Random House 2007), but in the profoundly nonlinear behavior of near-singular matrices, as easily hidden in large-scale econometric models. Such near-singularities reflect strongly correlated phenomena, of which stock market evaluations are a prime example, since they are affected both by hard data and by herd ("bull" or "bear") psychology. Unless we deal with systems that are inherently stable, the possibility that they can become instable cannot be discounted. And unless we realize the uncertainty and collinearity of our input data and assumptions, the combination of oversimplified computer models, wishful thinking and/or greed and hubris of some will again get all of us into trouble.

There is yet another factor to consider. While outliers are by definition rare events, their *risk* is the *product* of their low probability times their potential consequences. Rejecting outliers just because their probability of occurrence is low, regardless of the risk involved, is irresponsible, just as it would be to abolish the building codes in San Francisco because earthquakes there don't occur very frequently.

10.21 For further reading

There are many good introductory books on matrix algebra. An outstanding, highly readable example is that of C. D. Meyer, *Matrix Analysis and Applied Linear Algebra* (SIAM, Philadelphia 2000).

More than half of this chapter is devoted to the description of some of Volpi's add-in matrix functions and macros. For more details read his *Tutorial of Numerical Analysis for Matrix.xla*, and the *Reference Guide for Matrix.xla*.

Chapter *11*

Spreadsheet reliability

This chapter will focus on three types of spreadsheet-related errors: those that are rather easy to make (but with care can often be avoided) on a spreadsheet, those that are hidden in Excel, and those that result from Excel's adherence to the IEEE-754 double-precision protocol.

This does not imply that any of these are the most significant errors you will encounter while processing your measurements in Excel. Errors can be caused by nonrepresentative samples, deficient experimental protocols, errors in data acquisition or data entry, instrumental distortion, inappropriate models, etc. All of these can result in inaccurate results, but the spreadsheet does not cause any of them.

Then there are experimental errors, often due to uncontrolled parameters such as temperature, pressure, truncation or round-off errors in analog-to-digital converters, etc., or to more fundamental fluctuations such as stochastic variations. These are typically put in the category of experimental imprecision and the spreadsheet, again, is not to blame for any of them.

Now back to the spreadsheet. The spreadsheet itself can certainly contribute to its unreliability, in the form of numerical approaches that magnify truncation errors, through the display of meaningless digits, through built-in functions and macros that sometimes yield faulty results, and through the ease of modifying the spreadsheet after it has been tested. Such errors, and especially ways to recognize and avoid many of them, are a main focus of this chapter. More often than most of us would like to admit, our spreadsheets also contain (possibly consequential) coding errors. While it doesn't seem humanly possible to create a nontrivial spreadsheet or to write a substantial amount of computer code without errors, we can often find and correct most of them before they do real damage. In section 11.1 we will consider some practices that make it easier to identify and remove many of those errors, preferably during the writing and testing stages. It often helps to have others check the code; in this respect, open-access code is unmatched because anyone so inclined can add to its debugging.

11.1 Good spreadsheet practices

For many scientific problems, Excel facilitates calculations that otherwise would require dedicated computer programs. The easy accessibility of Excel, its user-friendliness, its many scientific functions, and its convenient graphics, have converted many scientists into do-it-yourself spreadsheet programmers. This has greatly helped to lower the activation barrier to computer use. But every advance comes with its own downside. In the case of Excel, the very flexibility that makes it so appealing to the novice can lead to spreadsheets that are so unstructured that it will be difficult (after some time even for their own authors) to follow their logic. Such spreadsheets are very hard to troubleshoot. It has been established that most large spreadsheets contain errors, and some of these have been quite serious and, where money is involved, costly.

In this the spreadsheet is, of course, not alone: like all human creations, computer programs contain errors, often benign, but sometimes catastrophic. Typical computer programs contain between 2 to 10 errors per 100 lines of code. Typical spreadsheets in business and finance have been found to contain similar error frequencies. There are no reasons to believe that scientific spreadsheets will do any better. (The opposite might even be true, since typically less money is involved, and scrutiny may therefore be more relaxed.) Below we list some aspects that are specific to the spreadsheet.

(1) Most scientific spreadsheet users are not trained in computer programming, and may therefore lack the professional discipline taught with that craft.

(2) It is not customary, as it is with commercial software, or even with financial spreadsheets, to have someone else validate your spreadsheet. Consequently, logic errors that might be caught by a reviewer are more likely to remain.

(3) It is seldom required, as it is with commercial software, to document the operation of a spreadsheet. That operation will be clear to you as you generate it, but will be much less obvious some time later, and even less conspicuous to someone else.

(4) An obvious invitation to problems is the ease with which an existing, working spreadsheet can be modified, by its creator or by subsequent users, *after* it has been tested. Especially error-prone are row and/or column insertions and deletions, which may play havoc with off-screen parts of the spreadsheet.

(5) Unlike most computer programs, spreadsheets can accept data uncritically, i.e., they need not perform checks on the input data, enhancing the likelihood of entering incorrect data, or of entering data incorrectly.

(6) Macros don't need to leave *any* trace of their involvement beyond the numbers they generate, making spreadsheets in which such macros were used well nigh impossible to troubleshoot.

For the above reasons, it is absolutely necessary to document any spreadsheet that you intend to keep for later use, and even more so for any spreadsheet that you can anticipate others will or may want to use.

Then there is the nasty problem of Excel's 'helpfulness' in guessing what the input data represent, and making corresponding, often *irreversible* changes, but *without alerting the user to the changes made*. When you enter the number 1/3, Excel may convert it into 3-Jan, without asking you whether this is what you meant. If you subsequently spot the problem and try to correct it by specifying the cell format as a number rather than a date, e.g., with Format ⇨ Cells ⇨ Number ⇨ Fraction ⇨ Up to one digit, you may find 40546 in 2011, 40911 in 2012, and so on. The original input is *irretrievably* gone, replaced by Excel's internal date serial number for that day in a particular year, counting from in Jan. 1, 1900 as day 1. (In this particular example, you could have avoided the problem by entering the data as =1/3, or by formatting the cell ahead of data entry.) We already encountered this type of pernicious problem in section 1.8, and the only solution is to be alert to such problems, and always verify your input data.

While the following steps will not prevent all errors from occurring, they might help to minimize potential problems with your spreadsheets.

(1) Keep the spreadsheet compact, and if possible avoid using more than one sheet per problem. If not modified, figures copied to another sheet respond to their sheet of origin. Formulas referring to data on other sheets are awkward because they must specify the sheet. Excel's built-in auditing tools do not work beyond their sheet of origin.

(2) Organize the spreadsheet with a clear, logical, and therefore easy-to-follow layout, with the flow from input data through processing to output either going to the right and/or, for a larger spreadsheet, going down. This implies that, in terms of the auditing "dependents" tools, the arrows should mostly point in these rightward and/or downward directions, and in their reverse for "precedents". (The only clear exception to this would be for the summary tables, which are often best placed at the very top of the spreadsheet, together with the summary figures.)

(3) Set aside spreadsheet space to document what the spreadsheet supposedly does, and how it does it.

(4) Throughout the spreadsheet, liberally use headings, block labels, cell and block frames and/or colors, to help illustrate the meanings of the data and the general flow of the analysis. When using colors, remember that black-and-white copies will often show light colors as white, and dark colors as black, but usually can print gray.

526

(5) Liberally use cell comments to document the outputs of macros and other special routines that otherwise leave no trace, in order to indicate where they came from.

(6) Always double-check that your input data were entered correctly, and were left unaltered by Excel.

(7) Use Excel's extensive auditing tools to make sure that the data flow is as intended.

(8) Place constants in easily found, clearly labeled cells or tables, so that updating them requires only one change, and thereby avoid the risk of uneven implementation.

(9) Avoid ambiguous formulas, such as =F3/F4/F5, but instead use brackets: =F3/(F4*F5).

(10) When writing VBA code, always use Option Explicit to minimize the risk that typos create phantom parameters, which might be difficult to identify during troubleshooting.

(11) Test your spreadsheet with data for which you know the end result of the computation, as well as with numbers that are non-integer and not exactly expressible as binary numbers, and over the widest possible range(s).

(12) Be very careful when modifying an existing spreadsheet after it has been tested. Especially adding or removing rows and/or columns can have many unintended consequences in spreadsheet areas beyond what is shown at that time on your monitor screen.

(13) Be as open as possible about your code: this way your friends rather than your competitors will find most of the errors you overlooked.

11.1.1 Organization

Different problems may require different spreadsheet layouts. Still, a few general suggestions may be helpful here. The Statistical Services Centre of the University of Reading, UK, has published a set of common-sense recommendations downloadable from http://www.reading.ac.uk/ssc/home.html.

(1) For spreadsheet documentation, set aside a fixed number of rows at the top of the spreadsheet. Use its top row for a title and date, and the next rows for a brief narrative, describing the function of the spreadsheet, its actions, where to place input data, and any additional information needed by a user unfamiliar with this particular spreadsheet. Include the date and method of testing and validating the spreadsheet, and any macros needed in operating the spreadsheet. Also list any subsequent modifications, with their dates. For a complicated calculation you may want to include a simple diagram outlining the data flow. Complicated equations can be displayed in the spreadsheet heading by typing them in the Equation Editor (the same as used in Word, and also used for equations shown in this book), available through Insert ⇨ Object ⇨ Microsoft Equation. (In order to save space, I have not followed this advice to self-document the small sample spreadsheets shown in this book, which has already become obese. But I can assure you that I do follow it myself in my research, and urge you to do likewise.)

(2) Use the available visual spreadsheet tools, such as colored, boldfaced and/or italic fonts, colored cell backgrounds, frames around data blocks, and/or empty rows and columns, to emphasize sets of data that functionally belong together. Use dark colors for fonts, light colors for cell backgrounds, but use the latter sparingly if the spreadsheet would otherwise become too gaudy.

(3) Use Insert ⇨ Comments to place relevant information with particular cells or cell blocks. In the default mode, the comment only shows when the pointer lingers over the red triangle in the top-right corner of the cell. Many of the macros in the MacroBundle use this method to identify the routine used, and to provide information regarding the input data, operational parameters, and output array used.

(4) If the spreadsheet requires that input data be placed in a particular location, then label that place (cell, array) with name and color, and use Data ⇨ Validation to ensure the correct input data type. You can, e.g., specify a minimum and maximum value for numerical data, and make sure that dates, times, text strings, etc., are not entered when numbers are expected, and vice versa. Invalid input data that happened to come in indirectly, 'under the wire' as it were, can be visualized with Tools ⇨ Auditing ⇨ Show Auditing Toolbar ⇨ Circle Invalid Data.

11.1.2 Auditing

Excel contains several helpful tools for use in auditing the spreadsheet. The first of these is the color coding that appears when you click on a cell containing a formula, and then click on that formula in the formula box. The colors shown correspond to those that will now outline the cells and cell blocks involved, provided that these are on the same sheet. This gives you a quick overview of the input data used in the highlighted cell, and may help to spot cells that are incorrectly providing input, such as can happen after a botched spreadsheet modification.

A more powerful set of auditing tools can be found under Tools ⇨ Auditing, where you will find Trace Precedents, Trace Dependents, Trace Error, Remove All Arrows, and Show Auditing Toolbar. The latter presents a few more options, including circling data identified as invalid with Data ⇨ Validation. The auditing feature replaces the Info Window used in versions preceding Excel 97.

Of these auditing tools, those for tracing precedents and dependents are the most useful, as they show with arrows which cells or cell blocks contribute to the value shown in a cell, and which cells or cell blocks in turn refer directly to that value. (Again this is restricted to the active sheet. When a precedent cell or cell block is located on another sheet, an arrow starting from an icon depicting a spreadsheet appears as the source of the information, alerting you to an off-sheet precedent, but the particular sheet involved is neither identified nor shows the tracer arrows. There is seldom a good reason to refer to other worksheets: if data from another worksheet are needed, copy them to the present worksheet, label them as such, and use these copies. With the choices available under Tools ⇨ Auditing you can remove all tracing arrows; with the Auditing Toolbar you can remove the arrows somewhat more selectively.

Errors are often introduced when a spreadsheet is extended or modified to accommodate new needs. Especially the insertion or deletion of new rows and columns may disrupt other parts of the spreadsheet, especially those outside the limited field of view of the monitor. In this respect, cut&paste (Ctrl∪x & Ctrl∪v) behaves differently from copy&paste (Ctrl∪c & Ctrl∪v)! Using the tracer arrows of the auditing tools can reveal anomalies and other artifacts created with such 'corrections' or 'updates'.

11.2 Excel's functions and macros

While much of the remainder of this chapter is about the numerical reliability of Excel itself, and how to improve it, this is, emphatically, *not* to suggest that that is the most common cause of unreliable data; in fact, it seldom is. A more probable order of importance of the various sources of spreadsheet errors might be (1) outright coding errors, (2) systematic errors in the data, such as might result from, e.g., poor sampling or lack of calibration, (3) flawed logic used in the data analysis, (4) experimental uncertainty, (5) faulty numerical procedures and (6) faulty Excel functions. Section 11.1 described some practices that can help minimize faulty code, or at least catch and correct some of those errors before they have consequences. A consideration of sampling bias and other sources of systematic errors lies well outside the context of this book (although deconvolution might help if sources of systematic error are identified after the measurements were taken), and chapters 2 through 8 have emphasized reducing random errors. We can say little about flawed logic, other than that it appears to be more common than you might think. Sections 11.3 through 11.8 will be devoted to some of the most prevalent sources of faulty numerical procedures, both on the spreadsheet, and in some of the (relatively few) cases in which the reliability of Excel functions is questionable.

The large number of built-in functions and macros is one of the features that make spreadsheets attractive for scientific data analysis. Most users will not question their reliability, but will assume that this aspect has been dealt with professionally, and that by now, more than a quarter century after their introduction, most errors have been weeded out. In many respects this is indeed the case, but there are still a fair number of exceptions. More disturbingly, many of these have been known and documented for years, but

Microsoft has been slow to correct them, even after recognizing them as such in its Knowledge Base. In fact, before Excel 2003, there were very few such corrections, and many well-known problems still persist. It is for this reason that Excel has earned a poor reputation among, e.g., statisticians.

Excel displays its numerical results in a flexible format of up to 15 decimals, regardless of their reliability. Many numerical procedures sharply reduce the number of significant figures in an answer, but Excel has no simple way to display which decimals are to be trusted, and which are not. This applies to all operations performed on the spreadsheet, as well as to the built-in Excel functions and macros. It would be ideal if all 15 decimals shown were correct, and we will see, starting in section 11.9, how this ideal is now within easy reach. But even without such more drastic action, it is useful to understand the most prevalent sources of such errors in numerical computations, both in Excel-provided functions and macros and in user-programmed code, and this will be the focus of the next few sections.

11.3 Cancellation errors

When we consider the four most basic mathematical operations, addition, subtraction, multiplication and division, the first two are typically learned first, and our greater ease and familiarity with them might suggest them to be the more reliable. However, in terms of numerical calculation they actually tend to be the more error-prone.

Beyond integers, only relatively few numbers can be represented exactly in the binary format in which the computer stores them. All other numbers are therefore represented with a small relative error, ε, in Excel typically of the order of 10^{-15}. In what follows we will make the usual assumption that these relative errors are indeed very much smaller than 1, so that we can neglect higher-order terms in ε.

Say that we want to multiply two numbers, a and b. Mathematically, this yields the product $a \times b$, but numerically we also have to consider their relative errors (because a and b will usually be manipulated by the cpu in their 64-bit binary representations), i.e., we have

$$a\,(1+\varepsilon_a) \times b\,(1+\varepsilon_b) = a \times b\,(1+\varepsilon_a+\varepsilon_b+\varepsilon_a\varepsilon_b) \approx a \times b\,(1+\varepsilon_a+\varepsilon_b) \qquad (11.3.1)$$

so that the resulting relative error is approximately the sum of the relative errors in a and b. Since both ε_a and ε_b are very much smaller than 1, the same will apply to their sum, i.e., $(1+\varepsilon_a+\varepsilon_b)$ will be close to 1, so that our answer will be close to $a \times b$.

For division we have a similar situation,

$$\frac{a(1+\varepsilon_a)}{b(1+\varepsilon_b)} = \frac{a}{b}(1+\varepsilon_a)(1-\varepsilon_b+\varepsilon_b^2-\varepsilon_b^3+\varepsilon_b^4-\cdots) \approx \frac{a}{b}\,(1+\varepsilon_a-\varepsilon_b) \qquad (11.3.2)$$

which is equally benign. But we have no such luck with addition or subtraction.

We only need to look at addition, because that will include subtraction as long as we don't specify the signs of a, b, and of the associated errors ε. Analogous to (11.3.1) and (11.3.2) we have for addition

$$a\,(1+\varepsilon_a) + b\,(1+\varepsilon_b) = (a+b)\left(1+\frac{a\varepsilon_a+b\varepsilon_b}{a+b}\right) = (a+b)\left(1+\frac{a}{a+b}\varepsilon_a+\frac{b}{a+b}\varepsilon_b\right) \qquad (11.3.3)$$

When a and b have the same sign, both $a/(a+b)$ and $b/(a+b)$ are always smaller than 1, and everything is fine. But when a and b have *different* signs, i.e., in what you normally would call a subtraction, all bets are off about the magnitudes of the multipliers of the ε's in (11.3.3). Especially when $a \approx -b$, so that a and b are much larger than $(a+b)$, the otherwise rather small errors (ε_a in a, and ε_b in b) can be magnified beyond recognition in the resulting value for $(a+b)$. This so-called *cancellation error* in additions and subtractions is one of the weak links in numerical computations. Fortunately, this type of error is often readily avoidable once we are aware of its existence and dangers.

11.4 The standard deviation

Perhaps no single feature of Excel has done more to make statisticians avoid it than its original implementation of the function StDev for the standard deviation, one of the most basic quantities of statistics. The sample standard deviation for fitting N repeat measurements of a single quantity q is given by (2.1.2), which we here repeat as

$$s = \sqrt{\frac{\sum\limits_{i=1}^{N}(q_i - a)^2}{N-1}} \qquad a = \frac{1}{N}\sum\limits_{i=1}^{N}q_i \qquad\qquad (11.4.1)$$

where q_i represents the ith measurement, and a the average of q_i over all N measurements. The expression in the numerator of (11.4.1) can be reformulated as

$$\sum_{i=1}^{N}(q_i - a)^2 = \sum_{i=1}^{N}\left(q_i^2 - 2aq_i + a^2\right) = \sum_{i=1}^{N}\left(q_i^2\right) - 2a\sum_{i=1}^{N}(q_i) + a^2 N$$

$$= \sum_{i=1}^{N}\left(q_i^2\right) - 2a\sum_{i=1}^{N}(q_i) + a\sum_{i=1}^{N}(q_i) = \sum_{i=1}^{N}\left(q_i^2\right) - a\sum_{i=1}^{N}(q_i)$$

so that (11.4.1) can be rewritten as

$$s = \sqrt{\frac{\sum\limits_{i=1}^{N}q_i^2 - \dfrac{1}{N}\left(\sum\limits_{i=1}^{N}q_i\right)^2}{N-1}} \qquad\qquad (11.4.2)$$

This second form, (11.4.2), was implemented on many early handheld calculators, because it only required three registers, one for counting up to N, the second for adding the terms q_i, and the third for summing the terms q_i^2. On these calculators, which had a very limited memory, direct implementation of (11.4.1) was not feasible, because that would require holding on to all individual q_i-values in order to determine a first, before the terms $(q_i - a)$ could be computed, while (11.4.2) did not pose such a problem. But even though (11.4.1) and (11.4.2) are *mathematically* equivalent, *numerically* they are not, because (11.4.1) keeps the differences $(q_i - a)$ small, whereas (11.4.2) involves differences between two large, near-equal sums of squares. Unfortunately, Microsoft initially based its Excel function StDev on (11.4.2) and, worse, waited until 2003 to upgrade that instruction to a numerically more accurate algorithm, long after the deficiency was pointed out, and even after Microsoft had acknowledged the problem in its KnowledgeBase. The self-documented spreadsheet of Fig. 11.4.1 illustrates this problem, using variations on the NIST StRD test data set Mavro as our test model. Its correct answer, 1, is transparent and easily tested. Cells E7, E12, etc. contain a simplified form of pE as defined in section 9.1, with an exclamation mark indicating a perfect score. The failures of (11.4.2) are emphasized in bold in cells E21:E22 and E31:E32.

It is clear from Fig. 11.4.1 that the problem with (11.4.2) in cell E21 lies in the values in E19 and E20, which have the same fifteen digits, so that their difference (F15-F16) in cell F17 is zero. In fact, since Excel carries 52 binary digits but in its display rounds those to 15 decimals, its zero may even be negative, as illustrated in cell E31 (to the amount of $-2.2E+12$, yet too small to show as a difference in E29 and E30) in which case taking the square root yields the error message #NUM!. Note that (11.4.1) produces correct answers even when the input values differ only in their least significant digits.

530

	A	B	C	D	E	F
1						
2		y	$y - y_{av}$		$y_{ref} = 1$	
3					**(11.4.1):**	
4		10000001	-1.0000	=B4-$E$4	10000002.0000	=SUM(B4:B6)/COUNT(B4:B6)
5		10000003	1.0000	=B5-$E$4	2.0000	=SUMSQ(C4:C6)
6		10000002	0.0000	=B6-$E$4	1.0000	=SQRT(E5/(COUNT(B4:B6)-1))
7					!	=IF(E6=1," ! ",-LOG(ABS((E6-$F$2)/$F$2)))
8					**(11.4.2):**	
9					300000120000014	=SUMSQ(B4:B6)
10					300000120000012	=(SUM(B4:B6)^2)/COUNT(B4:B6)
11					1.0000	=SQRT((E9-E10)/(COUNT(B4:B6)-1))
12					!	=IF(E11=1," ! ",-LOG(ABS((E11-$F$2)/$F$2)))
13					**(11.4.1):**	
14		100000001	-1.0000	=B14-$E$14	100000002.0000	=SUM(B14:B16)/COUNT(B14:B16)
15		100000003	1.0000	=B15-$E$14	2.0000	=SUMSQ(C14:C16)
16		100000002	0.0000	=B16-$E$14	1.0000	=SQRT(E15/(COUNT(B14:B16)-1))
17					!	=IF(E16=1," ! ",-LOG(ABS((E16-$F$2)/$F$2)))
18					**(11.4.2):**	
19					30000001200000000	=SUMSQ(B14:B16)
20					30000001200000000	=(SUM(B14:B16)^2)/COUNT(B14:B16)
21					**0.0000**	=SQRT((E19-E20)/(COUNT(B14:B16)-1))
22					**0**	=IF(E21=1," ! ",-LOG(ABS((E21-$F$2)/$F$2)))
23					**(11.4.1):**	
24		100000000000001	-1.0000	=B24-$E$24	100000000000002	=SUM(B24:B26)/COUNT(B24:B26)
25		100000000000003	1.0000	=B25-$E$24	2.0000	=SUMSQ(C24:C26)
26		100000000000002	0.0000	=B26-$E$24	1.0000	=SQRT(E25/(COUNT(B24:B26)-1))
27					!	=IF(E26=1," ! ",-LOG(ABS((E26-$F$2)/$F$2)))
28					**(11.4.2):**	
29					3.00000000000012E+28	=SUMSQ(B24:B26)
30					3.00000000000012E+28	=(SUM(B24:B26)^2)/COUNT(B24:B26)
31					**#NUM!**	=SQRT((E29-E30)/(COUNT(B24:B26)-1))
32					**#NUM!**	=IF(E31=1," ! ",-LOG(ABS((E31-$F$2)/$F$2)))

Fig. 11.4.1: A spreadsheet illustrating the mathematically equivalent equations (11.4.1) and (11.4.2) used in pre-2003 and post-2003 Excel respectively to implement the instruction StDev for the sample standard deviation.

11.5   The quadratic formula

The well-known quadratic formula $ax^2 + bx + c = 0$ has two roots,

$$x_{\pm} = \frac{-b \pm \sqrt{b^2 - 4ac}}{2a} \tag{11.5.1}$$

Equation (11.5.1) is *mathematically* correct, as was (11.4.2) in the preceding example, but it can yield poor or nonsensical *numerical* results when b^2 is much larger than $4ac$, so that the positive square root approaches $+b$, in which case the numerator can become too small for the computer to represent, leading to a catastrophic cancellation error. Just try (11.5.1) in Excel with, e.g., $a = 1$, $b = 10^6$, and $c = 10^{-6}$, in which case x_+ is found as $-7.27595761418343E-12$ instead of $-1.00000000000000E-11$. And for $a = 1$, $b = 10^6$, and $c = 10^{-7}$ we find $x_+ = 0$ rather than the correct answer, $-1.00000000000000E-13$.

How do we know the "correct" answers? By expanding the square root in terms of the series

$$\sqrt{1 + \delta} = 1 + \frac{1}{2}\delta - \frac{1 \times 1}{2 \times 4}\delta^2 + \frac{1 \times 1 \times 3}{2 \times 4 \times 6}\delta^3 - \frac{1 \times 1 \times 3 \times 5}{2 \times 4 \times 6 \times 8}\delta^4 + \cdots$$

531

which converges rapidly for $|\delta| \ll 1$, so that

$$x_+ = \frac{-b+b\sqrt{1-4ac/b^2}}{2a} = \frac{-b+b\left(1-\dfrac{2ac}{b^2}-\dfrac{2a^2c^2}{b^4}-\dfrac{4a^3c^3}{b^6}-\cdots\right)}{2a}$$

$$= -\frac{c}{b}-\frac{ac^2}{b^3}-\frac{2a^2c^3}{b^5}-\cdots \qquad \text{for } 4ac/b^2 \ll 1 \tag{11.5.2}$$

When we multiply both numerator and denominator in (11.5.1) by $-b-\sqrt{(b^2-4ac)}$ we obtain

$$x_\pm = \frac{-2c}{b \pm \sqrt{b^2-4ac}} \tag{11.5.3}$$

which transfers the problem to x_-. For the same parameter values, Excel in this case cannot find an answer, because it now computes the denominator as zero.

The above are obvious examples of cancellation errors. In this simple case, the errors can be avoided by using, e.g., the pair of expressions

$$x_1 = \frac{-2c}{-b+\text{sign}(b)\times\sqrt{b^2-4ac}} \tag{11.5.4}$$

$$x_2 = \frac{b+\text{sign}(b)\times\sqrt{b^2-4ac}}{-2a} \tag{11.5.5}$$

where the factor sign $(b) = b/|b|$ kicks in when b is negative. Equations (11.5.4) and (11.5.5) therefore provide a *workaround* for this problem. An equivalent alternative would be code such as

```
Discr = Sqr(b ^ 2 - 4 * a * c)
If b > 0 Then y = -0.5 * (b + Discr) Else y = -0.5 * (b - Discr)
x1 = c / y
x2 = y / a
```

where we first compute the larger root y, and then find the smaller one using the property $x_1 x_2 = c/a$.

Here are some more examples of cancellation errors, taken from W. Gautschi, *Numerical Analysis*, Birkhäuser (1997).

Exercise 11.5.1:
(1) Make a spreadsheet with four columns: one for a, one for b, one for $(a-b)$^2, and one for $a^2-2*a*b+b$^2.
(2) In its first row of data, enter $a = 33554430$, and in the ten rows below it, increment a by 1.
(3) In the second column, compute b as $a-1$, and in the next two columns, compute $(a-b)^2$ and $a^2-2ab+b^2$ respectively.
(4) Are $(a-b)^2$ and $a^2-2ab+b^2$ mathematically and/or numerically identical? Explain what you observed by substituting $b = a-1$ in $(a-b)^2$ and $a^2-2ab+b^2$ respectively. See also appendix D.10.

Exercise 11.5.2:
(1) For small values of δ, the expression $y = \sqrt{(x+\delta)} - \sqrt{x}$ is a likely source of cancellation error. Multiplication of both sides by $\sqrt{(x+\delta)} + \sqrt{x}$ plus the realization that $[\sqrt{(x+\delta)} - \sqrt{x}] \times [\sqrt{(x+\delta)} + \sqrt{x}] = (x+\delta) - x = \delta$ leads to the mathematically equivalent expression $y = \delta/[\sqrt{(x+\delta)} + \sqrt{x}]$, which does not involve a difference.
(2) Use the spreadsheet to compute y using both formulas for $x = 1$ and $\delta = 1, 10^{-1}, 10^{-2}$, etc., and see how small a value of δ will still get you an answer with either formula. What factor limits each range?

Exercise 11.5.3:
(1) Use the spreadsheet to calculate $y = \cos(x+\delta) - \cos(x)$ for $x = 0$ and $x = \pi/2$, with δ decreasing a factor of 10 at each step.
(2) Alternatively, use the mathematically equivalent expression $y = -2\sin(\delta/2)\sin(x+\delta/2)$, and compare the two. Clearly, the method that avoids calculating a difference between two nearly equal numbers yields the better results.
(3) You might expect $\cos(x+\delta)$ to become indistinguishable from $\cos(x)$ for $\delta < 10^{-15}$, but the computation under point (1) fails much earlier. Can you explain why that might be the case? Hint: consider how the computer computes the cosine.

11.6 Accumulation errors

In cancellation errors, as in computing $a - b$ where $a \approx b$, the numbers themselves partially cancel, but the errors don't necessarily follow suit. But while differences between large, near-equal numbers are a well-known source of errors, addition is not always error-free either. It is quite common to get large errors by systematically adding quite small ones, while the primary answer stays more or less constant. The effect is, of course, further enhanced when the value of the function itself decreases as the errors add up. We already encountered such errors in section 7.1 and, more dramatically, in section 7.12. In both those cases, we used numerical simulations, and the functions used contained no 'experimental' errors. Below is another example of such an *accumulation* of errors, taken from G. Hämmerlin & K.-H. Hoffmann, *Numerical Mathematics*, Springer (1991).

Assume that we need to evaluate integrals of the type

$$I_n = \int_0^1 \frac{x^n}{x+5} dx \qquad (11.6.1)$$

for different values of the positive integer n, and realize that this can be done by using the recursion

$$I_n + 5I_{n-1} = \int_0^1 \frac{x^n + 5x^{n-1}}{x+5} dx = \int_0^1 x^{n-1} dx = \frac{1}{n} \qquad (11.6.2)$$

It is easy to find the first term of (11.6.1),

$$I_0 = \int_0^1 \frac{x^0}{x+5} dx = \int_0^1 \frac{1}{x+5} dx = \ln \frac{6}{5} \qquad (11.6.3)$$

so that we can use

$$I_n = \frac{1}{n} - 5I_{n-1} \qquad (11.6.4)$$

to evaluate I_n for successively larger values of n, as illustrated below.

Exercise 11.6.1:

(1) Make a spreadsheet with two columns: one for n, one for I_n.
(2) In the column for n, deposit values from 0 to 25.
(3) In the second column, in the row for $n = 0$, place the instruction =LN(6/5).
(4) In the next row of the second column, for $n = 1$, deposit the instruction compute I_1 as $1/n - 5I_0$, and copy this instruction down the column.
(5) Plot the results.

There is clearly something wrong here: integrating x between 0 and 1 for positive values of n cannot possibly yield a negative result, yet that is what you will find for even values of n above 20, where the computed function will start to swing wildly.

Because this is caused by the accumulation of small errors in I, each time multiplied by 5, we might instead want to take the opposite tack, starting from high n-values on down, using

$$I_n = \left(\frac{1}{n+1} - I_{n+1} \right) \Big/ 5 \qquad (11.6.5)$$

But in that case, how do we start the process? Actually, it doesn't much matter: almost any reasonable guess value will do! Just try it.

Exercise 11.6.1 (continued):

(6) Add one or more columns, and on the bottom line place numbers such as 0, or even 1 or −1.
(7) On the penultimate line express (11.6.5) in code.
(8) Copy that code up to the top row, for $n = 0$.
(9) Add these new data to the plot.
(10) Compare the answers in the top row, where the known answer is ln(6/5).

Now here is the surprise: despite our quite arbitrary starting value for I_{25}, the resulting value for I_0 is right-on. Even when we start with more outrageous values, such as $I_{25} = +1$ or -1, the results will reach the correct answers for much smaller n-values, after some initial oscillations. This is so because these starting values are well within the amplitudes obtained with (11.6.4), which yields $I_{25} = +11.84$. The results for n from 1 to 25 are actually better for larger starting numbers n_{max} when the value of $I_{n_{max}}$ is kept constant at, say, zero. In using this recurrence formula, it is apparently more important to keep the errors down than to have a good initial guess value.

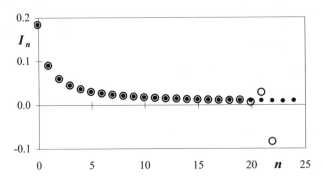

Fig. 11.6.1: Results of the recursive solution of (11.6.1) starting at $n = 0$ from the known result $I_0 = \ln(6/5)$ (large open circles), or starting at $n = 25$ with the guess value $I_{25} = 0$ and working one's way down to lower n-values (small solid circles). The oscillations in the results starting from $n = 0$ are clearly visible above $n \approx 20$. When working back from $n = 25$, the oscillations from (11.6.4) are smaller than those from (11.6.5) as long as the assumed value of I_{25} lies within the envelope of the results obtained with (11.6.4).

11.7 The inverse hyperbolic sine

Excel users who ignore cancellation and accumulation errors do so at their own risk. Such errors sometimes even crop up in Excel's built-in functions, for which users typically will not have access to the underlying algorithm, and over which they therefore have little control.

A careful study of the numerical precision of Excel's many statistical functions by Cook, Cox, Dainton & Harris, *NPL Report CISE*27/99, downloadable from http://www.npl.co.uk/ssfm/download/documents/cise 27_99.pdf, found that the computation of the inverse hyperbolic sine, arsinh(x), gave small, seemingly random errors for x-values between -100 and 0. The reported relative errors were rather inconsequential, affecting only the last few decimals, but they suggested that there might be a systematic problem.

In this case, a simple solution suggests itself: use of the property

$$\text{arsinh}(-x) = -\text{arsinh}(x) \tag{11.7.1}$$

should eliminate the problem. And so it does. Moreover, when we instead apply the usual formula

$$\text{arsinh}(x) = \ln\left(x + \sqrt{x^2 + 1}\right) \tag{11.7.2}$$

we recover the erroneous results reported by Cook et al., *point for point*. Clearly, for $x < 0$, (11.7.2) sets a numerical trap similar to that for $b < 0$ in (11.5.1), and Excel falls right into it. A simple fix, therefore, would be to check the sign of x, and then use (11.7.1) for $x < 0$.

Now that we are at it, we might as well look at the function over its entire range. Even though the function arsinh(x) has only one continuous argument, x, that argument can assume an infinity of values between the IEEE-754 limits of, approximately, -1.8×10^{308} and $+1.8 \times 10^{308}$. We will therefore take representative samples to test our results. In the present case this is relatively easy, since arsinh(x) is a continuous, smoothly varying function of x.

534

But first, why would we need to go to such extreme values of x? The answer is that users might not be aware of the magnitude of the argument when arsinh(x) is embedded in a computation. Even for $x \approx 10^{308}$, near the upper limit of values that can be used in Excel, arsinh(x) is not much larger than 700, certainly not an excessively large number. It is therefore best to ensure that the function operates properly for all numerically possible input values x.

The Excel function ASinH(x) accepts x-values between approximately -6.72×10^7 and $+1.34 \times 10^{154}$. However, below $x = +0.2$, the accuracy of the Excel function deteriorates as x becomes smaller, as can be seen in Fig. 11.7.1. This is, once more, a case of cancellation error: for $x^2 \ll 1$, the square root in (11.7.2) numerically approaches 1, so that the term $\ln(x+1)$ approaches zero as $x - x^2/2 + x^3/3 - x^4/4 + \dots$. The correct approach for $x^2 \ll 1$ is $\sqrt{(x^2+1)} \to 1 + x^2/2 - x^4/(2\cdot4) + 3x^6/(2\cdot4\cdot6) - (3\cdot5)x^8/(2\cdot4\cdot6\cdot8) + \dots$ which leads to the series expansion for $|x| < 1$

$$\text{arsinh}(x) = x - \frac{1}{2} \times \frac{x^3}{3} + \frac{1\cdot3}{2\cdot4} \times \frac{x^5}{5} - \frac{1\cdot3\cdot5}{2\cdot4\cdot6} \times \frac{x^7}{7} + \cdots \tag{11.7.3}$$

with the limit arsinh(x) $\to x$ (rather than 0) for $x^2 \ll 1$.

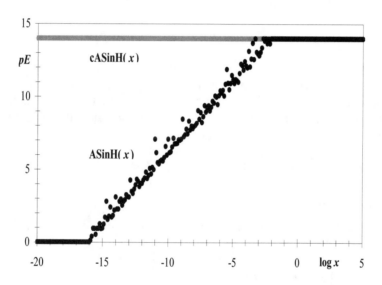

Fig. 11.7.1: Error plot of ASinH(x) and the corrected function cASinH(x), here both shown for the limited range $10^{-20} \le x \le 10^5$. The Excel function ASinH(x) remains at pE = 14 for $10^{-2} \le x \le 1.34 \times 10^{154}$, while the cFunction cASinH(x) yields pE = 14 over the entire range, $-1.8 \times 10^{308} \le x \le +1.8 \times 10^{308}$.

For x larger than about 1.34×10^{154}, the term x^2 in (11.7.2) exceeds the capacity of Excel, which is why ASinH(x) then yields no answer at all. But for such large values of x, one need not stay with (11.7.2), but instead can use the approximation arsinh(x) $\approx \ln(2x)$. Finally, for $x < 0$, we use (11.7.1).

The above results are incorporated in a *corrected* function cASinH() computed with the code shown below. It has a minimum pE of 14 when compared with high-precision results computed with XN, as discussed later in this chapter. Incidentally, Excel 2010 finally has a corrected version of ASINH().

```
Function cASINH(X) As Double
' Accuracy: minimum pE = 14
Dim n As Integer
Dim Sum As Double, Term As Double
Dim Y As Double, Z As Double
```

```
Y = Abs(X)
If Y > 10 ^ 150 Then
  Z = Log(2 * Y)
ElseIf Y <= 10 ^ 150 And Y >= 0.2 Then
  Z = Log(Y + Sqr(1 + Y ^ 2))
ElseIf Y < 0.2 And Y > 0 Then
  Term = -2 * (Y ^ 3) / 3
  Sum = Y + Term
  n = 2

  Do
    Term = -Term * 2 * n * (Y ^ 2) / (2 * n + 1)
    Sum = Sum + Term
    n = n + 1
  Loop Until Abs(Term) < 1E-30
  Z = Sum * Sqr(1 + Y ^ 2)
ElseIf Y = 0 Then
  Z = Log(1)
End If
cASINH = Sgn(X) * Z

End Function
```

11.8 The error function

The error function

$$\text{erf}(x) = \frac{2}{\sqrt{\pi}} \int_0^x e^{-t^2} \, dt \tag{11.8.1}$$

is another example of sloppy Excel programming. The error function is basic to both engineering and statistics, and appears in many problems of heat and mass transport that describe 'random walk' processes, such as heat conduction and molecular diffusion. As its name indicates, the error function is also related to the cumulative Gaussian ('normal') error distribution curve

$$\frac{1}{\sigma\sqrt{2\pi}} \int_{-\infty}^x e^{-(t-\mu)^2/2\sigma^2} \, dt = \frac{1}{2}\left[1 + \text{erf}\left(\frac{x-\mu}{\sigma\sqrt{2}}\right)\right] \tag{11.8.2}$$

with mean μ and standard deviation σ.

Excel's error function takes two forms, one following the common definition (11.8.1), the other the rather unusual, two-parameter form

$$\text{erf}(a,b) = \frac{2}{\sqrt{\pi}} \int_a^b e^{-t^2} \, dt = \text{erf}(b) - \text{erf}(a) \tag{11.8.3}$$

which we will not consider here, but which exhibits the same problem.

For negative values of x, we have the simple symmetry relation

$$\text{erf}(-x) = -\text{erf}(x) \tag{11.8.4}$$

while for positive values of x there is a straightforward, non-alternating power series

$$\text{erf}(x) = \frac{2}{\sqrt{\pi}} e^{-x^2} \sum_{n=0}^{\infty} \frac{2^n x^{2n+1}}{1 \cdot 3 \cdot \ldots \cdot (2n+1)} \tag{11.8.5}$$

For $x > 6$, we have erf$(x) = 1$ to at least 15 figures, so that the function need not be computed. A VBA code reflecting these properties is shown below. Figure 11.8.1 shows the errors of the Excel function Erf(x) and of our cErf(x), and speaks for itself. Again, the results were checked against the same function computed with much longer numberlength. As with ASINH(), Excel 2010 has a corrected version for the error function. Even prodding a giant can sometimes work.

```
Function cErf(X)

' Based on Abramowitz & Stegun eq.(7.1.6)

Dim n As Integer
Dim Factor, Term, Y

If X < -6 Then
  Y = -1
  GoTo A
ElseIf X > 6 Then
  Y = 1
  GoTo A
ElseIf Abs(X) < 1E-8 Then
  Y = 2 * X / Sqr([Pi()])
  GoTo A
Else
  Term = X * Exp(-X * X)
  Y = Term
  n = 1
  Do
    Factor = 2 * X * X / (2 * n + 1)
    Term = Term * Factor
    Y = Y + Term
    n = n + 1
  Loop Until Abs(Term / Y) < 1E-50
  Y = 2 * Y / Sqr([Pi()])
End If

A:
cErf = Y

End Function
```

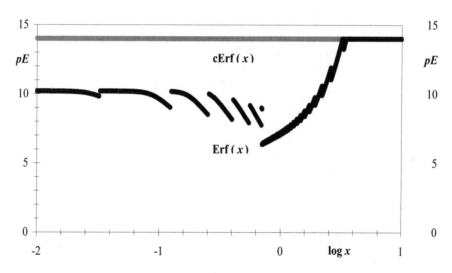

Fig. 11.8.1: Error plots of Erf(x) (black) and its corrected version cErf(x) (gray). For $x < 0$, Erf(x) gives no result, for $0 < x \lesssim 10^{-2}$ it is good to only 10 decimal figures (apparently because of an error in the value of $2/\sqrt{\pi}$ used), around $x = 0.707$ its accuracy dips to pE = 6.3, and for $x > 1.57 \times 10^{162}$ it again fails to give a result. Moreover, as shown here, the curve of Erf(x) vs. x shows a number of spurious discontinuities. By contrast, the function cErf is smooth and accurate to at least 14 significant decimal digits over the entire range of possible input values, $2.2 \times 10^{-308} \le |x| \le 1.8 \times 10^{308}$.

11.9 Double precision add-in functions and macros

Almost as a casual byproduct of his extended-precision XNumbers software, Leonardo Volpi generated a set of double-precision functions that were more accurate than their Excel equivalents, and also created many new functions not provided by Microsoft. John Beyers further added to these, making XN a quite large collection of useful functions that greatly extends the Excel toolkit. Of course, the extended precision functions listed in Table 11.11.1 and in appendix D can also yield double-precision answers when DgtMax is specified as 16, but it is better to use a larger value for DgtMax (such as 28 or 35) and to convert the results back to double precision with xCDbl.

537

Table 11.9.1 is a categorized listing of a number of double-precision *functions* that are accessible in this way, with a brief description, and Table 11.9.2 lists the double-precision *macros* available by clicking on the Macro button of the XN toolbar. For details on their operation, often with worked-out examples, see the XN manual, which you can access from Excel by pressing the Help button on the XN toolbar. If your monitor screen is wide enough to display the essential part of your spreadsheet and the help file side-by-side, without overlap, you can work in the spreadsheet while the help file shows. Many XN double-precision functions for operating with complex numbers were already listed in table 9.7.1, and are therefore not included here. Moreover, whole categories of functions in that table are not even discussed here, such as those for polynomial operations with names starting with "Poly", or the "ODE" solvers for ordinary *d*ifferential *e*quations. If these interest you, read up on them in the XN Help menu.

The abbreviations A, H, and N in the right-most column of Table 11.9.1 refer to chapters or sections in A: the *A*tlas of Functions by K. Oldham, J. Myland & J. Spanier, 2nd ed., Springer 2009, H: the *H*andbook of Mathematical Functions edited by M. Abramowitz & I. Stegun, NBS 1964, reprinted many times since by Dover, and N: the *N*IST Handbook of Mathematical Functions, edited by F. W. J. Olver, D. W. Lozier, D. F. Boisvert and C. W. Clark, Cambridge Univ. Press 2010.

function	brief description	symbol	refs.
Special functions			
AiryA	Airy function Ai(x)	$Ai(x)$	A56, H10.4, N9
AiryAD	First derivative of the Airy function Ai(x)	$Ai'(x)$	A56, H10.4, N9
AiryB	Airy function Bi(x)	$Bi(x)$	A56, H10.4, N9
AiryBD	First derivative of the Airy function Bi(x)	$Bi'(x)$	A56, H10.4, N9
BesselIx	Modified Bessel function of the 1st kind $I_n(x)$	$I_n(x)$	A49, H9, N10
BesseldI	First derivative of the modified Bessel function $I_n(x)$	$I_n'(x)$	A49, H9, *N10*
BesselJx	Bessel function of the 1st kind $J_n(x)$	$J_n(x)$	A52, H9, N10
BesseldJ	First derivative of the Bessel function $J_n(x)$	$J_n'(x)$	A52, H9, *N10*
BesselKx	Modified Bessel function of the 2nd kind $K_n(x)$	$K_n(x)$	A51, H9, N10
BesseldK	First derivative of the modified Bessel function $K_n(x)$	$K_n'(x)$	A51, H9, N10
BesselYx	Bessel function of the 2nd kind $Y_n(x)$	$Y_n(x)$	A54, H9, N10
BesseldY	First derivative of the Bessel function $Y_n(x)$	$Y_n'(x)$	A32.13, H10.1, N10
BesselSphJ	Spherical Bessel function of the 1st kind $J_n(x)$	$j_n(x)$	A32.13, H10.1, N10
BesselSphY	Spherical Bessel function of the 2nd kind $Y_n(x)$	$y_n(x)$	A32.13, H10.1, N10
DiGamma	Digamma function	$\psi(x)$	A44, H6.3, N5
ErrFun	Error function	erf(x)	A40, H7, N7
ErrFunC	Error function complement	erfc(x)	A40, H7, N7
HypGeom	Hypergeometric function	$F(a,b;c;z)$	A18.14, H15, H15
Zeta	Riemann zeta function	$\zeta(x)$	A3, H23.2, H25
Trigonometric operations			
Serie_Trig	Generates a trigonometric series from its harmonics		
Serie2D_Trig	Generates a 2-D trigonometric series from its harmonics		
Polynomial operations			
Poly	Evaluates polynomial at x		
PolyAdd	Adds two polynomials		
PolyBuild	Builds a polynomial for given roots		
PolyCenter	Center of polynomial roots		
PolyDiv	Quotient of two polynomials		
PolyInt	Transformation to polynomial with same roots but integer coefficients		
PolyInterp	Polynomial interpolation		
PolyInterpCoef	Coefficients of polynomial interpolation		
PolyMult	Product of two polynomials		
Polyn	Value of polynomial $P(z)$ for specified real or complex argument z		
Polyn2	Value of bivariant polynomial $P(w, z)$ for specified for real or complex arguments w, z		
PolyRadius	Radius of polynomial roots		

538

PolyRem	Remainder of polynomial division		
PolyShift	Shifts a polynomial from x to $x + x_0$		
PolySolve	Finds all roots of a polynomial		
PolySub	Subtracts two polynomials		
PolyTerms	Extracts vector of polynomial coefficients		
PolyWrite	Constructs polynomial from its coefficients		

Orthogonal polynomials

Poly_ChebychevT	Evaluates Chebychev polynomial of 1st kind	$T_n(x)$	A22, H22, N18
Poly_Weight_ChebychevT	Weight of Chebychev polynomial of 1st kind		A21, H22, N18
Poly_ChebychevU	Evaluates Chebychev polynomial of 2nd kind	$U_n(x)$	A22, H22, N18
Poly_Weight_ChebychevU	Weight of Chebychev polynomial of 2nd kind		A21, H22, N18
Poly_Gegenbauer	Evaluates Gegenbauer polynomial	$C_n^{(\alpha)}(x)$	A22, H22, N18
Poly_Weight_Gegenbauer	Weight of Gegenbauer polynomial		A21, H22, N18
Poly_Hermite	Evaluates Hermite polynomial	$H_n(x)$	A24, H22, N18
Poly_Weight_Hermite	Weight of Hermite polynomial		A21, H22, N18
Poly_Jacobi	Evaluates Jacobi polynomial	$P_n^{(\alpha,\beta)}(x)$	A22, H22, N18
Poly_Weight_Jacobi	Weight of Jacobi polynomial		A21, H22, N18
Poly_Laguerre	Evaluates Laguerre polynomial	$L_n(x)$	A23, H22, N18
Poly_Weight_Laguerre	Weight of Laguerre polynomial		A21, H22, N18
Poly_Legendre	Evaluates Legendre polynomial	$P_n(x)$	A21, H22, N18
Poly_Weight_Legendre	Weight of Legendre polynomial		A21, H22, N18

Special integrals

Convol	Convolution integral of two vectors	$v_1 \otimes v2$	
SinIntegral	Sine integral	$Si(x)$	A38, H5.2, N6
CosIntegral	Cosine integral	$Ci(x)$	A38, H5.2, N6
Exp_Integr	Exponential integral $Ei(x)$	$Ei(x)$	A37, H5, N6
Expn_Integr	Entire exponential integral $Ein(x)$	$Ein(x)$	A37, H5, N6
Fresnel_Sin	Fresnel sine integral	$S(x)$	A39, H7, N7
Fresnel_Cos	Fresnel cosine integral	$C(x)$	A39, H7, N7
IElliptic1	Elliptic integral of the 1st kind		A61, H17, N19
IElliptic2	Elliptic integral of the 2nd kind		A61, H17, N19
Kummer1	Confluent hypergeometric function of 1st kind	$M(a,b,x)$	A47, H13, N13
Kummer2	Confluent hypergeometric function of 2nd kind	$U(a,b,x)$	A48, H13, N13

Distributions

default (dtype = 0) = probability function; dtype = 1 yields cumulative function

DSBeta	Beta distribution	A26.5
xBetaI	Incomplete beta function	
DSBinomial	Binomial distribution	
DSCauchy	Cauchy (Lorentz) distribution	
DSChi	Chi distribution	A26.4
DSErlang	Erlang distribution	
DSGamma	Gamma distribution	
xGammaI	incomplete gamma function	
DSLevy	Levy distribution	
DSLogistic	Logistic distribution	
DSLogNormal	Lognormal distribution	
DSMaxwell	Maxwell distribution	
DSMises	Von Mises distribution	
DSNormal	Normal (Gaussian) distribution	A26.2
DSPoisson	Poisson distribution	
DSRayleigh	Rayleigh distribution	
DSRice	Rice distribution	
DSStudent	Student distribution	A26.7
DSWeibull	Weibull distribution	

Least squares alternatives

RegLinMM   Straight line fit minimizing the sum of absolute values

RegLinRM   Straight line fit minimizing the deviations from the median

Differentiation   *see section 9.2.11*

Diff1   First derivative of $f(x)$ $f'(x)$

Diff2   Second derivative of $f(x)$ $f''(x)$

DPoly   Value of nth order derivative of polynomial $P(x)$ at specified x

Dpolyn   Value of nth order derivative of polynomial $P(z)$ at specified real or complex argument z

Grad   Vector of first derivatives of multivariate function

Hessian   Hessian matrix of a multivariate function

Jacobian   Jacobian matrix of a vector function

Integration

Integr   Integrates $f(x)$ between a and b

Integr_DE   Integrates $f(x)$ using double exponential transformation

Integr_2D   2-D integration of $f(x,y)$

Integr_NC   Newton-Cotes integration of $f(x)$ between a and b

Integr_Ro   Romberg integration of $f(x)$ between a and b

IntegrData   trapezoidal integration of 1st, 3rd (default), or 5th degree

IntegrData2D   bidimensional trapezoidal integration of a piecewise-rectangular grid

IntegrDataC   Newton-Cotes integration of a complex data vector v

IntPowSin   Integrates $\sin^n(x)$

IntPowCos   Integrates $\cos^n(x)$

Fourier transformations

FFT   Fast Fourier transform of $N = 2^n$ real input data

FFT_INV   Fast inverse Fourier transform of 2^n real input data

FFT2D   Fast 2-D Fourier transform

FFT2D_INV   Fast 2-D inverse Fourier transform

DFT   Discrete Fourier transform of any number N of real input data

DFT_INV   Discrete inverse Fourier transform of any number N of real input data

DFSP   Amplitude and phase angle determined by discrete Fourier transform

DFSP_INV   The inverse of DFSP, viz. the reconstitution of $f(t)$ from the DFT amplitude and phase angle

Fourier_Sin   Integrates $f(x) \sin(kx)$ from a to ∞

Integr_fSin   Integrates $f(x) \sin(kx)$ with Filon's formula

Fourier_Cos   Integrates $f(x) \cos(kx)$ from a to ∞

Integr_fCos   Integrates $f(x) \cos(kx)$ with Filon's formula

Equation solvers

DiophEqu   Solves the diophantine equation $ax + by = c$

PellEqu   Solves Brouncker-Pell equation $x^2 - dy^2 = 1$

SysPoly2   Solves system of two 2nd-degree polynomials

Zero_Bisec   Finds root of $f(x)$ by bisection

Zero_Sec   Finds root of $f(x)$ with the secant method

ODE solvers

ODE_COR   Solves ODE with multi-step corrector

ODE_PC2I   Solves ODE with implicit 2nd-order predictor-corrector

ODE_PC4   Solves ODE with 2nd-order Adams-Bashforth-Moulton method

ODE_PRE   Solves ODE with multi-step predictor

ODE_RK4   Solves ODE with 4th-order Runge-Kutta method

ODE_SYSL   Solves linear system of ODEs with constant coefficients

Interpolating tools

CSpline_Coeff	Coefficients of cubic spline
CSpline_Eval	Interpolates using fast cubic spline interpolation
CSpline_Interp	Interpolates using cubic spline interpolation
CSpline_Pre	Second derivative of cubic spline
FracInterp	Interpolation with continued fraction
FracInterpCoef	Coefficients of interpolation with continued fraction
Interp_Mesh	Linear interpolation in a rectangular mesh of data points

Extrapolating tools

ExtDelta2	Aitken's delta-square extrapolation

Primes

Factor	Decomposes an integer into its prime factors
NextPrime	First prime beyond n for primes $< 2^{53}$
PrevPrime	First prime before n for primes $< 2^{53}$
Totient	Euler's Totient function
Prime	Yields "P" if prime, smallest factor if not prime

Measures of data agreement

DgMat	Number of matching most-significant digits between x_1 and x_2
FDgMat	$= pE$ using second argument as reference
LRE	$= pE$ using second argument as reference
mjkLRE	$= pE$ using second argument as reference

Data conversions

cvBinDec	Convert from binary to decimal
cvDecBin	Convert from decimal to binary
cvBaseDec	Converts from any base-n system ($1 < n < 27$) to decimal
cvDecBase	Converts from decimal to any base-n system ($1 < n < 27$)
s2Dbl	Converts string to double precision

Miscellany

dBel	Yields the decibel level, $db(x) = 20 \log(x)$
Flip	Inverts order of vector elements
Fract	Approximates decimal fraction as a quotient of two integers
FractCont	Continued fraction of x in double precision
FractContSqr	Continued fraction of $\sqrt{n}$
MCD	Maximum (largest, greatest) common divisor
MCM	Minimum (smallest, least) common multiplier
SumDigits	Sums the values of the digits of an integer

Table 11.9.1: The double-precision functions in XN.xla(m). Advise: before first use of one of these functions, consult the relevant page in the Xnumbers v.6.0 Help file ⇨ Contents ⇨ Index of Functions, which you find on your computer by clicking on the Help button of the short XN toolbar.

macro	brief description	symbol
Matrix operations		
Transpose		$\mathbf{A}^{T}$
Add		$\mathbf{A} + \mathbf{B}$
Subtract		$\mathbf{A} - \mathbf{B}$
Scalar multiply		$k\,\mathbf{A}$
Matrix multiply		$\mathbf{A}\,\mathbf{B}$
Scalar product		$\mathbf{A}^{T}\mathbf{B}$
Invert		$\mathbf{A}^{-1}$
Determinant		
Similarity transformation		$\mathbf{B}^{-1}\mathbf{A}\,\mathbf{B}$
Solve a linear system		$\mathbf{A}\,\mathbf{X} = \mathbf{B}$
Solve an overdetermined linear system ($n > m$)		$\mathbf{A}\,\mathbf{X} = \mathbf{B}$
Norm		$\|\mathbf{A}\|$
Crout decomposition		LU
Cholesky decomposition		LL^{T}
Singular value decomposition		$\mathbf{U}\,\mathbf{D}\,\mathbf{V}^{T}$
Integration		
Double integration		
Triple integration		
Integration from $-\infty$ to $+\infty$		
Fourier transformation		
Discrete Fourier transformation		
2-D discrete Fourier transformation		
Sampler (of a specified function)		
Number theory		
Factors		
Prime number generation		
Prime test		
Integer relation finder	of polynomial or polyvariate relations	
Polynomials		
Rootfinder		
Builder		
Factors		
Orthogonal zero		
Orthogonal coeff.		
Optimizers		
Downhill simplex	Multivariate Nelder-Mead algorithm, robust & derivative-free	
Downhill simplex / Resets		
1-D divide & conquer	Monovariate, bisection-based algorithm, robust and derivative-free	
Least squares		
Linear		
Mesh fill		
ODE Solvers		
IVP Solver		
Slope grid		
Polynomial		

Table 11.9.2: The double-precision macros in XN.xla(m), accessible from the XN toolbar under Macros. For information, consult the relevant page in the Xnumbers v.6.0 Help file ⇨ Contents ⇨ Index of Macros.

11.10 Going beyond standard numberlength

11.10.1 Hardware solutions

A practical limitation to higher numerical accuracy of standard computer software lies in the arithmetic unit (or *central processing unit*, cpu) used. The cpu performs the basic algebraic operations of addition, subtraction, multiplication, and division usingy efficient, dedicated hardware.

Some of the mathematically elegant solutions described so far, such as singular value decomposition and various types of centering, are attempts to reduce some consequences of having only 54 bits available to represent the mantissas of 'double precision' numbers. Numberlength in digital computers is usually expressed either in its basic unit of one *bit* (**bi**nary uni**t**), which can be either 0 or 1, or in 8-bit *bytes*, which therefore can represent $2^8 = 256$ different integers, say from 0 through 255.

Most personal computers use the IEEE-754 format, which specifies 2 bytes (16 bits) for so-called *single-precision* integers (Excel's Integer type) ranging from $-32K$ to $+32K$ ($2^{16} = 65,536$ or 64K), and 4 bytes (32 bits) for *double precision* (Excel's Long type) to handle integers to approximately ± 4 billion ($\pm 4 \times 10^9$ or $\pm 4G$ since $2^{32} = 4,294,967,296$). For *floating-point* numbers (in scientific notation), 'single precision' (Excel's Single) uses 4 bytes or 32 bits, the regular numberlength in 32-bit processors, to represent from about $\pm 10^{-45}$ to $\pm 3 \times 10^{38}$. Excel's Double ('double precision') covers between roughly $\pm 5 \times 10^{-324}$ and $\pm 1.8 \times 10^{308}$, processing two 4-byte 'words' as if they were one. Of the resulting 64 bits, one bit specifies the sign, 9 are used for the exponent, while 54 are devoted to the mantissa. These 54 bits translate to about 16 decimals ($2^{54} \approx 1.8 \times 10^{16}$) of which Excel displays only 15 to keep a margin of error. Still, it is usually not clear how many of these digits are significant. This is where *numerical accuracy* comes in.

Many modern cpu's with the facility to calculate in *quadruple precision* (i.e., using 128 bits) have been incorporated in personal computers produced since 2003, when AMD introduced them; Intel followed suit the next year. Specifically, many AMD Athlon, Opteron, Turon and Semperon processors, as well as many Intel Xeon, Celeron, Pentium and Core2 cpu's, now have the necessary ('x64') hardwired facilities to manipulate 128-bit numbers in their basic computations. However, absent serious competition for its flagship Office bundle, Microsoft has not yet upgraded Excel's computational engine to take advantage of the capabilities of 64-bit computing in *calculating* its results, although the 64-bit version of Excel 2010 can use x64 for *addressing* an even larger spreadsheet than that of Excel 2007. That may be helpful for using Excel as a low-grade database, but does nothing for serious computations.

11.10.2 Software solutions

Hardwired mathematical manipulations are by far the fastest, but one can achieve higher computational accuracy by performing operations in software, albeit with slower performance. There are several ways in which this can be accomplished. Some software systems, such as Mathematica and Maple, use symbolic algebra, and can compute results to arbitrary precision. Other approaches convert numbers longer than the arithmetic unit can handle into two or more parts that can be manipulated separately. One way to do this is to convert all numbers to a large base, such as base 256, perform all internal operations in that base (in software), and then convert the results back into decimal (base 10) code. For example, the six-digit decimal number $(456789)_{10}$ would be converted into its three-digit base-256 equivalent $(6)_{256}$ $(248)_{256}$ $(85)_{256}$ (because $456789 = 6 \times 256^2 + 248 \times 256 + 85 \times 1$), and then be handled as String = chr(6) & chr(248) & chr(85). This method, which obviously takes an approach that is the opposite of the usual conversion of decimal numbers into their binary equivalents, evaluates rather quickly, but it is difficult for its designers to debug. It is apparently not (yet) available for Excel from any source.

Another approach is to represent long decimal numbers in shorter packets (such as splitting the number 12345678987654321 into packets of up to six decimals as 12345, 678987, 654321), and to perform all basic arithmetic operations on such packets, see D. H. Bailey, ACM Trans. Math. Software 19 (1993)

288-319. This method was used in MPFUN, a freely available extended-precision software routine for Fortran77, which has since been extended to Fortran90 and C^{++} in ARPREC, software that allows for *arbitrary precision* limited only by the size of the available memory. In this approach the decimal numbers remain recognizable, which makes it much easier to debug the code. In section 11.11 we will consider an early, limited application of this approach in Volpi's BigMatrix.xla, before we devote the remainder of this chapter to its extensive subsequent implementation in XN.xla and XN.xlam, John Beyers' extensions of Leonardo Volpi's XNumbers.xla. The add-in programs BigMatrix.xla, XNumbers.xla and Xnumbers.dll are freely downloadable from Volpi's web site, and XN.xla, and (for **07**,**10**XN.xlam) can be found at http://thetropicalevents.com/XNumbers60. All of these can also be downloaded from my excellaneous website. But first we will briefly describe a software solution Microsoft introduced ten years ago without much fanfare.

11.10.3 Excel's Decimal data type and the xq functions

Since 2000, Excel VBA has had a Decimal data type, in which it represents numbers with 96 bits to yield 29-decimal numbers in string format. This seldom advertised and poorly documented mode appears to be designed especially for financial transactions, where the repeated use of a binary representation of fractional currency (such as 1¢ as $0.01) can lead to accumulating round-off errors. At this time, however, this option has limited applicability in scientific computation, because the only mathematical operations it can use appear to be addition, subtraction, multiplication, division, and taking the natural logarithm.

In using this special mode, it is necessary to enter numbers exceeding 15 decimal places as a string (i.e., within quotation marks) and to convert them into the special *dec*imal format (a subset of the Variant data type) with the command CDec. The following code illustrates how you can add two 32-decimal numbers in decimal mode and obtain an answer good to ±1 in its last (29th) decimal place. The result is shown as a message box on the spreadsheet, and in the Immediate Window.

```
Sub TestDecimalAddition()

Dim dA, dB, dSum
dA = "1000000000000.0000000000000234567"
dB = "2000000000000.0000000000000456789"
Debug.Print "a = " & dA
Debug.Print "b = " & dB
vSum = CDec(dA) + CDec(dB)
MsgBox "a      = " & dA & vbCr & _
    "b      = " & dB & vbCr & _
    "a + b = " & dSum
Debug.Print "a + b = " & dSum

End Sub
```

For a more extensive exploration use the MacroMorsel routines Decimal Operations (from which the above segment was lifted) and Counting Pennies. The decimal mode is clearly optimized for calculating interest rates and for balancing the books to the penny in large financial institutions, but its very limited instruction set makes it unsuitable for most scientific calculations.

Leonardo Volpi and his 'foxes' built his xq functions on this Decimal mode, and John Beyers further expanded that collection. The resulting xq functions listed in Table 11.10.1 combine with Excel's Decimal functions to cover a set of basic mathematical operations with quadruple precision, extending that collection more than five-fold. Their main advantage over XN functions lies in their speed. They typically get at least 25 decimals correct. You have access to them when XN is loaded. Exercise 11.10.1 illustrates their advantage over double precision numbers when a common function hits close to a rough spot, as the $\cos(\alpha)$ does near $\alpha = \pi/2$.

Exercise 11.10.1:

(1) In cells B3:B15 of a new spreadsheet place the numbers 1 (1) 13.

(2) In C2 deposit the label α and in C3 the formula =ROUND(PI()/2,B3) which yields an approximation of $\pi/2$ to B3 digits past the decimal point.

(3) In D2 put the label COS(α) and in D3 the instruction =COS(C3).

(4) In F2 place the label xqCos(α), and below it the instruction =xqCos(C3).

(5) Since we already use XN, we will now cheat a little by anticipating its full use, which will be discussed in the following sections. Just place the label xCos(α,35) in H2, and the instruction =xCos(C3,35) in H3, which will calculate the answer to 35 decimals. Make columns C, D, F, and H wide enough to accommodate the full lengths of their answers.

(6) In E2 place the label pE and below it use the equation =xRound(xLRE(D3,H3),2). Similarly, in G3 compute =xRound(xLRE(F3,H3),2). The rounding merely serves to keep these columns narrow.

(7) Highlight C3:H3, and click on its handle to copy these instructions down to row 15.

(8) Notice how the relative precision of your answers decreases as the value in column C approaches $\pi/2$. However, your answers have at least 7 extra correct decimals when you use xqCos(α) rather than COS(α) in this nasty problem, close to the zero crossing of the cosine, where the series expansion used to compute its value always gives trouble.

xqAdd(x,y)	xAdd	add, $x + y$
xqSub(x,y)	xSub	subtract, $x - y$
xqMult(x,y)	xMult	multiply, $x * y$
xqDiv(x,y)	xDiv	divide, x / y
xqAbs(x)	xAbs	absolute value, $\|x\|$
xqInt(x)	xInt	integer value, $x - \text{xDec}(x)$
xqDec(x)	xDec	remainder past decimal point, including sign(x)
xqRound(x)	xRound	round, optional: # of digits past decimal point (default = 0)
xqACosH(x)	xACosH	inverse hyperbolic cosine, arcosh(x)
xqAngleC(x)	xAngleC	right-angle complement of x, $\pi/2 - x$
xqASin(x)	xASin	inverse sine, arcsin(x)
xqASinH(x)	xASinH	inverse hyperbolic sine, arsinh(x)
xqATan(x)	xATan	inverse tangent, arctan(x)
xqATan2(x)	xATan2	inverse tangent, arctan(y/x)
xqATanH(x)	xTanH	inverse hyperbolic tangent, artanh(x)
xqCos(x)	xCos	cosine, cos(x)
xqCosH(x)	xCosH	hyperbolic cosine, cosh(x)
xqErf(x)	xErf	error function, erf(x)
xqErfC(x)	xErfC	error function complement, erfc(x)
xqExp(x)	xExp	exponentiation, e^x
xqExpA(x)	xExpA	a raised to the xth power, a^x
xqLn(x)	xLn	natural logarithm, ln(x)
xqLog(x)	xLog	10-based logarithm, log(x)
xqPow(x)	xPow	x raised to the nth power
xqRoot(x)	xRoot	n^{th} root of x, $x^{1/n}$
xqSin(x)	xSin	sine, sin(x)
xqSinH(x)	xSinH	hyperbolic sine, sinh(x)
xqSqr(x)	xSqr	square root of x, $x^{1/2}$
xqTan(x)	xTan	tangent, tan(x)
xqTanH(x)	xTanH	hyperbolic tangent, tanh(x)

Table 11.10.1: The additional quadruple precision functions in XN.xla(m), and corresponding multi-precision XN functions.

11.10.4 The BigMatrix macros

BigMatrix also provides quadruple precision for a few specific matrix operations with a minimum of fuss: matrix multiplication, scalar multiplication, matrix inversion, solving a system of linear equations, and linear least squares. It works its wonders in the background, taking in 15-decimal numbers and producing 15-decimal results while doing the processing using 30-decimal numbers. BigMatrix can also execute the more mundane matrix operations such as matrix addition, subtraction, transposition.

BigMatrix.xla is installed as an add-in function, even though it behaves as (and is) a set of macros. It includes one- and two-dimensional fast Fourier transformation, but these are performed in standard 'double precision', and will not be considered here. Unlike Volpi's other routines, the code of BigMatrix is password-protected.

Using it typically starts with the sequence $\underline{T}$ools $\Rightarrow$ Big Matrices $\Rightarrow$ Manager, which brings up a Matrix Manager input box with three rows of windows (for matrices A, B, and C) plus, in its bottom left-hand corner, a window to select a particular operation. Entering a matrix can be done by specifying its first and last cell, its first cell and its number of rows and columns, or just its first cell in case the matrix is completely surrounded by blank cells. Matrix inversion requires you to specify one input matrix A and the location of its inverse, in B, while multiplication obviously involves two input matrices in A and B, and one output matrix in C. For the output matrix it suffices to specify only the first (top left) cell; it is up to you to make sure that the output will not overwrite valuable data. After you have entered the matrix locations and specified the desired operation, click OK. If you want to read the relevant section in the documentation first, click on Help.

For small matrices, instructions are implemented almost instantaneously, but for larger matrices you will notice their nonzero execution times. BigMatrix certainly does not hide this, and instead displays its execution time as the price you pay for its higher numerical accuracy. For example, inversion of a dense (rather than sparse) matrix of dimension 50×50 typically takes of the order of 1 second on a 1 MHz processor; inversion of a 100×100 matrix takes about eight times longer, while inversion of a 200×200 matrix will consume slightly more than a minute, i.e., the execution time of matrix inversion is roughly proportional to the cube of the matrix dimension. For sparse matrices (i.e., with many zero elements) the inversion is faster.

Table 11.10.2 lists the BigMatrix instructions that use quadruple numberlength, and how your unknowns should be entered in its Manager to get the desired answers. For full details and examples see the BigMatrix tutorial on the Help button of the Manager dialog box. Here we will merely give one example, the linear least squares analysis of the Filip data set already considered in sections 10.8 and 10.13, to let you see what BigMatrix can do.

	Mat. A	**Mat. B**	**Mat. C**	**in extra input box**
matrix multiplication	input: $\mathbf{A}\,(m \times n)$	input: $\mathbf{B}\,(n \times p)$	output: $\mathbf{C}\,(m \times p)$	
scalar multiplication	input: $\mathbf{A}\,(m \times n)$	input: $\mathbf{B}\,(m \times p)$	output: $\mathbf{C}\,(n \times p)$	
matrix inversion	input: $\mathbf{A}\,(m \times m)$	output: $\mathbf{A}^{-1}\,(m \times m)$		
solving a linear system	input: $\mathbf{A}\,(m \times m)$	input: $\mathbf{B}\,(m \times n)$	output: $\mathbf{C}\,(m \times n)$	
multivariate regression	input: $\mathbf{A}\,(m \times n)$	input: $\mathbf{B}\,(n \times 1)$	output: $\mathbf{C}\,(m{+}1 \times n)$	
polynomial regression	input: $\mathbf{A}\,(m \times 1)$	input: $\mathbf{B}\,(m \times 1)$	output: $\mathbf{C}\,(p{+}1 \times 1)$	enter intercept (if fixed) and degree p

Table 11.10.2: How to enter the various matrices in the BigMatrix Manager.

Exercise 11.10.2:

(1) Copy the data of Filip.dat, either from its original source (http://www.itl.nist.gov/div898/strd/lls/data/LINKS/DATA/Filip.dat) or from exercise 10.8.2, so that the column headings are in, say, row 3, the y-values are listed in cells B5:B86, the corresponding values of x are deposited in D5:D86, and the integer powers $x^2, x^2, \ldots, x^{10}$ of x are computed in E5:M86.

(2) Call the BigMatrix Manager with $\underline{T}$ools $\Rightarrow$ Big matrices $\Rightarrow$ Manager. Enter D5 as the first cell of Mat. A, and M86 as its Last cell, or merely specify the First cell of Mat. A as D5 in that window. (Since D5:M86 has empty borders, you

need not even specify 82 rows and 10 columns. Illustrating this convenient feature of the BigMatrix Manager was the reason to separate y in B5:B86 from **X** in D5:M86 by the empty row C. Alternatively you could have entered D5:M86 in the First cell window, or D5 as First cell, Rows as 82, and Columns as 1. The Manager understands.)

(3) Deposit B5 in the window for matrix B, and O5 in the window for C. Select Linear Regression as the operation, and press OK. You should now have the answers in O5:O15. If you want, note the time taken, then press Exit.

(4) List the certified answers in, say, Q5:Q15, and then compute pE by comparing O5 with Q5, O6 with Q6, etc. In section 10.8 you found pE = 0; here you will find pE–values for a_0 through a_{10} between 6.4 and 6.6, certainly an improvement.

In sections 10.8 and 10.13 you saw that many problems are caused by the limited numberlength of 32-bit 'double precision' computing of the higher powers of x, and we indicated a rather laborious way around that problem. But it is certainly easier to prevent it, simply by using extended numberlength to compute the powers x^2 through x^{10}. The Polynomial Regression operation of BigMatrix includes computing those powers with 30-decimal precision.

Exercise 11.10.2 (continued):
(5) Call <u>T</u>ools ⇨ Big matrices ⇨ Manager, specify D5:D86 as x in Mat. A, B5 or B5:B86 as y in Mat. B, O22 as output in Mat. C, specify the operation as Polynomial Regression, and in the small extra dialog box enter degrees as 10. Click OK. Polynomial regression neither uses nor needs spreadsheet-computed higher powers of x.

(6) Analyze the results in O22:O32 as you did earlier with those in O5:O15. Here is the happy surprise: using BigMatrix, without polynomial centering or singular value decomposition, you get all your coefficients right to pE = 14.

BigMatrix can also perform rectangular to polar and polar to rectangular conversion, one-dimensional forward and inverse Fourier transformation on up to 16K data points, and two-dimensional on up to 250 × 250 points. It aces all of the NIST linear least squares StRD test sets, including those with a 'high level of difficulty', Wampler n, Longley, and Filip, with pE ≥ 14. BigMatrix is now superseded by XN.xla(m), which has a much larger set of functions. However, if nothing else, BigMatrix was an early illustration of the potential usefulness of extended-numberlength computing in Excel.

11.11 The XN functions for extended precision

Leonardo Volpi wrote two general programs using extended numberlength, implemented in VB and VBA as XNumbers.xla for incorporation in functions and directly in the spreadsheet, and as XNumbers.dll as a *d*igital *l*inking *l*ibrary (dll) for use in macros. Both can still be downloaded from Volpi's web site, http://digilander.libero.it/foxes/SoftwareDownload.htm. However, they are no longer updated, and XNumbers.dll cannot be used in Excel 2007 or Excel 2010. Fortunately, John Beyers has greatly extended XNumbers.xla, made it readily usable in macros, relabeled this updated version XN.xla, and also made it available for Excel 2007 and 2010 as XN.xlam. These are freely downloadable from the website http.www.thetropicalevents.com/XNumbers60 and are relayed on my excellaneous website. It is this recent version of XNumbers.xla that will be used below, because it can be used everywhere in Excel: on the spreadsheet, and (after its installation in VBA) in functions and in subroutines, including macros. Installing XN.xla or XN.xlam is described in section 1.2.6. Moreover, you have already encountered its double-precision contributions in earlier chapters. Here we will emphasize its uses for high numerical precision.

The best explanation of all changes John Beyers has made in Xnumbers, plus a list of the many new functions he has added, can be found once XN and its XN toolbar are installed. You do the latter by clicking once on the XN book icon. (It is a toggle switch: clicking on the book icon once more will close the toolbar.) Then click on the Help button of that XN toolbar, select Help on-line, and in the resulting Xnumbers version 6.0 file click at the end of its first paragraph on "changes to version 6.0". One special aspect of XN is that it can be configured. Fortunately, there is no need to change the pre-configured settings, which will do fine for most functions.

In what follows we will use XN.xla6051-7A, as of this writing the latest version in its simplest (and fastest) incarnation, which can operate with numbers of up to 630 decimals. Slightly slower versions with higher maximum precisions (of up to 4030 decimals) can also be downloaded, as can the corresponding

Excel 2007/2010 versions of XN.xlam. Apart from their speed and maximum precision, all versions operate in identical fashion. Near the upper limit of available precision, the last few decimals are not always reliable, and it is therefore better to stay away from that very edge by two packets (i.e., by 14 decimals for 7-decimal packets) assigned in the XNToolbar under X-Edit ⇨ Configuration ⇨ Digit Max Adjustment as internal guard decimals. Also keep in mind that some XN functions can be rather slow at or near maximal precision, prime examples being xErf and xErfc, and the functions that use these: xNormal, xNormalS, and xMaxwell. By staying away from the limit by two packets as indicated above, the speed problem largely disappears: with DgtMax = 500, xErf computes its result in less than one second, and it is virtually instantaneous for DgtMax = 100. Operations on large matrices can also be slow, because the number of operations typically increases with some power larger than one of the number of elements involved. And especially slow can be iterative matrix computations, such as xSVD. But if you really need the result, what's a few seconds?

Personally I have never encountered a problem that required even 500 decimals of precision. I use 35 as my default value for all but the most difficult problems, and sometimes 28 to keep the numbers short.

Here are the advantages of XN:

(1) XN provides for a variable numerical precision. The desired precision can be specified for the entire spreadsheet, function, or subroutine, while still remaining adjustable for each individual instruction.

(2) XN can present its results either in full length or in regular, double precision format. In the latter case, i.e., when the output is converted back to double precision with an the instruction such as =xCDbl, it does not require any modifications of the input and output stages of already existing functions or macros, while the data processing is done in background at the selected higher precision.

(3) XN can be used directly on the spreadsheet. Many Excel instructions now have XN equivalents, including *all* of its engineering, statistical, and trigonometric functions. Moreover, there are many new functions. The required code changes in existing VBA functions and subroutines are relatively minor.

(4) If you want to make sure that data processing errors are kept to a minimum, and that at least the first 14 of the 15 decimals displaying your spreadsheet results are not distorted by limited computer precision, XN is your best bet.

Here are its disadvantages:

(1) While you can use XN functions on your spreadsheet, upgrading existing functions and macros to extended precision is only possible when you have access to their source code. Fortunately, that automatically includes your own, custom-made creations, and all open-access functions and macros (including those in the MacroBundle) that you can find in the literature.

(2) XN can be noticeably slow in execution, especially when we combine high precision with repeated use, as in multiply nested loops. This reflects the trade-off between speed and accuracy.

(3) If you want to share your active spreadsheets with colleagues (rather than just its results as, say, a pdf), they will need to install XN.xla(m) on their machines. Since XN is free, that is not much of a disadvantage, unless your institution blocks it. In that case, consult your IT manager..

While these disadvantages are rather minor compared with the possible gains, I do not recommend that you use XN for routine use, where it may often be overkill. Keep it for critical applications, and for double-checking that your intermediary and final results do not lose needed accuracy to numerically insufficient precision. Therefore, its principal applications will likely be to problems where double precision is known to produce substandard results, typically because of algorithmic cancellation and/or accumulation errors. XN can also be very useful as a final check on numerical results of consequence, and as a high-precision reference for testing algorithms and their spreadsheet implementations. Even such occasional uses fully warrant its inclusion in a book on *advanced* Excel.

Below you will find a short alphabetical list of the XN functions currently available in the XN.xla(m) downloads. In an effort to streamline the nomenclatures used in Matrix.xla(m) and XN.xla(m), some function names have recently been modified, such as xMatMult for extended-precision matrix inversion, which has become xMMult, to be more compatible with MMULT in Excel and with xMMultC and xMMultSC in XN. Check in your Paste Function (or Insert Function) dialog box which commands your version expects; the 13 function names which used Mat instead of M to specify that they were matrix functions are identified below with asterisks. Earlier versions are grandfathered, and are still listed in the Paste Function dialog box. They will be translated automatically into their most recent names, so that spreadsheets using older function names will still work properly as spreadsheet *functions*. But VBA has become more demanding, and *macros* using older names may have to be updated to use their current names. Not featured here (but listed in the PasteFunction box) are a number of functions with the last letter R, which stands for "raw" and are meant for use inside VBA programs, where they are some 10% faster.

As for all Excel functions, capitalization is ignored by Excel (except in quoted text), and is used here merely to enhance readability by emphasizing the different parts of compound terms. A categorized listing with somewhat greater detail can be found in appendix D, and specific examples are often available by consulting the on-screen Help file accessible after you have loaded the small XN toolbar.

extended preci-sion function	*brief function description*	*Excel double precision equivalent*
vRoundR	relative banker's rouding, default: to 15 decimal relative precision	
x_And	Boolean logic AND	AND
x_If	Boolean logic IF, including condition test on numeric strings	IF
x_Not	Boolean logic NOT	NOT
x_Or	Boolean logic OR	OR
x2Dbl	converts to double precision, slower than xCDbl, more accurate, but seldom needed	
x2Pi	$2\pi \approx 6.283\ldots$	
xAbs	absolute value	ABS
xACos	inverse cosine of an angle, $=\arccos(\alpha)$	ACOS
xACosH	inverse hyperbolic cosine of a number, $=\operatorname{arcosh}(x)$	ACOSH
xAdd	add	+
xAddMod	modular addition	
xAdj2Pi	adjusted angle, in rad between 0 and $+2\pi$	
xAdjPi	adjusted angle, in rad between $-\pi$ and $+\pi$	
xALog	10-based antilogarithm, 10^x	
xAngleC	complement of angle α, $=\pi/2 - \alpha$	
xASin	inverse sine of an angle, $=\arcsin(\alpha)$	ASIN
xASinH	inverse hyperbolic sine of a number, $=\operatorname{arsinh}(x)$	ASINH
xATan	inverse tangent of an angle, $=\arctan(\alpha)$	ATAN
xATan2	arctan in rad between $-\pi$ and $+\pi$	
xATanH	inverse hyperbolic tangent of a number, $=\operatorname{artanh}(x)$	ATANH
xAveDev	average of the absolute deviation from the mean	AVEDEV
xBaseChange	base converter	BASECHANGE
xBeta	beta function	
xBinomial	binomial distribution	BINOMDIST
xCalc	formula evaluator or parser	
xCat	concatenate	&
xCDbl	convert to double precision	
xCeil	ceiling	CEILING
xClip	yields Ceil for T $\geq$ Ceil, T for Floor < T < Ceiling, and Floor for T $\leq$ Floor	
xComb	binomial coefficient	
xComb_Big	binomial coefficient for large numbers	
xComp	comparison, yields 1 for $a > b$, 0 for $a = b$, and -1 for $a < b$; yields sign of a if b absent	IF
xComp1	absolute comparison, yields 1 for xAbs > 1, 0 for xAbs = 1, and -1 for xAbs < 1	
xCorrel	correlation coefficient	CORREL
xCos	cosine of an angle, $=\cos(\alpha)$	
xCosH	hyperbolic cosine of a number, $=\cosh(x)$	
xCoVar	covariance	COVAR

xCplx	builds complex number z from real and imaginary component, selects i or j as $\sqrt{-1}$.	COMPLEX
xCplxAbs	absolute value of complex number, $|z|$	IMABS
xCplxACos	complex inverse cosine, $\arccos(z)$	
xCplxACosH	complex inverse hyperbolic cosine, $\operatorname{arsinh}(z)$	
xCplxAdd	complex addition	
xCplxArg	argument of complex number, $\arctan(\mathrm{Im}/\mathrm{Re})$	IMARGUMENT
xCplxASin	complex inverse sine, $\arcsin(z)$	
xCplxASinH	complex inverse hyperbolic sine, $\operatorname{arsinh}(z)$	
xCplxATan	complex inverse tangent, $\arctan(z)$	
xCplxATanH	complex inverse hyperbolic tangent, $\operatorname{artanh}(z)$	
xCplxConj	complex conjugate	IMCONJUGATE
xCplxCos	complex cosine, $\cos(z)$	IMCOS
xCplxCosH	complex hyperbolic cosine, $\cosh(z)$	
xCplxDiv	complex division	IMDIV
xCplxExp	complex exponentiation, e^z	IMEXP
xCplxInv	complex inversion, $1/z$	
xCplxLn	complex natural logarithm, $\ln(z)$	IMLN
xCplxLog	complex logarithm to any base n, $\log_n(z)$	
xCplxLog10	complex 10-based logarithm, $\log(z)$	IMLOG10
xCplxLog2	complex 2-based logarithm, $\log_2(z)$	IMLOG2
xCplxMult	complex multiplication	
xCplxNeg	complex negation, $-z$	
xCplxPolar	converts complex number from rectangular to polar	
xCplxPow	raises complex number to integer power n, z^n, default $n = 2$	IMPOWER
xCplxRect	converts complex number from polar to rectangular	
xCplxRoot	n^{th} root of complex number, $z^{1/n}$, default $n = 2$	
xCplxSin	complex sine, $\sin(z)$	IMSIN
xCplxSinH	complex hyperbolic sine, $\sinh(z)$	
xCplxSqr	complex square root, $\sqrt{z}$	IMSQRT
xCplxSub	complex subtraction	IMSUB
xCplxTan	complex tangent, $\tan(z)$	
xCplxTanH	complex hyperbolic tangent, $\tanh(z)$	
xCStr	converts a double-precision number to a string, default Digit_Max = 767	
xCvExp	converts into scientific notation, $x = \text{mantissa} \times 10^{\text{exponent}}$, default exponent = 0	
xDec	decimal part of number	
xDecr	decrements a number by 1, $\mathrm{xSub}(x,1)$	
xDegrees	converts radians into degrees	DEGREES
xDelta	tests whether two numbers are equal	DELTA
xDevSq	sum of squares of deviations from sample average	DEVSQ
xDgMat	number of matching digits	
xDgt	the number of digits	
xDgtS	the number of significant digits	
xDiff	n^{th}-order derivative ($1 \le n \le 20$) of a function $f(x)$, default $n = 1$	
xDiff1	first-order derivative with choice of forward, central, or backward differencing	
xDiff2	second-order derivative with choice of forward, central, or backward differencing	
xDiffI	n^{th}-order derivative with choice of forward, central, or backward differencing	
xDiffOpt	displays n^{th}-order derivative plus values of h and d used	
xDiv	division	/
xDivInt	integer division	\
xDivMod	modular division	
xDivTrunc	truncated quotient $Q = \mathrm{xTrunc}(N/D)$	
xDLGI	1st derivative of Lagrange interpolation polynomial at specified x-value	
xDPoly	1st derivative of polynomial at specified x-value	
xE	$e \approx 2.718\ldots$, the base of natural logarithms	
xErF	error function	ERF

550

xErFC	error function complement	ERFC
xEu	Euler's gamma	
xEval	formula parser, evaluates quasi-algebraic expressions	
xEvalI	much slower version of xEval, can associate labels with input data	
xEven	rounds to nearest even number	EVEN
xExp	exponentiation, e^x	EXP
xExpa	raises a to the power x, a^x	
xExpBase	raises a to the power x, a^x	
xExponent	the exponent of a number $x = $ mantissa $\times 10^{exponent}$	
xExtDelta2	Aitken's delta-square extrapolation	
xFact	factorial, n!	FACT
xFact2	double-step (odd/even) factorial	FACTDOUBLE
xFib	Fibonacci number	
xFisher	Fisher transformation	FISHER
xFishInv	inverse Fisher transformation	FISHERINV
xFloor	rounds towards zero to nearest significant multiple	FLOOR
xFmt	formats string with selectable lead zeroes, trailing zeroes, and rounding	
xFormat	formats number in groups of n digits	FORMAT
xFract	numerator and denominator of a fraction	
xFractCont	continued fraction	
xGamma	gamma function, $\Gamma(x)$	GAMMADIST
xGammaF	Fisher's gamma distribution	
xGammaLn	natural logarithm of the gamma function, $\ln \Gamma(x)$	GAMMALN
xGammaLog	10-based logarithm of the gamma function, $\ln \Gamma(x)$	
xGammaQ	ratoio of two gamma functions, $\Gamma(x_1) / \Gamma(x_2)$	
xGEstep	threshold comparison, $= 1$ if $x \geq$ step, otherwise $= 0$	GESTEP
xGm	Euler's gamma, $=$xEu	
xGMmean	geometric mean	GEOMEAN
xGrad	gradient vector, i.e., first derivatives of a function $f(x,y,...)$	
xHMean	harmonic mean	HARMEAN
xImag	imaginary part of complex number	IMAGINARY
xIncr	increments by 1, $=$xAdd$(x,1)$	
xInt	integer part of number	
xIntercept	intercept of least squares straight line with y-axis	INTERCEPT
xIntLog10	$=$Int$[\log(|x|)/\log(10)]$	
xIntLog2	$=$Int$[\log(|x|)/\log(2)]$	
xIntMod	remainder R $=$ sign(D) $*$ { N $-$ D $*$ xInt(N/D) }	
xIntQR	quotient Q $=$ xInt(N/D) and remainder R $=$ N $-$ D $*$ Q	
xInv	inverse, $1/x$	
xIsErr	0 if no errors in range, otherwise 1	
xIsErrNA	0 if no errors in range, otherwise 1, ignoring N/A errors	
xIsEven	TRUE if trunc(x) $=$ even, FALSE if odd	ISEVEN
xIsInteger	TRUE if integer, FALSE if not	
xIsNumeric	$= 0$ for non-numeric, 1 for double precision, 2 for extended precision	
xIsOdd	TRUE if trunc(x) $=$ odd, FALSE if even	ISODD
xIsSquare	TRUE if perfect square	
xIsXNumber	TRUE if extended precision number that cannot be converted into double precision	
xJacobian	Jacobian matrix of a vector function	
xIElliptic1	elliptic integral of 1st kind	
xIElliptic2	elliptic integral of 2nd kind	
xLGI	interpolates Lagrange polynomial	
xLn	natural logarithm	LN
xLn10	$= \ln(10) \approx 2.302...$	
xLn2	$= \ln(2) \approx 0.693...$	
xLog	logarithm of any integer base n, $\log_n$, default $n = 10$	LOG
xLogistic	logistic distribution	

xLogNorm		lognormal distribution	
xLRE		negative logarithm of relative or absolute error	
xMAbs		modulus of matrix or vector, $\|\mathbf{M}\|$	
xMAbsC		Euclidian norm of complex matrix $\mathbf{C}$	
xMAdd		matrix addition, $= \mathbf{M}_1 + \mathbf{M}_2$	
xMAddC		complex matrix addition, $= \mathbf{C}_1 + \mathbf{C}_2$	
xMantissa		mantissa of a number x = mantissa $\times 10^{\text{exponent}}$	
xMatAbs	*	modulus of matrix or vector, $\|\mathbf{M}\|$, now xMAbs	
xMatAdd	*	matrix addition, $= \mathbf{M}_1 + \mathbf{M}_2$, now xMAdd	
xMatBAB	*	similarity transformation, $= \mathbf{B}^{-1} \mathbf{A} \mathbf{B}$, now xMBAB	
xMatDet	*	determinant of a matrix, now xMDet	MDETERM
xMatInv	*	inversion of a square matrix, $= \mathbf{M}^{-1}$, now xMInv	MINVERSE
xMatLL	*	Cholesky decomposition, $= \mathbf{L} \mathbf{L}^{\text{H}}$, now xMCholesky	
xMatLU	*	lower/upper decomposition $= \mathbf{L} \mathbf{U}$ with Crout's algorithm, now xMLU	MLU
xMatMult	*	matrix multiplication, $\mathbf{M}_1 \mathbf{M}_2$, now xMMult	MMULT
xMatPow	*	raising a square matrix to an integer power n, $= \mathbf{M}^n$, now xMPow	
xMatSub	*	subtraction of two real matrices, $= \mathbf{M}_1 - \mathbf{M}_2$, now xMSub	
xMax		maximum value in a range of values	
xMaxwell		Maxwell-Boltzmann distribution	
xMBAB		similarity transformation, $= \mathbf{B}^{-1} \mathbf{A} \mathbf{B}$	
xMCD		maximum common divisor = greatest common denominator	GCD
xMCharC		characteristic polynomial of complex matrix	
xMCholesky		Cholesky decomposition, $= \mathbf{L} \mathbf{L}^{\text{H}}$	
xMCM		minimum common multiple = least common multiple	LCM
xMCond		condition number κ of a real matrix	
xMCondC		condition number κ of a complex matrix	
xMCplx		converts two real matrices into one complex matrix	
xMDet		determinant of a matrix	MDETERM
xMDetC		determinant of a complex matrix	
xMean		arithmetic mean	AVERAGE
xMedian		median	MEDIAN
xMExp		matrix series expansion	
xMExpC		complex series expansion for $\exp(\mathbf{C})$	
xMExpErr		truncation error of xMatExp	
xMExpErrC		truncated error of complex series expansion for $\exp(\mathbf{C})$	
xMin		minimum value in a range of values	
xMInv		inversion of a square matrix, $= \mathbf{M}^{-1}$	MINVERSE
xMInvC		regular inverse of complex square matrix, $= \mathbf{C}^{-1}$	
xMLU		lower/upper decomposition $= \mathbf{L} \mathbf{U}$ with Crout's algorithm	MLU
xMMopUp		removes matrix elements a_{ij} when $\|a_{ij}\| <$ ErrMin	
xMMult		matrix multiplication, $\mathbf{M}_1 \mathbf{M}_2$	MMULT
xMMultC		multiplies two complex matrices, $\mathbf{C}_1 + \mathbf{C}_2$	
xMMultCS		multiplies a complex matrix and a complex scalar, $= \mathbf{C} \mathbf{S}$	
xMNormalize		normalizes the column vectors of a real matrix	
xMNormalizeC		normalizes the column vectors of a complex matrix	
xMode		most frequently occurring number in range of numbers	MODE
xMpCond		negative 10-based logarithm of condition number $\text{p}\kappa$ of a real matrix κ	
xMpCondC		negative 10-based logarithm of condition number $\text{p}\kappa$ of a complex matrix	
xMPow		raising a square matrix to an integer power n, $= \mathbf{M}^n$	
xMPowC		raise complex square matrix $\mathbf{C}$ to an integer power n, $= \mathbf{C}^n$	
xMPseudoInv		pseudo-inverse of matrix based on real SVD	
xMPseudoInvC		pseudo-inverse of matrix based on complex SVD	
xMRound		rounds a number to the nearest multiple	MROUND
xMSub		subtraction of two real matrices, $= \mathbf{M}_1 - \mathbf{M}_2$	
xMSubC		subtraction of two complex matrices, $= \mathbf{C}_1 - \mathbf{C}_2$	

552

xMTC	transpose of a complex matrix **C**	
xMTH	Hermitian (conjugate, adjoint) transpose of a complex matrix **C**	
xMult	multiplication	*
xMultinom	generates a multinomial	MULTINOMIAL
xMultMod	modular multiplication	
xNeg	negation, $= -x$	–
xNormal	normal distribution	NORMDIST
xNormalS	cumulative normal distribution	⑩ : NORM.S.DIST
xNormS	cumulative standard normal distribution	NORMSDIST
xOdd	rounds up to the nearest odd integer	ODD
xOddDen	checks if denominator is odd (TRUE) or even (FALSE)	
xPearson	Pearson product moment correlation coefficient	PEARSON
xPerm	the number of possible permutations	PERMUT
xPi	$\pi \approx 3.141...$	PI()
xPi2	$\pi / 2 \approx 1.570...$	
xPi4	$\pi / 4 \approx 0.785...$	
xPoly	evaluates polynomial $P(x)$ at specified x	
xPolyAdd	adds two polynomials in x	
xPolyDiv	divides two polynomials in x	
xPolyMult	multiplies two polynomials in x	
xPolyRem	the remainder of polynomial division	
xPolySub	subtracts two polynomials in x	
xPolyTerms	extracts polynomial coefficients as a vector	
xPow	raises number to power n, XN, n integer for $x < 0$	
xPow2	integer powers of 2, 2^n	
xPowMod	modular power, $a^p \bmod m$	
xProd	the product of two or more numbers	PRODUCT
xProdScal	scalar product of real vectors	
xProdScalC	scalar product of complex vectors	
xProdVect	vector product of two 3D vectors	
xQMean	quadratic mean	
xRad12	$=\sqrt{12}$	
xRad5	$=\sqrt{5}$	
xRadians	converts degrees to radians	RADIANS
xRand	generates random numbers with uniform distribution $U(0,1)$ between 0 and 1	RAND
xRandD	generates random numbers with uniform distribution $U(a,b)$ between a and b	RANDBETWEEN
xRandI	generates random numbers with uniform distribution $U(m,n)$ between integers m and n	
xRank	the rank of a number in a list of numbers	RANK
xRayleigh	Rayleigh distribution	
xRDown	rounds towards zero, default rounds to an integer	ROUNDDOWN
xReal	real component of complex number	IMREAL
xRegLinCoef	coefficients of a multivariate least squares fit	
xRegLinCov	covariance matrix of the coefficients of a multivariate least squares fit	
xRegLinErr	standard deviations of the coefficients of a multivariate least squares fit	
xRegLinEval	evaluates the least squares results at a specified value of x	
xRegLinStat	R^2 and standard deviation s_f of a multivariate least squares fit	
xRegPolyCoef	coefficients of the least squares fit to an internally computed polynomial in x	
xRegPolyErr	standard deviations of the coefficients of the least squares fit to that polynomial in x	
xRegPolyStat	R^2 and standard deviation of the least squares fit to that polynomial in x	
xRegrL	coefficients of a SVD-based multivariate linear least squares	
xRegrLC	coefficients of a SVD-based complex multivariate linear least squares	
xRoot	n^{th} root, $=x^{1/n}$	
xRound	rounding, with ending-5 rounded away from zero, default rounds to an integer	ROUND
xRoundR	relative rounding, default to 15 decimals	
xRSq	square of the Pearson product moment correlation coefficient	RSQ

xRUp	rounds away from zero, default rounds up to an integer	ROUNDUP
xSerie	generates a series for $f(x)$ over a specified range in x	
xSerie2D	generates a doubleseries for $f(x,y)$ over specified ranges in x and y	
xSerSum	sums a power series	SERIESSUM
xSin	sine of an angle, $=\sin\alpha$)	SIN
xSinH	hyperbolic sine of a number, $=\sinh(x)$	SINH
xSlope	slope of least squares fit to a straight line	SLOPE
xSplit	splits a number $x =$ mantissa $\times 10^{\text{exponent}}$ into its mantissa and exponent	
xSqr	square root, $=\sqrt{x}$	SQRT
xSqrPi	square root of pi, $=\sqrt{\pi}$	
xStatis	univariate statistical summary	
xStDev	sample standard deviation of repeat measurements	STDEV
xStDevP	population standard deviation of repeat measurements	STDEVP
xSub	subtract	–
xSubMod	modular subtraction	
xSum	sum of a range of cells	SUM
xSumProd	sum product of two cell ranges	SUMPRODUCT
xSumSq	sum of squares of terms in an array	SUMSQ
xSumX2mY2	sum of the differences of squares of corresponding terms in two arrays	SUMY2MY2
xSumX2pY2	sum of the sum of squares of corresponding terms in two arrays	SUMY2PY2
xSumXmY2	sum of the squares of the differences between corresponding terms in two arrays	SUMYMY2
xSVDD	Σ matrix of singular value decomposition $\mathbf{M} = \mathbf{U}\,\Sigma\,\mathbf{V}^{\mathrm{T}}$ of a rectangular matrix $\mathbf{M}$ with only real components	
xSVDDC	Σ matrix of singular value decomposition $\mathbf{M} = \mathbf{U}\,\Sigma\,\mathbf{V}^{\mathrm{H}}$ of a rectangular matrix with complex components	
xSVDU	$\mathbf{U}$ matrix of singular value decomposition $\mathbf{M} = \mathbf{U}\,\Sigma\,\mathbf{V}^{\mathrm{T}}$ of a rectangular matrix with only real components	
xSVDUC	$\mathbf{U}$ matrix of singular value decomposition $\mathbf{M} = \mathbf{U}\,\Sigma\,\mathbf{V}^{\mathrm{H}}$ of a rectangular matrix with complex components	
xSVDV	$\mathbf{V}$ matrix of singular value decomposition $\mathbf{M} = \mathbf{U}\,\Sigma\,\mathbf{V}^{\mathrm{T}}$ of a rectangular matrix with only real components	
xSVDVC	$\mathbf{V}$ matrix of singular value decomposition $\mathbf{M} = \mathbf{U}\,\Sigma\,\mathbf{V}^{\mathrm{H}}$ of a rectangular matrix with complex components	
xSysLin	Gauss-Jordan solution of linear system $\mathbf{A}\,\mathbf{x} = \mathbf{B}$	
xSysLinC	Gauss-Jordan solution of complex linear system $\mathbf{A}\,\mathbf{x} = \mathbf{B}$	
xTan	tangent of an angle, $=\tan(\alpha)$	TAN
xTanH	hyperbolic tangent of a number, $=\tanh(x)$	TANH
xTrunc	truncation to fixed number n of placed past the decimal point, default $n = 0$	TRUNC
xTruncMod	remainder $R = N - D * \text{xTrunc}(N/D)$, with sign of numerator N	
xTruncQR	truncate (number, divisor) to yield (quotient Q, remainder R)	
xTruncR	truncate to fixed number n of significant digits	
xUnformat	removes all formatting characters	
xVar	sample variance of a set of repeat measurements	VAR
xVarP	population variance of a set of repeat measurements	VARP
xWeibull	Weibull distribution	
xZeta	zeta distribution	

Table 11.11.1: Alphabetical listing of the XN functions with extended precision (beyond quadruple), readily identifiable by their prefix x. Some "raw" duplicate functions (with last letter R) have been omitted. For the sake of uniformity with the function names in Matrix.xla(m), those indicated with * were updated to function names that started with xM instead of xMat, but were grandfathered so that you can still use the older spreadsheets.

11.12 Using XN functions directly on the spreadsheet

XN is designed for use in and together with Excel, and therefore needs instructions that are clearly distinguishable from Excel, which it typically accomplishes with the prefix x. XN uses the same syntax as that of most Excel functions, except for the few algebra-like simple operations such as a plus sign for addition, an asterisk for multiplication, a slant for division, or ^ for exponentiation. Note that Excel also drops that quasi-algebraic notation in its matrix and complex functions, such as in MMult (M1,M2) or IMSUM (z_1, z_2). Exercise 11.12.1 lets you write some simple instructions in Excel and XN, and Fig. 11.12.1 shows the resulting spreadsheet.

	A	B	C	D	E	F	G	H
1								
2		$a = 7$			*Excel implementation:*	*operation:*	*XN implementation:*	
3		$b = 3$						
4				C2+C3=	10	$a+b$	10	=xAdd(C2,C3)
5				C2-C3=	4	$a-b$	4	=xSub(C2,C3)
6				C2*C3=	21	ab	21	=xMult(C2,C3)
7				C2/C3=	2.3333333333333300	a/b	2.3333333333333333333333333333	=xDiv(C2,C3)
8				EXP(C3)=	20.0855369231877000	e^b	20.085536923187766774092852965	=xExp(C3)
9				LN(C3)=	1.0986122886681100	$\ln b$	1.0986122886681096913952452 37	=xLn(C3)
10				LOG(C3)=	0.477121255	$\log b$	0.47712125471966624372950279033	=xLog(C3)
11				C2^C3=	343	a^b	343	=xPow(C2,C3)
12				C2*LN(C3)=	7.6902860206767700	$a \ln b$	7.6902860206767678397667 16659	=xMult(C2,xLn(C3))
13								
14						a/b	2.33333333333333333333333333333333333333	
15								=xDiv(C2,C3,35)

Fig. 11.12.1: A spreadsheet sampler comparing some of the basic operations of Excel and XN. For the value of *a* in cell C2, and *b* in cell C3, and the operations listed in column F, columns D and H show the codes, and columns E and G the results in Excel and XN respectively.

Exercise 11.12.1:

(1) Open a new spreadsheet, and in it enter some simple values in, say, cells C2 and C3.

(2) In E4:E12 enter the simple Excel commands shown in column D of Fig. 11.12.1, and verify that you get the same answers. You may have to widen column E to display its contents in scientific notation with 16 Decimal places.

(3) In G4 deposit the instruction =xAdd(C2,C3) which is the XN equivalent of Excel's =C2+C3. Likewise, in G5:G12 place the XN instructions shown in cells H5:H12. We have left-aligned G2:H13.

(4) The resulting spreadsheet should now look like Fig. 11.12.1.

We see that the XN-results in G4 through G6 as well as in G11 are identical to those of Excel, because XN does not show unnecessary (i.e., nonsignificant) trailing (or leading) zeroes. The first difference in Fig. 11.12.1 between results obtained with Excel or XN occurs in cell G7, which here displays *a/b* with 28 significant digits (as preset when you download XN from Steve Beyers' or my website), whereas E7 shows the same quotient with 15 significant digits plus added (but incorrect) "filler" zeroes, because the display format specifies 16 decimals past the decimal point. The same applies to cells E8, E9 and E12.

Please note the following aspects.

(1) The XN results are shown here with 28 decimals, i.e., in approximately quadruple precision, which is used in these intial illustrations as the default *D*-value, in which case it need not be specified in the instructions after it has been set as the default. When you want to use a different numberlength *D*, you must specify that precision with an added parameter, as in =xExp(C3,35) or =xMult(C5,C6,35), which will then show its answer to 35 decimals, or to whatever numberlength you have specified. This is illustrated in cells G14:H15. If you want to use a *D*-value different from 28 as the default, you must change it in the XN Configuration setting, in which case you can still overwrite it in specific calls.

(2) For a given XN instruction, the number of spreadsheet address locations within brackets contains a fixed minimum, e.g., two in H4:H7, one in H8:H10. An additional, optional number or cell address will then specify the numerical precision. In this way we need not spell out that the last value in the argument has a different meaning than the preceding one(s), but it does imply a convention that you need to follow. You can specify the default numerical precision, specify its value with a particular instruction (as in G14:H15), or store it in a spreadsheet cell to which instructions refer. The latter approach is convenient when you want to change the numerical precision of a complex computation involving many instructions, because the stored number then serves as the master switch for *D*. For instance, if we were to specify the number 70 in cell C15 of Fig. 11.12.1, then =xExp(C6,C15) would yield e^3 to 70 decimals. Please note the confusing nomenclature: the term Decimal places in Excel's Format ⇨ Cells ⇨ Number refers specif-

ically to the number of digits *past the decimal point*, whereas decimals, *D*, or DgtMax in XN denotes *all decimals used* in the representation, regardless of the position of the decimal point. The latter usage is more suitable for science and engineering, but clearly not for accounting.

(3) Be careful: when you replace the instruction in E4 with =C2+C3+C15 you will get 80 if C15 contains the value 70, but if you were to "translate" this into =xAdd(C5,C6,C15) you would get 10, computed to 70 decimals, but only displaying its one significant trailing zero, because XN adds the first and second quantities, and interprets the third number as specifying the required precision. Specifying four or more quantities in the argument of xAnd() will yield the #VALUE! error message, and you get the same message if you write, e.g., =xAdd(C3:C5). Incidentally, XN's interpretation of =xAdd(C5,C6,C15) illustrates that you can specify the desired computational numberlength either as a number, or as the address where its value can be found.

(4) Being able to compute in extended precision is often very useful, but displaying a result in its extended glory is often (except for checking purposes) unnecessary, space wasting, and may even come across as somewhat pompous. You cannot control the numberlength displayed in G7:G15 with the usual F<u>o</u>rmat ⇨ C<u>e</u>lls ⇨ Number sequence (try it!), because the results of XN are strings, even though their numerical values are recognized by both Excel and XN. Instead, use the fact that Excel allows cells containing text strings to overflow into adjacent cells, but only as long as these adjacent cells are *empty*. Therefore, as soon as you place some data or text in cells H7:H12, the maximum number of decimals displayed in G7:G12 is controlled by the width of column G and the font type and size used. Moreover, if you want to restrict the size of the XN output but have nothing useful to place in the adjacent column, just enter the non-showing apostrophe, '. Again, try out how this works. In cell G14 we specifically wanted to show all 35 decimals, and therefore left cell H14 untouched, instead placing the corresponding explanation in H15.

(5) Restricting the number of digits displayed in this way only works properly when you format the output cells as *left aligned*, otherwise you may only see a middle part or the tail end of the computed result. However, this means that exponents are not displayed; to visualize those, you need to switch temporarily to right alignment. Convince yourself on the spreadsheet that things indeed are as described here. Incidentally, outputting the results on the spreadsheet after conversion into double precision while at the same time showing them in full with Debug.Print statements in the Immediate Window avoids any such problems.

(6) Assuming that there is a good reason to go beyond double precision, such as when you anticipate that there might be a numerical problem with the method used, you should not round any intermediate results, because that may just undo the extra effort. However, it may well be appropriate to convert the *final* result back to double precision, e.g., with the instruction =xCDbl.

Exercise 11.12.2:

(1) Open a new spreadsheet, and in cell C5 enter =1/3. (If you just type 1/3 and Enter, Excel will consider it a date, and change it in that sense, *irreversibly*. You can prevent this most readily with the equal sign, which makes Excel expect a formula, or by pre-labeling cell C5 with F<u>o</u>rmat ⇨ C<u>e</u>lls ⇨ Number and by then specifying, e.g., Fraction.

(2) In D5 place the instruction =C5, and format that cell to show 16 digits past the decimal point. In cell F5 place the instruction =xCStr(C5,35) or =xAdd(C5,0,35) which shows the first 35 decimals of the exact decimal representation of how C5 is actually stored in the computer in binary form. (You only see 20 decimals because the rest are trailing, nonsignificant zeroes, and are therefore not displayed by XN.)

(3) In F6 deposit the instruction =xDiv(1,3,35) to show what 1/3 really should look like with 35 decimals. If you need to enter 1/3 in an XN calculation, do it this way; don't take it from the spreadsheet, because it will read the binary version of it, which in this case is clearly approximate beyond its sixteenth decimal.

(4) In D7 deposit the instruction =xCDbl(F6) to illustrate how you can easily retrieve the standard Excel format from an XN spreadsheet number.

(5) If you enter 12345.6789 in cell C9, and copy the instructions from D5:F5 to D9, you will again see some "junk" in the tail of F9. If you want to enter the input data as shown in C7, without the distortion caused by converting from decimal to binary representation, enter the number in C9 within quotation marks, as with =xAdd("12345.6789",0,35), as shown in cell F10. If you don't want to go through the bother of placing quotation marks around the input data, first

truncate them with `=xTruncR(C9,10)`, or include that in the instruction, as shown in cell F11. Such methods are only needed for noninteger numbers that cannot be represented exactly in binary format.

(6) Converting XN data back to Excel's double precision format is done with the instruction `=xCDbl`, as when placing the instruction `=xCDbl(F6)` in cell D7. Many applications of XN will involve functions and macros, and will end with this conversion back to double precision before returning their results to the spreadsheet. Since XN stays in the decimal domain, it avoids the errors inherent in converting from base-10 to base-2 and vice versa.

(7) Figure 11.12.2 summarizes these operations.

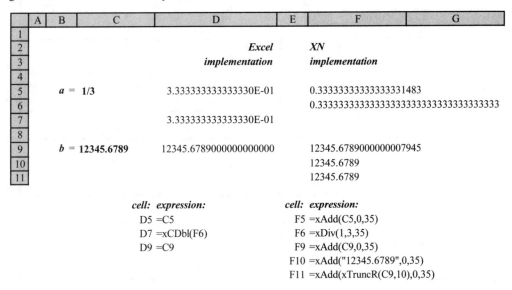

		Excel implementation	XN implementation
$a =$	1/3	3.333333333333330E-01	0.33333333333333331483
			0.333333333333333333333333333333333333
		3.333333333333330E-01	
$b =$	12345.6789	12345.6789000000000000	12345.6789000000007945
			12345.6789
			12345.6789

cell:	expression:		cell:	expression:
D5	=C5		F5	=xAdd(C5,0,35)
D7	=xCDbl(F6)		F6	=xDiv(1,3,35)
D9	=C9		F9	=xAdd(C9,0,35)
			F10	=xAdd("12345.6789",0,35)
			F11	=xAdd(xTruncR(C9,10),0,35)

Fig. 11.12.2: Moving between Excel's double-precision format and XN.

Exercise 11.12.3 is another example, this one involving matrices. We will first analyze a matrix with Matrix.xla(m), then with XN.xla(m). To illustrate some special features, we will use a singular matrix.

Exercise 11.12.3:

(1) Open a new sheet, and in cell block B3:**D**7 enter the values shown in Fig. 11.12.3. In E3 enter the instruction =B3−C3+D3, and copy this down to E7. This will ensure that the matrix **M** in B3:E7 is singular, because E3:E7 is now a linear function of the other three columns.

(2) Highlight B10:E14, then type =SVDU(B3:E7) and block-enter this instruction. Likewise, in B17:E20 compute **Σ** with an equal sign followed by the formula indicated in cell B16, and in B23:E26 do the same to find **V**.

(3) We will compute two more matrices of this set, to verify that our results obtained with Matrix are correct. In B29:E33 calculate the product **U Σ**, and in B36:E40 the product **U Σ V**^{T}, which should be equal to **M** in B3:E7. Annotate the matrices as illustrated in Fig. 11.12.3, so that it will be easy to see what is what. Note that the fourth singular value, in E20, is essentially zero, as it should be because there are only three independent columns in **M**, and therefore only three valid singular values. Therefore, the last column in **Σ**, E17:E20, as well as its last row, B20:E20, are really (disregarding round-off errors) zero. as is the last column in **U Σ**, E29:E33, here shown with five digits past the decimal point.

(4) For the moment, leave G3:J7 blank, and in G10:J14 compute **U** with =xSVDU(B3:E7). By not specifying DgtMax we adopt its automatic default value, 28.

(5) Make sure that G1:K40 is left-aligned, so that you can see the leading digits of the values shown. Place an apostrophe in cell K1, and copy it all the way down to row 40. This will keep the numbers in column J from overflowing into the neighboring columns to its right.

(6) There is one danger in displaying XN results this way, viz. that you will miss any added exponents, such as E-34 in cell J20. (Missing 34 orders of magnitude might lead to nontrivial errors!) Therefore, highlight G10:J14, and right-align. This will allow you to inspect the tail ends of the values, where those exponents can be found. It also helps to have columns B:E for comparison. In our example, you will find several numbers with the exponent E-2: in G11, I12, and H13, as well as in J14. You may want to display these in bold, italics and/or color, as a reminder that they have a (non-showing) exponent. For J14 you have space to put the exponent in its adjacent cell, H14. Then return to left-alignment.

	A	B	C	D	E	F	G	H	I	J	K
2							xCDbl(G36:J40)				
3	**M** =	5	4	-13	-12	**M**$_{rec}$ =	5	4	-13	-12	
4		4	3	-1	0		4	3	-1	9.73E-31	
5		3	5	8	6		3	5	8	6	
6		2	-2	5	9		2	-2	5	9	
7		1	6	-1	-6		1	6	-1	-6	
9		SVDU(B3:E7)					xSVDU(B3:E7)				
10	**U** =	-0.78690	0.19669	-0.44775	0.36896	**U** =	-0.7868988	0.19668776	0.447745434	-0.35349403	
11		-0.06810	0.40100	-0.37892	-0.74456		**-6.8100236**	0.40100124	0.378918964	0.82805308	
12		0.36020	0.75087	0.04834	0.48087		0.36020442	0.750873281	**-4.83370245**	-0.2695504	
13		0.42270	0.08576	-0.60694	-0.01489		0.42269696	**8.57594591**	0.60693754	-0.3352938	
14		-0.26026	0.47890	0.53407	-0.27938		-0.2602550	0.478901401	-0.53407377	**-6.55030596**E-2	
16		SVDD(B3:E7)					xSVDD(B3:E7)				
17	**Σ** =	23.49462	0	0	0	**Σ** =	23.4946159	0	0	0	
18		0	10.51076	0	0		0	10.5107581	0	0	
19		0	0	6.2870491	0		0	0	6.287049089	0	
20		0	0	0	*1.3E-15*		0	0	0	**1.29893555**E-34	
22		SVDV(B3:E7)					xSVDV(B3:E7)				
23	**V** =	-0.10816	0.52237	-0.68223	-0.5	**V** =	-0.1081585	0.52236802	0.68222678	0.5	
24		-0.16846	0.80356	0.27553	0.5		-0.1684555	0.80355865	-0.27552898	-0.5	
25		0.66199	0.28532	0.47996	-0.5		0.66198826	0.285320991	-0.47996194	0.5	
26		0.72229	0.00413	-0.47779	0.5		0.72228526	**4.13035953**	0.477793814	-0.5	
28		MMULT(B10:E14,B17:E20)					xMMult(G10:J14,G17:J20)				
29	**U Σ** =	-18.4879	2.06734	-2.81500	0.00000	**U Σ** =	-18.487885	2.067337546	2.814997524	**-4.5916599**E-35	
30		-1.59999	4.21483	-2.38228	0.00000		-1.5999889	4.214827082	2.382282131	**1.07558759**E-34	
31		8.46286	7.89225	0.30390	0.00000		8.46286455	7.892247466	-0.30389724	**-3.5012867**E-35	
32		9.93110	0.90140	-3.81585	0.00000		9.93110275	0.901396933	3.815846111	**-4.3552505**E-35	
33		-6.11459	5.03362	3.35775	0.00000		-6.1145915	5.033616821	-3.35774803	**-8.5084252**E-36	
35		MMULT(B29:E33,MT(BC23:E26))					xMMult(G29:J333,xMT(G23:J26))				
36	**U Σ V**^{T} =	5	4	-13	-12	**U Σ V**^{T} =	4.99999999	3.99999999	-12.9999999	-11.9999999	
37		4	3	-1	6.146E-16		4.00000000	3.00000000	-0.99999999	**9.73035478**E-31	
38		3	5	8	6		3.00000000	5.00000000	8.00000000	6.00000000	
39		2	-2	5	9		1.99999999	-1.99999999	5.00000000	8.99999999	
40		1	6	-1	-6		1.00000000	6.00000000	-0.99999999	-6.00000000	

Fig. 11.12.3a: The left half of the spreadsheet of Exercise 11.12.3. Thin internal borders were inserted in columns G:J for better readability. Note that the italicized values in cells G11, I12, H13 and H26 don't show their corresponding exponents.

(7) Now you can compare the numbers in G10:J14 with those in B10:E14, keeping in mind that the values shown the italics should actually start with 0.0. You will notice that these two sets agree, except for the fourth column, a point to which we will return below.

(8) In G17:J20 compute **Σ** with =xSVDD(B3:E7). Again it is useful to specify the exponent right next to the fourth singular value, because you will then notice that it is again close to zero *for the numerical precision used*.

(9) Similarly, calculate **V**, **U Σ** and **U Σ V**^{T} in G23:J26, G29:J33, and G36:J40 respectively. G36:J40 should now display the original matrix M, and it does. For ease of comparison you may also want to compute =xCDbl(xMMult(G29: J33,xMT(G23:J26)) in G3:J7. Figure 11.12.3 shows all the above results.

558

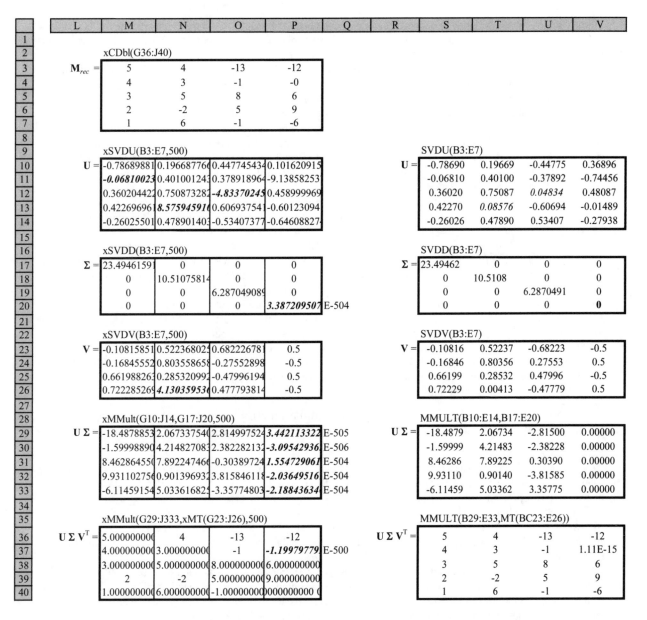

Fig. 11.12.3b: The right half of the spreadsheet of Exercise 11.12.3 including, in columns S through V, the reconstitution of **M** after setting the fourth singular value to zero.

(10) To see the effect of higher numerical precision, copy F1:K40 to L1, then adjust all matrices to use, e.g., DgtMax = 500. You can do this by highlighting every matrix, one at a time, adding , 500 to its argument, and block-entering the modified matrix instruction. Alternatively, you may want to place such a value somewhere on the spreadsheet, say in cell R1, and then add R1 instead of the fixed value 500 to each XN instruction (except xMT). That would make it easier to change the XN precision.

(11) You will notice that the numbers obtained do not vary much from columns B:E to G:J and, finally, M:P, except in two respects. First, the fouth singular value is not at all constant, but roughly scales with the precision used. That is a clear indication that it is not a realistic number, but an artifact of the computations. It is, indeed, always of the order of magnitude of the precision used. If you want to find out whether a small singular value is realistic or not, changing the numerical precision of computing Σ provides a convenient test.

(12) A second aspect is that the numbers in the fourth column of $U \Sigma$ exhibit similarly irregular behavior, not surprisingly because they all use σ_4 as their multiplier. And the same applies to the element (2,4) of $U \Sigma V^T$. Those values are not reliable.

(13) Finally, note that the reconstitution of M in M3:P7 as =xCDbl(M36:P40) yields a 0 (in this case, with a minus sign!) in cell P4 rather than a small value in scientific notation, such as we encountered in cell J4. This simply results from the fact that Excel cannot represent a very small number such as E–500, see Table 8.5.1.

(14) Moreover, the numbers in P10:P14 are again different from, but of a similar order of magnitude as those in J10:J14 and E10:E14. What is going on here? These numbers really should be zero, because the matrix M is singular, and therefore has only three nonzero singular values. Remember that the columns of U represent the eigenvectors of the matrix M M^T, where M actually should be a 3-by-5 matrix so that M^T is 5-by-3 and M M^T 3-by-3, and therefore can only have 3 eigenvalues and 3 corresponding eigenvectors. The numbers in E10:E14, J10:J14, and P10:P14 therefore should be zero. Why, then, don't they scale with DgtMax?

(15) Here is the explanation. The numbers are purely numerical artifacts, and as such should scale with DgtMax. But such artifacts can get multiplied in some matrix operations by a factor κ, the condition number of the source matrix. And that will just keep their order of magnitude independent of DgtMax, because when σ_4 gets smaller, $\kappa = \sigma_1/\sigma_4$ gets larger by the same factor! This clearly illustrates the perverse effect of working with very ill-conditioned matrices.

(16) What happens when we just set σ_4 equal to zero? Try it out in columns R:V. Here we will do it in double precision, using the corresponding Matrix.xla instructions. (Check out for yourself that you get equivalent results with XN.) For U, simply copy A9:E14 to R9:V14, and similarly copy V from A22:E26 to R22:V26, and then change their arguments from S3:V7 back to B3:E7. But if you were to do the same for Σ, you would not be able to change σ_4 because it is an individual matrix element. Therefore, first fill S23:V26 (or at least all of its off-diagonal elements) with zeroes, then copy σ_1 from B17 to S17, and likewise copy σ_2 and σ_3 to their equivalent places, but set σ_4 in V20 to zero.

(17) Now you can copy A29:E40 to R29; it will automatically adjust to the new arguments. The result in S36:V40 suggests that only element 2,4 is changed, but that is not the case: if you look with higher precision, you will see that all elements of the reconstituted matrix are affected, i.e., you redistribute the round-off error in σ_4, but you will see it only in element 2,4 when you display the result with limited precision.

In section 11.6 we considered an example of accumulation errors. Since these are clearly related to the finite precision of numerical calculations, let's see what XN can do for us in that case.

Exercise 11.12.4:

(1) In cell B2 of a new spreadsheet place a column heading for n, and in C2 one for I_n. In B4:B104 place the integers 0 (1) 100, in cell C4 enter the instruction =LN(6/5), in C5 the formula =1/B5-5*C4, and copy this down to row 104. Plot C4:C103 versus B4:B104. You should get a result such as Fig. 11.6.1 or 11.12.4*a*.

(2) In cell D1 place the label D =, and in E1 a corresponding value, such as 28. In D4 place the instruction =xLn(xDiv(6,5,E$1),E$1), in D5 put the formula =xSub(xDiv(1,$B5,E$1),xMult(5,D4,E$1),$1), and again copy this last instruction down. Visually inspect the results, and verify that they start out correctly, and only begin to oscillate at much higher n-values than in Fig. 11.12.4*a*.

(3) But when you try to plot D4:D104 versus B4:B104, you get zeroes in your plot, again because Excel's plotting routine cannot read XN output. If you were to remedy this, by embedding the instructions in column D in xCDbl(....), you would find oscillations similar to those in Fig. 11.12.4*a*, because the instructions at a given value of n refer to the value in the cell directly above it, at $n-1$, where it finds and therefore reads the double-precision value.

(4) The solution to this conundrum is to leave column D alone, and to do the conversion in a separate column. In E4 therefore place =xCDbl(D4), copy this down to row 104, and plot E4:E104 vs. B4:B104. This time you should find results such as shown in Fig. 11.12.4*b*.

(5) Now copy D1:E104 to F1, change the value in G1 to, say, 70, then plot G4:G104 against B4:B104. You should now see something like Fig. 11.12.4c, and the top of your spreadsheet should resemble Fig. 11.12.5.

You see that XN doesn't cure the problem of accumulation errors, but delays its reckoning. In this example, double precision gives you correct integrals I_n to about $n = 20$, quadruple precision (DgtMax = 28) yields correct results to about $n = 40$, and you need DgtMax = 70 = 5 × 14 to push the oscillations out of the way till about $n = 100$, and even then there is still plenty of slack in DgtMax. However, when you extend the n-scale far enough, you will eventually find the limits of any numerical representation of finite precision.

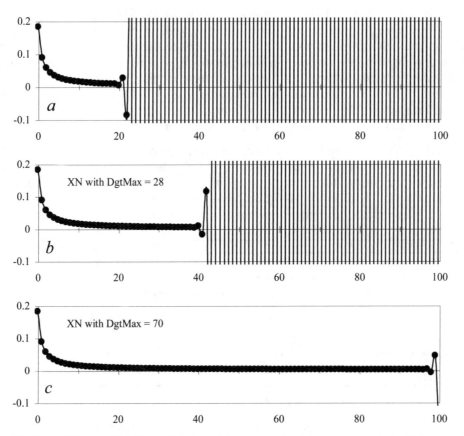

Fig. 11.12.4: The integral I_n of eq.(11.6.1) as a function of the nonnegative integer n, computed with the recursive formula (11.6.4) and starting from $I_0 = \ln(5/6)$. Panels a, b, and c use standard double precision, quadruple precision, and 70-decimal precision respectively. The higher precision doesn't abolish the oscillations, but pushes them to larger n-values.

	A	B	C	D	E	F	G
1				D = 28		D = 70	
2		*n*	I_n	I_n		I_n	
3				XN	xCDbl	XN	xCDbl
4		0	0.182322	0.18232155	0.182322	0.18232155	0.182322
5		1	0.088392	0.08839221	0.088392	0.08839221	0.088392
6		2	0.058039	0.05803891	0.058039	0.05803891	0.058039
7		3	0.043139	0.04313873	0.043139	0.04313873	0.043139
8		4	0.034306	0.03430632	0.034306	0.03430632	0.034306
9		5	0.028468	0.02846835	0.028468	0.02846835	0.028468
10		6	0.024325	0.02432490	0.024325	0.02432490	0.024325
11		7	0.021233	0.02123261	0.021233	0.02123261	0.021233

cell: instruction: *copied to:*

C4 = LN(6/5)
C5 = 1/B5-5*C4   C6:C104
D4 = xLn(xDiv(6,5,E$1),E$1)
D5 = xSub(xDiv(1,$B5,E$1),xMult(5,D4,E$1),E$1) D6:D104
E4 = xCDbl(D4)   E5:E104

Fig. 11.12.5: The annotated top of the spreadsheet of Exercise 11.12.4. Columns B, C, E, and G are centered, and the last three of these are set to display 6 places past the decimal point, correctly rounded.

A second observation is that the Excel plotting routine cannot use XN data as its input, because it sees them as the text strings they are, rather than as numbers. Therefore, if you want to display intermediate results, make a second column where you use xCDbl to convert them back to double precision, and use these for the plotting routine. In a well-written XN macro you will not encounter this, because all values that will be plotted should be computed first, and only then should the results (including those for any graphs) be converted into double precision and returned to the spreadsheet. In general, whenever an XN function depends on another XN function, you should not use intermediate answers rounded to double precision as input for the second XN function. Only round the final outputs, just before you display them.

In exercise 11.12.5 we revisit the Hilbert matrix, which can give serious numerical difficulties upon its inversion, see section 10.18.2. These difficulties are of two kinds: the conversion from fractions such as 1/7 to binary is inexact, and Hilbert matrices of large dimensions are quite ill-conditioned, which can easily invalidate their inversion. Such problems are readily solved using XN, by performing both the division of integers (as in 1/7) as well as the matrix inversion at higher precision.

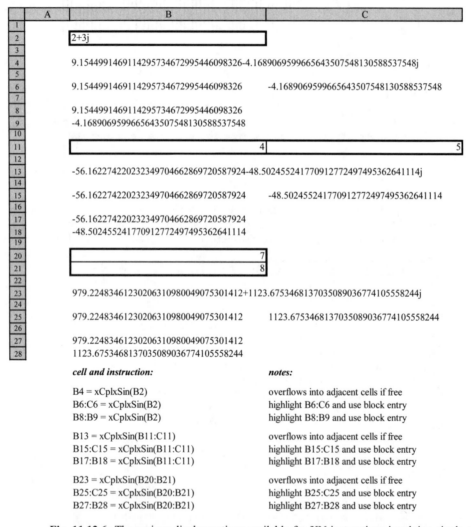

	A	B	C
1			
2		2+3j	
3			
4		9.15449914691142957346729954460983226-4.16890695996656435075481305885375548j	
5			
6		9.15449914691142957346729954460983226	-4.16890695996656435075481305885375548
7			
8		9.15449914691142957346729954460983226	
9		-4.16890695996656435075481305885375548	
10			
11		4	5
12			
13		-56.1622742202323497046628697205879244-48.502455241770912772497495362641114j	
14			
15		-56.1622742202323497046628697205879244	-48.502455241770912772497495362641114
16			
17		-56.1622742202323497046628697205879244	
18		-48.502455241770912772497495362641114	
19			
20		7	
21		8	
22			
23		979.224834612302063109800490753014122+1123.67534681370350890367741055558244j	
24			
25		979.224834612302063109800490753014122	1123.67534681370350890367741055558244
26			
27		979.224834612302063109800490753014122	
28		1123.67534681370350890367741055558244	

cell and instruction:	notes:
B4 = xCplxSin(B2)	overflows into adjacent cells if free
B6:C6 = xCplxSin(B2)	highlight B6:C6 and use block entry
B8:B9 = xCplxSin(B2)	highlight B8:B9 and use block entry
B13 = xCplxSin(B11:C11)	overflows into adjacent cells if free
B15:C15 = xCplxSin(B11:C11)	highlight B15:C15 and use block entry
B17:B18 = xCplxSin(B11:C11)	highlight B17:B18 and use block entry
B23 = xCplxSin(B20:B21)	overflows into adjacent cells if free
B25:C25 = xCplxSin(B20:B21)	highlight B25:C25 and use block entry
B27:B28 = xCplxSin(B20:B21)	highlight B27:B28 and use block entry

Fig. 11.12.6: The various display options available for XN instructions involving single complex numbers, here illustrated for D set to a default value of 35. In each case the input used is shown inside a heavy box. In cell B2 the imaginary unit (i or j) must be identified as such.

562

Exercise 11.12.5:

(1) In cells B3:M14 enter a 12×12 Hilbert matrix.

(2) Highlight B17:M28 and enter the block instruction =MInv(B3:M14).

(3) In cell B31 place the instruction (B17-ROUND(B17,0))/ROUND(B17,0), and copy it to B31:M42. You will see relative errors exceeding 0.1% in the left-top corner of B31:M42. For a 16×16 Hilbert matrix you wouldn't get a single valid answer in the inverse.

(4) In N1 place the label D =, in O1 deposit a numerical value for DgtMax, say 35, in N3:N14 place the numbers 0 (1) 11, and in P1:AA1 the numbers 1 (1) 12.

(5) In P3 enter the formula =xDiv(1,xAdd($N3,P$1,$O$1),$O$1) and copy this to P3:AA14. This will generate your Hilbert matrix in extended precision.

(6) In P17:AA28 use =xMInv(P3:AA14,O1) to compute the inverse of the Hilbert matrix.

(7) In cell P31 use =xCDbl(xDiv(xSub(P17,xRound(P17,0),$O$1),xRound(P17,0),$O$1)) to compute the relative errors of the inverted Hilbert matrix. You will find relative errors less than 1E-20. This is as you would expect with D = 35 and $p\kappa \approx 16$, because that should leave you with at least $(D - p\kappa) \approx 19$ significant digits.

(8) Vary the value of D, say from 28 to 70 to 210, and verify that this relationship between $D - p\kappa$ and the relative errors in the answer indeed holds. Upon using xMInv to invert this particular Hilbert matrix, with $p\kappa \approx 16$, you lose about 15 decimals to insignificance. The value of $(D - p\kappa)$ is therefore a useful guide to anticipate what precision D you will need to keep your relative errors in such an inversion below a given level.

Finally, the coding for instructions of single complex numbers in different input and output formats has been streamlined, as illustrated in Fig. 11.12.6.

First you select to use either i or j for $\sqrt{(-1)}$ in the XN toolbox under X_Edit ⇨ Configuration by deleting or selecting the option Use j instead of i; in this book we use j. You can now move freely between single-cell or double-cell (across or down) notation for either input or output merely by the formats of the selected input and output cells or cell blocks. The nine resulting options are illustrated in Fig. 11.12.6. For array operations this approach would be ambiguous, and you therefore still need to use the optional Ctype unless you want to use the default (1 = horizontal split).

11.13 Using XN functions in custom routines

Now that you have used extended-precision functions directly on the spreadsheet, let's see how to use them in background, in custom functions and macros. To do so, make sure that XN.xla(m) is properly installed in the VBEditor, as described in section 1.2.6. Check that the XN toolbar is activated, otherwise do so by clicking once on the XN (purple book) icon. The latter has a very practical reason. When an XN function or macro yields an error message (which will happen at some time, typically during the initial development or subsequent refinement of a custom routine), it will often get you inside the XN code. To extricate yourself from there, while realizing that the error most likely lies elsewhere, you not only should push the reset (Alt⌣R⌣R) but thereafter also the Help ⇨ ReInit Mem Variables button on the XN toolbar. Then fix the code you wrote, as it is almost always safe to assume that the XN code is correct. If you don't use ReInit Mem Variables, you may have to reactivate XN in the VBEditor, on some versions of Excel a major pain as it may involve more than one hundred manual priority-up pushes!

Exercise 11.13.1 will give you a taste of writing some simple functions, and Fig. 11.13.1 will illustrate them. If you wish, you can add Debug.Print statements to display intermediate results in the Immediate Window; in that case, remove them after testing is no longer necessary. Don't select a *function* name that is interpretable as a spreadsheet address. We therefore have used the unambiguous name F1F rather than F1 or FF1. This applies to functions but not to macros or, in general, to subroutines, which do not show as instructions on the spreadsheet.

Exercise 11.13.1:

(1) In a spreadsheet, open a new VBEditor module, and open its Immediate Window. Now type the following functions in the VBEditor module:

```
Function F1F()
F1F = xMult(3, xPi())
End Function
```

Then switch back to the spreadsheet and in cell B2 enter the instruction =F1F(). You should see the result in default (quadruple) precision. Note that F1F() is a function without an argument, just like the Excel function Pi() and the XN function xPi().

(2) In the VBEditor now type:
```
Function F2F()
F2F = xMult(3, xPi(35),35)
End Function
```
and in cell B3 enter the instruction =F2F(). The answer should now show with 35 decimals. Comparison with the result from F1F shows that the answer shown uses truncation rather than rounding of its least significant decimal. If you want to avoid this, instead use `F1F = xRoundR(xMult(3,xPi(35),35)28)`. Without this relative rounding, the last digit of your answer may be off by ±1 because of truncation.

(3) In cell A4 place a number. Then create the function
```
Function F3F(a)
F3F = xMult(a, xPi())
End Function
```
and in B4 use the instruction =F3F(A4).

(4) In cell B5 use the instruction =F3F(B2).

(5) In the VBEditor write the function
```
Function F4F(a)
F4F = xMult(a, xPi(35),35)
End Function
```
and apply it in cell B6 as the instruction =F4F(B2). The answer should now show in 35 decimals.

(6) Copy cell B6 to B7. Why is the answer slightly different from that in B6?

(7) Write the function
```
Function F5F(a)
F5F = xCDbl(xMult(a, xPi(35),35))
End Function
```
and in cell B8 enter the instruction =F5F(B3). Now highlight B2:B8, and set its numerical display to 4 decimals beyond the decimal point. Note that this will only affect cell B8

Writing XN macros is also fairly straightforward, but there are some extra precautions you should take. The most important of these is that any variables that will be used by XN should only be dimensioned by name (or, if it is a vector or matrix, by name *and* size), but *not* by data type, because their dimensioning As Single or As Double will override their extended precision. Exercise 11.13.2 illustrates some of the above points, and also uses Debug.Print statements to display intermediate and/or final results in the Immediate Window.

	A	B	C	D	E	F
1						
2		9.4247779607693797153879301149				=F1F()
3		9.4247779607693797153879301498385087				=F2F()
4	1.234	3.8767253345298048116208370327				=F3F(A4)
5		29.60881320326807585650347299				=F3F(B2)
6		29.6088132032680758565034729996994201				=F4F(B2)
7		29.6088132032680758565034729999628454				=F4F(B3)
8		29.6088				=F5F(B3)

Fig. 11.13.1: The simple custom functions of exercise 11.13.1 using XN.xla(m), shown here for DgtMax = 28. If not overridden, the automatic alignment shows whether a function is a right-aligned number, such as in A4 and B8, or a left-aligned text string, as in B2:B3 and B5:B7.

We also need to avoid hidden, unintentional redimensioning by using double-precision operations, because these will also overwrite the extended precision. Especially pernicious in this respect are the common algebra-like instructions such as +, −, *, /, and ^, which must be replaced by xAdd, xNeg (for negation) or xSub (for subtraction), xMult, xDiv, xPow (for integer powers) and xExpa or xExpBase (for arbitrary powers) respectively. The only exception to the above rules are those variables that are used to count

564

repeats in For Next or Do loops, or that act as numbering indices in program labels, and other such parameters that will not be converted to extended precision. The latter can be dimensioned `As Integer`, `As Long`, etc.

Exercise 11.13.2:

(1) In spreadsheet cell B2 place a number, and highlight it. Now write the following macro:

```
Sub M1()
Dim b, c
a = Selection.Value
b = "1234567890.0987654321"
c = xMult(a, b)
Debug.Print "a = " & a
Debug.Print "b = " & b
Debug.Print "c = " & c
Selection.Offset(1, 1).Select
Selection.Value = " ' " & c
End Sub
```

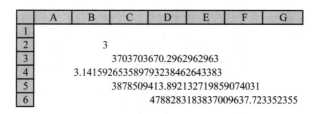

	A	B	C	D	E	F	G
1							
2		3					
3		3703703670.2962962963					
4		3.14159265358979323846264383					
5		3878509413.8921327198590740331					
6		4788283183837009637.723352355					

Fig. 11.13.2: The output of the test macro M1 after highlighting cell B2 is shown in C3, that of highlighting B4 in C5, and that of using C5 as input for the macro in D6.

Note that the penultimate line of code first inserts an apostrophe, otherwise that number will automatically be truncated to 15 decimals. And you can read that result again with XN as well as with an XN macro or function, as illustrated in cell D6 of Fig. 11.13.2, which uses C5 as its input. You can, of course, control the number of decimals of c displayed in that one-but-last line with, e.g., `vRoundR(c, 20)`.

The above examples deal with very simple functions and macros. When arrays are involved, the rules get slightly more complicated. Here are several aspects that require special attention.

When developing a complicated XN macro, we invariably stumble onto something that doesn't work as desired, resulting in an error message. In VBA we can readily clear the deck by clicking on the Debug button of the pop-up window, diagnosing and correcting the problem, and then resetting VBA with Alt⌣R⌣R and continue. But with XN.xla(m) we may then lose our anchor in VBA, in which case we have to start it up again, a royal nuisance, because moving Xnumbers60 up to the activated top of the References may take more up pushes than most morning exercises take push-ups! Avoid that with the following three lines near the beginning of the program:

```
xNumInvAppCallFlg = True
xNumACCols = ColsMax
xNumACRows = RowsMax
```

and a single line at its end, just before closing the macro,

```
xNumInvAppCallFlg = False
```

provided that we have activated the XN Toolbar, and follow resetting VBA with Ctrl⌣R⌣R by pressing the Toolbar Help ⇨ ReInit Mem Variables. These instructions with ColsMax and RowsMax scan the spreadsheet code for information on the maximal dimensions used, and should therefore appear after the largest matrices have been (re)dimensioned. Alternatively, if you know the maximum dimensions, you can make the code more efficient by specifying them, as is done in the next example, in section 11.14. In both cases, place the three lines starting with setting the `XnumInvAppCallFlg = True` past where the code has extracted all its row and column counts from the spreadsheet.

Finally: a small but sometimes pesky detail. Excel97 through Excel2003 had a problem with nested functions, because it would not allow more than 255 characters in an inner function. As a consequence, xCos(xPi2(550),550) works, but xCos(xPi2(255),255) would yield the error message #VALUE! because xPi2(255) including its decimal point takes up 256 characters. Fortunately, there is no problem making the calculation in two steps, up to the limit of D, because the problem appears only when the functions are nested. This bug was fixed in Excel2007.

Here is our last exercise, the application of the XN function xRegPolyCoef to the NIST test data set Filip.dat. It will illustrate a few tricks that will be used again in the next section, 11.14.

Exercise 11.13.3:

(1) Go to the NIST website http://itl.nist.gov/div898/strd/, click on Dataset Archives ⇨ Linear Regression ⇨ Filip ⇨ Data file (ASCII Format), where at the bottom of the page you will find Data: x y followed by two columns of data. Highlight these columns, starting with 0.8116 and ending with –3.2644011, and copy this block to the clipboard with, e.g., Ctrl‿c. Minimize but do not yet close the NIST website; you will need it again under point (9).

(2) On your computer go to Start ⇨ All Programs ⇨ Accessories ⇨ Notepad, and paste the copied Filip.dat data into Notepad. Make sure all data entries are aligned the same way; sometimes the first line needs some adjustment, which is most readily made here. Then save this file somewhere under a title, such as Filip.txt.

(3) On your spreadsheet select Data ⇨ Get External Data ⇨ Import Text File, direct the wizard Look in: window to the location where Filip.txt is filed, in the file name window type Filip.txt, and push Import. This will open up the Text Import Wizard.

(4) If not already indicated, select Fixed width, click on Next>, then on Finish, select a starting address such as B3, select either an Existing worksheet or a New worksheet, and press OK. You now should have the data file properly entered onto your spreadsheet as two separate columns. In cell B1 place the label y, and in C1 put the heading x. You may have to widen column C to show the full ten-decimal x-values.

(5) If you were to read these data directly into an XN function, you would read their stored values, which differ from those you see displayed in up to 15 decimals on the screen because they are stored in binary, which often must approximate them. (As long as you stay in double precision, such subtle differences between displayed and stored data fly under your radar, but in extended precision they can make a noticeable difference.) To make sure the corresponding distortion will not affect your analysis, in cell E3 place the instruction xCStr(xRoundR(B3,15)), then copy it to E3:F84. This will generate a data set on your computer that literally represents the NIST Filip.dat values, without binary distortion. Also copy the headings from B1:C1 to E1:F1.

(6) After all these preliminaries, you are finally ready to use the XN function xRegPolyCoef. Highlight the eleven-cells-wide block H3:R3, deposit the instruction =xRegPolyCoef(E3:E84,F3:F84,10) and block-enter. The third argument, 10, informs the function of the highest order in the polynomial in x. Left-align them so that you can see their leading digits.

(7) Highlight H3:R3, copy it, highlight H5, then use Edit ⇨ Paste Special, activate Values and Transpose, and click on OK to convert the data into column form. They are still in extended precision string format. For easy comparison, now convert them back to 15-decimal double precision format with the instruction =xCDbl(xRoundR(H3,15)) in cell H17, which you then copy to H18:H27, then highlight H17:H27, and change its number format with Format ⇨ Cells ⇨ Scientific with 14 Decimal places. If your column H is wide enough, you can see the difference between H5:H15 and H17:H27 that this clean-up operation makes.

(8) Return to the NIST minimized website, go back one page, select Certified Values, and of these copy the Certified Regression Statistics to NotePad, and finally the data in its middle column, labeled Estimate, into cells I17:I27 of your spreadsheet.

(9) Compare your output in H17:H27 with the NIST reference data in I17:I27. You see that the agreement is perfect; if you wish, you can confirm this by using the Macrobundle function PE or the equivalent XN functions xPE or xLRE. Your result is illustrated in Fig. 11.13.3.

(10) In the next section we will expand this approach with a custom macro that does the same and more. Note that both xRegPolyCoef and xnLS are open-access routines. If you want to modify them for your own purposes, the linear coding in xnLS may be more convenient than the more compact, modularized logic of xRegPolyCoef, but that is a matter of personal taste.

11.14 A specific example: xnLS

The example we will use here is the macro xnLS, which is an XN version of LS in the MacroBundle. It is used here to highlight several additional aspects.

(1) For all but the simplest macros it is advisable to write and test the macro first in double precision. The reason is that it is easier, because it avoids having to deal with XN at the same time that you may also struggle with the usual problems of writing code. Moreover, you may already have access to existing double-precision code, as in this example, and merely want to upgrade it to XN.

(2) This example illustrates a second aspect of converting to extended precision, because you may need to do more than just replace the instructions with their XN equivalents. Remember that the NIST test file Filip.dat used ten-decimal x-values raised to up to the tenth power. When you let Excel compute these without proper polynomial averaging (as described in section 10.7), you have already lost half the battle, and no matter how good your least squares algorithm is, you will not get the right answers. But even averaging is a nuisance as well as a stopgap measure, and we will therefore incorporate the power-raising aspect *inside* the extended-precision routine. This approach is also used in the Polynomial Regression macro of BigMatrix.

	E	F	G	H	I	J
1	*y*	*x*				
2						
3	0.8116	-6.860120914		-1467.48961422979588228784851530729087	-2772.17959193342392802	-2316.3710
4	0.9072	-4.324130045				
5	0.9052	-4.358625055		-1467.48961422979588228784851530729087		
6	0.9039	-4.358426747		-2772.17959193342392800284475566496031		
7	0.8053	-6.955852379		-2316.37108160893075882196791650105008		
8	0.8377	-6.661145254		-1127.97394098371569857167001526625226		
9	0.8667	-6.355462942		-354.4782337033487716107384852595209		
10	0.8809	-6.118102026		-75.12420173937571389052207557481206		
11	0.7975	-7.115148017		-10.87531803553425108528108118290086		
12	0.8162	-6.815308569		-1.06221498588946766459661122205916002		
13	0.8515	-6.519993057		-0.06701911545934083759267341228848863		
14	0.8766	-6.204119983		-2.46781078275478650840854452418919953E-3		
15	0.8885	-5.853871964		-4.02962525080403671297131548527643777E-5		
16	0.8859	-6.109523091				
17	0.8959	-5.79832982		-1.46748961422980E+03	-1.46748961422980E+03	
18	0.8913	-5.482672118		-2.77217959193342E+03	-2.77217959193342E+03	
19	0.8959	-5.171791386		-2.31637108160893E+03	-2.31637108160893E+03	
20	0.8971	-4.851705903		-1.12797394098372E+03	-1.12797394098372E+03	
21	0.9021	-4.517126416		-3.54478233703349E+02	-3.54478233703349E+02	
22	0.909	-4.143573228		-7.51242017393757E+01	-7.51242017393757E+01	
23	0.9139	-3.709075441		-1.08753180355343E+01	-1.08753180355343E+01	
24	0.9199	-3.499489089		-1.06221498588947E+00	-1.06221498588947E+00	
25	0.8692	-6.300769497		-6.70191154593408E-02	-6.70191154593408E-02	
26	0.8872	-5.953504836		-2.46781078275479E-03	-2.46781078275479E-03	
27	0.89	-5.642065153		-4.02962525080404E-05	-4.02962525080404E-05	
28	0.891	-5.031376979				
29	0.8977	-4.680685696				
30	0.9035	-4.329846955				

Fig. 11.13.3: Part of the output of spreadsheet of exercise 11.13.3, showing some of the Filip data in columns E and F, part of the result of xRegPolyCoef in H3:R3 and, transposed, all of them in H5:H15, the same in double precision in H17:H27, and for comparison the corresponding NIST reference data in I17:I27.

567

(3) There is yet another, more subtle aspect. When you enter data in the spreadsheet, either manually or by importing a data file, their values will be stored as their binary approximations. When a function or macro then reads these data, it doesn't read them from the screen, but from where they are stored, as binary values. In double precision that is fine, but in higher precision the binary approximation may just keep you from perfect agreement.

Enter the first *x*-value in Filip.dat, –6.860120914, in say cell B3 of Excel. Examining what is stored in B3 with =xCStr(B3,500) yields -6.86012091400000034724371289485134184360504150390625 instead, but xCStr(vRoundR(B3,15)) returns –6.860120914. Once this problem is recognized, it is therefore readily avoided by rounding all input data *a* read from the spreadsheet using vRoundR(a,15) to reconstruct the intended decimal data. You might consider this unnecessary nitpicking, because the difference between -6.86012091400000034724371289485134184360504150390625 and -6.860120914 is only in the 17th digit. But remember, an ill-conditioned matrix can greatly amplify small errors, so why take that risk? In section 11.15 we will see that it can indeed make a small but perceptible difference.

Below we will print the XN instructions in bold, to make it easy for you to compare xnLS with its precursor, LS, which is in the MacroBundle, and can easily be displayed or printed out for line-by-line comparison. We also bold-print the other changes that are specific to using extended precision, such as those involved in computing the higher powers of *x*, and in rounding the input data to 15 decimals. This makes it easy to see how much of LS does *not* need modification.

Here, then, are the driver macros xnLS0 and xnLS1 together with the subroutine xnLeastSquares that does the actual work. This package is complete: no other subroutines are needed, as long as XN has been installed.

```
' This is the XN version of LS for extended precision. If there are three or
' more input columns, it checks whether a power series in x is used and, if so,
' computes it internally. If that is inappropriate, comment out the lines of code
' in the paragraph between START OF INTERNAL POWER CALCULATION and its END.

Sub xnLS0()        ' for extended precision, unweighted least squares
                   ' through the origin
Dim P As Integer
P = 0
Call xnLeastSquares(p)
End Sub

''''''''''''''''''''''''''''''''''''''''''''''''''''''''''''''''''''''''''''''''''

Sub xnLS1()        ' for extended precision, general unweighted least squares
Dim P As Integer
P = 1
Call xnLeastSquares(p)
End Sub

''''''''''''''''''''''''''''''''''''''''''''''''''''''''''''''''''''''''''''''''''

Sub XNLeastSquares(P)

Dim Poly As Boolean
Dim DD As Integer, D As Integer
Dim CMax As Long, CCMax As Long, RMax As Long
Dim Answer As Integer, i As Long, j As Long
Dim Cell As Variant, myRange As Range
Dim a As Double

' The following dimension statements are for string variables.
' They are dimensioned here by name only to avoid problems in
' some Mac implementations of Excel

Dim Q, Root, Sf, SSR, varY, aD
Dim myAddress1, myAddress2, BoxAddress
```

```
' The following dimension statements are by name only

Dim BArray, BtArray, CArray, DataArray
Dim lccArray, OutputArray, PArray, PiArray, QArray
Dim XArray, XBArray, XtArray, YArray, YtArray

' Make sure that XN is loaded properly in the VBEditor

On Error Resume Next
DD = GetXnDefaultDigits()
If Err Then
  MsgBox "Make sure that Xnumbers60 is selected from" & vbLf & _
         "the Tools/References Menu in the VBEditor."
  End
End If

' Select the desired numerical precision.

Const vRR As Integer = 15 ' value to be used for relative
                          ' rounding of output results

' The automatic default value is hard-coded by SetXnDefaultDigits,
' which is set here to quintuple precision, but can readily be changed.
' If you don't want any other precision, and want to avoid having to
' respond to an input box every time you use this macro, simply comment
' out the instructions between this and the next comment line.

Dim NumberLength
Select Case GetXBase()
  Case 6: D = 36
  Case 7: D = 35
  Case 8: D = 32
  Case 13: D = 39
  Case Else: D = DD
End Select

TryAgain:

NumberLength = InputBox _
  ("Enter the desired decimal number-" & vbCr _
  & "length, preferably a multiple of " & GetXBase() & "." & _
  vbCr & vbCr & "The default value is " & DD & "." _
  , "Decimal numberlength", D)
If NumberLength = vbNullString Then End
i = CInt(NumberLength)
If i > GetDigitsLimit() Then
  MsgBox "The numberlength can be no" & _
    vbLf & "larger than " & GetDigitsLimit() & ". Try again."
  GoTo TryAgain
ElseIf i < 0 Then
  MsgBox "The numberlength must be >= 0. Try again."
  GoTo TryAgain
ElseIf i > 0 Then
  D = i
  SetXnDefaultDigits D
Else
  D = DD
End If

' Determine the array size:

Begin:
RMax = Selection.Rows.Count
CMax = Selection.Columns.Count
CCMax = CMax - 1 + P ' Set output Max Dimension
```

```
xNumInvAppCallFlg = True
xNumACCols = RMax
xNumACRows = RMax

' If area is not highlighted before the macro is called

If RMax = 1 And CMax = 1 Then
  Answer = MsgBox("You forgot to highlight" _
    & vbLf & "the block of input data." _
    & vbLf & "Do you want to do so now?" _
    , vbYesNo, "xn Least Squares Fit")
  If Answer = vbNo Then GoTo LastLine
  On Error Resume Next
  Set myRange = Application.InputBox(Prompt:= _
    "The input data are located in:", Type:=8)
  If Err Then GoTo LastLine
  myRange.Select
  GoTo Begin
End If

' Check that the number of columns is at least 2:

If CMax < 2 Then
  MsgBox "There must be at least two columns," & _
    vbLf & "one for Y, and one or more for X.", _
    , "XN Least Squares Fit"
  GoTo LastLine
End If

' Check that there are more data than coefficients:

If RMax - CCMax <= 0 Then
  MsgBox "With " & RMax & " data, xnLS" & P & _
    " can only deter-" & vbLf & "mine " & RMax - 1 & _
    " least squares coefficients." & vbLf & vbLf & _
    "Add more data, or reduce the re-" & vbLf & _
    "quested number of coefficients.", , _
    "xn Least Squares Fit"
  GoTo LastLine
End If

' Dimension the arrays, but by name and size only:

ReDim XArray(1 To RMax, 1 To CCMax)
ReDim YArray(1 To RMax, 1 To 1)
ReDim lccArray(1 To CCMax, 1 To CCMax)

' Read the dataArray, then fill YArray and XArray.

Selection.Offset(0, 0).Select
DataArray = Selection.Value
aD = Selection.Address

For i = 1 To RMax
  If IsEmpty(DataArray(i, 1)) Then
    MsgBox "Y-value(s) missing", , "XN Least Squares Fit"
    GoTo LastLine
  End If
  YArray(i, 1) = DataArray(i, 1)
Next i

' For P = 0 fill the CMax - 1 columns of XArray with the
' data in the x-columns. For P = 1 fill the first column
' of XArray with ones, and the remaining CMax - 1 columns
' of XArray with the data in the x-column(s).

For j = 2 To CMax
```

570

```
      For i = 1 To RMax
        If IsEmpty(DataArray(i, j)) Then
          MsgBox "X-value(s) missing", , " XN Least Squares Fit"
          GoTo LastLine
        End If
        XArray(i, j - 1 + P) = DataArray(i, j)
      Next i
    Next j

    If P = 1 Then
      For i = 1 To RMax
        XArray(i, 1) = 1
      Next i
    End If
```

' START OF INTERNAL POWER CALCULATION:

' Determine whether the columns beyond the second involve x^2,
' x^3, etc. Note: this will NOT catch irregular power series.

```
If CCMax > 2 Then
  For i = 1 To RMax
    For j = 3 To CCMax
      If DataArray(i, j) <> DataArray(i, j - 1) _
        * DataArray(i, 2) Then GoTo SkipPower
    Next j
  Next i
End If
```

' If so, then replace these columns by x^2, x^3, etc.,
' to be recomputed here at the chosen numberlength.

```
Poly = True
For i = 1 To RMax
  For j = 3 To CCMax
    XArray(i, j) = xPow(DataArray(i, 2), j - 1) '
  Next j
Next i
```

' END OF INTERNAL POWER CALCULATION:

SkipPower:

```
' QArray is the Moore-Penrose pseudo-inverse of XArray,
' CArray is the covariance matrix. The labels ' or t denote
' transposition, and " or i indicate inversion. The
' various arrays, their names, and their sizes are:
'                              rows      columns
'   Y             = YArray    ( RMax   , 1      )
'   X             = XArray    ( RMax   , CCMax  )
'   X'            = XtArray   ( CCMax  , RMax   )
'   X' X          = PArray    ( CCMax  , CCMax  )
'  (X' X)"        = PiArray   ( CCMax  , CCMax  )
'  (X' X)" X'     = QArray    ( CCMax  , RMax   )
'  (X' X)" X' Y   = BArray    ( CCMax  , 1      )
'   Y'            = YtArray   ( 1      , RMax   )
'   B'            = BtArray   ( 1      , CCMax  )
'   X B           = XBArray   ( RMax   , 1      )
'   C             = CArray    ( CCMax  , CCMax  )

XtArray = xMT(XArray)
PArray = xMMult(XtArray, XArray)
PiArray = xMInv(PArray)
```

```
QArray = xMMult(PiArray, XtArray)
BArray = xMMult(QArray, YArray)
YtArray = xMT(YArray)
BtArray = xMT(BArray)
XBArray = xMMult(XArray, BArray)

' Calculate SSR = Sum(Y - X B) ^ 2; then compute the
' variance of y as varY = SSR/(RMax-CCMax); and the
' covariance matrix CArray as V = (X'X)" times varY.

SSR = xSumSq(xMSub(YArray, XBArray))
varY = xDiv(SSR, (RMax - CCMax))
Sf = xSqr(xAbs(varY))
If CCMax = 1 Then        ' Fix output variables for indexing
  Q = BArray
  ReDim CArray(1 To 1, 1 To 1), BArray(1 To 1, 1 To 1)
  CArray(1, 1) = xMult(PiArray, varY)
  BArray(1, 1) = Q
Else
  CArray = xMMultS(PiArray, varY)
End If

' Check against overwriting spreadsheet data

Set myRange = Range(ActiveCell.Offset(RMax, 1 - P), _
  ActiveCell.Offset(RMax + 2 + CCMax, CMax - 1))
OutputArray = myRange
For Each Cell In OutputArray
  If Not IsEmpty(Cell) Then
    Answer = MsgBox("There are data in the " _
      & 3 + CCMax & " lines below the" & vbLf & _
      "input data array. Can they be overwritten?", _
      vbYesNo, "Overwrite?")
    If Answer = vbNo Then GoTo LastLine Else Exit For
  End If
Next

Application.ScreenUpdating = False

' Prepare the output format

With myRange
  .Clear
  .NumberFormat = "@"
  .Font.Italic = True
  .HorizontalAlignment = xlCenter
  .Rows(1).Font.Bold = True
  .Rows(1).Font.ColorIndex = 1
End With

' Prepare the output labels, suppressing them when space
' for them is unavailable or data will be overwritten

ActiveCell.Offset(RMax, 0).Select
If P = 1 Then If ActiveCell.Column = 1 Then GoTo NoLabel

ActiveCell.Offset(0, -P).Select

If P = 1 Then _
  If Not IsEmpty(ActiveCell) Then _
    If ActiveCell.Value <> "Coeff:" Then _
      ActiveCell.Offset(0, P).Select: _
      GoTo NoLabel

With ActiveCell        ' Make label for Coeff
  .Value = "Coeff:"
  .Font.Bold = True
```

572

```
      .Font.Italic = True
      .Font.ColorIndex = 1
      .Interior.ColorIndex = xlNone
      .ClearComments
      .HorizontalAlignment = xlRight
      .Offset(1, 0).Select
End With

If P = 1 Then _
   If Not IsEmpty(ActiveCell) Then _
     If ActiveCell.Value <> "StDev:" Then _
       ActiveCell.Offset(-1, P).Select: _
       GoTo NoLabel

With ActiveCell         ' Make label for StDev
   .Value = "StDev:"
   .Font.Bold = True
   .Font.Italic = True
   .Font.ColorIndex = 1
   .Interior.ColorIndex = xlNone
   .HorizontalAlignment = xlRight
   .ClearComments
   .AddComment
   .Comment.Visible = False
   .Comment.Text Text:= _
     "Color code for StDev:" & vbLf & _
     "Q = abs(P/S);  Colors:" & vbLf & _
     "gray:        3 < Q <= 5" & vbLf & _
     "orange:   2 < Q <= 3" & vbLf & _
     "red:         1 < Q <= 2" & vbLf & _
     "bold red:        Q <= 1"
   .Comment.Shape.TextFrame.AutoSize = True
   .Offset(1, 0).Select
End With

If P = 1 Then _
   If Not IsEmpty(ActiveCell) Then _
     If ActiveCell.Value <> "Sf:" Then _
       ActiveCell.Offset(-1, P).Select: _
       GoTo NoLabel

With ActiveCell        ' Make label for Sf
   .Value = "Sf:"
   .Font.Bold = True
   .Font.Italic = True
   .Font.ColorIndex = 1
   .Interior.ColorIndex = xlNone
   .ClearComments
   .HorizontalAlignment = xlRight
   .Offset(-1, P).Select
End With

If CCMax = 1 Then _
   ActiveCell.Offset(-1, P).Select: _
   GoTo NoLabel

ActiveCell.Offset(3, -P).Select
If P = 1 Then _
   If Not IsEmpty(ActiveCell) Then _
     If ActiveCell.Value <> "CM:" Then _
       ActiveCell.Offset(-3, P).Select: _
       GoTo NoLabel

ActiveCell.Offset(-1, 0).Select
With ActiveCell          ' Make label for CM
```

```
        .Value = "CM:"
        .Font.Bold = True
        .Font.Italic = True
        .Font.ColorIndex = 5
        .Interior.ColorIndex = xlNone
        .ClearComments
        .HorizontalAlignment = xlRight
        .Offset(-3, P).Select
End With

NoLabel:

' Output the least squares coefficients Coeff

ActiveCell.Offset(0, 1 - P).Select
For j = 1 To CCMax
    ActiveCell.Offset(0, j - 1).Value = vRoundR(BArray(j, 1), vRR)
Next j
ActiveCell.Offset(1, 0).Select

' Displaying the standard deviation in color code, and
' warning when the variance is computed as negative.

'     bold red when Q <= 1
'     red       when 1 < Q <= 2
'     orange    when 2 < Q <= 3
'     gray      when 3 < Q <= 5
'     black     when Q > 5

' Output the corresponding standard deviation StDev

' When the variance is computed as negative, a light gray
' background color and a cell comment are used as alerts,
' and the standard deviation is displayed in bold pink.

For j = 1 To CCMax
    With ActiveCell
        Q = xSqr(xAbs(CArray(j, j)))
        .Value = vRoundR(Q, vRR)
        Q = xDiv(xAbs(BArray(j, 1)), Q)
        Select Case xComp(CArray(j, j))
        Case Is >= 0
            .Font.ColorIndex = 3                    'red
            Select Case xCDbl(Q)
                Case Is <= 1: .Font.Bold = True      'bold red
                Case Is > 5: .Font.ColorIndex = 1    'black
                Case Is > 3: .Font.ColorIndex = 16   'gray
                Case Is > 2: .Font.ColorIndex = 46   'orange
            End Select
        Case Else
            .Font.Bold = True
            .Font.ColorIndex = 7                     'bold pink
            .Interior.ColorIndex = 15                'light gray
            .AddComment
            .Comment.Visible = False
            .Comment.Text Text:="Q = " & vRoundR(Q, vRR)
            .Comment.Shape.TextFrame.AutoSize = True
        End Select
        .Offset(0, 1).Select
    End With
Next j

' Output the residual standard deviation Sf

ActiveCell.Offset(1, -CCMax).Select
ActiveCell.Value = vRoundR(Sf, vRR)
```

574

```
' Setup the descriptor cell

ActiveCell.Offset(0, 1).Select
If CCMax = 1 Then ActiveCell.Offset(1, -1).Select
With ActiveCell
   .Value = "xnLS" & P
   .Font.Bold = True
   .Font.Italic = False
   .Font.ColorIndex = 5
   .Interior.ColorIndex = 20

' In a comment box, identify the macro used, its
' optional parameters, and its date & time of use

   .AddComment
   .Comment.Visible = False
   If Poly Then
     .Comment.Text Text:= _
       "xnLS" & P & " version 11" & vbLf & _
       "Numberlength: " & D & vbLf & _
       "Input: " & aD & vbLf & _
       "Higher-order powers" & vbLf & _
       "of x computed internally" & vbLf & _
       "N = " & RMax & ",    P = " & CCMax & vbLf & _
       "Date = " & Date & vbLf & "Time = " & Time
   Else
     .Comment.Text Text:= _
       "xnLS" & P & " version 11" & vbLf & _
       "Numberlength: " & D & vbLf & _
       "Input: " & aD & vbLf & _
       "N = " & RMax & ",    P = " & CCMax & vbLf & _
       "Date = " & Date & vbLf & "Time = " & Time
   End If
   .Comment.Shape.TextFrame.AutoSize = True
   aD = .Address
End With
If CCMax = 1 Then GoTo LastLine

' Write the covariance matrix

ActiveCell.Offset(1, -1).Select
For i = 1 To CCMax
  For j = 1 To CCMax
    ActiveCell.Value = vRoundR(CArray(i, j), vRR)
    ActiveCell.Font.ColorIndex = 5
    ActiveCell.Offset(0, 1).Select
  Next j
  ActiveCell.Offset(1, -CCMax).Select
Next i

Application.ScreenUpdating = True

' Provide as optional output the array of linear
' correlation coefficients. The user specifies
' the cell block in which to write this array

Answer = MsgBox("Do you want to see the " _
  & "matrix of linear correlation" & vbLf _
  & "coefficients? It will need a block of " _
  & CCMax & " by " & CCMax & " cells.", _
  vbYesNo, "xn Least Squares Fit")
If Answer = vbNo Then GoTo LastLine
```

```
' Read location of active cell

ActiveCell.Select
myAddress1 = Selection.Address
ActiveCell.Offset(CCMax - 1, CCMax - 1).Select
myAddress2 = Selection.Address
BoxAddress = myAddress1 & ":" & myAddress2
ActiveCell.Offset(1 - CCMax, 1 - CCMax).Select

OutlineMatrix:

On Error Resume Next
Set myRange = Application.InputBox(Prompt:= _
  "Select the default array location with OK," _
  & vbCr & "otherwise type in your own coordinates:", _
  Default:=BoxAddress, Type:=8)
If Err Then GoTo LastLine
On Error GoTo 0
myRange.Select

' Make sure that the selected block has the correct size

If Selection.Rows.Count <> CCMax Then
  MsgBox "The selected range does not have " _
    & CCMax & " rows. Please correct.", _
    , "XN Least Squares Fit"
  GoTo OutlineMatrix
End If
If Selection.Columns.Count <> CCMax Then
  MsgBox "The selected range does not have " _
    & CCMax & " columns. Please correct", _
    , "XN Least Squares Fit"
  GoTo OutlineMatrix
End If

' Make sure that no valuable data will be overwritten

Application.ScreenUpdating = False

OutputArray = Selection.Value
For Each Cell In OutputArray
  If Not IsEmpty(Cell) Then
    Application.ScreenUpdating = True
    Answer = MsgBox("There are data in the " _
    & CCMax & " lines below the" & vbLf & _
    "input data array. " & "Can they be overwritten?", _
    vbYesNo, "Overwrite?")
    If Answer = vbNo Then GoTo LastLine
    Application.ScreenUpdating = False
    Exit For
  End If
Next Cell

' Draw a box around the reserved area

With Selection
  .Clear
  .NumberFormat = "@"
  .Borders(xlEdgeTop).LineStyle = xlDashDot
  .Borders(xlEdgeTop).Weight = xlThin
  .Borders(xlEdgeRight).LineStyle = xlDashDot
  .Borders(xlEdgeRight).Weight = xlThin
  .Borders(xlEdgeBottom).LineStyle = xlDashDot
  .Borders(xlEdgeBottom).Weight = xlThin
  .Borders(xlEdgeLeft).LineStyle = xlDashDot
  .Borders(xlEdgeLeft).Weight = xlThin
```

576

```
' Format cells in array

   .HorizontalAlignment = xlCenter
   .Font.Italic = True

' Write the array of linear correlation coefficients

   For i = 1 To CCMax
     For j = 1 To CCMax
       Root = xSqr(xAbs(xMult(CArray(i, i), CArray(j, j))))
       lccArray(i, j) = vRoundR(xDiv(CArray(i, j), Root), vRR)
     Next j
   Next i
   .Value = lccArray

' Format and color-code the cells in the CC array
' Color alerts indicating collinearity:
'   black        for              abs(CoVar) < 0.90
'   gray         for 0.90 <= abs(CoVar) < 0.95
'   orange       for 0.95 <= abs(CoVar) < 0.98
'   red          for 0.98 <= abs(CoVar) < 0.99
'   bold red     for 0.99 <= abs(CoVar) < 1

   For Each Cell In .Cells
     a = Cell.Value
     Select Case Abs(a)
     Case Is < 0.9: Cell.Font.ColorIndex = 1    ' black
     Case Is < 0.95: Cell.Font.ColorIndex = 16  ' gray
     Case Is < 0.98: Cell.Font.ColorIndex = 46  ' orange
     Case Is < 0.99: Cell.Font.ColorIndex = 3   ' red
     Case Else: If a = 1 Then _
       Cell.Font.Italic = False Else _
       Cell.Font.ColorIndex = 3: _
       Cell.Font.Bold = True                    ' bold red
     End Select
   Next Cell
End With

' Do not color-code the main diagonal

For i = 1 To CCMax
  Selection(i, i).Font.Italic = False
  Selection(i, i).Font.Bold = False
  Selection(i, i).Font.ColorIndex = 1
Next i

' Label the linear correlation coefficients

ActiveCell.Select
If ActiveCell.Column > 1 Then ActiveCell.Offset(0, -1).Select
If P = 0 Or IsEmpty(ActiveCell) Or _
  ActiveCell.Value = "CC:" Then
  With ActiveCell
    .Value = "CC:"
    .Font.Bold = True
    .Font.Italic = True
    .Font.ColorIndex = 1
    .Interior.ColorIndex = xlNone
    .HorizontalAlignment = xlRight
  End With
Else
  If ActiveCell.Column > 1 Then ActiveCell.Offset(0, 1).Select
End If
```

```
' Make comment for Color alerts indicating collinearity:

With ActiveCell
  .ClearComments
  .AddComment
  .Comment.Visible = False
  .Comment.Text Text:= _
    "Collinearity alerts:" & vbLf & _
    "gray:         abs(CC) >= 0.90" & vbLf & _
    "orange:   abs(CC) >= 0.95" & vbLf & _
    "red:          abs(CC) >= 0.98" & vbLf & _
    "bold red: abs(CC) >= 0.99"
  .Comment.Shape.TextFrame.AutoSize = True
End With

LastLine:

' Set active cell to description

On Error Resume Next ' in case it is invalid
Range(aD).Select
' Reset XN and DD to their original values

xNumInvAppCallFlg = SetXnDefaultDigits(DD)

End Sub
```

Here are a few special aspects of this macro, insofar as they differ from LS.

(1) In order to prevent errors when XN is not loaded in the VBEditor, a simple error trap is provided.

(2) In the section that selects the desired numerical precision, we first store the value of DgtMax as DD, use the function `GetXBase` to retrieve the packet length from XN.xla(m), then use `xBase` to specify the default value in the input box specifying Numberlength. Similarly, `GetDigitsLimit` retrieves the maximum numberlength for XN.xla(m) These commands are used to differentiate between the various versions of XN.xla(m). At the end of the macro we use DD to reset DgtMax to its pre-macro value.

(3) The macro reads RMax and CMax from the highlighted spreadsheet area. Since no matrix dimension will exceed RMax, it then sets both `xNumACCols` and `xNumACRows` equal to RMax. This, plus setting a flag with `xNumInvAppCallFlg`, will prevent some inadvertent visits to XN functions. The flag is reset after the last matrix operation, just before the end of the macro.

(4) The function xMT is identical to MT, because transposition does not affect the values of the matrix elements, but only their indices, i.e., the order in which they will be stored. The function xMT is used here so that you need not have Matrix.xla loaded to run this XN macro. Note that we cannot use the Excel function Transpose because it does not work in VBA, not even with the usual `Application.` prefix.

(5) The instruction `Selection.NumberFormat = "@"` retains the text string format.

(6) The instruction `On Error GoTo 0` deactivates error trapping; note that 0 is not defined.

(7) The cell comment identifying the macro was of course modified to add the extra information specific to XN.xla(m).

(8) The instruction `xNumInvAppCallFlg = SetXnDefaultDigits(DD)` resets `Flg` to `False` and returns the value of D to its earlier-saved value `DD`.

11.15 Filip, once more

We will use Filip.dat to test xnLS, because it has been modified specifically to accommodate high powers of high-precision x-values by computing x^n inside the macro. Table 11.15.1 shows our results, for various D-values, in terms of their pE-values based on the NIST values as reference. As you can see in that table, we find complete agreement with the NIST-published values for all coefficients and all standard deviations, i.e., to $pE = 15$, when we use $D \geq 34$. At $D = 18$ we obtain $pE = 0$, in agreement with the total failure of LS to solve Filip.dat in double precision with the traditional least squares algorithm. The contrast could not be starker!

578

Both xRegPolyCoeff and xnLS clearly illustrate the power and convenience of XN. With the relatively small additions of negating the distortion involved in binary data storage, where necessary computing the higher powers of x internally, and replacing a limited number of instructions by the corresponding XN functions, we have transformed a primitive custom algorithm LS that could not get a single coefficient of Filip.dat right to one that passes this most difficult of all NIST linear least squares tests. No specialized knowledge about the subtleties of matrix inversion (such as embedded in singular value decomposition) are needed. Our "brute force" approach to use higher computer precision with an inferior algorithm certainly beats most commercial statistical software packages in fitting Filip.dat. Not bad for free, open-access spreadsheet software. The various results obtained in this book with Filip.dat are summarized in Table 11.15.2.

D	$pE(a_i)$	$pE(s_i)$	D	$pE(a_i)$	$pE(s_i)$	D	$pE(a_i)$	$pE(s_i)$
18	0.00	0.00	24	5.11	5.45	30	11.53	11.85
19	0.00	0.00	25	5.99	6.32	31	12.99	13.34
20	2.02	0.17	26	6.92	7.25	32	13.39	13.68
21	2.58	0.69	27	8.33	8.64	33	14.03	14.46
22	2.95	2.88	28	9.07	9.41	**34**	**15.00**	**15.00**
23	5.55	3.97	29	10.52	10.85	**35**	**15.00**	**15.00**

Table 11.15.1: The dependence of the results obtained by xnLS with Filip.dat to the NIST StRD reference values for the coefficients a_i and the standard deviations s_i, as measured by its lowest pE-value in each category as a function of the specified decimal precision D used. For $D > 35$ the pE is always 15.

software used	least squares coefficients a_i	standard deviations s_i	covariances v_{ij}
classical least suares (LS)	0	0	0
pre-2003 LinEst and Regression	0	0	–
BigMatrix linear regression	6.4	–	–
singular value decomposition (SVD)	7.7	–	–
post-2003 LinEst and Regression	7.7	7.5	–
LS + polynomial centering	10	–	✔
SVD + polynomial centering	13.7	–	–
post-2003 LinEst + polynomial centering	13.7	7.5	–
BigMatrix polynomial regression[#]	14	–	–
xRegPolyCoef[#] $D \geq 34$	**15**	–	–
xnLS1[#] with $D \geq 34$	**15**	**15**	✔

Table 11.15.2: A score card of linear least squares analyses of Filip.dat in terms of the error criterion pE_{min}. Only LS and xnLS provide the covariance matrix, but these are merely check-marked here, because NIST provides no reference values for comparison. $D = 35$ is our recommended default (quintuple) precision. Routines that compute x^n internally are indicated with [#].

test data set	D	test data set	D	test data set	D
Norris	19	Filip	34	Wampler3	25
Pontius	20	Longley	23	Wampler4	25
NoInt1	16*	Wampler1	28	Wampler5	25
NoInt2	16*	Wampler2	23		

Table 11.15.3: The minimum number of decimals D needed to get all coefficients a_i, their standard deviations s_i, and the standard deviation of the fit s_f, to all specified 15 decimals with xnLS. *: $pE = 15$ is already obtained with the standard double-precision macro LS.

Table 11.15.3 shows how many decimals xnLS needs for each of the eleven NIST StRD linear least squares test data to get all its least squares coefficients and standard deviations correct to all 15 decimals specified by NIST. Note that you don't always need extended precision to get $pE = 15$: with NoInt1 and NoInt2 you can already obtain this with the standard double-precision macro LS. As our test we used the function xpE based on (9.1.1), but modified here by making that criterion readily user-selectable (as the value of C in the function code), and using the more stringent precision criterion of 15 rather than the 14 used in (9.1.2). The actual function xpE used for Table 11.15.3 relies on relative rounding, and is shown here:

```
Function xpE(number, reference, Optional vRR)
' vRR is the value for Relarive Rounding used, here with
' a default of 15 (decimals) for "double precision"
Dim N, R, pE
If IsMissing(vRR) Then vRR = 15
N = vRoundR(number, vRR)
R = vRoundR(reference, vRRC)
If xComp(N, R) = 0 Then pE = C
If (xComp(N, R) <> 0 And xComp(R, 0) = 0) Then _
  pE = xNeg(xLog(xAbs(N)))
If (xComp(N, R) <> 0 And xComp(R, 0) <> 0) Then _
  pE = xNeg(xLog(xAbs(xDiv(xSub(N, R), R))))
If xComp(pE, 0) <= 0 Then pE = 0
If xComp(pE, C) = 1 Then pE = vRR
xpE = vRoundR(pE, vRR)
End Function
```

Given the central role of least squares analysis in this book, it was perhaps fitting to return to Filip.dat as our last example. We encountered the traditional least squares formalism in section 10.5, but its implementation in our custom macro LS could not make any sense of Filip.dat, and neither could the pre-2003 Excel routines LinEst and Regression, which were likewise based on the classical pseudo-inverse $(\mathbf{X}^{\mathrm{T}}\mathbf{X})^{-1}\mathbf{X}^{\mathrm{T}}$. Singular value decomposition described in section 10.11 made it possible to find the coefficients a_i to $pE \geq 7.5$, and the same applied to Excel's LinEst and Regression since their 2003 update, because they use the related QR factorization. Further progress could be made by polynomial centering, see section 10.7, and their combined results came close to the NIST reference data for the coefficients a_i, with a minimum pE of 13.7, i.e., with relative errors no larger than 2×10^{-14}. BigMatrix has a macro that, with quadruple precision and internally computing the powers of x, can even achieve slightly better results, with $pE \geq 14$ for both the coefficients a_i and their standard deviations s_i. However, all of these would still leave us without the covariances v_{ij}. In section 11.14 we therefore modified LS with XN, in order to suit all of our requirements.

Why so much emphasis on the covariances? First, look at the data obtained from Filip.dat for not only a_i but also s_i. The ratios a_i/s_i are less than five for all eleven coefficients, indicating that the answers are not very precise. But let's assume that Filip.dat reflects actually observed data, as claimed by NIST. In that case we can either fit them to a simple empirical model, using as few parameters as possible, to describe the overall character of the results of our measurement, and be able to interpolate them and, perhaps, even extrapolate them to adjacent x-values, or we can use a theoretical framework. In the first case, a simple empirical fit to the general shape of the curve would certainly not use a power series in x, see *Am. J. Phys.* 75 (2007) 617, especially since a tenth-order polynomial will start to oscillate violently just outside the measurement range, making it unsuitable for extrapolation, and even questionable for interpolation. The polynomial model therefore implies some theoretical basis, in which the parameters obtained should be interpretable. And therein lies the rub: if any conclusions drawn from the fitting coefficients a_i involve more than one coefficient, we definitely need the covariances, because the standard deviations by themselves are then powerless to provide reliable uncertainty estimates. Why? Just do the fit with xnLS, observe its output on your monitor screen or send the output to a color printer, and look at the linear correlation coefficients r_{ij}, as defined in (2.10.2), between the various coefficients a_i. It is a veritable sea of red ink, indicating that these coefficients show very high mutual dependencies. Every r_{ij} of adjacent powers of x (i.e., every r_{ij} for which $j = i \pm 1$) is at least 0.9996, every r_{ij} where $j = i \pm 2$) is at least 0.9985, etc., and even the least strongly coupled coefficient, that between a_0 and a_{10}, has an r_{ij} of 0.965. The mutual dependence of these coefficients is so strong that, without their covariances, no valid uncertainties can be assigned to any functions depending on two or more a_i-values.

Incidentally, you might well ask how realistic Filip.dat is as a test set. NIST labels it as from an "observed" rather than a "generated" source, but that does not necessarily exclude a large amount of doctoring. One seldom encounters raw experimental data that are significant to ten decimal places, with such uniformly high covariances, that would need to be fitted to a tenth-order polynomial. But even if Filip.dat was artfully crafted, perhaps starting from a set of real experimental data, it is a vivid illustration of the potential liabilities of numerical least squares analysis in a double-precision environment. This is why it has been a recurring theme in this book, and why table 11.15.2 summarized the results of our encounters with it. It does inspire confidence when software can pass even unrealistically severe tests in real problem areas, especially when it is within such easy reach as through the combination of Excel and XN.

The power of XN is that it directly addresses the *root cause* of most problems specific to numerical analysis, viz. the limited precision provided by software based on the IEEE 754 protocol. In fact, XN has far more numerical precision than you may ever need, and this spare precision makes it ready for much tougher problems. Using 600 decimals for Filip.dat is certainly overkill for the NIST data: with xnLS you can get identical results with just 34 decimals. But when you reduce that number to 28, the fit is poor, mainly because of errors in computing the higher powers of x, and with $D < 20$ you will get no valid answers whatsoever, see Table 11.15.1. Because the double precision of IEE-754 is really the limiting factor, and XN completely bypasses it, there is no need to introduce SVD into xnLS, which would merely slow it down.

11.16 Overview of XN rules

Finally, at the risk of being repetitive, here is a summary of the rules for writing XN functions or subroutines (including macros), or for modifying existing code to use extended precision.

(1) Always start with a functioning standard VBA routine. If one is already available, as was LS in the example shown in section 11.14, by all means use it, and otherwise start from scratch, write a standard double-precision routine that fits your requirements except for its limited precision, then debug and save it.

(2) Make a copy of the regular function or subroutine, and give it a distinct name, such as one starting with XN. Then modify that copy by introducing XN functions in all critical places, and adjusting the dimensioning accordingly. Matrices need not be dimensioned by size either. High-precision functions and subroutines should not be used as routine updates of their double-precision equivalents, because they are relatively slow, even when set to the standard double precision of about 15 decimals. This is so because much of the extra execution time is up front, regardless of the precision specified. This is also why I suggest using a default value of 35 (rather than 28) for DgtMax, because the extra time involved is trivial, and you will seldom need more. Its slightly slower performance is usually not even noticeable, and even when it is, it is a price you'd be glad to pay for peace of mind.

(3) In the dimension statements of extended-precision functions and subroutines, remove the dimension specifiers `As Single` and `As Double` from any parameter you want to use in extended number-length, because these dimension statements will otherwise overrule XN and keep the parameters in their Excel-specified precisions. Be especially vigilant to check all quasi-algebraic signs, such as $+$, $-$, $*$, $/$, and $\wedge$, because their familiarity makes them easy to overlook. Yet they may thwart your higher precision when an operation is left unchanged that should have been modified to XN.

(4) Modify all precision-critical instructions to fit the XN format. For complicated expressions, either break up the expression into several simpler parts, or use the `xEval` function.

(5) Before testing your VBA code, make sure that the small XN toolbar has been activated (you can do that by clicking on the XN icon, the purple book with an X on its cover. You will need this to press Help

⇨ ReInit Mem Variables, after you encounter an error message, correct the error, and reset the code with Alt⌣R⌣R. Otherwise you may have to re-install XN.xla(m) in the VBEditor module with Tools ⇨ References, where XNumbers60 may take many repeat pushes of the Priority Up button from the bottom of the alphabetical pile to its top.

For subroutines (including macros) the following additional rules apply:

(6) If you want a precision different from its default value, make it so that the user can specify it in, e.g., an input box.

(7) After the dimensions of your matrices are known by, e.g., reading the data from the spreadsheet, but before XN matrix computations are made with them, insert the lines

```
XNumInvAppCallFlg = True
XNumACCols = ColsMax
XNumACRows = RowsMax
```

or, as is the case with xnLS, declare their specific maximum values. And just before the end of the subroutine, insert the line

```
XNumInvAppCallFlg = False
```

These simple precautions will prevent a number of unwelcome excursions into the XN code.

By comparing, e.g., the macro xnLS in the xnMacroBundle with its parent LS in the MacroBundle, you will see that its conversion to extended numberlength does not involve very much work, because you need not rethink the structure of your code, but merely include one extra calculation and modify a number of instructions. All input and output statements and their formatting remain unchanged. For more specifics, including additional functions and more details, see the XN Help file.

In summary, with XN.xla(m) and a few relatively minor modifications of your functions and subroutines (including macros), you can have high-precision computations while the structure of these routines, while your data input and output formats remain unchanged. This can provide a very useful back-up for any custom macros, as it allows you to check the accuracy of your code. It can also help you identify areas of code where it is worthwhile to pay extra attention to algorithmic accuracy. Some of the macros of the MacroBundle have already spawned XN-versions, which you can find in the xnMacroBundle. You are of course welcome to try them out. Please let me know by e-mail, at rdelevie@bowdoin.edu, when you encounter any problems with them.

11.17 Summary

This chapter has focused on the limits of Excel, and described some approaches to stretch some of them. The likelihood of software errors is an ever-present concern. Moreover, such errors can be unusually dangerous, because numerical results tend to have an aura of authority, sometimes even more so than the printed word, and printed but erroneous numbers are the worst in this respect. Section 11.1 therefore described some methods to reduce the frequency of errors by keeping the spreadsheet well organized, well documented, and as simple and as auditable as possible. Ultimately, the best defenses are a self-critical attitude, and a willingness to have others verify your results. Open access to the source code certainly facilitates and even invites such independent testing by others.

Sections 11.3 through 11.8 illustrated several types of common but often readily avoidable algorithmic errors in standard numerical procedures. The watchword here is, again, to be on the lookout for trouble, to be especially skeptical of your own results, to keep testing them until you are fully satisfied that they are indeed correct, and even then remain open to criticism and suggestions. The problems of limited precision described here are often magnified by manipulating large data arrays, such as in matrix operations, as we already saw in chapter 10.

Finally, we have devoted considerable space to a description of XN.xla(m), a huge contribution by Leonardo Volpi that was further expanded and enhanced by John Beyers. It greatly boosts the numerical prowess of Excel. The NIST Standard Reference Datasets illustrate that, with XN, Excel can compete successfully with the best of the specialized statistical software packages in terms of linear least squares, while still retaining its general advantages of wide availability, transparency, and ease of use. The availability of both Matrix and XN functions for real as well as complex singular value decomposition should make this task much easier, because so many new statistical approaches are based on SVD. The aspect still missing (although accessible through R, see section 1.2.7) is a more extensive set of specialized statistical routines.

Only members of the statistical community, i.e., those intimately familiar with the customs and needs of that community, can write these statistical routines. For those readers to whom this applies, consider this an open invitation. Your contributions will be welcomed and used in gratitude by many of your colleagues and students, who usually prefer the convenience and directness of spreadsheet functions and macros over having to type instructions in a command-line interface. Moreover, by keeping your routines open-access, you can readily modify them to suit their own needs and preferences.

For nonlinear least squares, the accuracy is mostly limited by Solver, a conjugate gradient method that is now bundled with all major spreadsheets, and has as its main advantages that it requires relatively little memory space (so that it can tackle problems with large numbers of adjustable parameters) and readily accepts constraints on those parameters. However, it does not always produce very accurate results. When the number of adjustable parameters is relatively small, higher accuracy may be obtained by more traditional methods, such as the Levenberg-Marquardt algorithm, of which an open-access VBA version has recently become available in the macro collection Optimiz of Luis Isaac Ramos Garcia that can be found on Volpi's web site as well as on my excellaneous site. Stay tuned for its XN version.

An essential difference between pure, formal math and numerical computation is that numerical calculations, by relying on specific data values, cannot be used to *prove* any general theorems. Secondly, but of primary concern here, there is a difference between closed-form and numerical calculations in that the latter typically use limited precision. This has stimulated much effort to optimize the algorithms, both in terms of efficiency (i.e., minimum number of operations) and accuracy, but such optimizations require specialized expertise and considerable time, which most physical scientists lack – after all, their main interest is usually not in the computer methods themselves, but in using these as tools to solve other problems. For those users, XN is a great gift, because it allows them to use widely available but often non-optimal numerical methods to derive sufficiently accurate results from their experimental data. XN does not solve the efficiency problem and, in fact, aggravates it, and it is therefore not well suited for very complex computations such as used in molecular docking, climate forecasting, or airplane design, which it would slow down unacceptably. But for most relatively small-scale scientific calculations, where speed is not as important as accuracy, XN often provides a very accessible and convenient bypass around the need for specialized knowledge of computer optimization. A central example used in this book, the solution of linear least squares problems, clearly illustrates this. A computer scientist will know how to avoid matrix inversion and construction of the pseudo-inverse, but a physical scientist will usually lack that specialized skill. The result may be a macro such as LS, which is primitive by the standards of computer science, yet gets the job done very well in extended precision. The latter therefore allows physical scientists to focus on solving the *scientific* problem at hand even without the optimal algorithm.

For experimental data, and for final results, the 15 decimals provided by Excel are almost always more than sufficient. Clearly, the need for extended precision in the analysis of scientific data comes neither from unrealistic expectations about the accuracy of the results of that analysis, nor from measurement uncertainty. Physical measurements often have only a few significant digits, and never 15 or more; not even the well-studied fundamental constants of physics and chemistry are known to such high relative accuracy. Instead, extended precision is primarily driven by *algorithmic* requirements, i.e., by problems of implementing numerical analysis on digital computers. Methods such as differentiation, high-order Romberg integration, and especially the inversion of ill-conditioned matrices or the solution of stiff differential equations, often need extended precision for their own, *internal* reasons. This is where XN can play a very useful role, especially since such requirements might not be obvious to the user of non-transparent ("black-box") computer programs. Another application of XN is as a source of reliable reference values, which makes it easy to verify custom-made spreadsheet routines, or to identify where regular code may still need special attention.

As can be seen in Table 11.15.3, quadruple precision ($D \geq 28$) suffices for most applications. John Beyers recommends $D = 28$, but I like to use the fast 7-digit packets ($D_{max} \approx 600$) with $D_{default} = 35$ just to make sure, because the additional computational time (for quintuple vs. quadruple precision) is usually negligible, except for difficult problems, which are typically where a somewhat higher precision may be needed. At the other extreme you can select $D_{max} \approx 4000$ with (at the same D-values) roughly two times slower packets of 13 decimals. XN provides all these options, so that you can make your own decisions.

11.18 For further reading

Many relevant papers of R. Panko on the prevalence of spreadsheet errors can be downloaded from his web site at http:// panko.shidler.hawaii.edu/ssr/Mypapers/whatknow.htm. Specific recommendations for organizing spreadsheets and verifying their results can be found at http://www.rdg.ac.uk under the heading publications/guides/topsde.html, and in a 2005 booklet by P. O'Beirne, *Spreadsheet Check and Control*.

For specific comments on the accuracy of Excel functions, consult the quoted papers by L. Knüsel and B. D. McCullough, the *NPL Report Cise27/99* by Cook, Cox, Dainton & Harris, downloadable from http:// www.npl.co.uk/ssfm/download/documents/cise27_99.pdf, and Heiser's tome on *Microsoft Excel 2000, 2003 and 2007 Faults, Problems, Workarounds and Fixes*, at http://www.daheiser.info.

When exploring BigMatrix, consult its tutorial (included in the download as a pdf file), *Linear Algebra for Big Matrices*, as well as the Help button of its Manager. For XN, consult appendix D, and use the documentation accompanying XN.xla(m), especially the XN Help file, based on version 6 of Volpi's *Xnumbers Multi-Precision Floating Point Arithmetic and Numerical Methods for Excel*, with an extensive update by John Beyers. A detailed programming guide for XN still remains to be written.

Appendix *A*

Some aspects of Excel

A.1 The basic spreadsheet operations

Symbol	Description	Comments	Precedence[1]

Numeric operators:

Symbol	Description	Comments	Precedence
–	Negation[2]	$-3\text{^}2 = 9$ but $0–3\text{^}2 = –9$; $–(3\text{^}2) = 0–(3\text{^}2) = –9$	1
^	Exponentiation	note: ** will not work; e or E may work[3]	2
*	Multiplication	note: × , · or . will not work[4]	3
/	Division		3
\	Integer division		4
Mod	Modulus	the remainder of a division	5
+	Addition		7
–	Subtraction[2]	$0–3\text{^}2 = –9$, $0–3\text{^}2 = –9$ (compare with negation, see above)	7
=	Assignment		9

String operators:

Symbol	Description	Comments	Precedence
&	Concatenation		8
=	Assignment		9
:	Range	as in: =SUM(B3:B15)	
,	Union	as in: =SUM(B3,D5,A7:F9)	
	Intersection	as in: =SUM(B3:B15 A7:F9)	

Notes: **1**: Precedence (ranging from 1 for highest to 9 for lowest) indicates the order in which operations will be performed *in the absence of brackets*. **2**: Excel uses the same symbol for negation and subtraction, but assigns them different precedences depending on what function it assigns to them. Therefore, *always use brackets in case of possible ambiguity*. **3**: E-notation *only* works for integer exponents. **4**: Multiplication *always* requires the explicit multiplication sign *****; *ab* is never interpreted as a product of *a* and *b*, but *a*b* always is.

Comparison operators:

Symbol	Description	Comments	Precedence
=	Equal to	as in: If x = 3 Then	1
<>	Unequal to	as in: If x <> 3 Then	2
<	Smaller than		3
>	Larger than		4
<=	Smaller than or equal to		5
>=	Larger than or equal to		6
Like	Pattern match	as in: If top Like t?p Then	7
Is	Object comparison		7
=	Assignment	as in: x = 3	8

585

Symbol	Description	Precedence[1]

Logical operators:

Symbol	Description	Precedence
Not	Negation	1
And	Conjunction	2
Or	Disjunction	3
Xor	Exclusion	4
Eqv	Equivalence	5
Imp	Implication	6
=	Assignment	8

A.2 Some common mathematical functions

Function	Description
ABS(x)	Absolute value
AVERAGE(*range*)	Average of the range specified
COUNT(*range*)	Counts number of entries in given range
COUNTA(*range*)	Counts number of non-blank values in range
COUNTBLANK(*range*)	Counts number of blank cells in given range
COUNTIF(*range, criterion*)	Counts only those values in the range that satisfy a given criterion
DEGREES(*angle in radians*)	Converts radians to degrees
EVEN(x)	Rounds a number to the nearest even integer away from zero
EXP(x)	Exponentiates, $= e^x$
FACT(n)	Factorial of a non-negative integer
FACTDOUBLE(n)	Double factorial of a non-negative number
INT(x)	Rounds a number down to the nearest integer
LN(x)	Natural logarithm of positive number
LOG(x [,n])	Logarithm of base n, where n is optional, with a default value of 10
LOG10(x)	Ten-based logarithm
MAX(*range*)	Finds the maximum value in 1 to 30 specified range(s)
MDETERM(*array*)	Yields the determinant of a square array of numbers
MEDIAN(*range*)	The median of a set of numbers
MIN(*range*)	Finds the smallest number in one or more ranges
MOD(x,y)	The remainder of the division x/y
ODD(x)	Rounds away from zero to the nearest odd number
PI( )	The number $\pi = 3.14159265358979$
POWER(x,y)	Raises x to the power y, $= x^y$
PRODUCT(*range*)	Product of numbers in specified range
RADIANS(*angle*)	Converts from degrees to radians
RAND( )	Yields a random number between 0 and 1
ROUND(x,n)	Rounds x, away from zero to n decimal places ROUNDDOWN(x,n)
ROUNDUP(x,n)	Rounds towards zero
SIGN(x)	Sign of (x)
SQRT(x)	Square root of non-negative number
SUM(*range*)	Sums values in specified range or ranges
SUMPRODUCT(*array*1,*array*2, …)	Computes the sums of the products of two or more arrays of equal dimensions

SUMSQ(*range*)	Sum of squares of specified range or ranges
SUMX2MY2(*xaray,yarray*)	$= \Sigma\,(x^2 - y^2)$
SUMX2PY2(*xaray,yarray*)	$= \Sigma\,(x^2 + y^2)$
SUMXMY2(*xaray,yarray*)	$= \Sigma\,(x - y)^2$
TRUNC(*x*)	Truncates a number to an integer

A.3 Trigonometric & related operations

Function	Description and example (all angles in radians)
ACOS(*x*)	The inverse cosine, $= \arccos(x)$
ACOSH(*x*)	The inverse hyperbolic cosine, $= \mathrm{arcosh}(x)$
ASIN(*x*)	The inverse sine, $= \arcsin(x)$
ASINH(*x*)	The inverse hyperbolic sine, $= \mathrm{arsinh}(x)$
ATAN(*x*)	The inverse tangent, $= \arctan(x)$
ATAN2(*x,y*)	$= \arctan(y/x)$
ATANH(*x*)	The inverse hyperbolic tangent, $= \mathrm{artanh}(x)$
COS(*x*)	The cosine, $= \cos(x)$
COSH(*x*)	The hyperbolic cosine, $= \cosh(x)$
SIN(*x*)	The sine, $= \sin(x)$
SINH(*x*)	The hyperbolic sine, $= \sinh(x)$
TAN(*x*)	The tangent, $= \tan(x)$
TANH(*x*)	The hyperbolic tangent, $= \tanh(x)$

A.4 Some engineering functions

In pre-2007 Excel these functions required loading the Analysis Toolpak.

Function	Description
BESSELI(*x,n*)	The modified Bessel function $I_n(x) = i^{-1} J_n(ix)$
BESSELJ(*x,n*)	The Bessel function $J_n(x)$
BESSELK(*x,n*)	The modified Bessel function $K_n(x)$
BESSELY(*x,n*)	The Bessel function $Y_n(x)$
CONVERT(*n,fromUnit,toUnit*)	Converts a number from one measurement system to another
DELTA(*n,m*)	Kronecker delta
ERF(*n*)	The error function
ERFC(*n*)	The complementary error function
GESTEP(*n,step*)	Tests whether a number *n* exceeds a threshold value *step*
RANDBETWEEN(*n,m*)	Generates a random integer between the integer values *n* and *m*; it will change every time a spreadsheet calculation is performed.

A.5 Functions for complex numbers

All angles in radians. In pre-2007 Excel these functions require that the Analysis ToolPak is loaded.

Function	Description
COMPLEX(*a,b*)	Converts the real numbers *a* and *b* into the complex number $a+bj$
IMABS("*a + bj*")	$= (a^2+b^2)^{1/2}$, the absolute value (modulus) of a complex number
IMAGINARY("*a + bj*")	$= b$, the imaginary component of a complex number
IMARGUMENT("*a + bj*")	$= \arctan(b/a)$, the argument of a complex number
IMCONJUGATE("*a + bj*")	$= a - bj$, the complex conjugate of a complex number

IMCOS("$a + bj$")	The cosine of a complex number
IMDIV("$a + bj$", "$c + dj$")	The quotient of two complex numbers
IMEXP("$a + bj$")	The exponential of a complex number
IMLN("$a + bj$")	The natural logarithm of a complex number
IMLOG10("$a + bj$")	The base-10 log of a complex number
IMLOG2("$a + bj$")	The base-2 log of a complex number
IMPOWER("$a + bj$",n)	$= (a^2+b^2)^n$, the complex number raised to an integer power
IMPRODUCT("$a + bj$", "$c + dj$")	The product of two complex numbers
IMREAL("$a + bj$")	$= a$, the real component of a complex number
IMSIN("$a + bj$")	The sine of a complex number
IMSQRT("$a + bj$")	The square root of a complex number
IMSUB("$a + bj$", "$c + dj$")	The difference between two (or more) complex numbers
IMSUM("$a + bj$","$c + dj$")	The sum of two (or more) complex numbers

Notes: Operations on complex numbers all start with IM, and use text strings to squeeze the two components of a complex number into one cell. In order to use the results of complex number operations, you must therefore first *extract* its real and imaginary components, using IMREAL() and IMAGINARY(). Instead of j you can use the default i to denote the square root of minus one (but before using j you must specify it as such), but you *cannot* use the corresponding capitals, I or J.

A.6   Matrix operations

Function	Description
INDEX(*array,row#,column#*)[1]	Yields an individual matrix element
MDETERM(*array*)	The determinant of a square matrix
MINVERSE(*array*)[2]	The inverse of a square matrix
MMULT(*array*1, *array*2)[2]	The product of two matrices.
TRANSPOSE(*array*)[1]	The transpose of a matrix

Notes: **1**: INDEX interprets a blank as the number 0, TRANSPOSE leaves it a blank, while the other three functions yield the error message #VALUE!
2: MINVERSE and MMULT work only on data *arrays*, i.e., rectangular blocks of cells, but not on single cells. To enter these instructions, enter the array with Ctrl⌣Shift⌣Enter (on the Mac: Command⌣Return).

A.7: Error messages

Error message	Problem
#DIV/0!	Division by zero or by the contents of an empty cell
#NAME?	Excel does not recognize the name; perhaps it has been deleted
#N/A	Some needed data are not available
#NULL!	The formula refers to a non-existing intersection of two ranges
#NUM!	The number is of incorrect type, e.g., is negative when a positive number is expected
#REF!	The reference is not valid; it may have been deleted
#VALUE!	The argument or operand is of the wrong type

A.8 Shortcut keystrokes for IBM & Mac formats

Excel operation	common to IBM & Mac	
	IBM	**Mac**
Copy	Ctrl‿c	
Paste	Ctrl‿v	
Cut	Ctrl‿x	
Bold toggle	Ctrl‿b	
Italics toggle	Ctrl‿i	
Underline toggle	Ctrl‿u	
Find	Ctrl‿f	
Replace	Ctrl‿h	
Fill down	Ctrl‿d	
Fill right	Ctrl‿r	
Repeat	Ctrl‿y	
Undo	Ctrl‿z	
Open new workbook	Ctrl‿n	
Select next worksheet	Ctrl‿PageDown	
Select previous worksheet	Ctrl‿PageUp	
Display Formula dialog box*	Ctrl‿a	

* after typing a formula name in a cell or in the formula bar

Display Find dialog box	Ctrl‿f	
Display Replace dialog box	Ctrl‿h	
Display GoTo dialog box	Ctrl‿g	
Display Define Name dialog box	Ctrl‿F3	
Insert a Cell Comment	Shift‿F2	
Display Paste Function dialog box	Shift‿F3	
Display Macro dialog box	**Alt‿F8**	**Opt‿F8**
Toggle between Excel and VBA	**Alt‿F11**	**Opt‿F11**

VBA operation	IBM & Mac	
	IBM	**Mac**
Run macro	F5	
Stop macro	Esc	
Step through macro	F8	
Toggle breakpoint	F9	
Toggle between Excel and VBA	**Alt‿F11**	**Opt‿F11**

Excel operation	IBM	Mac
Enter / end of line	**Enter**	**Return**
Get properties	**right-click**	**Ctrl‿click**
Specify a range or matrix	**Ctrl‿Shift‿Enter**	**Command‿Return**

A.9 Installation requirements & suggestions

In order to make full use of the methods described in this book, you will *need* the following:

(1) Excel 97 or a more recent version of Excel, installed on your computer. If you start by installing Excel, load its *full* version rather than its 'typical' or 'small' option in order to avoid having to add separately the items listed under (2).

(2) If needed, install the items listed below, automatically included when installing the full version of Excel. If you do not find them installed on a computer with pre-installed Excel, the following items should be added from the original Microsoft Windows or Excel installation disk. For institutional users, ask your IT manager.

Analysis ToolPak	see section 1.2.1	(No longer needs to be loaded separately in Excel 2007/2010.)
Analysis ToolPak – VBA	see section 1.2.1	(No longer needs to be loaded separately in Excel 2007/2010.)
Solver add-in	see section 1.2.2	
Solver.xla	see section 1.2.2	
VBA Help file	see section 1.2.3	

(3) The MacroBundle, containing the custom macros used in this book, should be downloaded as a Word text file (.doc) from the web site http:// www.bowdoin.edu/~rdelevie/excellaneous, and entered into a VBA module, see section 1.7.4. For most convenient access, then install the MBToolbar.

(4) From the excellaneous website also download Matrix.xla(m) (written by Leonardo Volpi and his foxes, and extended by John Beyers) if you want to use the matrix and complex number tools described in chapter 10, BigMatrix.xla (or from Volpi's original website at http:// digilander . libero . it / foxes), and XN.xla(m) (or from Beyer's website, at http://www.thetropicalevents.com.) for chapter 11.

The following *optional* files, downloadable from the same web sites that contains the MacroBundle, are not required, but are made available for your convenience:

(5) If you write some sample macros used in this book, but want to avoid typing them, download the SampleMacros file. You can then readily copy a sample macro whenever you need it, and paste it into your spreadsheet.

(6) Likewise, if you want to check a particular exercise with an external data set used in this book, but wish to avoid its (tedious as well as error-prone) manual data entry, download the SampleData file, and when needed copy and paste a data set from it into your spreadsheet.

(7) Especially in connection with chapter 8 you may also want to download the MacroMorsels. Also download the XNMacroBundle when you need examples of coding with XN.

(8) Additional optional files are recommended in Table 1.2.1 on page 6.

Appendix *B*

MacroBundles & MacroMorsels

This appendix describes some details of the subroutines used in this book. Macros are those subroutines that can be called directly from the spreadsheet or, in terms of VBA, those subroutines that have no argument, and therefore start with the heading `Sub name()` with empty brackets. From the user's point of view, this distinction may be meaningless, especially when the macro may do nothing more than set a constant (such as to differentiate between LS0 and LS1 by setting p to either 0 or 1), and then calls a subroutine to do the actual work. In this appendix we therefore consider macros and subroutines together.

While the main focus of this book is on the appropriate choice and use of data analysis procedures, such procedures often require custom functions and subroutines. Functions can only return information (i.e., numbers or text), while subroutines can also perform spreadsheet actions. (Because of their greater power, malicious macros are also more dangerous, and are therefore more carefully screened by Excel.) Moreover, macros and subroutines are more difficult to write than functions, as they involve the often not very transparent interface between Excel and VBA. While the MacroMorsels highlight the details of writing VBA code for custom routines, the MacroBundle illustrates what a finished product might look like, while at the same time providing a number of directly useful macros for commonly used scientific data analysis procedures. For some of these procedures, Matrix.xla(m) and/or XN.xla(m) offer alternative solutions.

Appendix B.1 lists the various custom macros available in the MacroBundle, Appendix B.2 does the same for those routines from the MacroBundle that have been adapted for extended precision, and appendix B.3 lists the macros of the current MacroMorsel collection. Appendix B.4 summarizes some aspects of least-squares and error analysis.

All macros in the MacroBundle and XNMacroBundle are self-documented, open-access, open-code routines that use the simplest, most transparent forms of data input. They are provided as text simple files, and can be imported directly, 'as is', into Excel modules.

The MacroBundle, XNMacroBundle, MacroMorsels, and FunctionFeatures introduced in this book are efforts to make Excel transparent in its applications to scientific data analysis. In this effort, contributions from others are very welcome, and the MacroBundle already includes some of these, such as the custom macro ELS kindly contributed by Philip Barak of the University of Wisconsin, and the custom macro Mapper written by William Craig of Georgetown University. Comments and suggestions are also welcome. Given the current status of Excel as the world's most widely used numerical software, any help in this respect is greatly appreciated and will of course be fully acknowledged.

B.1 The contents of the MacroBundle

The macros in this MacroBundle are offered as examples of macro writing. They can also be used as finished tools in scientific data analysis. Moreover, they can be modified by their users to suit their individual needs, or can even be scavenged for useful parts. They are provided under the GNU General - Public License.

These macros fall into three rather broad categories: least squares and error analysis, Fourier transformation and (de)convolution, and miscellaneous. Below is a listing and brief description of each of them. For more detailed notes on least squares and error analysis see section B.4.

B.1.1 Linear least squares, nonlinear least squares & error analysis:

LS is a traditional, general least squares routine for linear (polynomial and/or multivariate) fitting, assuming one dependent variable. LS0 forces the fit through the origin, LS1 does not. The output provides the parameter values a_i, their standard deviations s_i, the standard deviation s_f of the over-all fit to the function, the covariance matrix CM, and (optionally) the matrix of linear correlation coefficients LCC. Note: on recent versions of Excel, LS1 may be rejected as identical to a cell address. In that case, just rename it to, e.g., LS01, LS0_ , or a similar non-rejected name. If you use the MBToolbar, also do this there.

LSPoly applies LS to polynomial fitting to a polynomial of gradually increasing order (up to 14), including criteria, such as s_i and the *F*-test, that may be useful in deciding how many power terms to include in the analysis.

LSMulti applies LS to an increasing number of terms of a multivariate least squares analysis.

LSPermute computes the standard deviation of the fit for all possible permutations of multivariate parameters of up to six terms.

GradeBySf computes the standard deviations of the fit s_f for all possible combinations and permutations of unweighted least squares fits of a user-specified multivariate expression of up to six terms.

ELS provides least squares smoothing and differentiation for an equidistant (in the independent variable) but otherwise arbitrary function using a 'Savitzky-Golay' moving polynomial fit. ELSfixed uses a fixed-order polynomial, ELSauto self-optimizes the order of the fitting polynomial as it moves along the function.

WLS is the equivalent of LS with the inclusion of user-assignable weights.

SolverAid provides uncertainty estimates (standard deviations and the covariance matrix) for Solver-derived parameter values.

SolverScan lets Solver scan a two-dimensional array of parameter values.

ColumnSolver applies Solver to column-organized data.

Propagation computes the propagation of uncertainty for a single function, for various independent input parameters with known standard deviations, or for mutually dependent parameters with a known covariance matrix.

B.1.2 Fourier transform & (de)convolution:

FT is a general-purpose Fourier transform macro for forward or inverse Fourier transformation of 2^n data where n is an integer larger than 2.

(De)convolve provides general convolution and deconvolution. The convolution macro is generally applicable, the deconvolution macro is not.

(De)ConvolveFT yields convolution and deconvolution based on Fourier transformation.

DeconvolveIt performs *it*erative (van Cittert) deconvolution. DeconvolveIt0 has no constraints, DeconvolveIt1 assumes that the function is non-negative everywhere.

Ortho is a Gram-Schmidt orthogonalization routine

Gabor provides time-frequency analysis.

B.1.3 Miscellaneous:

InsertMBToolbar provides a toolbar for easy access to the macros of the MacroBundle. Users can of course add their own macros to this toolbar, and/or remove undesirable macros from it. In Excel 97 through 2003, the toolbar will be placed and displayed with all other toolbars; in Excel 2007 it can only be displayed in the Developer ribbon.

RemoveMTToolbar

Deriv1 uses a refinement of central differencing to estimate the first (partial) derivative $dF(x)/dx$ (or $\partial F(x)/\partial x$) of a function $F(x)$.

Trapez uses trapezoidal integration. TrapezAuto reconstructs the equation, whereas TrapezSpecify requires the user to supply the function.

Romberg implements Romberg integration for more efficient trapezoidal integration. RombergAuto reconstructs the equation, while RombergSpecify needs a user-supplied function.

Mapper generates colored or gray-scale 2-D maps.

ScanF generates an array of a function $F(x,y)$ for subsequent use by Mapper, or of an input list suitable for making contour maps in SimonLuca Santoro's IsoL

RootFinder finds a single root by bisection.

Semi-integrate & semi-differentiate comprises two small macros for cyclic voltammetry assuming planar diffusion

MovieDemos contain the code for the simple demos of section 1.6.

B.2 The contents of the extended-precision MacroBundles

B.2.1 The new XNMacroBundle:

The XNMacroBundle will contain extended-numberlength versions of those routines in the MacroBundle that most benefit from higher computational accuracy. Apart from their likewise extended execution times, their functioning is mostly the same to those of the corresponding macros in the MacroBundle, and therefore need no further comment. They can be used as is, or used as examples of how to introduce XN.xla(m) into existing VBA macros. This list is still under construction; for its current status check my Excellaneous website.

B.2.1 The old xMacroBundle:

The old xMacroBundle was based on using Xnumbers.dll, and was described extensively in the 2nd edition of my *Advanced Excel for scientific data analysis*. It is still available for downloading, together with Xnumbers.dll, but these are no longer supported because they cannot be used with Excel 2007 or more recent versions of Excel.

If you have written routines based on xNumbers.dll, you will find it quite easy to convert them to XN. If for some reason that cannot be done, and you need to use them on Excel2007/2010, here is a suggestion, courtesy of Mark Parris of the Microsoft Excel team. Click on the START button, then click on Run, which will open a small Run dialog box in the bottom left corner of the screen. In its window type

REGSVR32   Xnumbers.dll

and click on the Run button. A box should appear with the message "DIIRegisterServer in Xnumbers.dll succeeded." That should do it. If your computer is part of a network, you may get a statement that access is denied, in which case you may have to contact the network administrator or IT person.

B.3 Currently available MacroMorsels

The MacroMorsels are small macros that highlight particular aspects of VBA coding, by restricting their scope to one specific question. In writing this book I have often found it useful to write Macro-Morsels to explore the scope and limitations of particular VBA operations, and they are offered here to illustrate how you can write your own when you need to explore solutions to VBA coding problems.

B.3.1 Data input & output MacroMorsels

ReadActiveCell
ReadActiveArray
InputBoxForNumber
InputBoxForCell
InputBoxForArray
InputBoxForRange
OutputASingleValue1
OutputASingleValue2
OutputSeveralValues
OutputAnArray1
OutputAnArray2
OutputAnArray3
ControlOutputFormat
FromArrayValuesToRangeValues
PreventCellOverwrite
PreventColumnOverwrite

B.3.2 Data analysis MacroMorsels

ImportingData
Rounding
Truncation
UseAnExcelFunction1
UseAnExcelFunction2
UseAnExcelFunction3
UseAnExcelFunction4
UseANestedExcelFunction
UseAnExcelMatrixOperation1
UseAnExcelMatrixOperation2
UseAnExcelMatrixOperation3
UseAnExcelMatrixOperation4
DetermineMatrixSize
ListMatrixElements
InvasiveComputing
CentralDifferencing1
CentralDifferencing2
DecimalOperations
CountingPennies

594

B.3.3 Spreadsheet management MacroMorsels

    ScanSymbolCode
    UseSymbolCode
    ControlANumericalDisplay
    DeconstructACellAddress
    DeconstructAnArrayAddress
    ReconstituteAnEquation1
    ReconstituteAnEquation2
    ReconstituteAnEquation3
    MoveAndResizeARange
    InhibitScreenUpdating
    KeepUserInformed
    AttachCellComments
    MakeTestToolbar
    DeleteTestToolar
    ErrorPrevention
    ErrorTrapping1
    ErrorTrapping2

B.4 Least squares & error analysis

Because of the important role assigned to least squares methods in this book, we here summarize some of its most salient aspects.

B.4.1 Inherent limitations of least squares methods

The power and ubiquity of least squares methods should not make us lose sight of its inherent limitations, of which we here emphasize three.

(a) Least squares methods are based on the analysis of *random*, non-deterministic deviations. They cannot recognize systematic errors in the data, let alone correct for them, and their error estimates only regard the statistical spread of the data around an assumed model, not any systematic bias or offset that may affect them. The resulting uncertainty estimates are, therefore, inherently over-optimistic, and there are many well-documented examples illustrating that systematic errors can dwarf the effects of random deviations. Since least squares analysis only deals with precision rather than accuracy, it is best to consider the resulting standard deviations as estimating *imprecision* rather than error.

(b) In a linear least squares analysis, we fit a particular model to a set of data. The analysis produces an answer to the question posed, i.e., it provides a fit *to that particular model*, based on minimizing the sum of squares of the differences between the data and the model used. While the analysis also yields uncertainty estimates of the fit to the model function, it does not consider other possible functions, and therefore neither confirms nor questions the appropriateness of the model to describe the data. It is, therefore, a purely quantitative method, which does not address the qualitative question (which should be answered first) of what model would be appropriate.

However, *within* a given model, least squares analysis can indicate whether a particular model *parameter* is of questionable statistical significance, e.g., by comparing the absolute value of that parameter with the magnitude of its estimated imprecision. When all or most model parameters fail that test, the model is most likely inadequate to its task.

(c) You can almost always use nonlinear least squares, and often also linear least squares. Linear least squares analysis gives an unambiguous answer, whereas the answer provided by nonlinear least squares can be wrong if you start out with initial values that are too far off. The applicability of linear least squares can be extended by using transformations and appropriately weighted linear least squares, see section 3.17, although this not always yields better results, see section 4.15.

(d) Perhaps the most generally applicable use of least squares is combination of nonlinear least squares with another method, such as numerical simulation. If you understand the underlying relations, you can almost always formulate the problem in terms of mathematical expressions. Using the methods described in chapter 7, you can then solve such a system of equations for a given set of parameter values, possibly including initial and/or boundary conditions. Any such answer is, of course, restricted to the particular values of the input parameters used. However, when you then let Solver of Levenberg-Marquardt vary these input parameters using a least squares (or other) criterion, you can quickly home in to a local solution that, if you are careful, is almost always also the global one. Examples of this approach are given in, e.g., sections 4.6 and 4.21. For periodic signals, another very powerful combination is that of least squares analysis and Fourier transformation, as illustrated in section 5.10.

B.4.2 The meaning of imprecision estimates

There is a fairly common misconception that imprecision estimates, such as embodied in 'error' bars, standard deviations, confidence limits, etc., indicate absolute limits to statistical uncertainty, a misconception perhaps encouraged by the common use of the shorthand symbol ± in front of quantities describing such estimates (as also used in this book). However, the *standard deviations* produced by least squares routines, and properties such as confidence limits derived from these standard deviations, are *characteristic parameters* describing the data reproducibility, rather than upper and lower limits of that reproducibility. No such upper and lower limits exist, and none can therefore be specified.

A Gaussian distribution is a smooth, continuous curve. One cannot say where it starts and where it ends because this never happens or, in a strictly mathematical sense, this only happens at infinity. Still, a *characteristic width* can be defined that, given a sufficiently large number of observations, would encompass a given *fraction f* of all likely deviations from its average value. Emphatically it does *not* mean that all such deviations fall within ± one characteristic width; instead, the fraction 1–*f* can be expected to fall outside these limits.

Perhaps the following analogy can help to clarify this point. Consider the exponential $e^{-t/\tau}$ as a function of time t. It decays gradually, approaching zero as t approaches $+\infty$. Of course one can define t-values where the integral

$$\int_0^T e^{-t/\tau}\,dt$$

has a particular value, such as 0.5, 0.9, 0.95, or 0.99, which in this example would occur at $T \approx 0.693\,\tau$, $2.303\,\tau$, $2.996\,\tau$, and $4.605\,\tau$ respectively. But since the choice of values such as 0.5, 0.9, etc. is rather arbitrary, and each merely is a constant factor times τ, one usually specifies the decay rate simply by its characteristic constant τ.

In physics, the same situation is encountered when a capacitor of capacitance C is discharged through a resistor of resistance R. The voltage and charge on the capacitor are exponentially decaying functions of time that gradually approach zero and, in principle, only reach full discharge after an infinitely long time. But although the decay curves are smooth and gradual, without any abrupt end, we can still identify a *characteristic* decay time, in this case of magnitude RC, during which time the fraction 1–e (about 63%) of the initial voltage or charge will have been lost. A first-order chemical reaction likewise decays exponentially, with a characteristic rate constant k; it does not imply that the reaction is complete after a time $1/k$, just as the capacitor is not fully discharged after a time $1/RC$.

In the same sense, the sample standard deviation s is the characteristic width of the Gaussian curve, and the area of that curve between $x = x_{av} - s$ and $x_{av} + s$ corresponds to only about 68.3% of its total area, i.e., it covers only 68.3% (about 2 out of 3) of all likely errors. And that only applies when the deviations are purely random, which they seldom are.

The confidence limits are more sophisticated than merely using different numerical values, because they also take into account the increased uncertainty associated with finite sample size. The 95% confidence limit is therefore not obtained by multiplying s by a fixed number, but by a function, the Student t, which also depends on sample size N. Still, the point remains that 5% of all measurements are expected to fall outside these 95% confidence limits. Do not consider standard deviation or confidence limits as absolute error limits.

Just as the numbers we derive from a least squares analysis are not cast in stone, but come with associated imprecisions, their imprecision estimates are also imprecise. This turns out to be a simple matter to define quantitatively, as described in section 2.12, and is mentioned here only to make sure that users of least squares macros are aware of it. Moreover, it is good to keep a healthy perspective of the accuracy and precision of *actual* data analyses, as illustrated in section 4.26.

B.4.3 The effects of mutually dependent parameters

Often we derive multiple parameters from one set of experimental data; this even happens with the lowly straight line plot, where we find a slope and intercept. If these parameters are subsequently used to compute a quantity that depends on more than one of these parameters, the propagation of uncertainty must take into account their mutual dependency. This can be done in two ways: either we avoid the problem by adopting an analysis method that is based on orthogonal parameters, or we specifically take the mutual interactions into account in terms of the covariance matrix. Both approaches work; and which one of these is selected often depends on matters of convenience. The custom macros LS, WLS, XNLS, and XNWLS provide the covariance matrix, as does SolverAid when applied to results obtained with Solver. Propagation can process either a covariance matrix or individual standard deviations, but in the latter case obviously cannot take their covariances into account. The important aspect here is that one should not neglect serious mutual dependencies between parameters, and it is therefore both best and easiest (because it avoids a value judgement every time you run the analysis) to *always* include them in the calculations, even when their effects may be negligible. Section 2.18 gives an example of what can happen when collinearity is ignored.

B.4.1.4 Choosing an appropriate least squares macro

Our recommended standard *linear* least squares workhorse is LS, because it provides the sought parameters, their standard deviations, and the covariance matrix. Its color code even warns you when a parameter is of questionable statistical significance, or (when you display the optional matrix of linear correlation coefficients) when the variables exhibit significant collinearity. It also comes with assistants: LSPoly may help you decide what order of polynomial to use in LS, while LSMulti, LSPermute, and ScaleBySf can help you sort out which variables to use in multivariate fitting with LS.

For computing the derivative of an equidistant curve with a moving least squares polynomial, use ELS. When you first transform your data to make them fit a straight line or a power series in x, use the weighted least squares routine WLS with the appropriate weighting factors, see section 3.17. However, the presence of substantial noise in your data may lead to unsatisfactory results, see section 3.20, in which case nonlinear least squares may be preferable.

Finally, you may encounter a problem involving high collinearity, i.e., a strong mutual dependency between some or all of the 'independent' variables, to which you will be alerted by color in the matrix of linear correlation coefficients of the latest version of LS. If you cannot handle it with multivariate or polynomial centering (see sections 10.6 and 10.7), combine centering with **RegrL**, a regression routine in Matrix.xla based on singular value decomposition, and therefore much more collinearity-resistant than LS. (Since Excel 2003, you can also use Excel's **LinEst** or **Regression**, which are now functionally equivalent to singular value decomposition.) Or you can use **Ortho**. Finally, if all else fails, use the Big-Matrix **Regression** routine described in section 11.10.4, or **XNLS**, which you can see in detail in section 11.14.

For nonlinear least squares, use **Solver** plus **SolverAid**. For repeated use of Solver, you may be able to organize your data such that you can use **ColumnSolver**. If the number of adjustable parameters is small, and a precise solution is desired, it may be wise to use Solver to generate first estimates of the sought parameters, and to refine these with a **Levenberg-Marquardt** routine.

Now that you've got the tools, and a book full of examples of how to apply them − go for it!

Appendix C

Some details of Matrix.xla

C.1 Matrix nomenclature

For the sake of notational compactness, we will denote a square *diagonal* matrix by **D** with elements d_{ii}, a square *tridiagonal* matrix by **T** with elements t_{ij} where $|j - i| \le 1$, most other *square* matrices by **S**, *rectangular* matrices by **R**, and all matrix elements by m_{ij}. A *vector* will be shown as **v**, with elements v_i, and a *scalar* as **s**. Particular values are denoted by x when real, and by z when complex. All optional parameters are shown in straight brackets, [ ]. All matrices, vectors, and scalars are assumed to be real, except when specified otherwise. All matrices are restricted to two dimensions, and vectors to one dimension. Table C.1 briefly explains some matrix terms that will be used in subsequent tables.

With some functions, the user is given the integer option *Int* of applying integer arithmetic. When a matrix only contains integer elements, selecting integer arithmetic may avoid most round-off problems. On the other hand, the range of integer arithmetic is limited, so that overflow errors may result if the matrix is large and/or contains large numbers. Another common option it *Tiny*, which defines the absolute value of quantities that can be regarded as most likely resulting from round-off errors, and are therefore set to zero. When not activated, the routine will use its user-definable default value.

Condition	of a matrix: ratio of its largest to smallest singular value
Diagonal	of a square matrix: the set of terms m_{ij} where $i = j$
Diagonal matrix **D**	square matrix with $m_{ij} = 0$ for all off-diagonal elements $i \ne j$.
Decomposition	or factorization: writing a matrix as the product of two or more special matrices
False	as optional parameter: False = 0
First lower subdiagonal	of a square matrix: the set of terms m_{ij} where $j = i+1$
First upper subdiagonal	of a square matrix: the set of terms m_{ij} where $j = i-1$
Inverse square matrix $\mathbf{S}^{-1}$	square matrix that satisfies $\mathbf{S}^{-1}\,\mathbf{S} = \mathbf{S}\,\mathbf{S}^{-1} = \mathbf{I}$
Hermitian matrix	a square matrix for which $\mathbf{S}^{*T} = \mathbf{S}$ where $\mathbf{S}^*$ denotes the complex conjugate of **S**; all symmetric real matrices are Hermitian
Hessenberg matrix **H**	a square matrix with $m_{ij} = 0$ for $j = i+k,\ k > 1$
Lower triangular matrix **L**	a square matrix with only 0's below its diagonal
Order	of a square matrix: its number of rows or columns
Orthogonal matrix	a real, square matrix with the property $\mathbf{S}^{-1} = \mathbf{S}^{T}$
Rank	order of largest nonsingular square submatrix of a matrix
Rectangular matrix **R**	a matrix with (in general) an unequal number of rows and columns
Square matrix **S**	a matrix with an equal number of rows and columns
Subdiagonal	the set of terms m_{ij} where $i = j\pm k$ where k is an integer
Symmetric matrix	a square matrix **S** with all $m_{ij} = m_{ji}$, hence $\mathbf{S} = \mathbf{S}^{T}$
Toeplitz matrix	a square matrix with constant elements on each diagonal parallel to the main diagonal
Transpose $\mathbf{R}^{T}$	matrix after interchanging its rows and columns
Triangular matrix **T**	matrix with non-zero terms only on its diagonal and first upper and lower subdiagonals
True	as optional parameter: True = 1
Uniform matrix	repeats its elements on its diagonal and each subdiagonal
Unit matrix **I**	square matrix of arbitrary dimension $m \times m$ with 1's on its diagonal, and 0's above and below it
Upper triangular matrix **U**	a square matrix with only 0's below its diagonal. (Exceptions: the upper triangular matrix **R** in QR decomposition; the orthogonal matrix **U** in singular value decomposition.)

Table C-1: The nomenclature used

C.2 Functions for basic matrix operations

C.2.1 Functions with a scalar output

Entering the functions listed below does not require the use of Ctrl⌣Shift⌣Enter.

MAbs(**R**) — Absolute value of **R** — $\sqrt{\sum_{i,j} m_{ij}^2}$

MCond(**R**) — Condition number κ of a matrix — κ
computed using singular value decomposition

MpCond(**R**) — $-\log_{10}$ of matrix condition number — $p\kappa = -\log(\kappa)$
computed using singular value decomposition

MDet(**S** [,Int] [,*Tiny*]) — Determinant of a square matrix **S** — $\det[\mathbf{S}]$
Similar to Excel's =MDETERM(**S**). Because of rounding errors, both
MDET and MDETERM can yield (often different) non-zero answers
For a singular matrix. When all elements of **S** are integer, and Integer is
set to True, MDET uses integer mode. Defaults: Integer = False, *Tiny* = 0.

MRank(**R**) — Rank of a matrix

MTrace(**S**) — Trace of a square matrix — $\mathrm{tr}(\mathbf{S}) = \sum_i m_{ii}$

C.2.2 Basic matrix functions

Entering the following functions requires the use of Ctrl⌣Shift⌣Enter

MAdd(**R**$_1$,**R**$_2$) — Addition of two matrices — $\mathbf{R}_1 + \mathbf{R}_2$
equivalent to Excel's =**R**$_1$+**R**$_2$, as in =B2:D5+F2:H5.

MSub(**R**$_1$,**R**$_2$) — Subtraction of two matrices — $\mathbf{R}_1 - \mathbf{R}_2$
Equivalent to Excel's = **R**$_1$–**R**$_2$, as in =B2:D5–F2:H5.

MT(**R**) — Transpose of a matrix — $\mathbf{R}^{\mathrm{T}}$
equivalent to Excel's function TRANSPOSE

MMult(**R**$_1$,**R**$_2$) — Product of two matrices — $\mathbf{R}_1\,\mathbf{R}_2$
Excel's function is listed here for the sake of completeness

MProd(**R**$_1$,**R**$_2$,**R**$_3$,...) — Product of two or more matrices — $\mathbf{R}_1\mathbf{R}_2\mathbf{R}_3...$
Pay attention to the dimensions, as the function MProd does *not* check them.

MMultS(**R**,*s*) — Product of a matrix and a scalar — $s\mathbf{R} = \mathbf{R}s$
equivalent to Excel's scalar multiplication, as in =3.21*B2:G9.

MPow(**S**,*n*) — $\mathbf{S}^n = \mathbf{S}\,\mathbf{S}\,\mathbf{S}\,...\,\mathbf{S}$ (*n* terms) — $\mathbf{S}^n$

MInv(**S** [,Int] [,*Tiny*]) — Inverse of **S** — $\mathbf{S}^{-1}$
similar to Excel's =MINVERSE(M). Because of rounding errors, both
M_INV(M) and MINVERSE(M) can yield (different) non-zero element values for a
singular matrix. When Integer is set to True, integer mode is used. Any result smaller
in absolute magnitude than *Tiny* is set to zero. Defaults: Integer = False, *Tiny* = 0.

MExp(**S** [,Algo] [,*n*]) — Matrix exponential — $e^{\mathbf{S}} = \sum_{n=0}^{\infty} \frac{\mathbf{S}^n}{n!}$

Uses Padé approximation (the default, Algo = "P"), otherwise the power method.
The default stops when convergence is reached. When *n* is specified, the resulting
error can be obtained with =MExpErr(**S**, *n*)

MExpErr (**S**,*n*) — Error term in matrix exponential

C.2.3 Vector functions

ProdScal($\mathbf{v}_1,\mathbf{v}_2$)	Scalar product of two vectors	$\mathbf{v}_1 \bullet \mathbf{v}_2$
ProdVect($\mathbf{v}_1,\mathbf{v}_2$)	Vector product of two vectors	$\mathbf{v}_1\,\mathbf{v}_2$
VectAngle($\mathbf{v}_1,\mathbf{v}_2$)	Angle between two vectors	$\arccos\left(\dfrac{\mathbf{v}_1 \bullet \mathbf{v}_2}{\lvert\mathbf{v}_1\rvert \cdot \lvert\mathbf{v}_2\rvert}\right)$

C.3: More sophisticated matrix functions

Diagonal or tridiagonal square matrices occur quite frequently in practical problems. When such matrices are of high orders, they can take up a large amount of space, even though most of it will be occupied by zeros. It is then often convenient to store and display $m{\times}m$ diagonal matrices $\mathbf{D}$ in compact notation as single $m{\times}1$ column vectors, and tridiagonal matrices $\mathbf{T}$ as $m{\times}3$ rectangular matrices. A number of special instructions are provided for this space-saving approach. Don't confuse compact notation with sparse notation, as used in connection with sparse matrices, see Table C.9.2.

MDetPar($\mathbf{S}$)	Determinant of $\mathbf{S}$ containing one symbolic parameter k Used with Ctrl⌣Shift⌣Enter yields vector, otherwise output shown as text string.	det[$\mathbf{S}$]
MDet3($\mathbf{T}$)	Determinant of $\mathbf{T}$ in $n{\times}3$ format There is no need to use Ctrl⌣Shift⌣Enter, because the output is a scalar.	det[$\mathbf{T}$]
MMult3($\mathbf{T},\mathbf{R}$)	Multiplies a tridiagonal matrix in tricolumnar format with a rectangular or square matrix $\mathbf{R}$, or even a vector $\mathbf{v}$.	$\mathbf{T\,R}$
MMultTpz ($\mathbf{S},\mathbf{v}$)	Multiplies a Toeplitz matrix in compact (columnar) format and a vector $\mathbf{v}$. For a Toeplitz matrix of order $2n+1$, $\mathbf{v}$ must be $n{\times}1$	
MBAB($\mathbf{S}_1,\mathbf{S}_2$)	Similarity transform	$\mathbf{S}_1^{-1}\,\mathbf{S}_2\,\mathbf{S}_1$
MBlock($\mathbf{S}$)	Transforms reducible, sparse square matrix into block-partitioned form	
MBlockPerm($\mathbf{S}$)	The permutation matrix for MBlock	
MDiag($\mathbf{v}$)	Convert vector $\mathbf{v}$ into $\mathbf{D}$	$m_{ii} = v_i$
MDiagExtr($\mathbf{S}[,d]$)	Extract the diagonal of $\mathbf{S}$ $d = 1$ for the diagonal, $i = j$ (the default), $d = 2$ for the first lower subdiagonal, $i = j+1$.	

C.4: Functions for matrix factorization

The terms matrix *factorization* and matrix *decomposition* refer to the same operations, in which a given matrix is expressed as the product of two or more special matrices. This approach is often used to facilitate finding the required solution. The differences between the various available approaches reflect their general applicability, numerical efficiency, tolerance of ill-conditioning, etc.

SVDD($\mathbf{R}$)	Yields $\mathbf{D}$ of $\mathbf{R} = \mathbf{U}^{\mathrm{T}}\,\mathbf{D}\,\mathbf{V}$ The central result of singular value decomposition, providing the singular values σ_i as well as easy routes to matrix rank r and condition number κ. When $\mathbf{R}$ is Hermitian, the σ_i are the absolute values of its eigenfunctions. Note: the traditional symbol $\mathbf{U}$ here does not imply an upper triangular matrix.	$\mathbf{D}$
SVDU($\mathbf{R}$)	Yields $\mathbf{U}$ of $\mathbf{R} = \mathbf{U}^{\mathrm{T}}\,\mathbf{D}\,\mathbf{V}$	$\mathbf{U}$
SVDV($\mathbf{R}$)	Yields $\mathbf{V}$ of $\mathbf{R} = \mathbf{U}^{\mathrm{T}}\,\mathbf{D}\,\mathbf{V}$	$\mathbf{V}$
MCholesky($\mathbf{S}$)	Cholesky decomposition of a symmetric matrix $\mathbf{M}$ into a lower triangular square matrix $\mathbf{L}$ and its transpose $\mathbf{L}^{\mathrm{T}}$	$\mathbf{S} = \mathbf{L}\,\mathbf{L}^{-1}$

MLU(**S** [,pivot])	LU decomposition into a lower (**L**) and upper (**U**) triangular square matrix. The optional pivot (the default) activates partial pivoting	$\mathbf{S} = \mathbf{L\,U}$
MOrthoGS(**R**)	Modified Gram-Schmidt orthogonalization	
MQH(**S**,**v**)	decomposition of **S** with vector **b** **Q** is orthogonal, **H** is Hessenberg. If **S** is symmetric, **H** is tridiagonal	$\mathbf{S} = \mathbf{Q\,H\,Q^T}$
MQR(**R**)	QR decomposition **Q** is orthogonal, **R** is upper triangular	$\mathbf{A} = \mathbf{Q\,R}$

MHessenberg(**S**)   Converts **S** into its Hessenberg form **H**

MChar(**S**, x)   Computes characteristic matrix at real value x
If x complex, use MCharC(**S**, z)

MCharPoly(**S**)   Computes characteristic polynomial of **S**
Can often be combined with PolyRoots(P)

PolyRoots(P)   Finds all roots of a polynomial P

PolyRootsQR(P)   Finds all roots of a polynomial P
using the QR algorithm

MNorm(**R** or **v** [,Norm])   Finds the matrix or vector norm   For matrix **R**: Norm: 0 (default) =
Frobenius, 1 = max. abs. column sum, 2 = Euclidian norm, 3 = max. abs. row sum.
For vector **v**: Norm: 1 = max. sum, 2 = Euclidian norm, 3 (default) = max. abs. value

MPerm(**p**)   generates a permutation matrix from a permutation vector **p**

MCmp(**v**)   Companion matrix of a monic polynomial P
where **v** contains the coefficients of P

MCovar(**R**)   covariance matrix

$$c_{ij} = \frac{\sum\limits_{k=1}^{m}(m_{ki} - m_{i,av})(m_{kj} - m_{j,av})}{m}$$

similar to Excel's COVAR(a_i, a_j)

MCorr(**R**)   correlation matrix (i.e., normalized covariance)

$$r_{ij} = \frac{m\sum\limits_{k=1}^{m}(m_{ki} - m_{i,av})(m_{kj} - m_{j,av})}{\sqrt{\sum\limits_{k=1}^{m}(m_{ki} - m_{i,av})}\sqrt{\sum\limits_{k=1}^{m}(m_{kj} - m_{j,av})}}$$

MExtract(**R**, row, $column$)   Creates a submatrix of **R** by extracting
a specified row and $column$

MMopUp(**R** [,$ErrMin$])   Eliminates round-off errors from **R**
by replacing by zero all elements $|a_{ij}| < ErrMin$ (default 10^{-15})

MRot(m, $theta$, p, q) Creates orthogonal matrix of order m that rotates by angle $theta$ in p,q plane
$p \neq q, p \leq m, q \leq m$

C.5 Eigenvalues & eigenvectors

The German word "eigen" in this context is best translated as "particular to": eigenvalues and eigenvectors of a matrix are scalars and vectors that are *particular to that matrix*. They are only defined for square matrices.

C.5.1: For general square matrices

MEigenvalJacobi(**S** [,*MaxIter*])   Jacobi sequence of orthogonality transforms
> *MaxIter* (default 100) is the max. # of iterations

MEigenvalMax(**S** [,*MaxIter*])   Finds maximum |eigenvalue by using the iterative power method
> *MaxIter* (default 1000) is the max. # of iterations

MEigenvecPow(**S** [,*Norm*] [,*MaxIter*])   Approximates eigenvalues for diagonizable **S**
> by using the power method. Normalizes eigenvector if *Norm* = True; default = False
> *MaxIter* (default 1000) is the max. # of iterations

MEigenvalQR(**S**)   Approximates the eigenvalues of **S** by QR decomposition
> Yields an $n \times 1$ array, or $n \times 2$ for complex eigenvalues

MQRIter(**S**[,*MaxIter*])   Iterative diagonalization of **M** to yield its eigenvalues
> based on QR decomposition *MaxIter* (default = 100) sets the max. # of iterations

MEigenvec(**S**, **eval** [,*MaxErr*])   Computes eigenvector of **S** for a given eigenvalue(s) in vector **eval**

MEigenvecInv(**S**, **eval**)   Computes eigenvectors for a given vector **eval** by inverse iteration

MEigenvecJacobi(**S**[,*MaxIter*])   Orthogonal similarity transforms of a symmetric matrix **S**
> *MaxIter* (default = 100) sets the max. # of iterations

MEigenvectMax(**S** [,*Norm*] [,*MaxIter*])   Yields eigenvector for dominant eigenvalue
> (i.e., with max. absolute value). Normalizes eigenvector if *Norm* = True; default = False

MEigenvecPow(**S** [,*Norm*] [,*MaxIter*])   Yields real eigenvectors for diagonizable **S**
> using the power method. Normalizes eigenvector if *Norm* = True; default = False.
> *MaxIter* (default 1000) is the max. # of iterations

MRotJacobi(**S**)   Jacobi orthogonal rotation of symmetric **S**

MEigenSortJacobi(**eval**, **evec** [,*n*])   Sorts eigenvectors by value of |eigenvalue|
> Optional *n* specifies number of eigenvectors shown

MNormalize(**R** [,Norm] [*Tiny*])   Normalize real matrix **R**
> Norm specifies normalizing denominator: $1 = |v_{min}|$,
> 2 (default) $= |v|$, $3 = |v_{max}|$; *Tiny* default $= 2 \times 10^{-14}$

C.5.2: For tridiagonal matrices

MEigenvalQL(**T** [,*MaxIter*])   Approximates eigenvalues of tridiago nal symmetric matrix
> using the QL algorithm accepts **T** in either regular or compact format.
> *MaxIter* (default 200) is the max. # of iterations

MEigenvalTTpz(*n*, *a*, *b*, *c*)   Computes eigenvalues for a tridiagonal
> Toeplitz matrix with elements *a*, *b*, *c*
> All eigenvalues are real if $ac > 0$, complex if $ac < 0$

MEigenvecT(**T**, eigenvalues [,*MaxErr*])   Approximates eigenvectors for given eigenvalue(s) of **T**
> Accepts **T** in either square or compact format

C.6 Linear system solvers

Linear system solvers solve a system of simultaneous linear equations in one single user operation. Int = True uses integer computation, otherwise use False (default). *Tiny* sets the minimum absolute round-off error that will be replaced by 0 (default: 10^{-15}).

SysLin (S, x [,Integer] [,*Tiny*]) Gauss-Jordan solution of linear system

> M is the matrix of independent (control) parameters, x is the unknown coefficient vector or matrix

SysLinIterG (S, x, x_0 [,*MaxIter*] [,w])   Iterative Gauss-Seidel solution of linear system

> using relaxation M is the matrix of independent (control) parameters, x is the unknown coefficient vector or matrix, x_0 its starting value, *MaxIter* (default = 200) is the max # of iteration (*MaxIter* = 1 can be used for step-by-step use), w (default = 1) is the relaxation factor

SysLinIterJ (S, x, x_0 [,*MaxIter*] [,w])   Iterative Jacobi solution of linear system

> S is the matrix of independent (control) parameters, x is the unknown coefficient vector or matrix, x_0 its starting value, *MaxIter* (default = 200) is the max # of iteration (*MaxIter* = 1 for step-by-step use).

SysLinT (T, x [,*Type*] [,*Tiny*]) Solution of triangular linear system

> by forward or backward substitution. T is either U (upper) or L (lower) diagonal; the optional (i.e., unnecessary) *Type* specifies U or L.

SysLin3 ($T3$, x [,Integer] [,*Tiny*]) SysLin for tridiagonal matrix $T3$

> where $T3$ is in compact notation

SysLinTpz (S, v)   Solves a Toeplitz linear system by Levinson's method

SysLinSing (S or R [,x] [,*MaxErr*]) Linear system analysis of a singular system

> The matrix can be square ($m \times m$) or rectangular ($m \times n$, where $m < n$, i.e., for an underdetermined system). When x is not specified, it is taken as 0. *MaxErr* (default = 10^{-13}) sets the relative precision. For degenerate (multiplicitous) eigenvalues a larger error tolerance may be needed, such as *MaxErr* = 10^{-10}. A system without solution returns a question mark.

TraLin (R ,X [,B])   Linear transformation $Y = RX + B$

> R is $m \times n$; X is $n \times p$, B is $m \times p$, and Y is $m \times p$. Also works when $p = 1$, in which case X, B, and Y are vectors.

C.7 Functions for complex matrices

There are many physical phenomena that are best described in terms of matrix algebra with complex rather than real numbers. For example, the concept of a dielectric permittivity ε of a medium can be extended from strictly transparent media to (partially or completely) light-absorbing ones by considering ε as a complex quantity. Electrical networks containing phase-shifting components are conveniently described in terms of complex quantities such as admittance and impedance; likewise, the linear (i.e., small-amplitude) response of an electrochemical interface is most completely described in terms of Rangarajan's matrix model (*J. Electroanal. Chem.* 55 (1974) 297-374) which includes complex quantities reflecting the time lags of mass transport and interfacial capacitance. Modern quantum theory uses complex wave functions.

The Excel functions involving complex quantities, as listed in Appendix A.5, only use the character string format. The matrix operations involving complex functions listed below allow the user, through the optional instruction parameter c, to select one of three notational formats. These formats are $c = 1$: split; $c = 2$: interlaced, and $c = 3$: character string. Figs. C.7.1 and C.7.2 illustrate these for when the real and imaginary components are integer or non-integer respectively.

In the split format each complex *entity* (scalar, vector, matrix) is displayed with its real components, and to its immediate right with its imaginary components. In the interlaced format, each complex *number* is represented in two adjacent cells on the same row. In the text string format, the numbers are displayed as character strings listing both the real and imaginary component, as in the Excel-supplied functions for complex numbers. In the latter case, the results may have to be decoded with =IMREAL() or =IMAGINARY(). These three ways of representing complex numbers are illustrated in Fig. C.7.2. The default mode is 1, the split format.

	A	B	C	D	E	F	G	H	I
1									
2	***Split format (default)***								
3	-2	8	0	0	5	7	=MDetC(A3:F5)		
4	3	4	6	5	-4	-2	9	-103	
5	-2	9	8	6	2	6			
6									
7	***Interlaced format***								
8	-2	0	8	5	0	7	=MDetC(A8:F10,2)		
9	3	5	4	-4	6	-2	9	-103	
10	-2	6	9	2	8	6			
11									
12	***Text string format***								
13	-2	8+5j	7j			=MDetC(A13:C15,3)			
14	3+5j	4-4j	6-2j				9-103j		
15	-2+6j	9+2j	8+6j						

Fig C.7.1: The three ways to display complex quantities: (1) "split", as entire quantities with real and imaginary components, the default mode; (2) "interlaced", in which each individual element is shown with its two components adjacent to each other; and (3) "string", as text strings. The matrix and its determinant contain only integer and imaginary components, in which case the text string format is often the more compact.

	A	B	C	D	E	F	G	H
1								
2	***Split format (default)***							
3	-2.42750	8.17185	0.04820	0	4.53980	6.84630	=MDetC(A3:F5)	
4	2.65938	4.07577	6.33463	5.28370	-4.32580	-1.68270	-20.96548	-78.61323
5	-2.36394	9.49214	7.88308	6.49700	2.01150	5.62860		
6								
7	***Interlaced format***							
8	-2.42750	0	8.17185	4.53980	0.04820	6.84630	=MDetC(A8:F10,2)	
9	2.65938	5.28370	4.07577	-4.32580	6.33463	-1.68270	-20.96548	-78.61323
10	-2.36394	6.49700	9.49214	2.01150	7.88308	5.62860		
11								
12	***Text string format***							
13	-2.4275	8.17185+4.5398j	0.0482+6.8463j				=MDetC(A13:C15,3)	
14	2.65938+5.2837j	4.07577-4.3258j	6.33463-1.6827j				-20.9654787597-78.6132259685j	
15	-2.36394+6.497j	9.49214+2.0115j	7.88308+5.6286j					

Fig C.7.2: The three ways to display complex quantities, when the numbers are not restricted to integers, in which case the text string format may require much wider columns.

MCplx ($\mathbf{R}_1$, $\mathbf{R}_2$ [,*c*])	Convert two real matrices **M** into one complex matrix **C**	$\mathbf{C} = \mathbf{R}_1 + i\mathbf{R}_2$
MAddC ($\mathbf{C}_1$, $\mathbf{C}_2$ [,*c*])	Add two complex matrices	$\mathbf{C}_1 + \mathbf{C}_2$
MSubC ($\mathbf{C}_1$, $\mathbf{C}_2$ [,*c*])	Subtract two complex matrices	$\mathbf{C}_1 + \mathbf{C}_2$
MAbsC (**C**[,*c*])	Absolute value of a complex vector	
MDetC (**C**)	Determinant of a complex square matrix **C**	Det(**C**)
MInvC (**C** [,*c*])	Invert of a complex square matrix	$\mathbf{C}^{-1}$
MMultC ($\mathbf{C}_1$, $\mathbf{C}_2$ [,*c*])	Product of two complex matrices $\mathbf{C}_1\,\mathbf{C}_2$	
MPowC ($\mathbf{C}_1$, $\mathbf{C}_2$, $\mathbf{C}_3$, ... [,*c*])	Product of two or more complex matrices	$\mathbf{C}_1\,\mathbf{C}_2\,\mathbf{C}_3\ldots$
MMultSC(**C**, *s* [,*c*])	Product of a complex matrix **C** and scalar *s*	$s\,\mathbf{C} = \mathbf{C}\,s$
MTC (**C** [,*c*])	Transpose of a complex matrix **C**	$\mathbf{C}^{\mathrm{T}}$

MTH ($\mathbf{C}$ [,c])	Hermitian (conjugate, adjoint) transpose of $\mathbf{C}$	$\mathbf{C}^H = \mathbf{C}^{*T} = \mathbf{C}^{T*}$
ProdScaleC ($\mathbf{v_1}, \mathbf{v_2}$)	Scalar product of complex vectors	$\mathbf{v_1} \bullet \mathbf{v_2}$

MNormalize ($\mathbf{C}$ [,Norm] [,c] [*Tiny*]) Normalize complex matrix $\mathbf{C}$
Norm specifies normalizing denominator: $1 = |v_{min}|$,
2 (default) $= |v|$, $3 = |v_{max}|$; *Tiny* default $= 2 \times 10^{-14}$

MCharC ($\mathbf{C}$, z [,c]) Compute characteristic matrix of $\mathbf{C}$ at value z
$\mathbf{M}$ and/or z can be real or complex

MCharPolyC ($\mathbf{C}$, [,c]) Compute the characteristic polynomial

PolyRootsQRC ($\mathbf{p}$, [,c]) Find all roots of a complex vector $\mathbf{p}$ of polynomial coefficients
using the QR algorithm

MEigenvalQRC ($\mathbf{C}$ [,c]) Approximates the eigenvalues of a complex square matrix $\mathbf{C}$
using QR decomposition

MEigenvecC ($\mathbf{C}$ [,c]) Compute complex eigenvector of $\mathbf{C}$ for given complex eigenvalue(s)

MEigenvecInvC ($\mathbf{C}$, eigenvalues [,c]) Compute eigenvector of $\mathbf{C}$ for given eigenvalue(s)
by inverse iteration

SysLinC ($\mathbf{C}$, $\mathbf{x}$ [,c]) Gauss-Jordan solution of complex linear system.
$\mathbf{C}$: vector or matrix of independent parameters, $\mathbf{x}$: is the unknown coefficient vector or matrix

C.8 Matrix generators

The following is a collection of routines for generating various types of matrices. It starts with the simplest, the identity matrix, and includes not only a number of named matrices but, also, routines to generate custom-ordered matrices, such as matrices with a given set of eigenvalues or with a given amount of sparsity. Often used option: Int = True (default) creates an integer matrix, otherwise use False.

MIde(m) Generates the identity matrix $\mathbf{I}$ of order m, i.e., $\mathbf{I}_{m \times m}$

MRnd(m [,n] [,Type] [,Int] [,$AMax$] [,$AMin$] [,$sparse$])
Generates a random $m \times n$ matrix (default: $n = m$). Type specifies the type of matrix: All (default) fills all cells, Sym generates a symmetrical matrix, Dia a diagonal one, Trd a tridiagonal, Tlw a tridiagonal lower, Tup a tridiagonal upper, and SymTrd a symmetrical tridiagonal matrix. *AMax* and *AMin* specify the maximum and minimum element values. *Sparse* accepts values from 0 to 1: 0 (default) for filled, 1 for very sparse.

MRndEig($\mathbf{v}$ [,Int]) Creates a random real matrix for a given vector $\mathbf{v}$ of eigenvalues
MRndEigSym($\mathbf{v}$) Creates a symmetrical random real matrix for a given vector $\mathbf{v}$ of eigenvalues

MRndRank(m [,$Rank$] [,Det] [,Int]) Creates a square real matrix with a given value of *Rank*
or *Determinant*. If Rank < m, Det = 0.

MRndSym(m [,$Rank$] [,Det] [,Int]) Creates a square real symmetrical matrix of dimension $m \times m$
with a given value of *Rank* or *Determinant*. If Rank < m, Det = 0.

MHilbert(m) Creates the $m \times m$ Hilbert matrix
The Hilbert matrix is ill-conditioned; its elements $h_{ij} = 1/(i+j+1)$ are shown in decimal form

MHilbertInv(m) Creates the $m \times m$ inverse Hilbert matrix
The elements of the inverse Hilbert matrix are all integer

MHouseholder($\mathbf{x}$) Creates the Householder matrix of vector $\mathbf{x}$

MTartaglia(m) Creates the $m \times m$ Tartaglia (or Pascal) matrix
Element values: $m_{i1} = m_{1j} = 1$; for $i > 1, j > 1$: $m_{ij} = m_{i-1,j} + m_{i,j-1}$

MVandermonde($\mathbf{x}$) Creates the Vandermonde matrix $\mathbf{X}$
of vector $\mathbf{x}$, as used in, e.g., the least squares formalism

606

C.9 Miscellaneous functions

C.9.1 Linear least squares routines

RegrL(**y**, **x** [,*Intercept*])   Linear least squares based on svd

> Equivalent to post-Excel2002 LinEst. **y**: $N \times 1$ vector of dependent variables, **x**: $N \times 1$ vector or $N \times m$ matrix of independent parameters for the monovariate and multivariate case respectively. *Intercept* = a_0 when specified; default leaves a_0 unspecified. First output column: coefficients a_i; 2nd output column: standard deviations s_i.

RegrP(*Order*, **y**, **x** [,*Intercept*])   Linear least squares polynomial fit

> based on svd, equivalent to post-Excel2002 LinEst. *Order* is the polynomial order, **y** the $N \times 1$ vector of dependent variables, **x** the $N \times 1$ vector of the independent parameter x. Powers of x are generated internally. *Intercept* = a_0 when specified; default leaves a_0 unspecified. Output: 1st column: coefficients a_i; 2nd column: standard deviations s_i.

RegrCir(**x**, **y**)   Least squares fit to a circle through all points (x_i, y_i), yields

> radius and x,y coordinates of circle center, with standard deviations

C.9.2 Optimization routine

Simplex(**y**, constraints [,optimum])   Simplex optimization

> **y** = $a_0 + a_1 x_1 + a_2 x_2 + ...$, as $1 \times m$ vector of the coefficients $a_0, a_1, a_2, ...$
> constraints: $<, >, =$; optimum: 1 (default) maximum, 0 minimum

C.9.3 Step-by-step demonstration

GJStep(**S** [,Type] [,Integer] [,*Tiny*])   Step-by-step (didactic) tracing of Gauss-Jordan elimination

> leading to either diagonal (Type = D) or triangular (Type = T) reduction. Integer = True conserves integer values, default = False. *Tiny* sets minimum round-off error; default = 2×10^{-15}. Copy & paste for the next step.

C.9.4 Economic optimization routines

MLeontInv (**S**,**v**)   Inverts the Leontief matrix encountered in economic input-output analysis

VarimaxIndex (**F** [,row-norm])   Varimax index for given factor loading matrix **F**.

> Row-normalization: False (default) or True

VarimaxRot (**F** [,row-norm] [,*MaxErr*] [,*MaxIter*])   Orthogonal rotation of factor loading matrix **F** in Kaiser's Varimax model.

> Row-normalization: False (default) or True; *MaxErr* default = 10^{-4}; *MaxIter* default = 500.

C.9.5 Minimum path routines

PathFloyd(**G**)   Computes the matrix of shortest-path pairs from an adjacency matrix **G**

PathMin(**G**)   Shows vectors of shortest paths

C.9.6 Routine for electrical circuit admittance

MAdm(**B**)   Creates an admittance matrix from a 3- or 4-column wide branch matrix **B**

> (two columns for the nodes, and 1 or 2 columns for the admittance of the individual circuit elements

C.10: Matrix macros

The Matrix Toolbar provides access to a set of matrix-related macros through three menu headings: Selector, Generator, and Macros. Below we will briefly describe each one of these.

C.10.1 The Selector tool

Use the Selector tool to select different parts of a matrix. Start with identifying a matrix (when that matrix is bordered by empty cells, just clicking on a single cell of that matrix will do), and then use the choices presented in the Selector dialog box. In other words, click on a cell in a matrix, click on Selector, click on a choice, such as Triang. low, again click on the Selector, then on the Paster (at the bottom of the Selector menu), select a starting cell, and click OK. You will see the lower triangular part of the selected matrix appear, starting at the selected starting cell. The available choices are listed in Table C.10.1. You can even arrange for diverse output formats through the Target range selector. When you do not specify a matrix ahead of time, click on Selector, and its dialog box will give you entry to the Selector choices.

Selector choice	Brief description
Full	the entire matrix
Triang. low	the lower triangle, including the diagonal
Triang. up	the upper triangle, including the diagonal
Diag. 1st	the (main) diagonal, from top-left to bottom-right
Diag. 2nd	the anti-diagonal, running from top-right to bottom-left
Tridiag. 1st	the tridiagonal, from top-left to bottom-right
Tridiag. 2nd	the anti-tridiagonal, from top-right to bottom-left
Subtriang. low	the lower triangle minus the diagonal
Subtriang. up	the upper triangle minus the diagonal
Adjoint	the matrix minus the row and column of the chosen cell

Table C.10.1: The choices offered in the Selector dialog box.

As its default, the Selector dialog box will copy the selected matrix parts as is, at your option leaving the unselected cells empty or filling them with zeros. By using its Target range you can also choose different output formats, such as vertical, horizontal, diagonal, transposed, etc. For the Adjoint output, also set the Target range at Adjoint.

C.10.2 The Generator tool

The Generator tool allows you to create matrices to your specifications. Apart from its four generators of specific matrices (Hilbert, inverse Hilbert, Tartaglia, and Toeplitz) of user-selectable order, it contains four random matrix generators, which are marvelous learning and teaching tools, especially when combined with some of the matrix functions described in the earlier sections to monitor their performance. Table C.10.2 lists the various choices available.

Generator choice	Brief description
Random	generates random matrices of user-selected dimensions, minimum and maximum element values, format (full, triangular, tridiagonal, integer, symmetric), and numerical resolution.
Rank/Determinant	generates random square matrices of user-selected order and determinant (the default, if rank = order) or rank (if det = 0).
Eigenvalues	generates random square matrices with user-selected eigenvalues.
Hilbert	generates the Hilbert matrix of given order.
Hilbert inverse	generates the inverse Hilbert matrix of given order.
Tartaglia	generates the Tartaglia matrix of given order.
Toeplitz	generates the Toeplitz matrix of given order.
Sparse	generates sparse square matrices of user-selected order, minimum and maximum element values, dominance factor, filling factor, and spreading factor. One can specify integer and/or symmetrical output, and regular (square) or sparse output display. In the latter case, all non-zero elements m_{ij} are listed in three adjacent columns as i, j, and m_{ij}.

Table C.10.2: The choices offered in the Generator dialog box.

C.10.3 The Macros tool

The Macros tool provides easy access to a number of macros. Many of these macros duplicate matrix functions already described in appendices B.2 to B.8, but the sparse matrix operations contains some additional features. The choices given in the Macros dialog box are listed in Table B.10.3. Some matrices can be selected by simply pointing to one cell of that matrix, and by then clicking on the smart selector icon, labeled with a rectangle. This method works only when the matrix in question is surrounded by empty cells and/or the spreadsheet border.

Macro choice	Brief description
Matrix operations	reproduces the most often used matrix functions
Complex matrix operations	duplicates many of the functions of section 9.7
Sparse matrix operations	applies the most common matrix operations to sparse matrices in sparse matrix format (i.e., in three adjacent columns: i, j, m_{ij}), thereby greatly facilitating handling large sparse matrices on the spreadsheet. It includes an efficient ADSOR (adaptive successive over-relaxation) Gauss-Seidel method.
Eigen-solving	provides eigenvalues, eigenvectors, the characteristic matrix, and the characteristic polynomial for a square (real, real tridiagonal, complex) matrix
Gauss step-by-step	a macro form of GJ_Step
Graph	includes Shortest Path and Draw
Methods	Clean-up and Round

Table C.10.3: The choices offered in the Macros dialog box.

610

XN extended-precision functions & macros

Here we list the major instructions available at present with XN.xla(m) version 6051. The further down the list, the sparser the annotations. A more complete listing is available once you have installed XN.xla(m), and its Toolbar, which can be toggled on and off by clicking on the XN purple book icon featuring an **X**. Because this software is still developing and growing; whenever information provided here differs from the documentation provided with your installed version, consider the latter as authoritative. For a quick guide on the format used, also consult the Paste (Insert) Function window by clicking on its icon, f_x. Note that numbers displayed by Excel are usually stored as their binary approximations; when they are text strings, they are shown within quotation marks " inside the function argument, or as 'a = .

For the list of available functions click on the Help button of the XN Toolbar, click on Help-on-line, which will open up the Xnumbers version 6.0 Help file. For the most recent list of functions, which includes the many recent updates from John Beyers, click on "changes to version 6.0" at the end of its first paragraph. For the older functions, use its Index of Functions or other items in its Contents. When in doubt, try them out!

In the list below, items shown within straight brackets [ ] are optional. The letter D is used as an abbreviation for DgtMax; I recommend a value of 35, which roughly corresponds to quintuple precision, as usually sufficient for final 15-decimal accuracy yet still very fast. This value ($D = 35$) is used here unless otherwise specified. As long as you avoid degrading its performance by mixing in double-precision operations, XN functions and macros with $D = 35$ pass all NIST StRD linear and nonlinear least squares tests with flying colors. Whether you will find $pE = 15$ or 'merely' $pE \geq 14$ may well depend on how you read in the data files. When you import test data, and then let a VBA routine read them from Excel, it will read the *stored* data, which are binary *approximations* of the data shown on the screen, see section 11.14. In the same vein, be careful with your input arguments. Instead of 1/3 use xDiv(3,10), replace 0.317 by "0.317", for -2 substitute xNeg(2) or "-2", etc., otherwise you may degrade the accuracy of your output.

To change the default D-value, use the XN Toolbar, select X-Edit ⇨ Configuration, and enter the desired value in the Default digits window. For 32-bit systems, the current D-values range from $D \leq 630$ for XN.xla(m)6051-7A or -7M, to $D \leq 4030$ for XN.xla(m)6051-13A or -13M. For best accuracy and speed, stay at least two packets (14 decimals for –7A and –7M, 26 decimals for –13A and –13M) below the upper edges of these ranges. Using a D-value much larger than needed merely slows you down.

D.1 Numerical constants

The brackets are required, even when empty, in which case D assumes its default value, here set to 35.

xPi([D])   **π, the ratio of circumference to diameter of a circle**   π

xPi() = 3.1415926535897932384626433832795029 when default D is 35;
xPi(58) = 3.1415926535897932384626433832795028841971693993751058209 75;
xPi(600) = 3.1415926535897932384626433832795028841971693993751058209 74
9445923078164062862089986280348253421170679821480865132823 0664709384
4609550582231725359408128481117450284102701938521105559644 6229489549
3038196442881097566593344612847564823378678316527120190914 5648566923
4603486104543266482133936072602491412737245870066063155881 7488152092
0962829254091715364367892590360011330530548820466521384146 9519415116
0943305727036575959195309218611738193261179310511854807446 2379962749
5673518857527248912279381830119491298336733624406566430860 2139494639
5224737190702179860943702770539217176293176752384674818467 66940513.

x2Pi([D])	**2π**	2π

xPi(50) = 6.2831853071795864769252867665590057683943387987502;
xPi(5) = 6.2832; xPi() = 6.2831853071795864769252867665590058.

xPi2([D])	**π/2**	π/2

xPi2(50) = 1.5707963267948966192313216916397514420985846996876.

xPi4([D])	**π/4**	π/4

xPi4(50) = 0.78539816339744830961566084581987572104929234984378.

xE([D])	**e, the base of the natural logarithm**	e

xE() = 2.7182818284590452353602874713526625 when the default D is 35

xEu([D]), **xGm**([D])	**γ, Euler's gamma**	γ

xEu(42) = xGm(42) = 0.577215664901532860606512090082402431042159.

xLn2([D])	**Natural logarithm of 2**	ln(2)

xLn2(50) = 0.69314718055994530941723212145817656807550013436026.

xLn10([D])	**Natural logarithm of 10**	ln(10)

xLn10(50) = 2.3025850929940456840179914546843642076011014886288.

xRad5([D])	**Square root of 5**	√(5)

xRad5(50) = 2.2360679774997896964091736687312762354406183596115.

xRad12([D])	**Square root of 12**	√(12)

xRad12(50) = 3.4641016151377545870548926830117447338856105076208.

D.2 Basic mathematical operations

xAbs(a)	**Absolute value**	$|a|$

Do not enter D in this instruction. xAbs("-1.2345") = 1.2345;
xAbs("-1234567890.0987654321") = 1234567890.0987654321;
xCos(xPi()) = -1 so that xAbs(xCos(xPi())) = 1.

xIncr(a)	**Increment a by 1**	a+1

e.g., xIncr(xPi()) = 4.1415926535897932384626433832795029 and
xIncr(xPi(28)) = 4.1415926535897932384626433383 for (π + 1), where
xPi([D]) has an optional D, while xIncr(xPi(),28) yields #VALUE!
because it incorrectly specifies D for xIncr(), which cannot handle it.

xAdd(a,b[,D])	**Addition**	a+b

e.g., Add(xPi(),xE()) = 5.8598744820488384738229308546321654,
xAdd(xPi(),xE(),21) = 5.85987448204883847382 for (π + e) with
35 (the default used here) or 21 decimals respectively.

xSum(A[,D])	**Summation of terms in a cell range**	Σ a_i

Ignores empty cells as well as cells containing text. Example: Place the
instruction =xPi() in cell B3, =xIncr(B3) in B4, and copy this down to
B8. In cell B10 then place the instruction =xSum(B3:B8), which will yield
33.849555921538759430775860299677017. In cell B11 verify that you get
the same answer with =xAdd(15,xMult(6,xPi())) for (1+2+3+4+5) + 6 π.

xNeg(a)	**Negation**	−a

Do *not* use −a because it will convert the result to double precision.
Instead, always use xNeg instead of a minus sign in XN, otherwise you
will revert to double precision. Using quotation marks surrounding a
fractional number uses it as shown, xNeg("-1234567890.0987654321") =
1234567890.0987654321 whereas xNeg(-1234567890.0987654321) =
1234567890.098759889602661133 uses the value stored by Excel approximating the 15-decimal number -1234567890.09876 in binary notation. No
such distortion (but still truncation to 15 decimals) occurs with integers:
xNeg(-12345678900987654321) = 12345678900987654321.

xSub$(a,b[,D])$	**Subtraction**	$a-b$

equivalent to xAdd(a, xNeg(b)). Do *not* use xAdd($a,-b$) because the notation $-b$ will make the result double precision. Example: $(\pi - e) \Rightarrow$ xSub(xPi(),xE()) = 0.42331082513074800310235591192684404. Also: xSub("1.00000000000000000012345678","1.00000000000000000023456789") = -1.1111111E-17, with all leading zeroes automatically deleted. And note: xSub(1.2345678901234," 1.2345678901234") = 6.9057879591E-17 illustrates the distortion due to decimal-to-binary conversion.

xMult$(a,b[,D])$	**Multiplication**	$a \times b$

e.g., xMult(6, Pi()) = 18.8495559215387594307758602996770I7, and xMult(6,Pi(42),42) = 18.8495559215387594307758602996770I7305183.

xProd$(a[,D])$	**Multiplication of components of a cell range**	$\Pi\, a_i$

Ignores empty cells as well as cells containing text.
The range can be a column, a row, or a rectangular array.

xInv(a)	**Inversion**	$1/a$

When $a = 0$, xInv(a) yields "?". Example: 1/9 in 42-decimal precision is xInv(9,42) = 0.111111111111111111111111111111111111111111

xDiv$(a,b[,D])$	**Division**	a/b

or: xMult(a, xInv(b)). When $b = 0$, xDiv(a,b) yields "?".
xDiv(7,9,42) = 0.777777777777777777777777777777777777777778

xDivInt(a,b)	**Integer division**	int (a/b)

xDivInt(a,0) $\Rightarrow$ "?". xDivInt(7,9) = 0; xDivInt(13,7) = 1; xDivInt(-13,7) = -2.

xPow$(a,p[,D])$	**Power**	a^p

where a can be positive or negative, and with integer or noninteger powers p
xPow(xPi(),xNeg("2.7"),21) = 4.54668999316115830687E-2
but xPow(xPi(),xNeg(2.7),21) = 4.54668999316115738232E-2; and watch this:
xPow(xNeg(xPi());xNeg("2.7"),21) = -2.67247732472589436167E-2
-3.67834947262189055211E-2j because $-\pi^{-2.7}$ has a complex root.

xPow2$(p[,D])$	**Power of 2**	2^p

where the power p can be positive or negative, integer or noninteger.
e.g. xPow2(xNeg("400.3") = 3.14552206294614155070350912629303O1E-121;
xMult(xPow2(xNeg("400.3")),xPow2("400.3"),34) = 1.

xExp$(p[,D])$	**Exponential**	e^p

xExp(80) = 55406223843935100525711733958316613, xExp(800)
= 2.7263745721125665673647795463672698E+347 and xExp(800,14)
= 2.7263745721126E+347. The latter two cannot be read by Excel or reduced to double precision, because Excel cannot store numbers beyond E308.

xExpa$(p[,a][,D])$	**Arbitrary power**	a^p

Note the *unusual argument order*: power first, then the value raised to it:
xExpa(3,7) = 343 = 7^3. When a is unspecified, $a = 10$: xExpa(3) = 1000;
xExpa(3,xPi()) = π^3 = 31.006276680299820175476315067101396,
xExpa(xNeg(3),xPi()) = $(-\pi)^3$ = -3.225153443319949295608274519613453E-2;
watch the commas: xExpa("3.01",17) = 5054.1863831357180932094218872658106 but
xExpa("3.01",,17) = 1023.2929922807541 and xExpa(3.01,,17) = 1023.2929922807536;
xExpa(xNeg("3.01")) = 31.363254111413810434877685894955175;
xExpa(xNeg("3.01"),xNeg(xPi()),21) = $(-\pi)^{-3.01}$ = -3.18844465707427014412E-2).

xExpBase$(a,x[,D])$	**Arbitrary power**	a^x

Arbitrary power of any base. Similar to xExpa($x,a[,D]$) but a not optional.

xSqr$(a[,D])$	**Square root of a**	$\sqrt{(a)}$

xSqr("4.7") = 2.1679483388678799418989624480732099 = $\sqrt{(4.7)}$,
xSqr("4.7",50) = 2.1679483388678799418989624480732099935826865748722.

xSqrPi(a[,D])	**Square root of a times π**	$\sqrt{(a\pi)}$

for $a \geq 0$. If a is omitted, $a = 1$. xSqrPi(,21) = 1.7724538509055160273 = $\sqrt{\pi}$, xSqrPi("4.7",21) = 3.8425883817905904 1156 = $\sqrt{(4.7\,\pi)}$ to 21 decimals.

xRoot(a[,b][,D])	**Arbitrary root**	$a^{1/b}$

b need not be an integer; default: $b = 2$. xRoot(9) = 3 = $\sqrt{2}$, as is xRoot(9,2), but xRoot(2,9) = 1.0800597388923061698729308312885969, and xRoot(2,,9) = 1.41421356; xRoot(78,9) = 1.6226794404526244307856240252218919 = $78^{1/9}$, while xRoot(78,"9.0001") = 1.6226707127436371883687249182251982.

xLn(a[,D])	**Natural logarithm**	$\ln a$

xLn(11,50) = 2.3978952727983705440619435779651292998217068539374.

xLog(a[,base][,D])	**General logarithm**	$\log_n a$, $\log a$

Optional base must be positive; default = 10. Analogous to Excel's LOG(a [,base]) where LOG(4,2) = 2 = $\log_2(4)$ and LOG(4) = 0.60206.. = $\log_{10}(4)$, XN uses xLog(30,3) = 3.0959032742893846042965675220214013 =$\log_3(30)$ at $D_{default}$ = 35, and xLog(30,,35) = xLog(30) = 1.4771212547196624372950279032551153 =$\log_{10}(30)$

D.3 Trigonometric and related operations

All angles are assumed to be in radians. The prefix ar stands for area, the prefix arc for arc.

xSin(α [,D])	**Sine**	$\sin \alpha$

xSin(0.5,50) = 0.47942553860420300027328793521557138808 18033679406; xSin(xPi()) = -1.5802830600624894179025055407692184E-35; xSin(xPi(46),46) = 3.7510582097494459230781640628620899862 80348253E-46; xSin(xSub(xPi(),0.00000001)) = 1.00000000000000000042558941617530493E-8; xSin(xSub(xPi(),"0.00000001")) = 9.9999999999999998333333333175305036E-9.

xCos(α [,D])	**Cosine**	$\cos \alpha$

xCos("0.5",50) = 0.87758256189037271611628158260382965199 164519710974 and xCos(0.5,50) = 0.8775825618903727161162815826038296519 9164519710974, because 0.5 = ½ is exactly convertible into binary notation, as are 0.75, 0.625, etc.; xCos(xPi2(),50) = 4.2098584699687552910487472296153908203 143104499314E-35. xCos(xPi2(50),50)=-4.7089512527703846091796856895500685982587328941466E-50.

xTan(α [,D])	**Tangent**	$\tan \alpha$

xTan(0.5,50) = 0.54630248984379051325517946578028538329 7 55172017979.

xASin(a[,D])	**Inverse sine**	$\arcsin a$

$|a| \leq 1$; xASin(1) = 1.5707963267948966192313216916397514; xASin(xNeg(1),48) = -1.57079632679489661923132169163975144209858469969.

xACos(a[,D])	**Inverse cosine**	$\arccos a$

$|a| \leq 1$; xACos(0,48) = 1.57079632679489661923132169163975144209858469969.

xATan(a[,D])	**Inverse tangent**	$\arctan a$

xATan(1,50) = 0.78539816339744830961566084581987572104929234984378.

xATan2(a, b[,D])	**Inverse tangent of quotient a/b**	$\arctan (a/b)$

xATan2(3,4,50) = 0.64350110879328438680280922871732263804151059111531; note that the order of a and b is reversed from that used in Excel's ATAN2.

xSinH(a[,D])	**Hyperbolic sine**	$\sinh a$

$\sinh a = (e^x - e^{-x}) / 2$; xSinH(3) = 10.017874927409901898974593619465828.

xCosH(a[,D])	**Hyperbolic cosine**	$\cosh a$

$\cosh a = (e^x + e^{-x}) / 2$; xCosH(0.3) = 1.0453385141288604816444546338323457 but xCosH(xDiv(3,10)) = xCosH("0.3") = 1.0453385141288604850253090463229121.

xTanH($a[,D]$)	**Hyperbolic tangent**	tanh a

tanh $a = (e^x - e^{-x}) / (e^x + e^{-x})$; xTanH("0.1",28) = 9.9667994624955817711830508368E-2

xASinH($a[,D]$)	**Inverse hyperbolic sine**	arsinh a

arsinh $a = \ln [a+\sqrt{(a^2+1)}]$; xASinH("0.1",28) = 0.099834078899207563327303124

xACosH($a[,D]$)	**Inverse hyperbolic cosine**	arcosh a

arcosh $a = \ln [a+\sqrt{(a^2-1)}]$, $a > 1$;

xATanH($a[,D]$)	**Inverse hyperbolic tangent**	artanh a

artanh $a = \frac{1}{2} \ln [(1+a)/(1-a)]$; xATanH(0.1,28) = 0.10033534773107558624291354 51;
xATanH("0.1",28) = 0.10033534773107558063572655 21.

xAngleC($a[,D]$)	**Complement of angle α**	$\pi/2-\alpha$

xAngleC(0.25,21) = 1.32079632679489661923132169 16397514;
xSub(xPi2(21),0.25,21) = 1.32079632679489661923132169 16397514.

xDegrees($a[,D]$)	**Converts radians into degrees**	radians→degrees

xDegrees(xPi4()) = 45; xdegrees(xMult(4,xPi()),28) = 720.

xRadians($a[,D]$)	**Converts degrees into radians**	degrees→radians

xRadians(180) = 3.14159265358979323846264338 32795029 = xPi()

xAdjPi($a[,D]$)	**Adjusted angle, in radians, between $-\pi$ and $+\pi$**	

xAdjPi(xMult(5.75,xPi()),21) = -2.3561944901923449 2885 = xMult(3,xNeg(xPi4()),21)

xAdj2Pi($a[,D]$)	**Adjusted angle, in radians, between 0 and 2π**	

xAdj2Pi(xMult(6.75,xPi()),21) = 2.356194490192344 92885 = xMult(3,xPi4(),21)

D.4 Statistical operations

A is an array of numbers a_i in a contiguous row, column, or block.

xMean(A$[,D]$)	**Mean**	$(\sum_{i=1}^{n} a_i)/n$

xMean(1,3,4,10) = xMean({1,3,4,10},21) = xMean(C14:C17,21) = 4.5
when C14:C17 contains 1, 3, 4, and 10 respectively.

xMedian(A)	**Median**

xMedian(1,3,4,10) = xMean(C14:C17,21) = 3.5 when C14:C17
contains 1, 3, 4, and 10 respectively. Do *not* specify D.

xGMean(A$[,D]$)	**Geometric mean**	$\sqrt[n]{a_1 \times a_2 \times \cdots \times a_n}$

xGMean({1,3,4,10},21) = xGMean(C14:C17,21) =
3.30975091964687310503 when C14:C17 contains 1, 3, 4,
and 10 respectively; A must be an array or a named range.

xHMean(A$[,D]$)	**Harmonic mean**	$n\Big/ \sum_{i=1}^{n}\left(\dfrac{1}{a_i}\right)$

xHMean({1,3,4,10},21) = xHMean(C14:C17,21) =
2.37623762376237623762 when C14:C17 contains 1, 3, 4,
and 10 respectively; A must be an array or a named range.

xQMean(A$[,D]$)	**Quadratic mean**	$(\sum_{i=1}^{n} a_i^2)/n$

xQMean({1,3,4,10},21) = xQMean(C14:C17,21) =
5.61248608016091207838 when C14:C17 contains 1, 3, 4,
and 10 respectively; A must be an array or a named range.

xStDev(A[,*D*])   **Standard deviation** $$\sqrt{\dfrac{\displaystyle\sum_{i=1}^{n}(a_i - a_{av})^2}{n-1}}$$

xStDev({3.1,3.2,3.3},21) = xStDev(B3:B5,21) = 9.99999999999998667732E-2 when B3:B5 contains 3.1, 3.2, and 3.3 respectively; xStDev({"3.1","3.2","3.3"},21) = 0.1

xStDevP(A[,*D*])   **Population standard deviation** $$\sqrt{\dfrac{\displaystyle\sum_{i=1}^{n}(a_i - a_{av})^2}{n}}$$

xStDevP({3.1,3.2,3.3},21) = xStDevP(B3:B5,21) = 0.081649658092772494494 when B3:B5 contains 3.1, 3.2, and 3.3 respectively; xStDev({"3.1","3.2","3.3"},21) = 8.16496580927726032732E-2.

xVar(A[,*D*])   **(Sample) variance** $$\dfrac{\displaystyle\sum_{i=1}^{n}(a_i - a_{av})^2}{n-1}$$

xVar({3.1,3.2,3.3},21) = xVar(B3:B5,21) = 9.99999999999997335465E-3 when B3:B5 contains 3.1, 3.2, and 3.3 respectively; xVar({"3.1","3.2","3.3"},21) = 0.01

xVarP(A[,*D*])   **Population variance** $$\dfrac{\displaystyle\sum_{i=1}^{n}(a_i - a_{av})^2}{n}$$

xVarP({3.1,3.2,3.3},21) = xVarP(B3:B5,21) = 6.6666666666666489031E-3 when B3:B5 contains 3.1, 3.2, and 3.3 respectively; xVar({"3.1","3.2","3.3"},21) = 6.66666666666666666667E-3.

xFact(*n*[,*D*])   **Factorial** $n!$

For *n* a positive integer; if not integer, *n* is rounded down to the next integer.
xFact(27) = 10888869450418352160768000000,
xFact(28) = 3.04888344611713860501504E+29,
xFact(1E7) = 1.20242340051590345611401534879443076E+65657059,
xFact(xFact(25)) = 3.567927957958848944858765294950 ×
                 E+384000963322077998379052338.

xFact2(*n*[,*D*])   **Double factorial**

$$n \text{ odd: } (2n-1)!! = \prod_{i=1}^{n}(2i-1) = \frac{(2n)!}{n!\,2^{k}}\,; \; n \text{ even: } (2n)!! = \prod_{i=1}^{n}(2i) = n!\,2^{k}$$

xFact(27) = 10888869450418352160768000000,
xFact(28) = 3.04888344611713860501504E+29,
xMult(xFact2(27),xFact2(28)) = 3.04888344611713860501504E+29 = xFact(28).

xComb(*n*,*m*[,*D*])   **Binomial coefficient** $\dbinom{n}{m} = \dfrac{n!}{m!\,(n-m)!}$

xComb(20,10) = 184756,
xComb(200,100) = 9.0548514656103281165404177077484164E+58,
xComb(2000,1000,45) = 2.0481516269894897143351625029808250 4439642489E+600
or, displayed in its full 600-decimal glory, as xComb(2000,1000, *D*) with *D* ≥ 601.

| **xComb_Big**$(n,m[,D])$ | **Binomial coefficient for large numbers** | $\dbinom{n}{m} = \dfrac{n!}{m!\,(n-m)!}$ |

xComb_Big(10000000,9000000,28) = 1.09354044606516776520 2685186E+1411814

| **xCorrel**$(A,B[,D])$ | **Correlation coefficient** | $r_{AB} = \dfrac{v_{AB}}{s_A\, s_B}$ |

xCorrel({1,2,3,4,5,6},{7,5,8,6,9,7},21) = 0.377964473009227227215;
xDiv(xCovar(A12:A17,A19:A24),xMult(xStDevP(A12:A17),xStDevP(A19:A24)),21)
= 0.377964473009227272145, see (2.10.2), when A12:A17 = {1,2,3,4,5,6} etc.
xCorrel({1,2,3,4,5,6},{3,4,5,6,7,8},21) = 1. A and B are data sets, addressed
either as a listing of their individual values (see the above examples) or by
reference to their spreadsheet addresses ranges. Note: in this book we deal
with physical laws, and a correlation coefficient $|r_{xy}| \leq 0.9$ is usually
considered insignificant. However, in the social sciences, where there are
often many complicating factors, and $|r_{xy}| = 0.9$ may be viewed as highly
significant. It all depends on the context.

| **xCovar**$(n,m[,D])$ | **Covariance** | $\dfrac{1}{N}\sum_{k=1}^{N}(a_{i,k} - a_{i,av})(a_{j,k} - a_{j,av})$ |

xCovar({1,2,3,4,5,6},{7,5,8,6,9,7}) = 0.833333333333333333333333333333333333,
xCorrel({1,2,3,4,5,6},{1,2.1,3,4,5,6}) = 0.99979520559482815691603169600455999.

xStatis$(A[,D])$ **Univariate statistical summary of a data range A**

Yields five parameters in row format (deposit the instruction with block-enter):
number of data N; their mean; sample standard deviation; population standard
deviation; and autocorrelation with lag $1 = \Sigma_1^{n-1}\{(x_i - x_{av})(x_{i+1} - x_{av})\}/\Sigma_1^{n}\{(x_i - x_{av})^2\}$.
xStatis({1,2,3,4,5,6},18) = {6, 3.5, 1.87082869338697069, 1.70782512765993306, 0.5}.

xRand$([,D])$ **Random number between 0 and 1** $U(0, 1)$

xRand() = 0.368847131729126017151222908115 38286.

xRandD$(a,b[,D])$ **Random number between a and b** $U(a, b)$

xRandD(4.1,4.3) = 4.19716314077377293399589 08101987838.
Note that a can be smaller or larger than b.

xRandI$(a,b[,D])$ **Random integer between a and b**

xRandI(4.2,-11.3) = -2; a can be smaller or larger than b, and neither needs to be integer.

D.5 Least squares functions

xIntercept$(\mathbf{y},\mathbf{x}[,D])$	**Intercept of least squares straight line with y-axis**	a_0
xSlope$(\mathbf{y},\mathbf{x}[,D])$	**Slope of least squares straight line**	a_1
xRegLinCoef$(\mathbf{y},\mathbf{x}[,D][,intercept])$	**Least squares coefficients**	a_0 through a_p

$\mathbf{y}$ is the vector of n dependent variables; $\mathbf{x}$ is the vector of n (or the matrix of $n{\times}m$)
independent variables; intercept forces the y-intercept through $y = $ intercept
for $x = 0$. The output yields the least squares coefficients, in row format.

xRegLinCov$(\mathbf{y},\mathbf{x},\mathbf{coef}\ [,D][,intercept])$ **Least squares covariance matrix**   CM

$\mathbf{y}$ is the vector of n dependent variables, $\mathbf{x}$ is the vector of n (or the matrix of $n{\times}m$)
independent variables, coef refers to the output of xRegLinCoef, and intercept forces
the y-intercept through $y = $ intercept for $x = 0$. The output yields the covariance matrix.

xRegLinErr(y, x, coef [,D][,intercept]) **Standard deviations of LS coefficients** s_0 through s_p

> **y** is the vector of n dependent variables; **x** is the vector of n (or the matrix of $n \times m$) independent variables; and intercept forces the y-intercept through y = intercept for $x = 0$. The output yields the standard deviations of the coefficients, in row format.

xRegLinEval(coef, x [,D]) **Evaluating a least squares fit at a specified x-value**

> Coef refers to the output of xRegLinCoef, and x is the specific value at which the fitting function is to be evaluated.

xRegLinStat(y, x, coef [,D][,intercept]) **More statistical least squares information** r^2 and s_f

> **y** is the vector of n dependent variables, **x** is the vector of n (or the matrix of $n \times m$) independent variables, coef refers to the output of xRegLinCoef, and intercept forces the y-intercept through y = intercept for $x = 0$. Outputs r^2 and s_f in row format.

xRegPolyCoef(y, x, degree [,D][,intercept]) **Least squares coefficients** a_0 through a_p

> **y** is the vector of n dependent variables; **x** is the vector of n independent variables; *degree* is the highest polynomial order; and intercept forces the y-intercept through y = intercept for $x = 0$. The default, intercept = TRUE, is to include a_0 in the analysis. In default mode ($D = 35$), xRegPolyCoef(B3:B84,C3:C84,10) aces the NIST LLS test Filip.dat (see exercise 11.13.3) provided that (1) the y-values in B3:B84, and the x-values in C3:C84, are in string format, i.e., preceded by an apostrophe, either manually or, faster, with the instruction xCStr(xRoundR(*number*,15)), and (2) the output data z are copied with the instruction = xCDbl(xRoundR((*address*,15)) where *number* is an input value read from the spreadsheet, and *address* an output result displayed there. If (1) and/or (2) are disregarded, the output may 'only' agree to pE = 14.0 instead of to pE = 15. Use a block-enter; the output is in row format.

xRegPolyErr(y, x, degree, coef [,D][,intercept]) **Standard deviations of LS coefficients** s_0 through s_p

> **y** is the vector of n dependent variables; **x** is the vector of n independent variables; *degree* is the highest polynomial order; and the optional intercept forces the y-intercept through y = intercept for $x = 0$. Do *not* forget to enter the coefficients from xRegPolyCoef! The default, intercept = TRUE, is to include a_0 in the analysis. The output yields the standard deviations s of the coefficients.

xRegPolyStat(y, x, degree, coef [,D][,intercept]) **More statistical least squares information** r^2 and s_f

> **y** is the vector of n dependent variables; **x** is the vector of n independent variables; *degree* is the highest polynomial order; and the optional intercept forces the y-intercept through y = intercept for $x = 0$. Do *not* forget to enter the coefficients from xRegPolyCoef! The default, intercept = TRUE, is to include a_0 in the analysis. The output yields r^2 and the standard deviations s_f of the over-all fit of the model function to the data.

xRegrL(y, x [,D][,intercept][,ε][,tol]) **Least squares coefficients obtained by SVD** a_0 through a_p

> This function uses SVD rather than the traditional pseudo-inverse; **y** is the vector of n dependent variables; **x** is the vector of n (or the matrix of $n \times m$) independent variables; and intercept forces the y-intercept through y = intercept for $x = 0$; ε is the resolution (default: 10^{-D}); tol (for tolerance, default: 0) specifies the largest absolute value that should be considerd round-off error and therefore can be set to 0 (similar to *Tiny*).

xRegrLC(y, x [,cf][,D][,intercept][,ε][,tol]) **Least squares coefficients of complex data by SVD**

> The extension of xRegrL to complex data. *cf* defines the complex format used; default = 1 for split format.

D.6 Statistical functions

Note: even though their names have the prefix x, the functions xGamma, xGammaLn, xGammaLog, xGammaQ and xBeta *used to be* double precision. John Beyers has now converted them to fully extended precision. If you have used them earlier in programs that plotted their output, make sure to use them now within an x CDbl() command so that their outputs will still be read properly by the graph. While Excel's functions treat numerical strings as numbers, Excel's graphs do not recognize such strings as valid input data.

xGamma$(x[,D])$ **Gamma function** $\Gamma(x)$

$\Gamma(n) = \pm\infty$ for n a non-positive integer, $\Gamma(n) = (n-1)!$, $\Gamma(1/2) = \sqrt{\pi}$.
xGamma(-101.01,50) = 1.013168130595368692581124058510337238551609 84E-158,
xGamma(0.5,40) = xSqr(xPi(40),40) = 1.772453850905516027298167483341145182798,
xGamma(1000,50) = 4.02387260077093773543702433923003985719374 86421071E+2564.
xGamma(0.000000001) = 999999999.4227842738059316758139 8533 for $D_{default} = 35$.

xGammaLn$(x[,D])$ **Natural logarithm of the gamma function** $\ln\Gamma(x)$

xGammaLn(0.5,70) = xLn(xGamma(0.5,70),70) = xLn(xSqr(xPi(70),70),70) =
0.5723649429247000870717136756765293558236474064576557857568115357360689.

xGammaLog$(x[,D])$ **10-based logarithm of the gamma function** $\log\Gamma(x)$

xGammaLog(1000,70) = xLog(xGamma(1000,70),,70) = xLog(xFact(999,70),,70) =
2567.6046442221328487714230578045236916771145131624634613100 44207289183.

xGammaQ$(x_1,x_2[,D])$ **Ratio of two gamma functions** $\Gamma(x_1)/\Gamma(x_2)$

xGammaQ(0.5,1000,25) = 4.40484584568092399142 1408E-2565, xGammaQ(0.5,1000,65) =
xDiv(xGamma(0.5,65),xGamma(1000,65),65) = xDiv(xSqr(xPi(70),70),xFact(999,65),65) =
4.404845845680923991421408051944532277770801007245629161 0680796307E-2568.

xBeta$(x,y[,D]$ **Complete Beta function** $B(x,y) = \int\limits_0^1 t^{x-1}(1-t)^{y-1}\,dt$

where $B(x, y) = \Gamma(x)\,\Gamma(y)\,/\,\Gamma(x+y)$, provides an easy check on the function.
Let B1, B2, etc are cell addresses, then for $x = 1.2$, $y = 3.4$ and $x+y = 4.6$ we have
B1: xGamma("1.2",50) = 0.9181687423997606106409516551858304006868 2199965868,
B2: xGamma("3.4",50) = 2.981206426810332971791368605443921181835 6413783808,
B3: xGamma("4.6",50) = 13.381285870932449355274522094100253203034374722681,
B4: xDiv(xMult(B1,B2,50),B3,40) = 0.2045581106435018057463802648086835068269,
finally in B5: xBeta("1.2","3.4") = 0.2045581106435018057463802 6480868351, and
xBeta("1.2","3.4",50) = 2.0455811064350180574638026480868350682689657512436E-1.

xZeta$(x[,D])$ **Riemann zeta function** $\zeta(x)$

$\zeta(x) = 0$ for x a negative even integer, $\pm\infty$ for $x = 1$: xZeta(1) = #VALUE!,
xZeta(-101,50) = -7.26120088036067163036772815107068472322350311 64793E+78,
xZeta(-9,60) = -7.575757575757575757575757575757575757575757575757576E-3,
xZeta(0.999999) = -999999.4227556522498020972335769 4814, xZeta(0,600)= 0.5,
xZeta(1.000001) = 1000000.57729800435533, xZeta(50,21) = 1.00000000000000088818

D.7 Statistical distributions

type = 0 or FALSE (default) for the probability density f; type = 1 or TRUE for the corresponding cumulative distribution F.

xNormal$(x,\mu,\sigma$ [,type] [,D]) **Normal distribution** $f(x,\mu,\sigma) = \dfrac{\exp[-(x-\mu)^2/(2\sigma^2)]}{\sigma\sqrt{2\pi}}$

Extended-precision version of Excel's NORMDIST:
xNormal(-1000,7,0.5,0,40) = 1.3545063340609621460561062176843454375 24E-880792,
xNormal(-10,7,0.5,,48)=7.58105280018573627361442359669669459333212880463E-252,
xNormal(0,7,0.5) = 2.1932131187779426125067829785218123E-43,
xNormal(10,7,0.5)=xNormal(10,7,0.5,0) = 1.2151765699646570973992615481363651E-8,
xNormal(45000,7,0.5) = 1.0582474958611311359386964761976518E-1306737131;
xNormal(-9876,7,0.5,1) = 9.66768695956483747239575107556894 08E-84838294,
xNormal(-10,7,0.5,1,45)=1.11389878557437938658195055559302360350188 09E-253,
xNormal(3,7,0.5,1) = 6.2209605742717841235159951725881884E-16,
xNormal(12,7,0.5,1,50) = 0.99999999999999999999992380146975839473934 02665675,
xNormal(14.6,7,0.5,1,50) = 1.

xNormalS$(z[,\text{type}][,D])$ **Standard normal distribution** $f(z) = \dfrac{\exp[-z^2/2]}{\sqrt{2\pi}}$

Extended-precision version of NORM.S.DIST of Excel 2010, with zero mean and unit
st. dev.: xNormalS(-1000,0,16)=xNormal(-1000,,16)=2.290648437187064E-2171486,
xNormalS(-10,0) = xNormal(-10,,1) = 7.69459862670641934633903358 00418772E-23,
xNormalS(0,0) = xNormal(0) = 0.398942280401432677939946059 93438187,
xNormalS(10,0) = xNormal(10) = 7.694598626706419346339033580 0418772E-23,
xNormalS(1000,0,21) = xNormal(1000,,21) = 2.29064843718706368675E-217148;
xNormalS(-1000, 1,21) = 7.04522365801717813535281616610508209E-217586,
xNormalS(-10, 1) = 7.61985302416052606597334325 15993084E-24,
xNormalS(0, 1) = 0.5,   xNormalS(10,1) = 0.99999999999999999999999238014697584,
xNormalS(1000, ,1) = 1.

xBinomial$(k,n,p[,\text{type}][,D])$ **Binomial distribution** $f(k,n,p) = \dfrac{n!\,p^k(1-p)^{n-k}}{k!(n-k)!}$

$k > 0$, $n > 0$, $p \neq 1$; typically, k and n are integer, with $k \leq n$, and $0 \leq p \leq 1$.
xBinomial(10,8,0.7) = xBinomial(10,8,0.7,0) = 0.31386138777777774857383467859235165,
xBinomial(100,80,0.7) = 9.2763880344798178286504175 93685876E-6,
xBinomial(100,80,0.5) = 8.2718061255302767487140869206996285E-25;
xBinomial(100,80,0.7,1) = 1.44837341111111107223573231024739338.

xLogistic$(x,\mu,s[,\text{type}][,D])$ **Logistic distribution** $f(x,\mu,s) = \dfrac{\exp[-(x-\mu)/s]}{s\big[1-\exp[-(x-\mu)/s]\big]^2}$

$s > 0$. xLogistic(1,1,0.5) = xLogistic(1,1,0.5,0) = 0.5,
xLogistic(0.1,1,0.5) = 0.2434586805741707832110798 8837114377,
xLogistic(0.5,1,0.5) = 0.3932238664829637050748494 6717181805,
xLogistic(2,1,0.5) = 0.20998717080701303469724 836952085072,
xLogistic(10,1,0.5) = 3.045995856161614597061650 5932086991E-8;
xLogistic(0.1,1,0.5,1) = 2.26481428783702350054744 13358600984E-2,
xLogistic(0.5,1,0.5,1) = 0.14973849934787756480856 989948056052,
xLogistic(1,1,0.5,1) = 0.38079707797788244405972 91413023968,
xLogistic(2,1,0.5,1) = 0.76159415595576488811945 828260479359,
xLogistic(10,1,0.5,1) = 0.8807970627479029312993 8019689418799.

xLogNorm$(x,\mu,\sigma[,\text{type}][,D])$ **Lognormal distribution** $f(x,\mu,\sigma) = \dfrac{\exp[-(\ln x - \mu)^2/(2\sigma^2)]}{x\sigma\sqrt{2\pi}}$

$x > 0$. xLogNorm(0.1,1,0.5,,28) = 2.6802846038819154286684 05659E-9,
xLogNorm(1,1,0.5,,20) = xLogNorm(1,1,0.5,0,20) = 0.1079819330263761039,
xLogNorm(10,1,0.5) = 2.68028460388191361194456 16856654493E-3;
xLogNorm(0.01,1,0.5,1) = 1.81397778835156884263893 18351031983E-29,
xLogNorm(1,1,0.5,1) = 2.27501319481792072002826 37166533437E-2,
xLogNorm(50,1,0.5,1) = 0.99999999712801243139612132792027695.

xMaxwell$(x,a[,\text{type}][,D])$ **Maxwell distribution** $f(x,a) = 4x^2 e^{-ax^2}\sqrt{a^3/\pi}$

Note that different authors define this distribution differently; here we use $a = m/2kT$
where m is mass, k is the Boltzmann constant, and T the absolute temperature.
xMaxwell(0.02,1,,28) = xMaxwell(0.02,1,1,28) = 9.023423245957835400 5919324E-4,
xMaxwell(1,1) = 0.83021499484118940668053649888267473,
xMaxwell(5,1) = 7.835433265508667654121684 1613105858E-10;
xMaxwell(0.02,1,1) = 6.016578105486313406526794 5144474112E-6,
xMaxwell(1,1,1) = 0.4275932955291201660009523 8564127189,
xMaxwell(5,1,1) = 0.99999999992010820755048528860859481.

xRayleigh$(x, \sigma[,type][,D])$ **Rayleigh distribution** $\qquad\qquad f(x,\sigma) = xe^{-x^2/2\sigma^2}/\sigma^2$

$x \geq 0$. xRayleigh(0.01,1,,60) = xRayleigh(0.01,1,0,60) =
9.9995000124997918774064006903279288318711046529804703483369 6E-3,
xRayleigh(1,1) = 0.60653065971263342360379953499118045,
xRayleigh(10,1) = 1.9287494879639177830173428165270126E-21;
xRayleigh(0.01,1,1) = 4.9998750020833075000834902025581322E-5,
xRayleigh(1,1,1) 0.39346934028736657639620046500881955,
xRayleigh(10,1,1) = 0.99999999999999999999980712501520361.

xWeibull$((x,k,\lambda[,type][,D])$ **Weibull distribution** $\qquad\qquad f(x,k,\lambda) = \dfrac{kx^{k-1}}{\lambda^k}e^{-(x/\lambda)^k}$

$x \geq 0$. xWeibull(0.01,1,0.5,,60) = xWeibull (0.01,1,0.5,0,60) =
1.9603973466135106036254488565805619061373641008489962365074 1,
xWeibull(1,1,0.5) = 0.27067056647322538378799898994496881,
xWeibull(10,1,0.5) = 4.1223072448771156559318807603116 42E-9;
xWeibull(0.01,1,0.5,1) = 1.9801326693244698187275571709719047E-2,
xWeibull(1,1,0.5,1) = 0.86466471676338730810600050502 75156,
xWeibull(10,1,0.5,1) = 0.99999999979388463775614421720340 5962.

D.8 Operations with complex numbers

Use the Configuration dialog box (under the X-Edit button on the XN toolbox) to select either i or j for $\sqrt{(-1)}$. Here we will use j. Complex numbers will be denoted by $z = a + j\,b$, and must be defined in terms of their separate, real and imaginary components, a and b. The notation has been simplified by allowing single-cell or split formatting of both input and output, simply by highlighting a single cell or specifying two (horizontally or vertically) adjacent cells, see Fig. 11.12.6. Here we will use (except for the first three functions) the default (1, horizontally split) format for both input and output. (Note that this simplified notation applies only to operations on individual complex numbers, as considered in this section; for arrays of complex numbers this short notation would be ambiguous, and cf must be specified when it differs from the chosen default.)

In B1 we have used =xCplx(3,4) to place 3+4j, and in E1 likewise =xCplx("5.6","7.8") to deposit 5.6+7.8j. The complex numbers $z_1 = 3 + 4\,j$ and $z_2 = 5.6 + 7.8j$ are stored as strings in row 2: as '3 in B2, '4 in C2, '5.6 in E2, and '7.8 in F2. They are also stored as regular spreadsheet numbers in row 3, i.e., as 3 in B3, as 4 in C3, as 5.6 in E3, and as 7.8 in F3. All examples will assume $D = 35$ unless otherwise indicated. Array output in adjacent cells will be shown as separated by a comma, and must of course be entered with the block enter combination Ctrl◡Shift◡Enter.

xCplx$(z[,D])$	**Converts Re(z) and Im(z) into a complex single-cell format**	
	xCplx(3,4) = 3+4j; xCplx("5.6","7.8") = 5.6+7.8j	
xReal$(z[,D])$	**Real part of a single-cell complex number**	$a = \text{Re}(a + jb)$
	xReal(xCplx(3,4)) = 3	
xImag$(z[,D])$	**Imaginary part of a single-cell complex number**	$b = \text{Im}(a + jb)$
	xImag(xCplx(3,4)) = 4	
xCplxAbs$(z[,D])$	**Absolute value of single-cell format**	$\lvert z \rvert = \lvert a + jb \rvert = \sqrt{a^2 + b^2}$
	xCplxAbs(B1) = xCplxAbs(B2:C2) = xCplxAbs(xCplx(3,4)) = 5	
xCplxArg$(z[,D])$	**Complex argument**	$\arg(z) = \arctan(b/a)$
	xCplxArg(B1,70) = xCplxArg(B2:C2,70) = xCplxArg(B2:C2,70) = 0.9272952180016122324285124629224288040570741085722405276218661774403957	
xCplxNeg$(z[,D])$	**Negation**	$-z = -(a + j\,b) = -a - j\,b$
	xCplxNeg(B1) = −3−4j; xCplxNeg(B2:C2) = xCplxNeg(B3:C3) = −3, −4	
xCplxConj$(z[,D])$	**Conjugate**	$z^* = a - j\,b$
	xCplxConj(B1) = 3−4j; xCplxConj(B2:C2) = xCplxConj(B3:C3) = 3, −4	

xCplxAdd$(z_1,z_2[,D])$ **Addition** $\qquad\qquad\qquad\qquad\qquad\qquad z_1+z_2 = (a_1+a_2)+j\,(b_1+b_2)$

xCplxAdd(B1,E1) = 8.6+11.8j;   xCplxAdd(B2:C2,E2:F2) = 8.6, 11.8;
xCplxAdd(B3:C3,E3:F3,21) = 8.59999999999999964473, 11.7999999999999998224

xCplxSub$(z_1,z_2[,D])$**Subtraction** $\qquad\qquad\qquad\qquad\qquad\qquad z_1-z_2 = (a_1-a_2)+j\,(b_1-b_2)$

xCplxSub(B1,E1) = -2.6-3.8j;   xCplxSub(B2:C2,E2:F2) = -2.6, -3.8;
xCplxSub(B3:C3,E3:F3,21) = -2.59999999999999964473, -3.79999999999999982236

xCplxMult$(z_1,z_2[,D])$ **Multiplication** $\qquad\qquad\qquad\qquad\quad z_1z_2 = (a_1a_2-b_1b_2)+j\,(a_1b_2+a_2b_1)$

xCplxMult(B1,E1) = -14.4+45.8j;   xCplxMult(2:C2,E2:F2) = -14.4, 45.8;
xCplxMult(B3:C3,E3:F3,21) = -14.4000000000000003553, 45.7999999999999998046

xCplxPow$(z,n[,D])$ **Integer power** $\qquad\qquad\qquad\qquad\qquad z^n = \sqrt{a^2+b^2}\,\exp[n\arctan(a/b)]$

xCplxPow(B1,2) = -7+24j;   xCplxPow(B2:C2,2) = xCplxPow(B3:C3,2) = -7, 24

xCplxRoot$(z,n[,D])$ **Integer root** $\qquad\qquad\qquad\qquad\qquad\qquad\qquad z^{1/n} = \sqrt[n]{a+jb}$

xCplxRoot(B1,2) = xCplxRoot(B3:C3,2) = 2+j, −2−j;   xCplxRoot(E1,2) =
xCplxRoot(E2:F2,2,21) = 2.75699864955772539922+1.41458175927131251328j in one
cell, and -2.75699864955772539922-1.41458175927131251328j in the next;   likewise,
xCplxRoot(E3:F3,2,21) = 2.75699864955772533513+1.41458175927131251395j in one
cell, and -2.75699864955772533513-1.41458175927131251395j in the next.

xCplxSqr$(z[,D])$ **Square root** $\qquad\qquad\qquad\qquad\qquad\qquad\qquad\qquad z^{\frac{1}{2}} = \sqrt{a+jb}$

xCplxSqr(B1) = 2+j;   xCplxSqr(B2:C2) = xCplxSqr(B3:C3) = 2, 1
xCplxSqr(E1,19) = xCplxSqr(E2:F2,19) = 2.756998649557725399, 1.414581759271312513
xCplxSqr(E2:F2,19) = 2.756998649557725335, 1.414581759271312514

xCplxDiv$(z_1,z_2[,D])$ **Division** $\qquad\qquad\qquad\qquad z_1/z_2 = \dfrac{(a_1a_2+b_2b_2)+j(-a_1b_2+a_2b_1)}{a_2^2+b_2^2}$

xCplxDiv(B2:C2,E2:F2,21) = 0.52060737527114967462, -1.08459869848156182213E-2
xCplxDiv(B3:C3,E3:F3,21) = 0.520607375271149693469, -1.08459869848156286485E-2

xCplxInv$(z[,D])$ **Inversion** $\qquad\qquad\qquad\qquad\qquad\qquad 1/z = \dfrac{1}{a+jb} = \dfrac{a-jb}{a^2+b^2}$

xCplxInv(B1) = 0.12-0.16j when placed in one cell; when placed in two cells,
xCplxInv(B1) = xCplxInv(B2:C2) = xCplxInv(B3:C3)= 0.12, −0.16;
xCplxInv(E2:F2,21) = 0.060737527114967462039, -8.45986984815618221258E-2
xCplxInv(E3:F3,21) = 6.0737527114967462625E-2, -8.45986984815618263928E-2

xCplxExp$(z[,D])$ **Exponential** $\qquad\qquad\qquad\qquad\qquad e^z = e^a\cos(a)+j\,e^b\cos(b)$

xCplxExp(E1,28)=14.5909705439244867111507082+270.032489548946360263111676j
xCplxExp(E2:F2,21) = 14.5909705439244867112, 270.032489548946360263
xCplxExp(E3:F3,21) = 14.5909705439245294948, 270.032489548946261736

xCplxLn$(z[,D])$ **Natural logarithm** $\qquad\qquad\qquad\qquad\qquad\qquad\qquad\qquad\qquad\qquad \ln z$

In one cell: xCplxLn(E1,21) = 2.26198006528127407189+0.948125538037829317382j,
in two: xCplxLn(E1,70) = xCplxLn(E2:F2,70) =
2.261980065281274071885982930024169450064511264424455256333274238956,
0.9481255380378293173815983411752882151513212835055453722109185788809796;
xCplxLn(E3:F3,25) = 2.2619800652812740352799931, 0.948125538037829336647 9415

xCplxLog$(z,b[,D])$ **Logarithm to base b** $\qquad\qquad\qquad\quad \log_b(z) = \ln(z)/\ln(b)$

Careful: xCplxLog(E1,,21) = 0.982365460526814654246+0.411765689321380975201j
which assumes that the non-specified base is 10, whereas xCplxLog(E1,21) =
0.7429671193268314006894268161861 6545+0.3114201184034633742533121651615121j
for $\log_{21}(z)$ with the default number of decimals, here 35. If you need the 10-based log, use:

622

xCplxLog10(*z*[,*D*]) **10-based logarithm** $\log(z) = \log_{10}(z) = \ln(z) / \ln(10)$

In two cells: xCplxLog10(E1,25) = xCplxLog10(E2:F2,70) =
0.98236546052681467014421035660595718198096856275524939383363525724175293,
0.41176568932138096683420481315007061658525052195624627864894980731 38795;
xCplxLog10(E3:F3,25) = 0.98236546052681 4654246404, 0.411765689321 3809752014713

xCplxLog2(*z*[,*D*]) **2-based logarithm** $\log_2(z) = \ln(z) / \ln(2)$

xCplxLog2(E2:F2,25)= 3.263347422770987814603177, 1.367856011867356597452088
xCplxLog2(E3:F3,25) =3.263347422770987761791808, 1.367856011867356625247546

xCplxSin(*z* [,*D*]) **Sine** $\sin(z)$

xCplxSin(E2:F2,25)= -770.335431725789249221414, 946.4236495468643587804233
xCplxSin(E3:F4,25)= -770.335431725 7894486197362, 946.4236495468639169837239

xCplxCos(*z*[,*D*]) **Cosine** $\cos(z)$

xCplxCos(E2:F2,25)= 946.4239673233332876174362, 770.3351730737666499652134
xCplxCos(E3:F4,25)= 946.4239673233328458207013, 770.3351730737668493633767

xCplxTan(*z*[,*D*]) **Tangent** $\tan(z)$

xCplxTan(E2:F2,24) = -3.28774083281655083 73533E-7, 0.99999993 1837917456442433
xCplxTan(E3:F4,24) = -3.28774083281655248 97145E-7, 0.99999993 1837917456442642

xCplxASin(*z*[,*D*]) **Inverse sine** $\arcsin(z)$

xCplxASin(E2:F2,24)= 0.620108349818012666322386, 2.95600293720697536127987
xCplxASin(E3:F4,24)= 0.620108349818012646903013, 2.95600293720697532483704

xCplxACos(*z*[,*D*]) **Inverse cosine** $\arccos(z)$

xCplxACos(E2:F2,24)= 0.950687976976883952908935, -2.95600293720697536127987
xCplxACos(E3:F4,24)= 0.950687976976883972328309, -2.95600293720697532483704

xCplxATan(*z*[,*D*]) **Inverse tangent** $\arctan(z)$

xCplxATan(E2:F2,24) = 1.50969874144921909210512, 8.44859768081672965961273E-2
xCplxATan(E3:F4,24) = 1.50969874144921909146551, 8.44859768081673008713949E-2

xCplxSinH(*z*[,*D*]) **Hyperbolic sine** $\sinh(z)$

xCplxSinH(E2:F2,24) = 7.29538551206624025612712, 135.018091013076278249296
xCplxSinH(E3:F4,24) = 7.29538551206626164758967, 135.018091013076228986589

xCplxCosH(*z*[,*D*]) **Hyperbolic cosine** $\cosh(z)$

xCplxCosH(E2:F2,24) = 7.29558503185824645502359, 135.014398535870082013816
xCplxCosH(E3:F4,24) = 7.29558503185826784721294, 135.014398535870032749833

xCplxTanH(*z* [,*D*]) **Hyperbolic tangent** $\tanh(z)$

xCplxTanH(E2:F2,24) = 1.00002718952482972149739, 2.94696926173800019499848E-6
xCplxTanH(E3:F4,24) = 1.00002718952482972151566, 2.94696926173801194879248E-6

xCplxASinH(*z*[,*D*]) **Inverse hyperbolic sine** $\text{arsinh}(z)$

xCplxASinH(E2:F2,24) = 2.954269101013251677 73266, 0.94554973566537043 1458319
xCplxASinH(E3:F4,24) = 2.954269101013251640 96493, 0.94554973566537045 0568323

xCplxACosH(*z*[,*D*]) **Inverse hyperbolic cosine** $\text{arcosh}(z)$

xCplxACosH(E2:F2,24) = 2.95600293720697536127987, 0.950687976976883952908935
xCplxACosH(E3:F4,24) = 2.95600293720697532483704, 0.950687976976883972328309

xCplxATanH(*z*[,*D*]) **Inverse hyperbolic tangent** $\text{artanh}(z)$

xCplxATanH(E2:F2,24)=6.03776070460713078765599E-2, 1.48608980485008744950066
xCplxATanH(E3:F4,24)=6.03776070460713084243571E-2, 1.48608980485008744524278

| **xCplxPolar**(z [,D]) | **Convert to polar** | $z = \rho\, e^{j\theta}$ |

xCplxPolar(E1,,35) = xCplxPolar(E2:F2,,35) = xCplxPolar(E2:F2) =
9.60208310732624309126871450256650,   0.94812553803782931738159834117528822
xCplxPolar(E3:F4,,25) = 9.60208310732624273977436l, 0.94812553803782933664794l5

| **xCplxRect**(z[,D]) | **Convert to rectangular** | $z = \rho\,\{\cos(\theta) + j\sin(\theta)\}$ |

xCplcRect(xCplxPolar(E1,,35),21)   = 5.6,   7.80000000000000000000000000000000001,
xCplcRect(xCplxPolar(E2:F2,35),21) = 5.6,   7.80000000000000000000000000000000001,
xCplcRect(xCplxPolar(E3:F3,21),21) = xCplcRect(xCplxPolar(E3:F3,500),21) =
5.59999999999999964472863212, 7.79999999999999982236431606.

D.9 Matrix and vector operations

D.9.1 Standard operations

We denote vectors as **v** with elements v_i. Matrices are either square real **S**, rectangular real **R** or (square or rectangular) complex **C**, all with elements m_{ij}. cf denotes the complex format used: 1 for split (= default), 2 for interspersed, 3 for Excel's string format. The number of rows of a vector or matrix is indicated by r, the number of colums by c. Absolute element values m_{ij} smaller than ε are set to zero as probable rounding errors; the default value for ε is 1E–D. Noninteger numbers should be placed between quotation marks when their exact rather than their Excel-stored values are to be used. We will use the compact matrix notation $\{m_{11}, m_{12}, \ldots; m_{21}, m_{22}, \ldots; m_{31}, m_{32}, \ldots; \ldots\}$ to denote a matrix with elements m_{ij} where commas separate individual elements in the same row, and semicolons separate different rows. $D_{default} = 35$.

| **xMAbs**(**R**[,D]) | **Absolute value of a real matrix** | $\|\mathbf{R}\| = \sqrt{\displaystyle\sum_{i=1}^{m}\sum_{j=1}^{n}(m_{i,j})^2}$ |

xMAbs({1,2;"3.1",-4}) = 5.53263047744922144100011616381675‌25;
xMAbs({1,2; 3.1,-4}) = 5.53263047744922149076583090461782‌64

| **xMAbsC**(**C**[,cf][,D]) | **Absolute value of a complex matrix** | $\|\mathbf{C}\| = \sqrt{\displaystyle\sum_{i=1}^{m}\sum_{j=1}^{n}(m_{i,j})^2}$ |

xMAbsC({1,2,0,-3; "3.1",-4,-1,0;6,5,2,1}) = 10.32521186223314257471‌3865204941196;
xMAbsC({1,2,0,-3; 3.1,-4,-1,0; 6,5,2,1}) = 10.32521186223314260138‌0176151460634

| **xMAdd**(**R**$_1$, **R**$_2$[,D]) | **Addition of two real matrices** | $\mathbf{R}_1 + \mathbf{R}_2$ |

R$_1$ and **R**$_2$ must have the same size $m{\times}n$, i.e., $c_1 = c_2$ *and* $r_1 = r_2$.

| **xMAddC**(**R**$_1$, **R**$_2$[,cf][,D]) | **Addition of two complex matrices** | $\mathbf{R}_1 + \mathbf{R}_2$ |

R$_1$ and **R**$_2$ must have the same size $m{\times}n$.

| **xMSub**(**R**$_1$, **R**$_2$[,D]) | **Subtraction of two real matrices** | $\mathbf{R}_1 - \mathbf{R}_2$ |

R$_1$ and **R**$_2$ must have the same size $m{\times}n$.

| **xMSubC**(**R**$_1$, **R**$_2$[,cf][,D]) | **Subtraction of two complex matrices** | $\mathbf{R}_1 - \mathbf{R}_2$ |

R$_1$ and **R**$_2$ must have the same size $m{\times}n$.

| **xProdScal**(**v**$_1$, **v**$_2$[,D]) | **Scalar product of two vectors (or matrices)** | $\mathbf{v}_1 \bullet \mathbf{v}_2$ |

v$_1$ and **v**$_2$ must have the same size m. The scalar product is zero if **v**$_1$ and **v**$_2$ are perpendicular. This function can also be applied to two matrices **R**$_1$ and **R**$_2$ where $c_1 = r_2$ in which case xProdScale(**R**$_1$,**R**$_2$) yields the product $\mathbf{R}_1^{\mathrm{T}}\mathbf{R}_2$

| **xProdScalC**(**v**$_1$, **v**$_2$[,cf][,D]) | **Complex scalar product of two vectors** | $\mathbf{v}_1 \bullet \mathbf{v}_2$ |

v$_1$ and **v**$_2$ must have the same size m. The scalar product is zero if **v**$_1$ and **v**$_2$ are perpendicular.

| **xProdVect**(**v**$_1$, **v**$_2$[,D]) | **Vector product** | $\mathbf{v}_1 \times \mathbf{v}_2$ |

v$_1$ and **v**$_2$ must have the same size m.

| **xMMult**(**R**$_1$, **R**$_2$[,D]) | **Multiplication of two real matrices** | $\mathbf{R}_1\,\mathbf{R}_2$ |

When **R**$_1$ is $m{\times}p$, **R**$_2$ must be $p{\times}n$, i.e., $c_1 = r_2$.

xMMultC($\mathbf{C}_1, \mathbf{C}_2[,cf][,D]$) **Multiplication of two complex matrices** $\qquad$ $\mathbf{C}_1\,\mathbf{C}_2$

> When $\mathbf{R}_1$ is $m{\times}p$, $\mathbf{R}_2$ must be $p{\times}n$, i.e., $c_1 = r_2$.

xMMultS($\mathbf{R},a[,D]$) **Multiplication of a real scalar a and a real matrix $\mathbf{R}$** $\qquad$ $a\,\mathbf{R}$

> Note the order of terms in the argument: first the matrix $\mathbf{R}$, then the scalar a,
> regardless of the matrix size. $a\mathbf{R}$ will have the size of $\mathbf{R}$.

xMMultSC($\mathbf{R},z[,cf][,D]$) **Multiplication of a complex scalar z and a complex matrix $\mathbf{C}$** $\quad$ $z\,\mathbf{C}$

> Note he order of terms in the argument: first the matrix $\mathbf{C}$, first, then the scalar z, regardless of
> The matrix size. This order is the reverse of that in the function name. $z\mathbf{C}$ will have the size of $\mathbf{C}$.

xMPow($\mathbf{S},n[,D]$) $\qquad$ **Integral power of a square, real matrix S** $\qquad$ $\mathbf{S}^n$

> n must be a positive integer.

xMPowC($\mathbf{C},n[,cf][,D]$) $\quad$ **Integral power of a complex matrix** $\mathbf{C}$ $\qquad$ $\mathbf{C}^n$

> n must be a positive integer.

xMInv($\mathbf{S}[,D]$) $\qquad$ **Inversion of a square real matrix** $\qquad$ $\mathbf{S}^{-1}$

> Uses Gauss-Jordan diagonalization with partial pivoting.

xMInvC($\mathbf{S}[,cf][,D]$) **Inversion of a square complex matrix** $\qquad$ $\mathbf{C}^{-1}$

> Uses Gauss-Jordan diagonalization with partial pivoting.

xMDivS($\mathbf{R},a[,D]$) $\qquad$ **Division of a real matrix $\mathbf{R}$ by a real scalar a** $\qquad$ $\mathbf{R}\,/\,a$

> Note the order of terms in the argument: first the matrix $\mathbf{R}$, then the scalar a,
> regardless of the matrix size. $\mathbf{R}\,/\,a$ will have the size of $\mathbf{R}$.

xMPseudoInv($\mathbf{R}[,D]$) $\quad$ **Pseudo-inverse of a rectangular real matrix** $\qquad$ $\mathbf{R}^+ = \mathbf{V}\,\boldsymbol{\Sigma}^{-1}\,\mathbf{U}^{\mathrm{T}}$

> based on SVD. When $\mathbf{R}$ is $m{\times}n$, $\mathbf{R}^+$ is $n{\times}m$. When R is square and nonsingular, its
> pseudoinverse is equal to its inverse. Uses Gauss-Jordan diagonalization with partial pivoting.

xMPseudoInvC($\mathbf{C}[,cf][,D]$) $\quad$ **Pseudo-inverse of a complex matrix** $\qquad$ $\mathbf{C}^+ = \mathbf{V}\,\boldsymbol{\Sigma}^{-1}\,\mathbf{U}^{\mathrm{T}}$

> based on SVD. When $\mathbf{R}$ is $m{\times}n$, $\mathbf{R}^+$ is $n{\times}m$. When R is square and nonsingular, its
> pseudoinverse is equal to its inverse. Uses Gauss-Jordan diagonalization with partial pivoting.

xMExp($\mathbf{S}[,n][,D]$) **Exponentiation of a square real matrix** $\qquad$ $e^{\mathbf{S}}$

> $\mathrm{Exp}(\mathbf{S}) = 1 + \mathbf{S} + \mathbf{S}^2/2 + \mathbf{S}^3/6 + \mathbf{S}^4/24 + \ldots + \mathbf{S}^n/n!$
> When n is deleted, the series is continues until it converges.

xMExpC($\mathbf{S}[,n][,cf][,D]$) $\quad$ **Exponentiation of a square complex matrix** $\qquad$ $e^{\mathbf{C}}$

> $\mathrm{Exp}(\mathbf{S}) = 1 + \mathbf{S} + \mathbf{S}^2/2 + \mathbf{S}^3/6 + \mathbf{S}^4/24 + \ldots + \mathbf{S}^n/n!$
> When n is deleted, the series is continues until it converges.

xMExpErr($\mathbf{S},n[,D]$) $\quad$ **Error term in xMExp** $\qquad$ $\left\|\mathbf{S}^n/n!\right\|$

> Note that n is required.

xMExpErrC($\mathbf{C},n[,cf][,D]$) $\quad$ **Error term in xMExpC** $\qquad$ $\left\|\mathbf{C}^n/n!\right\|$

> Note that n is required.

xMMopUp($\mathbf{S}[,errMin][,cf][,D]$) **Cleans up matrix errors close to zero**

> Replaces matrix elements smaller than ErrMin or ε by 0.

D.9.2 More sophisticated matrix operations

xMDet($\mathbf{S}[,D]$) $\qquad$ **Determinant of a square real matrix** $\qquad$ $|\mathbf{S}|$

> Uses Gauss-Jordan diagonalization with partial pivoting. Returns "?" when $\mathbf{S}$ is singular.
> xMDet({1,2;"3.1",-4}) = -10.2
> xMDet({1,2; 3.1,-4}) = -10.200000000000017763568394

xMDetC($\mathbf{C}[,D]$) $\qquad$ **Determinant of a square complex matrix** $\qquad$ $|\mathbf{C}|$

> xMDetC({1,2,0,-3;"3.1",-4,1,7}) = -13.2, 14.3; xMDetC({1,2,0,-3;3.1,-4,1,7}) =
> -13.200000000000017763568394, 14.300000000000026645352591

xMCond$(\mathbf{R}[,D])$ **Condition number of a real matrix** κ

> Based on SVD. xMCond({1,2;"3.1",-4}) = 2.6191817659615200272394889923128097;
> xMCond({1,2;3.1,-4}) = 2.6191817659615200292582110124456817

xMCondC$(\mathbf{C}[\text{Cformat},D,\varepsilon,\text{tol}])$ **Condition number of a complex matrix** κ

> Based on SVD. xMCondC({1,2,0,-3;"3.1",-4,1,7},,21) = 4.37608205969300766727,
> 4.37608205969300766727; xMCondC({1,2,0,-3; 3.1,-4,1,7},,21) =
> 4.37608205969300761817, 4.37608205969300761817

xMpCond$(\mathbf{R}[\text{Cformat},D,\varepsilon,\text{tol}])$ **$-\log_{10}$ of the condition number of a real matrix** $-\log_{10}(\kappa)$

> xMpCond({1,2;"3.1",-4}) = -0.41816563863710134091248426474409013;
> xMpCond({1,2; 3.1,-4}) = -0.41816563863710134124721469286252258

xMpCondC$(\mathbf{C}[\text{Cformat},D,\varepsilon,\text{tol}])$ **$-\log_{10}$ of the condition number of a complex matrix** $-\log_{10}(\kappa)$

> xMpCondC({1,2,0,-3;"3.1",-4,1,7},,2) = xMpCondC({1,2,0,-3;3.1,-4,1,7},,2) = -0.64

xMNormalize$(\mathbf{R}[,\text{normtype}][,\text{tiny}][,D])$ **Normalize a real matrix** $v_i\Big/\sqrt{\sum v_i^2}$

> Normtype: all nonzero vertical vectors normalized; default = 2 for Euclidean norm.
> $$\mathbf{R} = \begin{vmatrix} 3 & 6.1 \\ 4 & -5 \end{vmatrix}, \text{xMNormalize}(R,,,21) = \begin{vmatrix} 0.6 & 0.7733921040021265705 \\ 0.8 & -0.6339279548542024763 \end{vmatrix}$$

xMNormalizeC$(\mathbf{C}[,\text{normtype}][,\text{Cformat}][,\text{tiny}][,D])$ **Normalize a complex matrix**

> Normtype: all nonzero vertical vectors normalized; default = 2 for Euclidean norm.
> $$\mathbf{C} = \begin{vmatrix} 3 & 6.1 & -7 & 0 \\ 4 & -5 & 9 & 8 \end{vmatrix}, \text{xMNormalize}(R,,,9) = \begin{vmatrix} 0.6 & 0.773392105 & -0.6139406135 & 0 \\ 0.8 & -0.633927955 & 0.789352217 & 1 \end{vmatrix}$$

xMT$(\mathbf{R})$ **Transpose a real matrix** $\mathbf{R}^{\mathrm{T}}$

> $$\mathbf{R} = \begin{vmatrix} 3 & 6.1 \\ 4 & -5 \end{vmatrix}, \text{xMT(R)} = \begin{vmatrix} 3 & 4 \\ 6.1 & -5 \end{vmatrix}, \text{do } \textit{not} \text{ specify } D.$$

xMTC$(\mathbf{C})$ **Transpose a complex matrix** $\mathbf{C}^{\mathrm{T}}$

> $$\mathbf{C} = \begin{vmatrix} 3 & 6.1 & -7 & 0 \\ 4 & -5 & 9 & 8 \end{vmatrix}, \text{xMTC(C)} = \begin{vmatrix} 3 & 4 & -7 & 9 \\ 6.1 & -5 & 0 & 8 \end{vmatrix}, \text{do } \textit{not} \text{ specify } D.$$

xMTH$(\mathbf{C})$ **Hermitian (conjugate, adjoint) transpose a complex matrix** $\mathbf{C}^{\mathrm{H}}$

> $$\mathbf{C} = \begin{vmatrix} 3 & 6.1 & -7 & 0 \\ 4 & -5 & 9 & 8 \end{vmatrix}, \text{xMTH(C)} = \begin{vmatrix} 3 & 4 & 7 & -9 \\ 6.1 & -5 & 0 & -8 \end{vmatrix}, \text{do } not \text{ specify } D.$$

D.9.3 Matrix decompositions

xMLU$(\mathbf{S}[,\text{Pivot}][,D])$ **LU decomposition** using Crout's algorithm $\mathbf{L}\,\mathbf{U}$

> Returns the Lower and Upper triangular matrices that satisfy
> $\mathbf{S} = \mathbf{L}\,\mathbf{U}$ or, when Pivot is True, $\mathbf{S} = \mathbf{P}\,\mathbf{L}\,\mathbf{U}$ where $\mathbf{P}$ is the permutation
> matrix. If Pivot = False, the first diagonal element of $\mathbf{S}$ cannot be zero.

xMCholesky$(\mathbf{S}[,D])$ **LL decomposition** $\mathbf{L}\,\mathbf{L}^{\mathrm{T}}$

> Cholesky decomposition of a square matrix.

xSysLin$(\mathbf{A},\mathbf{B}[,D])$ **Solves simultaneous real linear equations** $\mathbf{X} = \mathbf{A}^{-1}\,\mathbf{B}$

> Uses the Gauss-Jordan diagonalization; $\mathbf{A}$, $\mathbf{X}$ and $\mathbf{B}$ must be real; $\mathbf{A}$ must be $m \times m$;
> $\mathbf{X}$ and $\mathbf{B}$ must both be $m \times 1$ or $m \times n$. Solves $\mathbf{A}\,\mathbf{X} = \mathbf{B}$ to yield $\mathbf{X} = \mathbf{A}^{-1}\,\mathbf{A}\;\mathbf{X} = \mathbf{A}^{-1}\,\mathbf{B}$.

xSysLinC$(\mathbf{A},\mathbf{B}[,D])$ **Solves simultaneous complex linear equations** $\mathbf{X} = \mathbf{A}^{-1}\,\mathbf{B}$

> Equivalent to xSysLin for complex arrays. $\mathbf{A}$, $\mathbf{X}$ and $\mathbf{B}$ must be complex; $\mathbf{A}$ must
> be $m \times m$; $\mathbf{X}$ and $\mathbf{B}$ must be $m \times 1$ or $m \times n$. Solves $\mathbf{A}\,\mathbf{X} = \mathbf{B}$ to yield $\mathbf{X} = \mathbf{A}^{-1}\,\mathbf{A}\;\mathbf{C} = \mathbf{A}^{-1}\,\mathbf{B}$.

xGaussJordan$(\mathbf{M},n,m,\text{Det, Algo, }D)$ **Gauss-Jordan elimination**

> Uses partial pivoting.

626

xSVDD($\mathbf{R}[,D][,\varepsilon]$) **Matrix Σ from SVD of a real rectangular matrix R**   **Σ**

SVD used in "compact" format; when $\mathbf{R}$ is $m{\times}n$, and $p = \min(m,n)$, $\mathbf{Σ}$ is $p{\times}p$.
$|\varepsilon|$ is the ignored rounding error; default: $|\varepsilon| \leq$ 1E–D.

xSVDDC($\mathbf{C}[,c][,D][,\varepsilon]$) **Matrix Σ from SVD of a complex rectangular matrix C**   **Σ**

SVD used in "compact" format; when $\mathbf{C}$ is $m{\times}n$, and $p = \min(m,n)$, $\mathbf{Σ}$ is $p{\times}p$.
Default format: $c = 1$ (split). $|\varepsilon|$ is the ignored rounding error; default: $|\varepsilon| \leq$ 1E–D.

xSVDU($\mathbf{R}[,D][,\varepsilon]$) **Matrix U from SVD of a real rectangular matrix R**   **U**

SVD used in "compact" format; when $\mathbf{R}$ is $m{\times}n$, and $p = \min(m,n)$, $\mathbf{U}$ is $n{\times}p$.
$|\varepsilon|$ is the ignored rounding error; default: $|\varepsilon| \leq$ 1E–D.

xSVDUC($\mathbf{C}[,c][,D][,\varepsilon]$) **Matrix U from SVD of a complex rectangular matrix C**   **U**

SVD used in "compact" format; when $\mathbf{C}$ is $m{\times}n$, and $p = \min(m,n)$, $\mathbf{U}$ is $n{\times}p$.
Default format: $c = 1$ (split). $|\varepsilon|$ is the ignored rounding error; default: $|\varepsilon| \leq$ 1E–D.

xSVDV($\mathbf{R}[,D][,\varepsilon]$) **Matrix V from SVD of a real rectangular matrix R**   **V**

SVD used in "compact" format; when $\mathbf{R}$ is $m{\times}n$, and $p = \min(m,n)$, $\mathbf{V}$ is $m{\times}p$.
$|\varepsilon|$ is the ignored rounding error; default: $|\varepsilon| \leq$ 1E–D.

xSVDVC($\mathbf{C}[,c][,D][,\varepsilon]$) **Matrix V from SVD of a complex rectangular matrix C**   **V**

SVD used in "compact" format; when $\mathbf{C}$ is $m{\times}n$, and $p = \min(m,n)$, $\mathbf{V}$ is $m{\times}p$.
Default format: $c = 1$ (split). $|\varepsilon|$ is the ignored rounding error; default: $|\varepsilon| \leq$ 1E–D.

D.10 Miscellaneous functions

D.10.1 Manipulating numbers

xCStr($x[,D]$)   **Converts a number x from double precision to string format**

Ignores $D_{default}$; when D is deleted, as many digits as needed (up to Digits_Limit) are displayed.
xCStr(1) = 1; xCStr(0.1) = 0.1000000000000000055511151231257827021181583404541015625;
xCStr("1.1") = 1.1; xCStr(1.1) = 1.100000000000000088817841970012523233890533447265625;
xCStr("4.1") = 4.1; xCStr(4.1) = 4.09999999999999964472863211994990706443786621093750.
When B2 holds the number 4.1, xCStr(B2) = xCStr(4.1), see above, but xCStr(""&B2&"") = 4.1,
i.e., the stored, binary value of x is read unless its spreadsheet value is selected with double quotes.
D can be used to limit the output: xCStr(B2,20) = xCStr(4.1,20) = 4.0999999999999996447.

xDec(a)   **Decimal part of number a**

xDec(2.99) = 0.99; xDec(–2.99) = –0.99.

xTrunc(a)   **Truncation**

xTrunc(2.99) = 2; xTrunc(–2.99) = –2; xTrunc(a) + xDec(a) = a.

xRound($a,[d][,D]$)   **Round**

Rounds a to d decimal places; default: $d = 0$. If least significant digit is 5, rounds it away
from zero. xRound(1.5) = 2; xRound(2.5) = 3; xRound(–1.5) = –2; xRound(–2.5) = –3.

vRoundR($a[,s][,D]$)**Relative round**

Uses *unbiased* (banker's) relative rounding. Rounds the mantissa of a to s significant
digits, while leaving its exponent alone. Note: the default (with s unspecified) is 15.

xRoundR($a[,s][,D]$)**Relative round**

Uses standard rounding to round the mantissa of a to s significant digits,
while leaving its exponent alone. Note: the default (with s unspecified) is 15.

xInt(a)   **Integer part**

Rounds down: xInt(2.99) = 2; xInt(–2.99) = –3. Warning: in general, for $a < 0$, xInt(a) + xDec(a) $\neq a$.

xComp($a[,b]$)   **Comparison of value of a with b**

xComp(a, b) = 1 for $a > b$, xComp(a, b) = 0 for $a = b$,
xComp(a, b) = –1 for $a < b$. The default assumes that $b = 0$.

xComp1(a)   **Comparison of absolute value of a with 1**

xComp1(a) = 1 for $|a| > 1$, xComp1(a) = 0 for $|a| = 1$, xComp1(a) = –1 for $|a| < 1$.

xDgt(*a*)   **Digit count**

xDgt(–2.99) = 3; xDgt(–0.00299) = 6.

xDgtS(*a*)   **Significant digit count**

Treats all trailing zeros as not significant: xDgtS(1234000) = 4;
xDgtS(1.234) = 28 (counting significant digits in corresponding string number);
xDgtS("–0.0029900") = 3; xDgtS(–0.0029900) = 28.

xCDbl(*a*)   **Converts from extended to double precision**

Converts an extended precision numerical string into a double precision number.
Example: xPi() = 3.14159265358979323846264338327950029; xCDbl(xPi()) =
3.1415927 with up to 15 digits depending on the cell formatting.

x2Dbl(*a*)   **Converts from extended to double precision**

Slower but in rare cases more precise version of xCDbl.

D.10.2 *Formatting instructions*

xFormat(*a*[,*Digit_Sep*])   **Format**

formats a string '*a* in comma-separated groups of *Digit_Sep*; default: *Digit_Sep* = 6.
For *a* = '1234567.89012345, xFormat(*a*) = 1,234567.890123,45 and xFormat(*a*,3) =
1,234,567.890,123,45; when *a* = 1234567.89012345, a spreadsheet number, the result
will reflect the stored value: xFormat(*a*) = 1,234,567.890,123,449,964,448,809,624.

xUnformat(*a*)   **Unformat**

Removes formatting commas from *a*

xSplit(*a*)   **Splits scientific notation over two cells**

Converts a number into scientific notation, spread over two adjacent cells.
xSplit(*a*) = {1.2345669999999999941758246258, 89} for *a* = 1.234567E+89;
xSplit(*a*) = {1.234567, 896} for *a* = 1234567E890 or *a* = 1234567E+890;
xSplit(*a*) = {1.234567, -884} for *a* = 1234567E-890.

xMantissa(*a*)   **Mantissa of *a* in scientific format**

Yields the mantissa of a numerical string *a*, e.g., xMantissa(a) = -123.4567 for *a* =
'-1.234567E-890 but -1.234560000000000004997855423 for *a* = –1.234567E-890.

xExponent(*a*)   **Exponent of *a* in scientific format**

Yields the exponent of a numerical string *a* or a number in the cell, e.g.,
xExponend(*a*) = -890 for either *a* = –1.234567E-890 or *a* = '-1.234567E-890
because the exponent is always integer.

xCvExp(*mant*[,*exp*])   **Converts scientific notation into mantissa and exponent**

=xCvExp(-123.456,789) yields -1.2345600000000000030695446185E+791, and
=xCvExp(-0.0000123456,0) generates -1.2345599999999999916351148266E-5,
in both cases showing decimal-to-binary conversion errors. You can avoid these
by setting *exp* to zero: =xCvExp("-0.0000123456",0) leads to –1.23456E-5.

D.10.3 *Logical functions*

x_And(*a*,*b*)   **Boolean logic AND**   AND(*a*,*b*)

x_And(*a*,*b*) = True only when $a \neq 0$ (or FALSE) *and* $b \neq 0$ (or FALSE);
a blank cell does not count as 0 (or FALSE).

x_Or(*a*,*b*)   **Boolean logic OR**   OR(*a*,*b*)

x_Or(*a*,*b*) = True when $a \neq 0$ (or FALSE) *or* $b \neq 0$ (or FALSE) *or both*,
a blank cell doesn't count.

x_If(*a*,*b*)   **Boolean logic IF**   IF()

x_If(*a*,*b*,*c*) = *b* when *a* = 1 or TRUE, x_If(*a*,*b*,*c*) = *c* when *a* = 0 or FALSE

x_Not(*a*)   **Boolean logic NOT**   NOT(*a*)

x_Not(*a*) = True when *a* = 0 (or FALSE). Non-zero numbers and strings evaluate as True.

D.10.4 Polynomial functions

xPolyTerms (*poly*[,*D*])   **Extract the coefficients of a polynomial**

When *poly* is, e.g., 'x^5-2.1+3*x^3+4*x^2 in cell B2,
xPolyTerms(B2) = {−2.1, 0, 4, 3, 0, 1}

xPoly (*a*,*coef*[,*D*])   **Evaluate a polynomial at *x***

When the polynomial is defined by its coefficients *coef* in, e.g.,
B4:G4 as {−2.1, 0, 4, 3, 0, 1}, xPoly(3,B4:G4) = −374.3.

xPolyAdd(*poly*1,*poly*2[,*D*])   **Adds two polynomials in *x***

The polynomials are *poly*1 and *poly*2. Block-enter their coefficients
in the same order. Missing coefficients will be interpreted as zero.
If enumerated in the argument, use ,, to indicate a missing coefficient.

xPolySub (*poly*1,*poly*2[,*D*])   **Subtracts two polynomials in *x***

The polynomials are *poly*1 and *poly*2. Block-enter their coefficients
in the same order. Missing coefficients will be interpreted as zero.
If enumerated in the argument, use ,, to indicate a missing coefficient.

xPolyMult (*poly*1,*poly*2[,*D*])   **Multiplies two polynomials in *x***

The polynomials are *poly*1 and *poly*2. Block-enter their coefficients
in the same order. Missing coefficients will be interpreted as zero.
If enumerated in the argument, use ,, to indicate a missing coefficient.
Assign space in the highlighted area for the higher-order cross-terms.

xPolyDiv (*a*[,*D*])   **Divides two polynomials in *x***

The polynomials are *poly*1 and *poly*2. Block-enter their coefficients
in the same order. Missing coefficients will be interpreted as zero.
If enumerated in the argument, use ,, to indicate a missing coefficient.

xPolyRem (*a*[,*D*])   **The remainder of polynomial division**

The polynomials are *poly*1 and *poly*2. Block-enter their coefficients
in the same order. Missing coefficients will be interpreted as zero.
If enumerated in the argument, use ,, to indicate a missing coefficient.

D.10.5 Integer operations

xPowMod(*a*,*p*[,*D*])   **Modular power** a^p mod *m*

Returns the remainder of the integer division d^p, i.e., $d^p - m\,(d^p \setminus m)$, e.g.,
xPowMod(10,3,7) = 6 because 10^3 = 1000 = 142*7 + 6 where 142*7 = 994.
Useful for finding the remainders of divisions of very large integers, as in
xPow(12,34567) = 1.1432260930295413791181531725537944E+37304 with
more than 3700 decimals, yet xPowMod(12,34567,89) = 52. This is the
remainder of dividing 12^{34567} by 89 despite the fact that XN-version used,
XN6051–7A, cannot hold more than 630 decimals.

xDivMod(*a*,*b*,*m*)   **Modular division**   (*a/b*) mod *m*

where *a* and *b* are integers, and *m* is a positive prime integer;
otherwise the function returns "?". Example: xPow(12,3939393) =
1.1127850718610753473503619921808241E+4251319, i.e., it is a
number with more than 4 million digits! While XN cannot perform
the regular division of such a giant number by the prime number
3001, it can find xPowMod(12,3939393,3001) = 2758.

D.10.6 Getting (& setting) XN configuration information

Here are a number of functions that allow you to read or "get" configuration settings, and to define or "set"
them. Since each Get function has a corresponding set counterpart, only the former are listed here; these Get
instructions must be followed by empty argument brackets to identify them as functions. A corresponding Set
function must have a replacement value as its argument, and is meant for use within a VBA function or macro.

GetDigitsLimit()	**Specifies the current DigitsLimit**
	For XN.xla605 the function =GetDigitsLimit() yields 630, its largest allowed *D*-value.
GetExcelAppVer()	**Specifies the current version of Excel used**
	For Excel97: =GetExcelAppVer() yields 8, 9 for 2000, 10 for 2002, 11 for 2003, 12 for 2007, and 14 for 2010.
GetxBase()	**Specifies the current packet size**
	For XN.xla605 the function =GetxBase() yields the value 7.
GetXnArgSep()	**Specifies the current VBA argument separator**
	In the US, =GetXnArgSep() should yield a comma.
GetXnCaseSen()	**Specifies the current case sensitivity**
	If case-insensitive (the default), =GetXnCaseSen() yields FALSE; if case-sensitive, TRUE.
GetXnConfigStatus()	**Specifies the current configuration settings**
	Needs a 19 rows high, 2 columns wide array to list the names and values of all 19 configuration settings.
GetXnDecSep()	**Specifies the current VBA decimal separator**
	In the US, =GetXnDecSep() should yield a period.
GetXnDefaultDigits()	**Specifies the currently selected default *D*-value**
	For the examples in this table, =GetXnDefaultDigits() should yield 35.
GetXnDefCStr()	**Specifies the current default value for default Dbl2Str digits**
	=GetXnDefCStr() yields 0 for vCStr, 15 to 28 for dCStr, 29 to Digits_Limit for xCStr.
GetXnSMPAdj()	**Specifies the Digit Max Adjustment of the Simulated Machine Precision**
	For 7-digit packets, the recommended value is $2 \times 7 = 14$ decimals.
GetXnAddAdj()	**Specifies the current Digit Max Adjustment for xAdd**
	The recommended value is 0 decimals for all versions of XN.
GetXnDivAdj()	**Specifies the current Digit Max Adjustment for xDiv**
	The recommended value is 0 decimals for all versions of XN.
GetXnMultAdj()	**Specifies the current Digit Max Adjustment for xMult**
	The recommended value is 2 packets for all versions of XN.

D.11 The Math Parser and related functions

The Math Parser can evaluate many formulas *f* written in quasi-algebra, as a function of the specified parameter Values. It thereby brings an aspect of symbolic calculus to numerical computation. Its formulas resemble those in Excel's VBA, as a function of the parameter Values. The Math Parser performs two functions: it first "parses" the formula, then evaluates its value. Its extended precision implementations xEval and xEvall, as implemented by John Beyers, uses the original parser developed for double precision expressions, but with XN for value evaluation. This can be especially helpful because writing complicated mathematical expressions in XN can be error-prone, a complication readily avoided by using xEval or xEvall. The Help-on-Line entry xEval (see the XN Toolbar under Help) gives many clear examples. xEvall uses a sophisticated search for the value labels which makes it about ten times slower than xEval; its use is therefore not recommended.

xEval(*f*, Values, [,*D*][,Angle][,*Tiny*][,IntSwapFix])   **Evaluates quasi-algebraic formulas**

xEvall(*f*, Values, [,*D*][,Angle][,*Tiny*][,IntSwapFix])   **xEval using top labels if present**

xEval assigns the parameter values in the order in which they are listed under Values. $D = 0$ will use the faster double-precision mode; $D = -1$ specifies quadruple precision in the Variant Decimal mode. Leaving *D* unspecified will use the value of Default Digits specified in the XN Toolbar under X-Edit ⇨ Configuration.

Angle provides a choice between the default rad(ians), deg(ree), and grad(s). *Tiny* defines the minimum absolute value that will be considered to be different from zero; for the optional IntSwapFix see the Help-on-Line file.

The formula *f* and its values can be fully specified in the argument, as in xEval("1/x^2+5*x*y+7*sqr(y)",{"2","3"},28) = 42.37435565298214105469212439, or the formula and/or its parameter values can be read from specified spreadsheet cells, as in =xEval("1/x^2+5*x*y+7*sqr(y)",I2:I3,28) or =xEval(I4,{"2","3"},28 or

=xEval(B4,B2:B3,28), which all give the same result when cell B4 contains the formula 1/x^2+5*x*y +7*sqr(y), and cells B2 and B3 the values 2 and 3 respectively..

For further details about the Math Parser see section 8.16 and, especially, the Help-on-Line entry on xEval. As described there, several functions can also use its quasi-algebraic code, such as the integration functions Integr(), Integr_2D, etc.

Here are two extended precision functions that use the Math Parser: xGrad and xJacobi.

xGrad(Values, f[,**x**][,D][,Labels])   **Gradient of a multivariate function f**
$$\begin{bmatrix} \partial f / \partial x_1 \\ \partial f / \partial x_2 \\ \vdots \\ \partial f / \partial x_m \end{bmatrix}$$

Approximates the gradient of a single function f of several variables, by default called x, y, z, and t in this order, as evaluated at the parameter Values in that same order, using 5-point expressions for the derivative. If you want to use other variable name Labels in your function, specify them as Labels and count your commas, see below.

You can specify the Values and the formula for f directly into the expression, as in =xGrad({-1,2,3,7},("(x+2*y-3*z^2)/LN(t)")), or read them from the spreadsheet, as in =xGrad(B2:B5,B6), when B2:B5 contain the values –1, 2, 3, and 7 respectively, and cell B6 the formula (x+2*y-3z^2)/ln(t).

In both cases you will get
$$\begin{bmatrix} 0.513898342369750690446493893018939 \\ 0.513898342369750690446493893018939 \\ -9.250170106555124780368900863409 \\ 0.905456529955800021614199338047098 \end{bmatrix}$$

Also in both cases, the expression must be written in Math Parser format. The Values, either enumerated or taken from B2:B5, must be in the order x,y,z,t. If you use other names, e.g., a, b, c, and d, then these must be defined in Labels as =xGrad(B2:B55,B6,,,A2:A5) where A2:A5 contains a, b, c, and d respectively.

xJacobian(Values,**f**,[,**x**][,D][,Labels][,MaxPrec])   **Jacobian of f**
$$\begin{bmatrix} \partial f_1/\partial x_1 & \partial f_1/\partial x_2 & \cdots & \partial f_1/\partial x_m \\ \partial f_2/\partial x_1 & \partial f_2/\partial x_2 & \cdots & \partial f_2/\partial x_m \\ \vdots & \vdots & \ddots & \vdots \\ \partial f_n/\partial x_1 & \partial f_n/\partial x_2 & \cdots & \partial f_n/\partial x_m \end{bmatrix}$$

Approximates the Jacobian of a vector **f** of n functions f, each of m variables, by default called x, y, z, and t in this order, as evaluated at the parameter Values listed in that same order, using 5-point expressions for the derivative. If you want to use other variable name Labels in your function, specify them as Labels and keep track of the commas.

As with xGrad you can specify the Values and the formula for f directly into the expression or, as is usually more convenient, read them from the spreadsheet, as in =xGrad(B2:B4,B5:B7), where B2:B5 contain the specific Values at which the function formulas (in Math Parser format) in B5:B7 must be evaluated:

$$\mathbf{J} = \begin{bmatrix} \partial f_1/\partial x_1 & \partial f_1/\partial x_2 & \cdots & \partial f_1/\partial x_m \\ \partial f_2/\partial x_1 & \partial f_2/\partial x_2 & \cdots & \partial f_2/\partial x_m \\ \vdots & \vdots & \ddots & \vdots \\ \partial f_n/\partial x_1 & \partial f_n/\partial x_2 & \cdots & \partial f_n/\partial x_m \end{bmatrix} \text{ for } \mathbf{f} = \begin{bmatrix} f_1(x_1,x_2,...,x_m) \\ f_2(x_1,x_2,...,x_m) \\ \vdots \\ f_n(x_1,x_2,...,x_m) \end{bmatrix} \text{ and } \mathbf{x} = \begin{bmatrix} x_1 \\ x_2 \\ \vdots \\ x_m \end{bmatrix}.$$

Author index

633

Subject index

*Courier font identifies VBA instructons.
Numbers refer to pages; italic numbers indicate
the starting page of section(s) primarily devoted
to that topic. Excel functions are shown in caps,
VBA. Matrix & XN functions in lower case.*

A

B

C

G

Gabor macro 296
Gabor transformation 295
Galton 61
gas-chromatographic ethanol analysis 110
Gauss elimination 466
Gaussian distribution 55, 73, 103
Gaussian noise 14
Gaussian peaks
   convolution of *291*
   vs. Lorentzian peaks 181
Gauss-Jordan elimination 467, 607
general least squares fit
   for a complex quantity 189
   to a straight line 186
General Public License 6
generator tool 608
Gibbs phenomenon 286
global minimum *181*
global weights 126, 189
  tables of global weights 128
glow-in-the-dark toys 160
GNU General Public License 6
Goal Seek 213
good graphing practices 18
good spreadsheet practices 50, *525*
GoTo 348
GradeBySf macro 119
gradient of multivariate function 631
Gram polynomials *107*, 111, 122
Gram-Schmidt orthogonalization 108
Gran plot 40
graph
   guidelines for good graphs 18
   inserts 18
   specifications 378
   2-D *13*
   3-D *19*
gridline control 11
Grinvald-Steinberg deconvolution 289
guidelines for good graphs 18

H

Hadamard transform 256
Hamming window 231
handle 2, 26
Hanes plot 130, 178
von Hann window 231
harmonic oscillator 95
Hartley transform 257
$H^{35}Cl$ infrared analysis 100
heat evolution in cement hardening 118

Heisenberg uncertainty 224, 273
help files 5
Hermitian matrix 491, 626
hidden links 51
Hilbert matrix *515*, 598
hotkey x, 1
hydrochloric acid infrared spectrum 100

I

ideal gas law 75
IEEE-754 protocol 6, *416*, *543*
If and Iff 49, 346
Iff 49, 346
If ... Then 346
If statements and Solver 291
ill-conditioned matrix 489
Immediate Window 337, *391*, 420
Impedance plot 189
implicit Euler integration 307
importing data *33*, 51
  and their possible corruption 33
through Notepad 33, 34
IMEP (International Measurement
  Evaluation Programme) 211
importing graphs into Word 33
imprecision
  band 71
  contours 71, 109
  in linear extrapolation 75
  measures 58
  of the imprecision 73
independent variable 57
infrared spectrum of $H^{35}Cl$ 100
initializing 39, 46
in-phase component 218
input box 352
  type designations 352
inserting
  a cell comment 3
  a macro in the Tools menu 9
  a chart 12
  a VBA module 7
  a toolbar 7, 12, 381
  a toolbar in Excel2007 12
  an additional Worksheet 26
  columns and/or rows 15
inserts in graphs 17
installation requirements 5, 590
integer operations 629
integration
  and chaos 331
  explicit Euler method *301*
  of ordinary differential equations *301*